College Preparatory Mathematics

Custom Edition for Stark State College

Modules 1–18

Taken from:

Prealgebra & Introductory Algebra, Third Edition
by Margaret L. Lial, Diana L. Hestwood, John Hornsby, and Terry McGinnis

Basic College Mathematics, Eighth Edition
by Margaret L. Lial, Stanley A. Salzman, Diana L. Hestwood

Intermediate Algebra, Ninth Edition
by Margaret L. Lial, John Hornsby, and Terry McGinnis

Learning Solutions

New York   Boston   San Francisco
London   Toronto   Sydney   Tokyo   Singapore   Madrid
Mexico City   Munich   Paris   Cape Town   Hong Kong   Montreal

Cover Art: *Regatta Single*, by Angela Sciaraffa

Taken from:

Prealgebra & Introductory Algebra, Third Edition
by Margaret L. Lial, Diana L. Hestwood, John Hornsby, and Terry McGinnis
Copyright © 2010, 2007, 2001 by Pearson Education, Inc.
Published by Addison Wesley
Boston, MA 02116

Basic College Mathematics, Eighth Edition
by Margaret L. Lial, Stanley A. Salzman, Diana L. Hestwood
Copyright © 2010, 2006, 2002, 1998, 1995, 1991, 1987, 1981 by Pearson Education, Inc.
Published by Addison Wesley

Intermediate Algebra, Ninth Edition
by Margaret L. Lial, John Hornsby, and Terry McGinnis
Copyright © 2010, 2007, 2001 by Pearson Education, Inc.
Published by Addison Wesley

This special edition published in cooperation with Pearson Learning Solutions.

All trademarks, service marks, registered trademarks, and registered service marks are the property of their respective owners and are used herein for identification purposes only.

Pearson Learning Solutions, 501 Boylston Street, Suite 900, Boston, MA 02116
A Pearson Education Company
www.pearsoned.com

Printed in the United States of America

4 5 6 7 8 9 10 V011 15 14 13 12 11

000200010270646579

MT

ISBN 10: 0-558-92659-2
ISBN 13: 978-0-558-92659-5

▶▶▶ CONTENTS

1

Whole Numbers

1.1 ▶▶▶ Reading and Writing Whole Numbers

OBJECTIVES

1. **Identify whole numbers.**
2. **Give the place value of a digit.**
3. **Write a number in words or digits.**
4. **Read a table.**

Knowing how to read and write numbers is an important step in learning mathematics.

OBJECTIVE 1 Identify whole numbers. The **decimal system** of writing numbers uses the ten digits

$$0, 1, 2, 3, 4, 5, 6, 7, 8, 9$$

to write any number. For example, these digits can be used to write **the whole numbers:**

$$0, 1, 2, 3, 4, 5, 6, 7, 8, 9, 10, 11, 12, 13 \ldots$$

The three dots indicate that the list goes on forever.

OBJECTIVE 2 Give the place value of a digit. Each digit in a whole number has a **place value,** depending on its position in the whole number. The following place value chart shows the names of the different places used most often and has the whole number 153,524 entered.

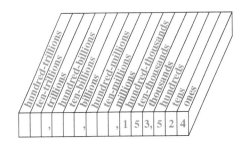

Starbucks sells 153,524 pounds of coffee each day. Each of the 5s in 153,524 represents a different amount because of its position, or **place value** within the number. The **place value** of the 5 on the left is 5 ten-thousands (50,000). The **place value** of the 5 on the right is 5 hundreds (500).

1 Identify the place value of the 4 in each whole number.

(a) 341

(b) 714

(c) 479

EXAMPLE 1 Identifying Place Values

Identify the place value of 8 in each whole number.

Each "8" has a different value.

(a) 28
⌐ 8 ones

(b) 85
⌐ 8 tens

(c) 869
⌐ 8 hundreds

Notice that the value of 8 in each number is different, depending on its location (place) in the number.

◀ *Work Problem* **1** *at the Side.*

EXAMPLE 2 Identifying Place Values

Identify the place value of each digit in the number 725,283.

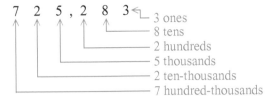

7 2 5 , 2 8 3 ↰ 3 ones
                      8 tens
                      2 hundreds
                      5 thousands
                      2 ten-thousands
                      7 hundred-thousands

ANSWERS

1. **(a)** tens **(b)** ones **(c)** hundreds

Notice the comma between the hundreds and thousands position in the number 725,283 in Example 2.

Work Problem **2** *at the Side.* ▶

Using Commas

Commas are used to separate each group of three digits, starting from the right. This makes numbers easier to read. (An exception: Commas are frequently omitted in four-digit numbers such as 9748 or 1329.) Each three-digit group is called a **period.** Some instructors prefer to just call them **groups.**

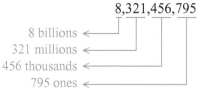

2 Identify the place value of each digit.

  (a) 14,218

  (b) 460,329

3 In the number 3,251,609,328 identify the digits in each period (group).

  (a) billions period

EXAMPLE 3   **Knowing the Period or Group Names**

Write the digits in each period of 8,321,456,795.

$$8,321,456,795$$

8 billions ←
321 millions ←
456 thousands ←
795 ones ←

  (b) millions period

Work Problem **3** *at the Side.* ▶

Use the following rule to read a number with more than three digits.

Writing Numbers in Words

Start at the left when writing a number in words or saying it aloud. Write or say the digit names in each period (group), followed by the name of the period, except for the period name "ones," which is *not* used.

  (c) thousands period

  (d) ones period

OBJECTIVE **3** **Write a number in words or digits.**   The following examples show how to write names for whole numbers.

EXAMPLE 4   **Writing Numbers in Words**

Write each number in words.

(a) 57
    This number means 5 tens and 7 ones, or 50 ones and 7 ones. Write the number as

fifty-seven.

Continued on Next Page

4 Write each number in words.

(a) 18

(b) 36

(c) 418

(d) 902

5 Write each number in words.

(a) 3104

(b) 95,372

(c) 100,075,002

(d) 11,022,040,000

6 Rewrite each number using digits.

(a) one thousand, four hundred thirty-seven

(b) nine hundred seventy-one thousand, six

(c) eighty-two million, three hundred twenty-five

ANSWERS

4. (a) eighteen
   (b) thirty-six
   (c) four hundred eighteen
   (d) nine hundred two
5. (a) three thousand, one hundred four
   (b) ninety-five thousand, three hundred seventy-two
   (c) one hundred million, seventy-five thousand, two
   (d) eleven billion, twenty-two million, forty thousand
6. (a) 1437   (b) 971,006   (c) 82,000,325

(b) 94

ninety-four

Remember: Start at the left to read a number.

(c) 874

eight hundred seventy-four

(d) 601

six hundred one

◄ *Work Problem* **4** *at the Side.*

CAUTION

The word *and* should never be used when writing whole numbers. You will often hear someone say "five hundred *and* twenty-two," but the use of "and" is not correct since "522" is a whole number. When you work with decimal numbers, the word *and* is used to show the position of the decimal point. For example, 98.6 is read as "ninety-eight *and* six tenths."

EXAMPLE 5   **Writing Numbers in Words by Using Period Names**

Write each number in words.

(a) 725,283

seven hundred twenty-five **thousand,** two hundred eighty-three

Number in period   Name   Number in period (not
   of period   necessary to write "ones")

(b) 7252

Careful: Do not use "and" when reading a whole number.

seven **thousand,** two hundred fifty-two

Name of period   No period name needed

(c) 111,356,075

one hundred eleven **million,** three hundred fifty-six **thousand,** seventy-five

(d) 17,000,017,000

seventeen **billion,** seventeen **thousand**

◄ *Work Problem* **5** *at the Side.*

EXAMPLE 6   **Writing Numbers in Digits**

Rewrite each number using digits.

(a) six **thousand,** twenty-two

6022   *With 4 digits or fewer, no comma is needed.*

(b) two hundred fifty-six **thousand,** six hundred twelve

256,612

(c) nine **million,** five hundred fifty-nine

9,000,559

Zeros indicate there are no thousands.

◄ *Work Problem* **6** *at the Side.*

🖩 **Calculator Tip**   Does your calculator show a comma between each group of three digits? Probably not, but try entering a long number such as 34,629,075. Notice that there is no key with a comma on it, so you do not enter commas. A few calculators may show the position of the commas *above* the digits, like this

$$34'629'075$$

Most of the time you will have to write in the commas where needed.

OBJECTIVE 4 Read a table.   A common way of showing number values is by using a **table.** Tables organize and display facts so that they are more easily understood. The following table shows some past facts and future predictions for the United States.

These estimated numbers give us a glimpse of what we can expect in the 21st century.

NUMBERS FOR THE 21ST CENTURY

Year	1990	2010	2020*
U.S. population	261 million	307 million	338 million
Births	16 million	14 million	13 million
Household income	$42,936	$49,564	$53,375
Average salary	$21,129	$25,743	$28,050

*Estimated figures
Source: Family Circle magazine; U.S. Census Bureau.

If you read from left to right along the row labeled "U.S. population," you find that the population in 1990 was 261 million, then the population in 2010 was 307 million, and the estimated population for 2020 is 338 million.

EXAMPLE 7   Reading a Table

Use the table to find each number, and write the number in words.

(a) The estimated household income in the year 2020
Read from left to right along the row labeled "Household income" until you reach the 2020 column and find $53,375.

Fifty-three thousand, three hundred seventy-five dollars

(b) The average salary in 1990.
Read from left to right along the row labeled "Average salary." In the 1990 column you find $21,129.

Twenty-one thousand, one hundred twenty-nine dollars

Remember: use hyphens when necessary.

Work Problem **7** *at the Side.* ▶

Note
Notice in Example 7 that hyphens are used when writing numbers in words. A hyphen is used when writing the numbers 21 through 99 (twenty-one through ninety-nine), except for numbers ending in zero (20, 30, 40, ... 90).

7 Use the table to find each number, and write the number in digits when given in words, or write the number in words when given in digits.

(a) The number of births in 2010

(b) The estimated number of births in 2020

(c) Household income in 1990

(d) The estimated average salary in 2020

Math in the Media

The Wedding Report recently released statistics showing the average wedding costs in the United States in 2008. In 2004, the cost of the average wedding was $24,168. This cost has increased as the average number of wedding guests has grown to over 200. The graph gives most of the costs involved in a wedding. Use this information to answer the questions that follow.

Numbers in the News

'Til Debt Do You Part

With over 200 guests, the cost of an average wedding has continued to grow. Most of the money is spent on the following:

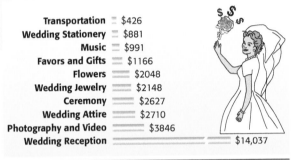

Transportation	$426
Wedding Stationery	$881
Music	$991
Favors and Gifts	$1166
Flowers	$2048
Wedding Jewelry	$2148
Ceremony	$2627
Wedding Attire	$2710
Photography and Video	$3846
Wedding Reception	$14,037

Source: The Wedding Report, *Wedding Statistics and Research for the Wedding Industry.*

1. What is the total of the costs shown in the graph?

2. How much more expensive was a wedding in 2008 compared with 2004?

3. The groom pays for the photography and video, the flowers, the wedding jewelry, the clergy ($500), and the groom's formal wear ($95). What is the total amount spent by the groom?

4. If you budgeted $65 per person for the wedding reception and you invited 225 guests to a wedding in 2004, how much would you have spent compared to the 2008 wedding reception costs?

5. If you budget $6000 for the wedding reception and the cost per person is $37, how many guests can you invite and how much of your budgeted amount will be left over?

6. If you budget $1000 for the wedding reception and the cost per person is $15, how many guests can you invite and how much of your budgeted amount will be left over?

7. What kind of an arithmetic problem did you work to get the answers to Problems 5 and 6? What is the mathematical term for the "left over" budget?

1.1 ▶▶▶ Exercises

Write the digit for the given **place value** *in each whole number. See Examples 1 and 2.*

1. 3065
thousands
tens

2. 4681
thousands
ones

3. 18,015
ten-thousands
hundreds

4. 86,332
ten-thousands
ones

5. 7,628,592,183
millions
thousands

6. 1,700,225,016
billions
millions

Write the digits for the given **period** *(group) in each whole number. See Example 3.*

7. 3,561,435
millions
thousands
ones

8. 28,785,203
millions
thousands
ones

9. 60,000,502,109
billions
millions
thousands
ones

10. 100,258,100,006
billions
millions
thousands
ones

11. Do you think the fact that humans have four fingers and a thumb on each hand explains why we use a number system based on ten digits? Explain.

12. The decimal system uses ten digits. Fingers and toes are often referred to as digits. In your opinion, is there a relationship here? Explain.

Write each number in words. See Examples 4 and 5.

13. 23,115

14. 37,886

15. 346,009

16. 218,033

17. 25,756,665

18. 999,993,000

Write each number using digits. See Example 6.

19. sixty-three thousand, one hundred sixty-three

20. ninety-five thousand, one hundred eleven

21. ten million, two hundred twenty-three

22. one hundred million, two hundred

Write the numbers from each sentence using digits. See Example 6.

23. There are three million, two hundred thousand parachute jumps in the United States each year. (*Source:* History Channel.)

24. The United States Postal Service set a record of two hundred eighty million, four hundred eighty-nine thousand postmarked pieces of mail on a single day. (*Source:* U.S. Postal Service.)

25. The number of cans of Pepsi Cola sold each day is fifty million, fifty-one thousand, five hundred seven. (*Source:* Andy Rooney, *60 Minutes*.)

26. The number of motorcycle owners in the world is twenty-three million, five hundred thirty-five thousand. (*Source:* Motorcycle Industry Council.)

27. There are fifty-four million, seven hundred fifty thousand Hot Wheels sold each year. (*Source:* Andy Rooney, *60 Minutes*.)

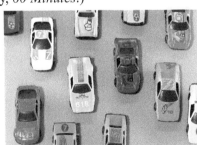

28. Burger King sells two million, four hundred thousand hamburgers each day, (*Source:* Andy Rooney, *60 Minutes*.)

29. Rewrite eight hundred trillion, six hundred twenty-one million, twenty thousand, two hundred fifteen by using digits.

30. Rewrite 70,306,735,002,102 in words

The table at the right shows various ways people get to work. Use the table to answer Exercises 31–34. See Example 7.

31. Which method of transportation is least used? Write the number in words.

32. Which method of transportation is most used? Write the number in words.

33. Find the number of people who walk to work or work at home, and write it in words.

GETTING TO WORK	
How workers 16 and over get to work:	
Drive alone	84,215,298
Carpool	15,377,634
Walk or work at home	7,894,911
Use public transportation	6,069,589

Source: U.S. Census Bureau.

34. Find the number of people who carpool, and write it in words.

Study Skills

> *Be sure to read Your Brain Can Learn Mathematics before this activity. You'll find out how your brain learns and remembers.*

Your textbook can be very helpful. Find out what it has to offer. First, let's look at some general features that will help in all chapters.

Each chapter is divided into sections, and each section has a number, such as 1.3 or 3.5. Your instructor will use these numbers to assign readings and homework.

$$\text{Chapter 3} \rightarrow \textbf{3.5} \leftarrow \text{Section 5 within Chapter 3}$$

There are four features to pay special attention to as you work in your book.

▶ **Objectives.** Each section lists the objectives in the upper corner of the first page. The objectives are listed again as each one is introduced. An objective tells you *what you will be able to do after you complete the section*. An excellent way to check your learning is to go back to the list of objectives when you are finished with a section and ask yourself if you can do them all.

▶ **Margin Exercises.** The exercises in the shaded margins of the pages in your textbook give you immediate practice. **This is a perfect way to get your dendrites growing right away!** The answers are given at the bottom, so you can check yourself easily.

▶ **Cautions, Pointers, Notes, and Calculator Tips.**
  • **Caution!** A bright yellow box is a comment about a common error that students make or a common trouble spot you will want to avoid.
  • **Pointers** are little "clouds" next to worked examples. They point to specific places where common mistakes are made and give on-the-spot reminders.
  • Look for the specially marked purple **Note** boxes. They contain hints, explanations, or interesting side comments about a topic.
  • A small picture of a red calculator ▦ appears several places. In the main part of the chapter, the icon means that there is a **Calculator Tip,** which helps you learn more about using your calculator. A calculator in an Exercise section is a recommendation to use your calculator to work that exercise.

How do you find out if you've worked the exercises correctly? Your textbook provides many of the answers. Throughout each chapter you should work the sample problems in the **margins.** The answers for those are at the **bottom of each page** in the margin area.

For homework, you can find the answers to all of the **odd-numbered section exercises** in the **Answers to Selected Exercises** section near the end of your textbook. Also, *all* of the answers are given for the Chapter Review Exercises and Chapter Tests. Check your textbook now, and find the page on which the Answers section begins.

OBJECTIVES

1 Explain the meaning of text features such as section numbering, objectives, margin exercises.

2 Locate the Index, Answers, and Solutions sections.

Table of Contents

Section Numbering

Chapter Features

> How will you make good use of the features at the end of each chapter?
> _____
> _____

End of Chapter Features

9

End of Chapter Features
(continued)

Answers

> *Flag the Answers section with a sticky note or other device, so that you can turn to it quickly.*

Solutions

Index

Why Are These Features Brain Friendly?

The textbook authors included text features that make it easier for you to understand the mathematics. **Your brain naturally seeks organization and predictability.** When you pay attention to the regular features of your textbook, you are allowing your brain to get familiar with all of the helpful tips, suggestions, and explanations that your book has to offer. You will make the best possible use of your textbook.

The Solutions section near the end of the book shows how to solve some of the harder odd-numbered exercises step by step. Look for the problem numbers with a square of blue shading around them. These are the ones that have a solution.

The Index is the last thing in your book. It lists all the topics, vocabulary, and concepts in alphabetical order. For example, look up the words below. Go to the page or pages listed and find each word. Write down the page that introduces or defines each one. There may be several subheadings listed under the main word, or several page numbers listed. Usually, the *first* place that a word appears in the textbook is where it is introduced and defined. So, the earliest page number is a good place to start.

> *Commutative property of multiplication* is defined on page _____.
> *Factors* of numbers are defined on page _____.
> *Rounding of mixed numbers* is explained on page _____.

> List a page number from Chapter 1 for each of these features:
> A *Caution* appears on page_____.
> A *Pointer* appears on page_____.
> A *Note* appears on page_____.
> A *Calculator Tip* appears on page_____.

1.2 ▶▶▶ Adding Whole Numbers

There are four soccer balls at the left and two at the right. In all, there are six soccer balls.

The process of finding the total is called **addition.** Here 4 and 2 were added to get 6. Addition is written with a + sign, so that

$$4 + 2 = 6.$$

OBJECTIVE 1 Add two single-digit numbers. In addition, the numbers being added are called **addends,** and the resulting answer is called the **sum** or **total.**

$$
\begin{array}{r}
4 \leftarrow \text{Addend} \\
+ 2 \leftarrow \text{Addend} \\
\hline
6 \leftarrow \text{Sum (total)}
\end{array}
$$

Addition problems can also be written horizontally, as follows.

$$
\begin{array}{ccccc}
4 & + & 2 & = & 6 \\
\uparrow & & \uparrow & & \uparrow \\
\text{Addend} & \text{Addend} & & \text{Sum}
\end{array}
$$

> **Commutative Property of Addition**
> By the **commutative property of addition,** changing the order of the addends in an addition problem does not change the sum.

For example, the sum of $4 + 2$ is the same as the sum of $2 + 4$. This allows the addition of the same numbers in a different order.

EXAMPLE 1 Adding Two Single-Digit Numbers

Add, and then change the order of numbers to write another addition problem.

(a) $5 + 3 = 8$ and $3 + 5 = 8$

(b) $7 + 8 = 15$ and $8 + 7 = 15$ *Changing the order in addition does not change the sum.*

(c) $8 + 3 = 11$ and $3 + 8 = 11$

(d) $8 + 8 = 16$

Work Problem ☐1 *at the Side.* ▶

> **Associative Property of Addition**
> By the **associative property of addition,** changing the grouping of the addends in an addition problem does not change the sum.

For example, the sum of $3 + 5 + 6$ may be found as follows.

$$(3 + 5) + 6 = 8 + 6 = 14 \qquad \text{Parentheses tell us to add } 3 + 5 \text{ first.}$$

Another way to add the same numbers is   *Changing the grouping of addends does not change the sum.*

$$3 + (5 + 6) = 3 + 11 = 14. \qquad \text{Parentheses tell us to add } 5 + 6 \text{ first.}$$

Either grouping gives a sum of 14 because of the associative property of addition.

1 Add, and then change the order of numbers to write another addition problem.

(a) $2 + 6$

(b) $9 + 5$

(c) $4 + 7$

(d) $6 + 9$

ANSWERS

1. (a) $8; 6 + 2 = 8$ **(b)** $14; 5 + 9 = 14$
   (c) $11; 7 + 4 = 11$ **(d)** $15; 9 + 6 = 15$

2 Add each column of numbers.

(a)   3
         8
         5
         4
       + 6

(b)   5
         6
         3
         2
       + 4

(c)   9
         6
         8
         7
       + 3

(d)   3
         8
         6
         4
       + 8

OBJECTIVE 2 Add more than two numbers. To add several numbers, first write them in a column. Add the first number to the second. Add this sum to the third number. Continue until all the numbers are used.

EXAMPLE 2 Adding More Than Two Numbers

Add 2, 5, 6, 1, and 4.

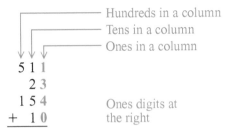

The sum is 18.

◀ *Work Problem* **2** *at the Side.*

Note

By the commutative and associative properties of addition, numbers may also be added starting at the bottom of a column. Adding from the top or adding from the bottom will give the same answer.

OBJECTIVE 3 Add when regrouping (carrying) is not required. If numbers have two or more digits, you must arrange the numbers in columns so that the ones digits are in the same column, tens are in the same column, hundreds are in the same column, and so on. Next, you add column by column starting at the right.

EXAMPLE 3 Adding without Regrouping

Add $511 + 23 + 154 + 10$.

First line up the numbers in columns, with the ones column at the right.

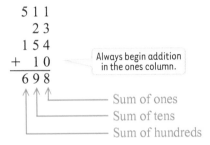

Now start at the right and add the ones digits. Add the tens digits next, and finally, the hundreds digits.

The sum of the four numbers is 698.

Work Problem 3 *at the Side.* ▶

OBJECTIVE 4 **Add with regrouping (carrying).** If the sum of the digits in any column is more than 9, use **regrouping** (sometimes called **carrying**).

EXAMPLE 4   **Adding with Regrouping**

Add 47 and 29.

Add ones.

$$\begin{array}{r} 47 \\ + 29 \\ \hline \end{array}$$

— 7 ones and 9 ones = 16 ones

Regroup 16 ones as 1 ten and 6 ones. Write 6 ones in the ones column and write 1 ten in the tens column.

$$\begin{array}{r} 1 \\ 47 \\ + 29 \\ \hline 6 \end{array}$$

Write 1 ten in the tens column.
7 ones and 9 ones = 16 ones
Write 6 ones in the ones column.

Add the digits in the tens column, including the regrouped 1.

$$\begin{array}{r} 1 \\ 47 \\ + 29 \\ \hline 76 \end{array}$$

— 1 ten + 4 tens + 2 tens = 7 tens

Work Problem 4 *at the Side.* ▶

EXAMPLE 5   **Adding with Regrouping**

Add 324 + 7855 + 23 + 7 + 86.

Step 1   Add the digits in the ones column.

$$\begin{array}{r} 2 \\ 324 \\ 7855 \\ 23 \\ 7 \\ + 86 \\ \hline 5 \end{array}$$

Write 2 tens in the tens column.
Sum of the ones column is 25 ones.
Write 5 ones in the ones column.

Notice that 25 ones are regrouped as 2 tens and 5 ones.

Step 2   Add the digits in the tens column, including the regrouped 2.

$$\begin{array}{r} 12 \\ 324 \\ 7855 \\ 23 \\ 7 \\ + 86 \\ \hline 95 \end{array}$$

Write 1 hundred in the hundreds column.
Sum of the tens column is 19 tens.

Notice that 19 tens are regrouped as 1 hundred and 9 tens.

Write 9 in the tens column.

Continued on Next Page

---

3 Add.

(a) $\begin{array}{r} 26 \\ + 73 \\ \hline \end{array}$

(b) $\begin{array}{r} 534 \\ + 265 \\ \hline \end{array}$

(c) $\begin{array}{r} 42,305 \\ + 11,563 \\ \hline \end{array}$

4 Add with regrouping

(a) $\begin{array}{r} 66 \\ + 27 \\ \hline \end{array}$

(b) $\begin{array}{r} 58 \\ + 33 \\ \hline \end{array}$

(c) $\begin{array}{r} 56 \\ + 37 \\ \hline \end{array}$

(d) $\begin{array}{r} 34 \\ + 49 \\ \hline \end{array}$

ANSWERS
3. **(a)** 99 **(b)** 799 **(c)** 53,868
4. **(a)** 93 **(b)** 91 **(c)** 93 **(d)** 83

5 Add by regrouping as necessary.

(a) 42
     651
     396
   + 87

(b)   162
     4271
      372
   + 8976

(c) 57
      4
    392
    804
     51
   + 27

(d) 7821
      435
       72
      305
   + 1693

6 Add by regrouping mentally.

(a) 816
     363
      17
       2
       5
   + 7654

(b) 3305
      650
      708
       29
       40
        6
   +   3

(c) 15,829
       765
        78
        15
         9
         7
   + 13,179

Step 3   Add the hundreds column, including the regrouped 1.

1 1 2
 324
7855
  23
   7
+ 86
 295

Sum of the hundreds column is 12 hundreds.

Write 1 thousand in the thousands column.

Notice that 12 hundreds are regrouped as 1 thousand and 2 hundreds.

Write 2 hundreds in the hundreds column.

Step 4   Add the thousands column, including the regrouped 1.

1 1 2
 324
7855
  23
   7
+ 86
8295

Sum of the thousands column is 8.

Finally, 324 + 7855 + 23 + 7 + 86 = 8295.

◀ *Work Problem* **5** *at the Side.*

Note

For additional speed, try to regroup mentally. Do not write the regrouped number, but just remember it as you move to the top of the next column. Try this method. If it works for you, use it.

◀ *Work Problem* **6** *at the Side.*

OBJECTIVE 5 Use addition to solve application problems.   In **Section 1.10** we will describe how to solve application problems in more detail. The next two examples are application problems that require adding.

EXAMPLE 6   **Applying Addition Skills**

On this map of the Walt Disney World area in Florida, the distance in miles from one location to another is written alongside of the road. Find the shortest route from Altamonte Springs to Clear Lake.

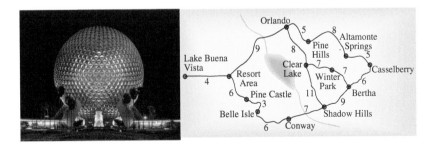

Continued on Next Page

Approach   Add the mileage along various routes to determine the distances from Altamonte Springs to Clear Lake. Then select the shortest route.

Solution   One way from Altamonte Springs to Clear Lake is through Orlando. Add the mileage numbers along this route.

8	Altamonte Springs to Pine Hills
5	Pine Hills to Orlando
+ 8	Orlando to Clear Lake
21 →	miles from Altamonte Springs to Clear Lake, going through Orlando

> Remember: Shortest distance is the fewest total miles.

Another way is through Casselberry, Bertha, and Winter Park. Add the mileage numbers along this route.

5	Altamonte Springs to Casselberry
6	Casselberry to Bertha
7	Bertha to Winter Park
+ 7	Winter Park to Clear Lake
25 →	miles from Altamonte Springs to Clear Lake through Bertha and Winter Park

The shortest route from Altamonte Springs to Clear Lake is 21 miles through Orlando.

Work Problem **7** *at the Side.* ▶

EXAMPLE 7   **Finding a Total Distance**

Use the map in Example 6 to find the total distance from Shadow Hills to Casselberry to Orlando and back to Shadow Hills.

Approach   Add the mileage from Shadow Hills to Casselberry to Orlando and back to Shadow Hills to find the total distance.

Solution   Use the numbers from the map.

9	Shadow Hills to Bertha
6	Bertha to Casselberry
5	Casselberry to Altamonte Springs
8	Altamonte Springs to Pine Hills
5	Pine Hills to Orlando
8	Orlando to Clear Lake
+ 11	Clear Lake to Shadow Hills
52 →	miles from Shadow Hills to Casselberry to Orlando and back to Shadow Hills

Work Problem **8** *at the Side.* ▶

EXAMPLE 8   **Finding a Perimeter**

Find the number of feet of floating pipe needed to contain the farm-raised salmon in the habitat shown.

The short way to write *feet* is *ft.*

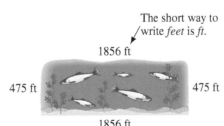

1856 ft

475 ft   475 ft

1856 ft

Approach   Find the **perimeter,** or total distance around the habitat, by adding the lengths of all the sides.

——— **Continued on Next Page**

7 Use the map in Example 6 to find the shortest route from Lake Buena Vista to Conway.

8 The road is closed between Orlando and Clear Lake, so this route cannot be used. Use the map in Example 6 to find the next shortest route from Orlando to Clear Lake.

ANSWERS

7. 19 miles
8.

5	Orlando to Pine Hills
8	Pine Hills to Altamonte Springs
5	Altamonte Springs to Casselberry
6	Casselberry to Bertha
7	Bertha to Winter Park
+7	Winter Park to Clear Lake
38 miles	

9 Solve the problem. Find the number of feet of fencing needed to enclose the solar electricity generating project shown.

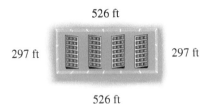

526 ft

297 ft   297 ft

526 ft

10 Check the following additions. If an answer is incorrect, find the correct answer.

(a)
```
    63
     4
     9
 + 28
   104
```

(b)
```
   927
   395
    64
 + 251
  1637
```

(c)
```
    79
   218
     7
 + 639
   953
```

(d)
```
   21,892
   11,746
 + 43,925
   79,563
```

Solution   Use the lengths shown.

```
    1856
     475
    1856
 +   475
    4662 ft
```

The amount of floating pipe needed is 4662 ft, which is the perimeter of (distance around) the habitat.

◀ *Work Problem* **9** *at the Side.*

OBJECTIVE 6 **Check the answer in addition.** Checking the answer is an important part of problem solving. A common method for checking addition is to re-add from bottom to top. This is an application of the commutative and associative properties of addition.

EXAMPLE 9 **Checking Addition**

Check the following addition.

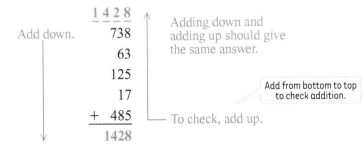

Add down.

```
   1428
    738
     63
    125
     17
 +  485
   1428
```

Adding down and adding up should give the same answer.

Add from bottom to top to check addition.

To check, add up.

Here the answers agree, so the sum is probably correct.

EXAMPLE 10 **Checking Addition**

Check the following additions. Are they correct?

(a)
```
    785        1033
     63         785
 +  185          63
   1033       + 185
              1033
```
Correct, because both answers are the same.

To check, add up.

(b)
```
    635        2454
     73         635
    831          73
 +  915         831
   2444       + 915
              2444
```
Error, because the answers are different.

To check, add up.

Avoid wrong answers by checking your work.

Re-add to find that the correct sum is 2454.

◀ *Work Problem* **10** *at the Side.*

Add. See Examples 1–3.

1. 43
+ 54

2. 18
+ 11

3. 56
+ 33

4. 83
+ 15

5. 317
+ 572

6. 574
+ 325

7. 318
151
+ 420

8. 135
253
+ 410

9. 6310
252
+ 1223

10. 121
5705
+ 3163

11. 932 + 44 + 613

12. 517 + 131 + 250

13. 1251 + 4311 + 2114

14. 3241 + 1513 + 2014

15. 12,142 + 43,201 + 23,103

16. 41,124 + 12,302 + 23,500

17. 3213 + 5715

18. 6344 + 1655

19. 38,204 + 21,020

20. 63,251 + 36,305

Add, regrouping as necessary. See Examples 4 and 5.

21. 87
+ 63

22. 19
+ 92

23. 86
+ 69

24. 37
+ 85

25. 47
+ 74

26. 97
+ 79

27. 67
+ 78

28. 96
+ 47

29. 73
+ 29

30. 68
+ 37

31. 746
+ 905

32. 621
+ 359

33. 306
+ 848

34. 798
+ 206

35. 278
+ 135

36. 172
+ 156

37. 928
+ 843

38. 686
+ 726

39. 526
+ 884

40. 116
+ 897

41.
$$3574 \\ +\ 2817$$

42.
$$6871 \\ +\ 7528$$

43.
$$7896 \\ +\ 3728$$

44.
$$9382 \\ +\ 7586$$

45.
$$9625 \\ +\ 7986$$

46.
$$5718 \\ 5623 \\ +\ 7436$$

47.
$$9056 \\ 78 \\ 6089 \\ +\ 731$$

48.
$$4022 \\ 709 \\ 8621 \\ +\ 37$$

49.
$$18 \\ 708 \\ 9286 \\ +\ 636$$

50.
$$1708 \\ 321 \\ 61 \\ +\ 8926$$

51.
$$422 \\ 6074 \\ 435 \\ +\ 8663$$

52.
$$6505 \\ 173 \\ 7044 \\ +\ 168$$

53.
$$321 \\ 9603 \\ 8 \\ 21 \\ +\ 1604$$

54.
$$7631 \\ 5983 \\ 7 \\ 36 \\ +\ 505$$

55.
$$2109 \\ 63 \\ 16 \\ 3 \\ +\ 9887$$

56.
$$322 \\ 6508 \\ 93 \\ 745 \\ 18 \\ +\ 2005$$

57.
$$553 \\ 97 \\ 2772 \\ 437 \\ 63 \\ +\ 328$$

58.
$$3187 \\ 810 \\ 527 \\ 76 \\ 2665 \\ +\ 317$$

59.
$$413 \\ 85 \\ 9919 \\ 602 \\ 31 \\ +\ 1218$$

60.
$$576 \\ 7934 \\ 60 \\ 781 \\ 5968 \\ +\ 371$$

Check each addition. If an answer is incorrect, find the correct answer. See Examples 9 and 10.

61.
$$832 \\ 468 \\ +\ 791 \\ \hline 2091$$

62.
$$326 \\ 852 \\ +\ 679 \\ \hline 1857$$

63.
$$179 \\ 214 \\ +\ 376 \\ \hline 759$$

64.
$$17 \\ 296 \\ 713 \\ +\ 94 \\ \hline 1220$$

65.
$$4713 \\ 28 \\ 615 \\ +\ 64 \\ \hline 5420$$

66.
$$3\ 628 \\ 72 \\ 564 \\ +\ 7\ 319 \\ \hline 11{,}583$$

67.
$$678 \\ 7\ 952 \\ 56 \\ 718 \\ +\ 2\ 173 \\ \hline 11{,}377$$

68.
$$516 \\ 8\ 760 \\ 24 \\ 189 \\ +\ 1\ 723 \\ \hline 11{,}212$$

69.
$$4\ 714 \\ 27 \\ 77 \\ 8\ 878 \\ +\ 636 \\ \hline 14{,}332$$

70.
$$6\ 715 \\ 283 \\ 9\ 617 \\ 13 \\ +\ 81 \\ \hline 16{,}719$$

71. Explain the commutative property of addition in your own words. How is this used when checking an addition problem?

72. Explain the associative property of addition. How can this be used when adding columns of numbers?

For Exercises 73–76, use the map to find the shortest route between each pair of cities. See Examples 6 and 7.

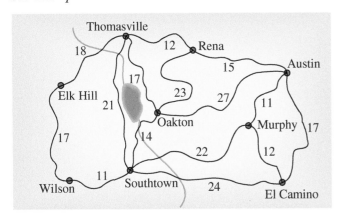

73. Southtown and Rena

74. Elk Hill and Oakton

75. Thomasville and Murphy

76. Murphy and Thomasville

Solve each application problem.

77. The Twin Lakes Food Bank raised $3482 at a flea market and $12,860 at their annual auction. Find the total amount raised at these two events.

78. A clothing store ordered 75 tops and 52 pairs of shorts. How many items were ordered?

79. There are 413 women and 286 men on the sales staff. How many people are on the sales staff?

80. One department in an office building has 283 employees while another department has 218 employees. How many employees are in the two departments?

81. This semester there are 13,786 students enrolled in on-campus day classes, 3497 students enrolled in night classes, and 2874 student's enrolled in on-line classes. Find the total number of students enrolled.

82. Robert and Crystal Hernandez have a car loan balance of $10,329 and a balance owed on their credit card of $2685. After receiving a home loan of $169,760, find the total amount of their loans.

Solve each problem involving perimeter. See Example 8.

83. Find the total distance around a lot that has been developed as a go-cart track.

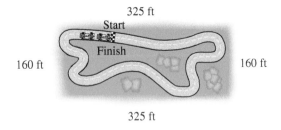

84. Because of heavy snowfall this winter, Maria needs to put new rain gutters around her entire roof. How many feet of gutters will she need?

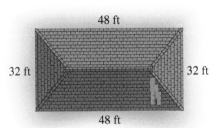

85. Martin plans to frame his back patio with redwood lumber. How many feet of lumber will he need?

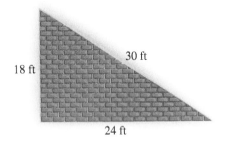

86. Due to a recent tornado, Carl Jones needs to replace all the fencing around his cow pasture. How many meters of fencing will he need?

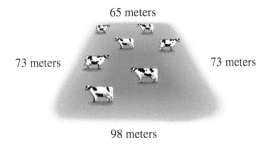

Relating Concepts (Exercises 87–94) For Individual or Group Work

Recall the place values of digits discussed in Section 1.1 and **work Exercises 87–94 in order.**

87. Write the largest four-digit number possible using the digits 4, 1, 9, and 2. Use each digit once.

88. Using the digits 4, 1, 9, and 2, write the smallest four-digit number possible. Use each digit once.

89. Write the largest five-digit number possible using the digits 6, 2, and 7. Use each digit at least once.

90. Using the digits 6, 2, and 7, write the smallest five-digit number possible. Use each digit at least once.

91. Write the largest seven-digit number possible using the digits 4, 3, and 9. Use each digit at least twice.

92. Using the digits 4, 3, and 9, write the smallest seven-digit number possible. Use each digit at least twice.

93. Explain your rule or procedure for writing the largest number in Exercise 91.

94. Explain your rule or procedure for writing the smallest number in Exercise 92.

1.3 ▶▶▶ Subtracting Whole Numbers

Suppose you have $9, and you spend $2 for parking. You then have $7 left. There are two different ways of looking at these numbers.

As an addition problem:

$$\$2 \;+\; \$7 \;=\; \$9$$

    ↑   ↑   ↑

  Amount   Amount   Original
   spent   left   amount

As a subtraction problem:

$$\$9 \;-\; \$2 \;=\; \$7$$

 ↑   ↑   ↑   ↑

 Original Subtraction Amount Amount
 amount   symbol   spent   left

OBJECTIVE 1 Change addition problems to subtraction and subtraction problems to addition.   As shown in the box above, an addition problem can be changed to a subtraction problem and a subtraction problem can be changed to an addition problem.

OBJECTIVES

1 Change addition problems to subtraction and subtraction problems to addition.

2 Identify the minuend, subtrahend, and difference.

3 Subtract when no regrouping (borrowing) is needed.

4 Check subtraction answers by adding.

5 Subtract with regrouping (borrowing).

6 Solve application problems with subtraction.

EXAMPLE 1   Changing Addition Problems to Subtraction

Change each addition problem to a subtraction problem.

(a) $4 + 1 = 5$
Two subtraction problems are possible:

$$5 - 1 = 4 \quad \text{or} \quad 5 - 4 = 1$$

These figures show each subtraction problem.

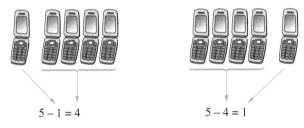

      $5 - 1 = 4$ $5 - 4 = 1$

(b) $8 + 7 = 15$

$$15 - 7 = 8 \quad \text{or} \quad 15 - 8 = 7$$

Work Problem **1** *at the Side.* ▶

EXAMPLE 2   Changing Subtraction Problems to Addition

Change each subtraction problem to an addition problem.

(a) $8 - 3 = 5$
   ↓   ↓   ↓
   $8 = 3 + 5$

It is also correct to write $8 = 5 + 3$.

Continued on Next Page

---

1 Write two subtraction problems for each addition problem.

(a) $7 + 2 = 9$

(b) $7 + 4 = 11$

(c) $15 + 22 = 37$

(d) $23 + 55 = 78$

ANSWERS

1. **(a)** $9 - 2 = 7$ or $9 - 7 = 2$
   (b) $11 - 4 = 7$ or $11 - 7 = 4$
   (c) $37 - 22 = 15$ or $37 - 15 = 22$
   (d) $78 - 55 = 23$ or $78 - 23 = 55$

2 Write an addition problem for each subtraction problem.

(a) $7 - 5 = 2$

(b) $9 - 4 = 5$

(c) $21 - 15 = 6$

(d) $58 - 42 = 16$

3 Subtract.

(a) $\begin{array}{r} 74 \\ -43 \\ \hline \end{array}$

(b) $\begin{array}{r} 68 \\ -24 \\ \hline \end{array}$

(c) $\begin{array}{r} 429 \\ -318 \\ \hline \end{array}$

(d) $\begin{array}{r} 3927 \\ -2614 \\ \hline \end{array}$

(e) $\begin{array}{r} 5464 \\ -324 \\ \hline \end{array}$

(b) $18 - 13 = 5$

$18 = 13 + 5$ or $18 = 5 + 13$

(c) $29 - 13 = 16$

$29 = 13 + 16$ or $29 = 16 + 13$

◀ *Work Problem* 2 *at the Side.*

OBJECTIVE 2 **Identify the minuend, subtrahend, and difference.** In subtraction, as in addition, the numbers in a problem have names. For example, in the problem $8 - 5 = 3$, the number 8 is the **minuend,** 5 is the **subtrahend,** and 3 is the **difference** or answer.

$$\underset{\underset{\text{Minuend}}{\uparrow}}{8} - \underset{\underset{\text{Subtrahend}}{\uparrow}}{5} = 3 \leftarrow \text{Difference}$$

The answer in subtraction is the difference.

$$\begin{array}{r} 8 \leftarrow \text{Minuend} \\ -5 \leftarrow \text{Subtrahend} \\ \hline 3 \leftarrow \text{Difference} \end{array}$$

OBJECTIVE 3 **Subtract when no regrouping (borrowing) is needed.** Subtract two numbers by lining up the numbers in columns so the digits in the ones place are in the same column. Next, subtract by columns, starting at the right with the ones column.

EXAMPLE 3 **Subtracting Two Numbers**

Subtract.

Ones digits are lined up in the same column.

(a) $\begin{array}{r} 53 \\ -21 \\ \hline 32 \end{array}$

3 ones − 1 one = 2 ones
5 tens − 2 tens = 3 tens

Ones digits are lined up.

(b) $\begin{array}{r} 385 \\ -165 \\ \hline 220 \end{array}$ ← Subtract from right to left.

5 ones − 5 ones = 0 ones
8 tens − 6 tens = 2 tens
3 hundreds − 1 hundred = 2 hundreds

(c) $\begin{array}{r} 9437 \\ -210 \\ \hline 9227 \end{array}$

7 ones − 0 ones = 7 ones
3 tens − 1 ten = 2 tens
4 hundreds − 2 hundreds = 2 hundreds
9 thousands − 0 thousands = 9 thousands

◀ *Work Problem* 3 *at the Side.*

OBJECTIVE 4 **Check subtraction answers by adding.** Use addition to check your answer to a subtraction problem. For example, check $8 - 3 = 5$ by *adding* 3 and 5.

$$3 + 5 = 8, \quad \text{so} \quad 8 - 3 = 5 \quad \text{is correct.}$$

ANSWERS

2. (a) $7 = 5 + 2$ or $7 = 2 + 5$
   (b) $9 = 4 + 5$ or $9 = 5 + 4$
   (c) $21 = 15 + 6$ or $21 = 6 + 15$
   (d) $58 = 42 + 16$ or $58 = 16 + 42$
3. (a) 31 (b) 44 (c) 111
   (d) 1313 (e) 5140

EXAMPLE 4   **Checking Subtraction by Using Addition**

Use addition to check each answer. If the answer is incorrect, find the correct answer.

(a)   89
        − 47
        ____
        42

Rewrite as an addition problem, as shown in Example 2.

Subtraction problem {
        89
        − 47
        ____
        42
        ____
        89
}   Addition problem

        47
        + 42
        ____
        89

Because 47 + 42 = 89, the subtraction was done correctly.   Avoid errors by checking answers.

(b) 72 − 41 = 21
        Rewrite as an addition problem.

$$72 = 41 + 21$$

But, 41 + 21 = 62, **not** 72, so the subtraction was done **incorrectly.** Rework the original subtraction to get the correct answer, 31. Then, 41 + 31 = 72.

(c)   374 ⟵ Match
        − 141
        ____
        233   141 + 233 = 374

The answer checks.

─────── Work Problem 4 at the Side. ▶

OBJECTIVE **5** **Subtract with regrouping (borrowing).** When a digit in the minuend is less than the one directly below it, **regrouping** is necessary (also called **borrowing**).

EXAMPLE 5   **Subtracting with Regrouping**

Subtract 19 from 57.

Write the problem vertically.

        57
        − 19
        ____

In the ones column, 7 is **less** than 9, so in order to subtract, we must regroup 1 ten as 10 ones.

5 tens − 1 ten = 4 tens ⟶ 4 17 ⟵ 1 ten = 10 ones, and
                        5̸ 7̸   10 ones + 7 ones = 17 ones
                        − 1 9

Now subtract 9 ones from 17 ones in the ones column. Then subtract 1 ten from 4 tens in the tens column.

        4 17
        5̸ 7̸
        − 1 9
        ____
        3 8   Difference

Finally, 57 − 19 = 38. Check by adding 19 and 38; you should get 57.

─────── Work Problem 5 at the Side. ▶

4 Use addition to determine whether each answer is correct. If incorrect, what should it be?

(a)   76
        − 45
        ____
        31

(b)   53
        − 22
        ____
        21

(c)   374
        − 251
        ____
        113

(d)   7531
        − 4301
        _____
        3230

5 Subtract.

(a)   58
        − 19

(b)   86
        − 38

(c)   41
        − 27

(d)   863
        − 47

(e)   762
        − 157

ANSWERS

4. (a) correct **(b)** incorrect; should be 31
   (c) incorrect; should be 123 **(d)** correct
5. (a) 39 **(b)** 48 **(c)** 14 **(d)** 816
   (e) 605

6 Subtract.

(a) 927
   − 43

(b) 675
   − 86

(c) 477
   − 389

(d) 1417
   − 988

(e) 8739
   − 3892

EXAMPLE 6 Subtracting with Regrouping

Subtract by regrouping when necessary.

(a) 7856
   − 137

Regroup 1 ten as 10 ones. ——— 10 ones + 6 ones = 16 ones

     4 16
  7 8 5̸ 6̸
 − 1 3 7
  7 7 1 9   Difference

(b)   635
    − 546

Regroup 1 ten as 10 ones. 10 ones + 5 ones = 15 ones

    2 15
  6 3̸ 5̸   Need to regroup
 − 5 4 6   further because
      9   2 is less than 4 in
             the tens column.

Regroup 1 hundred as 10 tens 10 tens + 2 tens = 12 tens

   5 12 15
  6̸ 3̸ 5̸
 − 5 4 6
    8 9   Difference

(c)   647
    − 489

    3 17
  6 4̸ 7   Need to regroup further
 − 4 8 9   because 3 is less than
      8   8 in the tens column.

   5 13 17
  6̸ 4̸ 7̸
 − 4 8 9
   1 5 8   Difference

◄ *Work Problem* **6** *at the Side.*

Sometimes a minuend has zeros in some of the positions. In such cases, regrouping may be a little more complicated than what we have shown so far.

EXAMPLE 7 Regrouping with Zeros

Subtract.

    4607
  − 3168

There are no tens that can be regrouped into ones. So you must first regroup 1 hundred as 10 tens.

Regroup 1 hundred as 10 tens. Write 10 tens.

    5 10
  4 6̸ 0 7
 − 3 1 6 8

Now we may regroup from the tens position.

         9 ← Regroup 1 ten as 10 ones;
   5 10 17   10 tens − 1 ten = 9 tens.
  4 6̸ 0̸ 7̸
 − 3 1 6 8   10 ones + 7 ones = 17 ones
         9

Continued on Next Page

Complete the problem.

$$
\begin{array}{r}
5\ \overset{9}{\cancel{10}}\ 17 \\
4\ \cancel{6}\ \cancel{0}\ \cancel{7} \\
-\ 3\ 1\ 6\ 8 \\
\hline
1\ 4\ 3\ 9 \quad \text{Difference}
\end{array}
$$

Check by adding 1439 and 3168; you should get 4607.

Work Problem **7** *at the Side.* ▶

EXAMPLE 8 **Regrouping with Zeros**

Subtract.

(a)
$$
\begin{array}{r}
708 \\
-\ 149 \\
\hline
\end{array}
$$

Write 10 tens. ┌── Regroup 1 ten as 10 ones.

Regroup 1 hundred as → 6 $\overset{9}{\cancel{10}}$ 18 ← 10 ones + 8 ones = 18 ones
10 tens.

$$
\begin{array}{r}
\cancel{7}\ \cancel{0}\ \cancel{8} \\
-\ 1\ 4\ 9 \\
\hline
5\ 5\ 9
\end{array}
$$

(b)
$$
\begin{array}{r}
380 \\
-\ 276 \\
\hline
\end{array}
$$

Regroup 1 ten as 10 ones. ──┐ ┌── Write 10 ones.

$$
\begin{array}{r}
7\ 10 \\
3\ \cancel{8}\ \cancel{0} \\
-\ 2\ 7\ 6 \\
\hline
1\ 0\ 4
\end{array}
$$

(c)
$$
\begin{array}{r}
9000 \\
-\ 6999 \\
\hline
\end{array}
$$

$$
\begin{array}{r}
8\ \overset{9}{\cancel{10}}\ \overset{9}{\cancel{10}}\ 10 \\
\cancel{9}\ \cancel{0}\ \cancel{0}\ \cancel{0} \\
-\ 6\ 9\ 9\ 9 \\
\hline
2\ 0\ 0\ 1
\end{array}
$$

Be extra careful when zeros are involved.

Work Problem **8** *at the Side.* ▶

As we have seen, an answer to a subtraction problem can be checked by adding.

EXAMPLE 9 **Checking Subtraction by Using Addition**

Use addition to check each answer.

Check

(a)
$$
\begin{array}{r}
613 \\
-\ 275 \\
\hline
338
\end{array}
\qquad
\begin{array}{r}
275 \\
+\ 338 \\
\hline
613 \quad \text{Correct}
\end{array}
$$

Match

Continued on Next Page

---

7 Subtract.

(a)
$$
\begin{array}{r}
206 \\
-\ 177 \\
\hline
\end{array}
$$

(b)
$$
\begin{array}{r}
703 \\
-\ 415 \\
\hline
\end{array}
$$

(c)
$$
\begin{array}{r}
7024 \\
-\ 2632 \\
\hline
\end{array}
$$

8 Subtract.

(a)
$$
\begin{array}{r}
308 \\
-\ 159 \\
\hline
\end{array}
$$

(b)
$$
\begin{array}{r}
570 \\
-\ 368 \\
\hline
\end{array}
$$

(c)
$$
\begin{array}{r}
1570 \\
-\ 983 \\
\hline
\end{array}
$$

(d)
$$
\begin{array}{r}
7001 \\
-\ 5193 \\
\hline
\end{array}
$$

(e)
$$
\begin{array}{r}
4000 \\
-\ 1782 \\
\hline
\end{array}
$$

ANSWERS

7. **(a)** 29 **(b)** 288 **(c)** 4392
8. **(a)** 149 **(b)** 202 **(c)** 587
(d) 1808 **(e)** 2218

9 Use addition to check each answer. If the answer is incorrect, find the correct answer.

(a) $\begin{array}{r} 357 \\ - 168 \\ \hline 189 \end{array}$

(b) $\begin{array}{r} 570 \\ - 328 \\ \hline 252 \end{array}$

(c) $\begin{array}{r} 14{,}726 \\ - 8\,839 \\ \hline 5\,887 \end{array}$

10 Use the table from Example 10 to find, on average,

(a) how much more a person with a Bachelor's degree earns each year than a person with an Associate of Arts degree.

(b) how much more a person with an Associate of Arts degree earns each year than a person who is not a high school graduate.

(b) $\begin{array}{r} 1915 \\ - 1635 \\ \hline 280 \end{array}$ *Match*   Check $\begin{array}{r} 1635 \\ + 280 \\ \hline 1915 \end{array}$ Correct

(c) $\begin{array}{r} 15{,}803 \\ - 7\,325 \\ \hline 8\,578 \end{array}$ *No Match*   Check $\begin{array}{r} 7\,325 \\ + 8\,578 \\ \hline 15{,}903 \end{array}$ Error

> It's always a good idea to check your work.

Rework the original problem to get the correct answer, 8478. Then, 7325 + 8478 **does** give 15,803.

◀ *Work Problem* **9** *at the Side.*

OBJECTIVE **6** **Solve application problems with subtraction.**
As shown in the next example, subtraction can be used to solve an application problem.

EXAMPLE 10 **Applying Subtraction Skills**

Use the table to find how much more, on average, a person with an Associate of Arts degree earns each year than a high school graduate.

EDUCATION PAYS
The more education adults get, the higher their annual earnings.

Education Level	Average Earnings
Not a high school graduate	$27,401
High school graduate	$32,860
Some college, no degree	$39,744
Associate of Arts degree	$43,094
Bachelor's degree	$56,655
Master's degree	$67,543
Doctoral degree	$92,035
Professional degree	$118,785

Note: Average annual earnings for workers between ages 25 and 64.

Source: U.S. Census Bureau.

Approach   The average earnings for a person with an Associate of Arts degree is $43,094 each year and the average for a high school graduate is $32,860. Find how much more a college graduate earns by subtracting $32,860 from $43,094.

Solution $\begin{array}{r} \$43{,}094 \\ - \$32{,}860 \\ \hline \$10{,}234 \end{array}$ ← Associate of Arts degree
← High school graduate
← More earnings

> Education pays.

On average, a person with an Associate of Arts degree earns $10,234 more each year than a high school graduate.

◀ *Work Problem* **10** *at the Side.*

Work each subtraction problem. Use addition to check each answer. See Examples 3 and 4.

1.	48 − 32	2.	17 − 13	3.	86 − 53	4.	78 − 35	5.	77 − 60

6.	87 − 63	7.	335 − 122	8.	602 − 301	9.	552 − 451	10.	888 − 215

11. 7352
   − 241

12. 4420
   − 310

13. 5546
   − 2134

14. 1875
   − 1362

15. 6259
   − 4148

16. 9654
   − 4323

17. 24,392
   − 11,232

18. 57,921
   − 34,801

19. 46,253
   − 5 143

20. 75,904
   − 3 702

Use addition to check each subtraction problem. If an answer is not correct, find the correct answer. See Example 4.

21. 54
   − 42
   ‾‾‾‾
   12

22. 87
   − 43
   ‾‾‾‾
   44

23. 89
   − 27
   ‾‾‾‾
   63

24. 47
   − 35
   ‾‾‾‾
   13

25. 382
   − 261
   ‾‾‾‾
   131

26. 754
   − 342
   ‾‾‾‾
   412

27. 4683
   − 3542
   ‾‾‾‾
   1141

28. 5217
   − 4105
   ‾‾‾‾
   1132

29. 8643
   − 1421
   ‾‾‾‾
   7212

30. 9428
   − 3124
   ‾‾‾‾
   6324

Subtract, regrouping when necessary. See Examples 5–8.

31. 75
   − 37

32. 86
   − 28

33. 94
   − 49

34. 68
   − 39

35. 57
   − 38

36. 47
   − 29

37. 828
   − 547

38. 916
   − 618

39. 771
   − 252

40. 973
   − 788

41. 7538
        − 479

42. 5863
        − 1295

43. 9988
        − 2399

44. 3576
        − 1658

45. 38,335
        − 29,476

46. 82,731
        − 14,826

47. 40
        − 37

48. 80
        − 73

49. 60
        − 37

50. 70
        − 27

51. 308
        − 289

52. 600
        − 599

53. 4041
        − 1208

54. 4602
        − 2063

55. 9305
        − 1530

56. 7120
        − 6033

57. 1580
        − 1077

58. 3068
        − 2105

59. 2006
        − 1850

60. 8203
        − 5365

61. 8240
        − 6056

62. 7050
        − 6045

63. 8503
        − 2816

64. 16,004
        − 5 087

65. 80,705
        − 61,667

66. 81,000
        − 55,456

67. 66,000
        − 34,444

68. 77,000
        − 65,308

69. 20,080
        − 13,496

70. 80,056
        − 23,869

Use addition to check each subtraction problem. If an answer is incorrect, find the correct answer. See Example 9.

71. 9428
        − 4509
        ─────
        4919

72. 1671
        − 1325
        ─────
        1346

73. 2548
        − 2278
        ─────
        270

74. 5274
        − 1130
        ─────
        4144

75. 93,758
        − 52,869
        ──────
        40,889

76. 82,357
        − 14,396
        ──────
        68,961

77. 36,778
        − 17,405
        ──────
        19,373

78. 34,821
        − 17,735
        ──────
        17,735

79. An addition problem can be changed to a subtraction problem and a subtraction problem can be changed to an addition problem. Give two examples of each to demonstrate this.

80. Can you use the commutative and the associative properties in subtraction? Explain.

Solve each application problem. See Example 10.

81. A man burns 187 calories during 60 minutes of sitting at a computer while a woman burns 140 calories at the same activity. How many fewer calories does a woman burn than a man? (*Source:* www.cookinglight.com)

82. A woman burns 302 calories during 60 minutes of walking, while a man burns 403 calories doing the same activity. How many more calories does a man burn than a woman? (*Source:* www.cookinglight.com)

83. Toronto's skyline is dominated by the CN Tower, which rises 1821 ft. The Sears Tower in Chicago is 1454 ft high. Find the difference in height between the two structures. (*Source:* Trizec Properties; *World Almanac.*)

1821 ft
d
1454 ft

CN Tower Sears Tower

84. The fastest animal in the world, the peregrine falcon, dives at 217 miles per hour (mph). A Boeing 747 cruises at 580 mph. How much faster is the plane?

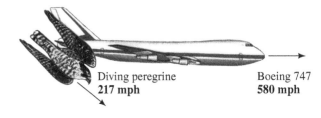

Diving peregrine
217 mph

Boeing 747
580 mph

85. A cruise ship has 1815 passengers. When in port at Grand Cayman, 1348 passengers go ashore for the day while the others remain on the ship. How many passengers remain on the ship?

86. In a recent three-month period there were 81,465 Ford Explorers and 70,449 Jeep Grand Cherokees sold. Which vehicle had greater sales? By how much? (*Source:* J. D. Power and Associates.)

87. Six years ago there were 6970 bridge and lock-tender jobs across the United States. Today there are 3700 that remain. How many of these jobs have been eliminated? (*Source:* Bureau of Labor Statistics.)

88. In 1964, its first year on the market, the Ford Mustang sold for $2500. In 2009, the Ford Mustang sold for $33,065. Find the increase in price. (*Source:* eBay.)

89. Patriot Flag Company manufactured 14,608 U.S. flags and sold 5069. How many flags remain unsold?

90. Eye exams have been given to 14,679 children in the school district. If there are 23,156 students in the school district, how many have not received eye exams?

91. The Jordanos now pay rent of $650 per month. If they buy a house, their housing expense will be $913 per month. How much more will they pay per month if they buy a house?

92. A retired couple who used to receive a Social Security payment of $1479 per month now receives $1568 per month. Find the amount of the monthly increase.

93. On Monday, 11,594 people visited Arcade Amusement Park, and 12,352 people visited the park on Tuesday. Which day had more people visit the park? How many more?

94. In the year 2020 it is predicted that we will need 2,820,000 nurses in the United States, while only 1,810,000 nurses will be available. Find the shortage in the number of nurses. (*Source:* American Hospital Association.)

Solve each application problem. Add or subtract as necessary.

95. A survey of large hotels found that the average salary for a general manager of a deluxe spa and tennis resort is one hundred one thousand, five hundred dollars per year, while spa and tennis directors earn $44,000. How much more does a general manager earn than a spa and tennis director?

96. This year there were 555,800 knee surgeries performed in the United States. The number of knee surgeries performed six years ago was 328,900. How many more of these surgeries were performed this year than six years ago? (*Source:* Agency for Healthcare Research and Quality.)

SUBWAY promotes healthy food choices by offering eight sandwiches that are low in fat. The nutritional information, printed on every SUBWAY napkin, appears below and includes information to answer Exercises 97–100. (Source: SUBWAY.)

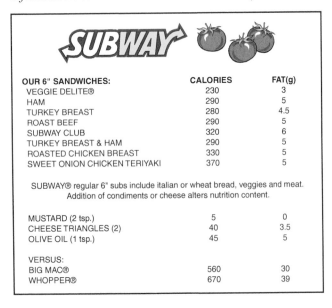

OUR 6" SANDWICHES:	CALORIES	FAT(g)
VEGGIE DELITE®	230	3
HAM	290	5
TURKEY BREAST	280	4.5
ROAST BEEF	290	5
SUBWAY CLUB	320	6
TURKEY BREAST & HAM	290	5
ROASTED CHICKEN BREAST	330	5
SWEET ONION CHICKEN TERIYAKI	370	5

SUBWAY® regular 6" subs include italian or wheat bread, veggies and meat. Addition of condiments or cheese alters nutrition content.

MUSTARD (2 tsp.)	5	0
CHEESE TRIANGLES (2)	40	3.5
OLIVE OIL (1 tsp.)	45	5
VERSUS:		
BIG MAC®	560	30
WHOPPER®	670	39

97. How many fewer calories and grams of fat are in a 6-inch Veggie Delite sandwich than a Big Mac?

98. How many fewer calories and grams of fat are in a 6-inch Turkey Breast and Ham sandwich than a Whopper?

99. Find the total number of calories and grams of fat in a Roasted Chicken Breast sandwich with mustard and olive oil.

100. A customer ate two sandwiches, one with the least calories and one with the most calories. Find the total number of calories and grams of fat in the two sandwiches.

1.4 ▶▶▶ Multiplying Whole Numbers

Suppose we want to know the total number of exercise bicycles available at the gym. The bicycles are arranged in four columns with three stations in each column. Adding the number 3 a total of 4 times gives 12.

$$3 + 3 + 3 + 3 = 12$$

This result can also be shown with a figure.

3 bicycles in each column

4 columns

OBJECTIVES

1 Identify the parts of a multiplication problem.

2 Do chain multiplication.

3 Multiply by single-digit numbers.

4 Use multiplication shortcuts for numbers ending in zeros.

5 Multiply by numbers having more than one digit.

6 Solve application problems with multiplication.

OBJECTIVE 1 Identify the parts of a multiplication problem.
Multiplication is a shortcut for repeated addition. In the exercise bicycle example, instead of *adding* $3 + 3 + 3 + 3$ to get 12, we can *multiply* 3 by 4 to get 12. The numbers being multiplied are called **factors.** The answer is called the **product.** For example, the product of 3 and 4 can be written with the symbol ×, a raised dot, or parentheses, as follows.

$$3 \leftarrow \text{Factor (also called } \textit{multiplicand}\text{)}$$
$$\underline{\times\ 4} \leftarrow \text{Factor (also called } \textit{multiplier}\text{)}$$
$$12 \leftarrow \text{Product (answer)}$$

$$3 \times 4 = 12 \quad \textbf{\textit{or}} \quad 3 \cdot 4 = 12 \quad \textbf{\textit{or}} \quad (3)(4) = 12 \quad \textbf{\textit{or}} \quad 3(4) = 12$$

Work Problem **1** *at the Side.* ▶

Commutative Property of Multiplication

> Multiply numbers in any order.

By the **commutative property of multiplication,** the product (answer) remains the same when the order of the factors is changed. For example,
$$3 \times 5 = 15 \quad \text{and} \quad 5 \times 3 = 15.$$

CAUTION
Recall that addition also has a commutative property. For example, $4 + 2$ gives the same sum as $2 + 4$. Subtraction, however, is **not** commutative.

EXAMPLE 1 Multiplying Two Numbers

Multiply.

(a) $3 \times 4 = 12$

(b) $6 \cdot 0 = 0$ (The product of any number and 0 is 0; if you give no money to each of 6 relatives, you give no money.)

(c) $4(8) = 32$

Continued on Next Page

1 Identify the factors and the product in each multiplication problem.

(a) $8 \times 5 = 40$

(b) $6(4) = 24$

(c) $7 \cdot 6 = 42$

(d) $(3)(9) = 27$

ANSWERS

1. (a) factors: 8, 5; product: 40
 (b) factors: 6, 4; product: 24
 (c) factors: 7, 6; product: 42
 (d) factors: 3, 9; product: 27

2 Multiply.

(a) 7×4

(b) 0×9

(c) $8(5)$

(d) $6 \cdot 5$

(e) $(3)(8)$

3 Multiply.

(a) $3 \times 2 \times 5$

(b) $4 \cdot 7 \cdot 1$

(c) $(8)(3)(0)$

You may want to review this multiplication table.

Multiplication Table

×	1	2	3	4	5	6	7	8	9
1	1	2	3	4	5	6	7	8	9
2	2	4	6	8	10	12	14	16	18
3	3	6	9	12	15	18	21	24	27
4	4	8	12	16	20	24	28	32	36
5	5	10	15	20	25	30	35	40	45
6	6	12	18	24	30	36	42	48	54
7	7	14	21	28	35	42	49	56	63
8	8	16	24	32	40	48	56	64	72
9	9	18	27	36	45	54	63	72	81

Know the "Times Table."

◀ Work Problem **2** at the Side.

OBJECTIVE 2 Do chain multiplication. Some multiplications involve more than two factors.

> **Associative Property of Multiplication**
> By the **associative property of multiplication,** grouping the factors differently does not change the product.

EXAMPLE 2 Multiplying Three Numbers

Multiply $2 \times 3 \times 5$.

$$(2 \times 3) \times 5 \qquad \text{Parentheses show what to do first.}$$
$$6 \quad \times 5 = 30$$

Also,

$$2 \times (3 \times 5)$$
$$2 \times \quad 15 = 30$$

Either grouping results in the same product.

◀ Work Problem **3** at the Side.

Calculator Tip The calculator approach to Example 2 uses chain calculations.

$$2 \; \boxed{\times} \; 3 \; \boxed{\times} \; 5 \; \boxed{=} \; \mathbf{30}$$

A problem with more than two factors, such as the one in Example 2, is called a **chain multiplication** problem.

Section 1.4 Multiplying Whole Numbers **33**
Section 1.4 Multiplying Whole Numbers **33**

OBJECTIVE 3 Multiply by single-digit numbers. Regrouping may be needed in multiplication problems with larger factors.

EXAMPLE 3 **Multiplying with Regrouping**

Multiply.

(a) 53
  × 4

Start by multiplying in the ones column.

$$\begin{array}{r} {}^{1}\!\!\leftarrow \\ 53 \\ \times\ 4 \\ \hline 2\!\!\leftarrow \end{array}$$

Write 1 ten in the tens column.
$4 \times 3 = 12$ ones
Write 2 ones in the ones column.

Next, multiply 4 times 5 tens.

$$\begin{array}{r} {}^{1} \\ 5\,3 \\ \times\ \ 4 \\ \hline 2 \end{array}$$

4×5 tens $=$ **20** tens

Add the 1 ten that was written at the top of the tens column.

$$\begin{array}{r} 1 \\ 5\,3 \\ \times\ \ 4 \\ \hline 212 \end{array}$$

20 tens + 1 ten = 21 tens

(b) 724
  × 5

Work as shown.

$$\begin{array}{r} 1\,2 \\ 724 \\ \times\ \ \ 5 \\ \hline 3620 \end{array}$$

Use regrouping here.

$5 \times 4 = $ **20** ones; write 0 ones; write 2 tens in the tens column.

$5 \times 2 = $ **10** tens; add the 2 regrouped tens to get 12 tens; write 2 tens; write 1 hundred in the hundreds column.

5×7 hundreds $= $ **35** hundreds; add the 1 regrouped hundred to get 36 hundreds.

Work Problem **4** *at the Side.* ▶

OBJECTIVE 4 Use multiplication shortcuts for numbers ending in zeros. The product of two whole number factors is also called a **multiple** of either factor. For example, since $4 \cdot 2 = 8$, the whole number 8 is a multiple of both 4 and 2. *Multiples of 10* are very useful when multiplying. A **multiple of 10** is a whole number that ends in 0, such as 10, 20, or 30; 100, 200, or 300; 1000, 2000, or 3000; and so on. There is a short way to multiply by these multiples of 10. Look at the following examples.

$$26 \times 1 = 26$$
$$26 \times 10 = 260$$
$$26 \times 100 = 2600$$
$$26 \times 1000 = 26{,}000$$

Do you see a pattern? These examples suggest the rule that follows.

4 Multiply.

(a) 53
  × 5

(b) 79
  × 0

(c) 758
  × 8

(d) 2831
  × 7

(e) 4714
  × 8

ANSWERS
4. **(a)** 265 **(b)** 0 **(c)** 6064
   (d) 19,817 **(e)** 37,712

5 Multiply.

(a) 63×10

(b) 305×100

(c) 714×1000

Multiplying by Multiples of 10

To multiply a whole number by 10, 100, or 1000, attach one, two, or three zeros, respectively, to the right of the whole number.

EXAMPLE 4 Using Multiples of 10 to Multiply

Multiply.

(a) $59 \times 10 = 590$
           ⌐ Attach 0.

(b) $74 \times 100 = 7400$
           ⌐ Attach 00.

(c) $803 \times 1000 = 803,000$ ← Attach 000.

◀ *Work Problem* **5** *at the Side.*

You can also find the product of other multiples of 10 by attaching zeros.

EXAMPLE 5 Using Multiples of 10 to Multiply

Multiply.

(a) 75×3000
Multiply 75 by 3, and then attach three zeros.

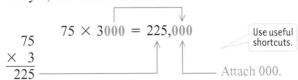

$$75 \times 3000 = 225,000$$

$$\begin{array}{r} 75 \\ \times\ 3 \\ \hline 225 \end{array}$$

Use useful shortcuts.

Attach 000.

(b) 150×70
Multiply 15 by 7, and then attach two zeros.

$$150 \times 70 = 10,500 \leftarrow \text{Attach 00.}$$

$$\begin{array}{r} 15 \\ \times\ 7 \\ \hline 105 \end{array}$$

◀ *Work Problem* **6** *at the Side.*

6 Multiply.

(a) 16×50

(b) 73×400

(c) $\begin{array}{r} 180 \\ \times\ 30 \end{array}$

(d) $\begin{array}{r} 4200 \\ \times\ 80 \end{array}$

OBJECTIVE **5** **Multiply by numbers having more than one digit.**
The next example shows multiplication when both factors have more than one digit.

EXAMPLE 6 Multiplying with More Than One Digit

Multiply 46 and 23.

First multiply 46 by 3.

$$\begin{array}{r} \overset{1}{4}6 \\ \times\ 3 \\ \hline 138 \end{array} \leftarrow 46 \times 3 = 138$$

Regrouping is needed here.

(e) $\begin{array}{r} 800 \\ \times\ 600 \end{array}$

Continued on Next Page

Now multiply 46 by 20.

$$\begin{array}{r} 1 \\ 46 \\ \times\ 20 \\ \hline 920 \end{array} \leftarrow 46 \times 20 = 920$$

Add the results.

$$\begin{array}{r} 46 \\ \times\ 23 \\ \hline 138 \\ +\ 920 \\ \hline 1058 \end{array} \begin{array}{l} \leftarrow 46 \times 3 \\ \leftarrow 46 \times 20 \end{array}$$

Add.

Both 138 and 920 are called **partial products.** To save time, the 0 in 920 is usually not written.

$$\begin{array}{r} 46 \\ \times\ 23 \\ \hline 138 \\ 92 \\ \hline 1058 \end{array} \leftarrow \begin{cases} \text{0 not written. Be very careful to} \\ \text{place the 2 in the tens column.} \end{cases}$$

Work Problem **7** *at the Side.* ▶

7 Complete each multiplication.

(a)
$$\begin{array}{r} 35 \\ \times\ 54 \\ \hline 140 \\ 175 \\ \hline \end{array}$$

(b)
$$\begin{array}{r} 76 \\ \times\ 49 \\ \hline 684 \\ 304 \\ \hline \end{array}$$

8 Multiply.

(a)
$$\begin{array}{r} 52 \\ \times\ 16 \\ \hline \end{array}$$

(b)
$$\begin{array}{r} 81 \\ \times\ 49 \\ \hline \end{array}$$

(c)
$$\begin{array}{r} 75 \\ \times\ 63 \\ \hline \end{array}$$

(d)
$$\begin{array}{r} 234 \\ \times\ 73 \\ \hline \end{array}$$

(e)
$$\begin{array}{r} 835 \\ \times\ 189 \\ \hline \end{array}$$

EXAMPLE 7 **Using Partial Products**

Multiply.

(a)
$$\begin{array}{r} 233 \\ \times\ 132 \\ \hline 466 \\ 699 \\ 233 \\ \hline 30{,}756 \end{array}$$

(Tens lined up)
(Hundreds lined up) — Be certain to align numbers in columns.
← Product

(b)
$$\begin{array}{r} 538 \\ \times\ 46 \\ \hline \end{array}$$

First multiply by 6.
$$\begin{array}{r} 24 \\ 538 \\ \times\ 46 \\ \hline 3228 \end{array} \leftarrow \text{Regrouping is needed here.}$$

Now multiply by 4, being careful to line up the tens.
$$\begin{array}{r} 13 \\ 24 \\ 538 \\ \times\ 46 \\ \hline 3228 \\ 2152 \\ \hline 24{,}748 \end{array} \text{— Finally, add the partial products.}$$

Work Problem **8** *at the Side.* ▶

Answers

7. **(a)** 1890 **(b)** 3724
8. **(a)** 832 **(b)** 3969 **(c)** 4725
   (d) 17,082 **(e)** 157,815

When 0 appears in the multiplier, be sure to move the partial products to the left to account for the position held by the 0.

9 Multiply.

(a) 28
    × 60

EXAMPLE 8 **Multiplying with Zeros**

Multiply.

(a)   1 3 7
      × 3 0 6
         8 2 2
         0 0 0   (Tens lined up)
         4 1 1   (Hundreds lined up)
       4 1,9 2 2

(b)   728
    × 50

(b)   1 4 0 6
        × 2 0 0 1   Use extra caution when   1 4 0 6
           1 4 0 6   working with 0s.   × 2 0 0 1
           0 0 0 0 ← (Zeros to line up tens)   1 4 0 6
           0 0 0 0 ← (Zeros to line up hundreds)
           2 8 1 2   2 8 1 2 0 0 ← Zeros are
         2,8 1 3,4 0 6   written so this
(c)   562   2,8 1 3,4 0 6   partial product
    × 109   starts in the
                                                                     thousands
                                                                     column.

Note

In Example 8(b) in the alternative method on the right, zeros were inserted so that thousands were placed in the thousands column. This is a commonly used shortcut.

(d)   3526
    × 6002

◀ *Work Problem* **9** *at the Side.*

OBJECTIVE **6** **Solve application problems with multiplication.**
The next example shows how multiplication can be used to solve an application problem.

10 Find the total cost of the following items.

EXAMPLE 9 **Applying Multiplication Skills**

Find the total cost of 53 portable DVD players priced at $78 each.

(a) 289 redwood planters at $12 per planter

Approach To find the cost of all the DVD players, multiply the number of players (53) by the cost of one player ($78).

Solution Multiply 53 by 78.

$$
\begin{array}{r}
53 \\
\times\ 78 \\
\hline
424 \\
371 \\
\hline
\$4134
\end{array}
$$

(b) 58 compound miter saws priced at $129 each

The total cost of the portable DVD players is $4134.

(c) 12 delivery vans at $28,300 per van

Calculator Tip If you are using a calculator for Example 9, you will do this calculation.

53 ⊗ 78 ⊜ 4134

◀ *Work Problem* **10** *at the Side.*

Work each chain multiplication. See Example 2.

1. $2 \times 6 \times 2$

2. $3 \times 5 \times 3$

3. $8 \times 6 \times 1$

4. $2 \times 4 \times 5$

5. $7 \cdot 8 \cdot 0$

6. $9 \cdot 0 \cdot 5$

7. $4 \cdot 1 \cdot 6$

8. $1 \cdot 5 \cdot 7$

9. $(4)(5)(2)$

10. $(4)(1)(9)$

11. $(3)(0)(7)$

12. $(0)(9)(4)$

13. Explain in your own words the commutative property of multiplication. How do the commutative properties of addition and multiplication compare to each other?

14. Explain in your own words the associative property of multiplication. How do the associative properties of addition and multiplication compare to each other?

Multiply. See Example 3.

15.   35
       $\times\ 6$

16.   53
       $\times\ 7$

17.   34
       $\times\ 7$

18.   76
       $\times\ 5$

19.   642
       $\times\ \ 5$

20.   472
       $\times\ \ 4$

21.   624
       $\times\ \ 3$

22.   852
       $\times\ \ 7$

23.   2153
       $\times\ \ \ 4$

24.   1137
       $\times\ \ \ 3$

25.   2521
       $\times\ \ \ 4$

26.   2544
       $\times\ \ \ 3$

27.   2561
       $\times\ \ \ 8$

28.   7326
       $\times\ \ \ 5$

29.   36,921
       $\times\ \ \ \ \ 7$

30.   28,116
       $\times\ \ \ \ \ 4$

Multiply. See Examples 4 and 5.

31.   40
       $\times\ 7$

32.   20
       $\times\ 7$

33.   80
       $\times\ 6$

34.   70
       $\times\ 5$

35.   740
       $\times\ 3$

36.   400
       $\times\ \ 8$

37.   600
       $\times\ \ 6$

38.   860
       $\times\ \ 7$

39.   125
       $\times\ 30$

40.   246
       $\times\ 50$

41. 1635
× 40

42. 7311
× 50

🌐 **43.** 900
× 300

44. 400
× 700

45. 43,000
× 2 000

46. 11,000
× 9 000

47. 970 · 50

48. 730 · 40

49. 800 · 900

50. 850 · 700

51. 9700 · 200

52. 10,050 · 300

Multiply. See Examples 6–8.

53. 28
× 17

54. 16
× 34

🌐 **55.** 75
× 32

56. 82
× 32

57. 83
× 45

58. (75)(21)

59. (58)(41)

60. (82)(67)

61. (67)(92)

62. (26)(33)

63. (28)(564)

64. (58)(312)

65. (619)(35)

66. (681)(47)

67. (55)(286)

68. 286
× 574

69. 735
× 112

70. 621
× 415

71. 538
× 342

72. 3228
× 751

73. 9352
× 264

74. 528
× 106

🌐 **75.** 215
× 307

76. 218
× 106

77. 428
× 201

78. 3706
× 208

79. 6310
× 3078

80. 3533
× 5001

81. 2195
× 1038

82. 1502
× 2009

83. A classmate of yours is not clear on how to use a shortcut to multiply a whole number by 10, by 100, or by 1000. Write a short note explaining how this can be done.

84. Show two ways to multiply when a 0 is in the multiplier. Use the problem 291 × 307 to show this.

Solve each application problem. See Example 9.

85. Carepanian Company, a health care supplier, purchased 300 cartons of Thera Bond Gym Balls. If there are 10 balls in each carton, find the total number of balls purchased.

86. A medical supply house has 30 bottles of vitamin C tablets, with each bottle containing 500 tablets. Find the total number of vitamin C tablets in the supply house.

87. Annie's Restaurant buys 15 cartons of eggs. If each carton contains 36 eggs, find the number of eggs purchased.

88. A hummingbird's wings beat about 65 times per second. How many times do the hummingbird's wings beat in 30 seconds?

89. The average amount of water used per person each day in the United States is 66 gallons. How much water does the average person use in one year? (1 year = 365 days). (*Source:* Okfam.)

90. Squid are being hauled out of the Santa Barbara Channel by the ton. They are then processed, renamed calamari, and exported. Last night 27 fishing boats each hauled out 40 tons of squid. What was the total catch for the night? (*Source: Santa Barbara News Press.*)

Find the total cost of the following items. See Examples 7–9.

91. 75 first-aid kits at $8 per kit

92. 38 gardeners at $64 per day

93. 65 rebuilt alternators at $24 per alternator

94. 62 wheelchair cushions at $44 per cushion

95. 206 desktop computers at $548 per computer

96. 520 printers at $219 per printer

Multiply.

97. 21 • 43 • 56

98. (600)(8)(75)(40)

Use addition, subtraction, or multiplication to solve each application problem.

99. In a forest-planting project, 450 trees are planted on each acre. Find the number of trees needed to plant 85 acres.

100. The largest living land mammal is the African elephant, and the largest mammal of all time is the blue whale. An African elephant weighs 15,225 pounds and a blue whale weighs 28 times that amount. Find the weight of the blue whale.

101. New York City has a population of 8,214,426, the largest in the country. Boston, in twenty-second place, has a population of 590,763. How many more people live in New York City than in Boston? (*Source:* Analysis of Census Bureau Estimates.)

102. Los Angeles, the second largest city in the country, has a population of 3,849,378. Dallas, at ninth largest, has a population of 1,232,940. Find the difference in the population of these two cities. (*Source:* Analysis of Census Bureau Estimates.)

103. A medical center purchased six laptop computers at $880 each, six printers at $235 each, and five fax machines at $140 each. Find the total cost of this equipment.

104. A motorcycle club traveled 640 miles on Saturday, 438 miles on Sunday, and 535 miles on Monday. Find the total number of miles traveled.

Relating Concepts (Exercises 105–114) For Individual or Group Work

Work Exercises 105–114 in order.

105. Add.
(a) $189 + 263$
(b) $263 + 189$

106. Your answers to Exercise 105(a) and (b) should be the same. This shows that the order of numbers in an addition problem does not change the sum. This is known as the _____ property of addition.

107. Add. Recall that parentheses show you what to do first.
(a) $(65 + 81) + 135$
(b) $65 + (81 + 135)$

108. Since the answers to Exercise 107(a) and (b) are the same, we see that grouping the numbers differently when adding does not change the sum. This is known as the _____ property of addition.

109. Multiply.
(a) 220×72
(b) 72×220

110. Since the answers to Exercise 109(a) and (b) are the same, we see that the product remains the same when the order of the factors is changed. This is known as the _____ property of multiplication.

111. Multiply. Recall that parentheses tell you what to do first.
(a) $(26 \times 18) \times 14$
(b) $26(18 \times 14)$

112. Since the answers to Exercise 111(a) and (b) are the same, we see that grouping the numbers differently when multiplying does not change the product. This is known as the _____ property of multiplication.

113. Do the commutative and associative properties apply to subtraction? Explain your answer using several examples.

114. Do you think that the commutative and associative properties will apply to division? Explain your answer using several examples.

1.5 ►►► Dividing Whole Numbers

Suppose the cost of lunch at a SUBWAY is $18 and is to be divided equally by three friends. Each person would pay $6, as shown here.

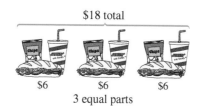

$18 total

$6 $6 $6
3 equal parts

OBJECTIVES

1 Write division problems in three ways.

2 Identify the parts of a division problem.

3 Divide 0 by a number.

4 Recognize that a number cannot be divided by 0.

5 Divide a number by itself.

6 Divide a number by 1.

7 Use short division.

8 Use multiplication to check the answer to a division problem.

9 Use tests for divisibility.

OBJECTIVE 1 Write division problems in three ways. Just as $3 \cdot 6$, 3×6, and $(3)(6)$ are different ways of indicating the multiplication of 3 and 6, there are several ways to write 18 divided by 3.

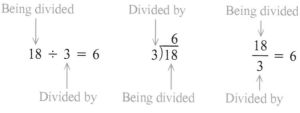

Being divided   Divided by   Being divided

$$18 \div 3 = 6 \qquad 3\overline{)18}^{\,6} \qquad \frac{18}{3} = 6$$

Divided by   Being divided   Divided by

We will use all three division symbols, $\div$, $\overline{)}\,$, and —. In courses such as algebra, a slash symbol, /, or a fraction bar, —, is most often used.

EXAMPLE 1 Using Division Symbols

Write each division problem using two other symbols.

(a) $18 \div 6 = 3$

This division can also be written as shown below.

$$6\overline{)18}^{\,3} \quad \text{or} \quad \frac{18}{6} = 3$$

Remember the three division symbols.

(b) $\dfrac{15}{5} = 3$

$$15 \div 5 = 3 \quad \text{or} \quad 5\overline{)15}^{\,3}$$

(c) $5\overline{)20}^{\,4}$

$$20 \div 5 = 4 \quad \text{or} \quad \frac{20}{5} = 4$$

Work Problem **1** *at the Side.* ►

OBJECTIVE 2 Identify the parts of a division problem. In division, the number being divided is the **dividend,** the number divided by is the **divisor,** and the answer is the **quotient.**

$$\text{dividend} \div \text{divisor} = \text{quotient}$$

$$\text{divisor}\overline{)\text{dividend}}^{\,\text{quotient}} \qquad \frac{\text{dividend}}{\text{divisor}} = \text{quotient}$$

1 Write each division problem using two other symbols.

(a) $24 \div 6 = 4$

(b) $9\overline{)36}^{\,4}$

(c) $48 \div 6 = 8$

(d) $\dfrac{42}{6} = 7$

ANSWERS

1. **(a)** $6\overline{)24}^{\,4}$ and $\dfrac{24}{6} = 4$

   (b) $36 \div 9 = 4$ and $\dfrac{36}{9} = 4$

   (c) $6\overline{)48}^{\,8}$ and $\dfrac{48}{6} = 8$

   (d) $6\overline{)42}^{\,7}$ and $42 \div 6 = 7$

2 Identify the dividend, divisor, and quotient.

(a) $15 \div 3 = 5$

(b) $18 \div 6 = 3$

(c) $\dfrac{28}{7} = 4$

(d) $9\overline{)27}$ with quotient 3

Identify the dividend, divisor, and quotient.

(a) $35 \div 7 = 5$

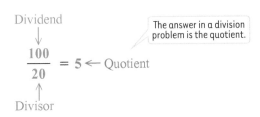

(b) $\dfrac{100}{20} = 5$

The answer in a division problem is the quotient.

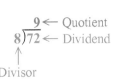

(c) $8\overline{)72}$ with quotient 9

$$\begin{array}{r} 9 \leftarrow \text{Quotient} \\ 8\overline{)72} \leftarrow \text{Dividend} \end{array}$$
            ↑
          Divisor

◀ Work Problem **2** at the Side.

3 Divide.

(a) $0 \div 5$

OBJECTIVE 3 Divide 0 by a number.   If no money, or $0, is divided equally among five people, each person gets $0. The general rule for dividing 0 follows.

> **Dividing 0 by a Number**
> The number **0** divided by any nonzero number is **0**.

(b) $\dfrac{0}{9}$

EXAMPLE 3   Dividing 0 by a Number

Divide.

(a) $0 \div 12 = 0$

(b) $0 \div 1728 = 0$

(c) $\dfrac{0}{24}$

(c) $\dfrac{0}{375} = 0$ Zero divided by any nonzero number is zero.

(d) $37\overline{)0}$

(d) $129\overline{)0}$

◀ Work Problem **3** at the Side.

Just as a subtraction such as $8 - 3 = 5$ can be written as the addition $8 = 3 + 5$, any division can be written as a multiplication. For example, $12 \div 3 = 4$ can be written as

$$3 \times 4 = 12 \quad \text{or} \quad 4 \times 3 = 12.$$

EXAMPLE 4 **Changing Division Problems to Multiplication**

Change each division problem to a multiplication problem.

(a) $\dfrac{20}{4} = 5$ becomes $4 \cdot 5 = 20$ or $5 \cdot 4 = 20$

(b) $8\overline{)48}$ (quotient 6) becomes $8 \cdot 6 = 48$ or $6 \cdot 8 = 48$

(c) $72 \div 9 = 8$ becomes $9 \cdot 8 = 72$ or $8 \cdot 9 = 72$

Work Problem **4** *at the Side.* ▶

4 Write each division problem as a multiplication problem.

(a) $5\overline{)15}$ (quotient 3)

OBJECTIVE **4** **Recognize that a number cannot be divided by 0.**
Division of any number by 0 cannot be done. To see why, try to find

$$9 \div 0 = ?$$

As we have just seen, any division problem can be converted to a multiplication problem so that

$$divisor \cdot quotient = dividend.$$

If you convert the preceding problem to its multiplication counterpart, it reads as follows.

$$0 \cdot ? = 9$$

You already know that 0 times any number must always be 0. Try any number you like to replace the "**?**" and you'll aways get 0 instead of 9. Therefore, the division problem $9 \div 0$ cannot be done. Mathematicians say it is **undefined** and have agreed never to divide by 0. However, $0 \div 9$ *can* be done. Check by rewriting it as a multiplication problem.

$$0 \div 9 = 0 \quad because \quad 9 \cdot 0 = 0 \text{ is true.}$$

(b) $\dfrac{32}{4} = 8$

Dividing a Number by 0
Since dividing any number by 0 cannot be done, we say that division by **0** is **undefined.** It is impossible to compute an answer.

(c) $45 \div 9 = 5$

EXAMPLE 5 **Dividing Numbers by 0**

All the following are undefined.

(a) $\dfrac{6}{0}$ is undefined.

(b) $0\overline{)8}$ is undefined.

(c) $18 \div 0$ is undefined. — You **cannot** divide a number by zero.

(d) $\dfrac{3}{0}$ is undefined.

5 Divide. If the division is not possible, write "undefined."

(a) $\dfrac{4}{0}$

(b) $\dfrac{0}{4}$

(c) $0\overline{)36}$

(d) $36\overline{)0}$

(e) $100 \div 0$

(f) $0 \div 100$

6 Divide.

(a) $8 \div 8$

(b) $15\overline{)15}$

(c) $\dfrac{37}{37}$

Division Involving 0

$$0 \div \text{nonzero number} = 0 \quad \text{and} \quad \frac{0}{\text{nonzero number}} = 0$$

but

$$\text{nonzero number} \div 0 \quad \text{and} \quad \frac{\text{nonzero number}}{0} \text{ are } \textbf{undefined.}$$

CAUTION
When 0 is the divisor in a problem, you write "undefined" as the answer. Never divide by 0.

◀ *Work Problem* **5** *at the Side.*

▦ **Calculator Tip**   Try these two problems on your calculator. Jot down your answers.

9 ⊕ 0 ⊜ _____   0 ⊕ 9 ⊜ _____

When you try to divide by 0, the calculator cannot do it, so it shows the word "Error" or the letter "E" (for error) in the display. But, when you divide 0 by 9 the calculator displays 0, which is the correct answer.

OBJECTIVE **5** **Divide a number by itself.**   What happens when a number is divided by itself? For example, what is $4 \div 4$ or $97 \div 97$?

Dividing a Number by Itself
Any *nonzero* number divided by itself is **1.**

EXAMPLE 6   **Dividing a Nonzero Number by Itself**

Divide.

(a) $16 \div 16 = 1$

(b) $32\overline{)32}^{\,1}$

(c) $\dfrac{57}{57} = 1$ —— A nonzero number divided by itself is 1.

◀ *Work Problem* **6** *at the Side.*

OBJECTIVE **6** **Divide a number by 1.**   What happens when a number is divided by 1? For example, what is $5 \div 1$ or $86 \div 1$?

Dividing a Number by 1
Any number divided by 1 is itself.

EXAMPLE 7 Dividing Numbers by 1

Divide.

(a) $5 \div 1 = 5$

(b) $1\overline{)26}$ with 26 above

(c) $\dfrac{41}{1} = 41$ — A number divided by one is itself.

Work Problem 7 at the Side. ▶

OBJECTIVE 7 Use short division. **Short division** is a method of dividing a number by a one-digit divisor.

EXAMPLE 8 Using Short Division

Divide: $3\overline{)96}$.

First, divide 9 by 3.

$$3\overline{)96} \quad \dfrac{9}{3} = 3$$

with 3 above

Next, divide 6 by 3.

$$3\overline{)96} \quad \dfrac{6}{3} = 2$$

with 32 above

Work Problem 8 at the Side. ▶

When two numbers do not divide exactly, the leftover portion is called the **remainder.** The remainder must always be less than the divisor.

EXAMPLE 9 Using Short Division with a Remainder

Divide 147 by 4.
Write the problem.

$$4\overline{)147}$$

Because 1 cannot be divided by 4, divide 14 by 4. Notice that the 3 is placed over the 4 in 14.

$$4\overline{)14^27} \quad \dfrac{14}{4} = 3 \text{ with 2 left over}$$

Next, divide 27 by 4. The final number left over is the remainder. Use **R** to indicate the remainder, and write the remainder to the side.

$$4\overline{)14^27} \quad 3\,6\,\mathbf{R}3 \quad \dfrac{27}{4} = 6 \text{ with 3 left over}$$

Work Problem 9 at the Side. ▶

7 Divide.

(a) $9 \div 1$

(b) $1\overline{)18}$

(c) $\dfrac{43}{1}$

8 Divide.

(a) $2\overline{)24}$

(b) $3\overline{)93}$

(c) $4\overline{)88}$

(d) $2\overline{)624}$

9 Divide.

(a) $2\overline{)125}$

(b) $3\overline{)215}$

(c) $4\overline{)538}$

(d) $\dfrac{819}{5}$

ANSWERS

7. **(a)** 9 **(b)** 18 **(c)** 43
8. **(a)** 12 **(b)** 31 **(c)** 22 **(d)** 312
9. **(a)** 62 **R**1 **(b)** 71 **R**2 **(c)** 134 **R**2 **(d)** 163 **R**4

10 Divide.

(a) $4\overline{)523}$

──

EXAMPLE 10 **Dividing with a Remainder**

Divide 1809 by 7.

Divide 18 by 7.

$$7\overline{)18^{4}09} \qquad \frac{18}{7} = 2 \text{ with 4 left over}$$

Divide 40 by 7.

$$7\overline{)18^{4}0^{5}9} \qquad \frac{40}{7} = 5 \text{ with 5 left over}$$

(b) $\dfrac{515}{7}$

Divide 59 by 7.

$$7\overline{)18^{4}0^{5}9} \,\text{ } 2\,5\,8\,\textbf{R3} \qquad \frac{59}{7} = 8 \text{ with 3 left over}$$

> The remainder must be less than the divisor.

◀ *Work Problem* **10** *at the Side.*

Note

Short division takes practice but is useful in many situations.

OBJECTIVE **8** **Use multiplication to check the answer to a division problem.** **Check** the answer to a division problem as follows.

(c) $3\overline{)1885}$

Checking Division

(divisor × quotient) + remainder = dividend

Parentheses tell you what to do first: Multiply the divisor by the quotient, then add the remainder.

(d) $6\overline{)1415}$

EXAMPLE 11 **Checking Division by Using Multiplication**

Check each answer.

(a) $5\overline{)458}$ with quotient 91 **R3**

(divisor × quotient) + remainder = dividend

$$(5 \times 91) + 3$$

> Be careful! Always add the remainder when checking division.

$$455 + 3 = 458$$

Matches original dividend, so the division was done correctly.

Continued on Next Page

(b) 6)1437   239 **R4**

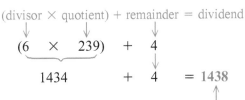

(divisor × quotient) + remainder = dividend

(6 × 239) + 4

1434 + 4 = 1438

Does not match original dividend.

The answer does **not** check. Rework the original problem to get the correct answer, 239 **R3**. Then, (6 × 239) + 3 **does** give 1437.

CAUTION

A common error when checking division is to forget to add the remainder. Be sure to add any remainder when checking a division problem.

Work Problem 11 *at the Side.* ▶

OBJECTIVE 9 Use tests for divisibility.   It is often important to know whether a number is *divisible* by another number. You will find this useful in Chapter 2 when writing fractions in lowest terms.

Divisibility

One whole number is **divisible** by another if the remainder is 0.

Use the following tests to decide whether one number is divisible by another number.

Tests for Divisibility

A number is divisible by

2   if it ends in 0, 2, 4, 6, or 8. These are the even numbers.

3   if the sum of its digits is divisible by 3.

4   if the last two digits make a number that is divisible by 4.

5   if it ends in 0 or 5.

6   if it is divisible by both 2 and 3.

7   has no simple test.

8   if the last three digits make a number that is divisible by 8.

9   if the sum of its digits is divisible by 9.

10   if it ends in 0.

> The most often used rules are for 2, 5, 10, and occasionally 3.

The most commonly used tests are those for 2, 3, 5, and 10.

11   Use multiplication to check each division. If an answer is incorrect, give the correct answer.

(a) 2)65   32 **R1**

(b) 7)586   83 **R4**

(c) 3)1223   407 **R2**

(d) 5)2383   476 **R3**

12 Which numbers are divisible by 2?

(a) 258

> **Divisibility by 2**
> A number is divisible by **2** if the number ends in 0, 2, 4, 6, or 8. All even numbers are divisible by 2.

EXAMPLE 12   **Testing for Divisibility by 2**

Are the following numbers divisible by 2?

(b) 307

(a) 986

↑
└─ Ends in 6

> All even numbers are divisible by 2.

Because the number ends in 6, which is an even number, the number 986 is divisible by 2.

(c) 4216

(b) 3255 is not divisible by 2.

↑
└─ Ends in 5, and not in 0, 2, 4, 6, or 8

◀ *Work Problem* **12** *at the Side.*

(d) 73,000

> **Divisibility by 3**
> A number is divisible by **3** if the sum of its digits is divisible by **3.**

13 Which numbers are divisible by 3?

(a) 743

EXAMPLE 13   **Testing for Divisibility by 3**

Are the following numbers divisible by 3?

(a) 4251
   Add the digits.

4 2 5 1

> If the sum of the digits is divisible by 3, the number is divisible by 3.

$4 + 2 + 5 + 1 = 12$

(b) 5325

Because 12 is divisible by 3, the number 4251 is also divisible by 3.

(b) 29,806
   Add the digits.

(c) 374,214

2 9 8 0 6

$2 + 9 + 8 + 0 + 6 = 25$

Because 25 is *not* divisible by 3, the number 29,806 is *not* divisible by 3.

(d) 205,633

> **CAUTION**
> Be careful when testing for divisibility by adding the digits. This method works only for the numbers 3 and 9.

◀ *Work Problem* **13** *at the Side.*

Divisibility by 5 and by 10

A number is divisible by **5** if it ends in 0 or 5.
A number is divisible by **10** if it ends in 0.

EXAMPLE 14   **Testing for Divisibility by 5**

Are the following numbers divisible by 5?

(a) 12,900 ends in 0 and is divisible by 5.

> If the number ends in 0 or 5,
> it's divisible by 5.

(b) 4325 ends in 5 and is divisible by 5.

(c) 392 ends in 2 and is not divisible by 5.

Work Problem 14 *at the Side.* ▶

EXAMPLE 15   **Testing for Divisibility by 10**

Are the following numbers divisible by 10?

> If the number ends in 0,
> it's divisible by 10.

(a) 700 and 9140 both end in 0 and are divisible by 10.

(b) 355 and 18,743 do not end in 0 and are not divisible by 10.

Work Problem 15 *at the Side.* ▶

---

14 Which numbers are divisible by 5?

(a) 180

(b) 635

(c) 8364

(d) 206,105

---

15 Which numbers are divisible by 10?

(a) 270

(b) 495

(c) 5030

(d) 14,380

ANSWERS

14. all but (c)
15. all but (b)

Math in the Media

As a college student, you need to plan a schedule to accommodate many responsibilities. These will include: preparing for and attending class, studying for exams, traveling to and from college, part-time work, family responsibilities, and personal time. Learning how to better manage your time is a skill presented by Stephen R. Covey at his Web site, stephencovey.com, and in his book *First Things First*. Dr. Covey says, "We're constantly making choices about the way we spend our time, from the major seasons to the individual moments of our lives. We're also living with the consequences of those choices." One of the first things you must do is calculate the amount of time dedicated to each of your obligations.

As an example, suppose that you are a full-time student enrolled in 12 credit hours of class: 4 credits of biology, 4 credits of computer science, 3 credits of mathematics, and 1 credit of physical education. Biology and computer science each have 3 hours of lecture and a 3-hour lab each week. Your biology and mathematics instructors recommend that you spend an additional 2 hours per week of study time for each hour of lecture time. Your physical education class is only 1 credit, but you are in class 3 hours each week.

Activity	Hours per Week
Class time	
Lab time	
Study time for mathematics and biology	
Travel time to and from college	5
Part-time work (including travel time)	25
Sleep (8 hours per day)	
Meals (3 hours per day)	
Hygiene (showers, dressing, etc.)	7
Other (housecleaning, laundry, etc.)	14

1. How many total hours are in one week?

2. Fill in the table entries for the number of hours in a week spent on class time, lab time, study time for biology and mathematics, sleep, and meals.

3. How many hours per week are spent on college-related activities?

4. How much more time is required for personal time (sleeping, eating, hygiene) than for college-related activities?

5. Based on the table data, how many hours per week are spent on the activities listed?

6. How many hours per week are available for other activities, such as dating, shopping, family responsibilities, and so on?

Write each division problem using two other symbols. See Example 1.

1. $24 \div 4 = 6$

2. $36 \div 3 = 12$

3. $\dfrac{45}{9} = 5$

4. $\dfrac{56}{8} = 7$

5. $2\overline{)16}$ with quotient 8

6. $8\overline{)48}$ with quotient 6

Divide. If the division is not possible, write "undefined." See Examples 3–7.

7. $9 \div 9$

8. $36 \div 9$

9. $\dfrac{14}{2}$

10. $\dfrac{10}{0}$

 11. $22 \div 0$

12. $6 \div 6$

13. $\dfrac{24}{1}$

14. $\dfrac{12}{1}$

15. $15\overline{)0}$

16. $\dfrac{0}{12}$

 17. $0\overline{)43}$

18. $\dfrac{8}{0}$

19. $\dfrac{15}{1}$

20. $\dfrac{6}{0}$

21. $\dfrac{8}{1}$

22. $\dfrac{0}{5}$

Divide by using short division. Use multiplication to check each answer. See Examples 8–10.

23. $3\overline{)75}$

24. $5\overline{)85}$

25. $7\overline{)126}$

26. $6\overline{)168}$

27. $4\overline{)1216}$

28. $5\overline{)2305}$

 29. $4\overline{)2509}$

30. $8\overline{)1335}$

31. $6\overline{)9137}$

32. $9\overline{)8371}$

33. $6\overline{)1854}$

34. $8\overline{)856}$

35. 12,020 ÷ 4   **36.** 8012 ÷ 4   **37.** 30,036 ÷ 6   **38.** 32,008 ÷ 8

39. 2434 ÷ 3   **40.** 5993 ÷ 7   **41.** 12,947 ÷ 5   **42.** 33,285 ÷ 9

43. 29,298 ÷ 4   **44.** 17,937 ÷ 6   **45.** 12,630 ÷ 4   **46.** 46,560 ÷ 7

47. 21,040 ÷ 8   **48.** $\dfrac{8199}{9}$ **49.** $\dfrac{74,751}{6}$ **50.** $\dfrac{72,543}{5}$

51. $\dfrac{71,776}{7}$ **52.** $\dfrac{77,621}{3}$ **53.** $\dfrac{128,645}{7}$ **54.** $\dfrac{172,255}{4}$

Use multiplication to check each answer. If an answer is incorrect, find the correct answer.
See Example 11.

55. $5\overline{)1877}$ with 375 R2
56. $3\overline{)1282}$ with 427 R1
57. $3\overline{)5725}$ with 1908 R2
58. $5\overline{)2158}$ with 432 R3

59. $7\overline{)4692}$ with 650 R2
60. $9\overline{)5974}$ with 663 R5
61. $6\overline{)21,409}$ with 3 568 R2
62. $6\overline{)3192}$ with 532

63. $8\overline{)16,019}$ with 2 002 R3
64. $8\overline{)33,664}$ with 4 208
65. $6\overline{)69,140}$ with 11,523 R2
66. $3\overline{)82,598}$ with 27,532 R1

67. $9\overline{)86,655}$ with 9 628 R7
68. $7\overline{)50,809}$ with 7 258 R4
69. $8\overline{)222,576}$ with 27,822
70. $4\overline{)311,216}$ with 77,804

71. Explain in your own words how to check a division problem using multiplication. Be sure to include what must be done if the quotient includes a remainder.

72. Describe the three divisibility rules that you feel might be most useful to you and tell why.

Solve each application problem.

73. The Carnival Cruise Line has 2624 linen napkins. If it takes eight napkins to set each table, find the number of tables that can be set. (*Source: USA Today.*)

74. A school district will distribute 1620 new science books equally among 12 schools. How many books will each school receive?

75. In one 8-hour day Dreyer's Edy's can produce 76,800 ice cream drumsticks. How many are produced each hour? (*Source:* History Channel, *Modern Marvels: Snack Food Tech.*)

76. Tootsie Roll Industries produces 415,000,000 Tootsie Rolls in a 5-day week. Find the number of Tootsie Rolls produced each day. (*Source:* History Channel, *Modern Marvels: Snack Food Tech.*)

77. Lottery winnings of $436,500 are divided equally among nine Starbucks employees. Find the amount received by each employee.

78. How many 5-pound bags of organic whole wheat flour can be filled from a 17,175-pound bin of flour?

79. If 8 gallons of fertilizer are needed for each acre of land, find the number of acres that can be fertilized with 1080 gallons of fertilizer.

80. A roofing contractor has purchased 1134 squares of roofing material. If each cabin needs 9 squares of material, find the number of cabins that can be roofed. (1 square measures 10 ft by 10 ft.)

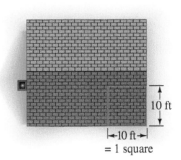

10 ft

|←10 ft→|
= 1 square

81. A class-action lawsuit settlement of $6,825,000 will be divided evenly among six injured people. Find the amount received by each person.

82. A 12,000-square foot condominium at the edge of Central Park in Manhattan sold for a record $45,000,000. If the buyer pays for the condominium in eight equal payments, find the amount of each payment. (*Source: USA Today.*)

83. The state of Maryland has the highest annual median household income of $65,148. How much income is this each month? (*Source:* U.S. Census Bureau.)

84. A professional basketball player has signed a 4-year contract for $21,937,500. How much is this each year?

Put a ✓ mark in the blank if the number at the left is divisible by the number at the top.
Put an X in the blank if the number is not divisible by the number at the top.
See Examples 12–15.

	2	3	5	10			2	3	5	10
85. 60	——	——	——	——		**86.** 35	——	——	——	——
87. 92	——	——	——	——		**88.** 96	——	——	——	——
89. 445	——	——	——	——		**90.** 897	——	——	——	——
91. 903	——	——	——	——		**92.** 500	——	——	——	——
93. 5166	——	——	——	——		**94.** 8302	——	——	——	——
95. 21,763	——	——	——	——		**96.** 32,472	——	——	——	——

1.6 ▶▶▶ Long Division

If the total cost of 42 Olympus digital cameras is $3066, we can find the cost of each camera using **long division.** Long division is used to divide by a number with more than one digit.

OBJECTIVE 1 Do long division.   In long division, estimate the various numbers by using a **trial divisor,** which is used to get a **trial quotient.**

OBJECTIVES

1 **Do long division.**

2 **Divide numbers ending in 0 by numbers ending in 0.**

3 **Use multiplication to check division answers.**

EXAMPLE 1 **Using a Trial Divisor and a Trial Quotient**

Divide. $42\overline{)3066}$

Because 42 is closer to 40 than to 50, use the first digit of the divisor as a trial divisor.

$$42$$

Using a trial divisor is a helpful tool.

Trial divisor

Try to divide the first digit of the dividend by 4. Since 3 cannot be divided by 4, use the first *two* digits, 30.

$$\frac{30}{4} = 7 \text{ with remainder } 2$$

$7 \leftarrow$ Trial quotient

$42\overline{)3066}$

7 goes over the 6, because $\frac{306}{42}$ is about 7.

Multiply 7 and 42 to get 294; next, subtract 294 from 306.

$$
\begin{array}{r}
7 \\
42\overline{)3066} \\
294 \quad \leftarrow 7 \times 42 \\
\hline
12 \quad \leftarrow 306 - 294
\end{array}
$$

Bring down the 6 at the right.

$$
\begin{array}{r}
7 \\
42\overline{)3066} \\
294\downarrow \\
\hline
126 \quad \leftarrow 6 \text{ brought down}
\end{array}
$$

Use the trial divisor, 4.

First two digits of 126 → $\frac{12}{4} = 3$

$$
\begin{array}{r}
73 \\
42\overline{)3066} \\
294 \\
\hline
126 \\
126 \quad \leftarrow 3 \times 42 = 126 \\
\hline
0
\end{array}
$$

The cost of each camera is $73.
Check the answer by multiplying 42 and 73. The product should be 3066.

1 Divide.

(a) $28\overline{)2296}$

CAUTION

The *first digit* of the quotient in long division must be placed in the proper position over the dividend.

◀ *Work Problem* **1** *at the Side.*

(b) $16\overline{)1024}$

EXAMPLE 2   **Dividing to Find a Trial Quotient**

Divide. $58\overline{)2730}$

Use 6 as a trial divisor, since 58 is closer to 60 than to 50.

First two digits of dividend $\longrightarrow$ $\dfrac{27}{6} = 4$ with 3 left over

4 ← Trial quotient

(c) $61\overline{)8784}$

$$58\overline{)2730}$$
$$\underline{232} \leftarrow 4 \times 58 = 232$$
$$41 \leftarrow 273 - 232 = 41 \text{ (smaller than 58, the divisor)}$$

Bring down the 0.

(d) $\dfrac{2697}{93}$

$$58\overline{)2730}$$
$$\underline{232}\downarrow$$
$$410 \leftarrow 0 \text{ brought down}$$

First two digits of 410 $\longrightarrow$ $\dfrac{41}{6} = 6$ with 5 left over

46 ← Trial quotient

2 Divide.

$$58\overline{)2730}$$
$$\underline{232}$$
$$410$$

(a) $24\overline{)1344}$

$$\underline{348} \leftarrow 6 \times 58 = 348$$
$$62 \leftarrow \text{Greater than 58}$$

Do not leave a remainder that is **greater** than the divisor.

(b) $72\overline{)4472}$

The remainder, 62, is greater than the divisor, 58, so 7 should be used instead of 6.

(c) $65\overline{)5416}$

$$\overset{47\ \mathbf{R4}}{58\overline{)2730}}$$
$$\underline{232}$$
$$410$$
$$\underline{406} \leftarrow 7 \times 58 = 406$$
$$4 \leftarrow 410 - 406$$

Now the remainder, 4, is *less* than the divisor, 58.

(d) $89\overline{)6649}$

◀ *Work Problem* **2** *at the Side.*

Sometimes it is necessary to write a 0 in the quotient.

EXAMPLE 3   **Writing Zeros in the Quotient**

Divide: 34)7068

Start as in Examples 1 and 2.

$$\begin{array}{r} 2 \\ 34\overline{)7068} \\ \underline{68} \quad \leftarrow 2 \times 34 = 68 \\ 2 \quad \leftarrow 70 - 68 = 2 \end{array}$$

Bring down the 6.

$$\begin{array}{r} 2 \\ 34\overline{)7068} \\ \underline{68}\downarrow \\ 26 \quad \leftarrow 6 \text{ brought down} \end{array}$$

Since 26 cannot be divided by 34, write a 0 in the quotient as a placeholder.

$$\begin{array}{r} 2\mathbf{0} \quad \leftarrow 0 \text{ in quotient} \\ 34\overline{)7068} \\ \underline{68} \\ 26 \end{array}$$

Use a zero to hold a place in the quotient.

Bring down the final digit, the 8.

$$\begin{array}{r} 20 \\ 34\overline{)7068} \\ \underline{68}\downarrow \\ 268 \leftarrow 8 \text{ brought down} \end{array}$$

Complete the problem.

$$\begin{array}{r} 207\ \mathbf{R}30 \\ 34\overline{)7068} \\ \underline{68} \\ 268 \\ \underline{238} \\ 30 \end{array}$$

The quotient is 207 **R**30.

> **CAUTION**
> There *must be a digit* in the quotient (answer) above every digit in the dividend once the answer has begun. Notice in Example 3 that a **0** was used to assure a digit in the quotient above every digit in the dividend.

Work Problem **3** *at the Side.* ▶

OBJECTIVE **2** **Divide numbers ending in 0 by numbers ending in 0.** When the divisor and dividend both contain zeros at the far right, recall that these numbers are multiples of 10. As with multiplication, there is a short way to divide these multiples of 10. Look at the following examples.

$$26,000 \div 1 = 26,000$$
$$26,000 \div 10 = 2600$$
$$26,000 \div 100 = 260$$
$$26,000 \div 1000 = 26$$

Do you see a pattern? These examples suggest the following rule.

3 Divide.

(a) 17)1823

(b) 23)4791

(c) 39)15,933

(d) 78)23,462

4 Divide.

(a) $70 \div 10$

(b) $2600 \div 100$

(c) $505,000 \div 1000$

Dividing a Whole Number by 10, 100, or 1000

Divide a whole number by 10, 100, or 1000 by dropping the appropriate number of zeros from the whole number.

EXAMPLE 4 **Dividing by Multiples of 10**

Divide.

One 0 in divisor

(a) $60 \div 10 = 6$

0 dropped

Two zeros in divisor

(b) $3500 \div 100 = 35$

00 dropped

Three zeros in divisor

(c) $915,000 \div 1000 = 915$

000 dropped

◀ *Work Problem* 4 *at the Side.*

Now we'll find the quotients for other multiples of 10 by dropping zeros.

EXAMPLE 5 **Dividing by Multiples of 10**

Divide:

5 Divide.

(a) $50\overline{)6250}$

(a) $40\overline{)11,000}$ Drop one zero from the divisor and the dividend.

$$
\begin{array}{r}
275 \\
4\overline{)1100} \\
\underline{8} \\
30 \\
\underline{28} \\
20 \\
\underline{20} \\
0
\end{array}
$$

(b) $130\overline{)131,040}$

Since $1100 \div 4$ is 275, then $11,000 \div 40$ is also 275.

(b) $3500\overline{)31,500}$ Drop two zeros from the divisor and the dividend.

$$
\begin{array}{r}
9 \\
35\overline{)315} \\
\underline{315} \\
0
\end{array}
$$

(c) $3400\overline{)190,400}$

Since $315 \div 35$ is 9, then $31,500 \div 3500$ is also 9.

Note

Dropping zeros when dividing by multiplies of 10 ***does not*** change the quotient (answer).

ANSWERS

4. (a) 7 (b) 26 (c) 505
5. (a) 125 (b) 1008 (c) 56

◀ *Work Problem* 5 *at the Side.*

OBJECTIVE **3** **Use multiplication to check division answers.**
Answers in long division can be checked just as answers in short division were checked.

EXAMPLE 6 **Checking Division by Using Multiplication**

Check each answer.

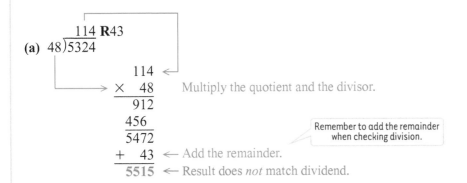

(a)

$$
48\overline{)5324} \quad 114\ \textbf{R}43
$$

114
× 48   Multiply the quotient and the divisor.
912
456
5472
+ 43 ← Add the remainder.
5515 ← Result does *not* match dividend.

Remember to add the remainder when checking division.

The answer does **not** check. Rework the original problem to get 110 **R**44. Then $(110 \times 48) + 44$ **does** give 5324.

(b)
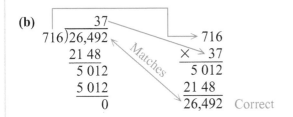

$$
716\overline{)26,492} \quad 37
$$

21 48
5 012
5 012
0

716
× 37
5 012
21 48
26,492 Correct

Matches

Calculator Tip To check the answer to Example 6(a), don't forget to add the remainder.

48 ⊗ 110 ⊕ 44 ⊜ **5324**

Add the remainder.

CAUTION
When checking a division problem, first multiply the quotient and the divisor. Then be sure to **add any remainder** before checking it against the original dividend.

Work Problem **6** *at the Side.* ▶

6 Decide whether each answer is correct. If the answer is incorrect, find the correct answer.

(a)
$$
16\overline{)608} \quad 38
$$
48
128
128
0

(b)
$$
426\overline{)19,170} \quad 42\ \textbf{R}178
$$
17 040
1 130
952
178

(c)
$$
514\overline{)29,316} \quad 57\ \textbf{R}18
$$
25 700
3 616
3 598
18

Math in the Media

It's just beginning to get dark, you're with family or friends in your car, you have plenty of pizza, popcorn, and other snacks, and the movie is about to start. You are at a drive-in movie theater.

A recent article in *USA Today* included some interesting facts about drive-ins. The first drive-in movie theater was opened in 1933 by the owner of an auto parts company and gas station to attract customers at night. It consisted of a sheet hanging between two trees. The popularity of drive-ins peaked in 1960, declined in the years that followed, but has remained fairly stable in recent years. The biggest reason for the decline of drive-ins has been the rising value of land and not a decline in popularity.

Use the drive-in movie theater facts below to answer the questions that follow.

Drive-in Movie Facts	States with the Most Open Drive-ins in 2008
1933: First drive-in movie	Pennsylvania: 35
1941: 12 open drive-ins	Ohio: 33
1958: 4063 open drive-ins	New York: 32
1960: 5000 open drive-ins	Indiana: 21
2008: 407 open drive-ins	California: 19
Typical screen size: 35 feet by 70 feet	Texas: 18
Typical popcorn machine cost: $12,500	Tennessee: 17
	Michigan: 14
	Illinois: 13
	Missouri: 13

(*Source: USA Today*)

1. What was the increase in the number of drive-in movies from 1941 to 1958?

2. Find the increase in the number of drive-in movies from 1958 to 1960.

3. How many less drive-ins were there in 2008 than in the peak year?

4. Find **(a)** the total number of drive-ins in the ten states with the most open drive-ins and **(b)** the number of open drive-ins in the remaining 40 states.

5. Find the cost of ten typical popcorn machines.

6. What is the area of the typical drive-in movie screen. (*Hint:* Area = width × height. The answer is to be expressed in square feet.)

7. Using your answer to Question 4(a), find the average number of open drive-ins in the ten states with the most open drive-ins. (The answer includes a remainder.)

60

Decide where the first digit in the quotient would be located. Then without finishing the division, you can tell which of the three choices is the correct answer. Circle your choice. See Examples 1 and 2.

1. 50)2650
  5   53   530

2. 14)476
  3   34   304

3. 18)4500
  2   25   250

4. 35)5600
  16   160   1600

5. 86)10,327
  12   120 **R7**   1200

6. 46)24,026
  5   52   522 **R14**

7. 26)28,735
  11   110   1105 **R5**

8. 12)116,953
  974 **R2**   9746 **R1**   97,460

9. 21)149,826
  71   713   7134 **R12**

10. 64)208,138
  325 **R2**   3252 **R10**   32,521

11. 523)470,800
  9 **R100**   90 **R100**   900 **R100**

12. 230)253,230
  11   110   1101

Divide by using long division. Use multiplication to check each answer. See Examples 1–3, 5, and 6.

13. 18)1319

14. 58)3654

15. 23)10,963

16. 83)39,692

17. 26)62,583

18. 28)84,249

19. 74)84,819

20. 238)186,948

21. 153)509,725

22. 308)26,796

23. 420)357,000

24. 900)153,000

Use multiplication to check each answer. If an answer is incorrect, find the correct answer.
See Example 6.

25. $35\overline{)3549}$ **101 R4**

26. $64\overline{)2712}$ **42 R26**

27. $28\overline{)18,424}$ **658 R9**

28. $145\overline{)34,776}$ **239 R121**

29. $614\overline{)38,068}$ **62 R3**

30. $557\overline{)97,286}$ **174 R368**

31. Describe in your own words a shortcut you can use to divide multiples of 10 by 10, by 100, or by 1000. Write an example problem and solve it.

32. Suppose you have a division problem with a remainder in the answer. Explain how to check your answer by writing an example problem that has a remainder.

Solve each application problem by using addition, subtraction, multiplication, or division as needed. See Examples 3–5.

33. Scientists using high-tech instruments have traced the travels of a tiger shark from Australia to South Africa—a total of 4950 miles in 99 days. On average, how far did the shark travel each day? (*Source: Discovery Channel, Shark Week.*)

34. A new bridge from Owensboro, Kentucky, to Rockport, Indiana, is 2200 feet long and cost $55,998,800. Find the construction cost per foot. (*Source:* Federal Highway Administration.)

35. Don Gracey, the Mountain Timesmith, has serviced and repaired 636 clocks this year. He has worked on 272 wall clocks and 308 table clocks. The rest were standing floor clocks. Find the number of floor clocks he worked on this year.

36. There are 24,000,000 business enterprises in the United States. If 7000 of these are larger businesses (over 500 employees), find the number of businesses that are small to mid-size. (*Source:* U.S. Census Bureau.)

37. To complete her college education, Judy Martinez received education loans of $34,080 including interest. Find her monthly payment if the loan is to be paid off in 96 months (8 years).

38. A consultant charged $13,050 for evaluating a school's compliance with the Americans with Disabilities Act. If the consultant worked 225 hours, find the rate charged per hour.

39. Each minute there is one diamond ring sold on eBay's U.S. site. Find the number of diamond rings sold in 30 days. (*Source: Time Style and Design.*)

40. A retired milkman in Indianapolis has eaten a Twinkie every day for the last 60 years. How many Twinkies has he eaten over this time period? *Hint:* Use a 365-day year, ignoring leap years. (*Source:* History Channel, *Modern Marvels: Snack Food Tech.*)

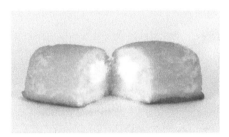

41. The average U.S. household of 2.5 people spent $2028 eating away from home last year. Find the average weekly household cost of eating away from home. *Hint:* 1 year equals 52 weeks. (*Source:* U.S. Bureau of Labor Statistics consumer expenditure surveys.)

42. Former professional basketball player Junior Bridgeman now owns 120 Wendy's restaurants with 4080 employees. Find the average number of employees at each restaurant. (*Source:* National Basketball Retired Players Association.)

Relating Concepts (Exercises 43–50) For Individual or Group Work

Knowing and using the rules of divisibility is necessary in problem solving.
Work Exercises 43–50 in order.

43. If you have $0 and you divide this amount among three people, how much will each receive?

44. When 0 is divided by any nonzero number, the result is _____.

45. Divide.
$8 \div 0$

46. We say that division by 0 is *undefined* because it is _____ to compute the answer. Give an
(possible/impossible)
example involving cookies that will support your answer.

47. Divide.
(a) $14 \div 1$
(b) $1\overline{)17}$
(c) $\dfrac{38}{1}$

48. Any number divided by 1 is the number itself. Is this also true when multiplying by 1? Give three examples that support your answer.

49. Divide.
(a) $32,000 \div 10$
(b) $32,000 \div 100$
(c) $32,000 \div 1000$

50. Write a rule that explains the shortcut for doing divisions like the ones in Exercise 49.

Math in the Media

The United States Postal Service posts a Web page on the Internet that gives a list of facts about their service. Some of those facts are listed in the table below.

Resource/Service	Number
1. Mail collection boxes	326,000
2. Post offices	36,895
3. Delivery points	146 million
4. Pieces of First Class mail delivered each year	213 billion
5. Processing plants sorting and shipping the mail	331
6. Pounds of mail carried on commercial airline flights annually	2.7 billion
7. Number of new deliveries each day	3500
8. Miles driven to move the mail annually	1.2 billion
9. Vehicles to pick up, transport, and deliver the mail	216,450
10. Customers each day who transact business at a post office	9 million

Source: United States Postal Service, www.usps.com

1. Write the number of delivery points entirely in digits. (Do not use the word "million" in your answer.)
2. Write the number of miles driven annually to move the mail entirely in digits.

3. Round the number of post offices to the nearest thousand.
4. Use your rounded number from Question 3 to compute the average number of customers who transact business each day per post office. Round the answer to the nearest person. (*Hint:* To find the average, divide the total number of customers per day by the number of post offices).

5. Find the total number of new deliveries each year. Write the result entirely in words. (*Hint:* Assume that new deliveries are added 365 days per year.)

6. Mail is sorted and shipped from processing plants to the post offices. Which of the following is a rough estimate of the number of post offices served by each processing plant: 10, 100, or 1000? Explain your choice.

UNITED STATES POSTAL SERVICE®

Summary Exercises on Whole Numbers

*Write the digit for the given **place value** in each whole number.*

1. 631,548

ten-thousands

tens

2. 76,047,309

millions

hundred-thousands

3. 9,181,576,423

hundred-millions

thousands

Write each number in words.

4. 86,002

5. 425,208,733

Add or subtract as indicated.

6.
$$\begin{array}{r} 46 \\ + 51 \\ \hline \end{array}$$

7. 166 + 739

8.
$$\begin{array}{r} 82 \\ - 61 \\ \hline \end{array}$$

9.
$$\begin{array}{r} 798 \\ - 389 \\ \hline \end{array}$$

10. 6382 + 4062 + 7129

11. 75 + 81,579 + 506 + 4

12.
$$\begin{array}{r} 1704 \\ - 1027 \\ \hline \end{array}$$

13.
$$\begin{array}{r} 55,000 \\ - 17,326 \\ \hline \end{array}$$

14.
$$\begin{array}{r} 70,552 \\ - 34,663 \\ \hline \end{array}$$

Multiply using the shortcut for multiples of 10.

15. 56 × 10

16. 140 × 40

17.
$$\begin{array}{r} 500 \\ \times \quad 700 \\ \hline \end{array}$$

18.
$$\begin{array}{r} 3600 \\ \times \quad 70 \\ \hline \end{array}$$

Write the numbers in each sentence using digits.

19. The world population is six billion, six hundred seventeen million, four hundred eighteen thousand, three hundred fifty-one people. (*Source:* U.S. Census Bureau.)

20. Each day there are twenty-four thousand, six hundred fifty-seven bags of Whiskas Cat Food sold. (*Source: Time* magazine.)

Multiply or divide as indicated. If the division cannot be done, write "undefined."

21. $8 \div 8$

22. $0 \div 9$

23. $\dfrac{12}{0}$

24. $\dfrac{15}{1}$

25. 7×8

26. $(6)(0)(5)$

27. $8 \cdot 4 \cdot 3$

28. $\dfrac{608}{2}$

29. $3\overline{)8252}$

30. $4569 \div 6$

31. $\begin{array}{r} 65 \\ \times\ 52 \\ \hline \end{array}$

32. $\begin{array}{r} 507 \\ \times\ 435 \\ \hline \end{array}$

33. $(28)(72)$

34. $(41)(36)$

35. $25\overline{)1950}$

36. $18\overline{)3780}$

37. $\begin{array}{r} 3602 \\ \times\ 5008 \\ \hline \end{array}$

38. $62\overline{)31,400}$

39. $630\overline{)32,760}$

40. $351\overline{)424,011}$

41. $4587 \div 8$

42. $72\overline{)2952}$

43. $\begin{array}{r} 662 \\ \times\ 315 \\ \hline \end{array}$

44. $\begin{array}{r} 2186 \\ \times\ 504 \\ \hline \end{array}$

1.7 ▶▶▶ Rounding Whole Numbers

One way to get a quick check on an answer is to *round* the numbers in the problem. **Rounding** a number means finding a number that is close to the original number, but easier to work with.

For example, the county planning commissioner might be discussing the need for more affordable housing. To demonstrate this, she probably would not need to say that the county is in need of 8235 more affordable housing units—she probably could say that the county needs 8200 or even 8000 housing units.

OBJECTIVE 1 Locate the place to which a number is to be rounded. The first step in rounding a number is to locate the *place to which the number is to be rounded.*

OBJECTIVES

1 Locate the place to which a number is to be rounded.

2 Round numbers.

3 Round numbers to estimate an answer.

4 Use front end rounding to estimate an answer.

EXAMPLE 1 Finding the Place to Which a Number Is to Be Rounded

Locate and draw a line under the place to which each number is to be rounded.

(a) Round 83 to the nearest ten. Is 83 closer to 80 or to 90?

83 is closer to 80. ◀— 83 is closer to 80 than to 90.

Tens place

(b) Round 54,702 to the nearest thousand. Is it closer to 54,000 or to 55,000?

54,702 is closer to 55,000.

Thousands place

(c) Round 2,806,124 to the nearest hundred-thousand. Is it closer to 2,800,000 or to 2,900,000?

2,806,124 is closer to 2,800,000.

Hundred-thousands place

Work Problem **1** *at the Side.* ▶

OBJECTIVE 2 Round numbers. Use the following rules for rounding whole numbers.

Rounding Whole Numbers

Step 1 Locate the *place* to which the number is to be rounded. Draw a line under that place.

Step 2(a) Look only at the next digit to the right of the one you underlined. If it is *5 or more, increase* the underlined digit by 1.

Step 2(b) If the next digit to the right is *4 or less, do not change* the digit in the underlined place.

Step 3 *Change* all digits to the right of the underlined place to zeros.

EXAMPLE 2 Using Rounding Rules for 4 or Less

Round 349 to the nearest hundred.

Step 1 Locate the place to which the number is being rounded. Draw a line under that place.

349

Hundreds place

Continued on Next Page

1 Locate and draw a line under the place to which each number is to be rounded. Then answer the question.

(a) 373 (nearest ten)

Is it closer to 370 or to 380?

_____

(b) 1482 (nearest thousand)

Is it closer to 1000 or to 2000?

_____

(c) 89,512 (nearest hundred)

Is it closer to 89,500 or to 89,600?

_____

(d) 546,325 (nearest ten-thousand)

Is it closer to 540,000 or to 550,000?

_____

ANSWERS

1. (a) 373 is closer to 370.
   (b) 1482 is closer to 1000.
   (c) 89,512 is closer to 89,500.
   (d) 546,325 is closer to 550,000.

2 Round to the nearest ten.

(a) 62

(b) 94

(c) 134

(d) 7543

3 Round to the nearest thousand.

(a) 3683

(b) 6502

(c) 84,621

(d) 55,960

Step 2   Because the next digit to the right of the underlined place is 4, which is 4 or less, do *not* change the digit in the underlined place.

Next digit is 4 or less.

349

4 or less, do not change underlined digit.

3 remains 3.

Step 3   Change all digits to the right of the underlined place to zeros.

349 rounded to the nearest hundred is 300.

In other words, 349 is closer to 300 than to 400.

◀ *Work Problem* **2** *at the Side.*

EXAMPLE 3   **Using Rounding Rules for 5 or More**

Round 36,833 to the nearest thousand.

Step 1   Find the place to which the number is to be rounded and draw a line under that place.

36,833

Thousands

Step 2   Because the next digit to the right of the underlined place is 8, which is 5 or more, add 1 to the underlined place.

Next digit is 5 or more.

36,833

5 or more, add 1 to underlined digit.

Change 6 to 7.

Step 3   Change all digits to the right of the underlined place to zeros.

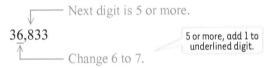

Change to 0.

36,833 rounded to the nearest thousand is 37,000.

Change 6 to 7.

In other words, 36,833 is closer to 37,000 than to 36,000.

◀ *Work Problem* **3** *at the Side.*

EXAMPLE 4   **Using Rounding Rules**

(a) Round 2382 to the nearest ten.

Step 1   2382

Tens place

Step 2   The next digit to the right is 2, which is 4 or less.

Next digit is 4 or less.

2382

Leave 8 as 8.

Step 3   2382   Change to 0.

2382 rounded to the nearest ten is 2380.
In other words, 2382 is closer to 2380 than to 2390.

Continued on Next Page

(b) Round 13,961 to the nearest hundred.

Step 1 13,961
$\uparrow$
Hundreds place

Step 2 The next digit to the right is 6.

Next digit is 5 or more.
$\downarrow$
13,961
Change 9 to 10; write 0 and regroup 1 into thousands place.
3 + regrouped 1 = 4
Change to 0

Step 3 14,061

13,961 rounded to the nearest hundred is 14,000.
In other words, 13,961 is closer to 14,000 than to 13,900.

Note

In Step 2 of Example 4(b), notice that the first three digits increased from 139 to 140 when we added 1 to the hundreds place.

13,961 rounded to 14,000

Work Problem **4** *at the Side.* ▶

EXAMPLE 5 **Rounding Large Numbers**

(a) Round 37,892 to the nearest ten-thousand.

Step 1 37,892
$\uparrow$
Ten-thousands place.

Remember to *underline* the place to which you are rounding.

Step 2 The next digit to the right is 7.

Next digit is 5 or more.
$\downarrow$
37892
$\uparrow$
Change 3 to 4.
Change 0.

Step 3 47,892

37,892 rounded to the nearest ten-thousand is 40,000.

(b) Round 528,498,675 to the nearest million.

Step 1 528,498,675
$\uparrow$
Millions place

Next digit is 4 or less.
$\downarrow$
Step 2 528,498,675
$\uparrow$
Leave 8 as 8
Change to 0.

Remember to change *everything* to the right of the place you have rounded to 0.

Step 3 528,498,675

528,498,675 rounded to the nearest million is 528,000,000.

Work Problem **5** *at the Side.* ▶

---

4 Round each number as indicated.

(a) 3458 to the nearest ten

(b) 6448 to the nearest hundred

(c) 73,077 to the nearest hundred

(d) 85,972 to the nearest hundred

5 Round each number as indicated.

(a) 14,598 to the nearest ten-thousand

(b) 724,518,715 to the nearest million

ANSWERS
4. **(a)** 3460   **(b)** 6400
   (c) 73,100   **(d)** 86,000
5. **(a)** 10,000   **(b)** 725,000,000

Sometimes a number must be rounded to different places.

6 Round each number to the nearest ten and to the nearest hundred.

(a) 458

EXAMPLE 6 **Rounding to Different Places**

Round 648 **(a)** to the nearest ten and **(b)** to the nearest hundred.

(a) to the nearest ten

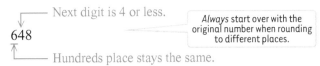

648 rounded to the nearest ten is 650.

(b) to the nearest hundred

┌— Next digit is 4 or less.
↓
648
↑
└— Hundreds place stays the same.

Always start over with the original number when rounding to different places.

648 rounded to the nearest hundred is 600.

    Notice that if 648 is rounded to the nearest ten (650), and then 650 is rounded to the nearest hundred, the result is 700. If, however, 648 is rounded directly to the nearest hundred, the result is 600 (not 700).

(b) 549

◀ *Work Problem* **6** *at the Side.*

CAUTION
Before rounding to a different place, always go back to the *original,* unrounded number.

EXAMPLE 7 **Applying Rounding Rules**

Round each number to the nearest ten, nearest hundred, and nearest thousand.

(a) 4358
    First round 4358 to the nearest ten.

┌— Next digit is 5 or more.
↓
4358
↑
└— Tens place (5 + 1 = 6)

(c) 9308

4358 rounded to the nearest ten in 4360.

    Now go back to 4358, the *original* number, before rounding to the nearest hundred.

┌— Next digit is 5 or more.
↓
4358
↑
└— Hundreds place (3 + 1 = 4)

Go back to the original number.

4358 rounded to the nearest hundred is 4400.

    Again, go back to the *original* number before rounding to the nearest thousand.

┌— Next digit is 4 or less.
↓
4358
↑
└— Thousands place stays the same.

4358 rounded to the nearest thousand is 4000.

Continued on Next Page

ANSWERS

6. (a) 460; 500
   (b) 550; 500
   (c) 9310; 9300

(b) 680,914

First, round to the nearest ten.

Next digit is 4 or less.

680,91**4**

Tens place stays the same.

680,914 rounded to the nearest ten is 680,910.

Go back to 680,914, the *original* number, to round to the nearest hundred.

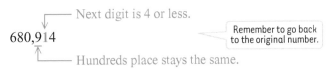

Next digit is 4 or less.

680,9**1**4

Remember to go back to the original number.

Hundreds place stays the same.

680,914 rounded to the nearest hundred is 680,900.

Go back to the *original* number to round to the nearest thousand.

Next digit is 5 or more.

680,**9**14

Thousands place (0 + 1 = 1)

680,914 rounded to the nearest thousand is 681,000.

Work Problem **7** *at the Side.* ▶

OBJECTIVE 3 Round numbers to estimate an answer. Numbers may be rounded to **estimate** an answer. An estimated answer is one that is close to the exact answer and may be used as a check when the exact answer is found. The "≈" sign is often used to show that an answer has been rounded or estimated and is almost equal to the exact answer; ≈ means "approximately equal to."

EXAMPLE 8 **Using Rounding to Estimate an Answer**

Estimate each answer by rounding to the nearest ten.

(a)
$$
\begin{array}{r}
76 \longrightarrow 80 \\
53 \longrightarrow 50 \\
38 \longrightarrow 40 \\
+ 91 \longrightarrow + 90 \\
\hline
260
\end{array}
$$
Rounded to the nearest ten

Estimated answer

(b)
$$
\begin{array}{r}
27 \\
- 14 \\
\hline
\end{array}
\qquad
\begin{array}{r}
30 \\
-10 \\
\hline
20
\end{array}
$$
Rounded to the nearest ten

Estimated answer

(c)
$$
\begin{array}{r}
16 \\
\times 21 \\
\hline
\end{array}
\qquad
\begin{array}{r}
20 \\
\times 20 \\
\hline
400
\end{array}
$$
Rounded to the nearest ten

Estimated answer

Work Problem **8** *at the Side.* ▶

---

7 Round each number to the nearest ten, nearest hundred, and nearest thousand.

(a) 4078

(b) 46,364

(c) 268,328

8 Estimate the answers by rounding each number to the nearest ten.

(a)
$$
\begin{array}{r}
16 \\
74 \\
58 \\
+ 31 \\
\hline
\end{array}
$$

(b)
$$
\begin{array}{r}
53 \\
- 19 \\
\hline
\end{array}
$$

(c)
$$
\begin{array}{r}
46 \\
\times 74 \\
\hline
\end{array}
$$

ANSWERS

7. **(a)** 4080; 4100; 4000
 (b) 46,360; 46,400; 46,000
 (c) 268,330; 268,300; 268,000
8. **(a)** 20 + 70 + 60 + 30 = 180
 (b) 50 − 20 = 30
 (c) 70 × 50 = 3500

9 Estimate the answers by rounding each number to the nearest hundred.

(a)   358
          743
          822
      +   978

(b)   842
      −   475

(c)   723
      ×   478

10 Use front end rounding to estimate each answer.

(a)   36
            3852
             749
        +   5474

(b)   2583
      −   765

(c)   648
      ×   67

EXAMPLE 9   **Using Rounding to Estimate an Answer**

Estimate each answer by rounding to the nearest hundred.

(a)   252 ⟶ 300
          749 ⟶ 700   } Rounded to the nearest hundred
          576 ⟶ 600
      +   819 ⟶ + 800
               ⟶ 2400   Estimated answer   ◁ The hundreds position is 3 places to the left.

(b)   780   800
      −   536   − 500   } Rounded to the nearest hundred
                    300   Estimated answer

(c)   664   700
      ×   834   × 800   } Rounded to the nearest hundred
                 560,000   Estimated answer

◀ *Work Problem* **9** *at the Side.*

OBJECTIVE **4** **Use front end rounding to estimate an answer.**
A convenient way to estimate an answer is to use *front end rounding*. With **front end rounding,** we round to the highest possible place so that all the digits become 0 except the first one. For example, suppose you want to buy a big flat-screen television for $2449, a home theater system for $1759, and a reclining chair for $525. Using front end rounding, you can estimate the total cost of these purchases.

Television	$2449 →	2000
Home theater system	$1759 →	2000
Reclining chair	$525 →	+ 500
		$4500 ← Estimated total cost

EXAMPLE 10   **Using Front End Rounding to Estimate an Answer**

Estimate each answer using front end rounding.

(a)   3825   4000
            72   70   } All digits changed to 0 except first digit, which is rounded
           565   600
      +   2389   + 2000
                    6670   Estimated answer

(b)   6712   7000
      −   825   − 800   } First digit rounded and all others changed to 0   ◁ Notice: Front end rounding leaves *only* one nonzero digit.
                    6200   Estimated answer

(c)   725   700
      ×   86   ×   90
                  63,000   Estimated answer

Note
When using front end rounding, all the digits become 0 except the highest-place digit (the first digit).

◀ *Work Problem* **10** *at the Side.*

1.7 ▶▶▶ **Exercises**

FOR
EXTRA
HELP

PRACTICE WATCH DOWNLOAD READ REVIEW

Round each number as indicated. See Examples 1–5.

1. 624 to the nearest ten

2. 509 to the nearest ten

3. 855 to the nearest ten

4. 946 to the nearest ten

5. 6771 to the nearest hundred

6. 5847 to the nearest hundred

7. 86,813 to the nearest hundred

8. 17,211 to the nearest hundred

9. 28,472 to the nearest hundred

10. 18,273 to the nearest hundred

11. 5996 to the nearest hundred

12. 4452 to the nearest hundred

13. 15,758 to the nearest thousand

14. 28,465 to the nearest thousand

15. 78,499 to the nearest thousand

16. 14,314 to the nearest thousand

17. 7,760,058,721 to the nearest billion

18. 44,706,892 to the nearest ten-million

19. 12,987 to the nearest ten-thousand

20. 6599 to the nearest ten-thousand

21. 595,008 to the nearest ten-thousand

22. 725,182 to the nearest ten-thousand

23. 4,860,220 to the nearest million

24. 13,713,409 to the nearest million

Round each number to the nearest ten, nearest hundred, and nearest thousand. See Examples 6 and 7.

	Ten	Hundred	Thousand			Ten	Hundred	Thousand
25. 4476	_____	_____	_____		**26.** 6483	_____	_____	_____
27. 3374	_____	_____	_____		**28.** 7632	_____	_____	_____
29. 6048	_____	_____	_____		**30.** 7065	_____	_____	_____

		Ten	Hundred	Thousand			Ten	Hundred	Thousand
31.	5343	_____	_____	_____	**32.**	7456	_____	_____	_____
33.	19,539	_____	_____	_____	**34.**	59,806	_____	_____	_____
35.	26,292	_____	_____	_____	**36.**	78,519	_____	_____	_____
37.	93,706	_____	_____	_____	**38.**	84,639	_____	_____	_____

39. Write in your own words the three steps that you would use to round a number when the digit to the right of the place to which you are rounding is 5 or more.

40. Write in your own words the three steps that you would use to round a number when the digit to the right of the place to which you are rounding is 4 or less.

Estimate the answer by rounding each number to the nearest ten. Then find the exact answer. See Example 8.

41. *Estimate:*   *Exact:*

Rounds to

$$
\begin{array}{r}
\text{_____} \leftarrow\ \ 25 \\
\text{_____} \leftarrow\ \ 63 \\
\text{_____} \leftarrow\ \ 47 \\
+\ \text{_____} \leftarrow\ +\ 84
\end{array}
$$

42. *Estimate:*   *Exact:*

$$
\begin{array}{r}
56 \\
24 \\
85 \\
+\ \text{_____} \quad +\ 71
\end{array}
$$

43. *Estimate:*   *Exact:*

$$
\begin{array}{r}
78 \\
-\ \text{_____} \quad -\ 43
\end{array}
$$

44. *Estimate:*   *Exact:*

$$
\begin{array}{r}
57 \\
-\ \text{_____} \quad -\ 24
\end{array}
$$

45. *Estimate:*   *Exact:*

$$
\begin{array}{r}
67 \\
\times\ \text{_____} \quad \times\ \ 34
\end{array}
$$

46. *Estimate:*   *Exact:*

$$
\begin{array}{r}
53 \\
\times\ \text{_____} \quad \times\ \ 75
\end{array}
$$

Estimate the answer by rounding each number to the nearest hundred. Then find the exact answer. See Example 9.

47. *Estimate:*   *Exact:*

Rounds to

$$
\begin{array}{r}
\text{_____} \leftarrow\ \ 863 \\
\text{_____} \leftarrow\ \ 735 \\
\text{_____} \leftarrow\ \ 438 \\
+\ \text{_____} \leftarrow\ +\ 792
\end{array}
$$

48. *Estimate:*   *Exact:*

$$
\begin{array}{r}
623 \\
362 \\
189 \\
+\ \text{_____} \quad +\ 736
\end{array}
$$

49. *Estimate:*   *Exact:*

－ _____   883
              － 448

50. *Estimate:*   *Exact:*

－ _____   614
              － 276

51. *Estimate:*   *Exact:*

                752
× _____   × 375

52. *Estimate:*   *Exact:*

                845
× _____   × 396

Estimate each answer using front end rounding. Then find the exact answer. See Example 10.

53. *Estimate:*   *Exact:*

              Rounds to
          ← _____   8215
          ← _____   56
          ← _____   729
+ _____   ← _____ + 3605

54. *Estimate:*   *Exact:*

                2685
                  73
                 592
+ _____   + 7183

55. *Estimate:*   *Exact:*

                687
－ _____   － 529

56. *Estimate:*   *Exact:*

                543
－ _____   － 174

57. *Estimate:*   *Exact:*

                939
× _____   × 29

58. *Estimate:*   *Exact:*

                864
× _____   × 74

59. The number 3492 rounded to the nearest hundred is 3500, and 3500 rounded to the nearest thousand is 4000. But when 3492 is rounded directly to the nearest thousand it becomes 3000. Why is this true? Explain.

60. The use of rounding is helpful when estimating the answer to a problem. Why is this true? Give an example using either addition, subtraction, multiplication, or division to show how this works.

61. In 1900, the population of the United States was 76 million. Today it's 303 million. Round each of these numbers to the nearest ten-million. (*Source:* Reiman Publications and U.S. Census Bureau.)

62. In 1900, the average workweek in the United States was 59 hours. Today it's 38 hours. Round each of these numbers to the nearest ten. (*Source:* Reiman Publications.)

63. There are 348,900 streets named Elm Street in the United States. Round this number to the nearest thousand and nearest ten-thousand. (*Source:* Expo Design Center.)

64. The most expensive item ever sold at a Costco Wholesale warehouse was a $235,000 diamond ring. Round this number to the nearest ten-thousand and the nearest hundred-thousand. (*Source:* Costco Stores magazine.)

65. In Chicago, the Sears Tower tenants recycled 1,667,300 pounds of paper last year. Round this number to the nearest ten-thousand, nearest hundred-thousand, and nearest million. (*Source:* Trizec Properties.)

66. The population of India is 1,129,866,154 people. Round the number to the nearest ten-thousand, nearest hundred-thousand, and nearest million. (*Source:* U.S. Census Bureau.)

67. American pharmaceutical companies spent $25,765,475,000 last year to develop new products. Round this amount to the nearest hundred-thousand, nearest hundred-million, and nearest billion. (*Source:* American Demographics.)

68. In one year the U.S. Federal Food Assistance Program paid out $18,915,762,568 in food stamps. Round this amount to the nearest hundred-thousand, nearest hundred-million, and nearest ten-billion. (*Source:* U.S. Department of Agriculture.)

Relating Concepts (Exercises 69–75) For Individual or Group Work

To see how both rounding and front end rounding are used in solving problems, **work Exercises 69–75 in order.**

69. A number rounded to the nearest thousand is 72,000. What is the *smallest* whole number this could have been before rounding?

70. A number rounded to the nearest thousand is 72,000. What is the *largest* whole number this could have been before rounding?

71. When front end rounding is used, a whole number rounds to 8000. What is the *smallest* possible original number?

72. When front end rounding is used, a whole number rounds to 8000. What is the *largest* possible original number?

The graph below shows the number of personal injuries in the United States each year for people participating in common activities.

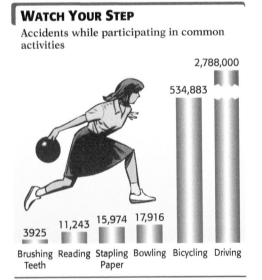

WATCH YOUR STEP

Accidents while participating in common activities

2,788,000

534,883

3925 11,243 15,974 17,916

Brushing Reading Stapling Bowling Bicycling Driving
Teeth   Paper

Source: AARP Magazine.

73. Round the number of accidents occurring in each activity to the nearest ten.

74. Use front end rounding to round the number of accidents in each activity.

75. (a) What is one advantage of using front end rounding instead of rounding to the nearest ten?

(b) What is one disadvantage?

1.8 ▶▶▶ Exponents, Roots, and Order of Operations

OBJECTIVE 1 Identify an exponent and a base. The product $3 \cdot 3$ can be written as 3^2 (read as "3 squared"). The small raised number 2, called an **exponent,** says to use 2 factors of 3. The number 3 is called the **base.** Writing 3^2 as 9 is called *simplifying the expression.*

EXAMPLE 1 Simplifying Expressions

Identify the exponent and the base, and then simplify each expression.

(a) 4^3

> The small raised number is the exponent.

Base $\rightarrow 4^3 \leftarrow$ Exponent $4^3 = 4 \times 4 \times 4 = 64$

(b) $2^5 = 2 \times 2 \times 2 \times 2 \times 2 = 32$
The base is 2 and the exponent is 5.

Work Problem **1** *at the Side.* ▶

OBJECTIVE 2 Find the square root of a number. Because $3^2 = 9$, the number 3 is called the **square root** of 9. The square root of a number is one of two identical factors of that number. Square roots of numbers are written with the symbol $\sqrt{}$.

$$\sqrt{9} = 3$$

> **Square Root**
> $$\sqrt{\text{number} \cdot \text{number}} = \sqrt{\text{number}^2} = \text{number}$$
> For example: $\sqrt{36} = \sqrt{6 \cdot 6} = \sqrt{6^2} = 6$ is the square root of 36.

To find the square root of 64 ask, "What number can be multiplied by itself (that is, *squared*) to give 64?" The answer is 8, so

$$\sqrt{64} = \sqrt{8 \cdot 8} = \sqrt{8^2} = 8.$$

A **perfect square** is a number that is the square of a *whole number.* The first few perfect squares are listed here.

> **Perfect Squares Table**
>
> | | | | |
> |---|---|---|---|
> | $0 = 0^2$ | $16 = 4^2$ | $64 = 8^2$ | $144 = 12^2$ |
> | $1 = 1^2$ | $25 = 5^2$ | $81 = 9^2$ | $169 = 13^2$ |
> | $4 = 2^2$ | $36 = 6^2$ | $100 = 10^2$ | $196 = 14^2$ |
> | $9 = 3^2$ | $49 = 7^2$ | $121 = 11^2$ | $225 = 15^2$ |

EXAMPLE 2 Using Perfect Squares

Find each square root.

(a) $\sqrt{16}$ Because $4^2 = 16$, $\sqrt{16} = 4$.   **(b)** $\sqrt{49} = 7$

(c) $\sqrt{0} = 0$ **(d)** $\sqrt{169} = 13$

Work Problem **2** *at the Side.* ▶

OBJECTIVE 3 Use the order of operations. Frequently problems may have parentheses, exponents, and square roots, and may involve more than one operation. Work these problems by following the **order of operations.**

OBJECTIVES

1 Identify an exponent and a base.

2 Find the square root of a number.

3 Use the order of operations.

1 Identify the exponent and the base, and then simplify each expression.

(a) 4^2

(b) 5^3

(c) 3^4

(d) 2^6

2 Find each square root.

(a) $\sqrt{4}$

(b) $\sqrt{25}$

(c) $\sqrt{36}$

(d) $\sqrt{225}$

(e) $\sqrt{1}$

ANSWERS

1. **(a)** 2; 4; 16 **(b)** 3; 5; 125
   (c) 4; 3; 81 **(d)** 6; 2; 64
2. **(a)** 2 **(b)** 5 **(c)** 6 **(d)** 15 **(e)** 1

3 Simplify each expression.

(a) $4 + 5 + 2^2$

(b) $3^2 + 2^3$

(c) $4 \cdot 6 \div 12 - 2$

(d) $60 \div \sqrt{36} \div 2$

(e) $8 + 6(14 \div 2)$

4 Simplify each expression.

(a) $12 - 6 + 4^2$

(b) $2^3 + 3^2 - (5 \cdot 3)$

(c) $2 \cdot \sqrt{64} - 5 \cdot 3$

(d) $20 \div 2 + (7 - 5)$

(e) $15 \cdot \sqrt{9} - 8 \cdot \sqrt{4}$

Order of Operations

1. Do all operations inside **parentheses** or **other grouping symbols.**
2. Simplify any expressions with **exponents** and find any **square roots.**
3. **Multiply** or **divide,** proceeding from left to right.
4. **Add** or **subtract,** proceeding from left to right.

EXAMPLE 3 Understanding the Order of Operations

Use the order of operations to simplify each expression.

(a) $8^2 + 5 + 2$

$$8^2 + 5 + 2$$
$$8 \cdot 8 + 5 + 2 \qquad \text{Evaluate exponent first; } 8^2 \text{ is } 8 \cdot 8.$$
$$64 + 5 + 2 \qquad \text{Add from left to right.}$$
$$69 \quad + 2 = 71$$

(b) $35 \div 5 \cdot 6 \qquad$ Divide first (start at left).
$$\quad 7 \quad \cdot 6 = 42 \qquad \text{Multiply.}$$

(c) $9 + (20 - 4) \cdot 3 \qquad$ Work inside parentheses first.
$$9 + \quad 16 \cdot 3 \qquad \text{Multiply.}$$
$$9 + \quad 48 = 57 \qquad \text{Add last.}$$

(d) $12 \cdot \sqrt{16} - 8(4) \qquad$ Find the square root first.
$$12 \cdot \quad 4 \quad - 8(4) \qquad \text{Multiply from left to right.}$$
$$48 \quad - \quad 32 = 16 \qquad \text{Subtract last.}$$

◀ *Work Problem* **3** *at the Side.*

EXAMPLE 4 Using the Order of Operations

Use the order of operations to simplify each expression.

(a) $15 - 4 + 2 \qquad$ Subtract first (start at left).
$$11 \quad + 2 = 13 \qquad \text{Add.}$$

(b) $8 + (7 - 3) \div 2 \qquad$ Work inside parentheses first.
$$8 + \quad 4 \quad \div 2 \qquad \text{Divide.} \qquad \boxed{\text{Add or subtract last.}}$$
$$8 + \quad 2 \quad = 10 \qquad \text{Add last.}$$

(c) $4^2 \cdot 2^2 + (7 + 3) \cdot 2 \qquad$ Work inside parentheses first.
$$4^2 \cdot 2^2 + \quad 10 \quad \cdot 2 \qquad \text{Evaluate exponents.}$$
$$16 \cdot 4 + \quad 10 \quad \cdot 2 \qquad \text{Multiply from left to right.}$$
$$64 \quad + \quad 20 = 84 \qquad \text{Add last.}$$

(d) $4 \cdot \sqrt{25} - 7 \cdot 2 + \dfrac{0}{5} \qquad$ Find the square root first. $\boxed{\text{Remember: Zero divided by any nonzero number is zero.}}$

$$4 \cdot \quad 5 \quad - 7 \cdot 2 + \dfrac{0}{5} \qquad \text{Multiply or divide from left to right.}$$
$$20 \quad - \quad 14 \quad + 0 = 6 \qquad \text{Add or subtract last.}$$

Note

Getting a correct answer depends on following the order of operations.

◀ *Work Problem* **4** *at the Side.*

1.8 ▶▶▶ **Exercises**

FOR
EXTRA
HELP
MyMathLab

Math XL
PRACTICE

WATCH

DOWNLOAD

READ

REVIEW

Identify the exponent and the base, and then simplify each expression. See Example 1.

1. 3^2

2. 2^3

3. 5^2

4. 4^2

🌐 **5.** 8^2

6. 10^3

7. 15^2

8. 11^3

Use the Perfect Squares Table on page 77 to find each square root. See Example 2.

🌐 **9.** $\sqrt{16}$

10. $\sqrt{25}$

11. $\sqrt{64}$

12. $\sqrt{36}$

13. $\sqrt{100}$

14. $\sqrt{49}$

15. $\sqrt{144}$

16. $\sqrt{225}$

Fill in each blank. See Example 2.

17. $6^2 = $ _____ so $\sqrt{} = 6$

18. $9^2 = $ _____ so $\sqrt{} = 9$

19. $20^2 = $ _____ so $\sqrt{} = 20$

20. $30^2 = $ _____ so $\sqrt{} = 30$

21. $35^2 = $ _____ so $\sqrt{} = 35$

22. $38^2 = $ _____ so $\sqrt{} = 38$

23. $25^2 = $ _____ so $\sqrt{} = 25$

24. $50^2 = $ _____ so $\sqrt{} = 50$

25. $100^2 = $ _____ so $\sqrt{} = 100$

26. $60^2 = $ _____ so $\sqrt{} = 60$

27. Describe in your own words a perfect square. Of the two numbers 25 and 50, identify which is a perfect square and explain why.

28. Use the following list of words and phrases to write the four steps in the order of operations.

add   square root

exponents   subtract

multiply   divide

parentheses or other grouping symbols

Simplify each expression by using the order of operations. See Examples 3 and 4.

29. $3^2 + 8 - 5$

30. $5^2 + 5 - 6$

31. $3 \cdot 7 - 6$

32. $5 \cdot 7 - 7$

33. $8 \cdot 5 \div 10$

34. $6 \cdot 8 \div 8$

35. $25 \div 5(8 - 4)$

36. $36 \div 18(7 - 3)$

37. $5 \cdot 3^2 + \dfrac{0}{8}$

38. $8 \cdot 3^2 - \dfrac{10}{2}$

39. $4 \cdot 1 + 8(9 - 2) + 3$

40. $3 \cdot 2 + 7(3 + 1) + 5$

41. $2^2 \cdot 3^3 + (20 - 15) \cdot 2$

42. $4^2 \cdot 5^2 + (20 - 9) \cdot 3$

43. $5\sqrt{36} - 2(4)$

44. $2 \cdot \sqrt{100} - 3(4)$

45. $8(2) + 3 \cdot 7 - 7 =$

46. $10(3) + 6 \cdot 5 - 20$

47. $2^3 \cdot 3^2 + 3\,(14 - 4)$

48. $3^2 \cdot 4^2 + 2\,(15 - 6)$

49. $7 + 8 \div 4 + \dfrac{0}{7}$

50. $6 + 8 \div 2 + \dfrac{0}{8}$

51. $3^2 + 6^2 + (30 - 21) \cdot 2$

52. $4^2 + 5^2 + (25 - 9) \cdot 3$

53. $7 \cdot \sqrt{81} - 5 \cdot 6$

54. $6 \cdot \sqrt{64} - 6 \cdot 5$

55. $8 \cdot 2 + 5\,(3 \cdot 4) - 6$

56. $5 \cdot 2 + 3\,(5 + 3) - 6$

57. $4 \cdot \sqrt{49} - 7\,(5 - 2)$

58. $3 \cdot \sqrt{25} - 6\,(3 - 1)$

59. $7\,(4 - 2) + \sqrt{9}$

60. $5\,(4 - 3) + \sqrt{9}$

61. $7^2 + 3^2 - 8 + 5$

62. $3^2 - 2^2 + 3 - 2$

63. $5^2 \cdot 2^2 + (8 - 4) \cdot 2$

64. $5^2 \cdot 3^2 + (30 - 20) \cdot 2$

65. $5 + 9 \div 3 + 6 \cdot 3$

66. $8 + 3 \div 3 + 6 \cdot 3$

67. $8 \cdot \sqrt{49} - 6\,(9 - 4)$

68. $8 \cdot \sqrt{49} - 6\,(5 + 3)$

69. $5^2 - 4^2 + 3 \cdot 6$

70. $3^2 + 6^2 - 5 \cdot 8$

71. $8 + 8 \div 8 + 6 + \dfrac{5}{5}$

72. $3 + 14 \div 2 + 7 + \dfrac{8}{8}$

73. $6 \cdot \sqrt{25} - 7(2)$

74. $8 \cdot \sqrt{36} - 4(6)$

75. $9 \cdot \sqrt{16} - 3 \cdot \sqrt{25}$

76. $6 \cdot \sqrt{81} - 3 \cdot \sqrt{49}$

77. $7 \div 1 \cdot 8 \cdot 2 \div (21 - 5)$

78. $12 \div 4 \cdot 5 \cdot 4 \div (15 - 13)$

79. $15 \div 3 \cdot 2 \cdot 6 \div (14 - 11)$

80. $9 \div 1 \cdot 4 \cdot 2 \div (11 - 5)$

81. $6 \cdot \sqrt{25} - 4 \cdot \sqrt{16}$

82. $10 \cdot \sqrt{49} - 4 \cdot \sqrt{64}$

83. $5 \div 1 \cdot 10 \cdot 4 \div (17 - 9)$

84. $15 \div 3 \cdot 8 \cdot 9 \div (12 - 8)$

85. $8 \cdot 9 \div \sqrt{36} - 4 \div 2 + (14 - 8)$

86. $3 - 2 + 5 \cdot 4 \cdot \sqrt{144} \div \sqrt{36}$

87. $2 + 1 - 2 \cdot \sqrt{1} + 4 \cdot \sqrt{81} - 7 \cdot 2$

88. $6 - 4 + 2 \cdot 9 - 3 \cdot \sqrt{225} \div \sqrt{25}$

89. $5 \cdot \sqrt{36} \cdot \sqrt{100} \div 4 \cdot \sqrt{9} + 8$

90. $9 \cdot \sqrt{36} \cdot \sqrt{81} \div 2 + 6 - 3 - 5$

Study Skills

Study the set of sample math notes in this section, and read the comments about them. Then try to incorporate the techniques into your own math note taking in class.

OBJECTIVES

1 Apply note taking strategies, such as writing problems as well as explanations.

2 Use appropriate abbreviations in notes.

▶ The **date and title** of the day's lecture topic are always at the top of every page. **Always begin a new day with a new page.**

▶ Note the **definitions** of base and exponent are written in parentheses—don't trust your memory!

▶ **Skipping lines** makes the notes easier to read.

▶ See how the **direction word** (*simplify*) is emphasized and explained.

▶ A **star marks an important concept.** This is a warning to avoid future mistakes. **Note the underlining,** too, which highlights the importance.

▶ Notice the two columns, which allow for the example and its explanation to be close together. **Whenever you know you'll be given a series of steps to follow, try the two-column method.**

▶ Note the **brackets and arrows,** which clearly show how the problem is set up to be simplified.

January 2   *Exponents*

Exponents used to show repeated multiplication.

         exponent

$3 \cdot 3 \cdot 3 \cdot 3$ *can be written* 3^4 *(how many times it's multiplied)*

     base (the number being multiplied)

Read 3^2 *as 3 to the 2nd power or 3 squared*

       3^3 *as 3 to the 3rd power or 3 cubed*

       3^4 *as 3 to the 4th power*

       etc.

Simplifying an expression with exponents

     actually do the repeated multiplication

     2^3 *means* $2 \cdot 2 \cdot 2$ *and* $2 \cdot 2 \cdot 2 = 8$

☆ *Careful!* 5^2 *means* $5 \cdot 5$ *NOT* $5 \cdot 2$

     so $5^2 = 5 \cdot 5 = 25$ *BUT* $5^2 \neq 10$

Example	*Explanation*
Simplify $2^4 \cdot 3^2$	*Exponents mean multiplication.*
$2 \cdot 2 \cdot 2 \cdot 2 \quad 3 \cdot 3$	*Use 2 as a factor 4 times.* *Use 3 as a factor 2 times.*
$16 \quad \cdot \quad 9$	$2 \cdot 2 \cdot 2 \cdot 2$ *is 16* $3 \cdot 3$ *is 9* $16 \cdot 9$ *is 144*
144	*Simplified result is 144 (no exponents left)*

Why Are These Notes Brain Friendly?

The notes are **easy to look at,** and you know that the brain responds to things that are visually pleasing. Other techniques that are visually memorable are the use of spacing (the two columns), stars, underlining, and circling. All of these methods **allow your brain to take note of important concepts and steps.**

The notes are also **systematic,** which means that they use certain techniques regularly. This way, your brain easily recognizes the topic of the day, the signals that show an important point, and the steps to follow for procedures. When you develop a system that you always use in your notes, your notes are easy to understand later when you are reviewing for a test.

Find one or two people in your math class to work with. Compare each other's lecture notes over a period of a week or so. Ask yourself the following questions as you examine the notes.

1. What are you doing in your notes to show the **main points** or larger concepts? (Such as underlining, boxing, using stars, capital letters, etc.)

2. In what ways do you **set off the explanations** for worked problems, examples, or smaller ideas (subpoints)? (Such as indenting, using arrows, circling or boxing)

3. What does **your instructor do** to show that he or she is moving from one idea to the next? (Such as saying "Next" or "Any questions," "Now," or erasing the board, etc.)

4. **How do you mark** that in your notes? (Such as skipping lines, using dashes or numbers, etc.)

5. What **explanations (in words) do you give yourself** in your notes, so when those new dendrites you grew in lecture are fading, you can read your notes and still remember the new concepts later when you try to do your homework?

6. What **did you learn** by examining your classmates' notes?

   •

   •

   •

7. What **will you try** in your own note taking? List **four** techniques that you will use next time you take notes in math class.

   •

   •

   •

   •

1.9 ▶▶▶ Solving Application Problems

Most problems involving applications of mathematics are written out in sentence form. You need to read the problem carefully to decide how to solve it.

OBJECTIVE 1 Find indicator words in application problems.
As you read an application problem, look for **indicator words** that help you determine whether to use addition, subtraction, multiplication, or division. Some of these indicator words are shown here.

Addition	Subtraction	Multiplication	Division	Equals
plus	less	product	divided by	is
more	subtract	double	divided into	the same as
more than	subtracted from	triple	quotient	equals
added to	difference	times	goes into	equal to
increased by	less than	of	divide	yields
sum	fewer	twice	divided equally	results in
total	decreased by	twice as much	per	are
sum of	loss of			
increase of	minus			
gain of	take away			

CAUTION
The word *and* does not always indicate addition, so it does not appear as an indicator word in the preceding table. Notice how the "and" shows the location of several different operation signs below.

The sum of 6 *and* 2 is $6 + 2$.
The difference of 6 *and* 2 is $6 - 2$.
The product of 6 *and* 2 is $6 \cdot 2$.
The quotient of 6 *and* 2 is $6 \div 2$.

OBJECTIVE 2 Solve application problems. Solve application problems by using the following six steps.

Solving an Application Problem

Step 1 **Read** the problem carefully and be certain you *understand* what the problem is asking. It may be necessary to read the problem several times.

Step 2 Before doing any calculations, **work out a plan** and try to visualize the problem. Draw a sketch if possible. Know which facts are given and which must be found. Use *indicator words* to help decide on the *plan* (whether you will need to add, subtract, multiply, or divide).

Step 3 **Estimate** a *reasonable answer* by using rounding.

Step 4 **Solve** the problem by using the facts given and your plan.

Step 5 **State the answer.**

Step 6 **Check** your work. If the answer does not seem reasonable, begin again by reading the problem.

Read and **understand** a problem before you begin.

Always **estimate** the final answer.

Check your answer to see if it is *reasonable*.

1 Pick the most reasonable answer for each problem.

(a) A grocery clerk's hourly wage: $1.40; $14; $140

(b) The total length of five sport-utility vehicles: 8 ft; 18 ft; 80 ft; 800 ft

(c) The cost of heart bypass surgery: $1000; $100,000; $10,000,000

> **CAUTION**
> Be certain that you know what the problem is asking before you try to solve it.

OBJECTIVE 3 Estimate an answer. The six problem-solving steps give a systematic approach for solving word problems. Each of the steps is important, but special emphasis should be placed on Step 3, estimating a *reasonable answer.* Many times an "answer" just does not fit the problem.

What is a reasonable answer? Read the problem and try to determine the approximate size of the answer. Should the answer be part of a dollar, a few dollars, hundreds, thousands, or even millions of dollars? For example, if a problem asks for the cost of a man's shirt, would an answer of $20 be reasonable? $2000? $2? $200?

> **CAUTION**
> Always estimate the answer, then look at your final result to be sure it fits your estimate and is reasonable. This step will give greater success in problem solving.

◀ *Work Problem* **1** *at the Side.*

EXAMPLE 1 **Applying Division**

A community group has raised $8260 for charity. Equal amounts are given to the Food Bank, Children's Center, Boy Scouts of America, and the Women's Shelter. How much did each group receive?

2 Solve each problem.

(a) On a recent geology field trip, 84 fossils were collected. If the fossils are divided equally among John, Sean, Jenn, and Kara, how many fossils will each receive?

Step 1 **Read.** A reading of the problem shows that the four charities divided $8260 equally.

Step 2 **Work out a plan.** The indicator words, *divided equally,* show that the amount each received can be found by dividing $8260 by 4.

Step 3 **Estimate.** Round $8260 to $8000. Then $8000 ÷ 4 = $2000, so a reasonable answer would be a little greater than $2000 each.

Step 4 **Solve.** Find the actual answer by dividing $8260 by 4.

$$\frac{2065}{4\overline{)8260}}$$

Step 5 **State the answer.** Each charity received $2065.

(b) This week there are 408 children attending a winter sports camp. If 12 children are assigned to each camp counselor, how many counselors are needed?

Step 6 **Check.** The exact answer of $2065 is reasonable, as $2065 is close to the estimated answer of $2000. Is the answer $2065 correct? Check by multiplying.

$2065 ← Amount received by each charity

$\underline{\times \quad 4}$ ← Number of charities

$8260 ← Total raised; matches number given in problem

> Remember: Check your work.

◀ *Work Problem* **2** *at the Side.*

ANSWERS

1. (a) $14 (b) 80 ft (c) $100,000
2. (a) 21 fossils (b) 34 counselors

EXAMPLE 2 **Applying Addition**

One week, Andrea Abriani, operations manager, decided to total the stroller production at Safe T First Strollers. The daily production figures were 7642 strollers on Monday, 8150 strollers on Tuesday, 7916 strollers on Wednesday, 8419 strollers on Thursday, and 7704 strollers on Friday. Find the total production for the week.

Step 1 **Read.** In this problem, the production for each day is given and the total production for the week must be found.

Step 2 **Work out a plan.** Add the daily production figures to arrive at the weekly total.

Step 3 **Estimate.** Because the production was about 8000 strollers per day for a week of five days, a reasonable estimate would be 5 • 8000 = 40,000 strollers.

Step 4 **Solve.** Find the exact answer by adding the production numbers for the 5 days.

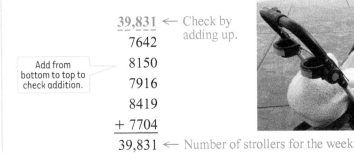

$$
\begin{array}{r}
\underline{39,831} \leftarrow \text{Check by} \\
7642 \quad \text{adding up.} \\
8150 \\
7916 \\
8419 \\
+\ 7704 \\
\hline
39,831 \leftarrow \text{Number of strollers for the week}
\end{array}
$$

Add from bottom to top to check addition.

Step 5 **State the answer.** Abriani's total production figure for the week was 39,831 strollers.

Step 6 **Check.** The exact answer of 39,831 strollers is close to the estimate of 40,000 strollers, so it is reasonable. Add up the columns to check the exact answer.

▦ **Calculator Tip**   The calculator solution to Example 2 uses chain calculations.

7642 ⊕ 8150 ⊕ 7916 ⊕ 8419 ⊕ 7704 ⊜ **39,831**

Work Problem 3 *at the Side.* ▶

EXAMPLE 3 **Determining Whether Subtraction Is Necessary**

The number of miles driven this year is 3028 fewer than the number driven last year. The miles driven last year was 16,735. Find the number of miles driven this year.

Step 1 **Read.** In this problem, the miles driven decreased from last year to this year. The miles driven last year and the decrease in miles driven are given. This year's miles driven must be found.

Step 2 **Work out a plan.** The indicator word, *fewer,* shows that subtraction must be used to find the number of miles driven this year.

Step 3 **Estimate.** Because the driving last year was about 17,000 miles, and the decrease in driving is about 3000 miles, a reasonable estimate would be 17,000 − 3000 = 14,000 miles.

Continued on Next Page

3 Solve each problem.

(a) During the semester, Cindy received the following points on examinations and quizzes: 92, 81, 83, 98, 15, 14, 15, and 12. Find her total points for the semester.

(b) Stephanie Dixon works at the telephone order desk of a catalog sales company. One week she had the following number of customer contacts: Monday, 78; Tuesday, 64; Wednesday, 118; Thursday, 102; and Friday, 196. How many customer contacts did she have that week?

ANSWERS

3. **(a)** 410 points   **(b)** 558 customer contacts

4 Solve each problem.

(a) A home has a living area of 1450 square feet, while an apartment has 980 square feet. Find the difference between the number of square feet in the two living areas.

Step 4   **Solve.** Find the exact answer by subtracting 3078 from 16,735.

$$\begin{array}{r} 16,735 \\ -\ \ 3078 \\ \hline 13,707 \end{array}$$

Step 5   **State the answer.** The driving this year is 13,707 miles.

Step 6   **Check.** The exact answer of 13,707 is reasonable, as it is close to the estimate of 14,000. Check by adding.

$$\begin{array}{r} 13,707 \leftarrow \text{miles driven this year} \\ +\ \ 3028 \leftarrow \text{decrease in miles driven} \\ \hline 16,735 \leftarrow \text{miles driven last year; matches number given in problem} \end{array}$$

◀ *Work Problem* **4** *at the Side.*

(b) The Antique Military Vehicle Collectors (AMVC) had $14,863 in their club treasury bank account. After writing a check for $1180 to rent a display hall, find the amount remaining in the club account.

EXAMPLE 4   **Solving a Two-Step Problem**

In May, a landlord received $720 from each of eight tenants. After paying $2180 in expenses, how much rent money did the landlord have left?

Step 1   **Read.** The problem asks for the amount of rent remaining after expenses have been paid.

Step 2   **Work out a plan.** The wording *from each of eight tenants* indicates that the eight rents must be totaled. Since the rents are all the same, use multiplication to find the total rent received. Then, subtract expenses.

Step 3   **Estimate.** The amount of rent is about $700, making the total rent received about $700 • 8 = $5600. The expenses are about $2000. A reasonable estimate of the amount remaining is $5600 − $2000 = $3600.

5 Solve each problem.

(a) Brenda is paid $685 for each kitchen remodeling job that she sells. If she sold 6 remodeling jobs and had $320 in sales expense deducted, how much did she make?

Step 4   **Solve.** Find the exact amount by first multiplying $720 by 8 (the number of tenants).

$$\begin{array}{r} \$\ 720 \\ \times\ \ \ \ \ 8 \\ \hline \$5760 \end{array}$$

Then subtract the $2180 in expenses from $5760.

$$\begin{array}{r} \$5760 \\ -\ \$2180 \\ \hline \$3580 \end{array}$$
The exact answer is close to the estimate and reasonable.

Step 5   **State the answer.** The amount remaining is $3580.

(b) An Internet book company had sales of 12,628 books with a profit of $6 for each book sold. If 863 books were returned, how much profit remains?

Step 6   **Check.** The exact answer of $3580 is reasonable, since it is close to the estimated answer of $3600. Check by adding the expenses to the amount remaining and then dividing by 8.

$$\$3580 + \$2180 = \$5760$$
Always check your work.
$$\begin{array}{r} \$720 \\ 8\overline{)5760} \end{array}$$
Matches the rent amount given in the problem

◀ *Work Problem* **5** *at the Side.*

1.9 ▶▶▶ **Exercises**

FOR
EXTRA
HELP **MyMathLab**

Math XL
PRACTICE

WATCH

DOWNLOAD

READ

REVIEW

Solve each application problem. First use front end rounding to estimate the answer. Then find the exact answer. See Examples 1–4.

1. Last week, SUBWAY sold 602 Veggie Delite sandwiches, 935 ham sandwiches, 1328 turkey breast sandwiches, 757 roast beef sandwiches, and 1586 SUBWAY club sandwiches. Find the total number of sandwiches sold.

Estimate:

Exact:

2. During a recent week, Radio Flyer, Inc. manufactured 32,815 Model #18 wagons, 4875 steel mini-wagons, 1975 wood 40-inch wagons, 15,308 scooters, and 9815 new-design plastic wagons. Find the total number of units manufactured.

Estimate:

Exact:

The graph shows the number of contaminated meat recalls by the U.S. Department of Agriculture over a five-year period. Use the graph for Exercises 3–4.

3. How many more meat recalls were there in 2003 than in 2007?

Estimate:

Exact:

4. How many fewer meat recalls were there in 2006 than in 2008?

Estimate:

Exact:

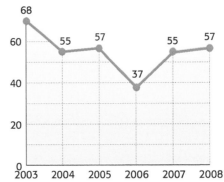

CONTAMINATED MEAT RECALLS

Source: U.S. Department of Agriculture.

5. A packing machine can package 236 first-aid kits each hour. At this rate, find the number of first-aid kits packaged in 24 hours.

Estimate:

Exact:

6. If 450 admission tickets to a classic car show are sold each day, how many tickets are sold in a 12-day period?

Estimate:

Exact:

7. Clarence Hanks, coordinator of Toys for Tots, has collected 2628 toys. If his group can give the same number of toys to each of 657 children, how many toys will each child receive?

Estimate:

Exact:

8. If profits of $680,000 are divided evenly among a firm's 1000 employees, how much money will each employee receive?

Estimate:

Exact:

9. The number of boaters and campers at the lake was 8392 on Friday. If this was 4218 more than the number of people at the lake on Wednesday, how many were there on Wednesday?

Estimate:

Exact:

10. The community has raised $52,882 for the homeless shelter. If the total amount needed for the shelter is $75,650, find the additional amount needed.

Estimate:

Exact:

11. Turn down the thermostat in the winter and you can save money and energy. In the upper Midwest, setting back the thermostat from 68° to 55° at night can save $34 per month on fuel. Find the amount of money saved in five months.

Estimate:

Exact:

12. The cost of tuition and fees at a community college is $785 per quarter. If Gale Klein has five quarters remaining, find the total amount that she will need for tuition and fees.

Estimate:

Exact:

The table shows the average annual earnings of those in careers that do not require a four year degree. Refer to the table to answer Exercises 13–16. First use front end rounding to estimate the answer. Then find the exact answer.

13. How much more does a dental hygienist earn than a flight attendant?

Estimate:

Exact:

14. How much more does an air traffic controller earn than a court reporter?

Estimate:

Exact:

No Degree? Apply Here?

Four years of college may be your best ticket to a high-paying career, but these solid jobs don't require an undergraduate degree:

Profession	Median Annual Earnings		
Air traffic controller	$87,930	Locomotive engineer	46,540
Nuclear power reactor operator	60,180	Telecom equipment installer/repairer*	46,390
Dental hygienist*	54,700	Funeral director*	42,010
Elevator installer/repairer	51,630	Aircraft mechanic*	41,990
Real estate broker	51,380	Brick mason	41,590
Commercial pilot (non-airline)	47,410	Police officer	40,970
Electrical power line installer/repairer	47,210	Electrician	40,770
		Flight attendant	40,600
		Court reporter*	40,410
		Real estate appraiser*	38,950

*Requires associate's degree or vocational diploma

Source: U.S. Department of Labor.

15. Mr. White is a locomotive engineer and Mrs. White is a court reporter. Mr. Easterly is an aircraft mechanic and Mrs. Easterly is a real estate broker.

(a) Which couple has higher earnings?

Estimate:

Exact:

(b) Find the difference in the earnings.

Estimate:

Exact:

16. Mr. Means is a funeral director and Mrs. Means is an electrician. Mr. Strong is a police officer and Mrs. Strong is a commercial pilot.

(a) Which couple has higher earnings?

Estimate:

Exact:

(b) Find the difference in the earnings.

Estimate:

Exact:

17. Ronda Biondi decides to establish a monthly budget. She will spend $695 for rent, $340 for food, $435 for child care, $240 for transportation, $180 for other expenses, and she will put the remainder in savings. If her monthly take-home pay is $2240, find her monthly savings.

Estimate:

Exact:

18. Robert Heisner had $2874 in his checking account. He wrote checks for $308 for auto repairs, $580 for child support, and $778 for an insurance payment. Find the amount remaining in his account.

Estimate:

Exact:

19. There are 43,560 square feet in one acre. How many square feet are there in 138 acres?

Estimate:

Exact:

20. The number of gallons of water polluted each day in an industrial area is 209,670. How many gallons of water are polluted each year? (Use a 365-day year.)

Estimate:

Exact:

The Internet was used to find the following minivan optional features and the price of each feature. Use this information to answer Exercises 21–24.

Safety and Security Options		Convenience and Comfort Options	
Option	Cost	Option	Cost
Integrated child bench seats	$400	Power sliding door	$400
Supplemental side air bags	$1395	8-way power seat	$395
Security alarm	$170	Roof rack	$250
Hands-free communication	$360	Power door locks	$315
Power adjustable pedal	$195	Keyless entry	$150
Full-size spare tire	$160	AM/FM stereo and CD	$350

Source: www.edmunds.com

21. Find the total cost of all Safety and Security Options listed.

Estimate:

Exact:

22. Find the total cost of all Convenience and Comfort Options listed.

Estimate:

Exact:

23. A new-car dealer offers an option value package that includes integrated child bench seats, security alarm, keyless entry, and a power sliding door at a cost of $980. If Jill buys the value package instead of paying for each option separately, how much will she save?

Estimate:

Exact:

24. A new-car dealer offers an option package that includes integrated child bench seats, security alarm, full-size spare tire, power door locks, 8-way power seat, and a roof rack for a total of $1550. How much will Samuel save if he buys the option package instead of paying for each option separately?

Estimate:

Exact:

25. The Enabling Supply House purchased 6 wheelchairs at $1256 each and 15 speech compression recorder-players at $895 each. Find the total cost.

Estimate:

Exact:

26. A college bookstore buys 17 desktop computers at $506 each and 13 printers at $482 each. Find the total cost.

Estimate:

Exact:

27. Being able to identify indicator words is helpful in determining how to solve an application problem. Write three indicator words for each of these operations: add, subtract, multiply, and divide. Write two indicator words that mean equals.

28. Identify and explain the six steps used to solve an application problem. You may refer to the text if you need help, but use your own words.

29. Write in your own words why it is important to estimate a reasonable answer. Give three examples of what might be a reasonable answer to a math problem from your daily activities.

30. First estimate by rounding to thousands, then find the exact answer to the following problem.

$$7438 + 6493 + 2380$$

Do the two answers vary by more than 1000? Why? Will estimated answers always vary from exact answers?

Estimate:

Exact:

Solve each application problem. See Examples 1–4.

31. Steve Edwards, manager, decided to total his sales at SUBWAY. The daily sales figures were $2358 on Monday, $3056 on Tuesday, $2515 on Wednesday, $1875 on Thursday, $3978 on Friday, $3219 on Saturday, and $3008 on Sunday. Find his total sales for the week.

32. The numbers of visitors at a war veteran's memorial during one week are 5318; 2865; 4786; 1998; 3899; 2343; and 7221. Find the total attendance for the week.

33. A car weighs 2425 pounds. If its 582-pound engine is removed and replaced with a 634-pound engine, what will the car weigh?

34. Barbara has $2324 in her preschool operating account. She spends $734 from this account, and then the class parents raise $568 in a rummage sale. Find the balance in the account after she deposits the money from the rummage sale.

35. In a recent survey of Reno/Lake Tahoe hotels, the cost per night at Harrah's in Reno was $45, while the cost at Harrah's in Lake Tahoe was $99 per night. Find the amount saved on a 7-night stay at Harrah's in Reno instead of staying at Harrah's in Lake Tahoe. (*Source:* Harrah's Casinos and Hotels.)

36. The most expensive hotel room in a recent study was the Ritz-Carlton at $645 per night, while the least expensive was Motel 6 at $74 per night. Find the amount saved in a 4-night stay at Motel 6 instead of staying at the Ritz-Carlton. (*Source:* Ritz-Carlton/Motel 6.)

37. A youth soccer association raised $7588 through fundraising projects. After expenses of $838 were paid, the balance of the money was divided evenly among the 18 teams. How much did each team receive?

38. Feather Farms Egg Ranch collected 3545 eggs in the morning and 2575 eggs in the afternoon. If the eggs are packed in flats containing 30 eggs each, find the number of flats needed for packing.

39. A theater owner wants to provide enough seating for 1250 people. The main floor has 30 rows of 25 seats in each row. If the balcony has 25 rows, how many seats must be in each balcony row to satisfy the owner's seating requirements?

40. Jennie makes 24 grapevine wreaths per week to sell to gift shops. She works 40 weeks a year and packages six wreaths per box. If she ships equal quantities to each of five shops, find the number of boxes each store will receive.

2

Fractions

2.1 ▶▶▶ Basics of Fractions

OBJECTIVES

1 Use a fraction to show which part of a whole is shaded.

2 Identify the numerator and denominator.

3 Identify proper and improper fractions.

In **Chapter 1** we discussed whole numbers. Many times, however, we find that parts of whole numbers are considered. One way to write parts of a whole is with **fractions.** Another way is with decimals.

OBJECTIVE 1 Use a fraction to show which part of a whole is shaded. The number $\frac{1}{8}$ is a fraction that represents 1 of 8 equal parts. Read $\frac{1}{8}$ as "one eighth."

EXAMPLE 1 Identifying Fractions

> A fraction represents part of a whole.

Use fractions to represent the shaded portions and the unshaded portions of each figure.

(a) The figure on the left has 6 equal parts. The 1 shaded part is represented by the fraction $\frac{1}{6}$. The *un*shaded part is $\frac{5}{6}$.

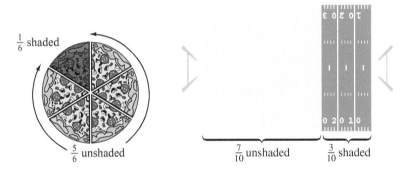

(b) The 3 shaded parts of the 10-part figure on the right are represented by the fraction $\frac{3}{10}$. The *un*shaded part is $\frac{7}{10}$.

◀ Work Problem **1** at the Side.

Fractions can be used to represent more than one whole object.

EXAMPLE 2 Representing Fractions Greater Than 1

Use a fraction to represent the shaded part of each figure.

(a)

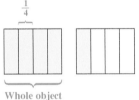

An area equal to 5 of the $\frac{1}{4}$ parts is shaded. Write this as $\frac{5}{4}$.

(b)

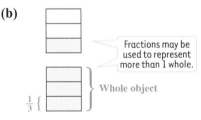

> Fractions may be used to represent more than 1 whole.

An area equal to 4 of the $\frac{1}{3}$ parts is shaded, so $\frac{4}{3}$ is shaded.

◀ Work Problem **2** at the Side.

OBJECTIVE 2 Identify the numerator and denominator. In the fraction $\frac{2}{3}$, the number 2 is the **numerator** and 3 is the **denominator.** The bar between the numerator and the denominator is the *fraction bar.*

$$\text{Fraction bar} \rightarrow \frac{2}{3} \begin{array}{l} \leftarrow \text{Numerator} \\ \leftarrow \text{Denominator} \end{array}$$

---

1 Write fractions for the shaded portions and the unshaded portions of each figure.

(a)

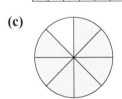

(b)

(c)

2 Write fractions for the shaded portions of each figure.

(a)

(b)

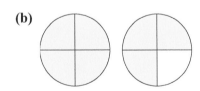

ANSWERS

1. (a) $\frac{3}{4}; \frac{1}{4}$ **(b)** $\frac{1}{6}, \frac{5}{6}$ **(c)** $\frac{7}{8}, \frac{1}{8}$

2. (a) $\frac{8}{7}$ **(b)** $\frac{7}{4}$

Numerators and Denominators

The **denominator** of a fraction shows the number of equivalent parts in the whole, and the **numerator** shows how many parts are being considered.

Note

Remember that a bar, —, is one of the division symbols, and that division by 0 is undefined. A fraction with a denominator of 0 is also undefined.

EXAMPLE 3 **Identifying Numerators and Denominators**

Identify the numerator and denominator in each fraction.

(a) $\dfrac{3}{4}$ (b) $\dfrac{8}{5}$

$\dfrac{3}{4}$ ← Numerator
← Denominator

$\dfrac{8}{5}$ ← Numerator
← Denominator

Work Problem **3** *at the Side.* ▶

OBJECTIVE 3 Identify proper and improper fractions. Fractions are sometimes called *proper* or *improper* fractions.

Proper and Improper Fractions

If the numerator of a fraction is *less* than the denominator, the fraction is a **proper fraction.** A proper fraction is less than 1 whole.

If the numerator is *greater than or equal to* the denominator, the fraction is an **improper fraction.** An improper fraction is greater than or equal to 1 whole.

Proper Fractions	**Improper Fractions**
$\dfrac{5}{8}\quad\dfrac{3}{5}\quad\dfrac{23}{24}$	$\dfrac{6}{5}\quad\dfrac{10}{10}\quad\dfrac{115}{112}$

EXAMPLE 4 **Classifying Types of Fractions**

(a) Identify all proper fractions in this list.

$$\dfrac{3}{4}\quad\dfrac{5}{9}\quad\dfrac{17}{5}\quad\dfrac{9}{7}\quad\dfrac{3}{3}\quad\dfrac{12}{25}\quad\dfrac{1}{9}\quad\dfrac{5}{3}$$

Proper fractions have a numerator that is smaller than the denominator. The proper fractions are shown below.

$\dfrac{3}{4}$ ← 3 is smaller than 4. $\dfrac{5}{9}\quad\dfrac{12}{25}\quad\dfrac{1}{9}$ — A proper fraction is less than 1.

(b) Identify all improper fractions in the list in part (a).

Improper fractions have a numerator that is equal to or greater than the denominator. The improper fractions are shown below.

$\dfrac{17}{5}$ ← 17 is greater than 5. $\dfrac{9}{7}\quad\dfrac{3}{3}\quad\dfrac{5}{3}$ — An improper fraction is equal to or greater than 1.

Work Problem **4** *at the Side.* ▶

3 Identify the numerator and the denominator. Draw a picture with shaded parts to show each fraction. Your drawings may vary, but they should have the correct number of shaded parts.

(a) $\dfrac{2}{3}$

(b) $\dfrac{1}{4}$

(c) $\dfrac{8}{5}$

(d) $\dfrac{5}{2}$

4 From the following group of fractions:

$$\dfrac{2}{3}\quad\dfrac{4}{3}\quad\dfrac{3}{4}\quad\dfrac{8}{8}\quad\dfrac{3}{1}\quad\dfrac{1}{3}$$

(a) list all proper fractions;

(b) list all improper fractions.

ANSWERS

3. (a) N: 2; D: 3
(b) N: 1; D: 4
(c) N: 8; D: 5
(d) N: 5; D: 2

4. (a) $\dfrac{2}{3},\dfrac{3}{4},\dfrac{1}{3}$ (b) $\dfrac{4}{3},\dfrac{8}{8},\dfrac{3}{1}$

Math in the Media

QUILT PATTERNS

People who make quilts often base their designs on a block that is cut into a grid of 4, 9, 16, 25, or 49 squares. The quilter chooses various colors for the pieces. Each quilt design shown was selected from Antique Quilt Designs at their Web site http://earlywomanmasters.net/quilts/index.html.

1. Identify the makeup of the block as 4, 9, 16, etc. Each color is what fractional part of the block?

Aunt Eliza's Star

Block size: _____

Tan: _____ Purple: _____

Green: _____

Barbara Fritchie Star

Block size: _____

Blue: _____ White: _____

Cobwebs

Block size: _____

Mauve: _____ Purple: _____

Yellow: _____

Farmer's Daughter

Block size: _____

Lavender: _____ White: _____

Yellow: _____

Tall Ships

Block size: _____

Blue: _____ Green: _____

Light gray: _____

Lincoln's Platform

Block size: _____

Blue: _____ Aqua: _____

Gold: _____

2. Use the blocks to design and color your own quilt patterns. Tell the fractional part of the block that is represented by each color.

3. Find the next two numbers in this pattern: 4, 9, 16, 25, _____, _____.

4. Explain how the pattern works:

FOR EXTRA HELP

Write fractions to represent the shaded and unshaded portions of each figure. See Examples 1 and 2.

1.

2.

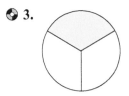**3.**

4.

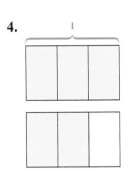

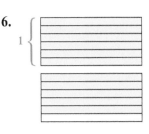**5.**

6.

7. What fraction of these 6 bills has a life span of 2 years or greater? What fraction has a life of 4 years or less? What fraction has a life of 9 years?

A BILL'S LIFE

A $1 bill lasts about 18 months as compared with the average lifespan of other denominations:

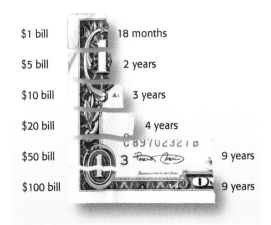

$1 bill	18 months
$5 bill	2 years
$10 bill	3 years
$20 bill	4 years
$50 bill	9 years
$100 bill	9 years

Source: Federal Reserve System; Bureau of Engraving and Printing.

8. What fraction of the 5 pets shown are dogs? What fraction are cats? What fraction of the pets are tan?

9. In an American Sign Language (ASL) class of 25 students, 8 are hearing impaired. What fraction of the students are hearing impaired?

10. Of 98 bicycles in a bike rack, 67 are mountain bikes. What fraction of the bicycles are not mountain bikes?

11. There are 520 rooms in a hotel. If 217 of the rooms are reserved for nonsmokers, what fraction of the rooms are for smokers?

12. Of the 46 employees at the college bookstore, 15 are full-time while the rest are part-time student help. What fraction of the bookstore employees work part-time?

Identify the numerator and denominator. See Example 3.

	Numerator	Denominator
13. $\frac{4}{5}$	_____	_____
15. $\frac{9}{8}$	_____	_____

	Numerator	Denominator
14. $\frac{5}{6}$	_____	_____
16. $\frac{7}{5}$	_____	_____

List the proper and improper fractions in each group. See Example 4.

	Proper	Improper
17. $\frac{8}{5}$ $\frac{1}{3}$ $\frac{5}{8}$ $\frac{6}{6}$ $\frac{12}{2}$ $\frac{7}{16}$	_____	_____
18. $\frac{1}{3}$ $\frac{3}{8}$ $\frac{16}{12}$ $\frac{10}{8}$ $\frac{6}{6}$ $\frac{3}{4}$	_____	_____
19. $\frac{3}{4}$ $\frac{3}{2}$ $\frac{5}{5}$ $\frac{9}{11}$ $\frac{7}{15}$ $\frac{19}{18}$	_____	_____
20. $\frac{12}{12}$ $\frac{15}{11}$ $\frac{13}{12}$ $\frac{11}{8}$ $\frac{17}{17}$ $\frac{19}{12}$	_____	_____

21. Write a fraction of your own choice. Label the parts of the fraction and write a sentence describing what each part represents. Draw a picture with shaded parts showing your fraction.

22. Give one example of a proper fraction and one example of an improper fraction. What determines whether a fraction is proper or improper? Draw pictures with shaded parts showing these fractions.

Fill in the blanks to complete each sentence.

23. The fraction $\frac{3}{8}$ represents _____ of the _____ equal parts into which a whole is divided.

24. The fraction $\frac{7}{16}$ represents _____ of the _____ equal parts into which a whole is divided.

25. The fraction $\frac{5}{24}$ represents _____ of the _____ equal parts into which a whole is divided.

26. The fraction $\frac{24}{32}$ represents _____ of the _____ equal parts into which a whole is divided.

Study Skills

It is best for your brain if you keep up with the reading and homework in your math class. Remember that the more times you work with the information, the more dendrites you grow! So, give yourself every opportunity to read, work problems, and review your mathematics.

You have two choices for reading your math textbook. Read the short descriptions below and decide which will be best for you.

Maddy learns best by listening to her teacher explain things. She "gets it" when she sees the instructor work problems on the board. She likes to ask questions in class and put the information in her notes. She has learned that it helps if she has *previewed* the section before the lecture, so she knows generally what to expect in class. *But after the class instruction*, when Maddy gets home, she finds that she can understand the math textbook easily. She remembers what her teacher said, and she can double-check her notes if she gets confused. So, Maddy does her **careful** reading of the section in her text **after** hearing the classroom lecture on the topic.

De'Lore, on the other hand, feels he learns well by reading on his own. He prefers to read the section and try working the example problems before coming to class. That way, he already knows what the teacher is going to talk about. Then, he can follow the teacher's examples more easily. It is also easier for him to take notes in class. De'Lore likes to have his questions answered right away, which he can do if he has already read the chapter section. So, De'Lore **carefully** reads the section in his text **before** he hears the classroom lecture on the topic.

Notice that there is **no one right way** to work with your textbook. You always must figure out what works best for you. Note also that both Maddy and De'Lore work with one section at a time. **The key is that you read the textbook regularly!** The rest of this activity will give you some ideas of how to make the most of your reading.

Try the following steps as you **read** your math textbook.

▶ Read slowly. Read only one section—or even part of a section—at a time.

▶ Do the sample problems in the margins **as you go.** Check them right away. The answers are at the bottom of the page.

▶ If your mind wanders, work problems on separate paper and write explanations in your own words.

▶ Make study cards as you read each section. Pay special attention to the yellow and blue boxes in the book. Make cards for new vocabulary, rules, procedures, formulas, and sample problems.

▶ **NOW**, you are ready to do your homework assignment!

OBJECTIVES

1 Select an appropriate strategy for homework.

2 Use textbook features effectively.

Preview before Class; Read Carefully after Class

Read Carefully before Class

Why Are These Reading Techniques Brain Friendly?

The steps at the left encourage you to be **actively working with the material** in your text. Your brain grows dendrites when it is doing something.

These methods require you to **try several different techniques,** not just the same thing over and over. Your brain loves variety!

Also, the techniques allow you to **take small breaks** in your learning. Those rest periods are crucial for good dendrite growth.

Now Try This ▶▶▶

Which steps for reading this book will be most helpful for you?

1. _____

2. _____

3. _____

Homework

Why Are These Homework Suggestions Brain Friendly?

Your brain will grow dendrites as you study the worked examples in the text and **try doing them yourself** on separate paper. So, when you see similar problems in the homework, you will already have dendrites to work from.

Giving yourself a practice test by trying to remember the steps (without looking at your card) is an excellent way to reinforce what you are learning.

Correcting errors right away is how you learn and reinforce the correct procedures. It is hard to unlearn a mistake, so always check to see that you are on the right track.

Teachers assign homework so you can grow your own dendrites (learn the material) and then coat the dendrites with myelin through practice (remember the material). Really! In learning, you get good at what you practice. So, completing homework every day will strengthen your neural network and prepare you for exams.

If you have read each section in your textbook according to the steps above, you will probably encounter few difficulties with the exercises in the homework. Here are some additional suggestions that will help you succeed with the homework.

▶ If you **have trouble with a problem,** find a similar worked example in the section. Pay attention to *every line* of the worked example to see how to get from step to step. Work it yourself too, on separate paper; don't just look at it.

▶ If it is **hard to remember the steps** to follow for certain procedures, write the steps on a separate card. Then write a short explanation of each step. Keep the card nearby while you do the exercises, but try *not* to look at it.

▶ If you **aren't sure you are working the assigned exercises correctly,** choose two or three odd-numbered problems that are a similar type and work them. Then check the answers in the Answers section of your book and see if you are doing them correctly. If you aren't, go back to the section in the text and review the examples and find out how to correct your errors. Finally, when you are sure you understand, try the assigned problems again.

▶ **Make sure you do some homework every day,** even if the math class does not meet each day!

Now Try This ▶▶▶

What are your biggest homework concerns?
List your two main concerns and a **brain friendly solution** for each one.

1. Concern: _____

   Solution: _____

2. Concern: _____

   Solution: _____

2.2 ▶▶▶ Mixed Numbers

Suppose you had three whole trays of muffins and half of another tray. You would state this as a whole number and a fraction.

OBJECTIVE 1 Identify mixed numbers. When a whole number and a fraction are written together, the result is a **mixed number.** For example, the mixed number

$$3\frac{1}{2} \quad \text{represents} \quad 3 + \frac{1}{2}$$

or 3 wholes and $\frac{1}{2}$ of a whole. Read $3\frac{1}{2}$ as "three and one-half." As this figure shows, the mixed number $3\frac{1}{2}$ is equal to the improper fraction $\frac{7}{2}$.

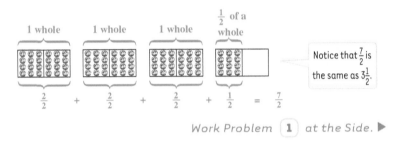

Notice that $\frac{7}{2}$ is the same as $3\frac{1}{2}$.

$$\underbrace{\frac{2}{2}}_{} + \underbrace{\frac{2}{2}}_{} + \underbrace{\frac{2}{2}}_{} + \underbrace{\frac{1}{2}}_{} = \frac{7}{2}$$

Work Problem **1** *at the Side.* ▶

OBJECTIVE 2 Write mixed numbers as improper fractions. Use the following steps to write $3\frac{1}{2}$ as an improper fraction without drawing a figure.

Step 1 Multiply 3 and 2.

$$3\frac{1}{2} \qquad 3 \cdot 2 = 6$$

Step 2 Add 1 to the product.

$$3\frac{1}{2} \qquad 6 + 1 = 7$$

Step 3 Use 7, from Step 2, as the numerator and 2 as the denominator.

$$3\frac{1}{2} = \frac{7}{2}$$

Same denominator

In summary, use the following steps to *write a mixed number as an improper fraction.*

Writing a Mixed Number as an Improper Fraction

Step 1 *Multiply* the denominator of the fraction and the whole number.

Step 2 *Add* to this product the numerator of the fraction.

Step 3 Write the result of Step 2 as the *numerator* and the original denominator as the *denominator.*

---

1 **(a)** Use these diagrams to write $1\frac{2}{3}$ as an improper fraction.

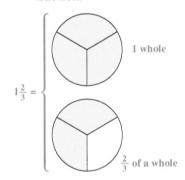

1 whole

$1\frac{2}{3} =$

$\frac{2}{3}$ of a whole

(b) Use these diagrams to write $2\frac{1}{4}$ as an improper fraction.

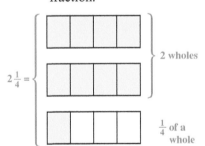

$2\frac{1}{4} =$

2 wholes

$\frac{1}{4}$ of a whole

ANSWERS

1. (a) $\frac{5}{3}$ (b) $\frac{9}{4}$

2 Write as improper fractions.

(a) $6\frac{1}{2}$

(b) $7\frac{3}{4}$

(c) $4\frac{7}{8}$

(d) $8\frac{5}{6}$

3 Write as whole or mixed numbers.

(a) $\frac{6}{5}$

(b) $\frac{9}{4}$

(c) $\frac{35}{5}$

(d) $\frac{78}{7}$

EXAMPLE 1 **Writing a Mixed Number as an Improper Fraction**

Write $7\frac{2}{3}$ as an improper fraction (numerator greater than denominator).

Step 1 $7\frac{2}{3}$ $7 \cdot 3 = 21$ Multiply 7 and 3.

Step 2 $7\frac{2}{3}$ $21 + 2 = 23$ Add 2. The numerator is 23.

Step 3 $7\frac{2}{3} = \frac{23}{3}$ Use the same denominator.

Always use the same denominator.

◀ *Work Problem* **2** *at the Side.*

OBJECTIVE 3 **Write improper fractions as mixed numbers.**
Write an improper fraction as a mixed number as follows.

> **Writing an Improper Fraction as a Mixed Number**
> Write an **improper fraction** as a mixed number by dividing the numerator by the denominator. The quotient is the whole number (of the mixed number), the remainder is the numerator of the fraction part, and the denominator remains unchanged.

EXAMPLE 2 **Writing Improper Fractions as Mixed Numbers**

Write each improper fraction as a mixed number.

Divide numerator by denominator.

(a) $\frac{17}{5}$ Divide 17 by 5. $\longrightarrow$ $\begin{array}{r} 3 \\ 5\overline{)17} \\ \underline{15} \\ 2 \end{array}$ ← **Whole number part**

← Remainder

The quotient **3** is the whole number part of the mixed number. The remainder **2** is the numerator of the fraction, and the denominator stays as **5**.

$$\frac{17}{5} = 3\frac{2}{5}$$ ← Remainder
Same denominator

We can check this by using a diagram in which $\frac{17}{5}$ is shaded.

$\frac{5}{5} = 1$ (whole) $\frac{5}{5} = 1$ (whole) $\frac{5}{5} = 1$ (whole) $\frac{2}{5}$

3 wholes

(b) $\frac{24}{4}$ Divide 24 by 4. $\longrightarrow$ $\begin{array}{r} 6 \\ 4\overline{)24} \\ \underline{24} \\ 0 \end{array}$ so $\frac{24}{4} = 6$

← No remainder

◀ *Work Problem* **3** *at the Side.*

Write each mixed number as an improper fraction. See Example 1.

1. $1\dfrac{1}{4}$

2. $2\dfrac{1}{2}$

3. $4\dfrac{3}{5}$

4. $5\dfrac{2}{3}$

5. $6\dfrac{1}{2}$

6. $5\dfrac{3}{5}$

⊕ **7.** $8\dfrac{1}{4}$

8. $8\dfrac{1}{2}$

9. $1\dfrac{7}{11}$

10. $4\dfrac{3}{7}$

11. $6\dfrac{1}{3}$

12. $8\dfrac{2}{3}$

13. $10\dfrac{1}{8}$

14. $12\dfrac{2}{3}$

15. $10\dfrac{3}{4}$

16. $5\dfrac{4}{5}$

17. $3\dfrac{3}{8}$

18. $2\dfrac{8}{9}$

19. $8\dfrac{3}{5}$

20. $3\dfrac{4}{7}$

21. $4\dfrac{10}{11}$

22. $11\dfrac{5}{8}$

23. $32\dfrac{3}{4}$

24. $15\dfrac{3}{10}$

25. $18\frac{5}{12}$

26. $19\frac{8}{11}$

27. $17\frac{14}{15}$

28. $9\frac{5}{16}$

29. $7\frac{19}{24}$

30. $9\frac{7}{12}$

Write each improper fraction as a whole or mixed number. See Example 2.

31. $\frac{4}{3}$

32. $\frac{11}{9}$

◑ **33.** $\frac{9}{4}$

34. $\frac{7}{2}$

35. $\frac{48}{6}$

36. $\frac{64}{8}$

37. $\frac{38}{5}$

38. $\frac{33}{7}$

39. $\frac{39}{8}$

40. $\frac{40}{9}$

41. $\frac{27}{3}$

42. $\frac{78}{78}$

43. $\frac{63}{4}$

44. $\frac{19}{5}$

45. $\frac{47}{9}$

46. $\frac{65}{9}$

47. $\frac{65}{8}$

48. $\frac{37}{6}$

49. $\frac{84}{5}$

50. $\frac{92}{3}$

51. $\frac{112}{4}$

52. $\frac{117}{9}$

53. $\frac{183}{7}$

54. $\frac{212}{11}$

55. Your classmate asks you how to change a mixed number to an improper fraction. Write a couple of sentences and give an example to show her how this is done.

56. Explain in a sentence or two how to change an improper fraction to a mixed number. Give an example to show how this is done.

Write each mixed number as an improper fraction.

57. $250\dfrac{1}{2}$

58. $185\dfrac{3}{4}$

⊕ **59.** $333\dfrac{1}{3}$

60. $138\dfrac{4}{5}$

61. $522\dfrac{3}{8}$

62. $622\dfrac{1}{4}$

Write each improper fraction as a whole or mixed number.

63. $\dfrac{617}{4}$

64. $\dfrac{760}{8}$

▦ **65.** $\dfrac{2565}{15}$

▦ **66.** $\dfrac{2915}{16}$

▦ **67.** $\dfrac{3917}{32}$

▦ **68.** $\dfrac{5632}{64}$

Knowing the basics of fractions is necessary in problem solving. **Work Exercises 69–74 *in order.***

69. Which of these fractions are proper fractions?

$$\frac{2}{3} \quad \frac{4}{5} \quad \frac{8}{5} \quad \frac{3}{4} \quad \frac{6}{6} \quad \frac{7}{10}$$

70. (a) The proper fractions in Exercise 69 are the ones where the _____ is less than the _____.

(b) Draw a picture with shaded parts to show each proper fraction in Exercise 69.

(c) The proper fractions in Exercise 69 are all _____ than 1.
(less/greater)

71. Which of these fractions are improper fractions?

$$\frac{5}{5} \quad \frac{3}{4} \quad \frac{10}{3} \quad \frac{2}{3} \quad \frac{5}{6} \quad \frac{6}{5}$$

72. (a) The improper fractions in Exercise 71 are the ones where the _____ is equal to or greater than the _____.

(b) Draw a picture with shaded parts to show each improper fraction in Exercise 71.

(c) The improper fractions in Exercise 71 are all equal to or _____ than 1.
(less/greater)

73. Identify which of these fractions can be written as whole or mixed numbers, and then write them as whole or mixed numbers.

$$\frac{5}{3} \quad \frac{7}{8} \quad \frac{7}{7} \quad \frac{11}{6} \quad \frac{4}{5} \quad \frac{15}{16}$$

74. (a) The fractions that can be written as whole or mixed numbers in Exercise 73 are _____ fractions, and their value is
(proper/improper)
always _____ 1.
(less than/greater than or equal to)

(b) Draw a picture with shaded parts to show each whole or mixed number in Exercise 73.

(c) Explain how to write an improper fraction as a whole or mixed number.

2.3 ⟩⟩⟩ Factors

OBJECTIVE 1 Find factors of a number. You will recall that numbers multiplied to give a product are called **factors.** Because 2 • 5 = 10, both 2 and 5 are factors of 10. The numbers 1 and 10 are also factors of 10, because

$$1 • 10 = 10$$

The various tests for divisibility show that 1, 2, 5, and 10 are the only whole number factors of 10. The products 2 • 5 and 1 • 10 are called **factorizations** of 10.

> **Note**
> The tests to decide whether one number is divisible by another number were shown in **Section 1.5.** You might want to review these. The tests that you will want to remember are those for 2, 3, 5, and 10.

EXAMPLE 1 Using Factors

Find all possible two-number factorizations of each number.

(a) 12

$$1 • 12 = 12 \qquad 2 • 6 = 12 \qquad 3 • 4 = 12$$

The factors of 12 are 1, 2, 3, 4, 6, and 12.

(b) 60

$$1 • 60 = 60 \qquad 2 • 30 = 60$$
$$3 • 20 = 60 \qquad 4 • 15 = 60$$
$$5 • 12 = 60 \qquad 6 • 10 = 60$$

> The factors of a number all divide evenly into that number.

The factors of 60 are 1, 2, 3, 4, 5, 6, 10, 12, 15, 20, 30, and 60.

Work Problem **1** *at the Side.* ▶

> **Composite Numbers**
> A number with a factor other than itself or 1 is called a **composite number.**

EXAMPLE 2 Identifying Composite Numbers

Which of the following numbers are composite?

(a) 6
Because 6 has factors of 2 and 3, numbers other than 6 or 1, the number 6 is composite.

(b) 11
The number 11 has only two factors, 11 and 1. It is *not* composite.

(c) 25
A factor of 25 is 5, so 25 is composite.

Work Problem **2** *at the Side.* ▶

OBJECTIVE 2 Identify prime numbers. Whole numbers that are not composite are called **prime numbers,** except 0 and 1, which are neither prime nor composite.

> **Prime Numbers**
> A **prime number** is a whole number that has exactly *two different* factors, *itself* and *1.*

OBJECTIVES

1 Find factors of a number.

2 Identify prime numbers.

3 Find prime factorizations.

1 Find all the whole number factors of each number.

(a) 18

(b) 16

(c) 36

(d) 80

2 Which of these numbers are composite?

2, 4, 5, 6, 8, 10, 11, 13, 19, 21, 27, 28, 33, 36, 42

ANSWERS

1. **(a)** 1, 2, 3, 6, 9, 18 **(b)** 1, 2, 4, 8, 16
   (c) 1, 2, 3, 4, 6, 9, 12, 18, 36
   (d) 1, 2, 4, 5, 8, 10, 16, 20, 40, 80
2. 4, 6, 8, 10, 21, 27, 28, 33, 36, 42

3 Which of the following are prime?

4, 7, 9, 13, 17, 19, 29, 33

4 Find the prime factorization of each number.

(a) 8

(b) 28

(c) 18

(d) 40

The number 3 is a prime number, since it can be divided evenly only by itself and 1. The number 8 is not a prime number (it is composite), since 8 can be divided evenly by 2 and 4, as well as by itself and 1.

> **CAUTION**
>
> A prime number has *only two* different factors, itself and 1. The number 1 is not a prime number because it does not have *two different* factors; the only factor of 1 is 1.

EXAMPLE 3 **Finding Prime Numbers**

Which of the following numbers are prime?

Only the number itself and 1 will divide evenly into a prime number.

2   5   11   15   27

The number 15 can be divided by 3 and 5, so it is not prime. Also, because 27 can be divided by 3 and 9, then 27 is not prime. The other numbers in the list, 2, 5, and 11, are divisible only by themselves and 1, so they are prime.

◀ *Work Problem* **3** *at the Side.*

OBJECTIVE **3** **Find prime factorizations.**   For reference, here are the prime numbers less than 50.

2	3	5	7	11
13	17	19	23	29
31	37	41	43	47

These are the prime numbers less than 50.

> **CAUTION**
>
> All prime numbers are odd numbers except the number 2. Be careful, though, because *all odd numbers are not prime numbers*. For example, 9, 15, and 21 are odd numbers but are *not* prime numbers.

The **prime factorization** of a number can be especially useful when we are adding or subtracting fractions and need to find a common denominator or write a fraction in lowest terms.

> **Prime Factorization**
>
> A **prime factorization** of a number is a factorization in which every factor is a *prime number.*

EXAMPLE 4 **Determining the Prime Factorization**

Find the prime factorization of 12.
    Try to divide 12 by the first prime, 2.

$$12 \div 2 = 6,$$

— First prime

so

$$12 = 2 \cdot 6$$

Try to divide 6 by the prime, 2.

$$6 \div 2 = 3,$$

so

$$12 = 2 \cdot \underline{2 \cdot 3}$$

— Factorization of 6

Because all factors are prime, the prime factorization of 12 is

$$2 \cdot 2 \cdot 3$$ All these factors are prime.

◀ *Work Problem* **4** *at the Side.*

EXAMPLE 5   **Factoring by Using the Division Method**

Find the prime factorization of 48.

$$2\overline{)48}$$ Divide 48 by 2 (first prime).

$$2\overline{)24}$$ Divide 24 by 2.

> The divisors are all prime factors.

$$2\overline{)12}$$ Divide 12 by 2.

$$2\overline{)6}$$ Divide 6 by 2.

$$3\overline{)3}$$ Divide 3 by 3 (second prime).

$$1$$ Continue to divide until the quotient is 1.

Because all factors (divisors) are prime, the prime factorization of 48 is

$$2 \cdot 2 \cdot 2 \cdot 2 \cdot 3$$

In Chapter 1, we wrote $2 \cdot 2 \cdot 2 \cdot 2$ as 2^4, so the prime factorization of 48 can be written, using exponents, as

$$48 = 2 \cdot 2 \cdot 2 \cdot 2 \cdot 3 = 2^4 \cdot 3$$

—————— *Work Problem* **5** *at the Side.* ▶

Note

When using the division method of factoring, the last quotient found is 1. The "1" is never used as a prime factor because 1 is neither prime nor composite. Besides, 1 times any number is the number itself.

EXAMPLE 6   **Using Exponents with Prime Factorization**

Find the prime factorization of 225.

$$3\overline{)225}$$ 225 is not divisible by 2; use 3.

$$3\overline{)75}$$ Divide 75 by 3.

> All the divisors are prime factors.

$$5\overline{)25}$$ 25 is not divisible by 3; use 5.

$$5\overline{)5}$$ Divide by 5.

> 1 is **not** a prime factor.

$$1$$ Continue to divide until the quotient is 1.

Write the prime factorization.

$$225 = 3 \cdot 3 \cdot 5 \cdot 5$$

Or, using exponents,

$$225 = 3^2 \cdot 5^2$$

—————— *Work Problem* **6** *at the Side.* ▶

5 Find the prime factorization of each number. Write the factorization with exponents.

(a) 36

(b) 54

(c) 60

(d) 81

6 Write the prime factorization of each number using exponents.

(a) 48

(b) 44

(c) 90

(d) 120

(e) 180

ANSWERS

5. (a) $2^2 \cdot 3^2$ **(b)** $2 \cdot 3^3$ **(c)** $2^2 \cdot 3 \cdot 5$
  (d) 3^4
6. (a) $2^4 \cdot 3$ **(b)** $2^2 \cdot 11$ **(c)** $2 \cdot 3^2 \cdot 5$
  (d) $2^3 \cdot 3 \cdot 5$ **(e)** $2^2 \cdot 3^2 \cdot 5$

Another method of factoring is a *factor tree*.

7 Complete each factor tree and give the prime factorization.

(a) 28

(b) 35

(c) 78

7. (a) 28

(b) 35

(c) 78

$$28 = 2 \cdot 2 \cdot 7 = 2^2 \cdot 7$$
$$35 = 5 \cdot 7$$
$$78 = 2 \cdot 3 \cdot 13$$

EXAMPLE 7 **Factoring by Using a Factor Tree**

Find the prime factorization of each number using a factor tree.

(a) 30

Try to divide by the first prime, 2. Write the factors under the 30. Circle the 2, since it is a prime.

Since 15 cannot be divided evenly by 2, try the next prime, 3.

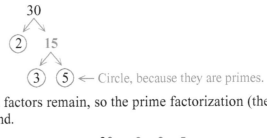

No uncircled factors remain, so the prime factorization (the circled factors) has been found.

$$30 = 2 \cdot 3 \cdot 5$$

(b) 24

Divide by 2.

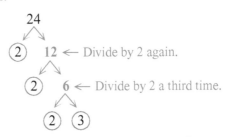

$$24 = 2 \cdot 2 \cdot 2 \cdot 3 \text{ or, using exponents, } 24 = 2^3 \cdot 3$$

(c) 45

Because 45 cannot be divided by 2, try 3.

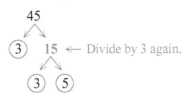

$$45 = 3 \cdot 3 \cdot 5 \text{ or, using exponents, } 45 = 3^2 \cdot 5$$

Note

The diagrams used in Example 7 look like tree branches, and that is why this method is referred to as using a factor tree.

◀ *Work Problem* **7** *at the Side.*

Find all the factors of each number. See Example 1.

1. 8

2. 12

3. 15

4. 28

5. 48

6. 30

7. 36

8. 20

9. 40

10. 60

11. 64

12. 84

Decide whether each number is prime *or* composite. *See Examples 2 and 3.*

13. 6

14. 9

15. 5

16. 7

17. 16

18. 10

19. 13

20. 65

21. 19

22. 17

23. 25

24. 26

25. 48

26. 47

27. 45

28. 53

Find the prime factorization of each number. Write answers with exponents when repeated factors appear. See Examples 4–7.

29. 8

30. 6

31. 20

32. 40

33. 36

34. 18

35. 25

36. 56

37. 68

38. 70

39. 72

40. 64

41. 44

42. 104

43. 100

44. 112

45. 125

46. 135

47. 180

48. 300

49. 320

50. 480

51. 360

52. 400

53. Give a definition in your own words of both a composite number and a prime number. Give three examples of each. Which whole numbers are neither prime nor composite?

54. With the exception of the number 2, all prime numbers are odd numbers. Nevertheless, all odd numbers are not prime numbers. Explain why these statements are true.

55. Explain the difference between finding all possible factors of 24 and finding the prime factorization of 24.

56. Use the division method to find the prime factorization of 36. Can you divide by 3s before you divide by 2s? Does the order of division change the answers?

Find the prime factorization of each number. Write answers using exponents.

57. 350

58. 640

59. 960

60. 1000

61. 1560

62. 2000

63. 1260

64. 2200

Relating Concepts (Exercises 65–70) For Individual or Group Work

An understanding of factors and factorization will be needed to solve fraction problems.
Work Exercises 65–70 in order.

65. A prime number is a whole number that has exactly two different factors, itself and 1. List all prime numbers less than 50.

66. Explain what it is about the numbers in Exercise 65 that makes them prime.

67. The number 2 is an even number and a prime number. Can any other even numbers be prime numbers? Explain.

68. Can a multiple of a prime number be prime (for example, 6, 9, 12, and 15 are multiples of 3)? Explain.

69. Find the prime factorization of 2100. Do not use exponents in your answer.

70. Write the answer to Exercise 69 using exponents for repeated factors.

2.4 ▶▶▶ Writing a Fraction in Lowest Terms

When working problems involving fractions, we must often compare two fractions to determine whether they represent the same portion of a whole. Look at the two cases of soda.

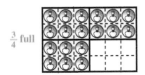 $\frac{3}{4}$ full   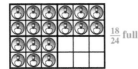 $\frac{18}{24}$ full

The cases of soda show areas that are $\frac{3}{4}$ full and $\frac{18}{24}$ full. Because the full areas are equivalent (the same portion), the fractions $\frac{3}{4}$ and $\frac{18}{24}$ are **equivalent fractions.** They each represent the same portion of the whole.

$$\frac{3}{4} = \frac{18}{24}$$

Because the numbers 18 and 24 both have 6 as a factor, 6 is called a **common factor** of the numbers. Other common factors of 18 and 24 are 1, 2, and 3.

Work Problem **1** *at the Side.* ▶

OBJECTIVE 1 Tell whether a fraction is written in lowest terms.
The fraction $\frac{3}{4}$ is written in *lowest terms* because the numerator and denominator have no common factor other than 1. However, the fraction $\frac{18}{24}$ is **not** in lowest terms because its numerator and denominator have common factors of 6, 3, 2, and 1.

Writing a Fraction in Lowest Terms

A fraction is written in **lowest terms** when the numerator and denominator have no common factor other than 1.

EXAMPLE 1   Understanding Lowest Terms

Are the following fractions in lowest terms?

(a) $\frac{3}{8}$ ⎯⎯ No common factors other than 1.

The numerator and denominator have no common factor other than 1, so the fraction is in lowest terms.

(b) $\frac{21}{36}$ ⎯⎯ 3 is a common factor of 21 and 36.

The numerator and denominator have a common factor of 3, so the fraction is **not in lowest terms.**

Work Problem **2** *at the Side.* ▶

OBJECTIVE 2 Write a fraction in lowest terms using common factors.   There are two common methods for writing a fraction in lowest terms. These methods are shown in the next examples. The first method works best when the numerator and denominator are small numbers.

OBJECTIVES

1 Tell whether a fraction is written in lowest terms.

2 Write a fraction in lowest terms using common factors.

3 Write a fraction in lowest terms using prime factors.

4 Determine whether two fractions are equivalent.

1 Decide whether the number in blue is a common factor of the other two numbers.

(a) 6, 12; 2

(b) 32, 64; 8

(c) 32, 56; 16

(d) 75, 81; 1

2 Are the following fractions in lowest terms?

(a) $\frac{4}{5}$

(b) $\frac{6}{18}$

(c) $\frac{9}{15}$

(d) $\frac{17}{46}$

ANSWERS

1. (a) yes (b) yes (c) no (d) yes
2. (a) yes (b) no (c) no (d) yes

3 Write in lowest terms.

(a) $\dfrac{8}{16}$

(b) $\dfrac{9}{12}$

(c) $\dfrac{28}{42}$

(d) $\dfrac{30}{80}$

(e) $\dfrac{16}{40}$

EXAMPLE 2   **Writing Fractions in Lowest Terms**

Write each fraction in lowest terms.

(a) $\dfrac{18}{24}$

The greatest common factor of 18 and 24 is 6. Divide both numerator and denominator by **6**.

$$\frac{18}{24} = \frac{18 \div 6}{24 \div 6} = \frac{3}{4}$$

Divide by the greatest common factor, 6.

(b) $\dfrac{30}{50} = \dfrac{30 \div 10}{50 \div 10} = \dfrac{3}{5}$ Divide both numerator and denominator by 10.

(c) $\dfrac{24}{42} = \dfrac{24 \div 6}{42 \div 6} = \dfrac{4}{7}$ Divide both numerator and denominator by 6.

(d) $\dfrac{60}{72}$

Suppose we thought that 4 was the greatest common factor of 60 and 72. Dividing by 4 would give

$$\frac{60}{72} = \frac{60 \div 4}{72 \div 4} = \frac{15}{18} \; \leftarrow \text{Not in lowest terms.}$$

But $\frac{15}{18}$ is not in lowest terms, because 15 and 18 have a common factor of 3. So we divide by 3.

$$\frac{15}{18} = \frac{15 \div 3}{18 \div 3} = \frac{5}{6}$$

Continue dividing until there is no common factor other than 1.

The fraction $\frac{60}{72}$ could have been written in lowest terms in one step by dividing by 12, the greatest common factor of 60 and 72.

$$\frac{60}{72} = \frac{60 \div 12}{72 \div 12} = \frac{5}{6} \; \leftarrow \text{Same answer as above.}$$

Continue dividing until the fraction is in lowest terms.

Note

Dividing the numerator and denominator by the same number results in an equivalent fraction.

In Example 2, we wrote fractions in lowest terms by dividing by a common factor. This method is summarized in the following steps.

The Method of Dividing by a Common Factor

Step 1 Find the greatest number that will divide evenly into both the numerator and denominator. This number is a ***common factor.***

Step 2 ***Divide*** both numerator and denominator by the common factor.

Step 3 ***Check*** to see whether the new fraction has any common factors (besides 1). If it does, repeat Steps 2 and 3. If the only common factor is 1, the fraction is in lowest terms.

ANSWERS

3. **(a)** $\dfrac{1}{2}$ **(b)** $\dfrac{3}{4}$ **(c)** $\dfrac{2}{3}$ **(d)** $\dfrac{3}{8}$ **(e)** $\dfrac{2}{5}$

◄ *Work Problem* **3** *at the Side.*

OBJECTIVE 3 Write a fraction in lowest terms using prime factors. The method of writing a fraction in lowest terms by division works well for fractions with small numerators and denominators. For larger numbers, when common factors are not obvious, use the method of *prime factors,* which is shown in the next example.

EXAMPLE 3 **Using Prime Factors**

Write each fraction in lowest terms.

(a) $\dfrac{24}{42}$

Write the prime factorization of both numerator and denominator. See **Section 2.3** for help.

$$\frac{24}{42} = \frac{2 \cdot 2 \cdot 2 \cdot 3}{2 \cdot 3 \cdot 7}$$

Just as with the method used in Example 2, divide both numerator and denominator by any common factors. Write a **1** by each factor that has been divided.

2 ÷ 2 is 1   3 ÷ 3 is 1

$$\frac{24}{42} = \frac{\overset{1}{\cancel{2}} \cdot 2 \cdot 2 \cdot \overset{1}{\cancel{3}}}{\underset{1}{\cancel{2}} \cdot \underset{1}{\cancel{3}} \cdot 7}$$

Multiply the remaining factors in both numerator and denominator.

$$\frac{24}{42} = \frac{1 \cdot 2 \cdot 2 \cdot 1}{1 \cdot 1 \cdot 7} = \frac{4}{7} \leftarrow \text{Lowest terms}$$

Finally, $\frac{24}{42}$ written in lowest terms is $\frac{4}{7}$.

(b) $\dfrac{162}{54}$

Write the prime factorization of both numerator and denominator.

$$\frac{162}{54} = \frac{2 \cdot 3 \cdot 3 \cdot 3 \cdot 3}{2 \cdot 3 \cdot 3 \cdot 3}$$

Now divide by the common factors. ***Do not forget to write the 1s.***

$$\frac{162}{54} = \frac{\overset{1}{\cancel{2}} \cdot \overset{1}{\cancel{3}} \cdot \overset{1}{\cancel{3}} \cdot \overset{1}{\cancel{3}} \cdot 3}{\underset{1}{\cancel{2}} \cdot \underset{1}{\cancel{3}} \cdot \underset{1}{\cancel{3}} \cdot \underset{1}{\cancel{3}}}$$

Remember to write in the 1s when dividing by a common factor.

$$= \frac{1 \cdot 1 \cdot 1 \cdot 1 \cdot 3}{1 \cdot 1 \cdot 1 \cdot 1} = \frac{3}{1} = 3$$

(c) $\dfrac{18}{90}$

$$\frac{18}{90} = \frac{\overset{1}{\cancel{2}} \cdot \overset{1}{\cancel{3}} \cdot \overset{1}{\cancel{3}}}{\underset{1}{\cancel{2}} \cdot \underset{1}{\cancel{3}} \cdot \underset{1}{\cancel{3}} \cdot 5} = \frac{1 \cdot 1 \cdot 1}{1 \cdot 1 \cdot 1 \cdot 5} = \frac{1}{5}$$

CAUTION
In Example 3(c) above, all factors of the numerator were divided. But 1 • 1 • 1 is still 1, so the final answer is $\frac{1}{5}$ (*not* 5).

In Example 3, we wrote fractions in lowest terms using prime factors. This method is summarized as follows.

4 Use the method of prime factors to write each fraction in lowest terms.

(a) $\dfrac{12}{36}$

> **Step 1** Write the **prime factorization** of both numerator and denominator.
>
> **Step 2** Use slashes to show you are **dividing** both numerator and denominator by common factors.
>
> **Step 3** **Multiply** the remaining factors in the numerator and denominator.

(b) $\dfrac{32}{56}$

◀ *Work Problem* **4** *at the Side.*

OBJECTIVE **4** **Determine whether two fractions are equivalent.**
The next example shows how to decide whether two fractions are equivalent.

EXAMPLE 4 **Determining Whether Two Fractions Are Equivalent**

(c) $\dfrac{74}{111}$

Determine whether each pair of fractions is equivalent. In other words, do both fractions represent the same part of a whole?

(a) $\dfrac{16}{48}$ and $\dfrac{24}{72}$

Use the method of prime factors to write each fraction in lowest terms.

(d) $\dfrac{124}{340}$

$$\frac{16}{48} = \frac{\cancel{2} \cdot \cancel{2} \cdot \cancel{2} \cdot \cancel{2}}{\cancel{2} \cdot \cancel{2} \cdot \cancel{2} \cdot \cancel{2} \cdot 3} = \frac{1 \cdot 1 \cdot 1 \cdot 1}{1 \cdot 1 \cdot 1 \cdot 1 \cdot 3} = \frac{1}{3} \leftarrow$$

Equivalent $\left(\dfrac{1}{3} = \dfrac{1}{3}\right)$

5 Is each pair of fractions equivalent?

(a) $\dfrac{24}{48}$ and $\dfrac{36}{72}$

$$\frac{24}{72} = \frac{\cancel{2} \cdot \cancel{2} \cdot \cancel{2} \cdot \cancel{3}}{\cancel{2} \cdot \cancel{2} \cdot \cancel{2} \cdot \cancel{3} \cdot 3} = \frac{1 \cdot 1 \cdot 1 \cdot 1}{1 \cdot 1 \cdot 1 \cdot 1 \cdot 3} = \frac{1}{3} \leftarrow$$

(b) $\dfrac{32}{52}$ and $\dfrac{64}{112}$

(b) $\dfrac{45}{60}$ and $\dfrac{50}{75}$

$$\frac{32}{52} = \frac{\cancel{2} \cdot \cancel{2} \cdot 2 \cdot 2 \cdot 2}{\cancel{2} \cdot \cancel{2} \cdot 13} = \frac{2 \cdot 2 \cdot 2}{1 \cdot 1 \cdot 13} = \frac{8}{13} \leftarrow$$

Not equivalent $\left(\dfrac{8}{13} \neq \dfrac{4}{7}\right)$

$$\frac{64}{112} = \frac{\cancel{2} \cdot \cancel{2} \cdot \cancel{2} \cdot \cancel{2} \cdot 2 \cdot 2}{\cancel{2} \cdot \cancel{2} \cdot \cancel{2} \cdot \cancel{2} \cdot 7} = \frac{1 \cdot 1 \cdot 1 \cdot 1 \cdot 2 \cdot 2}{1 \cdot 1 \cdot 1 \cdot 1 \cdot 7} = \frac{4}{7} \leftarrow$$

(c) $\dfrac{20}{4}$ and $\dfrac{110}{22}$

(c) $\dfrac{75}{15}$ and $\dfrac{60}{12}$

$$\frac{75}{15} = \frac{\cancel{3} \cdot \cancel{5} \cdot 5}{\cancel{3} \cdot \cancel{5}} = \frac{1 \cdot 1 \cdot 5}{1 \cdot 1} = 5 \leftarrow$$

(d) $\dfrac{120}{220}$ and $\dfrac{180}{320}$

Equivalent $(5 = 5)$

$$\frac{60}{12} = \frac{\cancel{2} \cdot \cancel{2} \cdot \cancel{3} \cdot 5}{\cancel{2} \cdot \cancel{2} \cdot \cancel{3}} = \frac{1 \cdot 1 \cdot 1 \cdot 5}{1 \cdot 1 \cdot 1} = 5 \leftarrow$$

◀ *Work Problem* **5** *at the Side.*

2.4 ▶▶▶	**Exercises**

FOR EXTRA HELP

MyMathLab   Math XL PRACTICE   WATCH   DOWNLOAD   READ   REVIEW

Put a ✓ mark in the blank if the number at the left is divisible by the number at the top.
Put an ✗ in the blank if the number is not divisible by the number at the top. (For help, see
Section 1.5.)

	2	3	5	10			2	3	5	10
1. 60	___	___	___	___		**2.** 90	___	___	___	___
3. 48	___	___	___	___		**4.** 36	___	___	___	___
5. 160	___	___	___	___		**6.** 175	___	___	___	___
7. 138	___	___	___	___		**8.** 150	___	___	___	___

Write each fraction in lowest terms. See Example 2.

9. $\dfrac{6}{8}$ **10.** $\dfrac{6}{12}$ **11.** $\dfrac{3}{12}$ **12.** $\dfrac{4}{12}$

13. $\dfrac{15}{25}$ **14.** $\dfrac{32}{48}$ **15.** $\dfrac{36}{42}$ **16.** $\dfrac{22}{33}$

17. $\dfrac{56}{64}$ **18.** $\dfrac{21}{35}$ **19.** $\dfrac{180}{210}$ **20.** $\dfrac{72}{80}$

⊕ 21. $\dfrac{72}{126}$ **22.** $\dfrac{73}{146}$ **23.** $\dfrac{12}{600}$ **24.** $\dfrac{8}{400}$

25. $\dfrac{96}{132}$ **26.** $\dfrac{165}{180}$ **27.** $\dfrac{60}{108}$ **28.** $\dfrac{112}{128}$

Write the numerator and denominator of each fraction as a product of prime factors and
divide by the common factors. Then write the fraction in lowest terms. See Example 3.

29. $\dfrac{18}{24}$ **30.** $\dfrac{16}{64}$ **⊕ 31.** $\dfrac{35}{40}$

32. $\dfrac{20}{32}$ **33.** $\dfrac{90}{180}$ **34.** $\dfrac{36}{48}$

35. $\dfrac{36}{12}$

36. $\dfrac{192}{48}$

37. $\dfrac{72}{225}$

38. $\dfrac{65}{234}$

Write each fraction in lowest terms. Then state whether the fractions are equivalent or not equivalent. See Example 4.

39. $\dfrac{3}{6}$ and $\dfrac{18}{36}$

40. $\dfrac{3}{8}$ and $\dfrac{27}{72}$

41. $\dfrac{10}{24}$ and $\dfrac{12}{30}$

42. $\dfrac{15}{35}$ and $\dfrac{18}{40}$

43. $\dfrac{15}{24}$ and $\dfrac{35}{52}$

44. $\dfrac{21}{33}$ and $\dfrac{9}{12}$

45. $\dfrac{14}{16}$ and $\dfrac{35}{40}$

46. $\dfrac{27}{90}$ and $\dfrac{24}{80}$

47. $\dfrac{48}{6}$ and $\dfrac{72}{8}$

48. $\dfrac{33}{11}$ and $\dfrac{72}{24}$

49. $\dfrac{25}{30}$ and $\dfrac{65}{78}$

50. $\dfrac{24}{72}$ and $\dfrac{30}{90}$

51. What does it mean when a fraction is expressed in lowest terms? Give three examples.

52. Explain what equivalent fractions are, and give an example of a pair of equivalent fractions. Show that they are equivalent.

Write each fraction in lowest terms.

53. $\dfrac{160}{256}$

54. $\dfrac{363}{528}$

55. $\dfrac{238}{119}$

56. $\dfrac{570}{95}$

Study Skills

> > > **USING STUDY CARDS**

OBJECTIVES

1 Create study cards for all new terms.

2 Create study cards for new procedures.

You may have used "flash cards" in other classes before. In math, study cards can be helpful, too. However, they are different because the main things to remember in math are *not* necessarily terms and definitions; they are *sets of steps to follow* to solve problems (and how to know which set of steps to follow) and *concepts about how math works* (principles). So, the cards will look different but will be just as useful.

In this two-part activity, you will find four types of study cards to use in math. Look carefully at what kinds of information to put on them and where to put it. Then use them the way you would any flash card:

▶ to quickly review when you have a few minutes,

▶ to do daily reviews,

▶ to review before a test.

Remember, the most helpful thing about study cards is making them. While you are making them, you have to do the kind of thinking that is most brain friendly, which improves your neural network of dendrites. After each card description you will find an assignment to try. It is marked **NOW TRY THIS.**

For **new vocabulary cards,** put the word (spelled correctly) and the page number where it is found on the front of the card. On the back, write:

New Vocabulary Cards

▶ the definition (in your own words if possible),

▶ an example, an exception (if there are any),

▶ any related words, and

▶ a sample problem (if appropriate).

Prime Numbers   *p. 122*

Front of Card

Definition: Whole numbers that can only be divided by themselves and 1.

★Must divide evenly, NO remainders!

Ex: 2, 3, 5, 7, 11, 13, 17 are the first few primes.
→ NOT 0 or 1
→ Used in factoring
→ Related word: composite number

Back of Card

Why Are Study Cards Brain Friendly?

• Making cards is **active.**

• Cards are **visually** appealing.

• **Repetition** is good for your brain.

For details see Using Study Cards Revisited following **Section 2.8.**

Now Try This ▶▶▶

> *List four new vocabulary words/concepts you need to learn right now. Make a card for each one.*
>
> _____   _____   _____   _____

Procedure ("Steps") Cards

For **procedure cards,** write the name of the procedure at the top on the front of the card. Then write each step *in words*. If you need to know abbreviations for some words, include them along with the whole words written out. On the back, put an example of the procedure, showing each step you need to take. You can review by looking at the front and practicing a new worked example, or by looking at the back and remembering what the procedure is called and what the steps are.

Writing a fraction in lowest terms using prime factors

Use this method with larger denominators.

Step 1:   Write prime factorization of numerator and denominator.

Step 2:   Divide out all common factors.

Step 3:   Multiply remaining factors.

Front of Card

Example: Write this fraction in lowest terms.

$$\frac{64}{112} = \frac{2 \cdot 2 \cdot 2 \cdot 2 \cdot 2 \cdot 2}{2 \cdot 2 \cdot 2 \cdot 2 \cdot 7} \quad \text{Prime factors of 64.} \quad \text{Prime factors of 112.}$$

Divide out common factors of 2

$$= \frac{\overset{1}{2} \cdot \overset{1}{2} \cdot \overset{1}{2} \cdot \overset{1}{2} \cdot 2 \cdot 2}{\underset{1}{2} \cdot \underset{1}{2} \cdot \underset{1}{2} \cdot \underset{1}{2} \cdot 7} = \frac{1 \cdot 1 \cdot 1 \cdot 1 \cdot 2 \cdot 2}{1 \cdot 1 \cdot 1 \cdot 1 \cdot 7} = \frac{4}{7}$$

multiply remaining factors   *lowest terms*

Back of Card

Now Try This ▶▶▶

> *What procedure are you learning right now? Make a "steps" card for it.*
>
> *Procedure:* _____

Summary Exercises on Fraction Basics

Write fractions to represent the shaded and unshaded portions of each figure.

1.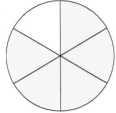

2.

3.

Identify the numerator and denominator.

	Numerator	**Denominator**			**Numerator**	**Denominator**

4. $\dfrac{3}{4}$ _____   _____

5. $\dfrac{8}{5}$ _____   _____

List the proper and improper fractions.

Proper   **Improper**

6. $\dfrac{8}{2}$ $\dfrac{3}{5}$ $\dfrac{16}{7}$ $\dfrac{8}{8}$ $\dfrac{4}{25}$ $\dfrac{1}{32}$ _____   _____

The bar graph below shows the countries that have produced the most men's winners in the New York City Marathon. Use this graph to answer Exercises 7–10.

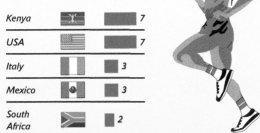

Kenyans Run to Marathon Glory

Former champions and Kenyans Martin Lel, Rodgers Rop, and Stephen Kiogora are among the favorites in Sunday's ING New York City Marathon. Countries that have produced the most men's winners:

Kenya 7
USA 7
Italy 3
Mexico 3
South Africa 2

Source: New York Road Runners.

7. What fraction of the winners were from Kenya?

8. What fraction of the winners were not from either Kenya or the United States?

9. What fraction of the winners were from either Mexico or South Africa?

10. What fraction of the winners were not from Kenya?

Write each improper fraction as a mixed number or whole number.

11. $\dfrac{5}{2}$

12. $\dfrac{11}{8}$

13. $\dfrac{9}{7}$

14. $\dfrac{8}{3}$

15. $\dfrac{64}{8}$

16. $\dfrac{45}{9}$

17. $\dfrac{36}{5}$

18. $\dfrac{47}{10}$

Write each mixed number as an improper fraction.

19. $3\frac{1}{3}$

20. $5\frac{3}{8}$

21. $6\frac{4}{5}$

22. $10\frac{3}{5}$

23. $12\frac{3}{4}$

24. $4\frac{10}{13}$

25. $11\frac{5}{6}$

26. $23\frac{5}{8}$

Write the prime factorization of each number using exponents.

27. 10

28. 55

29. 36

30. 81

31. 280

32. 360

Write each fraction in lowest terms.

33. $\frac{4}{12}$

34. $\frac{7}{14}$

35. $\frac{4}{16}$

36. $\frac{15}{25}$

37. $\frac{18}{24}$

38. $\frac{30}{36}$

39. $\frac{56}{64}$

40. $\frac{6}{300}$

41. $\frac{25}{200}$

42. $\frac{125}{225}$

43. $\frac{88}{154}$

44. $\frac{70}{126}$

Write the numerator and denominator of each fraction as a product of prime factors and divide by the common factors. Then write the fraction in lowest terms.

45. $\frac{24}{36}$

46. $\frac{80}{160}$

47. $\frac{126}{42}$

48. $\frac{96}{112}$

2.5 ▶▶▶ Multiplying Fractions

OBJECTIVE 1 Multiply fractions.   Suppose that you give $\frac{1}{2}$ of your Energy Bar to your kickboxing partner Jennifer. Then Jennifer gives $\frac{1}{2}$ of her share to Tony. How much of the Energy Bar does Tony get to eat?

Start with a sketch showing the Energy Bar cut in half (2 equal pieces).

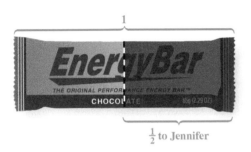

$\frac{1}{2}$ to Jennifer

Next, take $\frac{1}{2}$ of the shaded area. (Here we are dividing $\frac{1}{2}$ into 2 equal parts and shading one darker than the other.)

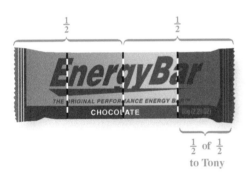

$\frac{1}{2}$ of $\frac{1}{2}$
to Tony

The sketch shows that Tony gets $\frac{1}{4}$ of the Energy Bar.

Tony gets $\frac{1}{2}$ of $\frac{1}{2}$ of the Energy Bar. When used between two fractions, the word *of* tells us to multiply.

$$\frac{1}{2} \text{ of } \frac{1}{2} \quad \text{means} \quad \frac{1}{2} \cdot \frac{1}{2}$$

Tony's share of the Energy Bar is

$$\frac{1}{2} \cdot \frac{1}{2} = \frac{1}{4}$$

Work Problem **1** *at the Side.* ▶

The rule for multiplying fractions follows.

> **Multiplying Fractions**
> Multiply two fractions by multiplying the numerators and multiplying the denominators.

OBJECTIVES

1. **Multiply fractions.**
2. **Use a multiplication shortcut.**
3. **Multiply a fraction and a whole number.**
4. **Find the area of a rectangle.**

1 Use these figures to find $\frac{1}{4}$ of $\frac{1}{2}$.

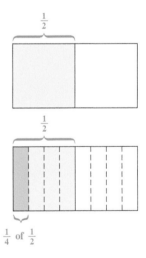

$\frac{1}{4}$ of $\frac{1}{2}$

ANSWER

1. $\frac{1}{8}$

Use this rule to find the product of $\frac{2}{3}$ and $\frac{1}{3}$ (multiply $\frac{2}{3}$ by $\frac{1}{3}$).

$$\frac{2}{3} \cdot \frac{1}{3} = \frac{2 \cdot 1}{3 \cdot 3} \leftarrow \text{Multiply numerators.} \atop \leftarrow \text{Multiply denominators.}$$

Finish multiplying.

$$\frac{2}{3} \cdot \frac{1}{3} = \frac{2 \cdot 1}{3 \cdot 3} = \frac{2}{9} \begin{array}{l} \leftarrow 2 \cdot 1 = 2 \\ \leftarrow 3 \cdot 3 = 9 \end{array}$$

Check that the final result is in lowest terms. $\frac{2}{9}$ is in lowest terms because 2 and 9 have no common factor other than 1.

---

2 Multiply. Write answers in lowest terms.

(a) $\dfrac{1}{2} \cdot \dfrac{3}{4}$

(b) $\dfrac{3}{5} \cdot \dfrac{1}{3}$

(c) $\dfrac{5}{6} \cdot \dfrac{1}{2} \cdot \dfrac{1}{8}$

(d) $\dfrac{1}{2} \cdot \dfrac{3}{4} \cdot \dfrac{3}{8}$

EXAMPLE 1 **Multiplying Fractions**

Multiply. Write answers in lowest terms.

(a) $\dfrac{5}{8} \cdot \dfrac{3}{4}$

Multiply the numerators and multiply the denominators.

$$\frac{5}{8} \cdot \frac{3}{4} = \frac{5 \cdot 3}{8 \cdot 4} = \frac{15}{32} \qquad \boxed{\text{Already in lowest terms}}$$

Notice that 15 and 32 have no common factors other than 1, so the answer is in lowest terms.

(b) $\dfrac{4}{7} \cdot \dfrac{2}{5}$

$$\frac{4}{7} \cdot \frac{2}{5} = \frac{4 \cdot 2}{7 \cdot 5} = \frac{8}{35} \leftarrow \text{Lowest terms}$$

(c) $\dfrac{5}{8} \cdot \dfrac{3}{4} \cdot \dfrac{1}{2}$

$$\frac{5}{8} \cdot \frac{3}{4} \cdot \frac{1}{2} = \frac{5 \cdot 3 \cdot 1}{8 \cdot 4 \cdot 2} = \frac{15}{64} \leftarrow \text{Lowest terms}$$

◀ *Work Problem* **2** *at the Side.*

OBJECTIVE **2** **Use a multiplication shortcut.** A **multiplication shortcut** that can be used with fractions is shown in Example 2.

EXAMPLE 2 **Using the Multiplication Shortcut**

Multiply $\frac{5}{6}$ and $\frac{9}{10}$. Write the answer in lowest terms.

$$\frac{5}{6} \cdot \frac{9}{10} = \frac{5 \cdot 9}{6 \cdot 10} = \frac{45}{60} \leftarrow \text{Not in lowest terms}$$

The numerator and denominator have a common factor other than 1, so write the prime factorization of each number.

$$\frac{5}{6} \cdot \frac{9}{10} = \frac{5 \cdot 9}{6 \cdot 10} = \frac{5 \cdot 3 \cdot 3}{2 \cdot 3 \cdot 2 \cdot 5} \qquad \boxed{\text{Write the prime factorization of each number.}}$$

Continued on Next Page

ANSWERS

2. (a) $\dfrac{3}{8}$ (b) $\dfrac{1}{5}$ (c) $\dfrac{5}{96}$ (d) $\dfrac{9}{64}$

Next, divide by the common factors of 5 and 3.

$$\frac{5}{6} \cdot \frac{9}{10} = \frac{5 \cdot 9}{6 \cdot 10} = \frac{\overset{1}{\cancel{5}} \cdot \overset{1}{\cancel{3}} \cdot 3}{2 \cdot \underset{1}{\cancel{3}} \cdot 2 \cdot \underset{1}{\cancel{5}}}$$

Finally, multiply the remaining factors in the numerator and in the denominator.

$$\frac{5}{6} \cdot \frac{9}{10} = \frac{1 \cdot 1 \cdot 3}{2 \cdot 1 \cdot 2 \cdot 1} = \frac{3}{4} \leftarrow \text{Lowest terms}$$

As a shortcut, instead of writing the prime factorization of each number, find the product of $\frac{5}{6}$ and $\frac{9}{10}$ as follows.

First, divide by 5, a common factor of both 5 and 10.
$$\frac{\overset{1}{\cancel{5}}}{6} \cdot \frac{9}{\underset{2}{\cancel{10}}}$$

Next, divide by 3, a common factor of both 6 and 9.
$$\frac{\overset{1}{\cancel{5}}}{\underset{2}{\cancel{6}}} \cdot \frac{\overset{3}{\cancel{9}}}{\underset{2}{\cancel{10}}}$$

Finally, multiply numerators and multiply denominators.
$$\frac{1 \cdot 3}{2 \cdot 2} = \frac{3}{4}$$

CAUTION
When using the multiplication shortcut, you are dividing a numerator and a denominator by a common factor. Be certain that you divide a numerator and a denominator **by the same number.** If you do all possible divisions, your answer will be in lowest terms.

EXAMPLE 3 Using the Multiplication Shortcut

Use the multiplication shortcut to find each product. Write the answers in lowest terms and as mixed numbers where possible.

(a) $\frac{6}{11} \cdot \frac{7}{8}$

Divide both 6 and 8 by their common factor of 2. Notice that 7 and 11 have no common factor. Then multiply.

$$\frac{\overset{3}{\cancel{6}}}{11} \cdot \frac{7}{\underset{4}{\cancel{8}}} = \frac{3 \cdot 7}{11 \cdot 4} = \frac{21}{44} \leftarrow \text{Lowest terms}$$

(b) $\frac{7}{10} \cdot \frac{20}{21}$

Divide a numerator and a denominator by the same number.

Divide 7 and 21 by 7, and divide 10 and 20 by 10.

$$\frac{\overset{1}{\cancel{7}}}{\underset{1}{\cancel{10}}} \cdot \frac{\overset{2}{\cancel{20}}}{\underset{3}{\cancel{21}}} = \frac{1 \cdot 2}{1 \cdot 3} = \frac{2}{3} \leftarrow \text{Lowest terms}$$

Continued on Next Page

3 Use the multiplication shortcut to find each product.

(a) $\dfrac{3}{4} \cdot \dfrac{2}{3}$

(b) $\dfrac{6}{11} \cdot \dfrac{33}{21}$

(c) $\dfrac{20}{4} \cdot \dfrac{3}{40} \cdot \dfrac{1}{3}$

(d) $\dfrac{18}{17} \cdot \dfrac{1}{36} \cdot \dfrac{2}{3}$

(c) $\dfrac{35}{12} \cdot \dfrac{32}{25}$

$$\dfrac{\overset{7}{\cancel{35}}}{\underset{3}{\cancel{12}}} \cdot \dfrac{\overset{8}{\cancel{32}}}{\underset{5}{\cancel{25}}} = \dfrac{7 \cdot 8}{3 \cdot 5} = \dfrac{56}{15} \quad \text{or} \quad 3\dfrac{11}{15} \; \leftarrow \text{Mixed number}$$

(d) $\dfrac{2}{3} \cdot \dfrac{8}{15} \cdot \dfrac{3}{4}$

$$\dfrac{\overset{1}{\cancel{2}}}{\underset{1}{\cancel{3}}} \cdot \dfrac{\overset{4}{\cancel{8}}}{15} \cdot \dfrac{\overset{1}{\cancel{3}}}{\underset{1}{\cancel{4}}} = \dfrac{1 \cdot 4 \cdot 1}{1 \cdot 15 \cdot 1} = \dfrac{4}{15} \; \leftarrow \text{Lowest terms}$$

This shortcut is especially helpful when the fractions involve large numbers.

> **Note**
>
> There is no specific order that must be used when dividing numerators and denominators, as long as both the numerator and the denominator are divided by the *same* number.

◀ *Work Problem* **3** *at the Side.*

OBJECTIVE 3 Multiply a fraction and a whole number. The rule for multiplying a fraction and a whole number follows.

> **Multiplying a Whole Number and a Fraction**
>
> Multiply a whole number and a fraction by writing the whole number as a fraction with a denominator of 1.

For example, write the whole numbers 8, 10, and 25 as follows.

$$8 = \dfrac{8}{1} \qquad 10 = \dfrac{10}{1} \qquad 25 = \dfrac{25}{1} \; \longleftarrow \boxed{\text{Write the whole number over 1.}}$$

EXAMPLE 4 Multiplying by Whole Numbers

Multiply. Write answers in lowest terms and as whole numbers where possible.

(a) $8 \cdot \dfrac{3}{4}$

Write 8 as $\frac{8}{1}$ and multiply.

$$8 \cdot \dfrac{3}{4} = \dfrac{\overset{2}{\cancel{8}}}{1} \cdot \dfrac{3}{\underset{1}{\cancel{4}}} = \dfrac{2 \cdot 3}{1 \cdot 1} = \dfrac{6}{1} = 6 \; \longleftarrow \boxed{\dfrac{6}{1} \text{ is the same as } 6 \div 1, \text{ which equals 6.}}$$

Continued on Next Page

ANSWERS

3. (a) $\dfrac{\overset{1}{\cancel{3}}}{\underset{2}{\cancel{4}}} \cdot \dfrac{\overset{1}{\cancel{2}}}{\underset{1}{\cancel{3}}} = \dfrac{1}{2}$ (b) $\dfrac{\overset{2}{\cancel{6}}}{\underset{1}{\cancel{11}}} \cdot \dfrac{\overset{3}{\cancel{33}}}{\underset{7}{\cancel{21}}} = \dfrac{6}{7}$

(c) $\dfrac{\overset{1}{\cancel{20}}}{4} \cdot \dfrac{\overset{1}{\cancel{3}}}{\underset{2}{\cancel{40}}} \cdot \dfrac{1}{\underset{1}{\cancel{3}}} = \dfrac{1}{8}$

(d) $\dfrac{\overset{1}{\cancel{18}}}{17} \cdot \dfrac{1}{\cancel{36}} \cdot \dfrac{\overset{1}{\cancel{2}}}{\underset{1}{\cancel{3}}} = \dfrac{1}{51}$

(b) $15 \cdot \dfrac{5}{6}$

$$15 \cdot \frac{5}{6} = \frac{\overset{5}{\cancel{15}}}{1} \cdot \frac{5}{\underset{2}{\cancel{6}}} = \frac{5 \cdot 5}{1 \cdot 2} = \frac{25}{2} = 12\frac{1}{2}$$

Work Problem **4** *at the Side.* ▶

OBJECTIVE 4 Find the area of a rectangle. To find the area of a rectangle (the amount of surface inside the rectangle), use the following formula.

> **Area of a Rectangle**
> The area of a rectangle is equal to the length multiplied by the width.
> **Area = length • width**

For example, the rectangle shown here has an area of 12 square feet (ft²).

Area = length • width ◁ Area is the amount of surface.
Area = 4 ft • 3 ft
Area = 12 ft²

Other units for measuring area are square inches (in.²), square yards (yd²), and square miles (mi²).

EXAMPLE 5 Applying Fraction Skills

Find the area of each rectangle.

(a) Find the area of each shower tile.

Area = length • width

Area $= \dfrac{11}{12} \cdot \dfrac{3}{4}$

$= \dfrac{11}{\underset{4}{\cancel{12}}} \cdot \dfrac{\overset{1}{\cancel{3}}}{4}$ Divide numerator and denominator by 3.

$= \dfrac{11}{16}$ ft²   This is less than 1 ft².

Continued on Next Page

---

4 Multiply. Write answers in lowest terms and as whole numbers or mixed numbers where possible.

(a) $8 \cdot \dfrac{1}{8}$

(b) $\dfrac{3}{4} \cdot 5 \cdot \dfrac{5}{3}$

(c) $\dfrac{3}{5} \cdot 40$

(d) $\dfrac{3}{25} \cdot \dfrac{5}{11} \cdot 99$

ANSWERS

4. **(a)** 1 **(b)** $6\dfrac{1}{4}$ **(c)** 24 **(d)** $5\dfrac{2}{5}$

5 Find the area of each rectangle.

(a)

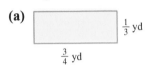

$\frac{1}{3}$ yd

$\frac{3}{4}$ yd

(b) a community college campus that is $\frac{3}{8}$ mile by $\frac{1}{3}$ mile

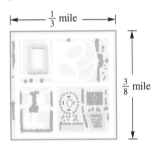

$\frac{1}{3}$ mile

$\frac{3}{8}$ mile

(b) Find the area of this polished diamond plate SUV running board.

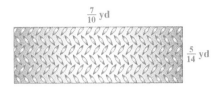

$\frac{7}{10}$ yd

$\frac{5}{14}$ yd

Multiply the length and width.

$$\text{Area} = \frac{7}{10} \cdot \frac{5}{14}$$

$$= \frac{\overset{1}{\cancel{7}}}{\underset{2}{\cancel{10}}} \cdot \frac{\overset{1}{\cancel{5}}}{\underset{2}{\cancel{14}}} \qquad \text{Divide 7 and 14 by 7.}$$
Divide 10 and 5 by 5.

$$= \frac{1}{4} \text{ square yard (yd}^2\text{)}$$

◀ *Work Problem* **5** *at the Side.*

(c) a parcel of subdivided land that is $\frac{9}{7}$ mile by $\frac{7}{12}$ mile

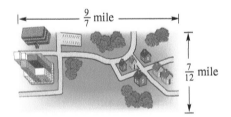

$\frac{9}{7}$ mile

$\frac{7}{12}$ mile

ANSWERS

5. (a) $\frac{1}{4}$ yd^2

(b) $\frac{1}{8}$ mi^2

(c) $\frac{3}{4}$ mi^2

Multiply. Write answers in lowest terms. See Examples 1–3.

1. $\dfrac{1}{3} \cdot \dfrac{3}{4}$

2. $\dfrac{2}{5} \cdot \dfrac{3}{4}$

3. $\dfrac{2}{7} \cdot \dfrac{1}{5}$

4. $\dfrac{2}{3} \cdot \dfrac{1}{2}$

5. $\dfrac{8}{5} \cdot \dfrac{15}{32}$

6. $\dfrac{5}{9} \cdot \dfrac{4}{3}$

7. $\dfrac{2}{3} \cdot \dfrac{7}{12} \cdot \dfrac{9}{14}$

8. $\dfrac{7}{8} \cdot \dfrac{16}{21} \cdot \dfrac{1}{2}$

9. $\dfrac{3}{4} \cdot \dfrac{5}{6} \cdot \dfrac{2}{3}$

10. $\dfrac{2}{5} \cdot \dfrac{3}{8} \cdot \dfrac{2}{3}$

11. $\dfrac{9}{22} \cdot \dfrac{11}{16}$

12. $\dfrac{5}{12} \cdot \dfrac{7}{10}$

13. $\dfrac{5}{8} \cdot \dfrac{16}{25}$

14. $\dfrac{6}{11} \cdot \dfrac{22}{15}$

15. $\dfrac{14}{25} \cdot \dfrac{65}{48} \cdot \dfrac{15}{28}$

16. $\dfrac{35}{64} \cdot \dfrac{32}{15} \cdot \dfrac{27}{72}$

17. $\dfrac{16}{25} \cdot \dfrac{35}{32} \cdot \dfrac{15}{64}$

18. $\dfrac{39}{42} \cdot \dfrac{7}{13} \cdot \dfrac{7}{24}$

Multiply. Write answers in lowest terms and as whole or mixed numbers where possible. See Example 4.

19. $5 \cdot \dfrac{4}{5}$

20. $20 \cdot \dfrac{3}{4}$

21. $\dfrac{5}{8} \cdot 64$

22. $\dfrac{5}{6} \cdot 24$

23. $36 \cdot \dfrac{2}{3}$

24. $30 \cdot \dfrac{3}{10}$

25. $36 \cdot \dfrac{5}{8} \cdot \dfrac{9}{15}$

26. $35 \cdot \dfrac{3}{5} \cdot \dfrac{1}{2}$

27. $100 \cdot \dfrac{21}{50} \cdot \dfrac{3}{4}$

28. $400 \cdot \dfrac{7}{8}$

29. $\dfrac{2}{5} \cdot 200$

30. $\dfrac{6}{7} \cdot 245$

31. $142 \cdot \dfrac{2}{3}$

32. $\dfrac{12}{25} \cdot 430$

33. $\dfrac{28}{21} \cdot 640 \cdot \dfrac{15}{32}$

34. $\dfrac{21}{13} \cdot 520 \cdot \dfrac{7}{20}$

35. $\dfrac{54}{38} \cdot 684 \cdot \dfrac{5}{6}$

36. $\dfrac{76}{43} \cdot 473 \cdot \dfrac{5}{19}$

Find the area of each rectangle. See Example 5.

37.
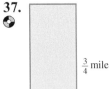
$\frac{3}{4}$ mile

$\frac{1}{3}$ mile

38.
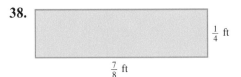
$\frac{1}{4}$ ft

$\frac{7}{8}$ ft

39. $\frac{3}{4}$ meter

12 meters

40. $\frac{3}{8}$ in.

8 in.

41. $\frac{3}{14}$ in.

$\frac{7}{5}$ in.

42.
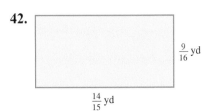
$\frac{9}{16}$ yd

$\frac{14}{15}$ yd

43. Write in your own words the rule for multiplying fractions. Make up an example problem to show how this works.

44. A useful shortcut when multiplying fractions is to divide a numerator and a denominator by the same number. Describe how this works and give an example.

Find the area of each rectangle in these application problems. Write answers in lowest terms and as whole or mixed numbers where possible. See Example 5.

45. Find the area of a heating-duct grill having a length of 2 yd and a width of $\frac{3}{4}$ yd.

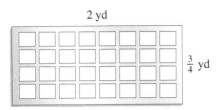

2 yd

$\frac{3}{4}$ yd

46. Find the area of the top of an office desk having a length of 2 yd and a width of $\frac{7}{8}$ yd.

$\frac{7}{8}$ yd

2 yd

47. A wildfire is contained in an area measuring $\frac{7}{8}$ mile by 4 miles. Find the total area of the containment.

48. A motorcycle racecourse is $\frac{2}{3}$ mile wide by 4 miles long. Find the area of the racecourse.

49. The Sunny Side Soccer Park is $\frac{1}{4}$ mile long and $\frac{3}{16}$ mile wide, while the Creek Side Soccer Park is $\frac{3}{8}$ mile long and $\frac{1}{8}$ mile wide. Which park has the larger area?

50. The Rocking Horse Ranch is $\frac{3}{4}$ mile long and $\frac{2}{3}$ mile wide. The Silver Spur Ranch is $\frac{5}{8}$ mile long and $\frac{4}{5}$ mile wide. Which ranch has the larger area?

Relating Concepts (Exercises 51–56) For Individual or Group Work

Front end rounding can be used to estimate an answer when multiplying fractions.
Work Exercises 51–56 in order. *Round exact answers to the nearest whole number.*

The bar graph shows the six largest fast-food chains by the number of stores.

Who's Hungry?

Largest Fast-Food Chains
(based on the number of stores)

Subway   20,775
McDonald's 13,774
Starbucks   9401
Pizza Hut   7532
Burger King 7178
Wendy's   5955

Source: Technomic.

51. Use front end rounding to estimate the total number of stores for the six largest chains.

52. Find the exact total number of stores for the six largest chains.

53. If $\frac{2}{3}$ of the Starbucks stores are in medium to large population areas, use front end rounding to estimate, and then find the exact number of stores in these population areas.

Estimate:

Exact:

54. If $\frac{2}{5}$ of the Pizza Hut stores are in shopping centers and food courts, use front end rounding to estimate, and then find the exact number of stores in these locations.

Estimate:

Exact:

Compare the estimated answers and the exact answers in Exercises 53 and 54. How can you get an estimated answer that is closer to the exact answer? Try rounding the number of stores to some multiple of the denominator in the fraction that has two *nonzero digits.*

55. Refer to Exercise 53. Round the number of Starbucks locations to some multiple of the denominator in $\frac{2}{3}$ that has *two* nonzero digits. Now estimate the answer, showing your work.

56. Refer to Exercise 54. Round the number of Pizza Hut stores to some multiple of the denominator in $\frac{2}{5}$ that has *two* nonzero digits. Now estimate the answer, showing your work.

2.6 ▶▶▶ Applications of Multiplication

OBJECTIVE **1** **Solve fraction application problems using multiplication.** Many application problems are solved by multiplying fractions. Use the following indicator words for multiplication.

product
double
triple
times
of (when "of" follows a fraction)
twice
twice as much

Always look for indicator words.

Look for these indicator words in the following examples.

OBJECTIVE

1 **Solve fraction application problems using multiplication.**

EXAMPLE 1 **Applying Indicator Words**

Lois Stevens gives $\frac{1}{10}$ of her income to her church. One month she earned $2980. How much did she give to the church that month?

Step 1 **Read** the problem. The problem asks us to find the amount of money given to the church.

Step 2 **Work out a plan.** The indicator word is *of:* Stevens gave $\frac{1}{10}$ *of* her income. When it follows a fraction, the word *of* indicates multiplication, so find the amount given to the church by multiplying $\frac{1}{10}$ and $2980.

Step 3 **Estimate** a reasonable answer. Round the income of $2980 to $3000. Then divide $3000 by 10 to find $\frac{1}{10}$ of the income (one of 10 equal parts). Our estimate is $3000 ÷ 10 = $300. (Recall the shortcut for dividing by 10; drop one 0 from the dividend.)

Step 4 **Solve** the problem.

$$\text{amount} = \frac{1}{\overset{}{\underset{1}{10}}} \cdot \frac{\overset{298}{\cancel{2980}}}{1} = \frac{298}{1} = 298$$

Step 5 **State the answer.** Stevens gave $298 to her church that month.

Step 6 **Check.** The exact answer, $298, is close to our estimate of $300.

Work Problem **1** *at the Side.* ▶

EXAMPLE 2 **Solving a Fraction Application Problem**

Of the 39 students in Carol Dixon's high school biology class, $\frac{2}{3}$ plan to go to college. How many plan to go to college?

Step 1 **Read** the problem. The problem asks us to find the number of students who plan to go to college.

Step 2 **Work out a plan.** Reword the problem to read

$\frac{2}{3}$ of the students plan to go to college.
     ↑
Indicator word for multiplication when it follows a fraction

Continued on Next Page

---

1 Solve each problem.

(a) Eric and Sabrina Means are saving $\frac{3}{8}$ of their income for the down payment on their first home. If they have a combined annual income of $81,576, how much can they save in a year?

(b) A retiring firefighter will receive $\frac{5}{8}$ of her highest annual salary as retirement income. If her highest annual salary is $62,504, how much will she receive as retirement income?

ANSWERS

1. **(a)** $30,591 **(b)** $39,065

2 At Sid's Pharmacy, $\frac{5}{16}$ of the prescriptions are paid by a third party (insurance company). If 3696 prescriptions are filled, find the number paid by a third party.

Use the six problem-solving steps.

Step 3   **Estimate** a reasonable answer. Round the number of students in the class from 39 to 40. Then, $\frac{1}{2}$ of 40 is 20. Since $\frac{2}{3}$ is more than $\frac{1}{2}$, our estimate is that "more than 20 students" plan to go to college.

Step 4   **Solve** the problem. Find the number who plan to go to college by multiplying $\frac{2}{3}$ and 39.

$$\text{number who plan to go} = \frac{2}{3} \cdot 39$$

$$= \frac{2}{\overset{}{\underset{1}{\cancel{3}}}} \cdot \frac{\overset{13}{\cancel{39}}}{1} = \frac{26}{1} = 26$$

Step 5   **State the answer.** 26 students plan to go to college.

Step 6   **Check.** The exact answer, 26, fits our estimate of "more than 20."

◀ *Work Problem* **2** *at the Side.*

---

3 At our college, $\frac{1}{3}$ of the students speak a foreign language. Of those speaking a foreign language, $\frac{3}{4}$ speak Spanish. What fraction of the students speak Spanish?

Use the six problem-solving steps.

EXAMPLE 3   Finding a Fraction of a Fraction

In her will, a woman divides her estate into 6 equal parts. Five of the 6 parts are given to relatives. Of the sixth part, $\frac{1}{3}$ goes to the Salvation Army. What fraction of her total estate goes to the Salvation Army?

Step 1   **Read** the problem. The problem asks for the fraction of an estate that goes to the Salvation Army.

Step 2   **Work out a plan.** Reword the problem to read

the Salvation Army gets $\frac{1}{3}$ of $\frac{1}{6}$.

Indicator word for multiplication when it follows a fraction

Step 3   **Estimate** a reasonable answer. If the estate is divided into 6 equal parts and each of these parts was divided into 3 equal parts, we would have $6 \cdot 3 = 18$ equal parts. Our estimate is $\frac{1}{18}$.

Step 4   **Solve** the problem. The Salvation Army gets $\frac{1}{3}$ of $\frac{1}{6}$.

Indicator word

To find the fraction that the Salvation Army is to receive, multiply $\frac{1}{3}$ and $\frac{1}{6}$.

$$\text{fraction to Salvation Army} = \frac{1}{3} \cdot \frac{1}{6}$$

$$= \frac{1}{18}$$

Step 5   **State the answer.** The Salvation Army gets $\frac{1}{18}$ of the total estate.

Step 6   **Check.** The exact answer, $\frac{1}{18}$, matches our estimate.

Remember to check your work.

◀ *Work Problem* **3** *at the Side.*

ANSWERS

2. 1155 prescriptions

3. $\frac{1}{4}$ speak Spanish

EXAMPLE 4 **Using Fractions with a Circle Graph**

The circle graph, or pie chart, shows where children 8 to 17 years of age make food purchases when away from home. If 2500 children were in the survey, find the number of children who buy food in the school cafeteria.

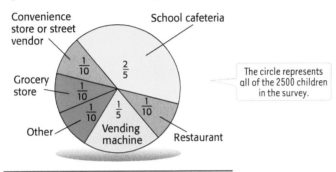

FINDING FOOD

Children ages 8 to 17 made food purchases at the following locations:

The circle represents all of the 2500 children in the survey.

Source: Pursuant Inc. for American Dietetic Association Foundation.

4 Solve each problem using the six problem-solving steps. Use the circle graph in Example 4.

(a) What fraction of the children buy food from vending machines?

Step 1 **Read** the problem. The problem asks for the number of children who buy food in the school cafeteria.

Step 2 **Work out a plan.** Reword the problem to read

$\frac{2}{5}$ of 2500 children buy food in the school cafeteria.
    ↑
Indicator word for multiplication when it follows a fraction

(b) What number of children buy food from vending machines?

Step 3 **Estimate** a reasonable answer. $\frac{1}{2}$ of 2500 people is 1250 people. $\frac{2}{5}$ is less than $\frac{1}{2}$, so our estimate is "less than 1250 people."

Step 4 **Solve** the problem. Find the number who buy food in the school cafeteria by multiplying $\frac{2}{5}$ and 2500.

$$\text{number in school cafeteria} = \frac{2}{5} \cdot 2500$$

$$= \frac{2}{5} \cdot \frac{2500}{1}$$

$$= \frac{2}{\overset{}{\underset{1}{5}}} \cdot \frac{\overset{500}{2500}}{1} \quad \text{Divide both numerator and denominator by 5.}$$

$$= \frac{1000}{1} = 1000$$

(c) What fraction of the children buy food from a convenience store or street vendor?

(d) What number of children buy food from a convenience store or street vendor?

Step 5 **State the answer.** 1000 children buy food in the school cafeteria.

Step 6 **Check.** The exact answer, 1000 children, fits our estimate of "less than 1250 children."

Work Problem **4** *at the Side.* ▶

ANSWERS

4. (a) $\frac{1}{5}$ (b) 500 children (c) $\frac{1}{10}$
   (d) 250 children

Math in the Media

HEART-RATE TRAINING ZONE

The Kaiser Permanente *Healthwise Handbook* says that "no one can prescribe the perfect fitness plan for you." However, your personal fitness plan should include aerobic conditioning that strengthens your heart and lungs. Activities that provide aerobic conditioning include brisk walking, running, stair climbing, biking, swimming, aerobic dance, or anything else that raises your heart rate to within your training zone for a minimum of 12 minutes.

If you train at the higher end of the training zone, you will burn glycogen and improve aerobic fitness. Training for longer periods at the lower end of the training zone results in your body using fat reserves for energy. Wickipedia, The Free Encyclopedia, at www.wickipedia.org, explains the calculations used to find maximum heart rates and training zones.

Example: The training zone (TZ) is based on your heart rate (HR) for one minute. To see if you are in the training zone, measure your heart rate for 15 seconds. Compare it to the 15-second training zone. Find the exact answer, and then round to the nearest whole number.

Instruction	Calculation	Example (age 22)
Calculate maximum heart rate (MHR).	$220 -$ your age	$220 - 22 = 198$
Calculate lower limit of training zone (TZ).	$\frac{3}{5} \times$ (MHR)	$\frac{3}{5} \times (198) = \frac{594}{5} = 118\frac{4}{5}$
Calculate upper limit of training zone (TZ).	$\frac{4}{5} \times$ (MHR)	$\frac{4}{5} \times (198) = \frac{792}{5} = 158\frac{2}{5}$
Calculate the exact 15-second training zone. Round the results to the nearest whole number.	$\left(\frac{1}{4} \times \text{lower TZ}, \right.$ $\left. \frac{1}{4} \times \text{Upper TZ}\right)$	$\frac{1}{4} \times \frac{594}{5} = 29\frac{7}{10}; \frac{1}{4} \times \frac{792}{5} = 39\frac{3}{5}$ HR between $29\frac{7}{10}$ and $39\frac{3}{5}$ HR between 30 and 40

1. Suppose you work in a physical fitness center and decide to design a poster to remind the clients of the training zone for their age. Compute the exact 15-second training zone for people of each of the ages in the table. Write fractions in lowest terms. Then round the answers to the nearest whole number.

2. Explain why the lower and upper training zones (TZ) are multiplied by $\frac{1}{4}$.

Age	MHR	Lower Limit of TZ	Upper Limit of TZ	15-Second TZ (exact)	15-Second TZ (rounded)
18					
25					
30					
40					
50					
60					

FOR EXTRA HELP

Solve each application problem. Look for indicator words. See Examples 1–4.

1. A file cabinet top is $\frac{3}{4}$ yd by $\frac{2}{3}$ yd. Find its area.

← $\frac{2}{3}$ yd →

$\frac{3}{4}$ yd

2. The rectangular floor of Darby's house measures $\frac{14}{15}$ yd by $\frac{3}{4}$ yd. Find its area.

3. A cookie sheet is $\frac{4}{3}$ ft by $\frac{2}{3}$ ft. Find its area.

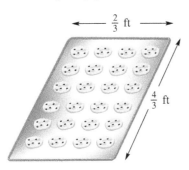

$\frac{2}{3}$ ft

$\frac{4}{3}$ ft

4. Each day there are 16 million people who shop at flea markets. If $\frac{2}{5}$ of these people purchase produce at the flea market, how many purchase produce? (*Source:* National Flea Market Association.)

5. Pete is helping Colin make a rectangular mahogany lamp table for Carolyn's birthday. Find the area of the top of the table if it is $\frac{4}{5}$ yd long by $\frac{3}{8}$ yd wide.

6. A convenience store sells 1650 items, of which $\frac{12}{25}$ are classified as junk food. How many of the items are junk food?

7. Dan Crump had expenses of $6848 during one semester of college. His part-time job provided $\frac{3}{8}$ of the amount he needed. How much did he earn on his job?

8. Erin Hernandez produces $5680 in profits for her employer. If her personal earnings are $\frac{2}{5}$ of these profits, find the amount of her earnings.

9. The city with the most expensive daily parking fee is New York City (Midtown) at $45. The daily parking fee in Boston (third most expensive) is $\frac{4}{5}$ as much as New York City. Find the daily parking fee in Boston. (*Source:* Colliers International.)

10. The daily parking fee in New York City (Downtown) is $36. In San Francisco (fifth most expensive), the daily parking fee is $\frac{3}{4}$ the cost of New York City (Downtown). How much is the daily parking fee in San Francisco? (*Source:* Colliers International.)

11. At the Garlic Festival Fun Run, $\frac{7}{12}$ of the runners are women. If there are 1560 runners, how many are women?

12. A hotel has 408 rooms. Of these rooms, $\frac{9}{17}$ are for nonsmokers. How many rooms are for nonsmokers?

Almost $\frac{1}{3}$ of all television owners own a TiVo or some other DVR recording device. The circle graph below shows how the owners of this device have changed their television viewing time. Use this information to work Exercises 13–18.

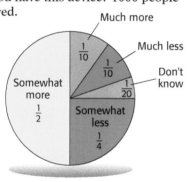

TV with TiVo

Do you watch more or less TV now that you have this device? 1000 people surveyed.

Source: Greenfield Online Omnibus

13. Which response was given by the least number of people? How many people gave this response?

14. Which response was given by the greatest number of people? How many gave this response?

15. Find the total number of people who said they watch less television.

16. Find the total number of people who said they watch more television.

17. Without actually adding the fractions given for all the groups, explain why their sum has to be 1.

18. Refer to Exercise 17. Suppose you added all the fractions for the groups and did not get 1 as an answer. List some possible explanations.

The table shows the earnings for the Owens family last year and the circle graph shows how they spent their earnings. Use this information to answer Exercises 19–24.

Month	Earnings	Month	Earnings
January	$4575	July	$5540
February	$4312	August	$3732
March	$4988	September	$4170
April	$4530	October	$5512
May	$4320	November	$4965
June	$4898	December	$6458

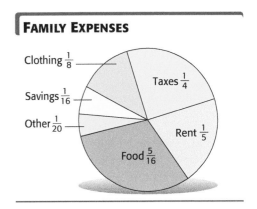

FAMILY EXPENSES

Clothing $\frac{1}{8}$

Savings $\frac{1}{16}$

Other $\frac{1}{20}$

Taxes $\frac{1}{4}$

Rent $\frac{1}{5}$

Food $\frac{5}{16}$

19. Find the Owens family's total income for the year.

20. How much of their annual earnings went to taxes?

21. Find the amount of their rent for the year.

22. How much did they spend for food during the year?

23. Find their annual savings.

24. How much of their annual income was spent on clothing?

25. Here is how one student solved a multiplication problem. Find the error and solve the problem correctly.

$$\frac{9}{10} \times \frac{20}{21} = \frac{\overset{3}{\cancel{9}}}{\underset{1}{\cancel{10}}} \times \frac{\overset{2}{\cancel{20}}}{\underset{3}{\cancel{21}}} = \frac{6}{3} = 2$$

26. When two whole numbers are multiplied, the product is always larger than the numbers being multiplied. When two proper fractions are multiplied, the product is always smaller than the numbers being multiplied. Are these statements true? Why or why not?

Solve each application problem.

27. The cost of Lasik eye surgery in the United States is $2000 for each eye. The same surgery in Thailand is $\frac{3}{8}$ of this amount. What is the cost of this procedure in Thailand? (*Source: Reader's Digest.*)

28. A knee replacement in the United States costs $36,300, while in Mexico the same procedure costs $\frac{3}{50}$ of this amount. Find the cost of a knee replacement in Mexico. (*Source: Reader's Digest.*)

29. A collector of scale model World War II ships wants to know the length of a $\frac{1}{128}$ scale model of a ship that was 256 feet in length. Find the length of the scale model. (*Source:* Lilliput Motor Company, LTD.)

30. Howard Martin, manager of Bayside Fishing, is adding $\frac{3}{32}$ of a quart of 2-cycle oil to each gallon of gasoline. How many quarts of oil will he need to add to 760 gallons of gasoline?

31. LaDonna Washington is running for city council. She needs to get $\frac{2}{3}$ of her votes from senior citizens and 27,000 votes in all to win. How many votes does she need from voters other than the senior citizens?

32. The start-up cost of a Subs and Sandwich Shop is $32,000. If the bank will loan you $\frac{9}{16}$ of the start up and you must pay the balance, how much more will you need to open a shop?

33. A will states that $\frac{7}{8}$ of an estate is to be divided among relatives. Of the remaining estate, $\frac{1}{4}$ goes to the American Cancer Society. What fraction of the estate goes to the American Cancer Society?

34. A couple has $\frac{2}{5}$ of their total investments in real estate. Of the remaining investments, $\frac{1}{3}$ is invested in bonds. What fraction of the total investments is in bonds?

2.7 ▶▶▶ Dividing Fractions

OBJECTIVE 1 Find the reciprocal of a fraction. To divide fractions, we need to know how to find the **reciprocal** of a fraction.

> **Reciprocal of a Fraction**
> Two numbers are reciprocals of each other if their product is 1. To find the reciprocal of a fraction, interchange the numerator and denominator.

For example, the reciprocal of $\frac{3}{4}$ is $\frac{4}{3}$.

Fraction $\frac{3}{4}$ ⤬ $\frac{4}{3}$ Reciprocal

> **Note**
> Notice that you invert, or "flip," a fraction to find its reciprocal.

EXAMPLE 1   Finding Reciprocals

Find the reciprocal of each fraction.

Flip a fraction to find the reciprocal.

(a) The reciprocal of $\frac{1}{4}$ is $\frac{4}{1}$ because $\frac{1}{4} \cdot \frac{4}{1} = \frac{4}{4} = 1$

(b) The reciprocal of $\frac{2}{3}$ is $\frac{3}{2}$ because $\frac{2}{3} \cdot \frac{3}{2} = \frac{6}{6} = 1$

(c) The reciprocal of $\frac{3}{5}$ is $\frac{5}{3}$ because $\frac{3}{5} \cdot \frac{5}{3} = \frac{15}{15} = 1$

(d) The reciprocal of 8 is $\frac{1}{8}$ because $\frac{8}{1} \cdot \frac{1}{8} = \frac{8}{8} = 1$ Think of 8 as $\frac{8}{1}$.

Work Problem **1** at the Side. ▶

> **Note**
> Every number has a reciprocal except 0. The number 0 has no reciprocal because there is no number that can be multiplied by 0 to get 1.
>
> $$0 \cdot (\text{reciprocal}) = 1$$
> ↑
> There is no number to use here that will give an answer of 1. When you multiply by 0, you always get 0.

OBJECTIVES

1 Find the reciprocal of a fraction.

2 Divide fractions.

3 Solve application problems in which fractions are divided.

1 Find the reciprocal of each fraction.

(a) $\frac{3}{4}$

(b) $\frac{3}{8}$

(c) $\frac{9}{4}$

(d) 16

In **Chapter 1,** we saw that the division problem $12 \div 3$ asks how many 3s are in 12. In the same way, the division problem $\frac{2}{3} \div \frac{1}{6}$ asks how many $\frac{1}{6}$ s are in $\frac{2}{3}$. The figure illustrates $\frac{2}{3} \div \frac{1}{6}$.

Ask: How many $\frac{1}{6}$ s are in $\frac{2}{3}$?

The figure shows that there are 4 of the $\frac{1}{6}$ pieces in $\frac{2}{3}$, or

$$\frac{2}{3} \div \frac{1}{6} = 4$$

OBJECTIVE 2 Divide fractions.   We will use reciprocals to divide fractions.

> **Dividing Fractions**
>
> To divide two fractions, multiply the first fraction by the reciprocal of the second fraction.

EXAMPLE 2   Dividing One Fraction by Another

Divide. Write answers in lowest terms and as mixed numbers where possible.

(a) $\dfrac{7}{8} \div \dfrac{15}{16}$

The reciprocal of $\dfrac{15}{16}$ is $\dfrac{16}{15}$

Reciprocals

$$\frac{7}{8} \div \frac{15}{16} = \frac{7}{8} \cdot \frac{16}{15}$$

Use $\frac{16}{15}$, the reciprocal of $\frac{15}{16}$, and multiply.

Change division to multiplication.

$$= \frac{7}{\overset{}{\underset{1}{8}}} \cdot \frac{\overset{2}{16}}{15} \qquad \text{Divide the numerator and denominator by 8.}$$

$$= \frac{7 \cdot 2}{1 \cdot 15} \qquad \text{Multiply.}$$

$$= \frac{14}{15} \quad \leftarrow \text{Lowest terms}$$

Continued on Next Page

(b) $\dfrac{\dfrac{4}{5}}{\dfrac{3}{10}}$

$$\dfrac{\dfrac{4}{5}}{\dfrac{3}{10}} = \dfrac{4}{5} \div \dfrac{3}{10} \qquad \text{Rewrite by using the} \div \text{symbol for division.}$$

$$= \dfrac{4}{\overset{}{\underset{1}{\cancel{5}}}} \cdot \dfrac{\overset{2}{\cancel{10}}}{3} \qquad \begin{array}{l}\text{The reciprocal of } \frac{3}{10} \text{ is } \frac{10}{3}. \text{ Change ``}\div\text{'' to `` } \cdot \text{ ''.} \\ \text{Divide the numerator and denominator by 5.}\end{array}$$

$$= \dfrac{4 \cdot 2}{1 \cdot 3} \qquad \text{Multiply.}$$

$$= \dfrac{8}{3} = 2\dfrac{2}{3} \qquad \text{Rewrite the answer as a mixed number.}$$

CAUTION
Be certain that the divisor fraction is changed to its reciprocal *before* you divide numerators and denominators by common factors.

Work Problem **2** *at the Side.* ▶

EXAMPLE 3   **Dividing with a Whole Number**

Divide. Write all answers in lowest terms and as whole or mixed numbers where possible.

(a) $5 \div \dfrac{1}{4}$

Write 5 as $\frac{5}{1}$. Next, use the reciprocal of $\frac{1}{4}$, which is $\frac{4}{1}$.

$$5 \div \dfrac{1}{4} = \dfrac{5}{1} \cdot \dfrac{4}{1} \qquad \text{Reciprocal of } \frac{1}{4} \text{ is } \frac{4}{1}.$$

Reciprocals

$$= \dfrac{5 \cdot 4}{1 \cdot 1} \qquad \text{Multiply.}$$

$$= \dfrac{20}{1} = 20 \qquad \text{Rewrite the answer as a whole number.}$$

Continued on Next Page

---

2 Divide. Write answers in lowest terms and as mixed numbers where possible.

(a) $\dfrac{1}{4} \div \dfrac{2}{3}$

(b) $\dfrac{3}{8} \div \dfrac{5}{8}$

(c) $\dfrac{\dfrac{2}{3}}{\dfrac{4}{5}}$

(d) $\dfrac{\dfrac{5}{6}}{\dfrac{7}{12}}$

3 Divide. Write answers in lowest terms and as whole or mixed numbers where possible.

(a) $10 \div \dfrac{1}{2}$

(b) $6 \div \dfrac{6}{7}$

(c) $\dfrac{4}{5} \div 6$

(d) $\dfrac{3}{8} \div 4$

4 Solve each problem using the six problem-solving steps.

(a) How many $\frac{3}{4}$-quart leafblower fuel tanks can be filled from 15 quarts of fuel?

(b) Find the number of $\frac{4}{5}$-quart bottles that can be filled from a 120-quart cask.

(b) $\dfrac{2}{3} \div 6$

Write 6 as $\frac{6}{1}$. The reciprocal of $\frac{6}{1}$ is $\frac{1}{6}$.

$$\frac{2}{3} \div \frac{6}{1} = \frac{2}{3} \cdot \frac{1}{6}$$

Reciprocals

*Careful! Divide out common factors **after** changing to the reciprocal and to multiplication.*

$$= \frac{\overset{1}{\cancel{2}}}{3} \cdot \frac{1}{\underset{3}{\cancel{6}}}$$
Divide the numerator and denominator by 2, then multiply.

$$= \frac{1 \cdot 1}{3 \cdot 3} = \frac{1}{9}$$ Lowest terms

◀ *Work Problem* **3** *at the Side.*

OBJECTIVE **3** **Solve application problems in which fractions are divided.** Many application problems require division of fractions. Recall that typical indicator words for division are *goes into, per, divide, divided by, divided equally,* and *divided into.*

EXAMPLE 4 **Applying Fraction Skills**

Goldie, the manager of the Burnside Deli, must fill a 10-gallon kosher dill pickle crock with salt brine. She has only a $\frac{2}{3}$-gallon container to use. How many times must she fill the $\frac{2}{3}$-gallon container and empty it into the 10-gallon crock?

Step 1 **Read** the problem. We need to find the number of times Goldie needs to use a $\frac{2}{3}$-gallon container in order to fill a 10-gallon crock.

Step 2 **Work out a plan.** We can solve the problem by finding the number of times 10 can be divided by $\frac{2}{3}$.

Step 3 **Estimate** a reasonable answer. Round $\frac{2}{3}$ gallon to 1 gallon. In order to fill the 10-gallon container, she would have to use the 1-gallon container 10 times, so our estimate is 10.

Step 4 **Solve** the problem.

Reciprocals

$$10 \div \frac{2}{3} = \frac{10}{1} \cdot \frac{3}{2}$$
The reciprocal of $\frac{2}{3}$ is $\frac{3}{2}$. Change "÷" to "·."

$$= \frac{\overset{5}{\cancel{10}}}{1} \cdot \frac{3}{\underset{1}{\cancel{2}}}$$
Divide the numerator and denominator by 2, and then multiply.

$$= \frac{15}{1} = 15$$

Step 5 **State the answer.** Goldie must fill the container 15 times.

Step 6 **Check.** The exact answer, 15 times, is reasonably close to our estimate of 10 times.

◀ *Work Problem* **4** *at the Side.*

EXAMPLE 5 **Applying Fraction Skills**

At the Happi-Time Day Care Center, $\frac{6}{7}$ of the total budget goes to classroom operation. If there are 18 classrooms and each one receives the same amount, what fraction of the operating amount does each classroom receive?

Step 1 **Read** the problem. Since $\frac{6}{7}$ of the total budget must be split into 18 parts, we must find the fraction of the classroom operating amount received by each classroom.

Step 2 **Work out a plan.** We must divide the fraction of the total budget going to classroom operation ($\frac{6}{7}$) by the number of classrooms (18).

Step 3 **Estimate** a reasonable answer. Round $\frac{6}{7}$ to 1. If all of the operating expenses (1 whole) were divided between 18 classrooms, each classroom would receive $\frac{1}{18}$ of the operating expenses, our estimate.

Step 4 **Solve** the problem. We solve by dividing $\frac{6}{7}$ by 18.

$$\frac{6}{7} \div 18 = \frac{6}{7} \div \frac{18}{1}$$

Write 18 as $\frac{18}{1}$

$$= \frac{\overset{1}{6}}{7} \cdot \frac{1}{\underset{3}{18}}$$

The reciprocal of $\frac{18}{1}$ is $\frac{1}{18}$. Change "÷" to " • ." Divide the numerator and denominator by 6.

$$= \frac{1}{21}$$

Multiply.

Step 5 **State the answer.** Each classroom receives $\frac{1}{21}$ of the total budget.

Step 6 **Check.** The exact answer, $\frac{1}{21}$, is close to our estimate of $\frac{1}{18}$.

Work Problem **5** *at the Side.* ▶

5 Solve each problem using the six problem-solving steps.

(a) The top 12 employees at Mayfield Manufacturing will divide $\frac{3}{4}$ of the annual bonus money. What fraction of the bonus money will each employee receive?

(b) A winning lottery ticket was purchased by 8 employees of United States Marketing and Promotions (USMP). They will donate $\frac{1}{5}$ of the total winnings to pay the medical expenses of a fellow employee, and then divide the remaining winnings evenly. What fraction of the prize money will each receive?

Math in the Media

Mathematics teachers attending conferences in New Orleans, Louisiana, and San Jose, California, found the following information about hotel rates on Internet Web sites. To find the hotel room rates in New Orleans, they went to www.hotel-rate.com/us/louisiana/neworleans/, while the hotel room rates in San Jose were found at www.sanjose.com.

Hotel New Orleans	Single	Double	Triple	Quad	Suites
Marriott	$229	$239	$249	$259	$806
Sheraton	$165	$174	$193	$223	$748
San Jose					
Crowne Plaza	$209	$209	$219	$219	—
Hilton Towers	$179	$179	$199	$219	—
Sainte Claire	$149	$149	$169	$189	$329

1. The double rate is for two people sharing a room. What fractional part does each person pay?

2. (a) Multiply the double rate at the Hilton Towers in San Jose by $\frac{1}{2}$. What is the result?

   (b) Divide the double rate at the Hilton Towers in San Jose by 2. What is the result?

   (c) Explain what happened. How much money would one person owe if he or she shared a double room at the Hilton Towers in San Jose?

3. The triple rate is for three people sharing a room. What fractional part does each person pay?

4. How much money would one person owe if he or she shared a triple room at the Sainte Claire in San Jose? How much money would each person save if he or she could book a triple room at the Sainte Claire instead of the Crowne Plaza? Find your answer using two different methods, based on your observations in Problem 2.

5. The quad rate is for four people sharing a room. What fractional part does each person pay?

6. How much money would one person owe if he or she shared a quad room at the Sheraton in New Orleans? Find your answer using two different methods, based on your observations in Problem 2.

7. How many people would have to share a suite at the Sheraton in New Orleans for the cost per person to be less than sharing a quad room at the same hotel? Round the answer to the nearest whole number. (*Hint:* Estimate the cost per person for a quad room first. Then estimate the number of people needed to share the cost of the suite. Check your work using actual values.)

DO NOT DISTURB

NO MOLESTE

PRIÈRE DE NE PAS DÉRANGER

BITTE NICHT STÖREN

2.7 ▶▶▶ **Exercises**

FOR EXTRA HELP

MyMathLab   Math**XL** PRACTICE   WATCH   DOWNLOAD   READ   REVIEW

Find the reciprocal of each number. See Example 1.

1. $\dfrac{3}{8}$

2. $\dfrac{2}{5}$

3. $\dfrac{5}{6}$

4. $\dfrac{12}{7}$

5. $\dfrac{8}{5}$

6. $\dfrac{13}{20}$

7. 4

8. 10

Divide. Write answers in lowest terms and as whole or mixed numbers where possible. See Examples 2 and 3.

9. $\dfrac{1}{2} \div \dfrac{3}{4}$

10. $\dfrac{5}{8} \div \dfrac{7}{8}$

11. $\dfrac{7}{8} \div \dfrac{1}{3}$

12. $\dfrac{7}{8} \div \dfrac{3}{4}$

13. $\dfrac{3}{4} \div \dfrac{5}{3}$

14. $\dfrac{4}{5} \div \dfrac{9}{4}$

15. $\dfrac{7}{9} \div \dfrac{7}{36}$

16. $\dfrac{5}{8} \div \dfrac{5}{16}$

17. $\dfrac{15}{32} \div \dfrac{5}{64}$

18. $\dfrac{7}{12} \div \dfrac{14}{15}$

19. $\dfrac{\frac{13}{20}}{\frac{4}{5}}$

20. $\dfrac{\frac{9}{10}}{\frac{3}{5}}$

21. $\dfrac{\frac{5}{6}}{\frac{25}{24}}$

22. $\dfrac{\frac{28}{15}}{\frac{21}{5}}$

23. $12 \div \dfrac{2}{3}$

24. $7 \div \dfrac{1}{4}$

25. $\dfrac{18}{\frac{3}{4}}$

26. $\dfrac{12}{\frac{3}{4}}$

27. $\dfrac{\frac{4}{7}}{8}$

28. $\dfrac{\frac{7}{10}}{3}$

Solve each application problem by using division. See Examples 4 and 5.

29. Veterinarian Jasmine Cato has $\frac{8}{9}$ quart of medication. She wishes to prescribe this medication for 4 cats in her pet hospital. If she divides the medication evenly, how much will each cat receive?

30. Harold Pishke, barber, has 15 quarts of conditioning shampoo. If he wants to put this shampoo into $\frac{3}{8}$-quart containers, how many containers can be filled?

31. Some college roommates want to make pancakes for their neighbors. They need 5 cups of flour, but have only a $\frac{1}{3}$-cup measuring cup. How many times will they need to fill their measuring cup?

32. A cross-country bike rider completes $\frac{5}{6}$ of her trip in 15 days. What fraction of her total trip does she complete each day?

33. How many $\frac{1}{8}$-ounce eye drop dispensers can be filled with 11 ounces of eye drops?

34. It is estimated that each guest at a party will eat $\frac{5}{16}$ pound of peanuts. How many guests may be served with 10 pounds of peanuts?

35. Pam Trizlia had a small pickup truck that could carry $\frac{2}{3}$ cord of firewood. Find the number of trips needed to deliver 40 cords of wood.

36. Manuel Servin has a 200-yard roll of weather stripping material. Find the number of pieces of weather stripping $\frac{5}{8}$ yard in length that may be cut from the roll.

37. Your classmate is confused on how to divide by a fraction. Write a short note telling him how this should be done.

38. If you multiply positive proper fractions, the product is smaller than the fractions multiplied. When you divide by a proper fraction, is the quotient smaller than the numbers in the problem? Prove your answer with examples.

Solve each application problem using multiplication or division.

39. The recipe for a Jelly Belly Express loafcake calls for $\frac{3}{4}$ pound of Jelly Belly jelly beans in assorted colors. If you want to make 16 cakes, how many pounds of Jelly Belly jelly beans will you need?

40. In a recent study, it was found that one month after leaving the hospital only $\frac{7}{8}$ of the 1520 heart attack patients were still taking the life-saving drugs prescribed for them. How many of these patients were still taking their drugs? (*Source:* Dr. Michael Ho, Denver Veterans Medical Center.)

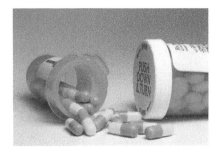

41. Broadly Plumbing finds that $\frac{3}{4}$ can of pipe joint compound is needed to plumb each new home. How many homes can be plumbed with 156 cans of compound?

42. A mechanic uses an average of $\frac{2}{3}$ gallon of gear lube to service each tractor differential. Find the number of tractors that can be serviced with 28 gallons of gear lube.

43. In recordings of 186 patient visits, doctors failed to mention a new drug's side effects or how long to take the drug in $\frac{2}{3}$ of the visits. In how many visits did doctors fail to discuss these issues with patients? (*Source:* Dr. Deijieng Tam, UCLA.)

44. Laura has been working on a job that will require 81 hours to complete. If she has completed $\frac{7}{9}$ of the job, how many hours has she worked?

45. A dish towel manufacturer requires $\frac{3}{8}$ yard of cotton fabric for each towel. Find the number of dish towels that can be made from 912 yards of fabric.

46. Each patient will receive $\frac{7}{10}$ vial of medication. How many patients can be treated with 3150 vials of medication?

Relating Concepts (Exercises 47–52) For Individual or Group Work

Many application problems are solved using multiplication and division of fractions.
Work Exercises 47–52 *in order.*

47. Perhaps the most common indicator word for multiplication is the word *of.* Circle the words in the list below that are also indicator words for multiplication.

more than	per
double	twice
times	product
less than	difference
equals	twice as much

48. Circle the words in the list below that are indicator words for division.

fewer	sum of
goes into	divide
per	quotient
equals	double
loss of	divided by

49. To divide two fractions, multiply the first fraction by the _____ of the second fraction.

50. Find the reciprocals for each number.

$$\frac{3}{4} \qquad \frac{7}{8} \qquad 5 \qquad \frac{12}{19}$$

The size of a U.S.A. first-class Forever postage stamp is shown here. Use this to answer Exercises 51 and 52.

51.(a) Explain how to find the perimeter of any regular 3-, 4-, 5-, or 6-sided figure using multiplication.

(b) Find the perimeter of the stamp using multiplication.

52. Find the area of the postage stamp. Explain how to find the area of any rectangle.

2.8 ▶▶▶ Multiplying and Dividing Mixed Numbers

In **Section 2.2** we worked with mixed numbers—a whole number and a fraction written together. Many of the fraction problems you encounter in everyday life involve mixed numbers.

OBJECTIVE 1 Estimate the answer and multiply mixed numbers.   When multiplying mixed numbers, it is a good idea to estimate the answer first. Then multiply the mixed numbers by using the following steps.

> **Multiplying Mixed Numbers**
>
> **Step 1** *Change* each mixed number to an improper fraction.
>
> **Step 2** *Multiply* as fractions.
>
> **Step 3** *Simplify* the answer, which means to write it in *lowest terms,* and change it to a mixed number or whole number where possible.

To estimate the answer, round each mixed number to the nearest whole number. If the numerator is *half* of the denominator or *more,* round up the whole number part. If the numerator is *less* than half the denominator, leave the whole number as it is.

$$1\frac{5}{8} \begin{array}{l} \leftarrow \text{5 is more than 4.} \\ \leftarrow \text{Half of 8 is 4.} \end{array} \Big\} \; 1\frac{5}{8} \text{ rounds up to 2}$$

$$3\frac{2}{5} \begin{array}{l} \leftarrow \text{2 is less than } 2\frac{1}{2}. \\ \leftarrow \text{Half of 5 is } 2\frac{1}{2}. \end{array} \Big\} \; 3\frac{2}{5} \text{ rounds to 3}$$

> Round mixed numbers to the nearest whole number when estimating.

Work Problem ① *at the Side.* ▶

OBJECTIVES

1. **Estimate the answer and multiply mixed numbers.**

2. **Estimate the answer and divide mixed numbers.**

3. **Solve application problems with mixed numbers.**

① Round each mixed number to the nearest whole number.

(a) $4\frac{2}{3}$

(b) $3\frac{2}{5}$

(c) $5\frac{3}{4}$

(d) $4\frac{7}{12}$

(e) $1\frac{1}{2}$

(f) $8\frac{4}{9}$

EXAMPLE 1 Multiplying Mixed Numbers

First estimate the answer. Then multiply to get an exact answer. Simplify your answers.

(a) $2\frac{1}{2} \cdot 3\frac{1}{5}$

Estimate the answer by rounding the mixed numbers.

$$2\frac{1}{2} \text{ rounds to 3} \quad \text{and} \quad 3\frac{1}{5} \text{ rounds to 3}$$

$$3 \cdot 3 = 9 \quad \text{Estimated answer}$$

To find the exact answer, change each mixed number to an improper fraction.

$$\text{Step 1} \quad 2\frac{1}{2} = \frac{5}{2} \quad \text{and} \quad 3\frac{1}{5} = \frac{16}{5}$$

Continued on Next Page

2 First estimate the answer. Then multiply to find the exact answer. Simplify your answers.

(a) $3\frac{1}{2}$ • $6\frac{1}{3}$

↓   ↓

_____ • _____

= _____ *estimate*

(b) $4\frac{2}{3}$ • $2\frac{3}{4}$

↓   ↓

_____ • _____

= _____ *estimate*

(c) $3\frac{3}{5}$ • $4\frac{4}{9}$

↓   ↓

_____ • _____

= _____ *estimate*

(d) $5\frac{1}{4}$ • $3\frac{3}{5}$

↓   ↓

_____ • _____

= _____ *estimate*

Next, multiply.

Step 1   *Step 2*   *Step 3*

$$2\frac{1}{2} \cdot 3\frac{1}{5} = \frac{5}{2} \cdot \frac{16}{5} = \frac{\overset{1}{\cancel{5}}}{\underset{1}{\cancel{2}}} \cdot \frac{\overset{8}{\cancel{16}}}{\underset{1}{\cancel{5}}} = \frac{1 \cdot 8}{1 \cdot 1} = \frac{8}{1} = 8$$

> Remember: Change to improper fractions, then divide out common factors, and finally multiply.

The estimated answer is 9 and the exact answer is 8. The exact answer is reasonable.

(b) $3\frac{5}{8} \cdot 4\frac{4}{5}$

$3\frac{5}{8}$ rounds to 4   and $4\frac{4}{5}$ rounds to 5

↓   ↓

$4 \cdot 5 = 20$ Estimated answer

Now find the exact answer.

Step 1   *Step 2*

$$3\frac{5}{8} \cdot 4\frac{4}{5} = \frac{29}{8} \cdot \frac{24}{5} = \frac{29}{\underset{1}{\cancel{8}}} \cdot \frac{\overset{3}{\cancel{24}}}{5} = \frac{29 \cdot 3}{1 \cdot 5} = \frac{87}{5}$$

Step 3

$$\frac{87}{5} = 17\frac{2}{5}$$

> Simplify this answer by writing it as a mixed number.

The estimate was 20, so the exact answer of $17\frac{2}{5}$ is reasonable.

(c) $1\frac{3}{5} \cdot 3\frac{1}{3}$

$1\frac{3}{5}$ rounds to 2   and $3\frac{1}{3}$ rounds to 3

↓   ↓

$2 \cdot 3 = 6$ Estimated answer

The exact answer is shown below.

$$1\frac{3}{5} \cdot 3\frac{1}{3} = \frac{8}{\cancel{5}} \cdot \frac{\overset{2}{\cancel{10}}}{3} = \frac{8 \cdot 2}{1 \cdot 3} = \frac{16}{3} = 5\frac{1}{3}$$

The estimate was 6, so the exact answer of $5\frac{1}{3}$ is reasonable.

◀ Work Problem **2** at the Side.

ANSWERS

2. (a) *Estimate:* 4 • 6 = 24; *Exact:* $22\frac{1}{6}$

    (b) *Estimate:* 5 • 3 = 15; *Exact:* $12\frac{5}{6}$

    (c) *Estimate:* 4 • 4 = 16; *Exact:* 16

    (d) *Estimate:* 5 • 4 = 20; *Exact:* $18\frac{9}{10}$

OBJECTIVE 2 Estimate the answer and divide mixed numbers.
Just as you did when multiplying mixed numbers, it is also a good idea to estimate the answer when dividing mixed numbers. To divide mixed numbers, use the following steps.

Dividing Mixed Numbers

Step 1   *Change* each mixed number to an improper fraction.

Step 2   Use the *reciprocal* of the second fraction (divisor).

Step 3   *Multiply.*

Step 4   *Simplify* the answer, which means to write it in *lowest terms,* and change it to a mixed number or whole number where possible.

Note

Recall that the reciprocal of a fraction is found by interchanging the numerator and the denominator.

EXAMPLE 2   Dividing Mixed Numbers

First estimate the answer. Then divide to find the exact answer. Simplify your answers.

(a) $2\frac{2}{5} \div 1\frac{1}{2}$

First estimate the answer by rounding each mixed number to the nearest whole number.

$$2\frac{2}{5} \quad \div \quad 1\frac{1}{2}$$

$$\Big\downarrow \quad \text{Rounded} \quad \Big\downarrow$$

$$2 \quad \div \quad 2 = 1 \qquad \text{Estimated answer}$$

To find the exact answer, first change each mixed number to an improper fraction.

$$\overset{\textit{Step 1}}{2\frac{2}{5} \div 1\frac{1}{2} = \frac{12}{5} \div \frac{3}{2}}$$

Next, use the reciprocal of the second fraction and multiply.

$$\underset{\text{Reciprocals}}{\frac{12}{5} \div \frac{3}{2}} = \overset{\textit{Step 2}}{\frac{\overset{4}{\cancel{12}}}{5} \cdot \frac{2}{\underset{1}{\cancel{3}}}} = \overset{\textit{Step 3}}{\frac{4 \cdot 2}{5 \cdot 1}} = \frac{8}{5} = \overset{\textit{Step 4}}{1\frac{3}{5}} \qquad \text{Exact answer simplified}$$

Remember: Use the reciprocal of the *second* fraction.

The estimate was 1, so the exact answer of $1\frac{3}{5}$ is reasonable.

Continued on Next Page

3 First estimate the answer. Then divide to find the exact answer. Simplify all answers.

(a) $3\dfrac{1}{8}$ $\div$ $6\dfrac{1}{4}$

$\downarrow$ $\downarrow$

_____ $\div$ _____

= _____ *estimate*

(b) $10\dfrac{1}{3}$ $\div$ $2\dfrac{1}{2}$

$\downarrow$ $\downarrow$

_____ $\div$ _____

= _____ *estimate*

(c) 8 $\div$ $5\dfrac{1}{3}$

$\downarrow$ $\downarrow$

_____ $\div$ _____

= _____ *estimate*

(d) $13\dfrac{1}{2}$ $\div$ 18

$\downarrow$ $\downarrow$

_____ $\div$ _____

= _____ *estimate*

(b) $8 \div 3\dfrac{3}{5}$

$$8 \quad \div \quad 3\dfrac{3}{5}$$

$\downarrow$ Rounded $\downarrow$

$$8 \quad \div \quad 4 = 2 \quad \text{Estimate}$$

Now find the exact answer.

Reciprocals

$$8 \div 3\dfrac{3}{5} = \dfrac{8}{1} \div \dfrac{18}{5} = \dfrac{8}{1} \cdot \dfrac{5}{18} = \dfrac{20}{9} = 2\dfrac{2}{9}$$

Write 8 as $\frac{8}{1}$.

Divide out common factors *only after* you have changed to the reciprocal and are multiplying.

The estimate was 2, so the exact answer of $2\frac{2}{9}$ is reasonable.

(c) $4\dfrac{3}{8} \div 5$

$$4\dfrac{3}{8} \quad \div \quad 5$$

$\downarrow$ Rounded $\downarrow$ Reciprocals

$$4 \quad \div \quad 5 = \dfrac{4}{1} \div \dfrac{5}{1} = \dfrac{4}{1} \cdot \dfrac{1}{5} = \dfrac{4}{5} \quad \text{Estimate}$$

The exact answer is shown below.

Reciprocals

$$4\dfrac{3}{8} \div 5 = \dfrac{35}{8} \div \dfrac{5}{1} = \dfrac{35}{8} \cdot \dfrac{1}{5} = \dfrac{7}{8}$$

Write 5 as $\frac{5}{1}$.

The estimate was $\frac{4}{5}$, so the exact answer of $\frac{7}{8}$ is reasonable.

◀ *Work Problem* **3** *at the Side.*

OBJECTIVE 3 Solve application problems with mixed numbers.
The next two examples show how to solve application problems involving mixed numbers.

EXAMPLE 3 **Applying Multiplication Skills**

The local Habitat for Humanity chapter is looking for 11 contractors who will each donate $3\frac{1}{4}$ days of labor to a community building project. How many days of labor will be donated in all?

Step 1   **Read** the problem. The problem asks for the total days of labor donated by the 11 contractors.

Step 2   **Work out a plan.** Multiply the number of contractors (11) and the amount of labor that each donates ($3\frac{1}{4}$ days).

Continued on Next Page

Step 3 **Estimate** a reasonable answer. Round $3\frac{1}{4}$ days to 3 days. Multiply 3 days by 11 contractors (3 • 11) to get an estimate of 33 days.

Step 4 **Solve** the problem. Find the exact answer.

$$11 \cdot 3\frac{1}{4} = 11 \cdot \frac{13}{4}$$

$$= \frac{11}{1} \cdot \frac{13}{4} = \frac{143}{4} = 35\frac{3}{4}$$

Always check to see if the answer is close to the estimate.

Step 5 **State the answer.** The community building project will receive $35\frac{3}{4}$ days of donated labor.

Step 6 **Check.** The exact answer, $35\frac{3}{4}$ days, is close to our estimate of 33 days.

Work Problem **4** *at the Side.* ▶

4 Use the six problem-solving steps. Simplify all answers.

(a) If one automobile requires $2\frac{5}{8}$ quarts of paint, find the number of quarts needed to paint 15 cars.

(b) Clare earns $9\frac{1}{4}$ per hour. How much would she earn in $6\frac{1}{2}$ hours? Write the answer as a mixed number.

EXAMPLE 4 **Applying Division Skills**

A dome tent for backpacking requires $7\frac{1}{4}$ yards of nylon material. How many tents can be made from $65\frac{1}{4}$ yards of material?

Step 1 **Read** the problem. The problem asks how many tents can be made from $65\frac{1}{4}$ yards of material.

Step 2 **Work out a plan.** Divide the number of yards of cloth ($65\frac{1}{4}$ yd) by the number of yards needed for one tent ($7\frac{1}{4}$ yd).

Step 3 **Estimate** a reasonable answer.

$$65\frac{1}{4} \quad \div \quad 7\frac{1}{4}$$

$$\downarrow \text{ Rounded } \downarrow$$

$$65 \quad \div \quad 7 \approx 9 \text{ tents} \qquad \text{Estimate}$$

Step 4 **Solve** the problem.

$$65\frac{1}{4} \div 7\frac{1}{4} = \frac{261}{4} \div \frac{29}{4}$$

$$= \frac{\overset{9}{\cancel{261}}}{\underset{1}{\cancel{4}}} \cdot \frac{\overset{1}{\cancel{4}}}{\underset{1}{\cancel{29}}} = \frac{9}{1} = 9 \qquad \text{Matches estimate}$$

Step 5 **State the answer.** 9 tents can be made from $65\frac{1}{4}$ yards of cloth.

Step 6 **Check.** The exact answer, 9, matches our estimate.

Work Problem **5** *at the Side.* ▶

5 Use the six problem-solving steps. Simplify all answers.

(a) The manufacture of one outboard engine propeller requires $4\frac{3}{4}$ pounds of brass. How many propellers can be manufactured from 57 pounds of brass?

(b) Jack Armstrong Trucking uses $21\frac{3}{4}$ quarts of motor oil for each oil change on his diesel engine truck. Find the number of oil changes that can be made with 609 quarts of oil.

Note

When rounding mixed numbers to estimate the answer to a problem, the estimated answer usually varies somewhat from the exact answer. However, the importance of the estimated answer is that it will show you whether your exact answer is reasonable or not.

ANSWERS

4. (a) *Estimate:* 3 • 15 = 45; *Exact:* $39\frac{3}{8}$ quarts

   (b) *Estimate:* 9 • 7 = 63; *Exact:* $\$60\frac{1}{8}$

5. (a) *Estimate:* 57 ÷ 5 ≈ 11; *Exact:* 12 propellers

   (b) *Estimate:* 600 ÷ 22 ≈ 27; *Exact:* 28 oil changes

Math in the Media

Alaska Burgers

1 pound 93% lean ground beef
$\frac{1}{2}$ medium Spanish onion, minced or
  processed
4 shakes Worcestershire sauce
$\frac{1}{4}$ teaspoon allspice (1 good pinch)
$\frac{1}{2}$ teaspoon ground cumin (two good
  pinches)
Cracked black pepper
$\frac{1}{3}$ pound brick of smoked cheddar
  cheese, cut into $\frac{1}{2}$ inch slices

4 fresh, crusty onion rolls
Thick-sliced tomato and lettuce to top

Mix beef, onion, Worcestershire, all-spice, cumin, and black pepper in a bowl. Separate a quarter of the mixture. Take a slice of the smoked cheese and place it in the middle of the mixture. Form the pattie shape around the cheese filling. Patties should be no more than $\frac{3}{4}$ inch thick. Repeat with rest of mixture to have a total of 4 patties.

Heat a nonstick griddle or frying pan to medium hot. Cook burgers 5 to 6 minutes on each side. Meat should be cooked through and cheese melted. Check each burger with an instant-read thermometer for an internal temp of 170°F for well done if undercooking concerns you. Or cut into one and check the color of the meat.

Salt burgers after preparation to your taste. (Salting beef before cooking draws out juices and flavor.) Top with tomato slices and lettuce. Serves 4.

Rachael Ray is a Food Network television host, bestselling cookbook author, and the editor of her own lifestyle magazine. Rachael Ray's recipes can be found on her Web site, www.rachaelray.com, on her television show, or in one of her many cookbooks. The recipe at the side is from her book Rachael Ray: 30-Minute Meals.

1. Following the recipe, **(a)** what is the weight of one $\frac{1}{2}$-inch slice of cheese, and **(b)** what is the thickness of a $\frac{1}{3}$-pound brick of smoked cheddar cheese?

2. According to the recipe, **(a)** how many teaspoons of allspice are in 8 good pinches, and **(b)** how many teaspoons of ground cumin are in 7 good pinches?

3. Suppose you are preparing Alaska Burgers for 18 guests. By what factor will you change the ingredient amounts?

4. You know that of the 15 guests at your next party, 5 large eaters will eat $1\frac{1}{2}$ burgers each, 5 children will eat $\frac{1}{2}$ burger each, and the rest of the guests will each eat 1 burger. **(a)** How many burgers will you need, and **(b)** by what factor will you change the ingredient amounts?

5. Fill in the blanks with the ingredient amounts needed to make 9 servings of Alaska Burgers

   Lean ground beef   _____
   Spanish onions   _____
   Worcestershire sauce _____
   Allspice   _____
   Ground cumin   _____
   Cheddar cheese   _____

6. If you have $5\frac{3}{4}$ pounds of beef, how many servings of Alaska Burgers can be prepared?

First estimate the answer. Then multiply to find the exact answer. Simplify all answers.
See Example 1.

1. *Exact:*

$$4\frac{1}{2} \cdot 1\frac{3}{4}$$

Estimate:

____ • ____ = ____

2. *Exact:*

$$2\frac{1}{2} \cdot 2\frac{1}{4}$$

Estimate:

____ • ____ = ____

 3. *Exact:*

$$1\frac{2}{3} \cdot 2\frac{7}{10}$$

Estimate:

____ • ____ = ____

4. *Exact:*

$$4\frac{1}{2} \cdot 2\frac{1}{4}$$

Estimate:

____ • ____ = ____

 5. *Exact:*

$$3\frac{1}{9} \cdot 1\frac{2}{7}$$

Estimate:

____ • ____ = ____

6. *Exact:*

$$6\frac{1}{4} \cdot 3\frac{1}{5}$$

Estimate:

____ • ____ = ____

7. *Exact:*

$$8 \cdot 6\frac{1}{4}$$

Estimate:

____ • ____ = ____

8. *Exact:*

$$6 \cdot 2\frac{1}{3}$$

Estimate:

____ • ____ = ____

9. *Exact:*

$$4\frac{1}{2} \cdot 2\frac{1}{5} \cdot 5$$

Estimate:

____ • ____ • ____ = ____

10. *Exact:*

$$5\frac{1}{2} \cdot 1\frac{1}{3} \cdot 2\frac{1}{4}$$

Estimate:

____ • ____ • ____ = ____

11. *Exact:*

$$3 \cdot 1\frac{1}{2} \cdot 2\frac{2}{3}$$

Estimate:

____ • ____ • ____ = ____

12. *Exact:*

$$\frac{2}{3} \cdot 3\frac{2}{3} \cdot \frac{6}{11}$$

Estimate:

____ • ____ • ____ = ____

First estimate the answer. Then divide to find the exact answer. Simplify all answers.
See Example 2.

 13. *Exact:*

$$1\frac{1}{4} \div 3\frac{3}{4}$$

Estimate:

____ ÷ ____ = ____

14. *Exact:*

$$1\frac{1}{8} \div 2\frac{1}{4}$$

Estimate:

____ ÷ ____ = ____

15. *Exact:*

$$2\frac{1}{2} \div 3$$

Estimate:

____ ÷ ____ = ____

16. *Exact:*

$$2\frac{3}{4} \div 2$$

Estimate:

____ ÷ ____ = ____

17. *Exact:*

$$9 \div 2\frac{1}{2}$$

Estimate:

____ ÷ ____ = ____

18. *Exact:*

$$5 \div 1\frac{7}{8}$$

Estimate:

____ ÷ ____ = ____

19. *Exact:*

$$\frac{5}{8} \div 1\frac{1}{2}$$

Estimate:

____ ÷ ____ = ____

20. *Exact:*

$$\frac{3}{4} \div 2\frac{1}{2}$$

Estimate:

____ ÷ ____ = ____

21. *Exact:*

$$1\frac{7}{8} \div 6\frac{1}{4}$$

Estimate:

____ ÷ ____ = ____

22. *Exact:*

$$8\frac{2}{5} \div 3\frac{1}{2}$$

Estimate:

____ ÷ ____ = ____

23. *Exact:*

$$5\frac{2}{3} \div 6$$

Estimate:

____ ÷ ____ = ____

24. *Exact:*

$$5\frac{3}{4} \div 2$$

Estimate:

____ ÷ ____ = ____

For Exercises 25–42, first estimate the answer. Then solve each application problem by using the six problem-solving steps. Simplify all answers. See Examples 3 and 4. Use the recipe for Carrot Cake Cupcakes to work Exercises 25–28.

CARROT CAKE CUPCAKES

12 paper bake cups
$1\frac{3}{4}$ cups flour
1 cup packed brown sugar
1 tsp. baking powder
1 tsp. baking soda
1 tsp. ground cinnamon
$\frac{1}{2}$ tsp. salt
1 cup shredded carrots
$\frac{3}{4}$ cup applesauce

$\frac{1}{3}$ cup vegetable oil
1 large egg
$\frac{1}{2}$ tsp. vanilla extract
1 container (16 oz.) ready-to-
    spread cream cheese frosting
Shredded coconut,
    tinted green
3 oz. Jelly Belly jelly beans,
    Orange Sherbet flavor

Preheat oven to 350° F. Place 12 bake cups in a muffin pan; set aside. In a large bowl, using a wire whisk, stir together flour, brown sugar, baking powder, baking soda, cinnamon, and salt. In a medium bowl, combine carrots, applesauce, oil, egg, and vanilla until blended. Add carrot mixture to flour mixture, stir well. Spoon batter into bake cups, filling $\frac{2}{3}$ full. Bake until toothpick inserted in center comes out clean,

20–25 minutes. Cool cupcakes in pan 10 minutes; remove to wire rack and cool completely. Frost with cream cheese frosting. To make carrot design on cupcakes, place gourmet Jelly Belly jelly beans in a carrot shape on each cupcake, top with green coconut for carrot top. Makes 12 cupcakes.

25. If 30 cupcakes are baked ($2\frac{1}{2}$ times the recipe), find the amount of each ingredient.

    (a) Applesauce

      Estimate:

      Exact:

    (b) Salt

      Estimate:

      Exact:

    (c) Flour

      Estimate:

      Exact:

26. If 18 cupcakes are baked ($1\frac{1}{2}$ times the recipe), find the amount of each ingredient.

    (a) Flour

      Estimate:

      Exact:

    (b) Applesauce

      Estimate:

      Exact:

    (c) Vegetable oil

      Estimate:

      Exact:

27. How much of each ingredient is needed if you bake one-half of the recipe?

(a) Vanilla extract

Estimate:

Exact:

(b) Applesauce

Estimate:

Exact:

(c) Flour

Estimate:

Exact:

28. How much of each ingredient is needed if you bake one-third of the recipe?

(a) Flour

Estimate:

Exact:

(b) Salt

Estimate:

Exact:

(c) Applesauce

Estimate:

Exact:

29. A new condominium conversion project requires $11\frac{3}{4}$ gallons of paint for each unit. How many units can be painted with 1316 gallons of paint?

Estimate:

Exact:

30. According to an old English system of time units, a moment is one and one-half minutes. How many moments are there in an 8-hour work day? (8 hours = 480 minutes). (*Source:* hightechscience.org/funfacts.htm)

Estimate:

Exact:

31. A manufacturer of floor jacks is ordering steel tubing to make the handles for the jack shown below. How much steel tubing is needed to make 135 of these jacks? The symbol for inches is ″, as in 5″ means 5 inches. (*Source:* Harbor Freight Tools.)

Estimate:

Exact:

32. A wheelbarrow manufacturer uses handles made of hardwood. Find the amount of wood that is necessary to make 182 handles. The longest dimension shown in the advertisement below is the handle length. (*Source:* Harbor Freight Tools.)

Estimate:

Exact:

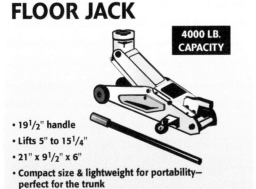

2-TON COMPACT FLOOR JACK   LOT NO. 36119

4000 LB. CAPACITY

- 19¹/₂″ handle
- Lifts 5″ to 15¹/₄″
- 21″ x 9¹/₂″ x 6″
- Compact size & lightweight for portability— perfect for the trunk

6.0 CUBIC FT.   LOT NO. 46852
WHEEL BARROW

- Steel construction with hardwood handles
- 14″ tubeless pneumatic tire
- Fully rolled edge for added tray strength
- Overall dimensions: 61¹/₂″ L x 27″ W x 24.9″ H

33. Write the three steps for multiplying mixed numbers. Use your own words.

34. Refer to Exercise 33. In your own words, write the additional step that must be added to the rule for multiplying mixed numbers to make it the rule for dividing mixed numbers.

35. A tire manufacturer uses $20\frac{3}{4}$ pounds of rubber to make a tire. Find the number of tires that can be manufactured with 51,460 pounds of rubber.

Estimate:

Exact:

36. The manager of the flooring department at The Home Depot determines that each apartment unit requires $62\frac{1}{2}$ square yards of carpet. Find the number of apartment units that can be carpeted with 6750 square yards of carpet.

Estimate:

Exact:

37. Mother Nature, manufacturer of bird feeders, cuts spacers from a tube that is $9\frac{3}{4}$ inches long. How many spacers can be cut from the tube if each spacer must be $\frac{3}{4}$ inch thick?

Estimate:

Exact:

38. A building contractor must move 12 tons of sand. If his truck can carry $\frac{3}{4}$ ton of sand, how many trips must he make to move the sand?

Estimate:

Exact:

Use the information on bottle jacks in the advertisement to answer Exercises 39–40. The " symbol is for inches.

12 TON HEAVY DUTY INDUSTRIAL BOTTLE JACKS

CENTRAL HYDRAULICS®

These all-purpose hydraulic jacks easily handle lifting jobs up to 12 tons, even at 45 degree and 90 degree angles. Rugged steel construction. Jacks feature twist tops for even more height. Certified to meet ASME standards. Base dimensions: 5-1/4" x 5-3/8"

17-3/4" MAXIMUM HEIGHT

Item 93378

STANDARD JACK

15-1/16" MAXIMUM HEIGHT

Item 93376

LOW PROFILE

$1999 REGULAR PRICE $29.99

SAVE 33%

39. A mechanic needs a hydraulic lift that will raise a car 4 times as high as the standard jack shown.

  (a) How high must it lift?

  (b) Will a mechanic 6 feet tall be able to fit under the vehicle without bending down? *Hint:* 1 ft = 12 in.

  (a) *Estimate:*   **(b)**

      Exact:

40. A race car driver needs a jack that will raise a vehicle only $\frac{1}{3}$ as high as the low-profile jack pictured.

  (a) How high must it lift?

  (b) Will a 6-inch part fit under the car?

  (a) *Estimate:*   **(b)**

      Exact:

41. A grape grower uses $6\frac{3}{4}$ gallons of a chemical for each acre of grapes. If she has $25\frac{1}{2}$ acres of grapes, how many gallons of the chemical are needed?

Estimate:

Exact:

42. A flooring contractor needs $24\frac{2}{7}$ boxes of tile to cover a kitchen floor. If there are 24 homes in a subdivision, how many boxes of tile are needed to cover all of the floors?

Estimate:

Exact:

Study Skills

USING STUDY CARDS REVISITED

This is the second part of the Study Cards activity. As you get further into a chapter, you can choose particular problems that will serve as a good test review. Here are two more types of study cards that will help you.

When you are doing your homework and find yourself saying, "This is really hard," or "I'm having trouble with this," make a **tough problem** study card! On the front, write out the procedure to work the type of problem *in words*. If there are special notes (like what *not* to do), include them. On the back, work at least one example; make sure you label what you are doing.

OBJECTIVES

1 Create study cards for difficult problems.

2 Create study cards of quiz problems.

Tough Problems Card

Front of Card

Warning: Division is NOT commutative. The order in which you write the numbers DOES matter.

Example: $1\frac{1}{3} \div 4 = \frac{1\!\!\!/4}{3} \cdot \frac{1}{4} = \frac{1}{3}$ ← Very different answers!

But $4 \div 1\frac{1}{3} = \frac{1\!\!\!/4}{1} \cdot \frac{3}{4\!\!\!/1} = \frac{3}{1} = 3$ ←

In an application problem, do NOT assume the numbers are given in the correct order. Use estimation to check that the answer is <u>reasonable</u>!

Back of Card

Maite painted 4 windows using $1\frac{1}{3}$ cans of paint. How much paint did she use on each window?

Try $4 \div 1\frac{1}{3}$

↓   ↓ (round)

$4 \div 1 = 4$ cans on each window ←— Estimate

<u>Not</u> reasonable — she only used $1\frac{1}{3}$ cans in all!

Need to find: paint on each window

↓   ↓   ↓

$1\frac{1}{3}$ cans $\div$ $4 = \frac{1\!\!\!/4}{3} \cdot \frac{1}{4\!\!\!/1} = \frac{1}{3}$ can

Reasonable!

Choose three types of difficult problems, and work them out on study cards. Be sure to put the words for solving the problem on one side and the worked problem on the other side.

◄◄◄ **Now Try This**

Practice Quiz Cards

Make up a few **quiz cards** for each type of problem you learn, and use them to prepare for a test. Choose two or three problems from the different sections of the chapter. Be sure you don't just choose the easiest problems! Put the problem **with the direction words** (like *solve, simplify, estimate*) on the front, and work the problem on the back. If you like, put the page number from the text there, too. When you review, you work the problem on a separate paper, and check it by looking at the back.

Front of Card

Solve this application problem.

Tiffany's monthly income is $1275. She spends $\frac{2}{5}$ of her income on rent and utilities. How much does she pay for rent and utilities?

Back of Card

Proper fraction followed by "of" indicates multiplication.

She spends $\frac{2}{5}$ of her income

$$\frac{2}{5} \cdot 1275 = \frac{2}{\underset{1}{\cancel{5}}} \cdot \frac{\overset{255}{\cancel{1275}}}{1} = \frac{510}{1} = 510$$

Tiffany spends $510 on rent and utilities.

Why Are Study Cards Brain Friendly?

First, making the study cards is an **active technique** that really gets your dendrites growing. You have to make decisions about what is most important and how to put it on the card. This kind of thinking is more in depth than just memorizing, and as a result, you will understand the concepts better and remember them longer.

Second, the cards are **visually appealing** (if you write neatly and try some color). Your brain responds to pleasant visual images, and again, you will remember longer and may even be able to "picture in your mind" how your cards look. This will help you during tests.

Third, because study cards are small and portable, you can review them easily whenever you have a few minutes. Even while you're waiting for a bus or have a few minutes between classes you can take out your cards and read them to yourself. Your **brain really benefits from repetition;** each time you review your cards your dendrites are growing thicker and stronger. After a while, the information will become automatic and you will remember it for a long time.

2.9 ▶▶▶ Adding and Subtracting Like Fractions

In **Chapter 2** we looked at the basics of fractions and then practiced with multiplication and division of fractions and mixed numbers. In this chapter we will work with addition and subtraction of fractions and mixed numbers.

OBJECTIVE **1** **Define like and unlike fractions.**   Fractions with the same denominators are **like fractions.** Fractions with different denominators are **unlike fractions.**

OBJECTIVES

1 **Define like and unlike fractions.**

2 **Add like fractions.**

3 **Subtract like fractions.**

EXAMPLE 1   **Identifying Like and Unlike Fractions**

(a) $\frac{3}{4}, \frac{1}{4}, \frac{5}{4}, \frac{6}{4},$ and $\frac{4}{4}$ are **like** fractions.

↑ ↑ ↑ ↑   ↑ —— All denominators are the same.

(b) $\frac{7}{12}$ and $\frac{12}{7}$ are **unlike** fractions.

↑   ↑ —— Denominators are different.

Note
Like fractions have the **same** denominator.

Work Problem **1** *at the Side.* ▶

OBJECTIVE **2** **Add like fractions.**   The figures below show you how to add the fractions $\frac{2}{7}$ and $\frac{4}{7}$.

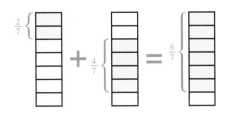

As the figures show,

$$\frac{2}{7} + \frac{4}{7} = \frac{6}{7}$$

Add like fractions as follows.

Adding Like Fractions

Step 1   Add the numerators to find the numerator of the sum.

Step 2   Write the denominator of the like fractions as the denominator of the sum.

Step 3   Write the sum in lowest terms.

1 Next to each pair of fractions write *like* or *unlike.*

(a) $\frac{2}{5}$ $\frac{3}{5}$ _____

(b) $\frac{2}{3}$ $\frac{3}{4}$ _____

(c) $\frac{7}{12}$ $\frac{11}{12}$ _____

(d) $\frac{3}{8}$ $\frac{3}{16}$ _____

ANSWERS

1. (a) like   **(b)** unlike   **(c)** like   **(d)** unlike

2 Add and write the sums in lowest terms.

(a) $\dfrac{3}{8} + \dfrac{1}{8}$

(b) $\dfrac{2}{9}$
  $+\dfrac{5}{9}$

(c) $\dfrac{3}{16} + \dfrac{1}{16}$

(d) $\dfrac{3}{10} + \dfrac{1}{10} + \dfrac{4}{10}$

EXAMPLE 2   **Adding Like Fractions**

Add and write the sum in lowest terms.

(a) $\dfrac{1}{5} + \dfrac{2}{5}$

Add numerators.

$$\dfrac{1}{5} + \dfrac{2}{5} = \dfrac{\overbrace{1+2}}{5} = \dfrac{3}{5} \leftarrow \text{Same denominator}$$

(b) $\dfrac{1}{12} + \dfrac{7}{12} + \dfrac{1}{12}$ | Fractions are ready to be added if they are *like* fractions.

Add numerators.

Step 1 $\dfrac{\overbrace{1+7+1}}{12}$

Step 2 $= \dfrac{9}{12} \begin{array}{l}\leftarrow \text{Sum of numerators}\\ \leftarrow \text{Same denominator}\end{array}$

Step 3 $= \dfrac{9 \div 3}{12 \div 3} = \dfrac{3}{4}$ In lowest terms

> **CAUTION**
> Fractions may be added **only** if they have like denominators.

◀ *Work Problem* **2** *at the Side.*

OBJECTIVE 3 Subtract like fractions.   The figures below show $\frac{7}{8}$ broken into $\frac{4}{8}$ and $\frac{3}{8}$.

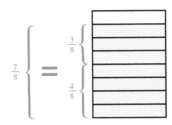

Subtracting $\frac{3}{8}$ from $\frac{7}{8}$ gives the answer $\frac{4}{8}$, or

$$\dfrac{7}{8} - \dfrac{3}{8} = \dfrac{4}{8}$$

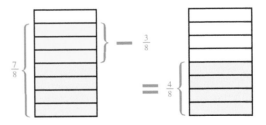

ANSWERS

2. (a) $\dfrac{1}{2}$ (b) $\dfrac{7}{9}$ (c) $\dfrac{1}{4}$ (d) $\dfrac{4}{5}$

Write $\frac{4}{8}$ in lowest terms.

$$\frac{7}{8} - \frac{3}{8} = \frac{4 \div 4}{8 \div 4} = \frac{1}{2}$$

The steps for subtracting like fractions are very similar to those for adding like fractions.

> **Subtracting Like Fractions**
>
> **Step 1** Subtract the numerators to find the numerator of the difference.
>
> **Step 2** Write the denominator of the like fractions as the denominator of the difference.
>
> **Step 3** Write the answer in lowest terms.

EXAMPLE 3 **Subtracting Like Fractions**

Find the difference and simplify the answer.

(a) $\dfrac{15}{16} - \dfrac{3}{16}$

Subtract numerators.

Step 1 $\dfrac{15}{16} - \dfrac{3}{16} = \dfrac{\overbrace{15 - 3}}{16}$

Step 2 $= \dfrac{12}{16}$ ← Difference of numerators
  ← Same denominator

Step 3 $= \dfrac{12 \div 4}{16 \div 4} = \dfrac{3}{4}$ In lowest terms

(b) $\dfrac{13}{4} - \dfrac{6}{4}$ Fractions are ready to be subtracted if they are *like* fractions.

Subtract numerators.

$\dfrac{13}{4} - \dfrac{6}{4} = \dfrac{\overbrace{13 - 6}}{4}$ ← Difference of numerators
  ← Same denominator

$= \dfrac{7}{4}$

To simplify the answer, write $\frac{7}{4}$ as a mixed number.

$$\frac{7}{4} = 1\frac{3}{4}$$

> **CAUTION**
> Fractions may be subtracted **only** if they have like denominators.

Work Problem ③ *at the Side.* ▶

3 Find the difference and simplify.

(a) $\dfrac{5}{6} - \dfrac{1}{6}$

(b) $\dfrac{16}{10}$
  $-\dfrac{7}{10}$

(c) $\dfrac{15}{3} - \dfrac{5}{3}$

(d) $\dfrac{25}{32}$
  $-\dfrac{6}{32}$

2.9 ▶▶▶ **Exercises**

Find the sum and simplify the answer. See Example 2.

1. $\dfrac{3}{8} + \dfrac{2}{8}$

2. $\dfrac{1}{5} + \dfrac{3}{5}$

3. $\dfrac{2}{6} + \dfrac{3}{6}$

4. $\dfrac{9}{11} + \dfrac{1}{11}$

 5. $\dfrac{1}{4} + \dfrac{1}{4}$

6. $\dfrac{1}{14} + \dfrac{1}{14}$

 7. $\begin{array}{r} \dfrac{9}{10} \\ + \dfrac{3}{10} \\ \hline \end{array}$

8. $\begin{array}{r} \dfrac{13}{12} \\ + \dfrac{5}{12} \\ \hline \end{array}$

9. $\begin{array}{r} \dfrac{2}{9} \\ + \dfrac{1}{9} \\ \hline \end{array}$

10. $\dfrac{7}{12} + \dfrac{3}{12}$

11. $\dfrac{6}{20} + \dfrac{4}{20} + \dfrac{3}{20}$

12. $\dfrac{1}{7} + \dfrac{2}{7} + \dfrac{3}{7}$

13. $\dfrac{4}{15} + \dfrac{2}{15} + \dfrac{5}{15}$

14. $\dfrac{5}{11} + \dfrac{1}{11} + \dfrac{4}{11}$

15. $\dfrac{3}{8} + \dfrac{7}{8} + \dfrac{2}{8}$

16. $\dfrac{4}{9} + \dfrac{1}{9} + \dfrac{7}{9}$

17. $\dfrac{2}{54} + \dfrac{8}{54} + \dfrac{12}{54}$

18. $\dfrac{7}{64} + \dfrac{15}{64} + \dfrac{20}{64}$

Find the difference and simplify the answer. See Example 3.

 19. $\dfrac{7}{8} - \dfrac{4}{8}$

20. $\dfrac{2}{3} - \dfrac{1}{3}$

21. $\dfrac{10}{11} - \dfrac{4}{11}$

22. $\dfrac{4}{5} - \dfrac{3}{5}$

23. $\dfrac{9}{10} - \dfrac{3}{10}$

24. $\dfrac{7}{14} - \dfrac{3}{14}$

25. $\begin{array}{r} \dfrac{31}{21} \\ - \dfrac{7}{21} \\ \hline \end{array}$

26. $\begin{array}{r} \dfrac{43}{24} \\ - \dfrac{13}{24} \\ \hline \end{array}$

 27. $\begin{array}{r} \dfrac{27}{40} \\ - \dfrac{19}{40} \\ \hline \end{array}$

28. $\begin{array}{r} \dfrac{38}{55} \\ - \dfrac{16}{55} \\ \hline \end{array}$

29. $\dfrac{47}{36} - \dfrac{5}{36}$

30. $\dfrac{76}{45} - \dfrac{21}{45}$

31. $\dfrac{73}{60} - \dfrac{7}{60}$

32. $\dfrac{181}{100} - \dfrac{31}{100}$

33. In your own words, write an explanation of how to add like fractions. Consider using three steps in your explanation.

34. Describe in your own words the difference between *like* fractions and *unlike* fractions. Give three examples of each type.

Solve each application problem. Write answers in lowest terms.

35. The Fair Oaks Save the Bluffs Committee raised $\frac{2}{9}$ of their target goal last year and another $\frac{5}{9}$ of the goal this year. What fraction of their goal has been raised?

36. After an initial payment to a winner at an arcade fundraiser, the organization still owed the winner $\frac{7}{10}$ of her total winnings. If the organization pays the winner another $\frac{3}{10}$ of the winnings, what fraction is still owed?

37. Robert Hernandez has saved $\frac{3}{7}$ of the amount needed for his children's college education fund. In the next five years he plans to save another $\frac{2}{7}$ of the total amount needed. What fraction of the amount needed will he have saved?

38. Phil Fravesi, general contractor, completes $\frac{3}{12}$ of a hobby and toy train addition to his home in April. In May, he completes another $\frac{5}{12}$ of the project. What portion of the project has he completed?

39. An organic farmer purchased $\frac{9}{10}$ acre of land one year and $\frac{3}{10}$ acre the next year. She then planted carrots on $\frac{7}{10}$ acre of the land and squash on the remainder. How much land is planted in squash?

40. A forester planted $\frac{5}{12}$ acre in seedlings in the morning and $\frac{11}{12}$ acre in the afternoon. If $\frac{7}{12}$ acre of seedlings were destroyed by frost, how many acres of seedlings remained?

Study Skills

▶▶▶ MANAGING YOUR TIME

OBJECTIVES

1 Create a semester schedule.

2 Create a "to do" list.

Why Are These Techniques Brain Friendly?

Your brain appreciates some order. It enjoys a little routine, for example, choosing the same study time and place each day. You will find that you quickly settle in to your reading or homework.

Also, your brain **functions better when you are calm.** Too much rushing around at the last minute to get your homework and studying done sends hostile chemicals to your brain and makes it more difficult for you to learn and remember. So, a little planning can really pay off.

Building rest into your schedule is good for your brain. Remember, it takes time for dendrites to grow.

We've suggested using color on your calendars. This too, is brain friendly. Remember, your brain **likes pleasant colors and visual material** that are nice to look at. Messy and hard to read calendars will not be helpful, and you probably won't look at them often.

Many college students find themselves juggling a difficult schedule and multiple responsibilities. Perhaps you are going to school, working part time, and managing family demands. Here are some tips to help you develop good time management skills and habits.

▶ **Read the syllabus for each class.** Check on class policies, such as attendance, late homework, and make-up tests. Find out how you are graded. Keep the syllabus in your notebook.

▶ **Make a semester or quarter calendar.** Put test dates and major due dates for *all* your classes on the same calendar. That way you will see which weeks are the really busy ones. Try using a different color pen for each class. Your brain responds well to the use of color. A semester calendar is on the next page.

▶ **Make a weekly schedule.** After you fill in your classes and other regular responsibilities (such as work, picking up kids from school, etc.), block off some study periods during the day that you can guarantee you will use for studying. Aim for 2 hours of study for each 1 hour you are in class.

▶ **Make "To Do" lists.** Then use them by crossing off the tasks as you complete them. You might even number them in the order they need to be done (most important ones first).

▶ **Break big assignments into smaller chunks.** They won't seem so big that way. Make deadlines for each small part so you stay on schedule.

▶ **Give yourself small breaks in your studying.** Do not try to study for hours at a time! Your brain needs rest between periods of learning. Try to give yourself a 10 minute break each hour or so. You will learn more and remember it longer.

▶ **If you get off schedule, just try to get back on schedule tomorrow.** We all slip from time to time. All is not lost! Make a new "To Do" list and start doing the most important things first.

▶ **Get help when you need it.** Talk with your instructor during office hours. Also, most colleges have some kind of Learning Center, tutoring center, or counseling office. If you feel lost and overwhelmed, ask for help. Someone can help you decide what to do first and what to spend your time on right away.

Which two or three of the suggestions above will you try this week? How do you think they will help you?

1. _____

2. _____

3. _____

SEMESTER CALENDAR

WEEK	MON	TUES	WED	THUR	FRI	SAT	SUN
1							
2							
3							
4							
5							
6							
7							
8							
9							
10							
11							
12							
13							
14							
15							
16							

2.10 ▶▶▶ Least Common Multiples

Only *like* fractions can be added or subtracted. Because of this, we must rewrite *unlike* fractions as *like* fractions before we can add or subtract them.

OBJECTIVE 1 Find the least common multiple. We can rewrite unlike fractions as like fractions by finding the *least common multiple* of the denominators.

> **Least Common Multiple (LCM)**
>
> The **least common multiple (LCM)** of two whole numbers is the smallest whole number divisible by both of those numbers.

EXAMPLE 1 Finding the Least Common Multiple

Find the least common multiple of 6 and 9.

First, find the multiples of 6.

$$\underbrace{6 \cdot 1}_{6}, \quad \underbrace{6 \cdot 2}_{12}, \quad \underbrace{6 \cdot 3}_{18}, \quad \underbrace{6 \cdot 4}_{24}, \quad \underbrace{6 \cdot 5}_{30}, \quad \underbrace{6 \cdot 6}_{36}, \quad \underbrace{6 \cdot 7}_{42}, \quad \underbrace{6 \cdot 8}_{48}, \ldots$$

(The three dots at the end of the list show that the list continues in the same pattern without stopping.) Now, find the multiples of 9.

$$\underbrace{9 \cdot 1}_{9}, \quad \underbrace{9 \cdot 2}_{18}, \quad \underbrace{9 \cdot 3}_{27}, \quad \underbrace{9 \cdot 4}_{36}, \quad \underbrace{9 \cdot 5}_{45}, \quad \underbrace{9 \cdot 6}_{54}, \quad \underbrace{9 \cdot 7}_{63}, \quad \underbrace{9 \cdot 8}_{72}, \ldots$$

The smallest number found in *both* lists is 18, so 18 is the **least common multiple** of 6 and 9; the number 18 is the smallest whole number divisible by both 6 and 9.

Multiples of 6: 6, 12, **18**, 24, 30, 36, 42, 48, . . .

Multiples of 9: 9, **18**, 27, 36, 45, 54, 63, 72, . . .

> The *smallest* number in *both* lists is the LCM.

18 is the smallest number found in both lists. **18** is the least common multiple (LCM) of 6 and 9.

◀ *Work Problem* **1** *at the Side.*

1 (a) List the multiples of 5.

5, ——, ——, ——,

——, ——, ——,

——, . . .

(b) List the multiples of 8.

8, ——, ——, ——,

——, ——, ——, . . .

(c) Find the least common multiple of 5 and 8.

OBJECTIVE 2 Find the least common multiple using multiples of the largest number. There are several ways to find the least common multiple. If the numbers are small, the least common multiple can often be found by inspection. Can you think of a number that can be divided evenly by both 3 and 4? The number 12 will work; it is the least common multiple of the numbers 3 and 4. A method that works well to find the least common multiple is to write multiples of the larger number.

In this case, 4 is larger than 3, so write the multiples of 4.

$$4, 8, 12, 16, 20, \ldots$$

Now, check each multiple of 4 to see if it is divisible by 3.

4 is *not* divisible by 3
8 is *not* divisible by 3
12 *is* divisible by 3

The first multiple of 4 that is divisible by 3 is 12, so 12 is the least common multiple of 3 and 4.

ANSWERS

1. (a) 10, 15, 20, 25, 30, 35, 40, . . .
   (b) 16, 24, 32, 40, 48, 56, . . .
   (c) 40

EXAMPLE 2   **Finding the Least Common Multiple**

Use multiples of the larger number to find the least common multiple of 6 and 9.

We start by writing the first few multiples of 9.

Multiples of 9

9, 18, 27, 36, 45, 54, . . .

Now, we check each multiple of 9 to see if it is divisible by 6. The first multiple of 9 that is divisible by 6 is 18.

9, **18**, 27, 36, 45, 54, . . .

First multiple divisible by 6, because $18 \div 6 = 3$

The least common multiple of the numbers 6 and 9 is 18.

◀ *Work Problem* 2 *at the Side.*

OBJECTIVE 3 **Find the least common multiple using prime factorization.**   Example 2 shows how to find the least common multiple of two numbers by making a list of the multiples of the *larger* number. Although this method works well if both numbers are fairly small, it is usually easier to find the least common multiple for larger numbers by using *prime factorization,* as shown in the next example.

EXAMPLE 3   **Applying Prime Factorization Knowledge**

Use prime factorization to find the least common multiple of 9 and 12.

We start by finding the prime factorization of each number.

Factors of 9

$9 = 3 \cdot 3$
$12 = 2 \cdot 2 \cdot 3$ $LCM = 3 \cdot 3 \cdot 2 \cdot 2 = 36$

Factors of 12

Check to see that 36 is divisible by 9 (yes) and by 12 (yes). The smallest whole number divisible by both 9 and 12 is 36.

CAUTION

Notice that we did *not* have to repeat the factors that 9 and 12 have in common. In this case, the **3** in $2 \cdot 2 \cdot 3 = 12$ was *not* used because 3 is already included in $3 \cdot 3 = 9$.

Work Problem 3 *at the Side.* ▶

2   Use multiples of the larger number to find the least common multiple in each set of numbers.

(a) 2 and 5

(b) 3 and 9

(c) 6 and 8

(d) 4 and 7

3   Use prime factorization to find the LCM for each pair of numbers.

(a) 15 and 18

(b) 12 and 20

4 Find the least common multiple of the denominators in each set of fractions.

(a) $\dfrac{3}{8}$ and $\dfrac{6}{5}$

(b) $\dfrac{5}{6}$ and $\dfrac{1}{14}$

(c) $\dfrac{4}{9}, \dfrac{5}{18},$ and $\dfrac{7}{24}$

5 Find the least common multiple for each set of numbers.

(a) 4, 8, 9

(b) 3, 6, 8

(c) 9, 36, 48

(d) 15, 20, 30, 40

EXAMPLE 4 **Using Prime Factorization**

Find the least common multiple of 12, 18, and 20.

Find the prime factorization of each number. Then use the prime factors to build the LCM.

$$12 = 2 \cdot 2 \cdot 3$$
$$18 = 2 \cdot 3 \cdot 3 \qquad \text{LCM} = 2 \cdot 2 \cdot 3 \cdot 3 \cdot 5 = 180$$
$$20 = 2 \cdot 2 \cdot 5$$

Check to see that 180 is divisible by 12 (yes) and by 18 (yes) and by 20 (yes). This smallest whole number divisible by 12, 18, and 20 is 180.

> **Note**
> The LCM did *not* repeat the factors that 12, 18, and 20 have in common.

◀ *Work Problem* **4** *at the Side.*

EXAMPLE 5 **Finding the Least Common Multiple**

Find the least common multiple for each set of numbers.

(a) 5, 6, 35
Find the prime factorization for each number.

$$5 = 5$$
$$6 = 2 \cdot 3 \qquad \text{LCM} = 2 \cdot 3 \cdot 5 \cdot 7 = 210$$
$$35 = 5 \cdot 7$$

The least common multiple of 5, 6, and 35 is 210.

(b) 10, 20, 24
Find the prime factorization for each number.

$$10 = 2 \cdot 5$$
$$20 = 2 \cdot 2 \cdot 5 \qquad \text{LCM} = 2 \cdot 2 \cdot 2 \cdot 3 \cdot 5 = 120$$
$$24 = 2 \cdot 2 \cdot 2 \cdot 3$$

The least common multiple of 10, 20, and 24 is 120.

◀ *Work Problem* **5** *at the Side.*

OBJECTIVE **4** **Find the least common multiple using an alternative method.** Some people like the following *alternative method* for finding the least common multiple for larger numbers. Try both methods, and *use the one you prefer.* As a review, a list of the first few prime numbers follows.

$$2, 3, 5, 7, 11, 13, 17$$

ANSWERS

4. (a)
$8 = 2 \cdot 2 \cdot 2 \qquad \text{LCM} = 2 \cdot 2 \cdot 2 \cdot 5 = 40$
$5 = 5$

(b)
$6 = 2 \cdot 3 \qquad \text{LCM} = 2 \cdot 3 \cdot 7 = 42$
$14 = 2 \cdot 7$

(c)
$9 = 3 \cdot 3 \qquad \text{LCM} = 2 \cdot 2 \cdot 2 \cdot 3 \cdot 3 = 72$
$18 = 2 \cdot 3 \cdot 3$
$24 = 2 \cdot 2 \cdot 2 \cdot 3$

5. (a) 72 **(b)** 24 **(c)** 144 **(d)** 120

EXAMPLE 6 **Alternative Method for Finding the Least Common Multiple**

Find the least common multiple for each set of numbers.

(a) 14 and 21

Start by trying to divide 14 and 21 by the first prime number in the list of prime numbers: 2, 3, 5, 7, 11, 13, and 17. Use the following shortcut. Divide by 2, the first prime.

$$2 \; | \underline{14 \quad 2\!\!\!/1}$$
$$ 7 \quad 21$$

Because 21 cannot be divided evenly by 2, cross out 21 and bring it down. Divide by 3, the second prime.

$$2 \; | \underline{14 \quad 2\!\!\!/1}$$
$$3 \; | \underline{\;7\!\!\!/ \quad 21}$$
$$ 7 \quad 7$$

Since 7 cannot be divided evenly by the third prime, 5, skip 5 and divide by the next prime, 7.
Divide by 7, the fourth prime.

Multiply these prime numbers to get the LCM.

$$2 \; | \underline{14 \quad 2\!\!\!/1}$$
$$3 \; | \underline{\;7\!\!\!/ \quad 21}$$
$$7 \; | \underline{\;7 \quad 7}$$
$$ 1 \quad 1 \qquad \text{All quotients are 1.}$$

When all quotients are 1, multiply the prime numbers on the left side.

$$\text{least common multiple} = 2 \cdot 3 \cdot 7 = 42$$

The least common multiple of 14 and 21 is 42.

(b) 6, 15, 18

Divide by 2.

$$2 \; | \underline{6 \quad 1\!\!\!/5 \quad 18}$$
$$ 3 \quad 15 \quad 9 \qquad \text{Cross out 15 and bring it down.}$$

Divide by 3.

$$2 \; | \underline{6 \quad 1\!\!\!/5 \quad 18}$$
$$3 \; | \underline{3 \quad 15 \quad 9}$$
$$ 1 \quad 5 \quad 3$$

Divide by 3 again, since the remaining 3 can be divided.

$$2 \; | \underline{6 \quad 1\!\!\!/5 \quad 18}$$
$$3 \; | \underline{3 \quad 15 \quad 9}$$
$$3 \; | \underline{1\!\!\!/ \quad 5\!\!\!/ \quad 3}$$
$$ 1 \quad 5 \quad 1$$

Finally, divide by 5.

$$2 \; | \underline{6 \quad 1\!\!\!/5 \quad 18}$$
$$3 \; | \underline{3 \quad 15 \quad 9}$$
$$3 \; | \underline{1\!\!\!/ \quad 5\!\!\!/ \quad 3}$$
$$5 \; | \underline{1\!\!\!/ \quad 5 \quad 1\!\!\!/}$$
$$ 1 \quad 1 \quad 1 \qquad \text{All quotients are 1.}$$

Multiply the prime numbers on the left side.

$$2 \cdot 3 \cdot 3 \cdot 5 = 90 \leftarrow \text{Least common multiple}$$

Work Problem **6** at the Side. ▶

6 In the following problems, the divisions have already been worked out. Multiply the prime numbers on the left to find the least common multiple.

(a)
$$2 \; | \underline{6 \quad 1\!\!\!/5}$$
$$3 \; | \underline{3 \quad 15}$$
$$5 \; | \underline{1\!\!\!/ \quad 5}$$
$$ 1 \quad 1$$

(b)
$$2 \; | \underline{20 \quad 36}$$
$$2 \; | \underline{10 \quad 18}$$
$$3 \; | \underline{5\!\!\!/ \quad 9}$$
$$3 \; | \underline{5\!\!\!/ \quad 3}$$
$$5 \; | \underline{5 \quad 1\!\!\!/}$$
$$ 1 \quad 1$$

ANSWERS

6. **(a)** 30   **(b)** 180

◀ Work Problem 7 at the Side.

7 Find the least common multiple of each set of numbers. Use whichever method you prefer.

(a) 3, 6, 10

OBJECTIVE 5 Write a fraction with an indicated denominator.
Before we can add or subtract *unlike* fractions, we must find the least common multiple, which is then used as the denominator of the fractions.

EXAMPLE 7   **Writing a Fraction with an Indicated Denominator**

Write the fraction $\frac{2}{3}$ with a denominator of 15
    Find a numerator, so that these fractions are equivalent.

$$\frac{2}{3} = \frac{?}{15}$$

To find the new numerator, first divide **15** by **3.**

$$\frac{2}{3} = \frac{?}{15} \qquad 15 \div 3 = 5$$

(b) 15 and 40

Multiply both numerator and denominator of the fraction $\frac{2}{3}$ by 5

$$\frac{2}{3} = \frac{2 \cdot 5}{3 \cdot 5} = \frac{10}{15}$$

This process is just the opposite of writing a fraction in lowest terms. Check the answer by writing $\frac{10}{15}$ in lowest terms; you should get $\frac{2}{3}$ again.

EXAMPLE 8   **Writing Fractions with a New Denominator**

Rewrite each fraction with the indicated denominator.

(c) 9, 24

(a) $\dfrac{3}{8} = \dfrac{?}{48}$

Divide 48 by 8, getting 6. Now multiply both the numerator and the denominator of $\frac{3}{8}$ by 6.

$$\frac{3}{8} = \frac{3 \cdot 6}{8 \cdot 6} = \frac{18}{48}$$

Multiply numerator and denominator by 6.

> Recall that multiplying a number by 1 does *not* change the number, and $\frac{6}{6} = 1$.

That is, $\frac{3}{8} = \frac{18}{48}$. As a check, write $\frac{18}{48}$ in lowest terms; you should get $\frac{3}{8}$ again.

(d) 8, 21, 24

(b) $\dfrac{5}{6} = \dfrac{?}{42}$

Divide 42 by 6, getting 7. Next, multiply both the numerator and the denominator of $\frac{5}{6}$ by 7.

$$\frac{5}{6} = \frac{5 \cdot 7}{6 \cdot 7} = \frac{35}{42}$$

Multiply numerator and denominator by 7.

> Notice that $\frac{7}{7} = 1$.

This shows that $\frac{5}{6} = \frac{35}{42}$. As a check, write $\frac{35}{42}$ in lowest terms. Did you get $\frac{5}{6}$ again?

Continued on Next Page

Note

In Example 7, on the previous page, the fraction $\frac{2}{3}$ was multiplied by $\frac{5}{5}$. In Example 8, the fraction $\frac{3}{8}$ was multiplied by $\frac{6}{6}$ and the fraction $\frac{5}{6}$ was multiplied by $\frac{7}{7}$. The fractions, $\frac{5}{5}$, $\frac{6}{6}$, and $\frac{7}{7}$ are all equal to 1.

$$\frac{5}{5} = 1 \qquad \frac{6}{6} = 1 \qquad \frac{7}{7} = 1$$

Recall that any number multiplied by 1 is the number itself.

Work Problem **8** *at the Side.* ▶

8 Rewrite each fraction with the indicated denominator.

(a) $\dfrac{1}{4} = \dfrac{?}{16}$

(b) $\dfrac{2}{3} = \dfrac{?}{15}$

(c) $\dfrac{7}{16} = \dfrac{?}{32}$

(d) $\dfrac{6}{11} = \dfrac{?}{33}$

2.10 ▶▶▶ Exercises

Use multiples of the larger number to find the least common multiple in each set of numbers. See Examples 1 and 2.

1. 3 and 6

2. 2 and 4

3. 3 and 5

4. 3 and 7

5. 4 and 9

6. 4 and 10

7. 2 and 7

8. 6 and 8

9. 6 and 10

10. 12 and 16

11. 20 and 50

12. 25 and 75

Find the least common multiple of each set of numbers. Use any method. See Examples 2–6.

13. 4, 10

14. 8, 10

15. 12, 20

16. 9 and 15

17. 6, 9, 12

18. 20, 24, 30

19. 4, 6, 8, 10

20. 8, 9, 12, 18

21. 12, 15, 18, 20

22. 6, 8, 9, 27, 36

23. 8, 10, 12, 16, 36

24. 5, 6, 8, 25, 30

Rewrite each fraction with a denominator of 24. See Examples 7 and 8.

25. $\dfrac{2}{3} =$

26. $\dfrac{3}{8} =$

27. $\dfrac{3}{4} =$

28. $\dfrac{5}{12} =$

29. $\dfrac{5}{6} =$

30. $\dfrac{7}{8} =$

Rewrite each fraction with the indicated denominator.

31. $\dfrac{1}{2} = \dfrac{}{6}$

32. $\dfrac{2}{3} = \dfrac{}{9}$

33. $\dfrac{3}{4} = \dfrac{}{16}$

34. $\dfrac{7}{10} = \dfrac{}{30}$

◐ 35. $\dfrac{7}{8} = \dfrac{}{32}$

36. $\dfrac{5}{12} = \dfrac{}{48}$

37. $\dfrac{3}{16} = \dfrac{}{64}$

38. $\dfrac{7}{8} = \dfrac{}{96}$

39. $\dfrac{8}{5} = \dfrac{}{20}$

40. $\dfrac{5}{8} = \dfrac{}{40}$

◐ 41. $\dfrac{9}{7} = \dfrac{}{56}$

42. $\dfrac{3}{2} = \dfrac{}{64}$

43. $\dfrac{7}{4} = \dfrac{}{48}$

44. $\dfrac{7}{6} = \dfrac{}{120}$

45. $\dfrac{8}{11} = \dfrac{}{132}$

46. $\dfrac{4}{15} = \dfrac{}{165}$

47. $\dfrac{3}{16} = \dfrac{}{144}$

48. $\dfrac{7}{16} = \dfrac{}{112}$

49. There are several methods for finding the least common multiple (LCM). Do you prefer the method using multiples of the largest number or the method using prime factorizations? Why? Would you ever use the other method?

50. Explain in your own words how to write a fraction with an indicated denominator. As part of your explanation, show how to change $\frac{3}{4}$ to a fraction having 12 as a denominator.

Find the least common multiple of the denominators of each pair of fractions.

51. $\dfrac{25}{400}, \dfrac{38}{1800}$

52. $\dfrac{53}{600}, \dfrac{115}{4000}$

53. $\dfrac{109}{1512}, \dfrac{23}{392}$

54. $\dfrac{61}{810}, \dfrac{37}{1170}$

Relating Concepts (Exercises 55–62) For Individual or Group Work

Most people think that addition and subtraction of fractions is more difficult than multiplication and division of fractions. This is probably because a common denominator must be used. **Work Exercises 55–62 in order.**

55. Fractions with the same denominators are _____ fractions and fractions with different denominators are _____ fractions.

56. To subtract like fractions, first subtract the _____ to find the numerator of the difference. Write the denominator of the like fractions as the _____ of the difference. Finally, write the answer in _____ terms.

57. The _____ common multiple (LCM) of two numbers is the _____ whole number (smallest/largest) divisible by both those numbers.

58. The following shows the common multiples for both 8 and 10. What is the least common multiple for these two numbers?

Multiples of 8: 8, 16, 24, 32, 40, 48, 56, 64, 72, 80, 88, ...

Multiples of 10: 10, 20, 30, 40, 50, 60, 70, 80, 90, ...

Find the least common multiple for each set of numbers.

59. 5, 7, 14, 10

60. 25, 18, 30, 5

61. Explain why the least common multiple for 8, 3, 5, 4, and 10 is not 240. Find the least common multiple.

62. Demonstrate that the least common multiple of 55 and 1760 is 1760.

2.11 ▶▶▶ Adding and Subtracting Unlike Fractions

OBJECTIVES

1 Add unlike fractions.

2 Add unlike fractions vertically.

3 Subtract unlike fractions.

4 Subtract unlike fractions vertically.

OBJECTIVE **1** **Add unlike fractions.** In this section, we add and subtract unlike fractions. To add unlike fractions, we must first change them to like fractions (fractions with the same denominator). For example, the figures below show $\frac{3}{8}$ and $\frac{1}{4}$.

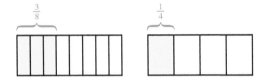

These fractions can be added by changing them to like fractions. Make like fractions by changing $\frac{1}{4}$ to the equivalent fraction $\frac{2}{8}$.

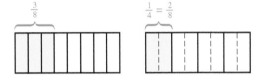

Now you can add the fractions.

$$\frac{3}{8} + \frac{1}{4} = \frac{3}{8} + \frac{2}{8} = \frac{5}{8}$$

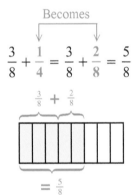

Use the following steps to add or subtract unlike fractions.

Adding or Subtracting Unlike Fractions

Step 1 Rewrite the *unlike fractions* as *like fractions* with the least common multiple as their new denominator. This new denominator is called the **least common denominator (LCD).**

Step 2 Add or subtract as with like fractions.

Step 3 Simplify the answer by writing it in lowest terms and as a whole or mixed number where possible.

EXAMPLE 1 **Adding Unlike Fractions**

Add $\frac{2}{3}$ and $\frac{1}{9}$.

The least common multiple of 3 and 9 is 9, so first write the fractions as like fractions with a denominator of 9. This is the *least common denominator (LCD)* of 3 and 9.

Continued on Next Page

Step 1

$$\frac{2}{3} = \frac{?}{9}$$

Divide 9 by 3, getting 3. Next, multiply numerator and denominator by 3.

$$\frac{2}{3} = \frac{2 \cdot 3}{3 \cdot 3} = \frac{6}{9}$$

Now, add the like fractions $\frac{6}{9}$ and $\frac{1}{9}$.

Becomes

Both fractions must have the *same* denominator **before** you add them.

Step 2

$$\frac{2}{3} + \frac{1}{9} = \frac{6}{9} + \frac{1}{9} = \frac{6+1}{9} = \frac{7}{9}$$

Step 3 Step 3 is not needed because $\frac{7}{9}$ is already in lowest terms.

Work Problem **1** *at the Side.* ▶

1 Add.

(a) $\dfrac{1}{2} + \dfrac{3}{8}$

(b) $\dfrac{3}{4} + \dfrac{1}{8}$

(c) $\dfrac{3}{5} + \dfrac{3}{10}$

EXAMPLE 2 **Adding Fractions**

Add each pair of fractions using the three steps. Simplify all answers.

(a) $\dfrac{1}{3} + \dfrac{1}{6}$

The least common multiple of 3 and 6 is 6. Rewrite both fractions as fractions with a least common denominator of 6.

Rewritten as like fractions

Step 1

$$\frac{1}{3} + \frac{1}{6} = \frac{2}{6} + \frac{1}{6}$$

6 is the LCD (least common denominator).

Add numerators.

Step 2

$$\frac{2}{6} + \frac{1}{6} = \frac{2+1}{6} = \frac{3}{6}$$

Only *like* fractions can be added.

Step 3

$$\frac{3}{6} = \frac{1}{2} \leftarrow \text{In lowest terms}$$

(d) $\dfrac{1}{12} + \dfrac{5}{6}$

(b) $\dfrac{6}{15} + \dfrac{3}{10}$

The least common multiple of 15 and 10 is 30, so rewrite both fractions with a least common denominator of 30.

Rewritten as like fractions

Step 1

$$\frac{6}{15} + \frac{3}{10} = \frac{12}{30} + \frac{9}{30}$$

The least common multiple of the denominators is the LCD.

Add numerators.

Step 2

$$\frac{12}{30} + \frac{9}{30} = \frac{12+9}{30} = \frac{21}{30}$$

Step 3

$$\frac{21}{30} = \frac{7}{10} \leftarrow \text{In lowest terms}$$

Work Problem **2** *at the Side.* ▶

2 Add. Simplify all answers.

(a) $\dfrac{3}{10} + \dfrac{1}{5}$

(b) $\dfrac{5}{8} + \dfrac{1}{3}$

(c) $\dfrac{1}{10} + \dfrac{1}{3} + \dfrac{1}{6}$

ANSWERS

1. (a) $\dfrac{7}{8}$ (b) $\dfrac{7}{8}$ (c) $\dfrac{9}{10}$ (d) $\dfrac{11}{12}$

2. (a) $\dfrac{1}{2}$ (b) $\dfrac{23}{24}$ (c) $\dfrac{3}{5}$

3 Add the following fractions vertically.

(a) $\dfrac{5}{8}$

$+\dfrac{1}{12}$

OBJECTIVE **2** **Add unlike fractions vertically.**   Fractions can also be added vertically (one fraction written below the other).

EXAMPLE 3   **Vertical Addition of Fractions**

Add the following fractions vertically.

(a) $\dfrac{3}{8} = \dfrac{3 \cdot 3}{8 \cdot 3} = \dfrac{9}{24}$ ← 24 is the LCD.

$+\dfrac{7}{12} = \dfrac{7 \cdot 2}{12 \cdot 2} = \dfrac{14}{24}$ ← Rewritten as like fractions

$\dfrac{23}{24}$ ← Add the numerators.
← Denominator is 24, the LCD.

(b) $\dfrac{2}{9} = \dfrac{2 \cdot 4}{9 \cdot 4} = \dfrac{8}{36}$

$+\dfrac{1}{4} = \dfrac{1 \cdot 9}{4 \cdot 9} = \dfrac{9}{36}$ ← Rewritten as like fractions

$\dfrac{17}{36}$ ← Add the numerators.
← Denominator is 36, the LCD.

◀ *Work Problem* **3** *at the Side.*

(b) $\dfrac{7}{16}$

$+\dfrac{1}{4}$

OBJECTIVE **3** **Subtract unlike fractions.**   The next example shows subtraction of unlike fractions.

EXAMPLE 4   **Subtracting Unlike Fractions**

Subtract. Simplify all answers.

As with addition, rewrite unlike fractions with a least common denominator.

(a) $\dfrac{3}{4} - \dfrac{3}{8}$

Rewritten as like fractions

Step 1 $\dfrac{3}{4} - \dfrac{3}{8} = \dfrac{6}{8} - \dfrac{3}{8}$ ← The LCD is 8.

Subtract numerators.

Step 2 $\dfrac{6}{8} - \dfrac{3}{8} = \dfrac{6 - 3}{8} = \dfrac{3}{8}$

Step 3   Not needed because $\frac{3}{8}$ is in lowest terms.

Continued on Next Page

(b) $\dfrac{3}{4} - \dfrac{7}{12}$

Rewritten as like fractions

Step 1 $\dfrac{3}{4} - \dfrac{7}{12} = \dfrac{9}{12} - \dfrac{7}{12}$

Subtract numerators.

Step 2 $\dfrac{9}{12} - \dfrac{7}{12} = \dfrac{9 - 7}{12} = \dfrac{2}{12}$ ← Subtract the numerators.
← Denominator is 12, the LCD.

Step 3 $\dfrac{2}{12} = \dfrac{1}{6}$ ← Lowest terms

Always write the final answer in lowest terms.

Work Problem **4** *at the Side.* ▶

4 Subtract. Simplify all answers.

(a) $\dfrac{5}{8} - \dfrac{1}{4}$

(b) $\dfrac{4}{5} - \dfrac{3}{4}$

OBJECTIVE **4** Subtract unlike fractions vertically.

EXAMPLE 5 **Vertical Subtraction of Fractions**

Subtract the following fractions vertically.

(a) $\dfrac{4}{5} = \dfrac{4 \cdot 8}{5 \cdot 8} = \dfrac{32}{40}$
$-\dfrac{3}{8} = \dfrac{3 \cdot 5}{8 \cdot 5} = \dfrac{15}{40}$

Rewritten as like fractions

$\dfrac{17}{40}$ ← Subtract numerators.
← Denominator is 40, the LCD.

(b) $\dfrac{3}{7} = \dfrac{3 \cdot 12}{7 \cdot 12} = \dfrac{36}{84}$
$-\dfrac{5}{12} = \dfrac{5 \cdot 7}{12 \cdot 7} = \dfrac{35}{84}$

Rewritten as like fractions

$\dfrac{1}{84}$ ← Subtract numerators.
← Denominator is 84, the LCD.

Work Problem **5** *at the Side.* ▶

5 Subtract vertically. Simplify all answers.

(a) $\dfrac{7}{8}$
$-\dfrac{2}{3}$

(b) $\dfrac{5}{6}$
$-\dfrac{1}{12}$

Add the following fractions. Simplify all answers. See Examples 1–3.

1. $\dfrac{3}{4} + \dfrac{1}{8}$

2. $\dfrac{1}{6} + \dfrac{2}{3}$

3. $\dfrac{2}{3} + \dfrac{2}{9}$

4. $\dfrac{3}{7} + \dfrac{1}{14}$

5. $\dfrac{9}{20} + \dfrac{3}{10}$

6. $\dfrac{5}{8} + \dfrac{1}{4}$

7. $\dfrac{3}{5} + \dfrac{3}{8}$

8. $\dfrac{5}{7} + \dfrac{3}{14}$

9. $\dfrac{2}{9} + \dfrac{5}{12}$

10. $\dfrac{5}{8} + \dfrac{1}{12}$

11. $\dfrac{1}{3} + \dfrac{3}{5}$

12. $\dfrac{2}{5} + \dfrac{3}{7}$

13. $\dfrac{1}{4} + \dfrac{2}{9} + \dfrac{1}{3}$

14. $\dfrac{3}{7} + \dfrac{2}{5} + \dfrac{1}{10}$

15. $\dfrac{3}{10} + \dfrac{2}{5} + \dfrac{3}{20}$

16. $\dfrac{1}{3} + \dfrac{3}{8} + \dfrac{1}{4}$

17. $\dfrac{4}{15} + \dfrac{1}{6} + \dfrac{1}{3}$

18. $\dfrac{5}{12} + \dfrac{2}{9} + \dfrac{1}{6}$

19. $\begin{array}{r} \dfrac{1}{4} \\ + \dfrac{1}{8} \\ \hline \end{array}$

20. $\begin{array}{r} \dfrac{7}{12} \\ + \dfrac{1}{8} \\ \hline \end{array}$

21. $\begin{array}{r} \dfrac{5}{12} \\ + \dfrac{1}{16} \\ \hline \end{array}$

22. $\begin{array}{r} \dfrac{3}{7} \\ + \dfrac{1}{3} \\ \hline \end{array}$

Subtract the following fractions. Simplify all answers. See Example 4.

23. $\dfrac{5}{6} - \dfrac{1}{3}$

24. $\dfrac{3}{4} - \dfrac{5}{8}$

25. $\dfrac{2}{3} - \dfrac{1}{6}$

26. $\dfrac{3}{4} - \dfrac{5}{8}$

🌐 **27.** $\dfrac{2}{3} - \dfrac{1}{5}$

28. $\dfrac{5}{6} - \dfrac{7}{9}$

29. $\dfrac{5}{12} - \dfrac{1}{4}$

30. $\dfrac{5}{7} - \dfrac{1}{3}$

31. $\dfrac{8}{9} - \dfrac{7}{15}$

32. $\dfrac{4}{5}$
$-\dfrac{1}{3}$

33. $\dfrac{7}{8}$
$-\dfrac{4}{5}$

34. $\dfrac{5}{8}$
$-\dfrac{1}{3}$

35. $\dfrac{5}{12}$
$-\dfrac{1}{16}$

36. $\dfrac{7}{12}$
$-\dfrac{1}{3}$

Solve each application problem.

4-Piece Chisel Set
LOT NO. 42429
• widths: $\frac{1}{4}$", $\frac{1}{2}$", $\frac{3}{4}$", and 1"
• Heat-treated, high-carbon steel
• $7\frac{1}{4}$" overall length
• Straight bevel

SALE!
$4⁹⁷

REGULAR PRICE $7.99

Use the newspaper advertisement for this 4-piece chisel set to answer Exercises 37–38. (*Source:* Harbor Freight Tools.)

37. Find the difference in the cutting-edge width of the two chisels with the widest blades. The symbol ″ is for inches.

38. Find the difference in the cutting-edge width of the two chisels with the narrowest blades. The symbol ″ is for inches.

39. A sports and entertainment center has $\frac{4}{5}$ of its total area devoted to seating of fans and guests. If $\frac{3}{8}$ of the seating area is used for general admission seating and the rest for reserved seating, find the fraction of the total area used for reserved seating.

40. Della Daniel wants to open a day care center and has saved $\frac{2}{5}$ of the amount needed for start-up costs. If she saves another $\frac{1}{8}$ of the amount needed and then $\frac{1}{6}$ more, find the total portion of the start-up costs she has saved.

41. When installing cabinets for The Home Depot, Sarah Bryn must be certain that the proper type and size of mounting screw is used. Find the total length of the screw shown.

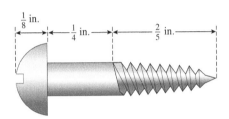

42. When installing a computer chassis, Bonnie Bottorff must be certain that the proper type and size of bolt is used. Find the total length of the bolt shown.

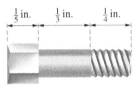

43. Bill Newton is a general contractor and begins a job with $\frac{3}{4}$ of a tank of fuel in his back-hoe. If he uses $\frac{1}{3}$ of the tank in the morning and $\frac{3}{8}$ of the tank in the afternoon, what fraction of the tank of fuel remains?

44. Adrian Ortega drives a tanker for the British Petroleum Company. He leaves the refinery with his tanker filled to $\frac{7}{8}$ of capacity. If he delivers $\frac{1}{4}$ of the tanker's capacity at the first stop and $\frac{1}{3}$ of the tanker's capacity at the second stop, find the fraction of the tanker's capacity remaining.

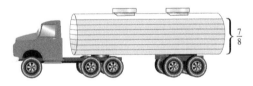

45. Step 1 in adding or subtracting unlike fractions is to rewrite the fractions so they have the least common multiple as a denominator. Explain in your own words why this is necessary.

46. Briefly list the three steps used for addition and subtraction of unlike fractions.

Refer to the circle graph to answer Exercises 47–50.

THE DAY OF THE STUDENT
(One day = 24 hours)

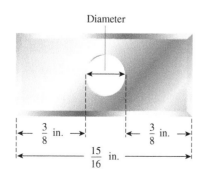

Work and Travel $\frac{1}{3}$

Class $\frac{1}{6}$

Study $\frac{1}{8}$

Sleep $\frac{7}{24}$

Other $\frac{1}{12}$

47. What fraction of the day was spent in class and study?

48. What fraction of the day was spent in work and travel and other?

49. In which activity was the greatest amount of time spent? How many hours did this activity take? What fraction of the day was spent on this activity and class time?

50. In which activity was the least amount of time spent? How many hours did this activity take? What fraction of the day was spent on this activity and studying?

51. Find the diameter of the hole in the mounting bracket shown. (The diameter is the distance across the center of the hole.)

Diameter

$\frac{3}{8}$ in. $\frac{3}{8}$ in.

$\frac{15}{16}$ in.

52. Chakotay is fitting a turquoise stone into a bear claw pendant. Find the diameter of the hole in the pendant. (The diameter is the distance across the center of the hole.)

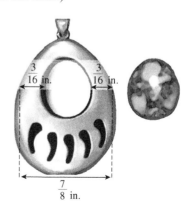

$\frac{3}{16}$ in. $\frac{3}{16}$ in.

$\frac{7}{8}$ in.

Study Skills

OBJECTIVES

1 **Create mind maps for appropriate concepts.**

2 **Visually show how concepts relate to each other using arrows or lines.**

Directions for Making a Mind Map

Why Is Mapping Brain Friendly?

Remember that your brain grows dendrites when you are **actively thinking** about and working with information. Making a map requires you to think hard about **how to place the information, how to show connections** between parts of the map, and **how color will be useful.** It also takes a lot of thinking to fill in all related details and **show how those details connect to the larger concept.** All that thinking will let your brain grow a complex, many-branched neural network of interconnected dendrites. It is time well spent.

Mind mapping is a visual way to show information that you have learned. It is an excellent way to review. Mapping is flexible and can be personalized, which is helpful for your memory. Your brain likes to see things that are **pleasing** to look at, **colorful,** and that **show connections** between ideas. Take advantage of that by creating maps that

▶ are easy to read,

▶ use color in a systematic way, and

▶ clearly show you how different concepts are related (using arrows or dotted lines, for example).

Here are some general directions for making a map. After you read them, work on completing the map that has been started for you on the next page. It is from Chapters 2 and 3: Fractions.

▶ To begin a mind map, write the concept in the center of a piece of paper and either circle it or draw a box around it.

▶ Make a line out from the center concept, and draw a box large enough to write the definition of the concept.

▶ Think of the other aspects (subpoints) of the concept that you have learned, such as procedures to follow or formulas. Make a separate line and box connecting each subpoint to the center.

▶ From each of the new boxes, add the information you've learned. You can continue making new lines and boxes or circles, or you can list items below the new information.

▶ Use color to highlight the major points. For example, everything related to one subpoint might be the same color. That way you can easily see related ideas.

▶ You may also use arrows, underlining, or small drawings to help yourself remember.

On a separate paper, make a map that summarizes Computations with Fractions. Follow the directions and use the starter map below.

Try This Fractions Mind Map Using Sections 2.5, 2.7, and 2.11

▶ The longest rectangles are *instructions* for all four operations. (The first one starts "Rewrite all numbers as fractions…" and the second one is at the bottom of the map.)

▶ Notice the wavy dividing lines that separate the map into two sides.

▶ Your job is to complete the map by writing the steps used in multiplying and dividing fractions (from **Sections 2.5 and 2.7**) and the steps used in adding and subtracting fractions (from **Section 2.11**).

Definition → numerator $\frac{3}{4}$ denominator

no. of parts used

total no. of parts in the whole

Fractions

computation

Rewrite all numbers as fractions
mixed → improper   whole number → write over 1

Multiply   **Divide**   **Add and Subtract**

Do **NOT** need common denominator   Need common denominator

Change ÷ to ·
flip 2nd number

Try larger denom.   Try multiples of larger denom.   Use prime factoring

Steps to fill in from Section 2.5   *then multiply*   Steps to fill in from Section 3.3

Simplify the answer
→ lowest terms
→ improper → mixed or whole number

2.12 ▶▶▶ Adding and Subtracting Mixed Numbers

1 Estimate an answer, then add or subtract mixed numbers.

2 Estimate an answer, then subtract mixed numbers by regrouping.

3 Add or subtract mixed numbers using an alternate method.

Recall that a mixed number is the sum of a whole number and a fraction. For example,

$$3\frac{2}{5} \quad \text{means} \quad 3 + \frac{2}{5}.$$

OBJECTIVE 1 Estimate an answer, then add or subtract mixed numbers. Add or subtract mixed numbers by adding or subtracting the fraction parts and then the whole number parts. It is a good idea to estimate the answer first, as we did when multiplying and dividing mixed numbers in **Section 2.8.**

◀ Work Problem **1** at the Side.

1 As a review of mixed numbers, write each mixed number as an improper fraction and each improper fraction as a mixed number.

(a) $\frac{9}{2}$

(b) $\frac{8}{3}$

(c) $4\frac{3}{4}$

(d) $3\frac{7}{8}$

EXAMPLE 1 Adding and Subtracting Mixed Numbers

First estimate the answer. Then add or subtract to find the exact answer.

(a) $16\frac{1}{8} + 5\frac{5}{8}$

Estimate: *Exact:*

$16 \xleftarrow{\text{Rounds to}} \left\{ 16\frac{1}{8} \right.$

$+ \ 6 \xleftarrow{\text{Rounds to}} \left\{ + \ 5\frac{5}{8} \right.$

First, estimate the answer. 22 $21\frac{6}{8} = 21\frac{3}{4}$ ← Lowest terms

Sum of whole numbers ⎯⎯⏐ ⏐⎯ Sum of fractions

In lowest terms $\frac{6}{8}$ is $\frac{3}{4}$, so the exact answer of $21\frac{3}{4}$ is in lowest terms. The exact answer is *reasonable* because it is close to the estimate of 22.

(b) $8\frac{5}{8} - 3\frac{1}{12}$

Estimate: *Exact:*

$9 \xleftarrow{\text{Rounds to}} \left\{ 8\frac{5}{8} = \ 8\frac{15}{24} \right.$

$- \ 3 \xleftarrow{\text{Rounds to}} \left\{ -3\frac{1}{12} = -3\frac{2}{24} \right.$

24 is the least common denominator.

6 $5\frac{13}{24}$

Subtract whole numbers. ⎯⎯⏐ ⏐⎯ Subtract fractions.

The exact answer of $5\frac{13}{24}$ is *reasonable* because it is close to the estimated answer of 6. Check by adding $5\frac{13}{24}$ and $3\frac{1}{12}$; the sum should be $8\frac{5}{8}$.

Continued on Next Page

ANSWERS

1. (a) $4\frac{1}{2}$ (b) $2\frac{2}{3}$ (c) $\frac{19}{4}$ (d) $\frac{31}{8}$

Note

When estimating, if the numerator is *half* of the denominator or *more*, round up the whole number part. If the numerator is *less* than *half* the denominator, leave the whole number part as it is.

Work Problem **2** *at the Side.* ▶

When you add the fraction parts of mixed numbers, the sum may be greater than 1. If this happens, simplify the fraction and regroup in the whole number column. (You cannot leave a whole number along with an improper fraction as the answer.)

EXAMPLE 2 **Simplify and Regroup When Adding Mixed Numbers**

First estimate, and then add $9\frac{5}{8} + 13\frac{7}{8}$.

Estimate: *Exact:*

$10 \xleftarrow{\text{Rounds to}} \left\{ 9\frac{5}{8} \right.$

First, add the fractions, then the whole numbers.

$+\ 14 \xleftarrow{\text{Rounds to}} \left\{ +\ 13\frac{7}{8} \right.$

24 $22\frac{12}{8}$

Sum of whole numbers ⟶ ⟵ Sum of fractions

The improper fraction $\frac{12}{8}$ can be written in lowest terms as $\frac{3}{2}$. Because $\frac{3}{2} = 1\frac{1}{2}$, the simplified sum is

Becomes

$22\frac{12}{8} = 22 + \frac{12}{8} = 22 + 1\frac{1}{2} = 23\frac{1}{2}.$

The estimate was 24, so the exact answer of $23\frac{1}{2}$ is reasonable.

Note

When adding mixed numbers, first add the fraction parts, then add the whole number parts. Then combine the two answers, simplifying the fraction part when necessary.

Work Problem **3** *at the Side.* ▶

OBJECTIVE 2 Estimate an answer, then subtract mixed numbers by regrouping. When subtracting mixed numbers, **regrouping** is necessary when the fraction part of the first number is less than the fraction part of the second number.

EXAMPLE 3 **Regroup When Subtracting Mixed Numbers**

First estimate, and then subtract to find the exact answer.

(a) $7 - 2\frac{5}{6}$

Continued on Next Page

2 First estimate, and then add or subtract to find the exact answer.

(a) *Estimate:*   *Exact:*

$7 \xleftarrow{\text{Rounds to}} \left\{ 6\frac{7}{8} = 6\frac{7}{8} \right.$

$+\ 2 \xleftarrow{\text{Rounds to}} \left\{ +\ 2\frac{1}{4} = 2\frac{2}{8} \right.$

(b) $25\frac{3}{5} + 12\frac{3}{10}$

Estimate:

___ + ___ = ___

Exact: ___

(c) *Estimate:*   *Exact:*

$\xleftarrow{\text{Rounds to}} \left\{ 4\frac{7}{9} \right.$

$- \xleftarrow{\text{Rounds to}} \left\{ -\ 2\frac{2}{3} \right.$

3 First estimate, and then add to find the exact answer.

(a) *Estimate:*   *Exact:*

$\xleftarrow{\text{Rounds to}} \left\{ 9\frac{3}{4} \right.$

$+ \xleftarrow{\text{Rounds to}} \left\{ +\ 7\frac{1}{2} \right.$

(b) *Estimate:*   *Exact:*

$\xleftarrow{\text{Rounds to}} \left\{ 15\frac{4}{5} \right.$

$+ \xleftarrow{\text{Rounds to}} \left\{ +\ 12\frac{2}{3} \right.$

ANSWERS

2. (a) $7 + 2 = 9; 9\frac{1}{8}$

(b) $26 + 12 = 38; 37\frac{9}{10}$

(c) $5 - 3 = 2; 2\frac{1}{9}$

3. (a) $10 + 8 = 18; 17\frac{1}{4}$

(b) $16 + 13 = 29; 28\frac{7}{15}$

$$\text{Estimate:} \qquad \text{Exact:}$$

$$7 \xleftarrow{\text{Rounds to}} \begin{cases} 7 \end{cases}$$

> There is no fraction here from which to subtract $\frac{5}{6}$.

$$\frac{-3}{4} \xleftarrow{\text{Rounds to}} \begin{cases} -2\frac{5}{6} \end{cases}$$

It is **not** possible to subtract $\frac{5}{6}$ without regrouping the whole number **7** first.

$$\text{Regroup 7 as } 6 + 1$$
$$7 = \overbrace{6 + 1}$$

$$1 = \frac{6}{6}$$
$$= 6 + \frac{6}{6}$$

$$= 6\frac{6}{6}$$

Now you can subtract.

$$7 = \qquad 6\frac{6}{6}$$

> 7 was written as $6\frac{6}{6}$.

$$-2\frac{5}{6} = \quad -2\frac{5}{6}$$
$$\overline{\qquad \qquad 4\frac{1}{6}}$$

The estimate was 4, so the exact answer of $4\frac{1}{6}$ is reasonable.

(b) $8\frac{1}{3} - 4\frac{3}{5}$

$$\text{Estimate:} \qquad \text{Exact:}$$

$$8 \xleftarrow{\text{Rounds to}} \begin{cases} 8\frac{1}{3} = \quad 8\frac{5}{15} \end{cases}$$

$$-5 \xleftarrow{\text{Rounds to}} \begin{cases} -4\frac{3}{5} = -4\frac{9}{15} \end{cases}$$
$$\overline{3}$$

> 15 is the least common denominator

It is **not** possible to subtract $\frac{9}{15}$ from $\frac{5}{15}$, so regroup the whole number **8.**

$$\text{Regroup 8 as } 7 + 1$$
$$8\frac{5}{15} = 8 + \frac{5}{15} = \overbrace{7 + 1} + \frac{5}{15}$$

$$1 = \frac{15}{15}$$
$$= 7 + \frac{15}{15} + \frac{5}{15}$$

$$= 7 + \frac{20}{15} \quad \leftarrow \frac{15}{15} + \frac{5}{15}$$

$$= 7\frac{20}{15}$$

Continued on Next Page

Now you can subtract.

$$8\frac{1}{3} = 8\frac{5}{15} = 7\frac{20}{15}$$

$$-4\frac{3}{5} = 4\frac{9}{15} = 4\frac{9}{15}$$

$$3\frac{11}{15}$$

The exact answer is $3\frac{11}{15}$ (lowest terms), which is reasonable because it is close to the estimate of 3.

Work Problem **4** *at the Side.* ▶

OBJECTIVE **3** **Add or subtract mixed numbers using an alternate method.** An alternate method for adding or subtracting mixed numbers is to first change the mixed numbers to improper fractions. Then rewrite the unlike fractions as like fractions. Finally, add or subtract the numerators and write the answer in lowest terms.

EXAMPLE 4 **Adding or Subtracting Mixed Numbers**

Add or subtract.

Rewrite $2\frac{3}{8}$ as $\frac{19}{8}$ and $3\frac{3}{4}$ as $\frac{15}{4}$.

(a) $2\frac{3}{8} = \frac{19}{8} = \frac{19}{8}$

$+3\frac{3}{4} = \frac{15}{4} = \frac{30}{8}$ —— 8 is the least common denominator.

$\frac{49}{8} = 6\frac{1}{8}$ Answer as mixed number

Change to improper fractions.

(b) $4\frac{2}{3} = \frac{14}{3} = \frac{70}{15}$

$-2\frac{1}{5} = \frac{11}{5} = \frac{33}{15}$ —— 15 is the least common denominator.

$\frac{37}{15} = 2\frac{7}{15}$ Simplify the answer by writing it as a mixed number.

Improper fractions

Work Problem **5** *at the Side.* ▶

Note

The advantage of this alternate method of adding or subtracting mixed numbers is that it eliminates the need to regroup. It is also the most useful method for working with algebraic fractions. However, if the mixed numbers are large, then the numerators of the improper fractions may become so large that they are difficult to work with. In such cases, you may want to keep the numbers as mixed numbers.

4 First estimate and then subtract to find the exact answer.

(a) *Estimate:*   *Exact:*

← Rounds to $\{7\frac{1}{3}$

$-$ ← Rounds to $\{-4\frac{5}{6}$

(b) *Estimate:*   *Exact:*

← $\{4\frac{5}{8}$

$-$ ← $\{-2\frac{15}{16}$

(c) *Estimate:*   *Exact:*

← $\{15$

$-$ ← $\{-6\frac{4}{9}$

5 Add or subtract by changing mixed numbers to improper fractions. Simplify answers.

(a) $3\frac{3}{8}$

$+2\frac{1}{2}$

(b) $6\frac{3}{4}$

$-4\frac{2}{3}$

ANSWERS

4. **(a)** $7 - 5 = 2$; $2\frac{1}{2}$

   (b) $5 - 3 = 2$; $1\frac{11}{16}$

   (c) $15 - 6 = 9$; $8\frac{5}{9}$

5. **(a)** $\frac{47}{8} = 5\frac{7}{8}$

   (b) $\frac{25}{12} = 2\frac{1}{12}$

FOR
EXTRA
HELP

MyMathLab

Math XL
PRACTICE

WATCH

DOWNLOAD

READ

REVIEW

First estimate the answer. Then add to find the exact answer. Write answers as mixed numbers. See Examples 1 and 2.

1. *Estimate:*   *Exact:*

Rounds to $\left\{ \; 5\dfrac{1}{2} \right.$

$+$ Rounds to $\left\{ \; +\,3\dfrac{1}{3} \right.$

2. *Estimate:*   *Exact:*

$6\dfrac{3}{5}$

$+$ $+\,7\dfrac{1}{10}$

3. *Estimate:*   *Exact:*

$7\dfrac{1}{3}$

$+$ $+\,4\dfrac{1}{6}$

4. *Estimate:*   *Exact:*

$10\dfrac{1}{4}$

$+$ $+\,5\dfrac{5}{8}$

5. *Estimate:*   *Exact:*

$\dfrac{5}{8}$

$+$ $+\,3\dfrac{7}{12}$

6. *Estimate:*   *Exact:*

$12\dfrac{4}{5}$

$+$ $+\,\dfrac{7}{10}$

7. *Estimate:*   *Exact:*

$24\dfrac{5}{6}$

$+$ $+\,18\dfrac{5}{6}$

8. *Estimate:*   *Exact:*

$14\dfrac{6}{7}$

$+$ $+\,15\dfrac{1}{2}$

9. *Estimate:*   *Exact:*

$33\dfrac{3}{5}$

$+$ $+\,18\dfrac{1}{2}$

10. *Estimate:*   *Exact:*

$18\dfrac{5}{8}$

$+$ $+\,6\dfrac{2}{3}$

11. *Estimate:*   *Exact:*

$22\dfrac{3}{4}$

$+$ $+\,15\dfrac{3}{7}$

12. *Estimate:*   *Exact:*

$7\dfrac{1}{4}$

$+$ $+\,25\dfrac{7}{8}$

13. *Estimate:*   *Exact:*

$$12\frac{8}{15}$$

$$18\frac{3}{5}$$

+ _____ $+14\frac{7}{10}$
_____

14. *Estimate:*   *Exact:*

$$14\frac{9}{10}$$

$$8\frac{1}{4}$$

+ _____ $+13\frac{3}{5}$
_____

First estimate the answer. Then subtract to find the exact answer. Simplify all answers.
See Examples 1 and 3.

15. *Estimate:*   *Exact:*

$$14\frac{7}{8}$$

− _____ $-12\frac{1}{4}$
_____

16. *Estimate:*   *Exact:*

$$14\frac{3}{4}$$

− _____ $-11\frac{3}{8}$
_____

17. *Estimate:*   *Exact:*

$$12\frac{2}{3}$$

− _____ $-1\frac{1}{5}$
_____

18. *Estimate:*   *Exact:*

$$11\frac{9}{20}$$

− _____ $-4\frac{3}{5}$
_____

19. *Estimate:*   *Exact:*

$$28\frac{3}{10}$$

− _____ $-6\frac{1}{15}$
_____

20. *Estimate:*   *Exact:*

$$15\frac{7}{20}$$

− _____ $-6\frac{1}{8}$
_____

21. *Estimate:*   *Exact:*

$$17$$

− _____ $-6\frac{5}{8}$
_____

22. *Estimate:*   *Exact:*

$$22$$

− _____ $-4\frac{5}{8}$
_____

23. *Estimate:*   *Exact:*

$$18\frac{3}{4}$$

− _____ $-5\frac{4}{5}$
_____

24. *Estimate:*   *Exact:*

$$14\frac{5}{8}$$

$-$ ___ $-\ 3\frac{2}{3}$

___   ___

25. *Estimate:*   *Exact:*

$$19\frac{2}{3}$$

$-$ ___ $-\ 11\frac{3}{4}$

___   ___

26. *Estimate:*   *Exact:*

$$20\frac{3}{5}$$

$-$ ___ $-\ 12\frac{7}{15}$

___   ___

Add or subtract by changing mixed numbers to improper fractions. Write answers as mixed numbers when possible. See Example 4.

27. $7\frac{5}{8}$

  $+\ 1\frac{1}{2}$

  ___

28. $8\frac{3}{4}$

  $+\ 1\frac{5}{8}$

  ___

29. $4\frac{2}{3}$

  $+\ 6\frac{5}{6}$

  ___

30. $7\frac{5}{12}$

  $+\ 6\frac{2}{3}$

  ___

31. $2\frac{2}{3}$

  $+\ 1\frac{1}{6}$

  ___

32. $4\frac{1}{2}$

  $+\ 2\frac{3}{4}$

  ___

33. $3\frac{1}{4}$

  $+\ 3\frac{2}{3}$

  ___

34. $2\frac{4}{5}$

  $+\ 5\frac{1}{3}$

  ___

35. $1\frac{3}{8}$

  $+\ 6\frac{3}{4}$

  ___

36. $1\frac{5}{12}$

  $+\ 1\frac{7}{8}$

  ___

37. $3\frac{1}{2}$

  $-\ 2\frac{2}{3}$

  ___

38. $4\frac{1}{4}$

  $-\ 3\frac{7}{12}$

  ___

39. $8\dfrac{3}{4}$

$-\ 5\dfrac{7}{8}$

40. $12\dfrac{2}{3}$

$-\ 7\dfrac{11}{12}$

41. $7\dfrac{1}{4}$

$-\ 4\dfrac{2}{3}$

42. $4\dfrac{1}{10}$

$-\ 3\dfrac{7}{8}$

43. $9\dfrac{1}{5}$

$-\ 3\dfrac{3}{4}$

44. $10\dfrac{2}{7}$

$-\ 5\dfrac{5}{14}$

45. $6\dfrac{3}{7}$

$-\ 2\dfrac{2}{3}$

46. $8\dfrac{2}{15}$

$-\ 6\dfrac{1}{2}$

47. In your own words, explain the steps you would take to add two large mixed numbers.

48. When subtracting mixed numbers, explain when you need to regroup. Explain how to regroup using your own example.

First estimate the answer. Then solve each application problem.

49. At the beginning of this chapter you read about Bryan Berg, who builds houses of cards. While in high school, Bryan built a house of cards $14\frac{1}{2}$ ft tall, setting his first world record. Today his current world record is $25\frac{3}{4}$ ft tall. How much taller is his current world record than his first world record?

(*Source: Guinness World Records.*)

Estimate:

Exact:

50. The heaviest marine mammal in the world is the blue whale at $143\frac{3}{10}$ tons. The sixth heaviest is the humpback whale at $29\frac{1}{5}$ tons. Find the difference in their weights. (*Source: Top 10 of Everything.*)

Estimate:

Exact:

Use the newspaper advertisement for this 6-piece jumbo wrench set
to answer Exercises 51–54. The symbol " is for inches.
(*Source:* Harbor Freight Tools.)

51. How much longer is the longest wrench than the
second-to-shortest wrench?

Estimate:

Exact:

52. Find the difference in length between the shortest
wrench and the second-to-longest wrench.

Estimate:

Exact:

53. What is the total length of the three longest
wrenches?

Estimate:

Exact:

54. What is the total length of the three shortest
wrenches?

Estimate:

Exact:

A mechanic buys the 34-piece hose clamp assortment
shown at the left. Use the advertisement to answer
Exercises 55–56. The symbol " is for inches. (*Source:*
Harbor Freight Tools.)

55. Find the difference in size between the largest hose
clamp and the smallest hose clamp.

Estimate:

Exact:

56. Find the difference in size between the second to
largest hose clamp and the smallest hose clamp.

Estimate:

Exact:

57. The four sides of Andre Herrebout's vegetable
garden are $15\frac{1}{2}$ feet, $18\frac{3}{4}$ feet, $24\frac{1}{4}$ feet, and $30\frac{1}{2}$ feet.
How many feet of fencing are needed to go around
the garden?

Estimate:

Exact:

58. On a recent vacation to Canada, Erin Gavin drove
for $7\frac{3}{4}$ hours on the first day, $5\frac{1}{4}$ hours on the second
day, $6\frac{1}{2}$ hours on the third day, and 9 hours on the
fourth day. How many hours did she drive
altogether?

Estimate:

Exact:

59. A craftsperson must attach a lead strip around all four sides of a stained glass window before it is installed. Find the length of lead stripping needed.

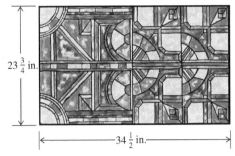

$23\frac{3}{4}$ in.

$\longleftarrow$ $34\frac{1}{2}$ in. $\longrightarrow$

Estimate:

Exact:

60. To complete a custom order, Zak Morten of Home Depot must find the number of inches of brass trim needed to go around the four sides of the lamp base plate shown. Find the length of brass trim needed.

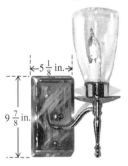

$\leftarrow 5\frac{1}{8}$ in. $\rightarrow$

$9\frac{7}{8}$ in.

Estimate:

Exact:

61. A museum humidifier contains 100 gallons of water. The system uses $10\frac{1}{4}$ gallons of water on Monday, $13\frac{1}{2}$ gallons on Tuesday, $8\frac{7}{8}$ gallons on Wednesday, $18\frac{3}{4}$ gallons on Thursday, $12\frac{3}{8}$ gallons on Friday, $9\frac{1}{2}$ gallons on Saturday, and $14\frac{1}{8}$ gallons on Sunday. Find the total number of gallons of water remaining.

Estimate:

Exact:

62. Marv Levinson bought 15 yards of Italian silk fabric. He made two shirts, needing a total of $3\frac{3}{4}$ yards of the material, a suit for his wife with $4\frac{1}{8}$ yards, and a jacket with $3\frac{7}{8}$ yards. Find the number of yards of material remaining.

Estimate:

Exact:

63. The exercise yard at the correction center has four sides and is surrounded by $527\frac{1}{24}$ ft of security fencing. If three sides of the yard measure $107\frac{2}{3}$ ft, $150\frac{3}{4}$ ft, and $138\frac{5}{8}$ ft, find the length of the fourth side.

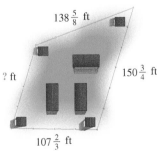

$138\frac{5}{8}$ ft

? ft $150\frac{3}{4}$ ft

$107\frac{2}{3}$ ft

Estimate:

Exact:

64. Three sides of a parking lot are $108\frac{1}{4}$ ft, $162\frac{3}{8}$ ft, and $143\frac{1}{2}$ ft. If the distance around the lot is $518\frac{3}{4}$ ft, find the length of the fourth side.

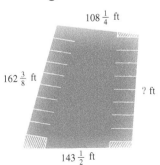

$108\frac{1}{4}$ ft

$162\frac{3}{8}$ ft

? ft

$143\frac{1}{2}$ ft

Estimate:

Exact:

65. A freight car is loaded with Morton Salt products consisting of $58\frac{1}{2}$ tons of coarse rock salt, $23\frac{5}{8}$ tons of medium rock salt, $16\frac{5}{6}$ tons of table salt, and $29\frac{1}{4}$ tons of animal salt lick blocks. If the weight of the freight car is $58\frac{1}{3}$ tons, find the weight of the loaded freight car.

Estimate:

Exact:

66. Bryan Berg, from the opening page of this chapter, built houses of cards reaching heights of $14\frac{1}{2}$ ft, $19\frac{3}{8}$ ft, $23\frac{5}{12}$ ft, and $25\frac{3}{4}$ ft (his current world record). Find the total height of these four houses of cards. (*Source: Reader's Digest.*)

Estimate:

Exact:

Find the unknown length, labeled with a question mark, in each figure.

67.

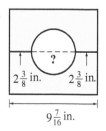

$2\frac{3}{8}$ in. ? $2\frac{3}{8}$ in.

$9\frac{7}{16}$ in.

68.

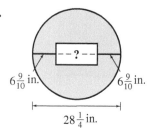

$6\frac{9}{10}$ in. ? $6\frac{9}{10}$ in.

$28\frac{1}{4}$ in.

69.

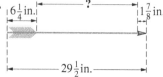

$6\frac{1}{4}$ in. ? $1\frac{7}{8}$ in.

$29\frac{1}{2}$ in.

70.

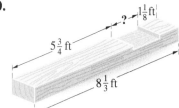

$5\frac{3}{4}$ ft ? $1\frac{1}{8}$ ft

$8\frac{1}{3}$ ft

Relating Concepts (Exercises 71–76) For Individual or Group Work

Most fraction problems include fractions with different denominators.
Work Exercises 71–76 in order.

71. To add or subtract fractions, we must first rewrite them as like fractions. Rewrite each fraction with the indicated denominator.

(a) $\dfrac{5}{9} = \dfrac{}{54}$

(b) $\dfrac{7}{12} = \dfrac{}{48}$

(c) $\dfrac{5}{8} = \dfrac{}{40}$

(d) $\dfrac{11}{5} = \dfrac{}{120}$

72. When rewriting unlike fractions as like fractions with the least common multiple as a denominator, the new denominator is called the _____ _____ _____, or LCD.

73. Add or subtract as indicated. Write answers in lowest terms.

(a) $\dfrac{5}{8} + \dfrac{1}{3}$

(b) $\dfrac{19}{20} - \dfrac{5}{12}$

(c) $\begin{array}{r} \dfrac{7}{12} \\ \dfrac{3}{16} \\ + \dfrac{3}{24} \\ \hline \end{array}$

(d) $\begin{array}{r} \dfrac{6}{7} \\ - \dfrac{2}{3} \\ \hline \end{array}$

74. A common method for adding or subtracting mixed numbers is to add or subtract the _____ _____ and then add or subtract the whole number parts

75. Another method for adding or subtracting mixed numbers is to first change the mixed numbers to _____ fractions. After adding or subtracting, write the answer in lowest terms and as a mixed number when possible. This method is difficult to use if the mixed numbers are _____.
(large/small)

76. Add or subtract these fractions as indicated. First use the method where you add or subtract fraction parts and then whole number parts. Then use the method where you change each mixed number to an improper fraction before adding or subtracting. Do you get the same answer using both methods? Which method do you prefer?

(a) $\begin{array}{r} 4\dfrac{5}{8} \\ + 3\dfrac{3}{4} \\ \hline \end{array}$

(b) $\begin{array}{r} 12\dfrac{2}{5} \\ - 8\dfrac{7}{8} \\ \hline \end{array}$

2.13 ▶▶▶ Order Relations and the Order of Operations

OBJECTIVES

1 Identify the greater of two fractions.

2 Use exponents with fractions.

3 Use the order of operations with fractions.

There are times when we want to compare the size of two numbers. For example, we might want to know which is the greater amount, the larger size, or the longer distance.

Fractions, like whole numbers, can be graphed on a number line. For fractions, divide the space between whole numbers into equal parts.

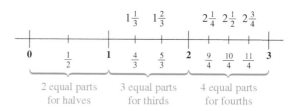

1 Locate each fraction on the number line.

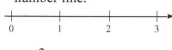

(a) $\dfrac{2}{3}$

OBJECTIVE 1 Identify the greater of two fractions. To compare the size of two numbers, place the two numbers on a number line and use the following rule.

> **Comparing the Size of Two Numbers**
> The number farther to the *left* on the number line is always *less*, and the number farther to the *right* on the number line is always *greater.*

For example, on the number line above, $\frac{1}{2}$ is to the *left* of $\frac{4}{3}$, so $\frac{1}{2}$ is *less than* $\frac{4}{3}$.

◀ Work Problem **1** at the Side.

(b) $1\dfrac{1}{2}$

Write *order relations* using the symbols shown below.

> **Symbols Used to Show Order Relations**
> $<$ is less than $>$ is greater than

EXAMPLE 1 Using Less-Than and Greater-Than Symbols

Rewrite the following using $<$ and $>$ symbols.

(a) $\dfrac{1}{2}$ is less than $\dfrac{4}{3}$

(c) $2\dfrac{3}{4}$

$\dfrac{1}{2}$ is less than $\dfrac{4}{3}$ is written as $\dfrac{1}{2} < \dfrac{4}{3}$ — The number farther to the *left* on the number line is *less.*

(b) $\dfrac{9}{4}$ is greater than 1

$\dfrac{9}{4}$ is greater than 1 is written as $\dfrac{9}{4} > 1$ — The number farther to the *right* on the number line is *greater.*

(c) $\dfrac{5}{3}$ is less than $\dfrac{11}{4}$

ANSWER

1.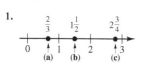

$\dfrac{5}{3}$ is less than $\dfrac{11}{4}$ is written as $\dfrac{5}{3} < \dfrac{11}{4}$

Continued on Next Page

> **Note**
> A number line is a very useful tool when working with order relations.

Work Problem **2** *at the Side.* ▶

The fraction $\frac{7}{8}$ represents 7 of 8 equivalent parts, while $\frac{3}{8}$ means 3 of 8 equivalent parts. Because $\frac{7}{8}$ represents more of the equivalent parts, $\frac{7}{8}$ is greater than $\frac{3}{8}$.

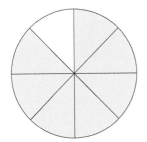 $\frac{7}{8} > \frac{3}{8}$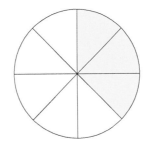

To identify the greater fraction, use the following steps.

> **Identifying the Greater Fraction**
>
> ***Step 1***   Write the fractions as like fractions (same denominators).
>
> ***Step 2***   Compare the numerators. The fraction with the greater numerator is the greater fraction.

EXAMPLE 2   **Identifying the Greater Fraction**

Determine which fraction in each pair is greater.

(a) $\frac{7}{8}, \frac{9}{10}$

First, write the fractions as like fractions. The least common multiple for 8 and 10 is 40.

$$\frac{7}{8} = \frac{7 \cdot 5}{8 \cdot 5} = \frac{35}{40} \quad \text{and} \quad \frac{9}{10} = \frac{9 \cdot 4}{10 \cdot 4} = \frac{36}{40}$$

> Rewrite both fractions with 40 as the denominator.

Look at the numerators. Because 36 is greater than 35, $\frac{36}{40}$ is greater than $\frac{35}{40}$. Then, because $\frac{36}{40}$ is equivalent to $\frac{9}{10}$,

$$\frac{9}{10} > \frac{7}{8} \quad \text{or} \quad \frac{7}{8} < \frac{9}{10}$$

The greater fraction is $\frac{9}{10}$.

(b) $\frac{8}{5}, \frac{23}{15}$

The least common multiple of 5 and 15 is 15.

$$\frac{8}{5} = \frac{8 \cdot 3}{5 \cdot 3} = \frac{24}{15} \quad \text{and} \quad \frac{23}{15} = \frac{23}{15}$$

This shows that $\frac{8}{5}$ is greater than $\frac{23}{15}$, or

$$\frac{8}{5} > \frac{23}{15}$$

Work Problem **3** *at the Side.* ▶

---

2 Use the number line on the previous page to help you write **<** or **>** in each blank to make a true statement.

(a) $1 \rule{2cm}{0.4pt} \frac{5}{4}$

(b) $\frac{8}{3} \rule{2cm}{0.4pt} \frac{3}{2}$

(c) $0 \rule{2cm}{0.4pt} 1$

(d) $\frac{17}{8} \rule{2cm}{0.4pt} \frac{8}{4}$

3 Write **<** or **>** in each blank to make a true statement.

(a) $\frac{7}{8} \rule{2cm}{0.4pt} \frac{3}{4}$

(b) $\frac{13}{8} \rule{2cm}{0.4pt} \frac{15}{9}$

(c) $\frac{9}{4} \rule{2cm}{0.4pt} \frac{7}{3}$

(d) $\frac{9}{10} \rule{2cm}{0.4pt} \frac{14}{15}$

ANSWERS

2. (a) <   **(b)** >   **(c)** <   **(d)** >
3. (a) >   **(b)** <   **(c)** <   **(d)** <

4 Simplify.

(a) $\left(\dfrac{1}{2}\right)^4$

OBJECTIVE **2** **Use exponents with fractions.** Exponents were used in **Section 1.8** to write repeated multiplication. For example,

$$3^2 = \underbrace{3 \cdot 3}_{\substack{\text{Two} \\ \text{factors of 3}}} = 9 \quad \text{and} \quad 5^3 = \underbrace{5 \cdot 5 \cdot 5}_{\substack{\text{Three} \\ \text{factors of 5}}} = 125$$

Exponent ↑ Exponent ↑

The next example shows exponents used with fractions.

EXAMPLE 3 **Using Exponents with Fractions**

Simplify.

(a) $\left(\dfrac{1}{2}\right)^3$

(b) $\left(\dfrac{3}{4}\right)^2$

$$\left(\dfrac{1}{2}\right)^3 = \overbrace{\dfrac{1}{2} \cdot \dfrac{1}{2} \cdot \dfrac{1}{2}}^{\text{Three factors of } \frac{1}{2}} = \dfrac{1}{8}$$

(b) $\left(\dfrac{5}{8}\right)^2$

$$\left(\dfrac{5}{8}\right)^2 = \overbrace{\dfrac{5}{8} \cdot \dfrac{5}{8}}^{\text{Two factors of } \frac{5}{8}} = \dfrac{25}{64}$$

(c) $\left(\dfrac{3}{4}\right)^2 \cdot \left(\dfrac{2}{3}\right)^3$

$$\left(\dfrac{3}{4}\right)^2 \cdot \left(\dfrac{2}{3}\right)^3 = \left(\dfrac{3}{4} \cdot \dfrac{3}{4}\right) \cdot \left(\dfrac{2}{3} \cdot \dfrac{2}{3} \cdot \dfrac{2}{3}\right)$$

(c) $\left(\dfrac{1}{2}\right)^3 \cdot \left(\dfrac{2}{3}\right)^2$

$$= \dfrac{\overset{1}{\cancel{3}} \cdot \overset{1}{\cancel{3}} \cdot \overset{1}{\cancel{2}} \cdot \overset{1}{\cancel{2}} \cdot \overset{1}{\cancel{2}}}{\underset{2}{\cancel{4}} \cdot \underset{2}{\cancel{4}} \cdot \underset{1}{\cancel{3}} \cdot \underset{1}{\cancel{3}} \cdot 3} \quad \text{Divide out all the common factors}$$

$$= \dfrac{1}{6} \quad \text{The fraction is in lowest terms after all common factors are divided out.}$$

◀ *Work Problem* **4** *at the Side.*

(d) $\left(\dfrac{1}{5}\right)^2 \cdot \left(\dfrac{5}{3}\right)^2$

OBJECTIVE **3** **Use the order of operations with fractions.** Recall the *order of operations* from **Section 1.8**.

Order of Operations

1. Do all operations inside *parentheses or other grouping symbols.*

2. Simplify any expressions with *exponents* and find any *square roots.*

3. *Multiply* or *divide,* proceeding from left to right.

4. *Add* or *subtract,* proceeding from left to right.

The next example shows how to apply the order of operations with fractions.

5 Simplify by using the order of operations.

> **EXAMPLE 4** **Using the Order of Operations with Fractions**

Simplify by using the order of operations.

(a) $\dfrac{1}{3} + \dfrac{1}{2}\left(\dfrac{4}{5}\right)$

Multiply $\frac{1}{2}\left(\frac{4}{5}\right)$ first because multiplication and division are done *before* adding.

(a) $\dfrac{5}{9} - \dfrac{3}{4}\left(\dfrac{2}{3}\right)$

| Do **not** add $\frac{1}{3} + \frac{1}{2}$ as the first step. | $\dfrac{1}{3} + \dfrac{1}{\underset{1}{\cancel{2}}}\left(\dfrac{\overset{2}{\cancel{4}}}{5}\right) = \dfrac{1}{3} + \dfrac{2}{5}$ |

Next, add. The least common denominator of 3 and 5 is 15.

$$\frac{1}{3} + \frac{2}{5} = \frac{5}{15} + \frac{6}{15} = \frac{11}{15}$$

(b) $\dfrac{3}{4}\left(\dfrac{2}{3} \cdot \dfrac{3}{5}\right)$

(b) $\dfrac{3}{8}\left(\dfrac{1}{2} + \dfrac{1}{3}\right)$

$$\frac{3}{8}\left(\frac{1}{2} + \frac{1}{3}\right) = \frac{3}{8}\underbrace{\left(\frac{3}{6} + \frac{2}{6}\right)}_{\text{Work inside parentheses first.}}$$

$$= \frac{3}{8}\left(\frac{5}{6}\right)$$

(c) $\dfrac{7}{8}\left(\dfrac{2}{3}\right) - \left(\dfrac{1}{2}\right)^2$

$$= \frac{\overset{1}{\cancel{3}}}{8}\left(\frac{5}{\underset{2}{\cancel{6}}}\right) \qquad \text{Divide numerator and denominator by 3.}$$

$$= \frac{5}{16} \qquad \text{Multiply.}$$

(c) $\left(\dfrac{2}{3}\right)^2 - \dfrac{4}{5}\left(\dfrac{1}{2}\right)$

$$\left(\frac{2}{3}\right)^2 - \frac{4}{5}\left(\frac{1}{2}\right) = \frac{4}{9} - \frac{4}{5}\left(\frac{1}{2}\right)$$

Simplify the expression with the exponent. $\frac{2}{3} \cdot \frac{2}{3}$ is $\frac{4}{9}$.

No work inside parentheses, so operations with exponents are next.

$$= \frac{4}{9} - \frac{\overset{2}{\cancel{4}}}{5}\left(\frac{1}{\underset{1}{\cancel{2}}}\right) \qquad \text{Now, multiply.}$$

(d) $\dfrac{\left(\dfrac{5}{6}\right)^2}{\dfrac{4}{3}}$

$$= \frac{4}{9} - \frac{2}{5}$$

$$= \frac{20}{45} - \frac{18}{45} \qquad \text{Subtract last. (Least common denominator is 45.)}$$

$$= \frac{2}{45}$$

Work Problem **5** *at the Side.* ▶

ANSWERS
5. **(a)** $\dfrac{1}{18}$ **(b)** $\dfrac{3}{10}$ **(c)** $\dfrac{1}{3}$ **(d)** $\dfrac{25}{48}$

2.13 ▶▶▶ **Exercises**

FOR EXTRA HELP

Locate each fraction in Exercises 1–12 on the following number line. See Margin Problem 1.

$$\begin{array}{c|c|c|c|c} + & | & | & | & | \rightarrow \\ 0 & 1 & 2 & 3 & 4 \end{array}$$

1. $\dfrac{1}{2}$ **2.** $\dfrac{1}{4}$ **3.** $\dfrac{3}{2}$ **4.** $\dfrac{5}{4}$ **5.** $\dfrac{7}{3}$ **6.** $\dfrac{11}{4}$

7. $2\dfrac{1}{6}$ **8.** $3\dfrac{4}{5}$ **9.** $\dfrac{7}{2}$ **10.** $\dfrac{7}{8}$ **11.** $3\dfrac{1}{4}$ **12.** $1\dfrac{7}{8}$

Write $<$ or $>$ to make a true statement. See Examples 1 and 2.

 13. $\dfrac{1}{2}$ —— $\dfrac{3}{8}$ **14.** $\dfrac{5}{8}$ —— $\dfrac{3}{4}$ **15.** $\dfrac{5}{6}$ —— $\dfrac{11}{12}$ **16.** $\dfrac{13}{18}$ —— $\dfrac{5}{6}$

17. $\dfrac{5}{12}$ —— $\dfrac{3}{8}$ **18.** $\dfrac{7}{15}$ —— $\dfrac{9}{20}$ **19.** $\dfrac{7}{12}$ —— $\dfrac{11}{18}$ **20.** $\dfrac{17}{24}$ —— $\dfrac{5}{6}$

21. $\dfrac{11}{18}$ —— $\dfrac{5}{9}$ **22.** $\dfrac{13}{15}$ —— $\dfrac{8}{9}$ **23.** $\dfrac{37}{50}$ —— $\dfrac{13}{20}$ **24.** $\dfrac{7}{12}$ —— $\dfrac{11}{20}$

Simplify. See Example 3.

25. $\left(\dfrac{1}{3}\right)^2$ **26.** $\left(\dfrac{2}{3}\right)^2$ **27.** $\left(\dfrac{5}{8}\right)^2$

28. $\left(\dfrac{7}{8}\right)^2$ **29.** $\left(\dfrac{3}{4}\right)^2$ **30.** $\left(\dfrac{3}{5}\right)^3$

31. $\left(\dfrac{4}{5}\right)^3$ **32.** $\left(\dfrac{4}{7}\right)^3$ **33.** $\left(\dfrac{3}{2}\right)^4$

34. $\left(\dfrac{4}{3}\right)^4$ **35.** $\left(\dfrac{3}{4}\right)^4$ **36.** $\left(\dfrac{2}{3}\right)^5$

37. Describe in your own words what a number line is, and draw a picture of one. Be sure to include how it works and how it can be used.

38. You have used the order of operations with whole numbers and again with fractions. List from memory the steps in the order of operations.

Use the order of operations to simplify each expression. See Example 4.

39. $2^4 - 4\,(3)$

40. $3^2 + 4\,(1)$

41. $3 \cdot 2^2 - \dfrac{6}{3}$

42. $5 \cdot 2^3 - \dfrac{6}{2}$

43. $\left(\dfrac{1}{2}\right)^2 \cdot 4$

44. $\left(\dfrac{1}{4}\right)^2 \cdot 4$

45. $\left(\dfrac{3}{4}\right)^2 \cdot \left(\dfrac{1}{3}\right)$

46. $\left(\dfrac{2}{3}\right)^3 \cdot \left(\dfrac{1}{2}\right)$

47. $\left(\dfrac{4}{5}\right)^2 \cdot \left(\dfrac{5}{6}\right)^2$

48. $\left(\dfrac{5}{8}\right)^2 \cdot \left(\dfrac{4}{25}\right)^2$

49. $6\left(\dfrac{2}{3}\right)^2 \left(\dfrac{1}{2}\right)^3$

50. $9\left(\dfrac{1}{3}\right)^3 \left(\dfrac{4}{3}\right)^2$

51. $\dfrac{3}{5}\left(\dfrac{1}{3}\right) + \dfrac{2}{5}\left(\dfrac{3}{4}\right)$

52. $\dfrac{1}{4}\left(\dfrac{3}{4}\right) + \dfrac{3}{8}\left(\dfrac{4}{3}\right)$

53. $\dfrac{1}{2} + \left(\dfrac{1}{2}\right)^2 - \dfrac{3}{8}$

54. $\dfrac{2}{3} + \left(\dfrac{1}{3}\right)^2 - \dfrac{5}{9}$

55. $\left(\dfrac{1}{3} + \dfrac{1}{6}\right) \cdot \dfrac{1}{2}$

56. $\left(\dfrac{3}{5} - \dfrac{3}{20}\right) \cdot \dfrac{4}{3}$

57. $\dfrac{9}{8} \div \left(\dfrac{2}{3} + \dfrac{1}{12}\right)$

58. $\dfrac{6}{5} \div \left(\dfrac{3}{5} - \dfrac{3}{10}\right)$

59. $\left(\dfrac{7}{8} - \dfrac{3}{4}\right) \div \dfrac{3}{2}$

60. $\left(\dfrac{4}{5} - \dfrac{3}{10}\right) \div \dfrac{4}{5}$

61. $\dfrac{3}{8}\left(\dfrac{1}{4} + \dfrac{1}{2}\right) \cdot \dfrac{32}{3}$

62. $\dfrac{1}{3}\left(\dfrac{4}{5} - \dfrac{3}{10}\right) \cdot \dfrac{4}{2}$

63. $\left(\dfrac{3}{4}\right)^2 - \left(\dfrac{1}{2} - \dfrac{1}{6}\right) \div \dfrac{4}{3}$

64. $\left(\dfrac{2}{3}\right)^2 - \left(\dfrac{5}{8} - \dfrac{1}{2}\right) \div \dfrac{3}{2}$

65. $\left(\dfrac{7}{8} - \dfrac{1}{4}\right) - \dfrac{2}{3}\left(\dfrac{3}{4}\right)^2$

66. $\left(\dfrac{5}{6} - \dfrac{7}{12}\right) - \dfrac{3}{4}\left(\dfrac{1}{3}\right)^2$

67. $\left(\dfrac{3}{4}\right)^2\left(\dfrac{2}{3} - \dfrac{5}{9}\right) - \dfrac{1}{4}\left(\dfrac{1}{8}\right)$

68. $\left(\dfrac{2}{3}\right)^2\left(\dfrac{1}{2} - \dfrac{1}{8}\right) - \dfrac{2}{3}\left(\dfrac{1}{8}\right)$

Solve each application problem.

69. The population of Las Vegas, Nevada has had an increase of $\frac{4}{25}$ since the turn of the century. During this same period, the population in Atlanta, Georgia has had an increase of $\frac{5}{30}$. Which city has had a higher rate of population growth? (*Source:* Census Bureau estimates.)

70. Two of the cities with the most expensive average home prices are Newport Beach, California (1\frac{5}{8}$ million) and Santa Barbara, California (1\frac{21}{32}$ million). Which city has the highest average home price? (*Source:* Coldwell Banker Home Price Comparison index.)

Relating Concepts (Exercises 71–80) For Individual or Group Work

You often need to use order relations and the order of operations when solving problems.
Work Exercises 71–80 in order.

71. When comparing the size of two numbers, the symbol —— means **is less than** and the symbol —— means **is greater than.**

72. (a) To identify the greater of two or more fractions, we must first write the fractions as _____ fractions and then compare the _____. The fraction with the greater _____ is the greater fraction.

(b) Write four pairs of fractions, all with different denominators. Write the symbol for **less than** or for **greater than** between each pair.

73. Fill in the blanks to complete the order of operations.

1. Do all operations inside _____ or other grouping symbols.

2. Simplify any expressions with _____ and find any _____ roots.

3. _____ or _____ proceeding from left to right.

4. _____ or _____ proceeding from left to right.

74. Use the order of operations to simplify the following.

$$\left(\frac{2}{3}\right)^2 - \left(\frac{4}{5} - \frac{3}{10}\right) \div \frac{5}{4}$$

Simplify, then place the results on the number line.

75. $\left(\dfrac{2}{3}\right)^2$

76. $\left(\dfrac{3}{2}\right)^2$

77. $\left(\dfrac{3}{5}\right)^3$

78. $\left(\dfrac{5}{4}\right)^2$

79. $4 + 2 - 2^2$

80. $\left(\dfrac{5}{8}\right)^2 + \left(\dfrac{7}{8} - \dfrac{1}{4}\right) \div \dfrac{1}{4}$

Summary Exercises on Fractions

Write proper *or* improper *for each fraction.*

1. $\dfrac{3}{4}$

2. $\dfrac{4}{3}$

3. $\dfrac{10}{10}$

4. $\dfrac{11}{12}$

Write each fraction in lowest terms.

5. $\dfrac{30}{36}$

6. $\dfrac{175}{200}$

7. $\dfrac{15}{35}$

8. $\dfrac{115}{235}$

Add, subtract, multiply, or divide as indicated. Simplify all answers.

9. $\dfrac{3}{4} \cdot \dfrac{2}{3}$

10. $\dfrac{7}{12} \cdot \dfrac{9}{14}$

11. $56 \cdot \dfrac{5}{8}$

12. $\dfrac{5}{8} \div \dfrac{3}{4}$

13. $\dfrac{35}{45} \div \dfrac{10}{15}$

14. $21 \div \dfrac{3}{8}$

15. $\dfrac{7}{8} + \dfrac{2}{3}$

16. $\dfrac{5}{8} + \dfrac{3}{4} + \dfrac{7}{16}$

17. $\dfrac{7}{12} + \dfrac{5}{6} + \dfrac{2}{3}$

18. $\dfrac{5}{6} - \dfrac{3}{4}$

19. $\dfrac{7}{8} - \dfrac{5}{12}$

20. $\dfrac{4}{5} - \dfrac{2}{3}$

First estimate the answer. Then add, subtract, multiply, or divide to find the exact answer.

21. *Exact:*

$3\dfrac{1}{2} \cdot 2\dfrac{1}{4}$

Estimate:

___ • ___ = ___

22. *Exact:*

$5\dfrac{3}{8} \cdot 3\dfrac{1}{4}$

Estimate:

___ • ___ = ___

23. *Exact:*

$8 \cdot 5\dfrac{2}{3} \cdot 2\dfrac{3}{8}$

Estimate:

___ • ___ • ___ = ___

24. *Exact:*

$4\dfrac{3}{8} \div 3\dfrac{3}{4}$

Estimate:

___ ÷ ___ = ___

25. *Exact:*

$6\dfrac{7}{8} \div 2$

Estimate:

___ ÷ ___ = ___

26. *Exact:*

$4\dfrac{5}{8} \div \dfrac{3}{4}$

Estimate:

___ ÷ ___ = ___

27. *Estimate:*   *Exact:*

←——Rounds to——— $\left\{ 5\dfrac{2}{3} \right.$

$+$ ___ ←——Rounds to——— $\left\{ +\, 4\dfrac{1}{4} \right.$

___

28. *Estimate:*   *Exact:*

$18\dfrac{5}{12}$

$+$ ___ $+\, 9\dfrac{3}{4}$

___

29. *Estimate:*   *Exact:*

$14\dfrac{3}{5}$

$+$ ___ $+\, 10\dfrac{2}{3}$

___

30. *Estimate:*   *Exact:*

$8\dfrac{3}{4}$

$-$ ___ $-\, 3\dfrac{4}{5}$

___

31. *Estimate:*   *Exact:*

14

$-$ ___ $-\, 7\dfrac{3}{8}$

___

32. *Estimate:*   *Exact:*

$31\dfrac{5}{6}$

$-$ ___ $-\, 22\dfrac{7}{12}$

___

Simplify by using the order of operations.

33. $\dfrac{1}{5}\left(\dfrac{2}{3} - \dfrac{1}{4} \right)$

34. $\dfrac{3}{4} \div \left(\dfrac{1}{2} + \dfrac{1}{3} \right)$

35. $\dfrac{2}{3} + \left(\dfrac{2}{3} \right)^2 - \dfrac{5}{6}$

Find the least common multiple of each set of numbers.

36. 8, 10

37. 9, 18, 24

38. 4, 12, 21

Rewrite each fraction with the indicated denominator.

39. $\dfrac{5}{6} = \dfrac{}{42}$

40. $\dfrac{3}{7} = \dfrac{}{28}$

41. $\dfrac{11}{12} = \dfrac{}{60}$

Write $<$ *or* $>$ *to make a true statement.*

42. $\dfrac{7}{8}$ ___ $\dfrac{15}{16}$

43. $\dfrac{16}{20}$ ___ $\dfrac{23}{30}$

44. $\dfrac{11}{15}$ ___ $\dfrac{7}{10}$

Chapter 2   ▶▶▶ Summary

▶ Key Terms

2.9	**like fractions**	Fractions with the same denominator are called *like fractions.*
	unlike fractions	Fractions with different denominators are called *unlike fractions.*
2.10	**least common multiple**	Given two or more whole numbers, the least common multiple is the smallest whole number that is divisible by all the numbers.
	LCM	The abbreviation for *least common multiple* is LCM.
2.11	**least common denominator**	When unlike fractions are rewritten as like fractions having the least common multiple as the denominator, the new denominator is the least common denominator.
	LCD	The abbreviation for *least common denominator* is LCD.
2.12	**regrouping when adding fractions**	Regrouping is used in the addition of mixed numbers when the sum of the fractions is greater than 1.
	regrouping when subtracting fractions	Regrouping is used in the subtraction of mixed numbers when the fraction part of the minuend is less than the fraction part of the subtrahend.

▶ New Symbols

$<$ is less than ($2 < 5$) $>$ is greater than ($4 > 2$)

▶ Test Your Word Power

See how well you have learned the vocabulary in this chapter. Answers follow the Quick Review.

1. Like fractions are
   A. fractions that are equivalent
   B. fractions that are not equivalent
   C. fractions that have the same numerator
   D. fractions that have the same denominator.

2. Two or more fractions are **unlike fractions** if
   A. they are not equivalent
   B. they have different numerators
   C. they have different denominators
   D. they are improper fractions.

3. The abbreviation **LCM** stands for
   A. the largest common multiple
   B. the longest common multiple
   C. the most likely common multiplier
   D. the least common multiple.

4. The **least common multiple** is
   A. the smallest whole number that is divisible by each of two or more numbers
   B. the smallest numerator
   C. the smallest denominator
   D. the smallest whole number that is not divisible by a group of numbers.

5. The abbreviation **LCD** stands for
   A. the largest common denominator
   B. the least common denominator
   C. the least common divisor
   D. the most likely common denominator.

6. The **least common denominator** is
   A. needed when multiplying fractions
   B. needed when dividing fractions
   C. the least common multiple of the denominators in a fraction problem
   D. any denominator that is common to a group of fractions.

▶ Quick Review

Concepts	Examples

(2.9) Adding Like Fractions

Add numerators and keep the same denominator. Write the result in lowest terms.

$$\frac{3}{4} + \frac{1}{4} + \frac{5}{4} = \frac{3+1+5}{4} = \frac{9}{4} = 2\frac{1}{4}$$

(2.9) Subtracting Like Fractions

Subtract numerators and keep the same denominator. Write the result in lowest terms.

$$\frac{7}{8} - \frac{5}{8} = \frac{7-5}{8} = \frac{2}{8} = \frac{2 \div 2}{8 \div 2} = \frac{1}{4}$$

(2.10) Finding the Least Common Multiple (LCM)

Method of using multiples of the larger number: List the first few multiples of the larger number. Check each one until you find the multiple that is divisible by the smaller number.

$$\frac{1}{3} + \frac{1}{4}$$

$4, 8, 12, 16, \ldots \longleftarrow$ Multiples of 4

First multiple divisible by 3 $(12 \div 3 = 4)$

The least common multiple (LCM) of 3 and 4 is 12.

(2.10) Finding the Least Common Multiple (LCM)

Method of prime numbers: First find the prime factorization of each number. Then use the prime factors to build the least common multiple.

Factors of 9

$$9 = 3 \cdot 3$$
$$15 = 3 \cdot 5$$

$$\text{LCM} = 3 \cdot 3 \cdot 5 = 45$$

Factors of 15

The least common multiple (LCM) of 9 and 15 is 45.

(2.11) Adding Unlike Fractions

Step 1 Find the least common multiple (LCM).
Step 2 Rewrite the fractions with the least common multiple as the denominator.
Step 3 Add the numerators, placing the sum over the common denominator, and simplify the answer.

$= 60$

$$\frac{1}{3} + \frac{1}{4} + \frac{1}{10}$$

$$\frac{1}{3} = \frac{20}{60} \quad \frac{1}{4} = \frac{15}{60} \quad \frac{1}{10} = \frac{41}{60} \quad \text{Lowest terms}$$

$$\frac{20}{1}$$

$$3$$

$$\frac{15}{24} \quad \frac{1}{3} = \frac{8}{24}$$

$\text{LCM} = 24$

(2.11) Subtracting Unlike Fractions

Step 1 Find the least common multiple (LCM)
Step 2 Rewrite the fractions with the least multiple as the denominator
Step 3 Subtract the numerator over the common the answer.

$$\frac{15}{24} - \frac{8}{24} = \frac{7}{24} \quad \text{Lowest Terms}$$

Concepts

Examples

2.12 Adding Mixed Numbers

Round the numbers and estimate the answer. Then find the exact answer using these steps.

Step 1 Add the fractions using a common denominator.

Step 2 Add the whole numbers.

Step 3 Combine the sums of the whole numbers and the fractions, simplifying the fraction part when necessary.

Compare the exact answer to the estimate to see if it is reasonable.

Estimate: *Exact:*

$$10 \xleftarrow{\text{Rounds to}} \begin{cases} 9\dfrac{2}{3} = 9\dfrac{8}{12} \end{cases}$$

$$+\ 7 \xleftarrow{\text{Rounds to}} \begin{cases} +\ 6\dfrac{3}{4} = 6\dfrac{9}{12} \end{cases}$$

$$17 \qquad\qquad 15\dfrac{17}{12} = 16\dfrac{5}{12}$$

The exact answer of $16\frac{5}{12}$ is reasonable because it is close to the estimate of 17.

2.12 Subtracting Mixed Numbers

Round the numbers and estimate the answer. Then find the exact answer using these steps.

Step 1 Subtract the fractions, regrouping if necessary.

Step 2 Subtract the whole numbers.

Step 3 Combine the differences of the whole numbers and the fractions, simplifying the fraction part when necessary.

Compare the exact answer to the estimate to see if it is reasonable.

Estimate: *Exact:*

$$9 \xleftarrow{\text{Rounds to}} \begin{cases} 8\dfrac{5}{8} = 8\dfrac{15}{24} = 7\dfrac{39}{24} \end{cases}$$

$$-\ 4 \xleftarrow{\text{Rounds to}} \begin{cases} -\ 3\dfrac{11}{12} = 3\dfrac{22}{24} = 3\dfrac{22}{24} \end{cases}$$

$$5 \qquad\qquad 4\dfrac{17}{24}$$

The exact answer of $4\frac{17}{24}$ is reasonable because it is close to the estimate of 5.

2.12 Adding or Subtracting Mixed Numbers Using an Alternate Method

Step 1 Change the mixed numbers to improper fractions.

Step 2 Rewrite the unlike fractions as like fractions.

Step 3 Add or subtract the numerators and simplify the answer.

Add.

$$2\dfrac{2}{3} = \dfrac{8}{3} = \dfrac{64}{24}$$

$$+\ 1\dfrac{3}{8} = \dfrac{11}{8} = +\dfrac{33}{24}$$

24 is the least common denominator.

$$\dfrac{97}{24} = 4\dfrac{1}{24} \quad \text{Answer as mixed number}$$

$\uparrow$ Improper fractions

Subtract.

$$8\dfrac{2}{3} = \dfrac{26}{3} = \dfrac{104}{12}$$

$$-\ 5\dfrac{3}{4} = \dfrac{23}{4} = -\dfrac{69}{12}$$

12 is the least common denominator.

$$\dfrac{35}{12} = 2\dfrac{11}{12} \quad \text{Answer as mixed number}$$

$\uparrow$ Improper fractions

(2.13) Identifying the Greater of Two Fractions

With unlike fractions, change to like fractions first. The fraction with the greater numerator is the greater fraction. Use these symbols:

$<$　　is less than

$>$　　is greater than

Identify the greater fraction.

$$\frac{7}{8}, \frac{9}{10}$$

$$\frac{7}{8} = \frac{7 \cdot 5}{8 \cdot 5} = \frac{35}{40}$$

$$\frac{9}{10} = \frac{9 \cdot 4}{10 \cdot 4} = \frac{36}{40}$$

$\frac{35}{40}$ is smaller than $\frac{36}{40}$, so $\frac{7}{8} < \frac{9}{10}$ or $\frac{9}{10} > \frac{7}{8}$.
$\frac{9}{10}$ is greater.

(2.13) Using the Order of Operations with Fractions

Follow the order of operations.
1. Do all operations inside parentheses or other grouping symbols.
2. Simplify any expressions with exponents and find any square roots.
3. Multiply or divide, proceeding from left to right.
4. Add or subtract, proceeding from left to right.

Simplify by using the order of operations.

$$\frac{1}{2}\left(\frac{2}{3}\right) - \left(\frac{1}{4}\right)^2 \qquad \text{Simplify fraction with exponent.}$$

$$= \frac{1}{2}\left(\frac{2}{3}\right) - \frac{1}{16} \qquad \text{Next, multiply.}$$

$$= \frac{1}{3} - \frac{1}{16}$$

$$= \frac{16}{48} - \frac{3}{48} \qquad \text{Change to common denominator and subtract.}$$

$$= \frac{13}{48}$$

ANSWERS TO TEST YOUR WORD POWER

1. D; *Example:* Because the fractions $\frac{3}{8}$ and $\frac{10}{8}$ both have 8 as a denominator, they are like fractions.

2. C; *Example:* The fractions $\frac{2}{3}$ and $\frac{3}{4}$ are unlike fractions because they have different denominators.

3. D; *Example:* LCM is the abbreviation for least common multiple.

4. A; *Example:* The least common multiple of 4 and 5 is 20 because 20 is the smallest number into which 4 and 5 will divide evenly.

5. B; *Example:* LCD is the abbreviation for least common denominator.

6. C; *Example:* The least common denominator of the fractions $\frac{2}{3}$ and $\frac{1}{2}$ is 6 because 6 is the least common multiple of 3 and 2.

　　When written using the least common denominator, $\frac{2}{3}$ and $\frac{1}{2}$ become $\frac{4}{6}$ and $\frac{3}{6}$, respectively.

Chapter 2 ▶▶▶ Review Exercises

[2.9] *Add or subtract. Write answers in lowest terms.*

1. $\dfrac{5}{7} + \dfrac{1}{7}$

2. $\dfrac{4}{9} + \dfrac{3}{9}$

3. $\dfrac{1}{8} + \dfrac{3}{8} + \dfrac{2}{8}$

4. $\dfrac{5}{16} - \dfrac{3}{16}$

5. $\dfrac{5}{10} + \dfrac{3}{10}$

6. $\dfrac{5}{12} - \dfrac{3}{12}$

7. $\dfrac{36}{62} - \dfrac{10}{62}$

8. $\dfrac{68}{75} - \dfrac{43}{75}$

Solve each application problem. Write answers in lowest terms.

9. Jaime Villagranna earns $\frac{7}{12}$ of his income installing kitchen cabinets for the Home Depot and $\frac{4}{12}$ of his income by operating his own cabinet business. What fraction of his total income comes from the two activities?

10. The Koats for Kids committee members completed $\frac{5}{8}$ of their Web-page design in the morning and $\frac{3}{8}$ in the afternoon. How much less did they complete in the afternoon than in the morning?

[2.10] *Find the least common multiple of each set of numbers.*

11. 5, 2

12. 3, 4

13. 10, 12, 20

14. 3, 8, 4

15. 6, 8, 5, 15

16. 15, 9, 20

Rewrite each fraction using the indicated denominator.

17. $\dfrac{2}{3} = \dfrac{}{12}$

18. $\dfrac{3}{8} = \dfrac{}{56}$

19. $\dfrac{2}{5} = \dfrac{}{25}$

20. $\dfrac{5}{9} = \dfrac{}{81}$

21. $\dfrac{4}{5} = \dfrac{}{40}$

22. $\dfrac{5}{16} = \dfrac{}{64}$

[2.9–2.11] *Add or subtract. Write answers in lowest terms.*

23. $\dfrac{1}{2} + \dfrac{1}{3}$

24. $\dfrac{1}{5} + \dfrac{3}{10} + \dfrac{3}{8}$

25. $\begin{array}{r} \dfrac{5}{12} \\[6pt] + \dfrac{5}{24} \\ \hline \end{array}$

26. $\dfrac{2}{3} - \dfrac{1}{4}$

27. $\begin{array}{r} \dfrac{7}{8} \\[6pt] - \dfrac{1}{3} \\ \hline \end{array}$

28. $\begin{array}{r} \dfrac{11}{12} \\[6pt] - \dfrac{4}{9} \\ \hline \end{array}$

Solve each application problem.

29. The San Juan School District operates an after school program for students. This year $\frac{2}{5}$ of the students played after school sports, $\frac{1}{6}$ participated in arts and crafts, and $\frac{1}{3}$ spent their time in tutoring and study hall. What fraction of the total students participated in these activities?

30. Lynn Couch Catering serves food and beverages when and where you like it. She finds that $\frac{1}{3}$ of her business is for company events, $\frac{3}{8}$ for wedding parties, and $\frac{1}{4}$ for club and membership events. What portion of her business comes from these three categories?

[2.12] *First estimate the answer. Then add or subtract to find the exact answer. Write exact answers as mixed numbers.*

31. *Estimate:*   *Exact:*

← Rounds to $\Big\{ 18\dfrac{5}{8}$

+ ___   ← Rounds to $\Big\{ + 13\dfrac{3}{4}$

32. *Estimate:*   *Exact:*

$22\dfrac{2}{3}$

+ ___ $+ 15\dfrac{4}{9}$

33. *Estimate:*   *Exact:*

$12\dfrac{3}{5}$

$8\dfrac{5}{8}$

+ ___ $+ 10\dfrac{5}{16}$

34. *Estimate:*   *Exact:*

$31\dfrac{3}{4}$

− ___ $- 14\dfrac{2}{3}$

35. *Estimate:*   *Exact:*

34

− ___ $- 15\dfrac{2}{3}$

36. *Estimate:*   *Exact:*

$215\dfrac{7}{16}$

− ___ $- 136$

Add or subtract by changing mixed numbers to improper fractions. Simplify all answers.

37. $5\dfrac{2}{5}$

$+ 3\dfrac{7}{10}$

38. $4\dfrac{3}{4}$

$+ 5\dfrac{2}{3}$

39. 5

$- 1\dfrac{3}{4}$

40. $6\dfrac{1}{2}$

$- 4\dfrac{5}{6}$

41. $8\dfrac{1}{3}$

$- 2\dfrac{5}{6}$

42. $5\dfrac{5}{12}$

$- 2\dfrac{5}{8}$

First estimate the answer and then find the exact answer for each application problem.

43. Two long-distance runners began an $18\frac{3}{4}$ mile run. They ran uphill $5\frac{5}{8}$ miles, downhill $7\frac{1}{3}$ miles, and the rest of the course was level. Find the distance of the level portion of the course.

Estimate:

Exact:

44. The Boys and Girls Clubs of America collected $28\frac{2}{3}$ tons of newspapers on Saturday and $24\frac{3}{4}$ tons on Sunday. Find the total weight of the newspapers collected.

Estimate:

Exact:

45. In a recent bass-fishing derby, Darrel Holmes caught three largemouth bass weighing $8\frac{7}{8}$ pounds, $9\frac{1}{2}$ pounds, and $6\frac{3}{4}$ pounds. Find their total weight.

Estimate:

Exact:

46. A developer wants to build a shopping center. She bought two parcels of land, one, $1\frac{11}{16}$ acres, and the other, $2\frac{3}{4}$ acres. If she needs a total of $8\frac{1}{2}$ acres for the center, how much additional land does she need to buy?

Estimate:

Exact:

[2.13] *Locate each fraction in Exercises 47–50 on the number line.*

47. $\frac{3}{8}$ **48.** $\frac{7}{4}$ **49.** $\frac{8}{3}$ **50.** $3\frac{1}{5}$

Write < or > in each blank to make a true statement.

51. $\frac{2}{3}$ ___ $\frac{3}{4}$ **52.** $\frac{3}{4}$ ___ $\frac{7}{8}$ **53.** $\frac{1}{2}$ ___ $\frac{7}{15}$ **54.** $\frac{7}{10}$ ___ $\frac{8}{15}$

55. $\frac{9}{16}$ ___ $\frac{5}{8}$ **56.** $\frac{7}{20}$ ___ $\frac{8}{25}$ **57.** $\frac{19}{36}$ ___ $\frac{29}{54}$ **58.** $\frac{19}{132}$ ___ $\frac{7}{55}$

Simplify each expression.

59. $\left(\frac{1}{2}\right)^2$ **60.** $\left(\frac{2}{3}\right)^2$ **61.** $\left(\frac{3}{10}\right)^3$ **62.** $\left(\frac{3}{8}\right)^4$

Simplify by using the order of operations.

63. $8\left(\dfrac{1}{4}\right)^2$

64. $12\left(\dfrac{3}{4}\right)^2$

65. $\left(\dfrac{2}{3}\right)^2 \cdot \left(\dfrac{3}{8}\right)^2$

66. $\dfrac{7}{8} \div \left(\dfrac{1}{8} + \dfrac{3}{4}\right)$

67. $\left(\dfrac{1}{2}\right)^2 \cdot \left(\dfrac{1}{4} + \dfrac{1}{2}\right)$

68. $\left(\dfrac{1}{4}\right)^3 + \left(\dfrac{5}{8} + \dfrac{3}{4}\right)$

▶▶▶ Mixed Review Exercises

Simplify. Use the order of operations as necessary.

69. $\dfrac{7}{8} - \dfrac{1}{8}$

70. $\dfrac{7}{10} - \dfrac{3}{10}$

71. $\dfrac{29}{32} - \dfrac{5}{16}$

72. $\dfrac{1}{4} + \dfrac{1}{8} + \dfrac{5}{16}$

73. $\begin{array}{r} 6\frac{2}{3} \\ -\ 4\frac{1}{2} \\ \hline \end{array}$

74. $\begin{array}{r} 9\frac{1}{2} \\ +\ 16\frac{3}{4} \\ \hline \end{array}$

75. $\begin{array}{r} 7 \\ -\ 1\frac{5}{8} \\ \hline \end{array}$

76. $\begin{array}{r} 2\frac{3}{5} \\ 8\frac{5}{8} \\ +\ \frac{5}{16} \\ \hline \end{array}$

77. $\begin{array}{r} 32\frac{5}{12} \\ -17 \\ \hline \end{array}$

78. $\dfrac{7}{22} + \dfrac{3}{22} + \dfrac{3}{11}$

79. $\left(\dfrac{1}{4}\right)^2 \cdot \left(\dfrac{2}{5}\right)^3$

80. $\dfrac{3}{8} \div \left(\dfrac{1}{2} + \dfrac{1}{4} \right)$

81. $\left(\dfrac{2}{3} \right)^2 \cdot \left(\dfrac{1}{3} + \dfrac{1}{6} \right)$

82. $\left(\dfrac{2}{3} \right)^3 + \left(\dfrac{2}{3} - \dfrac{5}{9} \right)$

Write < or > in each blank to make a true statement.

83. $\dfrac{2}{3}$ ___ $\dfrac{7}{12}$

84. $\dfrac{8}{9}$ ___ $\dfrac{15}{8}$

85. $\dfrac{17}{30}$ ___ $\dfrac{36}{60}$

86. $\dfrac{5}{8}$ ___ $\dfrac{17}{30}$

Find the least common multiple of each set of numbers.

87. 12, 18

88. 6, 8, 10, 12

89. 9, 14, 21

Rewrite each fraction using the indicated denominator.

90. $\dfrac{2}{3} = \dfrac{}{27}$

91. $\dfrac{9}{12} = \dfrac{}{144}$

92. $\dfrac{4}{5} = \dfrac{}{75}$

First estimate the answer and then find the exact answer for each application problem.

93. A cement contractor needs $13\frac{1}{2}$ ft of wire mesh for a concrete walkway and $22\frac{3}{8}$ ft of wire mesh for a driveway. If the contractor starts with a roll of wire that is $92\frac{3}{4}$ ft long, find the number of feet remaining after the two jobs have been completed.

Estimate:

Exact:

94. A baker had four 50-pound bags of sugar. If she used $68\frac{1}{2}$ pounds of sugar to bake cakes, $76\frac{5}{8}$ pounds for baking pies, and $33\frac{1}{4}$ pounds for baking cookies, how many pounds of sugar remain?

Estimate:

Exact:

Chapter 2 ▷▷▷ **Test**   Use the Chapter Test Prep Video CD to see fully worked-out solutions to any of the exercises you want to review

Add or subtract. Write answers in lowest terms.

1. _____

1. $\dfrac{5}{8} + \dfrac{1}{8}$

2. $\dfrac{1}{16} + \dfrac{7}{16}$

2. _____

3. _____

4. _____

3. $\dfrac{7}{10} - \dfrac{3}{10}$

4. $\dfrac{7}{12} - \dfrac{5}{12}$

Find the least common multiple of each set of numbers.

5. _____

5. 2, 3, 4

6. 6, 3, 5, 15

7. 6, 9, 27, 36

6. _____

7. _____

Add or subtract. Write answers in lowest terms.

8. _____

8. $\dfrac{3}{8} + \dfrac{1}{4}$

9. $\dfrac{2}{9} + \dfrac{5}{12}$

9. _____

10. _____

10. $\dfrac{7}{8} - \dfrac{2}{3}$

11. $\dfrac{2}{5} - \dfrac{3}{8}$

11. _____

First estimate the answer. Then add or subtract to find the exact answer; simplify exact answers.

12. *Estimate:* _____

12. $7\dfrac{2}{3} + 4\dfrac{5}{6}$

13. $16\dfrac{2}{5} - 11\dfrac{2}{3}$

   Exact: _____

13. *Estimate:* _____

   Exact: _____

14. *Estimate:* _____

14. $18\dfrac{3}{4} + 9\dfrac{2}{5} + 12\dfrac{1}{3}$

15. $24 - 18\dfrac{3}{8}$

   Exact: _____

15. *Estimate:* _____

   Exact: _____

16. Most students say that "addition and subtraction of fractions is more difficult than multiplication and division of fractions." Why do you think they say this? Do you agree with these students?

16. _____

17. Devise and explain a method of estimating an answer to addition and subtraction problems involving mixed numbers. Might your estimated answer vary from the exact answer? If it did, what would the estimation accomplish?

17. _____

First estimate the answer and then find the exact answer for each application problem.

18. In one week, a kennel owner used $10\frac{3}{8}$ pounds of puppy chow, $84\frac{1}{2}$ pounds of dry kibble, $36\frac{5}{6}$ pounds of high-protein mature dog mix, and $8\frac{1}{3}$ pounds of fresh ground meat products. Find the total number of pounds used.

18. *Estimate:* _____

Exact: _____

19. A painting contractor arrived at a 6-unit apartment complex with $147\frac{1}{2}$ gallons of exterior paint. If his crew sprayed $68\frac{1}{2}$ gallons on the wood siding, rolled $37\frac{3}{8}$ gallons on the masonry exterior, and brushed $5\frac{3}{4}$ gallons on the trim, find the number of gallons of paint remaining.

19. *Estimate:* _____

Exact: _____

Write < or > between each pair of fractions to make a true statement.

20. $\frac{3}{4}$ _____ $\frac{17}{24}$

21. $\frac{19}{24}$ _____ $\frac{17}{36}$

20. _____

21. _____

Simplify. Use the order of operations as needed.

22. $\left(\frac{1}{3}\right)^3 \cdot 54$

23. $\left(\frac{3}{4}\right)^2 - \left(\frac{7}{8} \cdot \frac{1}{3}\right)$

22. _____

23. _____

24. $4\left(\frac{7}{8} - \frac{7}{16}\right)$

25. $\frac{5}{6} + \frac{4}{3}\left(\frac{3}{8}\right)$

24. _____

25. _____

Study Skills

OBJECTIVES

1. Apply suggestions to tests and quizzes.
2. Develop a set of "best practices" to apply while testing.

Improving Your Test Score

To Improve Your Test Score	Comments
Come prepared with a pencil, eraser, and calculator, if allowed. If you are easily distracted, sit in the corner farthest from the door.	*Working in pencil lets you erase,* keeping your work neat and readable.
Scan the entire test, note the point value of different problems, and plan your time accordingly. Allow at least five minutes to check your work at the end of the testing time.	If you have 50 minutes to do 20 problems, $50 \div 20 = 2.5$ minutes per problem. *Spend less time on easy ones,* more time on problems with higher point values.
Read directions carefully, and circle any significant words. When you finish a problem, read the directions again to make sure you did what was asked.	*Pay attention to announcements* written on the board or made by your instructor. Ask if you don't understand. You don't want to get problems wrong because you misread the directions!
Show your work. Most math teachers give partial credit if some of the steps in your work are correct, even if the final answer is wrong. *Write neatly.* If you like to scribble when first working or checking a problem, do it on scratch paper.	*If your teacher can't read your writing, you won't get credit for it.* If you need more space to work, ask if you can use extra pieces of paper that you hand in with your test paper.
Check that the *answer to an application problem is reasonable* and makes sense. Read the problem again to make sure you've answered the question.	*Use common sense.* Can the father really be seven years old? Would a month's rent be $32,140? Label your answer: $, years, inches, etc.
To check for careless errors, you need to *rework the problem again, without looking at your previous work.* Cover up your work with a piece of scratch paper, and pretend you are doing the problem for the first time. Then compare the two answers.	If you just "look over" your work, your mind can make the same mistake again without noticing it. Reworking the problem from the beginning *forces you to rethink it.* If possible, use a different method to solve the problem the second time.

Reducing Anxiety

To Reduce Anxiety	Comments
Do not try to review up until the last minute before the test. Instead, go for a walk, do some deep breathing, and arrive just in time for the test. Ignore other students.	Listening to anxious classmates before the test *may cause you to panic.* Moderate exercise and deep breathing will calm your mind.

To Reduce Anxiety	Comments
Do a "knowledge dump" as soon as you get the test. Write important notes to yourself in a corner of the test paper: formulas, or common errors you want to watch out for.	Writing down tips and things that you've memorized **lets you relax;** you won't have to worry about forgetting those things and can refer to them as needed.
Do the easy problems first in order to build confidence. If you feel your anxiety starting to build, *immediately* stop for a minute, close your eyes, and take several slow, deep breaths.	Greater confidence helps you **get the easier problems correct.** Anxiety causes shallow breathing, which leads to confusion and reduced concentration. Deep breathing calms you.
As you work on more difficult problems, **notice your "inner voice."** You may have negative thoughts such as, "I can't do it," or "who cares about this test anyway." In your mind, yell, "STOP" and take several deep, slow breaths. Or, replace the negative thought with a positive one.	Here are **examples of positive statements.** Try writing one of them on the top of your test paper. • I know I can do it. • I can do this one step at a time. • I've studied hard, and I'll do the best I can.
If you still can't solve a difficult problem when you come back to it the second time, **make a guess and do not change it.** In this situation, your first guess is your best bet. Do not change an answer just because you're a little unsure. **Change it only if you find an obvious mistake.**	If you are thinking about changing an answer, be sure you have a good reason for changing it. If you cannot find a specific error, leave your first answer alone. **When the tests are returned, check to see if changing answers helped or hurt you.**
Read the harder problems twice. Write down *anything* that might help solve the problem: a formula, a picture, etc. If you still can't get it, circle the problem and **come back to it later.** Do *not* erase any of the things you wrote down.	If you know even a *little* bit about the problem, write it down. The **answer may come to you** as you work on it, or you may get partial credit. Don't spend too long on any one problem. Your subconscious mind will work on the tough problem while you go on with the test.
Ignore students who finish early. Use the entire test time. *You do not get extra credit for finishing early.* Use the extra time to rework problems and correct careless errors.	Students who leave early are often the ones who didn't study or who are too anxious to continue working. If they bother you, **sit as far from the door as possible.**

Reducing Anxiety
(*continued*)

> **Why Are These Suggestions Brain Friendly?**
>
> Several suggestions address anxiety. **Reducing anxiety allows your brain to make the connections between dendrites;** in other words, you can think clearly.
>
> Remember that **your brain continues to work on a difficult problem** even if you skip it and go on to the next one. Your subconscious mind will come through for you if you are open to the idea!
>
> Some of the suggestions ask you to **use your common sense.** Follow the directions, show your work, write neatly, and pay attention to whether your answers really make sense.

Cumulative Review Exercises ▶▶▶ Chapters 1–2

1. In this number, name the digit that has the given place value. 5,639,428

millions   ten-thousands

thousands   hundreds

2. Round 59,803 to the nearest ten, then to the nearest hundred, and finally to the nearest thousand.

Use front end rounding to estimate each answer. Then find the exact answer.

3. *Estimate:*   *Exact:*

— _____   24,276
                             − 9,887

4. *Estimate:*   *Exact:*

_____   35)112,385
)

Add, subtract, multiply, or divide as indicated.

5.   375,899
          521,742
       + 357,968

6.   3,896,502
       − 1,094,807

7. 5(8)(4)

8.   962
        × 384

9. 8)1080

10. 13,467 ÷ 5

Use front end rounding to estimate the answer to each application problem. Then find the exact answer.

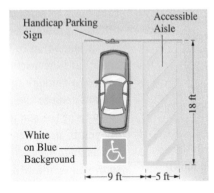

Handicap Parking Sign

Accessible Aisle

White on Blue Background

18 ft

◄—9 ft—►◄–5 ft–►

11. The Americans with Disabilities Act provides the single parking space design shown at the left. Find the perimeter of (distance around) this parking space, including the accessible aisle.

Estimate:

Exact:

12. The single parking space design in Exercise 22 measures 18 ft by 14 ft. Find its area.

Estimate:

Exact:

Round the mixed numbers in each problem to the nearest whole number and estimate the answer. Then find the exact answer.

13. The top of a rectangular pool table is $1\frac{3}{4}$ yards by $2\frac{2}{3}$ yards. Find its area.

Estimate:

Exact:

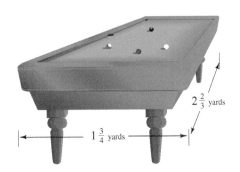

$2\frac{2}{3}$ yards

$1\frac{3}{4}$ yards

14. Fleas can jump 130 times higher than their own height. In human terms, how far could a $70\frac{1}{4}$ inch person jump? (*Source:* High Tech Productions Science and Technology Center.)

Estimate:

Exact:

Simplify.

15. $2^4 \cdot 3^2$

16. $5^2 - 2(8)$

17. $\sqrt{25} + 5 \cdot 9 - 6$

18. $\frac{2}{3}\left(\frac{4}{5} - \frac{2}{3}\right)$

19. $\frac{3}{4} \div \left(\frac{1}{3} + \frac{1}{2}\right)$

20. $\frac{7}{8} + \left(\frac{3}{4}\right)^2 - \frac{3}{8}$

21. $\frac{3}{4} \cdot \frac{2}{3}$

22. $42 \cdot \frac{7}{8}$

23. $\frac{25}{40} \div \frac{10}{35}$

24. $9 \div \frac{2}{3}$

First estimate the answer and then add or subtract to find the exact answer. Write exact answers as mixed numbers.

25. *Estimate:*   *Exact:*

$\xleftarrow{\text{Rounds to}}$ $\begin{cases} 3\frac{3}{8} \\ \\ +\ 4\frac{1}{2} \end{cases}$

$+$ $\xleftarrow{\text{Rounds to}}$

___

26. *Estimate:*   *Exact:*

$21\frac{7}{8}$

$+$ $+\ 4\frac{5}{12}$

___   ___

27. *Estimate:*   *Exact:*

5

$-$ $-\ 2\frac{3}{8}$

___   ___

Locate each fraction in Exercises 28–31 on the number line at the right.

28. $2\frac{3}{4}$

29. $\frac{1}{9}$

30. $\frac{5}{3}$

31. $\frac{10}{3}$

number line: 0 1 2 3 4

Write < or > in each blank to make a true statement.

32. $\frac{3}{5}$ ___ $\frac{5}{8}$

33. $\frac{17}{20}$ ___ $\frac{3}{4}$

34. $\frac{7}{12}$ ___ $\frac{11}{18}$

3

Real Number System

3.1 ▶▶▶ Introduction to Signed Numbers

OBJECTIVE 1 **Write positive and negative numbers used in everyday situations.** The whole numbers are either 0 or greater than 0. Numbers *greater* than 0 are called *positive numbers*. But many everyday situations involve numbers that are *less* than 0, called *negative numbers*. Here are a few examples.

OBJECTIVES

1 Write positive and negative numbers used in everyday situations.

2 Graph signed numbers on a number line.

3 Use the < and > symbols to compare integers.

4 Find the absolute value of integers.

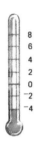

At midnight the temperature dropped to 4 degrees *below* zero.

−4 degrees

Jean had $30 in her checking account. She wrote a check for $40.75. We say she is now $10.75 "in the hole," or $10.75 "in the red," or *overdrawn* by $10.75.

−$10.75

The Packers football team *gained* 6 yards on the first play. On the second play they *lost* 9 yards. We can write the results using a positive number and a negative number.

+6 yards   and   **−9 yards**

A plane took off from the airport and climbed to 20,000 feet *above* sea level. We can write this using a positive number.

+20,000 feet

A scuba diver swam down to $25\frac{1}{2}$ feet *below* the surface. We can write this using a negative number.

−$25\frac{1}{2}$ feet

Note

To write a negative number, put a negative sign (a dash) in front of it: −10. Notice that the negative sign looks exactly like the subtraction sign, as in 5 − 3 = 2. The negative sign and subtraction sign do *not* mean the same thing (more on that in the next section). To avoid confusion for now, we will write negative signs in red and put them up higher than subtraction signs.

⁻10   means   negative 10   14 − 10 means 14 minus 10
↑
└─── Raised dash

Starting in **Chapter 5,** we will write negative signs in the traditional way. However, if you use a graphing calculator, it may show negative signs in the raised position.

Positive numbers can be written two ways:

1. Write a positive sign in front of the number: ⁺2 is *positive* 2. We will write the sign in the raised position to avoid confusion with the sign for addition, as in 6 + 3 = 9.

2. Do not write any sign. For example, 16 is assumed to be *positive* 16.

1 Write each negative number with a raised negative sign. Write each positive number in two ways.

(a) The temperature is $5\frac{1}{2}$ degrees below zero.

(b) Cameron lost 12 pounds on a diet.

(c) I deposited $210.35 in my checking account.

(d) I wrote too many checks, so my account is overdrawn by $65.

(e) The submarine dived to 100 feet below the surface of the sea.

(f) In this round of the card game, I won 50 points.

2 Graph each set of numbers.

(a) $^-2$ (b) 2 (c) 0

(d) $^-4$ (e) 4

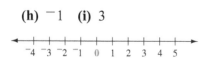

(f) $^-3\frac{1}{2}$ (g) $\frac{1}{2}$

(h) $^-1$ (i) 3

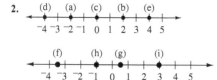

EXAMPLE 1   **Writing Positive and Negative Numbers**

Write each negative number with a raised negative sign. Write each positive number in two ways.

(a) The river rose to 8 feet above flood stage.

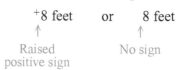

$^+8$ feet   or   8 feet
       ↑   ↑
   Raised   No sign
positive sign

(b) Michael lost $500 in the stock market.

$^-\$500$
↑
Raised negative sign

◀ Work Problem **1** at the Side.

OBJECTIVE 2   Graph signed numbers on a number line.
Mathematicians often use a **number line** to show how numbers relate to each other. A number line is like a thermometer turned sideways. *Zero* is the dividing point between the positive and negative numbers.

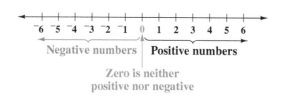

Negative numbers | Positive numbers

Zero is neither
positive nor negative

The number line could be shown with positive numbers on the left side of 0 instead of the right side. But it helps if everyone draws it the same way, as shown above. This method will also match what you do when graphing points and lines.

EXAMPLE 2   **Graphing Numbers on a Number Line**

Graph each number on the number line.

(a) $^-5$ (b) 3   (c) $1\frac{1}{2}$ (d) 0   (e) $^-1$ [0 separates negative numbers from positive numbers.]

Draw a dot at the correct location for each number.

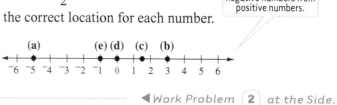

◀ Work Problem **2** at the Side.

OBJECTIVE 3   Use the < and > symbols to compare integers.
For the rest of this chapter, you will work only with *integers*. A list of **integers** can be written like this:

$$\ldots, \,^-6, \,^-5, \,^-4, \,^-3, \,^-2, \,^-1, 0, 1, 2, 3, 4, 5, 6, \ldots$$

The dots show that the list goes on forever in both directions.

ANSWERS

1. (a) $^-5\frac{1}{2}$ degrees (b) $^-12$ pounds
   (c) $210.35 or $^+\$210.35$ (d) $^-\$65$
   (e) $^-100$ feet (f) 50 points or $^+50$ points

2.

(d) (a) (c) (b) (e)
$^-4$ $^-3$ $^-2$ $^-1$ 0 1 2 3 4 5

(f) (h) (g) (i)
$^-4$ $^-3$ $^-2$ $^-1$ 0 1 2 3 4 5

We can use the number line to compare two integers.

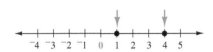   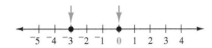

When comparing 1 and 4,
1 is to the *left* of 4.
1 is *less than* 4.
Use < to mean "is less than."

$$1 \quad < \quad 4$$

1 is less than 4

When comparing 0 and ⁻3,
0 is to the *right* of ⁻3.
0 is *greater than* ⁻3.
Use > to mean "is greater than."

$$0 \quad > \quad {}^-3$$

0 is greater than ⁻3

> **Note**
> One way to remember which symbol to use is that the "smaller end of the symbol" points to the "smaller number" (the number that is less).
>
> $$1 < 4 \qquad\qquad 0 > {}^-3$$
>
> Smaller number ⎺⎹ ⎸⎺ Smaller end   Smaller end ⎹⎺ ⎺⎸ Smaller number
> of symbol   of symbol

EXAMPLE 3 **Comparing Integers, Using the < and > Symbols**

Write < or > between each pair of numbers to make a true statement.

(a) 0 ___ 2

0 is to the *left* of 2 on the number line, so 0 is *less than* 2. Write $0 < 2$.

(b) 1 ___ ⁻4

1 is to the *right* of ⁻4, so 1 is *greater than* ⁻4. Write $1 > {}^-4$.

(c) ⁻4 ___ ⁻2

⁻4 is to the *left* of ⁻2, so ⁻4 is *less than* ⁻2. Write ${}^-4 < {}^-2$.

Work Problem **3** *at the Side.* ▶

OBJECTIVE **4** **Find the absolute value of integers.**   In order to graph a number on the number line, you need to ask two things:

1. Which *direction* is it from 0? It can be in a positive direction or a negative direction. You can tell the direction by looking for a positive sign (or no sign, which means positive), or a negative sign.

2. How *far* is it from 0? The distance from 0 is the *absolute value* of a number.

> **Absolute Value**
> The **absolute value** of a number is its distance from 0 on the number line. *Absolute value* is indicated by two vertical bars. For example,
>
> $$|6| \quad \text{is read} \quad \text{"the absolute value of 6."}$$

---

3 Write < or > between each pair of numbers to make a true statement.

(a) 5 ___ 4

(b) 0 ___ 2

(c) ⁻3 ___ ⁻2

(d) ⁻1 ___ ⁻4

(e) 2 ___ ⁻2

(f) ⁻5 ___ 1

ANSWERS
3. **(a)** > **(b)** < **(c)** < **(d)** >
   (e) > **(f)** <

4 Find each absolute value.

(a) $|13|$

(b) $|^-7|$

(c) $|0|$

(d) $|^-350|$

(e) $|6000|$

The absolute value of a number will *always* be positive (or 0), because it is the *distance* from 0. A distance is never negative. (You wouldn't say that your living room is $^-16$ feet long.) So absolute value concerns only *how far away* the number is from 0; we don't care which direction it is from 0.

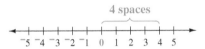

Finding Absolute Values

Find each absolute value.

(a) $|4|$ The distance from 0 to 4 on the number line is 4 spaces. So, $|4| = 4$.

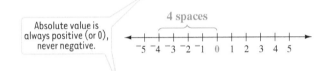

(b) $|^-4|$ The distance from 0 to $^-4$ on the number line is also 4 spaces. So, $|^-4| = 4$.

Absolute value is always positive (or 0), never negative.

(c) $|0|$ $|0| = 0$ because the distance from 0 to 0 on the number line is 0 spaces.

◀ *Work Problem* **4** *at the Side.*

3.1 ▶▶▶ Exercises

*Write each negative number with a raised negative sign. Write each positive number in
two ways. See Example 1.*

1. Mount Everest, the tallest mountain in the world, rises 29,035 feet above sea level. (*Source: World Almanac.*)

2. The bottom of Lake Baikal in Siberia, Russia, is 5371 feet below the surface of the water. (*Source: Guinness World Records.*)

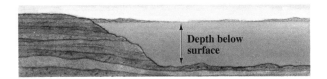

◑ 3. The coldest temperature ever recorded on Earth is 128.6 degrees below zero in Antarctica. (*Source: Fact Finder.*)

4. Normal body temperature is 98.6 degrees Fahrenheit, although it varies slightly for some people. (*Source:* Mayo Clinic *Health Letter.*)

5. During the first three plays of the football game, the Trojans lost a total of 18 yards.

6. The Jets gained 25 yards on a pass play.

◑ 7. Angelique won $100 in a prize drawing at the shopping mall.

8. Derice overdrew his checking account by $37.

9. Keith lost $6\frac{1}{2}$ pounds while he was sick with the flu.

10. The mice in an experiment gained $2\frac{1}{2}$ ounces.

Graph each set of numbers. See Example 2.

◑ 11. $^-3, 3, 0, ^-5$

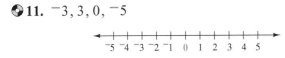

12. $^-2, 2, 0, 5$

13. $^-1, 4, ^-2, 5$

14. $3, ^-4, 1, ^-5$

15. $^-4\frac{1}{2}, \frac{1}{2}, 0, ^-8$

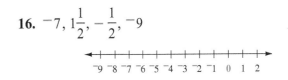

16. $^-7, 1\frac{1}{2}, -\frac{1}{2}, ^-9$

Write < or > between each pair of numbers to make a true statement. See Example 3.

17. 10 ___ 2

18. 6 ___ 0

19. ⁻1 ___ 0

20. ⁻3 ___ ⁻1

21. ⁻10 ___ 2

22. ⁻9 ___ 7

23. ⁻3 ___ ⁻6

24. 0 ___ ⁻1

25. ⁻10 ___ ⁻2

26. ⁻1 ___ ⁻5

27. 0 ___ ⁻8

28. 6 ___ ⁻4

29. 10 ___ ⁻2

30. ⁻2 ___ 1

31. ⁻4 ___ 4

32. 9 ___ ⁻9

Find each absolute value. See Example 4.

33. |15|

34. |10|

35. |⁻3|

36. |⁻8|

37. |0|

38. |100|

39. |200|

40. |⁻99|

41. |⁻75|

42. |⁻6320|

43. |⁻8042|

44. |0|

Relating Concepts (Exercises 45–48) For Individual or Group Work

A special type of X-ray, called a DEXA test, is a quick way to screen patients for osteoporosis (brittle bone disease). Use the information on the Patient Report Form to **work Exercises 45–48 in order.**

Patient Report Form

Your T score measures your bone density compared to that of a young, healthy woman when peak bone mass is achieved.

T Score	Interpretation
Above 0	Above normal
0 to ⁻1	Normal
Below ⁻1	You may be at risk; further discussion with your health care provider is recommended.

Source: Health Partners, Inc.

45. Here are the T scores for four patients. Draw a number line and graph the four scores.

Patient A: ⁻1.5   Patient C: ⁻1

Patient B: 0.5   Patient D: 0

46. List the patients' scores in order from lowest to highest.

47. What is the interpretation of each patient's score?

48. (a) What could happen if patient A did not understand the importance of a negative sign?

(b) For which patient does the sign of the score make no difference? Explain your answer.

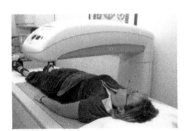

Taking a DEXA test of a patient's spine.

Study Skills

It is best for your brain if you keep up with the reading and homework in your math class. Remember that the more times you work with the information, the more dendrites you grow! So, give yourself every opportunity to read, work problems, and review your mathematics.

You have two choices for reading your math textbook. Read the short descriptions below and decide which will be best for you.

Maddy learns best by listening to her teacher explain things. She "gets it" when she sees the instructor work problems on the board. She likes to ask questions in class and put the information in her notes. She has learned that it helps if she has *previewed* the section before the lecture, so she knows generally what to expect in class. *But after the class instruction,* when Maddy gets home, she finds that she can understand the math textbook easily. She remembers what her teacher said, and she can double-check her notes if she gets confused. So, Maddy does her **careful** reading of the section in her text **after** hearing the classroom lecture on the topic.

De'Lore, on the other hand, feels he learns well by reading on his own. He prefers to read the section and try working the example problems before coming to class. That way, he already knows what the teacher is going to talk about. Then, he can follow the teacher's examples more easily. It is also easier for him to take notes in class. De'Lore likes to have his questions answered right away, which he can do if he has already read the chapter section. So, De'Lore **carefully** reads the section in his text **before** he hears the classroom lecture on the topic.

Notice that there is **no one right way** to work with your textbook. You always must figure out what works best for you. Note also that both Maddy and De'Lore work with one section at a time. **The key is that you read the textbook regularly!** The rest of this activity will give you some ideas of how to make the most of your reading.

Try the following steps as you **read** your math textbook.

▶ Read slowly. Read only one section—or even part of a section—at a time.

▶ Do the sample problems in the margins **as you go.** Check them right away. The answers are at the bottom of the page.

▶ If your mind wanders, work problems on separate paper and write explanations in your own words.

▶ Make study cards as you read each section. Pay special attention to the yellow and blue boxes in the book. Make cards for new vocabulary, rules, procedures, formulas, and sample problems.

▶ **NOW,** you are ready to do your homework assignment!

OBJECTIVES

1 Select an appropriate strategy for homework.

2 Use textbook features effectively.

Preview before Class; Read Carefully after Class

Read Carefully before Class

Why Are These Reading Techniques Brain Friendly?

The steps at the left encourage you to be **actively working with the material** in your text. Your brain **grows dendrites when it is doing something.**

These methods require you to **try several different techniques,** not just the same thing over and over. Your brain loves variety!

Also, the techniques allow you to take small breaks in your learning. Those **rest periods are crucial for good dendrite growth.**

> **Which steps for reading this book will be most helpful for you?**
>
> 1. _____
>
> 2. _____
>
> 3. _____

Homework

> **Why Are These Homework Suggestions Brain Friendly?**
>
> **Your brain will grow dendrites** as you study the worked examples in the text and try doing them yourself on separate paper. So, when you see similar problems in the homework, you will already have dendrites to work from.
>
> **Giving yourself a practice test** by trying to remember the steps (without looking at your card) is an excellent way to reinforce what you are learning.
>
> **Correcting errors right away** is how you learn and reinforce the correct procedures. It is hard to unlearn a mistake, so always check to see that you are on the right track!

Teachers assign homework so you can grow your own dendrites (learn the material) and then coat the dendrites with myelin through practice (remember the material). Really! In learning, you get good at what you practice. So, completing homework every day will strengthen your neural network and prepare you for exams.

If you have read each section in your textbook according to the steps above, you will probably encounter few difficulties with the exercises in the homework. Here are some additional suggestions that will help you succeed with the homework.

▶ If you **have trouble with a problem,** find a similar worked example in the section. Pay attention to *every line* of the worked example to see how to get from step to step. Work it yourself too, on separate paper; don't just look at it.

▶ If it is **hard to remember the steps** to follow for certain procedures, write the steps on a separate card. Then write a short explanation of each step. Keep the card nearby while you do the exercises, but try *not* to look at it.

▶ If you **aren't sure you are working the assigned exercises correctly,** choose two or three odd-numbered problems that are a similar type and work them. Then check the answers in the Answers section at the back of your book to see if you are doing them correctly. If you aren't, go back to the section in the text and review the examples and find out how to correct your errors. When you are sure you understand, try the assigned problems again.

▶ **Make sure you do some homework every day,** even if the math class does not meet each day!

> **What are your biggest homework concerns?**
> List your two main concerns below. Then write a **brain friendly solution** for each one.
>
> 1. Concern: _____ Solution: _____
>
> 2. Concern: _____ Solution: _____

3.2 ▶▶▶ Adding Integers

OBJECTIVE 1 Add integers. Numbers that you are adding are called **addends,** and the result is called the **sum.** You can add integers while watching a football game. On each play, you can use a *positive* integer to stand for the yards *gained* by your team, and a *negative* integer for yards *lost.* Zero indicates no gain or loss. For example,

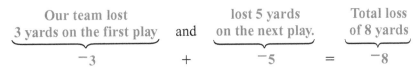

Our team gained 6 yards on the first play   and   gained 4 yards on the next play.   Total gain of 10 yards

6 + 4 = 10

Our team lost 3 yards on the first play   and   lost 5 yards on the next play.   Total loss of 8 yards

$^-3$ + $^-5$ = $^-8$

A drawing of a football field can help you add integers. Notice how similar the drawing is to a number line. Zero marks your team's starting point.

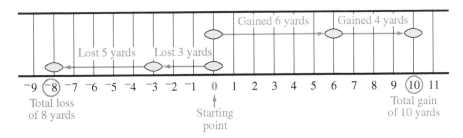

EXAMPLE 1 Using a Number Line to Add Integers

Use a number line to find $^-5 + ^-4$.

Think of the number line as a football field. Your team starts at 0. On the first play it lost 5 yards. On the next play it lost 4 yards. The total loss is 9 yards.

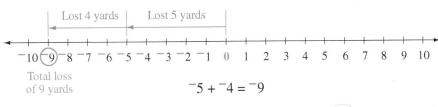

$^-5 + ^-4 = ^-9$

Work Problem **1** *at the Side.* ▶

Do you see a pattern in the margin problems you just did? The first two sums are $^-4$ and 4. They are the same, *except for the sign.* The same is true for the next two sums, $^-11$ and 11, and for the last two sums, $^-10$ and 10. This pattern leads to a rule for adding two integers when the signs are the same.

Adding Two Integers with the Same Sign

Step 1 *Add* the absolute values of the numbers.

Step 2 Use the *common sign* as the sign of the sum. If both numbers are positive, the sum is positive. If both numbers are negative, the sum is negative.

OBJECTIVES

1 Add integers.

2 Identify properties of addition.

1 Find each sum. Use the number line to help you.

(a) $^-2 + ^-2$

(b) $2 + 2$

(c) $^-10 + ^-1$

(d) $10 + 1$

(e) $^-3 + ^-7$

(f) $3 + 7$

ANSWERS

1. **(a)** $^-4$ **(b)** 4 **(c)** $^-11$
   (d) 11 **(e)** $^-10$ **(f)** 10

2 Find each sum.

(a) $^-6 + {}^-6$

(b) $9 + 7$

(c) $^-5 + {}^-10$

(d) $^-12 + {}^-4$

(e) $13 + 2$

EXAMPLE 2 **Adding Two Integers with the Same Sign**

Add.

(a) $^-8 + {}^-7$

> **Step 1** *Add* the absolute values.
>
> $$|^-8| = 8 \quad \text{and} \quad |^-7| = 7$$
>
> Add $8 + 7$ to get 15.

> **Step 2** Use the *common sign* as the sign of the sum. Both numbers are negative, so the sum is negative.
>
> $$^-8 + {}^-7 = {}^-15$$
>
> Both negative   Sum is negative.

(b) $3 + 6 = 9$

Both positive   Sum is positive.

In Step 1, when both numbers are positive, their absolute values are also positive, so we only need to show Step 2.

◀ *Work Problem* **2** *at the Side.*

You can also use a number line (or drawing of a football field) to add integers with *different* signs. For example, suppose that your team gained 2 yards on the first play and then lost 7 yards on the next play. We can represent this as $2 + {}^-7$.

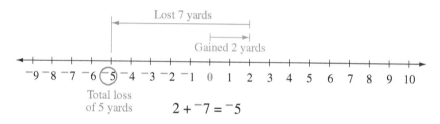

$$2 + {}^-7 = {}^-5$$

Or, try this one. On the first play your team gained 10 yards, but then it lost 4 yards on the next play. We can represent this as $10 + {}^-4$.

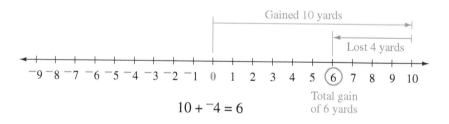

$$10 + {}^-4 = 6$$

These examples illustrate the rule for adding two integers with unlike, or different, signs.

Adding Two Integers with Unlike Signs

Step 1 *Subtract* the smaller absolute value from the larger absolute value.

Step 2 Use the sign of the number with the *larger absolute value* as the sign of the sum.

EXAMPLE 3 **Adding Two Integers with Unlike Signs**

Add.

(a) $^-8 + 3$

Step 1 $|^-8| = 8$ and $|3| = 3$

Subtract $8 - 3$ to get 5.

Step 2 $^-8$ has the *larger absolute value* and is negative, so the sum is also negative.

$$^-8 + 3 = ^-5$$

(b) $^-5 + 11$

Step 1 $|^-5| = 5$ and $|11| = 11$

Subtract $11 - 5$ to get 6.

Step 2 11 has the *larger absolute value* and is positive, so the sum is also positive.

$$^-5 + 11 = {}^+6 \quad \text{or} \quad 6$$

Work Problem ③ *at the Side.* ▶

EXAMPLE 4 **Adding Several Integers**

A football team has to gain at least 10 yards during four plays in order to keep the ball. Suppose that your college team lost 6 yards on the first play, gained 8 yards on the second play, lost 2 yards on the third play, and gained 7 yards on the fourth play. Did the team gain enough to keep the ball?

When you're adding several integers, work from left to right.

```
  1st play   2nd play       3rd play   4th play
     ↓          ↓              ↓          ↓
  ⁻6 yards + 8 yards   +  ⁻2 yards + 7 yards    First add ⁻6 + 8.
        2 yards        +  ⁻2 yards + 7 yards    Add 2 + ⁻2.
             0 yards              + 7 yards     Add 0 + 7.
                        7 yards
```

The team gained 7 yards, which is *not* enough yards to keep the ball.

Work Problem ④ *at the Side.* ▶

OBJECTIVE ② **Identify properties of addition.** In our football model for adding integers, we said that 0 indicated no gain or loss, that is, no change in the position of the ball. This example illustrates one of the *properties of addition*. The properties of addition apply to all addition problems, regardless of the specific numbers you use.

Addition Property of 0

Adding 0 to any number leaves the number unchanged.

Some examples are shown below.

$$0 + 6 = 6 \qquad ^-25 + 0 = {}^-25 \qquad 72{,}399 + 0 = 72{,}399$$
$$0 + {}^-100 = {}^-100$$

③ Find each sum.

(a) $^-3 + 7$

(b) $6 + {}^-12$

(c) $12 + {}^-7$

(d) $^-10 + 2$

(e) $5 + {}^-9$

(f) $^-8 + 9$

④ Write an addition problem and solve it for each situation.

(a) The temperature was $^-15$ degrees this morning. It rose 21 degrees during the day, then dropped 10 degrees. What is the new temperature?

(b) Andrew had $60 in his checking account. He wrote a $20 check for gas and a $75 check for groceries. Later in the day he deposited an $85 tax refund in his account. What is the balance in his account?

5 Rewrite each sum using the commutative property of addition. Check that the sum is unchanged.

(a) $175 + 25 =$ __ $+$ __

Both sums are ____.

Another property of addition is that you can change the *order* of the addends and still get the same sum. For example,

Gaining 2 yards, then losing 7 yards, gives a result of $^-5$ yards.

Losing 7 yards, then gaining 2 yards, also gives a result of $^-5$ yards.

Commutative Property of Addition

Changing the **order** of two addends does *not* change the sum.

Here are some examples.

$$84 + 2 = 2 + 84 \qquad \text{Both sums are 86.}$$

$$^-10 + 6 = 6 + {^-10} \qquad \text{Both sums are } ^-4.$$

(b) $7 + {^-37} =$ __ $+$ __

Both sums are ____.

EXAMPLE 5 **Using the Commutative Property of Addition**

Rewrite each sum, using the **commutative property of addition.** Check that the sum is unchanged.

(a) $65 + 35$

$$65 + 35 = 35 + 65$$
$$100 \quad = \quad 100$$

Both sums are 100, so the sum is unchanged.

> Adding two numbers in a different order does *not* change the sum.

(b) $^-20 + {^-30}$

(c) $^-16 + 16 =$ __ $+$ __

Both sums are ____.

$$^-20 + {^-30} = {^-30} + {^-20}$$
$$^-50 \quad = \quad ^-50$$

Both sums are $^-50$, so the sum is unchanged.

◀ *Work Problem* **5** *at the Side.*

When there are three addends, parentheses may be used to tell you which pair of numbers to add first, as shown below.

$(3 + 4) + 2$ First add $3 + 4$.	$3 + (4 + 2)$ First add $4 + 2$.
$7 \quad + 2$ Then add $7 + 2$.	$3 + \quad 6$ Then add $3 + 6$.
9	9

(d) $^-9 + {^-41} =$ __ $+$ __

Both sums are ____.

Both sums are 9. This example illustrates another property of addition.

Associative Property of Addition

Changing the **grouping** of addends does *not* change the sum.

Some examples are shown below.

$(^-5 + 5) + 8 = {^-5} + (5 + 8)$	$3 + (^-4 + {^-6}) = (3 + {^-4}) + {^-6}$
$0 \quad + 8 = {^-5} + \quad 13$	$3 + \quad ^-10 \quad = \quad ^-1 \quad + {^-6}$
$8 \quad = \quad 8$	$^-7 \quad = \quad ^-7$
Both sums are 8.	Both sums are $^-7$.

We can use the associative property to make addition problems easier. Notice in the first example in the blue box at the bottom of the previous page that it is easier to group $^-5 + 5$ (which is 0) and then add 8. In the second example in the box, it is helpful to group $^-4 + ^-6$ because the sum is $^-10$, and it is easy to work with multiples of 10.

EXAMPLE 6 **Using the Associative Property of Addition**

In each addition problem, pick out the two addends that would be easiest to add. Write parentheses around those addends. Then find the sum.

(a) $6 + 9 + ^-9$

Group $9 + ^-9$ because the sum is 0.

> Use the associative property to add the easiest numbers first.

$$6 + \underbrace{(9 + ^-9)}$$
$$\underbrace{6 + \quad 0}$$
$$6$$

(b) $17 + 3 + ^-25$

Group $17 + 3$ because the sum is 20, which is a multiple of 10.

$$\underbrace{(17 + 3)} + ^-25$$
$$\underbrace{20 \quad + ^-25}$$
$$^-5$$

Note

When using the associative property to make the addition of a group of numbers easier:

1. Look for two numbers whose sum is 0.

2. Look for two numbers whose sum is a multiple of 10 (the sum ends in 0, such as 10, 20, 30, or $^-100$, $^-200$, etc.).

If neither of these occurs, look for two numbers that are easier for you to add. For example, in $98 + 43 + 5$, you may find that adding $43 + 5$ is easier than adding $98 + 43$.

Work Problem 6 *at the Side.* ▶

---

6 In each problem, write parentheses around the two addends that would be easiest to add. Then find the sum.

(a) $^-12 + 12 + ^-19$

(b) $31 + 75 + ^-75$

(c) $16 + ^-1 + ^-9$

(d) $^-8 + 5 + ^-25$

ANSWERS

6. (a) $\underbrace{(^-12 + 12)} + ^-19$
$$\underbrace{0 \quad + ^-19}$$
$$^-19$$

(b) $31 + \underbrace{(75 \ + ^-75)}$
$$\underbrace{31 + \quad 0}$$
$$31$$

(c) $16 + \underbrace{(^-1 + ^-9)}$
$$\underbrace{16 + \quad ^-10}$$
$$6$$

(d) $^-8 + \underbrace{(5 + ^-25)}$
$$\underbrace{^-8 + \quad ^-20}$$
$$^-28$$

Math in the Media

GOLF SCOREBOARDS

At the 2007 PGA Championship golf tournament in Atlanta, Georgia, 72 strokes was the "par" score for each round of play. A negative score indicates that the player had less than 72 strokes for that round, and a positive score indicates that the player had more than 72 strokes. The scoreboard below shows the scores for several of the players.

Player	Round 1	Round 2	Round 3	Round 4
Tiger Woods	⁻6	⁻7	⁻6	⁻4
Zach Johnson	⁺1	⁻4	⁻10	⁻2
Sergio Garcia	⁻2	⁻6	⁻6	0

Source: www.pgatour.com

1. Identify the round and the player who had each score. There may be more than one correct answer.

   (a) Seven strokes less than par.

   (b) One stroke more than par.

   (c) Six strokes less than par.

2. What score did Garcia have in Round 4? Is the score positive or negative? What does that score tell you?

3. Graph Johnson's scores on the number line below. Label the round for each score that you graph.

⁻12 ⁻11 ⁻10 ⁻9 ⁻8 ⁻7 ⁻6 ⁻5 ⁻4 ⁻3 ⁻2 ⁻1 0 ⁺1 ⁺2 ⁺3 ⁺4 ⁺5

4. (a) List Johnson's scores from least to greatest.

   (b) List Woods' scores from least to greatest.

   (c) List Garcia's scores from least to greatest.

5. To win at golf, you must get the least number of strokes. Which round was the best round for (a) Woods; (b) Johnson; (c) Garcia?

6. Find the total score for each player on the scoreboard.

Tiger Woods won the 2007 PGA Championship.

3.2 ▶▶▶ Exercises

Add by using the number line. See Example 1.

1. $^-2 + 5$

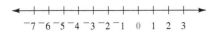

2. $^-3 + 4$

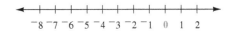

🌐 **3.** $^-5 + ^-2$

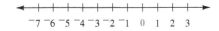

4. $^-2 + ^-2$

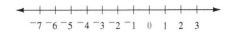

5. $3 + ^-4$

6. $5 + ^-1$

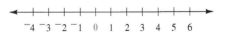

Add. See Example 2.

7. (a) $^-5 + ^-5$ | **8. (a)** $^-9 + ^-9$ | **9. (a)** $7 + 5$ | **10. (a)** $3 + 6$

(b) $5 + 5$ | **(b)** $9 + 9$ | **(b)** $^-7 + ^-5$ | **(b)** $^-3 + ^-6$

11. (a) $^-25 + ^-25$ | **12. (a)** $^-30 + ^-30$ | **13. (a)** $48 + 110$ | **14. (a)** $235 + 21$

(b) $25 + 25$ | **(b)** $30 + 30$ | **(b)** $^-48 + ^-110$ | **(b)** $^-235 + ^-21$

15. What pattern do you see in your answers to Exercises 7–14? Explain why this pattern occurs.

16. In your own words, explain how to add two integers that have the same sign.

Add. See Example 3.

17. (a) $^-6 + 8$

(b) $6 + ^-8$

18. (a) $^-3 + 7$

(b) $3 + ^-7$

19. (a) $^-9 + 2$

(b) $9 + ^-2$

20. (a) $^-8 + 7$

(b) $8 + ^-7$

21. (a) $20 + ^-25$

(b) $^-20 + 25$

22. (a) $30 + ^-40$

(b) $^-30 + 40$

23. (a) $200 + ^-50$

(b) $^-200 + 50$

24. (a) $150 + ^-100$

(b) $^-150 + 100$

25. What pattern do you see in your answers to Exercises 17–24? Explain why this pattern occurs.

26. In your own words, explain how to add two integers that have different signs.

Add. See Examples 2–4.

27. $^-8 + 5$

28. $^-3 + 2$

29. $^-1 + 8$

30. $^-4 + 10$

31. $^-2 + ^-5$

32. $^-7 + ^-3$

33. $6 + ^-5$

34. $11 + ^-3$

35. $4 + ^-12$

36. $9 + ^-10$

37. $^-10 + ^-10$

38. $^-5 + ^-20$

39. $^-17 + 0$

40. $0 + ^-11$

41. $1 + ^-23$

42. $13 + ^-1$

43. $^-2 + ^-12 + ^-5$

44. $^-16 + ^-1 + ^-3$

45. $8 + 6 + ^-8$

46. $^-5 + 2 + 5$

47. $^-7 + 6 + ^-4$

48. $^-9 + 8 + ^-2$

49. $^-3 + ^-11 + 14$

50. $15 + ^-7 + ^-8$

51. $10 + ^-6 + ^-3 + 4$

52. $2 + ^-1 + ^-9 + 12$

53. $^-7 + 28 + ^-56 + 3$

54. $4 + ^-37 + 29 + ^-5$

Write an addition problem for each situation and find the sum.

55. The football team gained 13 yards on the first play and lost 17 yards on the second play. How many yards did the team gain or lose in all?

56. At penguin breeding grounds on Antarctic islands, temperatures routinely drop to $^-15$ °C. Temperatures in the interior of the continent may drop another 60 °C below that. What is the temperature in the interior?

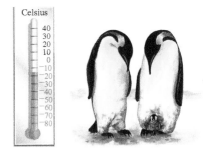

57. Nick's checking account was overdrawn by $62. He deposited $50 in his account. What is the balance in his account?

58. Cynthia had $100 in her checking account. She wrote a check for $83 and was charged $17 for overdrawing her account last month. What is her account balance?

59. $88 was stolen from Jay's car. He got $35 of it back. What was his net loss?

60. Marion lost 4 pounds in April, gained 2 pounds in May, and gained 3 pounds in June. How many pounds did she gain or lose in all?

61. Use the score sheet to find each player's point total after three rounds in a card game.

	Jeff	Terry
Round 1	Lost 20 pts	Won 42 pts
Round 2	Won 75 pts	Lost 15 pts
Round 3	Lost 55 pts	Won 20 pts

62. Use the information in the table on flood water depths to find the new flood level for each river.

	Red River	Mississippi
Monday	Rose 8 ft	Rose 4 ft
Tuesday	Fell 3 ft	Rose 7 ft
Wednesday	Fell 5 ft	Fell 13 ft

The table below shows the number of pounds gained or lost by several health club members during a four-month period. A negative number indicates a loss of pounds. A positive number indicates a gain. Find the total pounds gained or lost by each member.

	Member	Month 1	Month 2	Month 3	Month 4	Total
63.	Angela	⁻2	0	5	⁻5	
64.	Syshe	⁻1	2	⁻6	0	
65.	Brittany	3	⁻2	⁻2	3	
66.	Nicole	1	1	⁻4	2	

Rewrite each sum, using the commutative property of addition. Show that the sum is unchanged. See Example 5.

67. ⁻18 + ⁻5 = _____ + _____

Both sums are _____.

68. ⁻12 + 20 = _____ + _____

Both sums are _____.

69. ⁻4 + 15 = _____ + _____

Both sums are _____.

70. 17 + 1 = _____ + _____

Both sums are _____.

In each addition problem, write parentheses around the two addends that would be easiest to add. Then find the sum. See Example 6.

71. 6 + ⁻14 + 14

72. 9 + ⁻9 + ⁻8

73. ⁻14 + ⁻6 + ⁻7

74. ⁻18 + 3 + 7

75. Make up three of your own examples that illustrate the addition property of 0.

76. Make up three of your own examples that illustrate the associative property of addition. Show that the sum is unchanged.

Find each sum.

77. ⁻7081 + 2965

78. ⁻1398 + 3802

79. ⁻179 + ⁻61 + 8926

80. 36 + ⁻6215 + 428

81. 86 + ⁻99,000 + 0 + 2837

82. ⁻16,719 + 0 + 8878 + ⁻14

3.3 ▶▶▶ Subtracting Integers

OBJECTIVE 1 Find the opposite of a signed number. Look at how the integers match up on this number line.

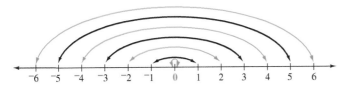

Each integer is matched with its *opposite*. **Opposites** are the same *distance* from 0 on the number line but are on *opposite sides* of 0.

$^+2$ is the opposite of $^-2$ and $^-2$ is the opposite of $^+2$

When you add opposites, the sum is always 0. The opposite of a number is also called its *additive inverse*.

$2 + {}^-2 = 0$ and $^-2 + 2 = 0$

> ### EXAMPLE 1 Finding the Opposites of Signed Numbers
>
> Find the opposite (additive inverse) of each number. Show that the sum of the number and its opposite is 0.
>
> *The sum of opposites is 0.*
>
> **(a)** 6   The opposite of 6 is $^-6$ and $6 + {}^-6 = 0$
>
> **(b)** $^-10$ The opposite of $^-10$ is 10   and $^-10 + 10 = 0$
>
> **(c)** 0   The opposite of 0 is 0 and $0 + 0 = 0$

Work Problem **1** *at the Side.* ▶

OBJECTIVE 2 Subtract integers. Now that you know how to add integers and how to find opposites, you can subtract integers. Every subtraction problem has the same answer as a related addition problem. The examples below illustrate how to change subtraction problems into addition problems.

$$6 - 2 = 4 \qquad \text{Same answer}$$
$$\downarrow \quad \downarrow$$
$$6 + {}^-2 = 4$$

$$8 - 3 = 5 \qquad \text{Same answer}$$
$$\downarrow \quad \downarrow$$
$$8 + {}^-3 = 5$$

> **Subtracting Two Integers**
>
> To subtract two numbers, *add* the first number to the *opposite* of the second number. Remember to change *two* things:
>
> **Step 1** Make one pencil stroke to change the subtraction symbol to an addition symbol.
>
> **Step 2** Make a second pencil stroke to change the *second* number to its *opposite*. If the second number is positive, change it to negative. If the second number is negative, change it to positive.

> **CAUTION**
> When changing a subtraction problem to an addition problem, do *not* make any change in the *first* number. The pattern is
>
> 1st number − 2nd number = 1st number + opposite of 2nd number.

OBJECTIVES

1 Find the opposite of a signed number.

2 Subtract integers.

3 Combine adding and subtracting of integers.

1 Find the additive inverse (opposite) of each number. Show that the sum of the number and its additive inverse is 0.

(a) 5

(b) 48

(c) 0

(d) $^-1$

(e) $^-24$

2 Subtract by changing subtraction to adding the opposite. (Make *two* pencil strokes.)

(a) $^-6 - 5$

(b) $3 - {}^-10$

(c) $^-8 - {}^-2$

(d) $0 - 10$

(e) $^-4 - {}^-12$

(f) $9 - 7$

EXAMPLE 2 **Subtracting Two Integers**

Make *two* pencil strokes to change each subtraction problem into an addition problem. Then find the sum.

Change 10 to $^-10$.

(a) $4 - 10 = 4 + {}^-10 = {}^-6$

Change subtraction to addition.

> Do **not** change 4.
> Change 10 to $^-10$.

Change $^-6$ to $^+6$.

(b) $^-9 - {}^-6 = {}^-9 + {}^+6 = {}^-3$

Change subtraction to addition.

> Do **not** change $^-9$.
> Change $^-6$ to $^+6$.

Change $^-5$ to $^+5$.

(c) $3 - {}^-5 = 3 + {}^+5 = 8$ Make *two* pencil strokes.

Change subtraction to addition.

> Do **not** change the first number when subtracting.

Change 9 to $^-9$.

(d) $^-2 - 9 = {}^-2 + {}^-9 = {}^-11$ Make *two* pencil strokes.

Change subtraction to addition.

◀ *Work Problem* 2 *at the Side.*

OBJECTIVE 3 **Combine adding and subtracting of integers.**
When adding and subtracting more than two signed numbers, first change all subtractions to adding the opposite. Then add from left to right.

3 Simplify.

(a) $6 - 7 + {}^-3$

(b) $^-2 + {}^-3 - {}^-5$

(c) $7 - 7 - 7$

(d) $^-3 - 9 + 4 - {}^-20$

EXAMPLE 3 **Combining Addition and Subtraction**

Simplify by completing all the calculations.

$^-5 - 10 - 12 + 1$ Change all subtractions to adding the opposite.
                       Change 10 to $^-10$. Change 12 to $^-12$.
$^-5 + {}^-10 + {}^-12 + 1$ Add from left to right. First add $^-5 + {}^-10$.

$^-15 + {}^-12 + 1$ Then add $^-15 + {}^-12$.

$^-27 + 1$ Finally, add $^-27 + 1$.

$^-26$

◀ *Work Problem* 3 *at the Side.*

▦ **Calculator Tip**   You can use the *change of sign* key +/– or +C– on your *scientific* calculator to enter negative numbers. To enter $^-5$, press ⑤ +/–. To enter $^+5$, just press ⑤. To enter Example 3 above, press the following keys.

5 +/– ⊖ 10 ⊖ 12 ⊕ 1 ⊜   The answer is $^-26$.

$^-5$ Subtract.

When using a calculator, you do *not* need to change subtraction to addition.

ANSWERS

2. (a) $^-11$ (b) 13 (c) $^-6$ (d) $^-10$
   (e) 8 (f) 2
3. (a) $^-4$ (b) 0 (c) $^-7$ (d) 12

3.3 ▶▶▶ Exercises

Find the opposite (additive inverse) of each number. Show that the sum of the number and its opposite is 0. See Example 1.

1. 6

2. 10

 3. $^-13$

4. $^-3$

5. 0

6. 1

Subtract by changing subtraction to addition. See Example 2.

7. $19 - 5$

8. $24 - 11$

 9. $10 - 12$

10. $1 - 8$

11. $7 - 19$

12. $2 - 17$

13. $^-15 - 10$

14. $^-10 - 4$

15. $^-9 - 14$

16. $^-3 - 11$

 17. $^-3 - {}^-8$

18. $^-1 - {}^-4$

19. $6 - {}^-14$

20. $8 - {}^-1$

21. $1 - {}^-10$

22. $6 - {}^-1$

23. $^-30 - 30$

24. $^-25 - 25$

25. $^-16 - {}^-16$

26. $^-20 - {}^-20$

27. $13 - 13$

28. $19 - 19$

29. $0 - 6$

30. $0 - 12$

31. (a) $3 - {}^-5$

(b) $3 - 5$

(c) $^-3 - {}^-5$

(d) $^-3 - 5$

32. (a) $9 - 6$

(b) $^-9 - 6$

(c) $9 - {}^-6$

(d) $^-9 - {}^-6$

33. (a) $4 - 7$

(b) $4 - {}^-7$

(c) $^-4 - 7$

(d) $^-4 - {}^-7$

34. (a) $8 - {}^-2$

(b) $^-8 - {}^-2$

(c) $8 - 2$

(d) $^-8 - 2$

Simplify. See Example 3.

35. $^-2 - 2 - 2$

36. $^-8 - 4 - 8$

37. $9 - 6 - 3 - 5$

38. $12 - 7 - 5 - 4$

39. $3 - {}^-3 - 10 - {}^-7$

40. $1 - 9 - {}^-2 - {}^-6$

 41. $^-2 + {}^-11 - {}^-3$

42. $^-5 - {}^-2 + {}^-6$

43. $4 - {}^-13 + {}^-5$

44. $6 - {}^-1 + {}^-10$

45. $6 + 0 - 12 + 1$

46. $^-10 - 4 + 0 + 18$

WINDCHILL
Temperature (degrees Fahrenheit)

Calm	40	35	30	25	20	15	10	5	0	−5	−10	−15	−20	−25	−30
5	36	31	25	19	13	7	1	−6	−11	−16	−22	−28	−34	−40	−46
10	34	27	21	15	9	3	−4	−10	−16	−22	−28	−35	−41	−47	−53
15	32	25	19	13	6	0	−7	−13	−19	−26	−32	−39	−45	−51	−58
20	30	24	17	11	4	−2	−9	−15	−22	−29	−35	−42	−48	−55	−61
25	29	23	16	9	3	−4	−11	−17	−24	−31	−37	−44	−51	−58	−64
30	28	22	15	8	1	−5	−12	−19	−26	−33	−39	−46	−53	−60	−67
35	28	21	14	7	0	−7	−14	−21	−27	−34	−41	−48	−55	−62	−69
40	27	20	13	6	−1	−8	−15	−22	−29	−36	−43	−50	−57	−64	−71

Wind Speed (miles per hour)

Shaded area: Frostbite occurs in 15 minutes or less.

Source: National Weather Service

This windchill table shows how wind increases a person's heat loss. For example, find the temperature of 15 °F along the top of the table. Then find a wind speed of 20 mph along the left side of the table. This column and row intersect at ⁻2 °F, the "windchill temperature." The actual temperature is 15 °F but the wind makes it feel like ⁻2 °F. The difference between the actual temperature and the windchill temperature is $15 - {}^-2 = 15 + {}^+2 = 17$ degrees difference.

Use the table to find the windchill temperature under each set of conditions in Exercises 47–48. Then write and solve a subtraction problem to calculate actual temperature minus windchill temperature.

47. **(a)** 30 °F; 10 mph wind

(b) 15 °F; 15 mph wind

(c) 5 °F; 25 mph wind

(d) ⁻10 °F; 35 mph wind

48. **(a)** 40 °F; 20 mph wind

(b) 20 °F; 35 mph wind

(c) 10 °F; 15 mph wind

(d) ⁻5 °F; 30 mph wind

49. Find, correct, and explain the mistake made in this subtraction.

$$\begin{array}{cc} {}^-6 & - & 6 \\ \downarrow & & \downarrow \\ {}^-6 & + & 6 = 0 \end{array}$$

50. Find, correct, and explain the mistake made in this subtraction.

$$\begin{array}{cc} {}^-7 & - & 5 \\ \downarrow & & \downarrow \\ {}^+7 & + & {}^-5 = 2 \end{array}$$

Simplify. Begin each exercise by working inside the absolute value bars or the parentheses.

51. $^-2 + {}^-11 + |{}^-2|$

52. $5 - |{}^-3| + 3$

53. $0 - |{}^-7 + 2|$

54. $|1 - 8| - |0|$

55. $^-3 - ({}^-2 + 4) + {}^-5$

56. $5 - 8 - (6 - 7) + 1$

Relating Concepts (Exercises 57–58) For Individual or Group Work

*Use your knowledge of the properties of addition to **work Exercises 57 and 58 in order.***

57. Look for a pattern in these pairs of subtractions.

$^-3 - 5 =$ ____ $^-4 - {}^-3 =$ ____

$5 - {}^-3 =$ ____ $^-3 - {}^-4 =$ ____

Explain what happens when you try to apply the commutative property to subtraction.

58. Recall the addition property of 0. Can 0 be used in a subtraction problem without changing the other number? Explain what happens and give several examples. (*Hint:* Think about *order* in a subtraction problem.)

3.4 ▶▶▶ Problem Solving: Rounding and Estimating

One way to get a rough check on an answer is to *round* the numbers in the problem. **Rounding** a number means finding a number that is close to the original number, but easier to work with.

For example, a superintendent of schools in a large city might be discussing the need to build new schools. In making her point, it probably would not be necessary to say that the school district has 152,807 students—it probably would be sufficient to say that there are about 153,000 students, or even 150,000 students.

OBJECTIVES

1 Locate the place to which a number is to be rounded.

2 Round integers.

3 Use front end rounding to estimate answers in addition and subtraction.

OBJECTIVE **1** **Locate the place to which a number is to be rounded.** The first step in rounding a number is to locate the *place to which the number is to be rounded.*

EXAMPLE 1 **Finding the Place to Which a Number Is to Be Rounded**

Locate and draw a line under the place to which each number is to be rounded. Then answer the question.

(a) Round ⁻23 to the nearest ten. Is ⁻23 closer to ⁻2̲0 or ⁻3̲0?

⁻23 is closer to ⁻20
Tens place

(b) Round $381 to the nearest hundred. Is it closer to $3̲00 or $4̲00?

$381 is closer to $400
Hundreds place

(c) Round ⁻54,702 to the nearest thousand. Is it closer to ⁻5̲4,000 or ⁻5̲5,000?

⁻54,702 is closer to ⁻55,000

Thousands place ———⌐

Work Problem **1** *at the Side.* ▶

OBJECTIVE **2** **Round integers.** Use these steps to round integers.

Rounding an Integer

Step 1 Locate the *place* to which the number is to be rounded. Draw a line under that place.

Step 2 Look only at the next digit to the right of the one you underlined. If the next digit is *5 or more, increase* the underlined digit by 1. If the next digit is *4 or less,* do *not* change the digit in the underlined place.

Step 3 *Change* all digits to the right of the underlined place to zeros.

---

1 Locate and draw a line under the place to which the number is to be rounded. Then answer the question.

(a) ⁻746 (nearest ten)

Is it closer to ⁻740 or

⁻750? _____

(b) 2412 (nearest thousand)

Is it closer to 2000 or

3000? _____

(c) ⁻89,512 (nearest hundred)

Is it closer to ⁻89,500 or

⁻89,600? _____

(d) 546,325 (nearest ten-thousand)

Is it closer to 540,000 or

550,000? _____

CAUTION

If you are rounding a negative number, be careful to write the negative sign in front of the rounded number. For example, ⁻79 rounds to ⁻80.

ANSWERS

1. **(a)** ⁻7̲46 is closer to ⁻750
   (b) 2̲412 is closer to 2̲000
   (c) ⁻89,5̲12 is closer to ⁻89,5̲00
   (d) 546,3̲25 is closer to 5̲50,000

2 Round to the nearest ten.

(a) 34

(b) ⁻61

(c) ⁻683

(d) 1792

EXAMPLE 2   **Using the Rounding Rule for 4 or Less**

Round 349 to the nearest hundred.

Step 1   Locate the place to which the number is being rounded. Draw a line under that place.

349

Hundreds place

Step 2   Because the next digit to the right of the underlined place is 4, which is *4 or less*, do *not* change the digit in the underlined place.

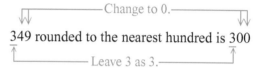

Next digit is *4 or less*.

349

3 remains 3.

Step 3   Change all digits to the right of the underlined place to zeros.

Change to 0.

349 rounded to the nearest hundred is 300

Leave 3 as 3.

In other words, 349 is closer to 300 than to 400.

> Think of money.
> $349 is closer to
> $300 than to $400.

◀ *Work Problem* **2** *at the Side.*

---

3 Round to the nearest thousand.

(a) 1725

(b) ⁻6511

(c) 58,829

(d) ⁻83,904

EXAMPLE 3   **Using the Rounding Rule for 5 or More**

Round 36,833 to the nearest thousand.

Step 1   Find the place to which the number is to be rounded. Draw a line under that place.

36,833

Thousands place

Step 2   Because the next digit to the right of the underlined place is 8, which is *5 or more*, add 1 to the underlined place.

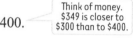

Next digit is *5 or more*.

36,833

Change 6 to 7.

Step 3   Change all digits to the right of the underlined place to zeros.

Change to 0.

36,833 rounded to the nearest thousand is 37,000

Change 6 to 7.

In other words, 36,833 is closer to 37,000 than to 36,000.

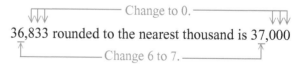

◀ *Work Problem* **3** *at the Side.*

EXAMPLE 4 | **Using the Rules for Rounding**

(a) Round ⁻2382 to the nearest ten.

Step 1 ⁻2382
⤒— Tens place

Step 2 The next digit to the right is 2, which is *4 or less*.

┌ Next digit is *4 or less*.
↓
⁻2382
⤒— Leave 8 as 8.

┌—Change to 0.—┐
↓   ↓
Step 3 ⁻2382 rounds to ⁻2380
⤒— Leave 8 as 8.—⤴

> Remember to keep the negative sign.

⁻2382 rounded to the nearest ten is ⁻2380.

(b) Round 13,961 to the nearest hundred.

Step 1 13,961
⤒— Hundreds place

Step 2 The next digit to the right is 6, which is *5 or more*.

┌ Next digit is *5 or more*.
↓
13,961
⤒⤒— Change 9 to 10; write 0 and regroup 1 into thousands place.
└— 3 + regrouped 1 = 4

┌— Change to 0. —┐
↓   ↓
Step 3 13,961 rounds to 14,000
⤒— Change 39 to 40.—⤴

> $13,961 is closer to $14,000 than to $13,900.

13,961 rounded to the nearest hundred is 14,000.

> **Note**
> In Step 2 above, when you added 1 to the hundreds place, notice that the first three digits increased from 139 to 140.
>
> 13,961   rounded to   14,000

Work Problem 4 *at the Side.* ▶

4 Round as indicated.

(a) ⁻6036 to the nearest ten

(b) 31,968 to the nearest hundred

(c) ⁻73,077 to the nearest thousand

(d) 4952 to the nearest thousand

(e) 85,949 to the nearest hundred

(f) 40,387 to the nearest thousand

ANSWERS

4. (a) ⁻6040 (b) 32,000 (c) ⁻73,000
(d) 5000 (e) 85,900 (f) 40,000

5 Round as indicated.

(a) −14,679 to the nearest ten-thousand

(b) 724,518,715 to the nearest million

(c) −49,900,700 to the nearest million

(d) 306,779,000 to the nearest hundred-million

EXAMPLE 5 **Rounding Large Numbers**

(a) Round −37,892 to the nearest ten-thousand.

Step 1 −37,892
        ⎣— Ten-thousands place

Step 2 The next digit to the right is 7, which is *5 or more*.

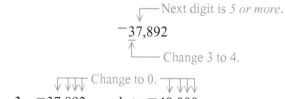

        ┌— Next digit is *5 or more*.
    −37,892
        ⎣— Change 3 to 4.

        ┌— Change to 0. —┐
Step 3 −37,892 rounds to −40,000
      ⎣—Change 3 to 4.—⎦

−37,892 rounded to the nearest ten-thousand is −40,000.

(b) Round 528,498,675 to the nearest million.

Step 1 528,498,675
        ⎣— Millions place

        ┌—Next digit is *4 or less*.
Step 2 528,498,675
        ⎣— Leave 8 as 8.

        ┌—Change to 0.—┐
Step 3 528,498,675 rounds to 528,000,000
      ⎣— Leave 8 as 8.—⎦

528,498,675 rounded to the nearest million is 528,000,000.

◀ *Work Problem* 5 *at the Side.*

OBJECTIVE 3 Use front end rounding to estimate answers in addition and subtraction. In many everyday situations, we can round numbers and **estimate** the answer to a problem. For example, suppose that you're thinking about buying a sofa for $988 and a chair for $209. You can round the prices and estimate the total cost as $1000 + $200 ≈ $1200. The ≈ symbol means "approximately equal to." The estimated total of $1200 is close enough to help you decide whether you can afford both items. Of course, when it comes time to pay the bill, you'll want the *exact* total of $988 + $209 = $1197.

Sofa		**Chair**			
$988	+	$209	=	$1197	← Exact cost
Rounds to		Rounds to			
↓		↓			
$1000	+	$200	=	$1200	← Estimated cost

In **front end rounding,** each number is rounded to the highest possible place, so all the digits become 0 except the first digit. Once the numbers have lots of zeros, working with them is easy. Front end rounding is often used to estimate answers.

EXAMPLE 6 **Using Front End Rounding**

Use front end rounding to round each number.

(a) $^-216$

Round to the highest possible place, that is, the leftmost digit. In this case, the leftmost digit, 2, is in the hundreds place, so round to the nearest hundred.

┌─ Next digit is *4 or less.*   ┌─Change to 0.─┐
$^-216$ $^-216$ rounds to $^-200$
└─ Leave 2 as 2.   └─Leave 2 as 2.─┘

The rounded number is $^-200$. Notice that all the digits in the rounded number are 0, except the first digit. Also, remember to write the negative sign.

(b) 97,203

The leftmost digit, 9, is in the ten-thousands place, so round to the nearest ten-thousand.

┌─ Next digit is *5 or more.*   ┌─Change to 0.─┐
97,203   97,203 rounds to 100,000
└── Change 9 to 10.   └─Change 9 to 10.─┘
                                       Regroup 1 into hundred-thousands place.

The rounded number is 100,000. Notice that all the digits in the rounded number are 0, except the first digit.

Work Problem **6** *at the Side.* ▶

EXAMPLE 7 **Using Front End Rounding to Estimate an Answer**

Use front end rounding to estimate an answer. Then find the exact answer.

Meisha's paycheck showed gross pay of $823. It also listed deductions of $291. What is her net pay after deductions?

Estimate: Use front end rounding to round $823 and $291.

┌─ Next digit is *4 or less.*   ┌─Next digit is *5 or more.*
$823 rounds to $800 $291 rounds to $300
└─Leave 8 as 8.─┘   └─Change 2 to 3.─┘

Use the rounded numbers and subtract to *estimate* Meisha's net pay.

$$\$800 - \$300 = \$500 \leftarrow \text{Estimate}$$

Exact: Use the original numbers and subtract to find the *exact* amount.

$$\$823 - \$291 = \$532 \leftarrow \text{Exact}$$

Meisha's paycheck will show the *exact* amount of $532. Because $532 is fairly close to the *estimate* of $500, Meisha can quickly see that the amount shown on her paycheck probably is correct. She might also use the estimate when talking to a friend, saying, "My net pay is about $500."

Continued on Next Page

---

6 Use front end rounding to round each number.

(a) $^-94$

(b) 508

(c) $^-2522$

(d) 9700

(e) 61,888

(f) $^-963,369$

7 Use front end rounding to estimate an answer. Then find the exact answer.

Pao Xiong is a bookkeeper for a small business. The company checking account is overdrawn by $3881. He deposits a check for $2090. What is the balance in the account?

Estimate:

Exact:

CAUTION

Always *estimate* the answer first. Then, when you find the *exact* answer, check that it is close to the estimate. If your exact answer is very far off, rework the problem because you probably made an error.

⊞ **Calculator Tip**   It's easy to press the wrong key when using a calculator. If you use front end rounding and estimate the answer *before* entering the numbers, you can catch many such mistakes. For example, a student thought that he entered Example 7 from the previous page correctly.

823 ⊖ 291 ⊜ | **1114** |

Front end rounding gives an estimated answer of $800 - 300 = 500$, which is very different from 1114. Can you figure out which key the student pressed incorrectly?

Answer: The student pressed ⊕ instead of ⊖.

◀ *Work Problem* **7** *at the Side.*

ANSWERS

7. *Estimate:* $^-\$4000 + \$2000 = {}^-\$2000$
    Exact: $^-\$3881 + \$2090 = {}^-\$1791$
    The account is overdrawn by $1791, which is fairly close to the estimate of $^-\$2000$.

3.4 ▶▶▶ **Exercises**

FOR
EXTRA
HELP **MyMathLab** | Math XL
PRACTICE | WATCH | DOWNLOAD | READ | REVIEW

Round each number to the indicated place. See Examples 1–5.

1. 625 to the nearest ten

2. 206 to the nearest ten

3. ⁻1083 to the nearest ten

4. ⁻2439 to the nearest ten

5. 7862 to the nearest hundred

6. 6746 to the nearest hundred

7. ⁻86,813 to the nearest hundred

8. ⁻17,211 to the nearest hundred

9. 42,495 to the nearest hundred

10. 18,273 to the nearest hundred

11. ⁻5996 to the nearest hundred

12. ⁻8451 to the nearest hundred

13. ⁻78,499 to the nearest thousand

14. ⁻14,314 to the nearest thousand

15. 5847 to the nearest thousand

16. 49,706 to the nearest thousand

17. 595,008 to the nearest ten-thousand

18. 725,182 to the nearest ten-thousand

19. ⁻8,906,422 to the nearest million

20. ⁻13,713,409 to the nearest million

21. 139,610,000 to the nearest million

22. 609,845,500 to the nearest million

23. 19,951,880,500 to the nearest hundred-million

24. 5,993,505,000 to the nearest hundred-million

25. 8,608,200,000 to the nearest billion

26. 703,750,678,005 to the nearest billion

Use front end rounding to round each number. See Example 6.

27. Tyrone's truck shows this number on the odometer.

28. Ezra bought a used car with this odometer reading.

29. From summer to winter the average temperature drops 56 degrees.

30. The flood waters fell 42 inches yesterday.

31. Jan earned $9942 working part time.

32. Carol deposited $285 in her checking account.

33. 60,950,000 Americans go to a video store each week. (*Source:* Video Software Dealer's Assoc.)

34. 95,840,000 U.S. households have cable TV. (*Source:* Nielsen Media Research.)

35. The submarine will dive to 255 feet below the surface of the ocean.

36. DeAnne lost $1352 in the stock market.

37. The population of Alaska is 670,053 people, and the population of California is 36,457,549 people. (*Source:* U.S. Census Bureau.)

38. Within forty years, it is estimated that the U.S. population will be 420,080,587 people and Canada's population will be 41,429,579 people. (*Source:* U.S. Census Bureau.)

39. Explain in your own words how to do front end rounding. Also show two examples of numbers and how you round them.

40. Describe two situations in your own life when you might use rounded numbers. Describe two situations in which exact numbers are important.

First, use front end rounding to estimate each answer. Then find the exact answer.
In Exercises 49–54, change subtraction to adding the opposite. See Example 7.

🌐 **41.** $^-42 + 89$

　　Estimate: _____ + _____ = _____

　　Exact:

42. $^-66 + 25$

　　Estimate: _____ + _____ = _____

　　Exact:

43. $16 + {}^-97$

　　Estimate: _____ + _____ = _____

　　Exact:

44. $58 + {}^-19$

　　Estimate: _____ + _____ = _____

　　Exact:

45. $^-273 + {}^-399$

　　Estimate:

　　Exact:

46. $^-311 + {}^-582$

　　Estimate:

　　Exact:

47. $3081 + 6826$

　　Estimate:

　　Exact:

48. $4904 + 1181$

　　Estimate:

　　Exact:

49. $23 - 81$

　　Estimate:

　　Exact:

50. $72 - 84$

　　Estimate:

　　Exact:

51. $^-39 - 39$

　　Estimate:

　　Exact:

52. $^-91 - 91$

　　Estimate:

　　Exact:

53. $^-106 + 34 - {}^-72$

　　Estimate:

　　Exact:

54. $52 - {}^-87 - 139$

　　Estimate:

　　Exact:

First use front end rounding to estimate the answer to each application problem.
Then find the exact answer. See Example 7.

55. The community has raised $52,882 for the homeless shelter. If the goal is $78,650, how much more needs to be collected?

Estimate:

Exact:

56. A truck weighs 9250 pounds when empty. After being loaded with firewood, it weighs 21,375 pounds. What is the weight of the firewood?

Estimate:

Exact:

57. Dorene Cox decided to establish a monthly budget. She will spend $845 for rent, $325 for food, $365 for child care, $182 for transportation, $240 for other expenses, and put the remainder in savings. If her monthly take-home pay is $2120, find her monthly savings.

Estimate:

Exact:

58. Jared Ueda had $2874 in his checking account. He wrote checks for $308 for auto repairs, $580 for child support, and $778 for tuition. Find the amount remaining in his account.

Estimate:

Exact:

59. In a laboratory experiment, a mixture started at a temperature of $^-102$ degrees. First the temperature was raised 37 degrees and then raised 52 degrees. What was the final temperature?

Estimate:

Exact:

60. A scuba diver was photographing fish at 65 feet below the surface of the ocean. She swam up 24 feet and then swam down 49 feet. What was her final depth?

Estimate:

Exact:

61. The White House in Washington, D.C., has 132 rooms, 412 doors, and 147 windows. What is the total number of doors and windows? (*Source: Scholastic Book of World Records.*)

Estimate:

Exact:

62. There are 30,096 McDonald's restaurants throughout the world in 119 different countries. Burger King has 11,204 restaurants in 69 countries. How many restaurants do the two companies have together? (*Source:* www.mcdonalds.com and www.bk.com)

Estimate:

Exact:

3.5 ▶▶▶ Multiplying Integers

OBJECTIVE **1** **Use a raised dot or parentheses to express multiplication.** In arithmetic we usually use "×" when writing multiplication problems. But in algebra, we use a raised dot or parentheses to show multiplication. The numbers being multiplied are called **factors** and the answer is called the **product.**

Arithmetic ─────────────**Algebra**─────────────

$3 \times 5 = 15$ $3 \cdot 5 = 15$ or $3(5) = 15$ or $(3)(5) = 15$

Factors Product   Factors Product   Factors Product   Factors Product

OBJECTIVES

1 Use a raised dot or parentheses to express multiplication.

2 Multiply integers.

3 Identify properties of multiplication.

4 Estimate answers to application problems involving multiplication.

EXAMPLE 1 **Expressing Multiplication in Algebra**

Rewrite each multiplication in three different ways, using a dot or parentheses. Also identify the factors and the product.

(a) 10×7

Raised dot
↓

Rewrite it as $10 \cdot 7$ or $10(7)$ or $(10)(7)$

The factors are 10 and 7. The product is 70.

(b) 4×80

Rewrite it as $4 \cdot 80$ or $4(80)$ or $(4)(80)$

The factors are 4 and 80. The product is 320.

───────────── *Work Problem* **1** *at the Side.* ▶

1 Rewrite each multiplication in three different ways using a dot or parentheses. Also identify the factors and the product.

(a) 100×6

Note
Parentheses are used to show several different things in algebra. When we discussed the associative property of addition earlier in this chapter, we used parentheses as shown below.

$6 + \underbrace{(9 + {}^{-}9)}$ ← Parentheses show which numbers to add first.

$\underbrace{6 + \quad 0}$

6

Now we are using parentheses to indicate multiplication, as in 3(5) or (3)(5).

(b) 7×12

OBJECTIVE **2** **Multiply integers.** Suppose that our football team gained 5 yards on the first play, gained 5 yards again on the second play, and gained 5 yards again on the third play. We can add to find the result.

$$5 \text{ yards} + 5 \text{ yards} + 5 \text{ yards} = 15 \text{ yards}$$

A quick way to add the same number several times is to multiply.

Our team made 3 plays	and	gained 5 yards each time.		Our team gained a total of 15 yards.
3	•	5	=	15

ANSWERS

1. (a) 100 • 6 or 100(6) or (100)(6)
The factors are 100 and 6; the product is 600.
(b) 7 • 12 or 7(12) or (7)(12)
The factors are 7 and 12; the product is 84.

When multiplying two integers, first multiply the absolute values. Then attach a positive sign or negative sign to the product according to the rules below.

Multiplying Two Integers

If two factors have *different signs,* the product is *negative.*
For example,

$$^-2 \cdot 6 = {}^-12 \qquad \text{and} \qquad 4 \cdot {}^-5 = {}^-20$$

If two factors have the *same sign,* the product is *positive.*
For example,

$$7 \cdot 3 = 21 \qquad \text{and} \qquad {}^-3 \cdot {}^-10 = 30$$

There are several ways to illustrate these rules. First we'll continue with football. Remember, you are interested in the results for *our* team. We will designate our team with a positive sign and their team with a negative sign.

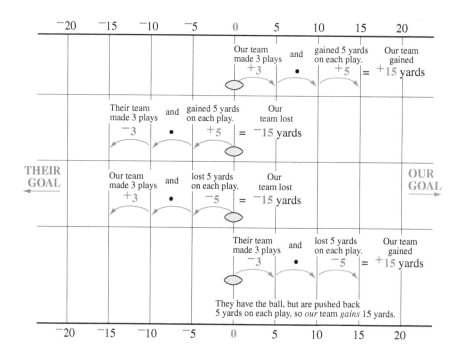

Here is a summary of the football examples.

When two factors have the *same* sign, the product is *positive.*

Both positive

$$3 \cdot 5 = 15$$

Product is positive.

Two factors with *matching* signs give a *positive* product.

$$^-3 \cdot {}^-5 = 15$$

Both negative

When two factors have *different* signs, the product is *negative.*

$$^-3 \cdot 5 = {}^-15$$

Product is negative.

Two factors with *different* signs give a *negative* product.

$$3 \cdot {}^-5 = {}^-15$$

There is another way to look at these multiplication rules. In mathematics, the rules or patterns must always be consistent.

Look for a pattern in this list of products.

$$4 \cdot 2 = 8$$
$$3 \cdot 2 = 6$$
$$2 \cdot 2 = 4$$
$$1 \cdot 2 = 2$$
$$0 \cdot 2 = 0$$
$$^-1 \cdot 2 = ?$$

Blue numbers decrease by 1.

Red numbers decrease by 2.

To keep the red pattern going, replace the ? with a number that is 2 *less than* 0, which is $^-2$.

So, $^-1 \cdot 2 = ^-2$. This pattern illustrates that the product of two numbers with *different* signs is *negative*.

Look for a pattern in this list of products.

$$4 \cdot ^-2 = ^-8$$
$$3 \cdot ^-2 = ^-6$$
$$2 \cdot ^-2 = ^-4$$
$$1 \cdot ^-2 = ^-2$$
$$0 \cdot ^-2 = 0$$
$$^-1 \cdot ^-2 = ?$$

Blue numbers decrease by 1.

Red numbers *increase* by 2.

To keep the red pattern going, replace the ? with a number that is 2 *more than* 0, which is $^+2$.

So, $^-1 \cdot ^-2 = ^+2$. This pattern illustrates that the product of two numbers with the *same* sign is *positive*.

EXAMPLE 2 Multiplying Two Integers

(a) $^-2 \cdot 8 = ^-16$ The factors have *different signs*, so the product is *negative*.
          Positive
          Negative

(b) $^-10 \, (^-6) = 60$ The factors have the *same sign*, so the product is *positive*.
          Both negative

(c) $(9) \, (^-11) = ^-99$ The factors have *different signs*, so the product is *negative*.
                    Negative
          Positive

Work Problem **2** *at the Side.* ▶

Sometimes there are more than two factors in a multiplication problem. If there are parentheses around two of the factors, multiply them first. If there aren't any parentheses, start at the left and work with two factors at a time.

EXAMPLE 3 Multiplying Several Factors

Multiply.

(a) $^-3 \cdot (4 \cdot ^-5)$ Parentheses tell you to multiply $4 \cdot ^-5$ first. The factors
         $^-3 \cdot \quad ^-20$ have *different* signs, so the product is *negative*.
                                  Then multiply $^-3 \cdot ^-20$. Both factors have the *same*
              60   sign, so the product is *positive*.

(b) $^-2 \cdot ^-2 \cdot ^-2$ There are no parentheses, so multiply $^-2 \cdot ^-2$ first. The
           $4 \quad \cdot ^-2$ factors have the *same sign*, so the product is *positive*.
                                  Then multiply $4 \cdot ^-2$. The factors have *different* signs,
              $^-8$ so the product is *negative*.

Continued on Next Page

2 Multiply.

(a) $7(^-2)$

(b) $^-5 \cdot ^-5$

(c) $^-1(14)$

(d) $10 \cdot 6$

(e) $(^-4)(^-9)$

3 Multiply.

(a) $5 \cdot (^-10 \cdot 2)$

(b) $^-1 \cdot 8 \cdot ^-5$

(c) $^-3 \cdot ^-2 \cdot ^-4$

(d) $^-2 \cdot (7 \cdot ^-3)$

(e) $(^-1)(^-1)(^-1)$

4 Multiply. Then name the property illustrated by each example.

(a) $819 \cdot 0$

(b) $1(^-90)$

(c) $25 \cdot 1$

(d) $(0)(^-75)$

> **CAUTION**
> In Example 3(b) you may be tempted to think that the final product will be *positive* because all the factors have the *same* sign. Be careful to **work with two factors at a time** and keep track of the sign at each step.

> **Calculator Tip**   You can use the *change of sign* key for multiplication and division, just as you did for adding and subtracting. To enter Example 3(b) on your scientific calculator, press the following keys.
>
>
>
> The answer is $^-8$.

◀ *Work Problem* **3** *at the Side.*

OBJECTIVE 3 Identify properties of multiplication.   Addition involving 0 is unusual because adding 0 does *not* change the number. For example, $7 + 0$ is still 7. (See **Section 3.2.**) But what happens in multiplication? Let's use our football team as an example.

Our team made 3 plays	and	didn't gain or lose yards on any play.		Altogether our team didn't gain or lose any yards.
3	•	0	=	0

This example illustrates one of the properties of multiplication.

> **Multiplication Property of 0**
> Multiplying any number by 0 gives a product of 0.
> Some examples are shown below.
> $$^-16 \cdot 0 = 0 \qquad (0)(5) = 0 \qquad 32{,}977(0) = 0$$

So, can you multiply a number by something that will *not* change the number?

$$6 \cdot \, ? = 6 \qquad ^-12(?) = ^-12 \qquad (?)(5876) = 5876$$

The number 1 can replace the ? in each example. This illustrates another property of multiplication.

> **Multiplication Property of 1**
> Multiplying a number by 1 leaves the number unchanged.
> Some examples are shown below.
> $$6 \cdot 1 = 6 \qquad ^-12(1) = ^-12 \qquad (1)(5876) = 5876$$

EXAMPLE 4   Using Properties of Multiplication

Multiply. Then name the property illustrated by each example.

(a) $(0)(^-48) = 0$ Illustrates the **multiplication property of 0.**

(b) $615(1) = 615$ Illustrates the **multiplication property of 1.**

◀ *Work Problem* **4** *at the Side.*

When adding, we said that changing the order of the addends did not change the sum (commutative property of addition). We also found that changing the *grouping* of addends did not change the sum (associative property of addition). These same ideas apply to multiplication.

> **Commutative Property of Multiplication**
> Changing the *order* of two factors does not change the product. For example,
> $$2 \cdot 5 = 5 \cdot 2 \quad \text{and} \quad {}^-4 \cdot 6 = 6 \cdot {}^-4$$

> **Associative Property of Multiplication**
> Changing the *grouping* of factors does not change the product. For example,
> $$9 \cdot (3 \cdot 2) = (9 \cdot 3) \cdot 2$$

EXAMPLE 5 **Using the Commutative and Associative Properties**

Show that the product is unchanged and name the property that is illustrated in each case.

(a) $\underbrace{{}^-7 \cdot {}^-4}_{28} = \underbrace{{}^-4 \cdot {}^-7}_{28}$ Multiplying two numbers in a different order does *not* change the product.

Both products are 28.

This example illustrates the **commutative property of multiplication.**

(b) $5 \cdot (10 \cdot 2) = (5 \cdot 10) \cdot 2$ Use the associative property to multiply the easiest numbers first.

$\underbrace{5 \cdot 20}_{100} = \underbrace{50 \cdot 2}_{100}$

Both products are 100.

This example illustrates the **associative property of multiplication.**

——— *Work Problem* **5** *at the Side.* ▶

Now that you are familiar with multiplication and addition, we can look at a property that involves both operations.

> **Distributive Property**
> Multiplication *distributes* over addition. An example is shown below.
> $$3(6 + 2) = 3 \cdot 6 + 3 \cdot 2$$

What is the **distributive property** really saying? Notice that there is an understood multiplication symbol between the 3 and the parentheses. To "distribute" the 3 means to multiply 3 times each number inside the parentheses.

Understood to be *multiplying* by 3

$3(6 + 2)$
↓
$3 \cdot (6 + 2)$

Using the distributive property,

$3 \cdot (6 + 2)$ can be rewritten as $3 \cdot 6 + 3 \cdot 2$

5 Show that the product is unchanged and name the property that is illustrated in each case.

(a) $(3 \cdot 3) \cdot 2 = 3 \cdot (3 \cdot 2)$

(b) $11 \cdot 8 = 8 \cdot 11$

(c) $2 \cdot {}^-15 = {}^-15 \cdot 2$

(d) ${}^-4 \cdot (2 \cdot 5) = ({}^-4 \cdot 2) \cdot 5$

ANSWERS

5. (a) $18 = 18$; associative property of multiplication
   (b) $88 = 88$; commutative property of multiplication
   (c) ${}^-30 = {}^-30$; commutative property of multiplication
   (d) ${}^-40 = {}^-40$; associative property of multiplication

6 Rewrite each product, using the distributive property. Show that the result is unchanged.

(a) $3(8 + 7)$

(b) $10(6 + {}^-9)$

(c) ${}^-6(4 + 4)$

EXAMPLE 6 Using the Distributive Property

Rewrite each product, using the distributive property. Show that the result is unchanged.

(a) $4(3 + 7)$

> Careful! Multiply *both* numbers by 4.

$$4(3 + 7) = 4 \cdot 3 + 4 \cdot 7$$
$$4(10) = 12 + 28$$
$$40 = 40 \qquad \text{Both results are 40.}$$

(b) ${}^-2({}^-5 + 1)$

> Multiple *both* numbers by ${}^-2$.

$${}^-2({}^-5 + 1) = {}^-2 \cdot {}^-5 + {}^-2 \cdot 1$$
$${}^-2({}^-4) = 10 + {}^-2$$
$$8 = 8 \qquad \text{Both results are 8.}$$

◀ *Work Problem* **6** *at the Side.*

OBJECTIVE 4 Estimate answers to application problems involving multiplication.   Front end rounding can be used to estimate answers in multiplication, just as we did when adding and subtracting (see **Section 3.4**). As a brief review, look at the pattern in these examples.

$${}^-3 \cdot 2 \text{ is } {}^-6$$
$${}^-30 \cdot 200 = {}^-6000$$

Total of three zeros   Write three zeros after the ${}^-6$.

$${}^-2 \cdot {}^-5 \text{ is } 10$$
$${}^-2000 \cdot {}^-5000 = 10{,}000{,}000$$

Total of six zeros   Write six zeros after the 10.

---

7 Use front end rounding to estimate an answer. Then find the exact answer.

An average of 27,095 baseball fans attended each of the 81 home games during the season. What was the total home game attendance for the season?

Estimate:

Exact:

EXAMPLE 7 Using Front End Rounding to Estimate an Answer

Use front end rounding to estimate an answer. Then find the exact answer.

Last year the Video Land store had to replace 392 defective videos at a cost of $19 each. How much money did the store lose on defective videos? (*Hint:* Because it's a loss, use a negative number for the cost.)

Estimate: Use front end rounding: 392 rounds to 400 and ${}^-\$19$ rounds to ${}^-\$20$. Use the rounded numbers and multiply to estimate the total amount of money lost.

$$4 \cdot {}^-2 \text{ is } {}^-8$$
$$400 \cdot {}^-\$20 = {}^-\$8000 \qquad \text{Estimate}$$

Total of three zeros   Write three zeros after the ${}^-8$.

Exact: $392 \cdot {}^-\$19 = {}^-\$7448$

Because the exact answer of ${}^-\$7448$ is fairly close to the estimate of ${}^-\$8000$, you can see that ${}^-\$7448$ probably is correct. The store manager could also use the estimate to say, "We lost about $8000 on defective videos last year."

◀ *Work Problem* **7** *at the Side.*

ANSWERS

6. (a) $3 \cdot 8 + 3 \cdot 7$; both results are 45.
(b) $10 \cdot 6 + 10 \cdot {}^-9$; both results are ${}^-30$.
(c) ${}^-6 \cdot 4 + {}^-6 \cdot 4$; both results are ${}^-48$.
7. (a) *Estimate:* $30{,}000 \cdot 80 = 2{,}400{,}000$ fans
(b) *Exact:* $27{,}095 \cdot 81 = 2{,}194{,}695$ fans

Multiply. See Examples 1–4.

1. (a) $9 \cdot 7$

    (b) $^-9 \cdot {}^-7$

    (c) $^-9 \cdot 7$

    (d) $9 \cdot {}^-7$

2. (a) $^-6 \cdot 9$

    (b) $6 \cdot {}^-9$

    (c) $^-6 \cdot {}^-9$

    (d) $6 \cdot 9$

3. (a) $7({}^-8)$

    (b) $^-7(8)$

    (c) $7(8)$

    (d) $^-7({}^-8)$

4. (a) $8(6)$

    (b) $^-8({}^-6)$

    (c) $^-8(6)$

    (d) $8({}^-6)$

5. $^-5 \cdot 7$

6. $^-10 \cdot 2$

7. $({}^-5)(9)$

8. $({}^-9)(4)$

9. $3({}^-6)$

10. $8({}^-9)$

11. $10({}^-5)$

12. $5({}^-11)$

13. $({}^-1)(40)$

14. $(75)({}^-1)$

15. $^-56 \cdot 1$

16. $1 \cdot {}^-87$

17. $^-8({}^-4)$

18. $^-3({}^-9)$

19. $11 \cdot 7$

20. $4 \cdot 25$

21. $25 \cdot 0$

22. $0 \cdot 30$

23. $^-19({}^-7)$

24. $^-21({}^-3)$

25. $^-13({}^-1)$

26. $^-1({}^-31)$

27. $(0)({}^-25)$

28. $({}^-50)(0)$

29. $^-4 \cdot {}^-6 \cdot 2$

30. $^-9 \cdot 3 \cdot {}^-3$

31. $({}^-4)({}^-2)({}^-7)$

32. $({}^-6)({}^-2)({}^-3)$

33. $5({}^-8)(4)$

34. $5(4)({}^-6)$

Write an integer in each blank to make a true statement.

35. $({}^-3)(\underline{\quad}) = {}^-15$

36. $6 \cdot \underline{\quad} = {}^-24$

37. $\underline{\quad} \cdot 10 = {}^-30$

38. $(\underline{\quad})({}^-4) = 16$

39. $^-17 = 17(\underline{\quad})$

40. $29 = {}^-29(\underline{\quad})$

41. $(\underline{\quad})({}^-350) = 0$

42. $\underline{\quad} \cdot 99 = 99$

43. $5 \cdot {}^-4 \cdot \underline{\quad} = {}^-100$

44. $\underline{\quad} \cdot 2 \cdot {}^-2 = {}^-24$

45. $(\underline{\quad})({}^-5)({}^-2) = {}^-40$

46. $({}^-3)(\underline{\quad})({}^-3) = {}^-27$

47. In your own words, explain the difference between the commutative and associative properties of multiplication. Show an example of each.

48. A student did this multiplication.

$$^-3 \cdot {}^-3 \cdot {}^-3 = 27$$

He knew that $3 \cdot 3 \cdot 3$ is 27. Since all the factors have the same sign, he made the product positive. Do you agree with his reasoning? Explain.

Relating Concepts (Exercises 49–50) For Individual or Group Work

*Look for patterns as you **work Exercises 49 and 50 in order**.*

49. Write three numerical examples for each of these situations:

(a) A positive number multiplied by $^-1$

(b) A negative number multiplied by $^-1$

Now write a rule that explains what happens when you multiply a signed number by $^-1$.

50. Do these multiplications.

$$^-2 \cdot {}^-2 = \underline{}$$

$$^-2 \cdot {}^-2 \cdot {}^-2 = \underline{}$$

$$^-2 \cdot {}^-2 \cdot {}^-2 \cdot {}^-2 = \underline{}$$

$$^-2 \cdot {}^-2 \cdot {}^-2 \cdot {}^-2 \cdot {}^-2 = \underline{}$$

Describe the pattern in the products. Then find the next three products without multiplying all the $^-2$s.

Rewrite each multiplication, using the stated property. Show that the result is unchanged. See Examples 5 and 6.

51. Distributive property
   $9(^-3 + 5)$

52. Distributive property
   $^-6(4 + {}^-5)$

53. Commutative property
   $25 \cdot 8$

54. Commutative property
   $^-7 \cdot {}^-11$

55. Associative property
   $^-3 \cdot (2 \cdot 5)$

56. Associative property
   $(5 \cdot 5) \cdot 10$

First use front end rounding to estimate the answer to each application problem.
Then find the exact answer. See Example 7.

57. Alliette receives $324 per week for doing child care in her home. How much income will she have for an entire year? There are 52 weeks in a year.

Estimate:

Exact:

58. Enrollment at our community college has increased by 875 students each of the last four semesters. What is the total increase?

Estimate:

Exact:

59. A new computer software store had losses of $9950 during each month of its first year. What was the total loss for the year?

Estimate:

Exact:

60. A cell phone company estimates that it is losing 95 customers each week. How many customers will it lose in a year?

Estimate:

Exact:

61. Tuition at the state university is $182 per credit for undergraduates. How much tuition will Wei Chen pay for 13 credits?

Estimate:

Exact:

62. Pat ate a dozen crackers as a snack. Each cracker had 17 calories. How many calories did Pat eat?

Estimate:

Exact:

63. There are 24 hours in one day. How many hours are in one year (365 days)?

Estimate:

Exact:

64. There are 5280 feet in one mile. How many feet are in 17 miles?

Estimate:

Exact:

Simplify.

65. $^-8 \cdot |^-8 \cdot 8|$

66. $^-7 \cdot |7| \cdot |^-7|$

67. $(^-37)\,(^-1)\,(85)\,(0)$

68. $^-1\,(9732)\,(^-1)\,(^-1)$

69. $|6 - 7| \cdot {}^-355{,}299$

70. $987 \cdot {}^-65{,}432 \cdot |9 - 9|$

Each of these application problems requires several steps and may involve addition and subtraction as well as multiplication.

71. Each of Maurice's four cats needed a $24 rabies shot and a $29 shot to prevent respiratory infections. There was also one $35 office visit charge. What was the total amount of Maurice's bill?

72. Chantele has three children. Her older daughter had a throat culture taken at the clinic today. Her baby received three immunization shots and her son received two shots. The co-pay amounts were $8 for each shot, an $18 office charge for each child, and $12 for the throat culture. How much did Chantele pay?

73. There is a 3-degree drop in temperature for every thousand feet that an airplane climbs into the sky. If the temperature on the ground is 50 degrees, what will be the temperature when the plane reaches an altitude of 24,000 feet? (*Source:* Lands' End.)

74. An unmanned research submarine descends to 150 feet below the surface of the ocean. Then it continues to go deeper, taking a water sample every 25 feet. What is its depth when it takes the 15th sample?

75. In Ms. Zubero's algebra class, there are six tests of 100 points each, eight quizzes of six points each, and 20 homework assignments of five points each. There are also four "bonus points" on each test. What is the total number of possible points?

76. In Mr. Jackson's prealgebra class, there are three group projects worth 25 points each, five 100-point tests, a 150-point final exam, and seven quizzes worth 12 points each. Find the total number of possible points.

3.6 ▷▷▷ Dividing Integers

OBJECTIVE **1** **Divide integers.** In arithmetic, we usually use $\overline{)}$ to write division problems so that we can do them by hand. Calculator keys use the $\div$ symbol for division. In algebra, we usually show division by using a fraction bar, a slash mark, or the $\div$ symbol. The answer to a division problem is called the **quotient.**

Arithmetic

$$\text{Divisor} \rightarrow 2\overline{)16} \begin{array}{l} \leftarrow \text{Quotient} \\ \leftarrow \text{Dividend} \end{array} \quad 8$$

Calculator and Algebra

$$\overset{\text{Dividend}}{\underset{}{16}} \div \overset{\text{Divisor}}{\underset{}{2}} = \underset{\text{Quotient}}{8}$$

$$\text{Dividend} \rightarrow \frac{16}{2} = \underset{\text{Quotient}}{8} \leftarrow \text{Divisor}$$

For every division problem, we can write a related multiplication problem. Because of this relationship, the sign rules for dividing integers are the same as the rules for multiplying integers. Examples:

$$\frac{16}{8} = 2 \qquad \text{because} \quad (2)(8) = 16$$

$$\frac{^-16}{^-8} = 2 \qquad \text{because} \quad (2)(^-8) = ^-16$$

$$\frac{^-16}{8} = ^-2 \qquad \text{because} \quad (^-2)(8) = ^-16$$

$$\frac{16}{^-8} = ^-2 \qquad \text{because} \quad (^-2)(^-8) = 16$$

> **Dividing Two Integers**
>
> If two numbers have *different signs,* the quotient is *negative.*
> Some examples are shown below.
>
> $$\frac{^-18}{3} = ^-6 \qquad \frac{40}{^-5} = ^-8$$
>
> If two numbers have the *same sign,* the quotient is *positive.*
> Some examples are shown below.
>
> $$\frac{^-30}{^-6} = 5 \qquad \frac{48}{8} = 6$$

EXAMPLE 1 **Dividing Two Integers**

(a) $\dfrac{^-20}{5}$ ⟵ Numbers have *different* signs, so the quotient is *negative.*
$\qquad \dfrac{^-20}{5} = ^-4$

(b) $\dfrac{^-24}{^-4}$ ⟵ Numbers have the *same* sign, so the quotient is *positive.*
$\qquad \dfrac{^-24}{^-4} = 6$

> The sign rules for dividing and multiplying are the same.

(c) $60 \div ^-2$ Numbers have *different* signs, so the quotient is *negative.*
$\qquad 60 \div ^-2 = ^-30$

Work Problem **1** *at the Side.* ▶

OBJECTIVES

1 Divide integers.

2 Identify properties of division.

3 Combine multiplying and dividing of integers.

4 Estimate answers to application problems involving division.

5 Interpret remainders in division application problems.

1 Divide.

(a) $\dfrac{40}{^-8}$

(b) $\dfrac{49}{7}$

(c) $\dfrac{^-32}{4}$

(d) $\dfrac{^-10}{^-10}$

(e) $^-81 \div 9$

(f) $^-100 \div ^-50$

ANSWERS
1. **(a)** $^-5$ **(b)** 7 **(c)** $^-8$ **(d)** 1
   (e) $^-9$ **(f)** 2

2 Divide. Then state the property illustrated by each division.

(a) $\dfrac{-12}{0}$

(b) $\dfrac{0}{39}$

(c) $\dfrac{-9}{1}$

(d) $\dfrac{21}{21}$

OBJECTIVE 2 Identify properties of division. You have seen that 0 and 1 are used in special ways in addition and multiplication. This is also true in division.

Examples			Pattern (Division Property)
$\dfrac{5}{5} = 1$	$\dfrac{-18}{-18} = 1$	$\dfrac{-793}{-793} = 1$	When a nonzero number is divided by itself, the quotient is 1.
$\dfrac{5}{1} = 5$	$\dfrac{-18}{1} = -18$	$\dfrac{-793}{1} = -793$	When a number is divided by 1, the quotient is the number.
$\dfrac{0}{5} = 0$	$\dfrac{0}{-18} = 0$	$\dfrac{0}{-793} = 0$	When 0 is divided by any other number (except 0), the quotient is 0.
$\dfrac{5}{0}$ is undefined.	$\dfrac{-18}{0}$ is undefined.		Division by 0 is *undefined.* There is no answer.

The most surprising property is that division by 0 *cannot be done.* Let's review the reason for that by rewriting this division problem as a related multiplication problem.

$$\frac{-18}{0} = ? \quad \text{can be written as the multiplication} \quad ? \bullet 0 = -18$$

If you thought the answer to $\frac{-18}{0}$ should be 0, try replacing ? with 0. It doesn't work in the related multiplication problem! Try replacing ? with any number you like. The result in the related multiplication problem is always 0 instead of -18. That is how we know that dividing by 0 cannot be done. Mathematicians say that it is *undefined* and have agreed never to divide by 0.

EXAMPLE 2 **Using the Properties of Division**

Divide. Then state the property illustrated by each example.

(a) $\dfrac{-312}{-312} = 1$ Any nonzero number divided by itself is 1.

(b) $\dfrac{75}{1} = 75$ Any number divided by 1 is the number.

(c) $\dfrac{0}{-19} = 0$ Zero divided by any nonzero number is 0.

> You *cannot* divide by 0. Write "undefined."

(d) $\dfrac{48}{0}$ is *undefined.*   Division by 0 is *undefined.*

▦ Calculator Tip Try Examples 2(c) and 2(d) above on your calculator. Use the change of sign key to enter -19 on a *scientific* calculator.

0 ÷ 19 +/– =   Answer is 0

$\underbrace{\qquad}_{-19}$

48 ÷ 0 =   Calculator shows "Error" or "ERR" or "E" for error because it cannot divide by 0.

ANSWERS

2. (a) undefined; division by 0 is undefined.
   (b) 0; 0 divided by any nonzero number is 0.
   (c) -9; any number divided by 1 is the number.
   (d) 1; any nonzero number divided by itself is 1.

◀ *Work Problem* **2** *at the Side.*

OBJECTIVE 3 Combine multiplying and dividing of integers.
When a problem involves both multiplying and dividing, first check to see if there are any parentheses. Do what is inside parentheses first. Then start at the left and work toward the right, using two numbers at a time.

EXAMPLE 3 **Combining Multiplication and Division of Integers**

Simplify.

(a) $6(^-10) \div (^-3 \cdot 2)$ Do operations inside parentheses first: $^-3 \cdot 2$ is $^-6$. The signs are *different*, so the product is *negative*.

$6(^-10) \div \quad ^-6$ Start at the left: $6(^-10)$ is $^-60$. The signs are *different*, so the product is *negative*.

$^-60 \quad \div \quad ^-6$ Finally, $^-60 \div ^-6$ is 10. The signs are the *same*, so the quotient is *positive*.

10

(b) $^-24 \div ^-2(4) \div ^-6$ No operations inside parentheses, so start at the left: $^-24 \div ^-2$ is 12. (*Same* signs, *positive* quotient.)

$12(4) \div ^-6$ Next, $12(4)$ is 48. (*Same* signs, *positive* product.)

$48 \div ^-6$ Finally, $48 \div ^-6$ is $^-8$. (*Different* signs, *negative* quotient.)

$^-8$

(c) $^-50 \div ^-5 \div ^-2$ There are no parentheses, so start at the left: $^-50 \div ^-5$ is 10. (*Same* signs, *positive* quotient.)

$10 \quad \div ^-2$ Now, $10 \div ^-2$ is $^-5$. (*Different* signs, *negative* quotient.)

$^-5$

Work Problem **3** *at the Side.* ▶

OBJECTIVE 4 Estimate answers to application problems involving division.   Front end rounding can be used to estimate answers in division just as you did when multiplying (see **Section 3.5**). Once the numbers have been rounded so that there are lots of zeros, you can use the division shortcut. As a brief review, look at the pattern in these examples.

$$400\cancel{0} \div ^-5\cancel{0} = 400 \div ^-5 = ^-80$$

Drop one 0 from both dividend and divisor.

$$^-6\cancel{000} \div ^-3\cancel{000} = ^-6 \div ^-3 = 2$$

Drop three zeros from both dividend and divisor.

3 Simplify.

(a) $60 \div ^-3(^-5)$

(b) $^-6(^-16 \div ^-8) \cdot 2$

(c) $^-8(10) \div 4(^-3) \div ^-6$

(d) $56 \div ^-8 \div ^-1$

4 First use front end rounding to estimate an answer. Then find the exact answer.

Laurie and Chuck Struthers lost $2724 on their stock investments last year. What was their average loss each month?

Estimate:

Exact:

EXAMPLE 4 **Using Front End Rounding to Estimate an Answer in Division**

First use front end rounding to estimate an answer. Then find the exact answer.

During a 24-hour laboratory experiment, the temperature of a solution dropped 96 degrees. What was the average drop in temperature each hour?

Estimate: Use front end rounding: $^-96$ degrees rounds to $^-100$ degrees and 24 hours rounds to 20 hours. To estimate the average, divide the rounded number of degrees by the rounded number of hours.

$$^-100 \text{ degrees} \div 20 \text{ hours} = {^-5} \text{ degrees each hour} \leftarrow \text{Estimate}$$

Exact: $^-96$ degrees $\div$ 24 hours = $^-4$ degrees each hour $\leftarrow$ Exact

Because the exact answer of $^-4$ degrees is close to the estimate of $^-5$ degrees, you can see that $^-4$ degrees probably is correct.

> ▦ **Calculator Tip**   The answer in Example 4 above "came out even." In other words, the quotient was an integer. Suppose that the drop in temperature had been 97 degrees. Do the division on your calculator.
>
> $$\underbrace{97 \;\boxed{+/-}}_{^-97} \;\boxed{\div}\; 24 \;\boxed{=} \qquad \text{Calculator shows } -4.041666667$$
>
> The quotient is *not* an integer. We will work with numbers like these in **Chapter 6,** Positive and Negative Decimals.

◀ *Work Problem* **4** *at the Side.*

OBJECTIVE **5** **Interpret remainders in division application problems.** In arithmetic, division problems often have a remainder, as shown below.

$$\begin{array}{r} 14 \text{ R10} \\ 25\overline{)360} \\ 25 \\ \hline 110 \\ 100 \\ \hline 10 \leftarrow \text{Remainder} \end{array}$$

But what does **R10** really mean? Let's look at this same problem by using money amounts.

EXAMPLE 5 **Interpreting Remainders in Division Applications**

Divide; then interpret the remainder in each application.

(a) The math department at Lake Community College has $360 in its budget to buy scientific calculators for the math lab. If the calculators cost $25 each, how many can be purchased? How much money will be left over?

We can solve this problem by using the same division as shown above. But this time we can decide what the remainder really means.

$$\begin{array}{r} 14 \leftarrow \text{Number of calculators purchased} \\ \text{Cost of one calculator} \rightarrow \$25\overline{)\$360} \leftarrow \text{Budget} \\ 25 \\ \hline 110 \\ 100 \\ \hline \$10 \leftarrow \text{Money left over} \end{array}$$

The remainder is the money that is left over.

The department can buy 14 calculators. There will be $10 left over.

Continued on Next Page

ANSWERS

4. *Estimate:* $^-\$3000 \div 10$ months = $^-\$300$ each month
Exact: $^-\$2724 \div 12$ months = $^-\$227$ each month

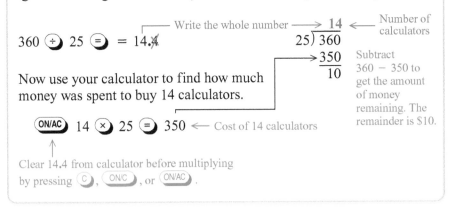

Calculator Tip You can use your calculator to solve Example 5(a) on the previous page. Recall that digits on the *right* side of the decimal point show *part* of one whole. You cannot order *part* of one calculator, so ignore those digits and use only the *whole number part* of the quotient.

Now use your calculator to find how much money was spent to buy 14 calculators.

Clear 14.4 from calculator before multiplying by pressing Ⓒ, Ⓞⁿ/ᶜ , or Ⓞⁿ/ᴬᶜ .

5 Divide; then interpret the remainder in each of these applications.

(a) Chad and Martha are baking cookies for a fund-raiser. They baked 116 cookies and are putting them into packages of a dozen each. How many packages will they have for the fund-raiser? How many cookies will be left over for them to eat?

(b) Luke's son is going on a Scout camping trip. There are 135 Scouts. Luke is renting tents that sleep 6 people each. How many tents should he rent?

We again use division to solve the problem. There is a remainder, but this time it must be interpreted differently than in the calculator example.

$$\begin{array}{r} 22 \\ 6\overline{)135} \\ \underline{12} \\ 15 \\ \underline{12} \\ 3 \end{array}$$

22 ← Number of tents with 6 Scouts each
$6\overline{)135}$ ← Total number of Scouts
Each tent holds →
3 ← Scouts left over

22 tents is *not* enough for all the Scouts.

If Luke rents 22 tents, 3 Scouts will have to sleep out in the rain. He must rent **23 tents** to accommodate all the Scouts. (One tent will have only 3 Scouts in it.)

Work Problem **5** *at the Side.* ▶

(b) Coreen is a dispatcher for a bus company. A group of 249 senior citizens is going to a baseball game. If the buses will each hold 44 people, how many buses should she send to pick up the seniors?

Math in the Media

Although prices can vary depending on where you live, average wedding costs in the United States increased from $15,208 in 1990 to the grand total you will calculate in the table below (in 2007). The average number of wedding guests is 165.

Category	Average Cost in 2007
Attire (bride's dress, men's formalwear, etc.)	$ 2710
Ceremony	2627
Favors and gifts	1166
Flowers	2048
Jewelry: engagement and wedding rings	4150
Music	991
Photography and video	3836
Reception	14,737
Stationery; invitations	881
Limousine	426
Grand Total	

Sources: www.costofwedding.com and *Bride's* magazine.

1. What is the grand total of expenses shown in the table?

2. How much more expensive was a wedding in 2007 compared to 1990?

3. If you budgeted $78 per person for the wedding reception and you invited 165 guests to a wedding in 2009, how much money would you have spent compared to the 2007 wedding reception costs?

4. If you budget $10,000 for the reception and the caterer charges $78 per person, how many guests can you invite? How much of your budget is left over?

5. If you budget $12,500 for the reception and the caterer charges $78 per person, how many guests can you invite? How much of your budget is left over?

6. What type of arithmetic problem did you work to get the answers to Problems 4 and 5? What is the mathematical term for the "left over" budget?

7. If you rent the limousine for six hours, what is the average cost per hour? When you solved this problem, which number was the dividend? the divisor? the quotient? Rewrite the division as a related multiplication.

3.6 ▶▶▶ Exercises

Divide. See Examples 1 and 2.

1. (a) $14 \div 2$

(b) $^-14 \div ^-2$

(c) $14 \div ^-2$

(d) $^-14 \div 2$

2. (a) $^-18 \div ^-3$

(b) $18 \div 3$

(c) $^-18 \div 3$

(d) $18 \div ^-3$

3. (a) $^-42 \div 6$

(b) $^-42 \div ^-6$

(c) $42 \div ^-6$

(d) $42 \div 6$

4. (a) $45 \div 5$

(b) $45 \div ^-5$

(c) $^-45 \div ^-5$

(d) $^-45 \div 5$

5. (a) $\dfrac{35}{35}$

(b) $\dfrac{35}{1}$

(c) $\dfrac{^-13}{1}$

(d) $\dfrac{^-13}{^-13}$

6. (a) $\dfrac{^-23}{1}$

(b) $\dfrac{^-23}{^-23}$

(c) $\dfrac{17}{1}$

(d) $\dfrac{17}{17}$

7. (a) $\dfrac{0}{50}$

(b) $\dfrac{50}{0}$

(c) $\dfrac{^-11}{0}$

(d) $\dfrac{0}{^-11}$

8. (a) $\dfrac{^-85}{0}$

(b) $\dfrac{0}{^-85}$

(c) $\dfrac{6}{0}$

(d) $\dfrac{0}{6}$

9. $\dfrac{^-8}{2}$

10. $\dfrac{^-14}{7}$

11. $\dfrac{21}{^-7}$

12. $\dfrac{30}{^-6}$

13. $\dfrac{^-54}{^-9}$

14. $\dfrac{^-48}{^-6}$

15. $\dfrac{55}{^-5}$

16. $\dfrac{70}{^-7}$

17. $\dfrac{^-28}{0}$

18. $\dfrac{^-40}{0}$

19. $\dfrac{14}{^-1}$

20. $\dfrac{25}{^-1}$

21. $\dfrac{^-20}{^-2}$

22. $\dfrac{^-80}{^-4}$

23. $\dfrac{^-48}{^-12}$

24. $\dfrac{^-30}{^-15}$

25. $\dfrac{^-18}{18}$

26. $\dfrac{50}{^-50}$

27. $\dfrac{0}{^-9}$

28. $\dfrac{0}{^-4}$

29. $\dfrac{^-573}{^-3}$

30. $\dfrac{^-580}{^-5}$

31. $\dfrac{163,672}{^-328}$

32. $\dfrac{^-69,496}{1022}$

Simplify. See Example 3.

33. $^-60 \div 10 \div {}^-3$

34. $36 \div {}^-4 \div 3$

35. $^-64 \div {}^-8 \div {}^-2$

36. $^-72 \div {}^-9 \div {}^-4$

37. $100 \div {}^-5({}^-2)$

38. $^-80 \div 4({}^-5)$

39. $48 \div 3 \cdot (12 \div {}^-4)$

40. $^-2 \cdot ({}^-3 \cdot {}^-7) \div 7$

41. $^-5 \div {}^-5({}^-10) \div {}^-2$

42. $^-9(4) \div {}^-36(50)$

43. $64 \cdot 0 \div {}^-8(10)$

44. $^-88 \div {}^-8 \div {}^-11(0)$

Relating Concepts (Exercises 45–50) For Individual or Group Work

Use your knowledge of the properties of multiplication as you **work Exercises 45–50 in order.**

45. Explain whether or not division is commutative like multiplication. Start by doing these two divisions on your calculator: $2 \div 1$ and $1 \div 2$.

46. Explain whether or not division is associative like multiplication. Start by doing these two divisions: $(12 \div 6) \div 2$ and $12 \div (6 \div 2)$.

47. Explain what is different and what is similar about multiplying and dividing two signed numbers.

48. In your own words, describe at least three division properties. Include examples to illustrate each property.

49. Write three numerical examples for each situation.

(a) A negative number divided by $^-1$

(b) A positive number divided by $^-1$

Now write a rule that explains what happens when you divide a signed number by $^-1$.

50. Explain why $\frac{0}{^-3}$ and $\frac{^-3}{0}$ do not give the same result.

Solve these application problems by using addition, subtraction, multiplication, or division. First use front end rounding to estimate the answer. Then find the exact answer. See Example 4.

51. The greatest ocean depth is 35,836 feet below sea level. If an unmanned research sub dives to that depth in 17 equal steps, how far does it dive in each step? (*Source: The Top 10 of Everything.*)

Estimate:

Exact:

52. Our college enrollment dropped by 3245 students over the last 11 years. What was the average drop in enrollment each year?

Estimate:

Exact:

53. When Ashwini discovered that her checking account was overdrawn by $238, she quickly transferred $450 from her savings to her checking account. What is the new balance in her checking account?

Estimate:

Exact:

54. The Tigers offensive team lost a total of 48 yards during the first half of the football game. During the second half they gained 191 yards. How many yards did they gain or lose during the entire game?

Estimate:

Exact:

55. The foggiest place in the United States is Cape Disappointment, Washington. It is foggy there an average of 106 days each year. How many days is it not foggy each year? (*Source:* National Weather Service.)

Estimate:

Exact:

56. The number of cell phone users in the United States in 1992 was 11 million. The number of users reached 233 million in 2007. What was the increase in the number of users during this 15-year period? (*Source: The World Almanac.*)

Estimate:

Exact:

57. A plane descended an average of 730 feet each minute during a 37-minute landing. How far did the plane descend during the landing?

Estimate:

Exact:

58. A discount store found that 174 items were lost to shoplifting last month. The average value of each item was $24. What was the total loss due to shoplifting?

Estimate:

Exact:

59. Mr. and Mrs. Martinez drove on the Interstate for five hours and traveled 315 miles. What was the average number of miles they drove each hour?

Estimate:

Exact:

60. Rochelle has a 48-month car loan for $15,072. How much is her monthly payment?

Estimate:

Exact:

Find the exact answer in Exercises 61–66. Solving these problems requires more than one step.

61. Clarence bowled four games and had scores of 143, 190, 162, and 177. What was his average score? (*Hint:* To find the average, add all the scores and divide by the number of scores.)

62. Sheila kept track of her grocery expenses for six weeks. The amounts she spent were $184, $111, $136, $110, $98, and $153. What was the average weekly cost of her groceries?

63. On the back of an oatmeal box, it says that one serving weighs 40 grams and that there are 13 servings in the box. On the front of the box, it says that the weight of the contents is 510 grams. What is the difference in the total weight on the front and the back of the box? (*Source:* Quaker Oats.)

64. A 2000-calorie-per-day diet recommends that you eat no more than 65 grams of fat. If each gram of fat is 9 calories, how many calories can you consume in other types of food? (*Source:* U.S. Department of Agriculture.)

65. Stephanie had $302 in her checking account. She wrote a $116 check for day care and a $548 check for rent. She also deposited her $347 paycheck. What is the balance in her account?

66. Gary started a new checking account with a $500 deposit. The bank charged him $18 to print his checks. He also wrote a $193 check for car repairs and a $289 check to his credit card company. What is the balance in his account?

Divide; then interpret the remainder in each application. See Example 5.

67. A cellular phone company is offering 1000 free minutes of air time to new subscribers. How many hours of free time will a new subscriber receive?

68. Nikki is catering a large party. If one pie will serve eight guests, how many pies should she make for 100 guests?

69. Hurricane victims are being given temporary shelter in a hotel. Each room can hold five people. How many rooms are needed for 163 people?

70. A college has received a $250,000 donation to be used for scholarships. How many $3500 scholarships can be given to students?

Simplify:

71. $|{}^-8| \div {}^-4 \cdot |{}^-5| \cdot |1|$

72. ${}^-6 \cdot |{}^-3| \div |9| \cdot {}^-2$

73. ${}^-6({}^-8) \div ({}^-5 - {}^-5)$

74. ${}^-9 \div {}^-9({}^-9 \div 9) \div (12 - 13)$

 75. Look back at the opening page of **Section 1.1.** You guessed how many days it would take to receive a million dollars if you got $1 each second. Here's how to use your calculator to get the answer. If you get $1 per second, it would take 1,000,000 seconds to receive $1,000,000. Press these keys.

1000000	÷ 60	= 16666.66667	÷ 60	= 277.7777778	÷ 24	= 11.57407407
	There are 60 seconds in one minute.	About 16,667 minutes	There are 60 minutes in one hour.	About 278 hours	There are 24 hours in one day.	About $11\frac{1}{2}$ days (11.5 is equivalent to $11\frac{1}{2}$.)

Notice that you do *not* have to re-enter the intermediate answers. When the answer 16666.66667 appears on your calculator display, just go ahead and enter ÷ 60.

Now use a *scientific* calculator to find how long it takes to receive a *billion* dollars. Start by entering 1000000000. Then follow the pattern shown above. You will need to do one more division step to get the number of years. (Assume that there are 365 days in one year.)

Summary Exercises on Operations with Integers

Simplify each expression.

1. $2 - 8$

2. $(^-16)(0)$

3. $^-14 - {}^-7$

4. $\dfrac{^-42}{6}$

5. $^-9(^-7)$

6. $\dfrac{^-12}{12}$

7. $(1)(^-56)$

8. $1 + {}^-23$

9. $5 - {}^-7$

10. $^-88 \div {}^-11$

11. $^-18 + 5$

12. $\dfrac{0}{^-10}$

13. $^-40 - {}^-40$

14. $^-17 + 0$

15. $8(^-6)$

16. $^-1 - 9$

17. $^-5(10)$

18. $\dfrac{30}{0}$

19. $0 - 14$

20. $\dfrac{18}{^-3}$

21. $^-13 + 13$

22. $\dfrac{^-16}{^-1}$

23. $20 - 50$

24. $\dfrac{^-7}{0}$

25. $(^-4)(^-6)(2)$

26. $^-2 + {}^-12 + {}^-5$

27. $^-60 \div 10 \div {}^-3$

28. $^-8 - 4 - 8$

29. $64(0) \div {}^-8$

30. $2 - {}^-5 + 9$

31. $^-9 + 8 + {}^-2$

32. $(^-6)(^-2)(^-3)$

33. $8 + 6 + {}^-8$

34. $9 - 0 - 16$

35. $^-25 \div {}^-1 \div {}^-5$

36. $1 - 32 + 0$

37. $^-72 \div {}^-9 \div {}^-4$

38. $^-7 + 28 + {}^-56 + 3$

39. $9 - 6 - 3 - 5$

40. $^-6({}^-8) \div ({}^-5 - 7)$

41. $^-1(9732)({}^-1)({}^-1)$

42. $^-80 \div 4({}^-5)$

43. $^-10 - 4 + 0 + 18$

44. $^-7 \cdot |7| \cdot |{}^-7|$

45. $5 - |{}^-3| + 3$

46. $^-2({}^-3)(7) \div {}^-7$

47. $^-3 - ({}^-2 + 4) - 5$

48. $0 - |{}^-7 + 2|$

49. Describe what happens in each situation.
  (a) Zero is divided by a nonzero number.

  (b) Any number is multiplied by 0.

  (c) A nonzero number is divided by itself.

50. Find, explain, and correct the errors in this student's work.

  (a) $\dfrac{15}{^-15} = 0$

  (b) $\dfrac{8}{0} = 8$

  (c) $^-10 \div {}^-2 \div {}^-5 = 1$

3.7 ▶▶▶ Exponents and Order of Operations

OBJECTIVE 1 Use exponents to write repeated factors. An **exponent** is a quick way to write repeated multiplication. Here is an example.

$$2 \cdot 2 \cdot 2 \cdot 2 \cdot 2 \quad \text{can be written} \quad 2^5 \leftarrow \text{Exponent}$$
$$\uparrow$$
$$\text{Base}$$

The *base* is the number being multiplied over and over, and the exponent tells how many times to use the number as a factor. This is called *exponential notation* or *exponential form*.

To simplify 2^5, actually do the multiplication.

$$2^5 = \underbrace{2 \cdot 2 \cdot 2 \cdot 2 \cdot 2}_{\text{Factored form}} = 32$$

Exponential form   Factored form   Simplified form

Here are some more examples, using 2 as the base.

$2 = 2^1$	is read	"2 to the **first power**."
$2 \cdot 2 = 2^2$	is read	"2 to the **second power**" or, more commonly, "2 **squared**."
$2 \cdot 2 \cdot 2 = 2^3$	is read	"2 to the **third power**" or, more commonly, "2 **cubed**."
$2 \cdot 2 \cdot 2 \cdot 2 = 2^4$	is read	"2 to the **fourth power**."
$2 \cdot 2 \cdot 2 \cdot 2 \cdot 2 = 2^5$	is read	"2 to the **fifth power**."

and so on.

We usually don't write an exponent of 1, so if no exponent is shown, you can assume that it is 1. For example, 6 is actually 6^1, and 4 is actually 4^1.

> **Note**
> Exponents can also be negative numbers or 0, for example, 2^{-3} and 2^0.

EXAMPLE 1 Using Exponents

Complete this table

	Exponential Form	Factored Form	Simplified	Read as
(a)		$5 \cdot 5 \cdot 5$		
(b)		$(4)(4)$		
(c)		7		

Work Problem 1 at the Side. ▶

OBJECTIVE 2 Simplify expressions containing exponents. Exponents are also used with signed numbers, as shown below.

$$(^-3)^2 = (^-3)(^-3) = 9$$ The factors have the same sign, so the product is positive.

$$(^-4)^3 = \underbrace{(^-4)(^-4)}(^-4)$$ Multiply two numbers at a time.

$$\underbrace{16 \quad (^-4)}$$ First, $(^-4)(^-4)$ is positive 16.

$$^-64$$ Then, $16(^-4)$ is $^-64$.

OBJECTIVES

1 Use exponents to write repeated factors.

2 Simplify expressions containing exponents.

3 Use the order of operations.

4 Simplify expressions with fraction bars.

---

1 Write each multiplication using exponents. Indicate how to read the exponential form.

(a) $3 \cdot 3 \cdot 3 \cdot 3$

(b) $6 \cdot 6$

(c) 9

(d) $(2)(2)(2)(2)(2)(2)$

ANSWERS

1. (a) 3^4 is read "3 to the fourth power."
 (b) 6^2 is read "6 squared" or "6 to the second power."
 (c) 9^1 is read "9 to the first power."
 (d) 2^6 is read "2 to the sixth power."

2 Simplify.

(a) $(^-2)^3$

(b) $(^-6)^2$

(c) $2^4(^-3)^2$

(d) $3^3(^-4)^2$

Simplify exponents before you do other multiplications, as shown below. Notice that the exponent applies only to the *first* thing to its *left*.

Exponent applies only to the 2. → $2^3(5)(4^2)$ ← Exponent applies only to the 4.

$(2)(2)(2)$ is 8. → $8(5)(16)$ ← $(4)(4)$ is 16.

$40(16)$

640

EXAMPLE 2 **Using Exponents with Negative Numbers**

Simplify.

(a) $(^-5)^2 = (^-5)(^-5) = 25$

(b) $(^-5)^3 = \underbrace{(^-5)(^-5)}(^-5)$ ← Be careful! Work with two factors at a time and watch the signs.

$\rightarrow \underbrace{25(^-5)}$

$^-125$

(c) $(^-2)^4 = (^-2)(^-2)(^-2)(^-2) = 16$

(d) $2^3(^-3)^2 = \underbrace{(2)(2)(2)}\underbrace{(^-3)(^-3)}$

$\rightarrow (8)(9) \leftarrow$

72

Calculator Tip On a *scientific* calculator, use the exponent key  to enter exponents. To enter 5^8, press the following keys.

5 $\boxed{y^x}$ 8 $\boxed{=}$ Answer is 390,625.
↑   ↑
Base   Exponent

Be careful when using your calculator's exponent key with a negative number, such as $(^-5)^3$. Different calculators use different keystrokes, so check the instruction manual, or experiment to see how your calculator works.

◀ Work Problem **2** at the Side.

OBJECTIVE **3** **Use the order of operations.** In **Sections 1.4** and **3.6,** you worked examples that mixed addition and subtraction or mixed multiplication and division. In those situations, you worked from left to right. Example 3 below is a review.

EXAMPLE 3 **Working from Left to Right**

Simplify.

(a) $\underbrace{^-8 - {}^-6} + {}^-11$ Do additions and subtractions from left to right.

$\underbrace{{}^-2 \quad + {}^-11}$

$^-13$

Continued on Next Page

(b) $^-15 \div {}^-3\,(6)$ Do multiplications and divisions from left to right.

$$\to 5\,(6)$$

$$30$$

Work Problem **3** *at the Side.* ▶

3 Simplify.

(a) $^-9 + {}^-15 - 3$

Now we're ready to do problems that use a mix of the four operations, parentheses, and exponents. Let's start with a simple example: $4 + 2 \cdot 3$.

If we work from left to right	If we multiply first
$4 + 2 \cdot 3$	$4 + 2 \cdot 3$
$6 \quad \cdot 3$	$4 + \quad 6$
18	10

↖ Which answer is correct? ↗

(b) $^-4 - 2 + {}^-6$

To be sure that everyone gets the same answer to a problem like this, mathematicians have agreed to do things in a certain order. The following order of operations shows that multiplying is done ahead of adding, so *the correct answer is 10*.

Order of Operations

Step 1 Work inside ***parentheses*** or ***other grouping symbols.***

Step 2 Simplify expressions with ***exponents.***

Step 3 Do the remaining ***multiplications and divisions*** as they occur from left to right.

Step 4 Do the remaining ***additions and subtractions*** as they occur from left to right.

(c) $3\,(^-4) \div {}^-6$

▦ **Calculator Tip**   Enter the example above in your calculator.

$$4 \;\oplus\; 2 \;\otimes\; 3 \;\ominus\;$$

Which answer do you get? If you have a scientific calculator, it automatically uses the order of operations and multiplies first to get the correct answer of 10. Some standard, four-function calculators may *not* have the order of operations built into them and will give the ***incorrect*** answer of 18.

(d) $^-18 \div 9\,(^-4)$

④ Simplify.

(a) $8 + 6(14 \div 2)$

(b) $4(1) + 8(9 - 2)$

(c) $3(5 + 1) + 20 \div 4$

⑤ Simplify.

(a) $2 + 40 \div (^-5 + 3)$

(b) $^-5(5) - (15 + 5)$

(c) $(^-24 \div 2) + (15 - 3)$

(d) $^-3(2 - 8) - 5(4 - 3)$

(e) $3(3) - (10 \cdot 3) \div 5$

(f) $6 - (2 + 7) \div (^-4 + 1)$

EXAMPLE 4 **Using the Order of Operations with Whole Numbers**

Simplify.

Do **not** start by adding $9 + 3$.

$9 + 3\,(20 - 4)\ \div\ 8$ Work inside parentheses first: $20 - 4$ is 16.
Bring down the other numbers and symbols that you haven't used.

$9 + \quad 3\,(16) \quad \div\ 8$ Look for exponents: none.
Move from left to right, looking for multiplying and dividing.

$9 + \quad 3\,(16) \quad \div\ 8$ Yes, here is multiplying: $3(16)$ is 48.

$9 + \quad 48 \quad \div\ 8$ Here is dividing: $48 \div 8$ is 6. There is no other multiplying or dividing, so look for adding and subtracting.

$9 + \qquad\quad 6$ Add last: $9 + 6$ is 15.

$\qquad\quad 15$

◀ Work Problem ④ at the Side.

EXAMPLE 5 **Using the Order of Operations with Integers**

Simplify.

(a) $^-8 \div (7 - 5) - 9$ Work inside parentheses first: $7 - 5$ is 2.
Bring down the other numbers and symbols that you haven't used.
Look for exponents: none.

$^-8 \div \quad (2) \quad - 9$ Move from left to right, looking for multiplying and dividing.

$^-8 \div \quad (2) \quad - 9$ Here is dividing: $^-8 \div 2$ is $^-4$. No other multiplying or dividing, so look for adding and subtracting.

$^-4 \qquad - 9$ Change subtracting to adding. Change 9 to its opposite.

$^-4 \qquad + {}^-9$ Add $^-4 + {}^-9$.

$^-13$

Do **not** start by adding $3 + 2$.

(b) $3 + 2\,(6 - 8) \cdot (15 \div 3)$ Work inside first set of parentheses.
Change $6 - 8$ to $6 + {}^-8$ to get $^-2$.

$3 + 2\ (^-2) \cdot (15 \div 3)$ Work inside second set of parentheses: $15 \div 3$ is 5.

$3 + 2\ (^-2) \cdot \quad 5$ Multiply and divide from left to right.
First multiply $2(^-2)$ to get $^-4$.

$3 + \quad ^-4 \quad \cdot \quad 5$ Then multiply $^-4 \cdot 5$ to get $^-20$.

$3 + \qquad ^-20$ Add last: $3 + {}^-20$ is $^-17$.

$^-17$

◀ Work Problem ⑤ at the Side.

ANSWERS

4. (a) 50 **(b)** 60 **(c)** 23
5. (a) $^-18$ **(b)** $^-45$ **(c)** 0
   (d) 13 **(e)** 3 **(f)** 9

EXAMPLE 6   **Using the Order of Operations with Exponents**

Simplify.

(a) $4^2 - (^-3)^2$ The only parentheses are around $^-3$, but there is no work to do inside these parentheses.

$\underbrace{4^2}_{} - \underbrace{(^-3)^2}_{}$ Simplify the exponents: $4^2 = (4)(4) = 16$, and $(^-3)^2 = (^-3)(^-3) = 9$.

$\underbrace{16 - \quad 9}_{7}$ There is no multiplying or dividing, so add and subtract: $16 - 9$ is 7.

(b) $(^-4)^3 - (4 - 6)^2(^-3)$ Work inside parentheses: $4 - 6$ becomes $4 + {^-6}$, which is $^-2$.

$\underbrace{(^-4)^3}_{} - \underbrace{(^-2)^2}_{}(^-3)$ Simplify the exponents next: $(^-4)^3$ is $(^-4)(^-4)(^-4) = {^-64}$, and $(^-2)^2$ is $(^-2)(^-2) = 4$.

$^-64 \quad - \quad \underbrace{4(^-3)}_{}$ Look for multiplying and dividing. Multiply $4(^-3)$ to get $^-12$.

$^-64 \quad - \quad ^-12$ Change subtraction to addition. Change $^-12$ to its opposite.

$\underbrace{^-64 \quad + \quad ^+12}_{^-52}$ Add: $^-64 + 12$ is $^-52$.

> **CAUTION**
> To help in remembering the order of operations, you may have memorized the letters **PEMDAS**, or the phrase "Please Excuse My Dear Aunt Sally."
>
> **P**lease   **E**xcuse   **M**y   **D**ear   **A**unt   **S**ally
>
> **P**arentheses; **E**xponents; **M**ultiply and **D**ivide; **A**dd and **S**ubtract
>
> Be careful! Do **not** automatically do all multiplication before division. Multiplying and dividing are done *from left to right* (after parentheses and exponents).

Work Problem **6** *at the Side.* ▶

6 Simplify.

(a) $2^3 - 3^2$

(b) $6^2 \div (^-4)(^-3)$

(c) $(^-4)^2 - 3^2(5 - 2)$

(d) $(^-3)^3 + (3 - 9)^2$

7 Simplify.

(a) $\dfrac{^{-}3\,(2^3)}{^{-}10 - 6 + 8}$

OBJECTIVE **4** **Simplify expressions with fraction bars.** A fraction bar indicates division, as in $\dfrac{^{-}6}{2}$, which means $^{-}6 \div 2$. In the expression

$$\frac{^{-}5 + 3^2}{16 - 7\,(2)}$$

the fraction bar also acts as a grouping symbol, like parentheses. It tells us to do the work in the numerator (above the bar) and then the work in the denominator (below the bar). The last step is to divide the results.

$$\frac{^{-}5 + 3^2}{16 - 7\,(2)} \longrightarrow \frac{^{-}5 + 9}{16 - 14} \longrightarrow \frac{4}{2} \longrightarrow 4 \div 2 = 2$$

The final result is 2.

(b) $\dfrac{(^{-}10)\,(^{-}5)}{^{-}6 \div 3\,(5)}$

EXAMPLE 7 **Using the Order of Operations with Fraction Bars**

Simplify $\dfrac{^{-}8 + 5(4 - 6)}{4 - 4^2 \div 8}$.

First do the work in the numerator.

Do **not** start by adding $^{-}8 + 5$.	$^{-}8 + 5\,(4 - 6)$	Work inside the parentheses.
	$^{-}8 + \ 5\,(^{-}2)$	Multiply.
	$^{-}8 + \ (^{-}10)$	Add.

Numerator $\longrightarrow \ ^{-}18$

(c) $\dfrac{6 + 18 \div (^{-}2)}{(1 - 10) \div 3}$

Now do the work in the denominator.

$4 - 4^2 \div 8$	There are no parentheses; simplify the exponent.
$4 - 16 \div 8$	Divide.
$4 - \ \ 2$	Subtract.

Denominator $\rightarrow 2$

(d) $\dfrac{6^2 - 3^2(4)}{5 + (3 - 7)^2}$

The last step is the division.

Numerator $\longrightarrow \dfrac{^{-}18}{2} = \ ^{-}9$
Denominator $\longrightarrow$

◀Work Problem **7** *at the Side.*

FOR EXTRA HELP    PRACTICE   WATCH   DOWNLOAD   READ REVIEW

Complete this table. See Example 1.

	Exponential Form	Factored Form	Simplified	Read as
1.	4^3		64	
2.	10^2		100	
3.		$2 \cdot 2 \cdot 2 \cdot 2 \cdot 2 \cdot 2 \cdot 2$		
4.		$3 \cdot 3 \cdot 3 \cdot 3 \cdot 3$		
5.		$5 \cdot 5 \cdot 5 \cdot 5$		
6.		$2 \cdot 2 \cdot 2 \cdot 2 \cdot 2 \cdot 2$		
7.				7 squared
8.				6 cubed
9.				10 to the first power
10.				4 to the fourth power

Simplify. See Examples 1 and 2.

11. (a) 10^1 **12. (a)** 5^1 **13. (a)** 4^1 **14. (a)** 3^1

(b) 10^2 **(b)** 5^2 **(b)** 4^2 **(b)** 3^2

(c) 10^3 **(c)** 5^3 **(c)** 4^3 **(c)** 3^3

(d) 10^4 **(d)** 5^4 **(d)** 4^4 **(d)** 3^4

15. 5^{10} **16.** 4^9 **17.** 2^{12} **18.** 3^{10}

19. $(^-2)^2$ **20.** $(^-4)^2$ **21.** $(^-5)^2$ **22.** $(^-10)^2$

23. $(^-4)^3$ **24.** $(^-2)^3$ **25.** $(^-3)^4$ **26.** $(^-2)^4$

27. $(^-10)^3$ **28.** $(^-5)^3$ **29.** 1^4 **30.** 1^5

31. $3^3 \cdot 2^2$ **32.** $4^2 \cdot 5^2$ **33.** $2^3 \, (^-5)^2$ **34.** $3^2 \, (^-2)^2$

35. $6^1 \, (^-5)^3$ **36.** $7^1 \, (^-4)^3$ **37.** $(^-2)(^-2)^4$ **38.** $^-6 \, (^-6)^2$

39. Simplify.

$(^-2)^2 = $ _____ $(^-2)^6 = $ _____

$(^-2)^3 = $ _____ $(^-2)^7 = $ _____

$(^-2)^4 = $ _____ $(^-2)^8 = $ _____

$(^-2)^5 = $ _____ $(^-2)^9 = $ _____

(a) Describe the pattern you see in the signs of the answers.

(b) What would be the sign of $(^-2)^{15}$ and the sign of $(^-2)^{24}$?

40. Explain why it is important to have rules for the order of operations. Why do you think our "natural instinct" is to just work from left to right?

Simplify. See Examples 3–7.

41. $12 \div 6 \, (^-3)$ **42.** $10 - 30 \div 2$ **43.** $^-1 + 15 - 7 - 7$

44. $9 + \, ^-5 + 2 \, (^-2)$ **45.** $10 - 7^2$ **46.** $5 - 5^2$

47. $2 - \, ^-5 + 3^2$ **48.** $6 - \, ^-9 + 2^3$ **49.** $3 + 5 \, (6 - 2)$

50. $4 + 3 \, (8 - 3)$ **51.** $^-7 + 6 \, (8 - 14)$ **52.** $^-3 + 5 \, (9 - 12)$

53. $2 \, (^-3 + 5) - (9 - 12)$ **54.** $3 \, (2 - 7) - (^-5 + 1)$ **55.** $^-5 \, (7 - 13) \div \, ^-10$

56. $^-4(9 - 17) \div {}^-8$

57. $9 \div (^-3)^2 + {}^-1$

58. $^-48 \div (^-4)^2 + 3$

59. $2 - {}^-5(^-2)^3$

60. $1 - {}^-10(^-3)^3$

61. $^-2(^-7) + 3(9)$

62. $4(^-2) + {}^-3(^-5)$

63. $30 \div {}^-5 - 36 \div {}^-9$

64. $8 \div {}^-4 - 42 \div {}^-7$

65. $2(5) - 3(4) + 5(3)$

66. $9(3) - 6(4) + 3(7)$

67. $4(3^2) + 7(3 + 9) - {}^-6$

68. $5(4^2) - 6(1 + 4) - {}^-3$

69. $(^-4)^2 \cdot (7 - 9)^2 \div 2^3$

70. $(^-5)^2 \cdot (9 - 17)^2 \div (^-10)^2$

71. $\dfrac{^-1 + 5^2 - {}^-3}{^-6 - 9 + 12}$

72. $\dfrac{^-6 + 3^2 - {}^-7}{7 - 9 - 3}$

73. $\dfrac{-2\,(4^2) - 4\,(6-2)}{-4\,(8-13) \div -5}$

74. $\dfrac{3\,(3^2) - 5\,(9-2)}{8\,(6-9) \div -3}$

75. $\dfrac{2^3 \cdot (-2-5) + 4\,(-1)}{4 + 5\,(-6 \cdot 2) + (5 \cdot 11)}$

76. $\dfrac{3^3 + 4\,(-1-2) - 25}{-4 + 4\,(3 \cdot 5) + (-6 \cdot 9)}$

77. $5^2\,(9-11)\,(-3)\,(-3)^3$

78. $4^2\,(13-17)\,(-2)\,(-2)^3$

79. $|-12| \div 4 + 2 \cdot |(-2)^3| \div 4$

80. $6 - |2 - 3 \cdot 4| + (-5)^2 \div 5^2$

81. $\dfrac{-9 + 18 \div -3\,(-6)}{32 - 4\,(12) \div 3\,(2)}$

82. $\dfrac{-20 - 15\,(-4) - -40}{14 + 27 \div 3\,(-2) - -4}$

4

Introduction to Variables/ Solving Equations

4.1 ▶▶▶ Introduction to Variables

OBJECTIVES

1 Identify variables, constants, and expressions.

2 Evaluate variable expressions for given replacement values.

3 Write properties of operations using variables.

4 Use exponents with variables.

OBJECTIVE 1 Identify variables, constants, and expressions.
You probably know that algebra uses letters, especially the letter x. But why use letters when numbers are easier to understand? Here is an example.

Suppose that you run your college bookstore. When deciding how many books to order for a certain class, you first find out the class limit, that is, the maximum number of students allowed in the class. You will need at least that many books. But you decide to order 5 extra copies for emergencies.

Rule for ordering books: Order the class limit + 5 extra

How many books would you order for a prealgebra class with a limit of 25 students?

Class limit — ↓   ↓ — Extra
$$25 + 5$$ You would order 30 prealgebra books.

How many books would you order for a geometry class that allows 40 students to register?

Class limit — ↓   ↓ — Extra
$$40 + 5$$ You would order 45 geometry books.

You could set up a table to keep track of the number of books to order for various classes.

Class	Rule for Ordering Books: Class Limit + 5 Extra	Number of Books to Order
Prealgebra	$25 + 5$	30
Geometry	$40 + 5$	45
College algebra	$35 + 5$	40
Calculus 1	$50 + 5$	55

A shorthand way to write your rule is shown below.

$$c + 5$$
↑
The c stands for class limit.

You can't write your rule by using just numbers because the class limit varies, or changes, depending on which class you're talking about. So you use a letter, called a **variable,** to represent the part of the rule that varies. Notice the similarity in the words *varies* and *variable*. When part of a rule does *not* change, it is called a **constant.**

The variable, or the part of
the rule that varies or changes
↓
$$c + 5$$
↑
The constant, or the part of
the rule that does *not* change

$c + 5$ is called an **expression.** It expresses (tells) the rule for ordering books. You could use any letter you like for the variable part of the expression, such as $x + 5$, or $n + 5$, and so on. But one suggestion is to use a letter that reminds you of what it stands for. In this situation, the letter c reminds us of "class limit."

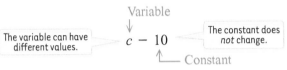

EXAMPLE 1 **Writing an Expression and Identifying the Variable and Constant**

Write an expression for this rule. Identify the variable and the constant.

Order the class limit minus 10 books because some students will buy used books.

Variable
↓

The variable can have different values. → $c - 10$ ← The constant does *not change.*

↑—— Constant

Work Problem **1** *at the Side.* ▶

1 Write an expression for this rule. Identify the variable and the constant.

Order the class limit plus 15 extra books because it is a very large class.

OBJECTIVE **2** **Evaluate variable expressions for given replacement values.**   When you need to figure out how many books to order for a particular class, you use a specific value for the class limit, like 25 students in prealgebra. Then you **evaluate the expression,** that is, you follow the rule.

Ordering Books for a Prealgebra Class

$c + 5$ Expression (rule for ordering books) is $c + 5$.
↓   Replace c with 25, the class limit for prealgebra.

$\underbrace{25 + 5}$ Follow the rule. Add $25 + 5$.

30   Order 30 prealgebra books.

EXAMPLE 2 **Evaluating an Expression**

Use this rule for ordering books: Order the class limit minus 10. The expression is $c - 10$.

(a) Evaluate the expression when the class limit is 32.

$c - 10$ Replace c with 32.
↓

$\underbrace{32 - 10}$ Follow the rule. Subtract to find $32 - 10$.

22   Order 22 books.

(b) Evaluate the expression when the class limit is 48.

$c - 10$ Replace c with 48.
↓

$\underbrace{48 - 10}$ Follow the rule. Subtract to find $48 - 10$.

38   Order 38 books.

Work Problem **2** *at the Side.* ▶

2 Use this expression for ordering books: $c + 3$.

(a) Evaluate the expression when the class limit is 25.

(b) Evaluate the expression when the class limit is 60.

In any career you choose, there will be many useful "rules" that need to be written using variables (letters) because part of the rule changes depending on the situation. This is one reason algebra is such a powerful tool. Here is another example.

Suppose that you work in a landscaping business. You are putting a fence around a square-shaped garden. Each side of the garden is 6 feet long. How much fencing material should you bring to finish the job? You could add the lengths of the four sides.

|← 6 feet →|

6 feet   6 feet

|← 6 feet →|

6 feet + 6 feet + 6 feet + 6 feet = 24 feet of fencing

ANSWERS

1. The expression is $c + 15$. The variable is c and the constant is 15.
2. **(a)** $25 + 3$ is 28; order 28 books
   (b) $60 + 3$ is 63; order 63 books

3 **(a)** Evaluate the expression 4*s* when the length of one side of a square table is 3 feet.

Or, recall that multiplication is a quick way to do repeated addition. The square garden has 4 sides, so multiply by 4.

$$4 \cdot 6 \text{ feet} = 24 \text{ feet of fencing}$$

So the rule for calculating the amount of fencing for a square garden is:

$$4 \cdot \text{length of one side}$$

Other jobs may require fencing for larger or smaller square shapes. The following table shows how much fencing you will need.

Length of One Side of Square Shape	Expression (Rule) to Find Total Amount of Fencing: 4 • Length of One Side	Total Amount of Fencing Needed
6 feet	4 • 6 feet	24 feet
9 feet	4 • 9 feet	36 feet
10 feet	4 • 10 feet	40 feet
3 feet	4 • 3 feet	12 feet

The expression (rule) can be written in shorthand form as shown below.

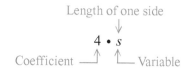

The number part in a *multiplication* expression is called the numerical coefficient, or just the **coefficient.** We usually don't write multiplication dots in expressions, so we do the following.

(b) Evaluate the expression 4*s* when the length of one side of a square park is 7 miles.

$$4 \cdot s \quad \text{is written as} \quad 4s$$

You can use the expression 4*s* any time you need to know the *perimeter* of a square shape, that is, the total distance around all four sides of the square.

CAUTION
If an expression involves adding, subtracting, or dividing, then you *do* have to write $+$, $-$, or $\div$. It is *only* multiplication that is understood without writing an operation symbol.

$4 + s$	$4 - s$	$4 \div s$	$4s$
↑	↑	↑	
Add *s*.	Subtract *s*.	Divide by *s*.	Multiply by *s*.

EXAMPLE 3 **Evaluating an Expression with Multiplication**

The expression (rule) for finding the perimeter of a square shape is 4*s*. Evaluate the expression when the length of one side of a square parking lot is 30 yards.

4*s*   Replace *s* with 30 yards.
↓
4 • 30 yards   There is no operation symbol between the 4 and the *s*, so it is understood to be multiplication. 4 times 30 is 120.
↓
120 yards ←— Total distance around the lot (perimeter) is 120 yards.

◀ *Work Problem* **3** *at the Side.*

ANSWERS
3. (a) 4 • 3 feet; 12 feet
   (b) 4 • 7 miles; 28 miles

Some expressions (rules) involve several different steps. An expression for finding the approximate systolic blood pressure of a person of a certain age is shown below.

$$100 + \frac{a}{2} \quad \longleftarrow \text{Age of person (the variable)}$$

Remember that a fraction bar means division, so $\frac{a}{2}$ is the person's age divided by 2. You also need to remember the order of operations, which means doing division before addition.

EXAMPLE 4   **Evaluating an Expression with Several Steps**

Evaluate the expression $100 + \frac{a}{2}$ when the age of the person is 24.

$$100 + \frac{a}{2} \quad \rceil \text{Replace } a \text{ with 24, the age of the person.}$$

$$100 + \frac{24}{2} \quad \lceil \begin{array}{l} \text{Follow the rule using the order of operations.} \\ \text{First divide: } 24 \div 2 \text{ is 12.} \end{array}$$

$$\underbrace{100 + 12} \quad \text{Now add: } 100 + 12 \text{ is 112.}$$

$$112 \quad \longleftarrow \text{The approximate systolic blood pressure is 112.}$$

Work Problem **4** *at the Side.* ▶

🔲 **Calculator Tip**   If you like to fish, you can use an expression (rule) like the one below to find the approximate weight (in pounds) of a fish you catch. Measure the length of the fish (in inches) and then use the correct expression for that type of fish. For a northern pike, the weight expression is shown below.

Variable (length of fish) ⟶

$$\frac{l^3}{3600}$$

where l is the length of the fish in inches. (*Source: InFisherman.*)

To evaluate this expression for a fish that is 43 inches long, follow the rule by calculating as follows.

$$\frac{43^3}{3600} \quad \begin{array}{l} \text{Replace } l \text{ with 43, the length of the} \\ \text{fish in inches.} \end{array}$$

In the numerator, you can multiply 43 • 43 • 43 or use the y^x key on your calculator. Then divide by 3600.

Enter 43 y^x 3 $\div$ 3600 $=$ Calculator shows 22.08527778
　　　↑　　　↑
　　Base Exponent

The fish weighs about 22 pounds.

Now use the expression to find the approximate weight of a northern pike that is 37 inches long. (Answer: about 14 pounds.)

(*continued*)

4 Evaluate the expression $100 + \frac{a}{2}$ when the age of the person is 40.

ANSWER

4. $100 + \dfrac{40}{2} \quad \longleftarrow$ Replace a with 40.

$\underbrace{100 + 20}$

$120 \quad \longleftarrow$ Approximate systolic blood pressure is 120.

Notice that variables are used on your calculator keys. On the y^x key, y represents the base and x represents the exponent. You first evaluated y^x by entering 43 as the base and 3 as the exponent for the first fish. Then you evaluated y^x again by entering 37 as the base and 3 as the exponent for the second fish.

5 (a) Use the expression for finding your average bowling score. Evaluate the expression if your total score for 4 games is 532.

Some expressions (rules) involve several variables. For example, if you go bowling and want to know your average score, you can use this expression.

$$\frac{t}{g}$$

$t \leftarrow$ Total score for all games (variable)

$g \leftarrow$ Number of games (variable)

EXAMPLE 5 **Evaluating Expressions with Two Variables**

(a) Find your average score if you bowl three games and your total score for all three games is 378.

Use the expression (rule) for finding your average score.

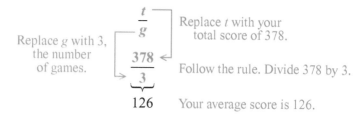

Replace g with 3, the number of games.

$$\frac{t}{g}$$ Replace t with your total score of 378.

$$\frac{378}{3}$$ Follow the rule. Divide 378 by 3.

126 Your average score is 126.

(b) Complete this table.

Value of x	Value of y	Expression $x - y$
16	10	16 − 10 is 6
100	5	
3	7	
8	0	

(b) Complete these tables to show how to evaluate each expression.

Value of x	Value of y	Expression (Rule) $x + y$
2	5	2 + 5 is 7
−6	4	__ + __ is __
0	16	__ + __ is __

Value of x	Value of y	Expression (Rule) xy
2	5	2 • 5 is 10
−6	4	__ • __ is __
0	16	__ • __ is __

The expression (rule) is to *add* the two variables. So the completed table is:

Value of x	Value of y	Expression (Rule) $x + y$
2	5	2 + 5 is 7
−6	4	−6 + 4 is −2
0	16	0 + 16 is 16

The expression (rule) is to *multiply* the two variables. We know that it's multiplication because there is no operation symbol between the x and y. So the completed table is:

Value of x	Value of y	Expression (Rule) xy
2	5	2 • 5 is 10
−6	4	−6 • 4 is −24
0	16	0 • 16 is 0

ANSWERS

5. (a) $\dfrac{532}{4}$; average score is 133.

(b) 100 − 5 is 95
3 − 7 is −4
8 − 0 is 8

◀ *Work Problem* **5** *at the Side.*

OBJECTIVE **3** **Write properties of operations using variables.**
Now you can use variables as a shorthand way to express the properties you learned about in **Sections 3.2, 3.5,** and **3.6.** We'll use the letters a and b to represent any two numbers.

Commutative Property **of Addition**	**Commutative Property** **of Multiplication**
$a + b = b + a$	$a \cdot b = b \cdot a$
	or, $ab = ba$

6 **(a)** Use the variable a to state this property: Multiplying any number by 0 gives a product of 0.

To get specific examples, you can pick values for a and b. For example, if a is $^-3$, replace every a with $^-3$. If b is 5, replace every b with 5.

$$a + b = b + \ a$$
$$^-3 + 5 = 5 + \ ^-3$$
$$2 \ = \ 2$$
Both sums are 2

$$ab = ba$$
$$^-3 \cdot 5 = 5 \cdot \ ^-3$$
$$^-15 \ = \ ^-15$$
Both products are $^-15$

Of course, you could pick many different values for a and b, because the commutative "rule" will always work for adding *any* two numbers or multiplying *any* two numbers.

EXAMPLE 6 **Writing Properties of Operations Using Variables**

Use the variable b to state this property: When any number is divided by 1, the quotient is the number.

Use the letter b to represent any number.

$$\frac{b}{1} = b$$

(b) Use the variables a, b, and c to state the associative property of addition: Changing the grouping of addends does not change the sum.

Work Problem **6** *at the Side.* ▶

OBJECTIVE **4** **Use exponents with variables.**   In **Section 3.7** we used an exponent as a quick way to write repeated multiplication. For example,

$$3 \cdot 3 \cdot 3 \cdot 3 \cdot 3 \quad \text{can be written} \quad 3^5 \leftarrow \text{Exponent}$$
3 is used as a factor 5 times.
$\qquad\qquad\qquad\uparrow\!\!\!\!\_\_\_$ Base

The meaning of an exponent is the same when a variable is the base.

$$c \cdot c \cdot c \cdot c \cdot c \quad \text{can be written} \quad c^5 \leftarrow \text{Exponent}$$
c is used as a factor 5 times.
$\qquad\qquad\qquad\uparrow\!\!\!\!\_\_\_$ Base

m^2 means $m \cdot m$ Here m is used as a factor 2 times.

$x^4 y^3$ means $x^4 \cdot y^3$ or $\underbrace{x \cdot x \cdot x \cdot x}_{x^4} \cdot \underbrace{y \cdot y \cdot y}_{y^3}$

$7b^2$ means $7 \cdot b \cdot b$ The exponent applies *only* to b.

$^-4xy^2z$ means $^-4 \cdot x \cdot y \cdot y \cdot z$ The exponent applies *only* to y.

7 Rewrite each expression without exponents.

(a) x^5

(b) $4a^2b^2$

(c) $^-10xy^3$

(d) s^4tu^2

EXAMPLE 7   **Understanding Exponents Used with Variables**

Rewrite each expression without exponents.

(a) y^6 can be written as $y \cdot y \cdot y \cdot y \cdot y \cdot y$

     y is used as a factor 6 times.

(b) $12bc^3$ can be written as $12 \cdot b \cdot c \cdot c \cdot c$ The exponent applies *only* to *c*.

     Coefficient is 12. c^3

(c) $^-2m^2n^4$ can be written as $^-2 \cdot m \cdot m \cdot n \cdot n \cdot n \cdot n$

     Coefficient is $^-2$. m^2 n^4

◀ *Work Problem* **7** *at the Side.*

To evaluate an expression with exponents, multiply all the factors.

EXAMPLE 8   **Evaluating Expressions with Exponents**

Evaluate each expression.

(a) x^2 when *x* is $^-3$

     x^2 means $x \cdot x$ Replace each *x* with $^-3$.

                 $^-3 \cdot {}^-3$ Multiply $^-3$ times $^-3$.

                   9

So x^2 becomes $(^-3)^2$, which is $(^-3)(^-3)$, or 9.

8 Evaluate each expression.

(a) y^3 when *y* is $^-5$

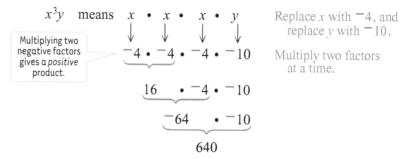

(b) x^3y when *x* is $^-4$ and *y* is $^-10$

     x^3y means $x \cdot x \cdot x \cdot y$ Replace *x* with $^-4$, and replace *y* with $^-10$.

     Multiplying two negative factors gives a *positive* product. $^-4 \cdot {}^-4 \cdot {}^-4 \cdot {}^-10$ Multiply two factors at a time.

               $16 \cdot {}^-4 \cdot {}^-10$

                  $^-64 \cdot {}^-10$

                    640

(b) r^2s^2 when *r* is 6 and *s* is 3

So x^3y becomes $(^-4)^3(^-10)$, which is $(^-4)(^-4)(^-4)(^-10)$, or 640.

(c) $10xy^2$ when *x* is 4 and *y* is $^-3$

(c) $^-5ab^2$ when *a* is 5 and *b* is 3

     $^-5ab^2$ means $^-5 \cdot a \cdot b \cdot b$ Replace *a* with 5, and replace *b* with 3.

     Multiplying two factors with *different* signs gives a *negative* product. $^-5 \cdot 5 \cdot 3 \cdot 3$ Multiply two factors at a time.

(d) $^-3c^4$ when *c* is 2

              $^-25 \cdot 3 \cdot 3$

                $^-75 \cdot 3$

                 $^-225$

So $^-5ab^2$ becomes $^-5(5)(3)^2$, which is $^-5(5)(3)(3)$, or $^-225$.

     Coefficient is $^-5$.

◀ *Work Problem* **8** *at the Side.*

Identify the variable and the constant in each expression. See Example 1.

1. $c + 4$

2. $d + 6$

3. $^-3 + m$

4. $^-4 + n$

Identify the parts of each expression. Choose from these labels: variable, constant, *and* coefficient.

5. $5h$

6. $3s$

7. $2c - 10$

8. $6b - 1$

9. $x - y$

10. xy

11. $^-6g + 9$

12. $^-10k + 15$

Evaluate each expression. See Examples 2–5.

13. The expression (rule) for ordering robes for the graduation ceremony at West Community College is $g + 10$, where g is the number of graduates. Evaluate the expression when

   (a) there are 654 graduates.

   (b) there are 208 graduates.

   (c) there are 95 graduates.

14. Crickets chirp faster as the weather gets hotter. The expression (rule) for finding the approximate temperature (in degrees Fahrenheit) is $c + 37$ where c is the number of chirps made in 15 seconds by a field cricket. (*Source:* AccuWeather.com) Evaluate the expression when the cricket

   (a) chirps 45 times.

   (b) chirps 33 times.

   (c) chirps 58 times.

15. The expression for finding the perimeter of a triangle with sides of equal length is $3s$, where s is the length of one side. Evaluate the expression when

   (a) the length of one side is 11 inches.

   (b) the length of one side is 3 feet.

16. The expression for finding the perimeter of a pentagon with sides of equal length is $5s$, where s is the length of one side. Evaluate the expression when

   (a) the length of one side is 25 meters.

   (b) the length of one side is 8 inches.

17. The expression for ordering brushes for an art class is $3c - 5$, where c is the class limit. Evaluate the expression when

(a) the class limit is 12.

(b) the class limit is 16.

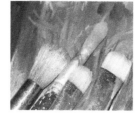

18. The expression for ordering doughnuts for the office staff is $2n - 4$, where n is the number of people at work. Evaluate the expression when

(a) there are 13 people at work.

(b) there are 18 people at work.

19. The expression for figuring a student's average test score is $\frac{p}{t}$, where p is the total points earned on all the tests and t is the number of tests. Evaluate the expression when

(a) 332 points were earned on 4 tests.

(b) there were 7 tests and 637 points were earned.

20. The expression for deciding how many buses are needed for a group trip is $\frac{p}{b}$, where p is the total number of people and b is the number of people that one bus will hold. Evaluate the expression when

(a) 176 people are going on a trip and one bus holds 44 people.

(b) a bus holds 36 people and 72 people are going on a trip.

Complete each table by evaluating the expressions. See Example 5.

21.

Value of x	Expression $x + x + x + x$	Expression $4x$
-2	$-2 + -2 + -2 + -2$ is -8	$4 \cdot -2$ is -8
12		
0		
-5		

22.

Value of y	Expression $3y$	Expression $y + 2y$
-6	$3(-6)$ is -18	$-6 + 2(-6)$ is $-6 + -12$, or -18
10		
-3		
0		

23.

Value of x	Value of y	Expression $-2x + y$
3	7	$-2(3) + 7$ is $-6 + 7$, or 1
-4	5	
-6	-2	
0	-8	

24.

Value of x	Value of y	Expression $-2xy$
3	7	$-2 \cdot 3 \cdot 7$ is -42
-4	5	
-6	-2	
0	-8	

25. Explain the words *variable* and *expression*.

26. Explain the words *coefficient* and *constant*.

Use the variable b to express each of these properties. See Example 6.

27. Multiplying a number by 1 leaves the number unchanged.

28. Adding 0 to any number leaves the number unchanged.

29. Any number divided by 0 is undefined.

30. Multiplication distributes over addition. (Use a, b, and c as the variables.)

Rewrite each expression without exponents. See Example 7.

31. c^6

32. d^7

33. x^4y^3

34. c^2d^5

35. $^-3a^3b$

36. $^-8m^2n$

37. $9xy^2$

38. $5ab^4$

39. $^-2c^5d$

40. $^-4x^3y$

41. a^3bc^2

42. x^2yz^6

Evaluate each expression when r is $^-3$, s is 2, and t is $^-4$. See Example 8.

43. t^2

44. r^2

45. rs^3

46. s^4t

47. $3rs$

48. $6st$

49. $-2s^2t^2$

50. $-4rs^4$

51. $r^2s^5t^3$

52. $r^3s^4t^2$

53. $-10r^5s^7$

54. $-5s^6t^5$

Evaluate each expression when x is 4, y is -2, and z is -6.

55. $|xy| + |xyz|$

56. $x + |y^2| + |xz|$

57. $\dfrac{z^2}{-3y + z}$

58. $\dfrac{y^2}{x + 2y}$

Relating Concepts (Exercises 59–60) For Individual or Group Work

At the beginning of this chapter, you read that there is an expression that tells your approximate distance from a thunderstorm. First, count the number of seconds from the time you see a lightning flash until you start to hear the thunder. Then, to estimate the distance (in miles), use the expression $\dfrac{s}{5}$, where s is the number of seconds. Use this expression as you **work Exercises 59 and 60 in order.** *(This expression is based on the fact that the light from the lightning travels faster than the sound from the thunder.)*

59. Evaluate the thunderstorm expression for each number of seconds. How far away is the storm?

   (a) 15 seconds

   (b) 10 seconds

   (c) 5 seconds

60. Explain how you can use your answers from Exercise 59 to:

   (a) Estimate the distance when the time is $2\frac{1}{2}$ seconds.

   (b) Find the number of seconds when the distance is $1\frac{1}{2}$ miles.

   (c) Find the number of seconds when the distance is $2\frac{1}{2}$ miles.

Study Skills

You may have used "flash cards" in other classes before. In math, study cards can be helpful, too. However, they are different because the main things to remember in math are *not* necessarily terms and definitions; they are *sets of steps to follow* to solve problems (and how to know which set of steps to follow) and *concepts about how math works* (principles). So, the cards will look different but will be just as useful.

In this two-part activity, you will find four types of study cards to use in math. Look carefully at what kinds of information to put on them and where to put it. Then use them the way you would any flash card:

▶ to quickly review when you have a few minutes,

▶ to do daily reviews,

▶ to review before a test.

Remember, the most helpful thing about study cards is making them. It is in the making of them that you have to do the kind of thinking that is most brain friendly and will improve your neural network of dendrites. After each card description you will find an assignment to try. It is marked "**NOW TRY THIS.**"

For **new vocabulary cards**, put the word (spelled correctly) and the page number where it is found on the front of the card. On the back, write:

▶ the definition (in your own words if possible),

▶ an example, an exception (if there are any),

▶ any related words, and

▶ a sample problem (if appropriate).

OBJECTIVES

1 **Create study cards for all new terms.**

2 **Create study cards for new procedures.**

New Vocabulary Cards

variable   p. 94

Front of Card

Definition: A letter representing a number that varies (changes) depending on the situation.

Example: $C + 5$ where c represents the class limit
variable   which varies for different classes.
constant   varies ⟷ variable

–Use any letter you like: a, b, c, d, h, k, m, n, o, p, x, y, etc.
–Related words: constant, coefficient

Back of Card

Why Are Study Cards Brain Friendly?

• Making cards is **active**.

• Cards are **visually** appealing.

• **Repetition** is good for your brain.

For details see *Using Study Cards Revisited* following **Section 4.2.**

List four new vocabulary words/concepts you need to learn right now. Make a card for each one.

_____   _____

_____   _____

Procedure ("Steps") Cards

For **procedure cards,** write the name of the procedure at the top on the front of the card. Then write each step *in words*. If you need to know abbreviations for some words, include them along with the whole words written out. On the back, put an example of the procedure, showing each step you need to take. You can review by looking at the front and practicing a new worked example, or by looking at the back and remembering what the procedure is called and what the steps are.

Front of Card

Evaluating an expression

Step 1: Replace each variable with the value you are given.

Step 2: Do the calculations, following the order of operations.

Back of Card

Example: Evaluate 3c – 5 when c is 20
must be given the replacement value

$3c - 5$
↓
$3(20) - 5$ Replace c with 20.
        Do the calculations.

$60 - 5$ Follow order of operations; multiply first, then subtract.

55 *No variables in final answer.*

Now Try This ▶▶▶

What procedure are you learning right now? Make a "steps" card for it.

Procedure: _____

4.2 ▶▶▶ Simplifying Expressions

OBJECTIVE 1 Combine like terms, using the distributive property. In **Section 4.1,** the expression for ordering math textbooks was $c + 5$. This expression was simple and easy to use. Sometimes expressions are *not* written in the simplest possible way. For example:

Evaluate this expression when c is 20.

$c + 5$ Replace c with 20.

$\underline{20 + 5}$ Add $20 + 5$.

25

Evaluate this expression when c is 20.

$2c - 10 - c + 15$ Replace c with 20.

$2 \cdot 20 - 10 - 20 + 15$ Multiply $2 \cdot 20$.

$40 - 10 - 20 + 15$ Change subtraction to adding the opposite.

$\underline{40 + {}^-10} + {}^-20 + 15$ Add from left to right.

$\underline{30 + {}^-20} + 15$

$\underline{10 + 15}$

25

These two expressions are actually equivalent. When you evaluate them, the final result is the same, but it takes a lot more work when you use the right-hand expression. To save a lot of work, you need to learn how to *simplify expressions*. Then you can rewrite $2c - 10 - c + 15$ in the simplest way possible, which is $c + 5$.

The basic idea in **simplifying expressions** is to *combine,* or *add,* like terms. Each addend in an expression is a **term.** Here are two examples.

Separates the terms

$c + 5$

Two terms

Separates the terms

$6x^2 + {}^-2xy + 8$

Three terms

In $6x^2 + {}^-2xy + 8$, the 8 is the *constant term*. There are also two *variable terms* in the expression: $6x^2$ is a variable term, and ^-2xy is a variable term. A **variable term** has a number part (coefficient) and a letter part (variable).

$6x^2$

Variable part is x^2.

Coefficient is 6.

^-2xy

Variable part is xy.

Coefficient is $^-2$.

If no coefficient is shown, it is assumed to be 1. Remember from **Section 3.5** that multiplying any number by 1 does *not* change the number.

c can be written $1 \cdot c$ or just $1c$

Coefficient is understood to be 1.   Variable part is c.

Also, ^-c can be written $^-1 \cdot c$. The coefficient of ^-c is understood to be $^-1$.

Like Terms

Like terms are terms with exactly the same variable parts (the same letters and exponents). The coefficients do *not* have to match.

1 List the like terms in each expression. Then identify the coefficients of the like terms.

(a) $3b^2 + {}^-3b + 3 + b^3 + b$

Like Terms		Unlike Terms	
$5x$ and $3x$	Variable parts match; both are x.	$3x$ and $3x^2$	Variable parts do *not* match; exponents are different.
${}^-6y^3$ and y^3	Variable parts match; both are y^3.	${}^-2x$ and ${}^-2y$	Variable parts do *not* match; letters are different.
$4a^2b$ and $5a^2b$	Variable parts match; both are a^2b.	a^3b and a^2b	Variable parts do *not* match; exponents are different.
${}^-8$ and 4	There are no variable parts; numbers are like terms.	${}^-8c$ and 4	Variable parts do *not* match; one term has a variable part, but the other term does not.

(b) ${}^-4xy + 4x^2y + {}^-4xy^2 + {}^-4 + 4$

EXAMPLE 1 **Identifying Like Terms and Their Coefficients**

List the like terms in each expression. Then identify the coefficients of the like terms.

(a) ${}^-5x + {}^-5x^2 + 3xy + x + {}^-5$
The like terms are ${}^-5x$ and x.
The coefficient of ${}^-5x$ is ${}^-5$, and the coefficient of x is understood to be 1.

(b) $2yz^2 + 2y^2z + {}^-3y^2z + 2 + {}^-6yz$
The like terms are $2y^2z$ and ${}^-3y^2z$.
The coefficients are 2 and ${}^-3$.

(c) $5r^2 + 2r + {}^-2r^2 + 5 + 5r^3$

(c) $10ab + 12 + {}^-10a + 12b + {}^-6$
The like terms are 12 and ${}^-6$.
The like terms are constants (there are no variable parts). *Numbers alone (no variable parts) are like terms.*

◄ *Work Problem* **1** *at the Side.*

(d) ${}^-10 + {}^-x + {}^-10x + {}^-x^2 + {}^-10y$

The distributive property (see **Section 3.5**) can be used "in reverse" to combine like terms. Here is an example.

$$\underbrace{3 \cdot x}_{3x} + \underbrace{4 \cdot x}_{4x} \quad \text{can be written as} \quad \underbrace{(3 + 4)}_{7} \cdot x$$
$$7 \cdot x$$
$$7x$$

Thus, $3x + 4x$ can be written in *simplified form* as $7x$. To check that $3x + 4x$ is the same as $7x$, evaluate each expression when x is 2.

$$3x + 4x \qquad\qquad 7x$$
$$\downarrow \quad\; \downarrow \qquad\qquad\quad \downarrow$$
$$3 \cdot 2 + 4 \cdot 2 \qquad\qquad 7 \cdot 2$$
$$\underbrace{6}_{} + \underbrace{8}_{} \qquad\qquad\quad 14$$
$$14$$

ANSWERS
1. (a) ${}^-3b$ and b; the coefficients are ${}^-3$ and 1.
  (b) ${}^-4$ and 4; they are constants.
  (c) $5r^2$ and ${}^-2r^2$; the coefficients are 5 and ${}^-2$.
  (d) ${}^-x$ and ${}^-10x$; the coefficients are ${}^-1$ and ${}^-10$.

Both results are 14, so the expressions are equivalent. But you can see how much easier it is to work with $7x$, the simplified expression.

CAUTION
Notice that $3x + 4x$ is simplified to $7x$, **not** to $7x^2$.

Variable part is unchanged.   Do *not* change x to x^2.

Combining Like Terms

Step 1 If there are any variable terms with no coefficient, write in the understood 1.

Step 2 If there are any subtractions, change each one to adding the opposite.

Step 3 Find *like* terms (the variable parts match).

Step 4 Add the coefficients (number parts) of like terms. ***The variable part stays the same.***

EXAMPLE 2 **Combining Like Terms**

Combine like terms.

(a) $2x + 4x + x$

$2x + 4x + x$ No coefficient; write understood 1.
There are no subtractions to change.

$2x + 4x + 1x$ Find like terms: $2x$, $4x$, and $1x$ are like terms, so add the coefficients, $2 + 4 + 1$.

$(2 + 4 + 1)x$ The variable part, x, stays the same.

$7x$

Therefore, $2x + 4x + x$ can be written as $7x$.

Do **not** write $7x^3$. Keep x as x.

(b) $^-3y^2 - 8y^2$

$^-3y^2 - 8y^2$ Both coefficients are shown.
Change subtraction to adding the opposite.

$^-3y^2 + \;^-8y^2$ Find like terms: $^-3y^2$ and $^-8y^2$ are like terms, so add the coefficients, $^-3 + \;^-8$.

$(^-3 + \;^-8)y^2$ The variable part, y^2, stays the same.

$^-11y^2$

Therefore, $^-3y^2 - 8y^2$ can be written as $^-11y^2$.

Work Problem **2** *at the Side.* ▶

2 Combine like terms.

(a) $10b + 4b + 10b$

(b) $y^3 + 8y^3$

(c) $^-7n - n$

(d) $3c - 5c - 4c$

(e) $^-9xy + xy$

(f) $^-4p^2 - 3p^2 + 8p^2$

(g) $ab - ab$

ANSWERS

2. **(a)** $24b$ **(b)** $9y^3$ **(c)** ^-8n **(d)** ^-6c
(e) ^-8xy **(f)** $1p^2$, or just p^2
(g) 0, because $1ab + \;^-1ab$ is $(1 + \;^-1)\,ab$, or $0ab$, and 0 times anything is 0.

OBJECTIVE **2** **Simplify expressions.** When simplifying expressions, be careful to combine only *like* terms—those having variable parts that match. You *cannot* combine terms if the variable parts are different.

3 Simplify each expression by combining like terms.

(a) $3b^2 + 4d^2 + 7b^2$

(b) $4a + b - 6a + b$

(c) $^-6x + 5 + 6x + 2$

(d) $2y - 7 - y + 7$

(e) $^-3x - 5 + 12 + 10x$

EXAMPLE 3 **Simplifying Expressions**

Simplify each expression by combining like terms.

(a) $6xy + 2y + 3xy$

The *like* terms are $6xy$ and $3xy$. We can use the commutative property to rewrite the expression so that the like terms are next to each other. This helps to organize our work.

$6xy + 3xy + 2y$ Combine *like* terms only.

$(6 + 3)xy + 2y$ Add the coefficients, $6 + 3$.
              The variable part, xy, stays the same.

$9xy + 2y$ Keep writing $2y$, the term that was not combined; it is still part of the expression.

The simplified expression is $9xy + 2y$.

(b) Here is the expression from the first page in this section.

$2c - 10 - c + 15$ Write the understood 1 as the coefficient of c.

$2c - 10 - 1c + 15$ Change subtractions to adding the opposite.

$2c + {}^-10 + {}^-1c + 15$ We can add in any order, so rewrite the expression so that like terms are next to each other.

$2c + {}^-1c + {}^-10 + 15$ Combine $2c + {}^-1c$.
              Also combine $^-10 + 15$.

$(2 + {}^-1)c + 5$

$1c + 5$

The simplified expression is $1c + 5$ or just $c + 5$

$1c$ is the same as c.

Note

In this book, when combining like terms we will usually write the variable terms in *alphabetical order*. A constant term (number only) will be written last. So, in Examples 3(a) and 3(b) above, the preferred and alternative ways of writing the expressions are as follows.

The simplified expression is $9xy + 2y$ (alphabetical order). However, by the commutative property of addition, $2y + 9xy$ is also correct.

The simplified expression is $c + 5$ (constant written last). However, by the commutative property of addition, $5 + c$ is also correct.

◄ *Work Problem* **3** *at the Side.*

We can use the associative property of multiplication to simplify an expression such as $4(3x)$.

$4(3x)$ can be written as $4 \cdot (3 \cdot x)$

Understood multiplications

Using the associative property, we can regroup the factors.

$4 \cdot (3 \cdot x)$ can be written as $(4 \cdot 3) \cdot x$ To simplify, multiply $4 \cdot 3$.

$12 \quad \cdot x$ Write $12 \cdot x$ without the multiplication dot.

$12x$

The simplified expression is $12x$.

EXAMPLE 4   Simplifying Multiplication Expressions

Simplify.

(a) $5(10y)$

Use the associative property.

$5 \cdot (10 \cdot y)$ can be written as $(5 \cdot 10) \cdot y$ Multiply $5 \cdot 10$.

$50 \quad \cdot y$ Write $50 \cdot y$ without the multiplication dot.

$50y$

So, $5(10y)$ simplifies to $50y$.

(b) $^-6(3b)$

Use the associative property.

$^-6(3b)$ can be written as $(^-6 \cdot 3)b$

^-18b

So, $^-6(3b)$ simplifies to ^-18b.

(c) $^-4(^-2x^2)$

Use the associative property.

$^-4(^-2x^2)$ can be written as $(^-4 \cdot {}^-2)x^2$

$8x^2$

So, $^-4(^-2x^2)$ simplifies to $8x^2$.

Work Problem **4** *at the Side.* ▶

OBJECTIVE 3 Use the distributive property to multiply.   The distributive property can also be used to simplify expressions such as $3(x + 5)$. You *cannot* add the terms inside the parentheses because x and 5 are *not* like terms. But notice the understood multiplication dot between the 3 and the parentheses.

$3(x + 5)$

$3 \cdot (x + 5)$

Thus you can *distribute* multiplication over addition, as you did in **Section 1.6.** That is, multiply 3 times each term inside the parentheses.

$3 \cdot (x + 5)$ can be written as $3 \cdot x + 3 \cdot 5$

$3x \quad + \quad 15$

So, $3(x + 5)$ simplifies to $3x + 15$.

└ Stays as addition ┘

4 Simplify.

(a) $7(4c)$

(b) $^-3(5y^3)$

(c) $20(^-2a)$

(d) $^-10(^-x)$

ANSWERS

4. **(a)** $28c$ **(b)** $^-15y^3$ **(c)** ^-40a **(d)** $10x$

Multiplication also distributes over subtraction.

5 Simplify.

(a) $7(a + 10)$

$4(y - 2)$ means $4 \cdot (y - 2)$ and can be written as $\underbrace{4 \cdot y}_{4y} - \underbrace{4 \cdot 2}_{8}$

So, $4(y - 2)$ simplifies to $4y - 8$.
↳ Stays as subtraction ↱

Notice that we did *not* need to change subtraction to adding the opposite.

(b) $3(x - 3)$

EXAMPLE 5 | **Using the Distributive Property**

Simplify.

(a) $6(y - 4)$ can be written as $\underbrace{6 \cdot y}_{6y} - \underbrace{6 \cdot 4}_{24}$

Remember to multiply $6 \cdot y$ **and** $6 \cdot 4$

Stays as subtraction

So, $6(y - 4)$ simplifies to $6y - 24$

(b) $5(3x + 2)$ can be written as $\underbrace{5 \cdot 3x}_{} + \underbrace{5 \cdot 2}_{}$

$\underbrace{5 \cdot 3 \cdot}_{} x + 10$

$\underbrace{15 \cdot}_{} x + 10$

$15x + 10$

(c) $4(2y + 6)$

So, $5(3x + 2)$ simplifies to $15x + 10$

(c) $^-2(4a + 3)$ can be written as $^-2 \cdot 4a + \underbrace{^-2 \cdot 3}_{}$

$\underbrace{^-2 \cdot 4 \cdot}_{} a + {}^-6$

$\underbrace{^-8}_{} \cdot a + {}^-6$

$^-8a + {}^-6$

(d) $^-5(3b + 2)$

Now we will use the definition of subtraction "in reverse" to rewrite $^-8a + {}^-6$.

Change $^-6$ to its opposite, $^+6$.

Write $^-8a + {}^-6$ as $^-8a - 6$

Change addition to subtraction.

Think back to the way we changed subtraction to adding the opposite. Here we are "working backward." From now on, whenever addition is followed by a negative number, we will change it to subtracting a positive number.

(e) $^-8(c + 4)$

$^-8a + {}^-6$
$\updownarrow \quad \updownarrow$ Equivalent expressions
$^-8a - 6$

So, $^-2(4a + 3)$ simplifies to $^-8a - 6$.

◀ *Work Problem* **5** *at the Side.*

Sometimes you need to do several steps to simplify an expression.

EXAMPLE 6   **Simplifying a More Complex Expression**

Simplify: $8 + 3(x - 2)$

$8 + 3(x - 2)$ $\qquad$ Do *not* add $8 + 3$. Use the distributive property first because multiplying is done *before* adding.

$8 + \underbrace{3 \cdot x} - \underbrace{3 \cdot 2}$ $\qquad$ Do the multiplications.

$8 + 3x \quad - \quad 6$ $\qquad$ Rewrite so that like terms are next to each other.

$3x + \underbrace{8 \quad - \quad 6}$ $\qquad$ Subtract to find $8 - 6$ or change to adding $8 + {}^{-}6$.

$3x + \quad 2$

The simplified expression is $3x + 2$.

CAUTION

Do *not* add $8 + 3$ as the first step in Example 6 above. Remember that the order of operations tells you to do multiplying *before* adding.

Work Problem **6** *at the Side.* ▶

6 Simplify.

(a) ${}^{-}4 + 5(y + 1)$

(b) $2(3w + 4) - 5$

(c) $5(6x - 2) + 3x$

(d) $21 + 7(a^2 - 3)$

(e) ${}^{-}y + 3(2y + 5) - 18$

Math in the Media

EXPRESSIONS AND TRAFFIC SIGNALS

Traffic engineers have to decide how long to have the green, yellow, and red lights showing on a traffic signal.

To find the number of seconds for the green light, the engineers use this expression.

$$2.1n + 3.7$$

The variable n stands for the average number of vehicles traveling in each lane of the street during one complete light cycle (green to yellow to red, and back to green again).

1. How many seconds should the green light be on if a street averages 5 vehicles in each lane per light cycle? Round to the nearest whole number.

2. How many seconds for the green light, to the nearest whole number, if the average is 10 vehicles per light cycle? If the average is 15 vehicles per light cycle?

3. As the average number of vehicles increases, what is happening to the number of seconds for the green light?

4. Based on the answers to Questions 1 and 2, make a guess on the number of seconds for the green light when the average is 20 vehicles per light cycle. Then calculate the number of seconds using the expression.

To decide the number of seconds that a yellow light should be on, traffic engineers use this expression.

$$\frac{5v}{100} + 1 \quad \text{where } v \text{ is the speed limit in miles per hour (mph).}$$

5. How many seconds should the yellow light be on if the speed limit is 20 mph? 40 mph? 60 mph?

6. Based on the answers you just calculated, how could you estimate the time for a yellow light if the speed limit is 30 mph? 50 mph?

7. Use the given expression to find the number of seconds that the yellow light should be on if the speed limit is 30 mph and 50 mph. Did you get the same result as in Question 6?

Source: Applying Mathematics: A Consumer/Career Approach.

4.2 ▶▶▶ **Exercises**

FOR
EXTRA
HELP   **MyMathLab** *Math* XL
PRACTICE
WATCH
DOWNLOAD   READ
REVIEW

Circle the like terms in each expression. Then identify the coefficients of the like terms.
See Example 1.

1. $2b^2 + 2b + 2b^3 + b^2 + 6$

2. $3x + x^3 + 3x^2 + 3 + 2x^3$

3. $^-x^2y + {}^-xy + 2xy + {}^-2xy^2$

4. $ab^2 + {}^-a^2b + 2ab + {}^-3a^2b$

5. $7 + 7c + 3 + 7c^3 + {}^-4$

6. $4d + {}^-5 + 1 + {}^-5d^2 + 4$

Simplify each expression. See Example 2.

7. $6r + 6r$

8. $4t + 10t$

9. $x^2 + 5x^2$

10. $9y^3 + y^3$

11. $p - 5p$

12. $n - 3n$

13. $^-2a^3 - a^3$

14. $^-10x^2 - x^2$

15. $c - c$

16. $b^2 - b^2$

17. $9xy + xy - 9xy$

18. $r^2s - 7r^2s + 7r^2s$

🌐 19. $5t^4 + 7t^4 - 6t^4$

20. $10mn - 9mn + 3mn$

21. $y^2 + y^2 + y^2 + y^2$

22. $a + a + a$

23. $^-x - 6x - x$

24. $^-y - y - 3y$

Simplify by combining like terms. Write each answer with the variables in alphabetical order and any constant term last. See Example 3.

25. $8a + 4b + 4a$

26. $6x + 5y + 4y$

27. $6 + 8 + 7rs$

28. $10 + 2c^2 + 15$

29. $a + ab^2 + ab^2$

30. $n + mn + n$

31. $6x + y - 8x + y$

32. $d + 3c - 7c + 3d$

33. $8b^2 - a^2 - b^2 + a^2$

34. $5ab - ab + 3a^2b - 4ab$

35. $^-x^3 + 3x - 3x^2 + 2$

36. $a^2b - 2ab - ab^3 + 3a^3b$

37. $^-9r + 6t - s - 5r + s + t - 6t + 5s - r$

38. $^-x - 3y + 4z + x - z + 5y - 8x - y$

Simplify by using the associative property of multiplication. See Example 4.

39. $3(10a)$

40. $8(4b)$

41. $^-4(2x^2)$

42. $^-7(3b^3)$

43. $5(^-4y^3)$

44. $2(^-6x)$

45. $^-9(^-2cd)$

46. $^-6(^-4rs)$

47. $7(3a^2bc)$

48. $4(2xy^2z^2)$

49. $^-12(^-w)$

50. $^-10(^-k)$

Use the distributive property to simplify each expression. See Example 5.

51. $6(b + 6)$

52. $5(a + 3)$

53. $7(x - 1)$

54. $4(y - 4)$

55. $3(7t + 1)$

56. $8(2c + 5)$

57. $^-2(5r + 3)$

58. $^-5(6z + 2)$

59. $^-9(k + 4)$

60. $^-3(p + 7)$

61. $50(m - 6)$

62. $25(n - 1)$

Simplify each expression. See Example 6.

63. $10 + 2(4y + 3)$

64. $4 + 7(x^2 + 3)$

65. $6(a^2 - 2) + 15$

66. $5(b - 4) + 25$

67. $2 + 9(m - 4)$

68. $6 + 3(n - 8)$

69. $^-5(k + 5) + 5k$

70. $^-7(p + 2) + 7p$

71. $4(6x - 3) + 12$

72. $6(3y - 3) + 18$

73. $5 + 2(3n + 4) - n$

74. $8 + 8(4z + 5) - z$

75. $^-p + 6(2p - 1) + 5$

76. $^-k + 3(4k - 1) + 2$

77. Explain the difference between *simplifying* an expression and *evaluating* an expression.

78. Simplify each expression. Are the answers equivalent? Explain why or why not.

$$5(3x + 2) \qquad 5(2 + 3x)$$

79. Explain what makes two terms *like* terms. Include several examples in your explanation.

80. Explain how to combine like terms. Include an example in your explanation.

81. Explain and correct the error made by a student who simplified this expression.

$$\underbrace{{}^-2x + 7x}_{} + 8$$
$$5x^2 \quad + 8$$

82. Explain and correct the error made by a student who simplified this expression.

$$\underbrace{{}^-10a + 6a}_{} \underset{\downarrow}{-} \underbrace{7 + 2}_{}$$
$${}^-4a \quad + \underset{\downarrow}{{}^-7 + 2}$$
$${}^-4a \quad + \quad {}^-5$$
$$4a - 5$$

Simplify.

83. $^-4(3y) - 5 + 2(5y + 7)$

84. $6(^-3x) - 9 + 3(^-2x + 6)$

85. $^-10 + 4(^-3b + 3) + 2(6b - 1)$

86. $12 + 2(4a - 4) + 4(^-2a - 1)$

87. $^-5(^-x + 2) + 8(^-x) + 3(^-2x - 2) + 16$

88. $^-7(^-y) + 6(y - 1) + 3(^-2y) + 6 - y$

Study Skills

This is the second part of the Study Cards activity. As you get further into a chapter, you can choose particular problems that will serve as a good test review. Here are two more types of study cards that will help you.

When you are doing your homework and find yourself saying, "This is really hard," or "I'm worried I'll make a mistake," make a **tough problem** study card! On the front, write out the procedure to work the type of problem *in words*. If there are special notes (like what *not* to do), include them. On the back, work at least one example; make sure you label what you are doing.

OBJECTIVES

1 Create study cards for difficult problems.

2 Create study cards of quiz problems.

Tough Problems Card

Simplifying Expressions

    Combine (add) <u>like</u> terms only.

    Like terms have variable parts that match.

    Use the distributive property if possible.

Front of Card

Example   Simplify this expression.

$7 + 3(2n - 4)$	*Do <u>not</u> add $7 + 3$!*
$7 + 3(2n - 4)$	*Use the distributive property.*
$7 + 3 \cdot 2n - 3 \cdot 4$	*Do the multiplications.*
$7 + 6n - 12$	*Rewrite so like terms are next to each other.*
$6n + 7 + {}^-12$	*Change subtraction to adding the opposite.*
$6n + \quad {}^-5$	*Do <u>not</u> stop here!*
$6n - \quad 5$	*Use definition of subtraction "in reverse."*

Back of Card

Choose three types of difficult problems or problems that have given you trouble, and work them out on study cards. Be sure to put the words for solving the problem on one side and the worked problem on the other side.

◁◁◁ **Now Try This**

Practice Quiz Cards

Make up a few **quiz cards** for each type of problem you learn, and use them to prepare for a test. Choose two or three problems from the different sections of the chapter. Be sure you don't just choose the easiest problems! Put the problem **with the direction words** (like *solve, simplify, evaluate*) on the front, and work the problem on the back. If you like, put the page number from the text there, too. When you review, you work the problem on a separate paper, and check it by looking at the back.

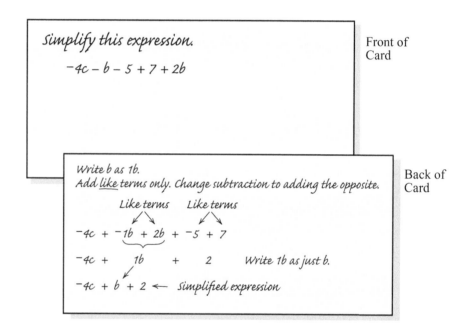

Front of Card

Back of Card

Why Are Study Cards Brain Friendly?

First, making the study cards is an **active technique** that really gets your dendrites growing. You have to make decisions about what is most important and how to put it on the card. This kind of thinking is more in depth than just memorizing, and as a result, you will understand the concepts better and remember them longer.

Second, the cards are **visually appealing** (if you write neatly and try some color). Your brain responds to pleasant visual images, and again, you will remember longer and may even be able to "picture in your mind" how your cards look. This will help you during tests.

Third, because study cards are small and portable, you can review them easily whenever you have a few minutes. Even while you're waiting for a bus or have a few minutes between classes you can take out your cards and read them to yourself. Your **brain really benefits from repetition;** each time you review your cards your dendrites are growing thicker and stronger. After a while, the information will become automatic and you will remember it for a long time.

Summary Exercises on Variables and Expressions

Identify the parts of each expression. Choose from these labels: variable, constant, coefficient.

1. $^-10 - m$

2. ^-8cd

3. $6 + 4x$

4. The expression for finding the perimeter of an octagon with sides of equal length is $8s$. Evaluate the expression when

    (a) the length of one side is 4 yards.

    (b) the length of one side is 15 inches.

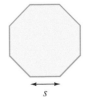

5. The expression for the total cost of a car is $d + mt$ where d is the down payment, m is the monthly payment, and t is the number of months you must make payments. Evaluate the expression when

    (a) the down payment is \$3000 and you make 36 monthly payments of \$280.

    (b) the down payment is \$1750 and you make 48 monthly payments of \$429.

Rewrite each expression without exponents.

6. ad^4

7. b^3cd

8. $^-7ab^5c^2$

Evaluate each expression when w is 5, x is $^-2$, y is $^-6$, and z is 0.

9. w^4

10. $5xz$

11. yz^2

12. wxy

13. x^3

14. ^-4wy

15. $3xy^2$

16. w^2x^5

17. $^-7wx^4y^3$

Simplify each expression.

18. $10b + 4b + 10b$

19. $^-3x - 5 + 12 + 10x$

20. $^-8(c + 4)$

21. $^-9xy + 9xy$

22. $^-4(^-3c^2d)$

23. $3f - 5f - 4f$

24. $2(3w + 4)$

25. $^-a - 6b - a$

26. $^-10(^-5x^3y^2)$

27. $5r^2 + 2r - 2r^2 + 5r^3$

28. $21 + 7(h^2 - 3)$

29. $^-3(m + 3) + 3m$

30. $^-4(8y - 5) + 5$

31. $2 + 12(3x - 1)$

32. $^-n + 5(4n - 2) + 11$

33. Explain and correct each error made by the student who simplified these expressions.

    (a) $6(n + 2)$
         $6n + 2$

    (b) $^-5(^-4a)$
         ^-20a

    (c) $\underbrace{3y + 2y}_{5y^2} - 10$
         $5y^2 \quad - 10$

34. Explain and correct the error made by this student.

$$\underbrace{^-8x + x}_{} \underset{\downarrow}{-} \underbrace{12}_{} \underset{\downarrow}{+ 3}$$
$$^-7x \quad + \quad \underbrace{^-12 + 3}_{}$$
$$^-7x \quad + \quad ^-9$$
$$7x - 9$$

4.3 ▶▶▶ Solving Equations Using Addition

Now you are ready for a look at the "heart" of algebra, writing and solving **equations.** *Writing* an equation is a way to show the relationship between what you *know* about a problem and what you *don't* know. Then, *solving* the equation is a way to figure out the part that you didn't know and answer your question.

The questions you can answer by writing and solving equations are as varied as the careers people choose. A zookeeper can solve an equation that answers the question of how long to incubate the egg of a particular tropical bird. An aerobics instructor can solve an equation that answers the question of how hard a certain person should exercise for maximum benefit.

OBJECTIVE 1 Determine whether a given number is a solution of an equation.   Let's start with the example from the beginning of this chapter: ordering textbooks for math classes. The expression we used to order books was $c + 5$, where c was the class limit (the maximum number of students allowed in the class). Suppose that 30 prealgebra books were ordered. What is the class limit for prealgebra? To answer this question, write an equation showing the relationship between what you know and what you don't know.

You don't know
the class limit.   You do know the total
                                    number of books ordered.

$$c + 5 = 30$$

You do know that 5 extra books were ordered.

> **Note**
>
> An equation has an equal sign. Notice the similarity in the words equation and equal. An *expression* does *not* have an equal sign.

The equal sign in an equation is like the balance point on a playground teeter-totter, or seesaw. To have a true equation, the two sides must balance.

These equations balance, so we can use the $=$ sign.

These equations do *not* balance, so we write $\neq$ to mean "is not equal to."

$$6 + 8 = 14$$

$$6 + 8 \neq 15$$

$$10 = 5 \cdot 2$$

$$10 \neq 4 \cdot 2$$

$$3 \cdot 2 = 5 + 1$$

$$4 + 5 \neq 5 \cdot 4$$

OBJECTIVES

1 Determine whether a given number is a solution of an equation.

2 Solve equations using the addition property of equality.

3 Simplify equations before using the addition property of equality.

When an equation has a variable, we **solve the equation** by finding a number that can replace the variable and make the equation balance. For the example about ordering prealgebra textbooks:

(a) Which of these numbers, 95, 65, or 70, is the solution of the equation $c + 15 = 80$?

$$\overline{c + 5 = 30}$$
$$\blacktriangle$$

What number can replace c so that the equation balances?

Try replacing c with 15. $15 + 5 \neq 30$ Does *not* balance: $15 + 5$ is only 20.

Try replacing c with 40. $40 + 5 \neq 30$ Does *not* balance: $40 + 5$ is more than 30.

Try replacing c with 25. $25 + 5 = 30$ Balances: $25 + 5$ is 30.

The **solution** is 25 because 25 is the *only* number that makes the equation balance. By solving the equation, you have answered the question about the class limit for prealgebra. The class limit is 25.

> **Note**
>
> Most of the equations that you will solve in **Chapters 4–7** have only one solution, that is, one number that makes the equation balance. Later in this book, you will solve equations that have two or more solutions.

(b) Which of these numbers, 20, 24, or 32, is the solution of the equation $28 = c - 4$?

EXAMPLE 1 **Identifying the Solution of an Equation**

Which of these numbers, 70, 40, or 60, is the solution of the equation $c - 10 = 50$?

Replace c with each of the numbers. The one that makes the equation balance is the solution.

$70 - 10 \neq 50$ $40 - 10 \neq 50$ $60 - 10 = 50$

Does *not* balance: $70 - 10$ is more than 50.   Does *not* balance: $40 - 10$ is only 30.   Balances: $60 - 10$ is 50.

The solution is 60 because, when c is 60, the equation balances.

◀ *Work Problem* **1** *at the Side.*

OBJECTIVE 2 Solve equations using the addition property of equality. When solving the book ordering equation, $c + 5 = 30$, you could just look at the equation and think, "What number, plus 5, would balance with 30?" You could easily see that c had to be 25. Not all equations can be solved this easily, so you'll need some tools for the harder ones. The first tool, called the **addition property of equality,** allows us to add the *same* number to *both* sides of an equation.

Addition Property of Equality

If $a = b$, then $a + c = b + c$.

In other words, you may add the same number to both sides of an equation and still keep it balanced.

Think of the teeter-totter. If there are 3 children of the same size on each side, it will balance. If 2 more children climb onto the left side, the only way to keep the balance is to have 2 more children of the same size climb onto the right side as well.

$$3 = 3$$

$$3 + 2 = 3 + 2$$

All the tools you will learn to use with equations have one goal.

Goal in Solving an Equation

The goal is to end up with the variable (letter) on one side of the equal sign balancing a number on the other side.

We work on the original equation until we get:

variable = number   or   number = variable

Once we have arrived at that point, the number balancing the variable is the solution to the original equation.

EXAMPLE 2   **Using the Addition Property of Equality**

Solve each equation and check the solution.

(a) $c + 5 = 30$

We want to get the variable, c, by itself on the left side of the equal sign. To do that, we add the *opposite* of 5, which is $^-5$. Then $5 + {}^-5$ will be 0.

$$c + 5 = 30$$

Add $^-5$ to the left side. $\longrightarrow$ $\underline{{}^-5 \quad {}^-5}$ $\longleftarrow$ To keep the balance, add $^-5$ to the right side also.

$$c + 0 = 25 \longleftarrow 30 + {}^-5 \text{ is } 25.$$

$5 + {}^-5$ is 0.

Recall that adding 0 to any number leaves the number unchanged, so $c + 0$ is c.

$$\underbrace{c + 0}_{} = 25$$
$$c \quad = 25$$

Because c *balances* with 25, the *solution* is 25.

Check the solution by replacing c with 25 in the *original equation*.

$$c + 5 = 30 \qquad \text{Original equation}$$
$$\underbrace{25 + 5}_{} = 30 \qquad \text{Replace } c \text{ with 25.} \qquad \boxed{\begin{array}{l}\text{The solution}\\ \text{is 25, \textbf{not} 30.}\end{array}}$$
$$30 \quad = 30 \qquad \text{Balances}$$

Because the equation balances when we use 25 to replace the variable, we know that **25 is the correct solution**. If it had *not* balanced, we would need to rework the problem, find our error, and correct it.

(b) $^-5 = x - 3$

We want the variable, x, by itself on the right side of the equal sign. (Remember, it doesn't matter which side of the equal sign the variable is on, just so it ends up by itself.) To see what number to add, we change the subtraction to adding the opposite.

$$^-5 = x - 3 \qquad \text{Change subtraction to adding}$$
$$\qquad\qquad\qquad\quad \text{the opposite.}$$
$$^-5 = x + {}^-3 \qquad \text{To get } x \text{ by itself on the right side,}$$

To keep the balance, add 3 to the left side also. $\underline{3 \qquad\qquad 3}$ add the opposite of $^-3$, which is 3. Then $^-3 + 3$ is 0.

$^-5 + 3$ is $^-2$. $\qquad ^-2 = \underbrace{x + 0}_{} \qquad$ Adding 0 to x leaves x unchanged.

$$^-2 = \quad x \qquad\qquad x \text{ balances with } ^-2, \text{ so } ^-2 \text{ is the}$$
$$\text{solution.}$$

We check the solution by replacing x with $^-2$ in the *original equation*. If the equation balances when we use $^-2$, we know that it is the correct solution. If the equation does *not* balance when we use $^-2$, we made an error and need to try solving the equation again.

Continued on Next Page

Check

$$-5 = x - 3 \quad \text{Original equation}$$

$$-5 = -2 - 3 \quad \text{Replace } x \text{ with } -2.$$

$$-5 = -2 + -3 \quad \text{Change subtraction to adding the opposite.}$$

$$-5 = -5 \quad \text{Balances; this shows } -2 \text{ is the correct solution.}$$

When x is replaced with -2, the equation balances, so -2 **is the correct solution.**

CAUTION

When checking the solution to Example 2(b) above, we ended up with $-5 = -5$. Notice that -5 is *not* the solution. The solution is -2, the number used to replace x in the original equation.

Work Problem **2** *at the Side.* ▶

OBJECTIVE **3** **Simplify equations before using the addition property of equality.** Sometimes you can simplify the expression on one or both sides of the equal sign. Doing so will make it easier to solve the equation.

EXAMPLE 3 **Simplifying before Solving Equations**

Solve each equation and check each solution.

(a) $y + 8 = 3 - 7$

You cannot simplify the left side because y and 8 are *not* like terms.

$$y + 8 = 3 - 7 \quad \text{Simplify the right side by changing subtraction to adding the opposite.}$$

$$y + 8 = 3 + -7 \quad \text{Add } 3 + -7.$$

$$y + 8 = -4$$

To get y by itself on the left side, add the opposite of 8, which is -8.

$8 + -8$ is 0.

$$\underline{\quad -8 \quad -8\quad} \quad \leftarrow \text{To keep the balance, add } -8 \text{ to the right side also.}$$

$$y + 0 = -12 \quad -4 + -8 \text{ is } -12.$$

$$y = -12$$

The solution is -12. Now check the solution.

Check

$$y + 8 = 3 - 7 \quad \text{Go back to the } \textit{original} \text{ equation and replace } y \text{ with } -12.$$

Add $-12 + 8$.

$$-12 + 8 = 3 - 7 \quad \text{Change } 3 - 7 \text{ to } 3 + -7.$$

$$-4 = 3 + -7 \quad \text{Add } 3 + -7.$$

$$-4 = -4 \quad \text{Balances; so } -12 \text{ is the correct solution.}$$

When y is replaced with -12, the equation balances, so -12 **is the correct solution (not** -4).

Continued on Next Page

---

2 Solve each equation and check each solution.

(a) $12 = y + 5$

Check

(b) $b - 2 = -6$

Check

3 Simplify each side of the equation when possible. Then solve the equation and check the solution.

(a) $2 - 8 = k - 2$

Check

(b) $4r + 1 - 3r = {}^-8 + 11$

Check

(b) ${}^-2 + 2 = {}^-4b - 6 + 5b$

Simplify the left side by adding ${}^-2 + 2$.

$$\underbrace{{}^-2 + 2} = {}^-4b - 6 + 5b$$

Simplify the right side by changing subtraction to adding the opposite.

$$0 = {}^-4b + {}^-6 + 5b \quad \text{Find like terms.}$$

$$0 = \underbrace{{}^-4b + 5b} + {}^-6 \quad \text{Combine } {}^-4b + 5b.$$

To keep the balance, add 6 to the left side also.

$$0 = 1b + {}^-6 \quad \text{To get } 1b \text{ by itself, add the opposite of } {}^-6, \text{ which is 6.}$$

$$\frac{6}{6}$$

$$6 = \underbrace{1b + 0}$$

$$6 = 1b \quad 1b \text{ is equivalent to } b.$$

$$6 = b$$

The solution is 6.

Check $\quad {}^-2 + 2 = {}^-4b - 6 + 5b \quad$ Go back to the *original* equation and replace each b with 6.

Add ${}^-2 + 2$. $\quad \underbrace{{}^-2 + 2} = \underbrace{{}^-4 \cdot 6} - 6 + \underbrace{5 \cdot 6} \quad$ On the right side, do multiplications first.

$$0 = \underbrace{{}^-24 + {}^-6} + 30 \quad \text{Change subtraction to adding the opposite.}$$

$$0 = \underbrace{{}^-30 + 30} \quad \text{Add from left to right.}$$

$$0 = 0 \quad \text{Balances}$$

When b is replaced with 6, the equation balances, so **6 is the correct solution (not** 0**).**

> **CAUTION**
> When checking a solution, always go back to the *original* equation. That way, you will catch any errors you made when simplifying each side of the equation.

◀ *Work Problem* **3** *at the Side.*

4.3 ▶▶▶ Exercises

FOR EXTRA HELP    PRACTICE   WATCH   DOWNLOAD   READ   REVIEW

In each list of numbers, find the one that is a solution of the given equation. See Example 1.

1. $n - 50 = 8$

    58, 42, 60

2. $r - 20 = 5$

    15, 30, 25

3. $^-6 = y + 10$

    $^-4, ^-16, 16$

4. $^-4 = x + 13$

    $17, ^-17, ^-9$

5. $t + 12 = 0$

    $0, ^-12, ^-24$

6. $b - 8 = 0$

    $8, 0, ^-8$

Solve each equation and check each solution. See Example 2.

7. $p + 5 = 9$ **Check** $p + 5 = 9$

8. $a + 3 = 12$ **Check** $a + 3 = 12$

9. $8 = r - 2$ **Check** $8 = r - 2$

10. $3 = b - 5$ **Check** $3 = b - 5$

11. $^-5 = n + 3$ **Check**

12. $^-1 = a + 8$ **Check**

13. $^-4 + k = 14$ **Check**

14. $^-9 + y = 7$ **Check**

15. $y - 6 = 0$ **Check**

16. $k - 15 = 0$ **Check**

17. $7 = r + 13$ **Check**

18. $12 = z + 19$ **Check**

19. $x - 12 = {}^-1$ **Check**

20. $m - 3 = {}^-9$ **Check**

21. ${}^-5 = {}^-2 + t$ **Check**

22. ${}^-1 = {}^-10 + w$ **Check**

A solution is given for each equation. Show how to check the solution. If the solution is correct, leave it. If the solution is not correct, solve the equation and check your new solution. See Example 2.

23. $z - 5 = 3$ **Check** $z - 5 = 3$
    The solution is ${}^-2$. $\downarrow$

24. $x - 9 = 4$ **Check** $x - 9 = 4$
    The solution is 13. $\downarrow$

25. $7 + x = {}^-11$ **Check**
    The solution is ${}^-18$.

26. $2 + k = {}^-7$ **Check**
    The solution is ${}^-5$.

27. ${}^-10 = {}^-10 + b$ **Check**
    The solution is 10.

28. $0 = {}^-14 + a$ **Check**
    The solution is 0.

Simplify each side of the equation when possible. Then solve the equation and check the solution. Show your work. See Example 3.

29. $c - 4 = {}^{-}8 + 10$ **Check**

30. $b - 8 = 10 - 6$ **Check**

31. ${}^{-}1 + 4 = y - 2$ **Check**

32. $2 + 3 = k - 4$ **Check**

33. $10 + b = {}^{-}14 - 6$ **Check**

34. $1 + w = {}^{-}8 - 8$ **Check**

35. $t - 2 = 3 - 5$ **Check**

36. $p - 8 = {}^{-}10 + 2$ **Check**

37. $10z - 9z = {}^{-}15 + 8$ **Check**

38. $2r - r = 5 - 10$ **Check**

39. ${}^{-}5w + 2 + 6w = {}^{-}4 + 9$ **Check**

40. ${}^{-}2t + 4 + 3t = 6 - 7$ **Check**

Solve each equation. Show your work. See Examples 2 and 3.

41. $^-3 - 3 = 4 - 3x + 4x$

42. $^-5 - 5 = {}^-2 - 6b + 7b$

43. $^-3 + 7 - 4 = {}^-2a + 3a$

44. $6 - 11 + 5 = {}^-8c + 9c$

45. $y - 75 = {}^-100$

46. $a - 200 = {}^-100$

47. $^-x + 3 + 2x = 18$

48. $^-s + 2s - 4 = 13$

49. $82 = {}^-31 + k$

50. $^-5 = 72 + w$

51. $^-2 + 11 = 2b - 9 - b$

52. $^-6 + 7 = 2h - 1 - h$

53. $r - 6 = 7 - 10 - 8$

54. $m - 5 = 2 - 9 + 1$

55. $^-14 = n + 91$

56. $66 = x - 28$

57. $^-9 + 9 = 5 + h$

58. $18 - 18 = 6 + p$

59. A student did this work when solving an equation. Do you agree that the solution is $^-7$? Explain why or why not.

$$^-8 + 1 = x + 7$$
$$^-7 = x + 7$$
$$\underline{^-7 \qquad \underline{\quad ^-7}}$$
$$^-14 = x + 0$$
$$^-14 = x$$

Check

$$^-8 + 1 = x + 7$$
$$^-8 + 1 = ^-14 + 7$$
$$^-7 = ^-7$$

Balances, so
$^-7$ is the solution.

60. A student did this work when solving an equation. Show how to check the solution. If the solution does not check, find and correct the errors.

$$^-3 - 6 = n - 5$$
$$^-3 + 6 = n - 5$$
$$3 = n - 5$$
$$\underline{^-5 \qquad \underline{\quad ^-5}}$$
$$^-2 = n + 0$$
$$^-2 = n$$

61. West Community College always orders 10 extra robes for the graduation ceremony. The college ordered 305 robes this year. Solving the equation $g + 10 = 305$ will give the number of graduates (g) this year. Solve the equation.

62. Refer to Exercise 61. The college ordered 278 robes last year. Solve the equation $g + 10 = 278$ to find the number of graduates last year.

63. The warmer the temperature, the faster a field cricket chirps. Solving the equation $92 = c + 37$ will give you the number of chirps (in 15 seconds) when the temperature is 92 degrees. Solve the equation.

64. Refer to Exercise 63. Solve the equation $77 = c + 37$ to find the number of times a field cricket chirps (in 15 seconds) when the temperature is 77 degrees.

65. During the summer months, Ernesto spends an average of only $45 per month on parking fees by riding his bike to work on nice days. This is $65 less per month than what he spends for parking in the winter. Solving the equation $p - 65 = 45$ will give you his monthly parking fees in the winter. Solve the equation.

66. By walking to work several times a week in the summer, Aimee spends an average of $56 less per month on parking fees. If she spends $98 per month on parking in the summer, solve the equation $p - 56 = 98$ to find her monthly parking fees in the winter.

Solve each equation. Show your work.

67. $^-17 - 1 + 26 - 38 = {}^-3 - m - 8 + 2m$

68. $19 - 38 - 9 + 11 = {}^-t - 6 + 2t - 6$

69. $^-6x + 2x + 6 + 5x = |0 - 9| - |^-6 + 5|$

70. $^-h - |^-9 - 9| + 8h - 6h = {}^-12 - |^-5 + 0|$

Relating Concepts (Exercises 71–72) For Individual or Group Work

*Use what you have learned about solving equations to **work Exercises 71 and 72 in order.***

71. (a) Write two *different* equations that have $^-2$ as the solution. Be sure that you have to use the *addition property of equality* to solve the equations. Show how to solve each equation. Use Exercises 7 to 22 as models.

   (b) Follow the directions in part (a), but this time write two equations that have 0 as the solution.

72. Not all equations have solutions that are integers. Try solving these equations.

   (a) $x + 1 = 1\dfrac{1}{2}$

   (b) $\dfrac{1}{4} = y - 1$

   (c) $\$2.50 + n = \$3.35$

   (d) Write two more equations that have fraction or decimal solutions.

4.4 ▶▶▶ Solving Equations Using Division

OBJECTIVE 1 Solve equations, using the division property of equality. In **Section 4.1** you worked with the expression for finding the perimeter of a square-shaped garden, that is, finding the total distance around all four sides of the garden:

4*s*, where *s* is the length of one side of the square

Suppose you know that 24 feet of fencing was used around a square-shaped garden. What was the length of one side of the garden? To answer this question, write an equation showing the relationship between what you know and what you don't know.

You don't know the length of one side.

You do know that
there are 4 sides.

You do know the
perimeter.

$$4\, s = 24$$

To solve the equation, what number can replace *s* so that the equation balances? You can see that *s* is 6 feet.

$$4 \cdot 6 = 24$$

Balances:
4 · 6 is exactly 24.

The **solution** is **6 feet** because **6** is the *only* number that makes the equation balance. You have answered the question about the length of one side: The length is 6 feet.

There is a tool that you can use to solve equations such as 4*s* = 24. Called the **division property of equality,** it allows you to *divide* both sides of an equation by the *same* number. (The only exception is that you cannot divide by 0.)

> **Division Property of Equality**
>
> If $a = b$, then $\dfrac{a}{c} = \dfrac{b}{c}$ as long as *c* is *not* 0.
>
> In other words, you may divide both sides of an equation by the same nonzero number and still keep it balanced.

In **Section 4.3,** you saw that *adding* the same number to both sides of an equation kept it balanced. We could also have *subtracted* the same number from both sides because subtraction is defined as adding the opposite. Now we're saying that you can *divide* both sides by the same number. In **Chapter 5** we'll *multiply* both sides by the same number.

> **Equality Principle for Solving an Equation**
>
> As long as you do the *same* thing to *both* sides of an equation, the balance is maintained. (The only exception is that you cannot divide by 0.)

OBJECTIVES

1 Solve equations using the division property of equality.

2 Simplify equations before using the division property of equality.

3 Solve equations such as $^{-}x = 5$.

1 Solve each equation and check each solution.

(a) $4s = 44$

Check

(b) $27 = {}^-9p$

Check

(c) ${}^-40 = {}^-5x$

Check

(d) $7t = {}^-70$

Check

ANSWERS

1. (a) $s = 11$
Check $\underbrace{4s}_{4 \cdot 11} = 44$
$4 \cdot 11 = 44$
Balances $\quad 44 = 44$

(b) $p = {}^-3$
Check $27 = \underbrace{{}^-9p}_{{}^-9 \cdot {}^-3}$
$27 = {}^-9 \cdot {}^-3$
Balances $\quad 27 = \quad 27$

(c) $x = 8$
Check $\underbrace{{}^-40}_{} = {}^-5x$
${}^-40 = \underbrace{{}^-5 \cdot 8}_{}$
Balances $\quad {}^-40 = {}^-40$

(d) $t = {}^-10$
Check $\underbrace{7t}_{} = {}^-70$
$\underbrace{7 \cdot {}^-10}_{} = {}^-70$
Balances $\quad {}^-70 = {}^-70$

EXAMPLE 1 **Using the Division Property of Equality**

Solve each equation and check each solution.

(a) $4s = 24$

As with any equation, the goal is to get the variable by itself on one side of the equal sign. On the left side we have $4s$, which means $4 \cdot s$. The variable is multiplied by 4. Division is the opposite of multiplication, so dividing by 4 can be used to "undo" multiplying by 4.

Divide $4s$ by 4. The fraction bar indicates division: $\longrightarrow$ $\dfrac{4s}{4} = \dfrac{24}{4}$ To keep the balance, divide the right side by 4 also: $4s \div 4$ is s. $\qquad\qquad\qquad\qquad\qquad$ $24 \div 4$ is 6

$$s = 6$$

So, as we already knew, 6 is the solution. We check the solution by replacing s with 6 in the original equation.

Check $\qquad 4s = 24 \qquad$ Original equation

$\qquad\qquad\qquad \underbrace{4 \cdot 6}_{} = 24 \qquad$ Replace s with 6.

$\qquad\qquad\qquad 24 = 24 \qquad$ Balances $\quad$ [The solution is 6, **not** 24.]

When s is replaced with 6, the equation balances, so **6 is the correct solution.**

(b) $42 = {}^-6w$

On the right side of the equation, the variable is *multiplied* by ${}^-6$. To undo the multiplication, *divide* by ${}^-6$.

To keep the balance, divide by ${}^-6$ on the left side also. $\qquad \dfrac{42}{{}^-6} = \dfrac{{}^-6w}{{}^-6}$ $\qquad$ Use division to undo multiplication: ${}^-6w \div {}^-6$ is w.

$${}^-7 = w$$

The solution is ${}^-7$.

Check $\qquad 42 = {}^-6w \qquad$ Original equation

$\qquad\qquad 42 = \underbrace{{}^-6 \cdot {}^-7}_{} \qquad$ Replace w with ${}^-7$. $\quad$ [The solution is ${}^-7$, **not** 42.]

$\qquad\qquad 42 = 42 \qquad$ Balances

When w is replaced with ${}^-7$, the equation balances, so ${}^-7$ **is the correct solution.**

CAUTION

Be careful to divide both sides by the *same* number as the coefficient of the variable term. In Example 1(b) above, the coefficient of ${}^-6w$ is ${}^-6$, so divide both sides by ${}^-6$. (Do ***not*** divide by the *opposite* of ${}^-6$, which is 6. Use the opposite only when you're *adding* the same number to both sides.)

◀ *Work Problem* **1** *at the Side.*

OBJECTIVE 2 Simplify equations before using the division property of equality. You can sometimes simplify the expression on one or both sides of the equal sign, as you did in **Section 4.3.**

EXAMPLE 2 Simplifying before Solving Equations

Solve each equation and check each solution.

(a) $4y - 7y = {}^-12$

Simplify the left side by combining like terms.	$4y - 7y = {}^-12$	The right side cannot be simplified.
Change subtraction to adding the opposite.	$4y + {}^-7y = {}^-12$	
Divide by the coefficient, which is $^-3$.	$\dfrac{{}^-3y}{{}^-3} = \dfrac{{}^-12}{{}^-3}$	To keep the balance, divide by $^-3$ on the right side.
	$y = 4$	$^-12 \div {}^-3$ is 4.

The solution is 4.

Check

	$4y - 7y = {}^-12$	Go back to the *original* equation and replace each y with 4.
Do multiplications first.	$4 \cdot 4 - 7 \cdot 4 = {}^-12$	
Change subtraction to adding the opposite.	$16 - 28 = {}^-12$	
	$16 + {}^-28 = {}^-12$	
	${}^-12 = {}^-12$	Balances

When y is replaced with 4, the equation balances, so **4 is the correct solution.**

(b) $3 - 10 + 7 = h + 7h$

Change subtraction to adding the opposite.	$3 - 10 + 7 = h + 7h$	Write the understood 1 as the coefficient of h.
Add from left to right.	$3 + {}^-10 + 7 = 1h + 7h$	Combine like terms.
	${}^-7 + 7 = 8h$	
To keep the balance, divide by 8 on the left side also.	$\dfrac{0}{8} = \dfrac{8h}{8}$	Divide by the coefficient, which is 8.
$0 \div 8$ is 0.	$0 = h$	

The solution is 0.

Check

	$3 - 10 + 7 = h + 7h$	Go back to the *original* equation and replace each h with 0.
	$3 + {}^-10 + 7 = 0 + 7 \cdot 0$	
	${}^-7 + 7 = 0 + 0$	
	$0 = 0$	Balances

When h is replaced with 0, the equation balances, so **0 is the correct solution.**

Work Problem **2** *at the Side.* ▶

2 Simplify each side of the equation when possible. Then solve the equation and check the solution.

(a) $^-28 = {}^-6n + 10n$

Check

(b) $p - 14p = {}^-2 + 18 - 3$

Check

ANSWERS

2. (a) $n = {}^-7$

Check
$$^-28 = {}^-6n + 10n$$
$$^-28 = {}^-6 \cdot {}^-7 + 10 \cdot {}^-7$$
$$^-28 = 42 + {}^-70$$
Balances $^-28 = {}^-28$

(b) $p = {}^-1$

Check
$$p - 14p = {}^-2 + 18 - 3$$
$$^-1 - 14({}^-1) = 16 - 3$$
$$^-1 - {}^-14 = 13$$
$$^-1 + {}^+14 = 13$$
Balances $\quad 13 = 13$

3 Solve each equation and check each solution.

(a) $^-k = ^-12$

Check

(b) $7 = ^-t$

Check

(c) $^-m = ^-20$

Check

OBJECTIVE 3 Solve equations such as $^-\mathbf{x} = \mathbf{5}$. When solving equations, do **not** leave a negative sign in front of the variable.

EXAMPLE 3 Solving an Equation of the Type $^-\mathbf{x} = \mathbf{5}$

Solve $^-x = 5$ and check the solution.

It may look as if there is nothing more we can do to the equation $^-x = 5$, but ^-x is *not* the same as x. To see this, we write in the understood $^-1$ as the coefficient of ^-x.

Coefficient is understood to be $^-1$.

$$^-x = 5 \quad \text{can be written} \quad ^-1x = 5$$

We want the coefficient of x to be $^+1$, not $^-1$. To accomplish that, we can divide both sides by the coefficient of x, which is $^-1$.

$$\frac{^-1x}{^-1} = \frac{5}{^-1} \qquad \text{Divide both sides by } ^-1.$$

On the left side, $^-1 \div ^-1$ is 1. $\qquad 1x = ^-5 \qquad$ On the right side, $5 \div ^-1$ is $^-5$.

Now x is by itself on one side of the equal sign and has a coefficient of $^+1$. The solution is $^-5$.

Check $\qquad ^-x = 5 \qquad$ Go back to the *original* equation.

$^-1x = 5 \qquad$ Write in the understood $^-1$ as the coefficient of ^-x.

$^-1 \cdot ^-5 = 5 \qquad$ Replace x with $^-5$. — The solution is $^-5$, **not** 5.

$5 \quad = 5 \qquad$ Balances

When x is replaced with $^-5$, the equation balances, so $^-5$ **is the correct solution.**

CAUTION
As the last step in solving an equation, do **not** leave a negative sign in front of a variable. For example, do *not* leave $^-y = ^-8$. Write in the understood $^-1$ as the coefficient, so that

$$^-y = ^-8 \quad \text{is written as} \quad ^-1y = ^-8$$

Then divide both sides by $^-1$ to get $y = 8$. The solution is 8.

◀ *Work Problem* **3** *at the Side.*

Solve each equation and check each solution. See Example 1.

1. $6z = 12$ **Check** $6z = 12$ **2.** $8k = 24$ **Check** $8k = 24$

3. $48 = 12r$ **Check**   **4.** $99 = 11m$ **Check**

5. $3y = 0$ **Check**   **6.** $5a = 0$ **Check**

7. $^-7k = 70$ **Check**   **8.** $^-6y = 36$ **Check**

9. $^-54 = ^-9r$ **Check**   **10.** $^-36 = ^-4p$ **Check**

11. $^-25 = 5b$ **Check**   **12.** $^-70 = 10x$ **Check**

Simplify where possible. Then solve each equation and check each solution. See Example 2.

13. $2r = ^-7 + 13$ **Check** $2r = \underbrace{^-7 + 13}$ **14.** $6y = 28 - 4$ **Check** $6y = \underbrace{28 - 4}$

15. $^-12 = 5p - p$ **Check**   **16.** $20 = z - 11z$ **Check**

Solve each equation. Show your work. See Examples 1 and 2.

17. $3 - 28 = 5a$

18. $^-55 + 7 = 8n$

19. $x - 9x = 80$

20. $4c - c = {}^-27$

21. $13 - 13 = 2w - w$

22. $^-11 + 11 = 8t - 7t$

23. $3t + 9t = 20 - 10 + 26$

24. $6m + 6m = 40 + 20 - 12$

25. $0 = {}^-9t$

26. $^-10 = 10b$

27. $^-14m + 8m = 6 - 60$

28. $7w - 14w = 1 - 50$

29. $100 - 96 = 31y - 35y$

30. $150 - 139 = 20x - 9x$

Use multiplication to simplify the side of the equation with the variable. Then solve each equation.

31. $3(2z) = {}^-30$

32. $2(4k) = 16$

33. $50 = {}^-5(5p)$

34. $60 = 4({}^-3a)$

35. ${}^-2({}^-4k) = 56$

36. ${}^-5(4r) = {}^-80$

37. ${}^-90 = {}^-10({}^-3b)$

38. ${}^-90 = {}^-5({}^-2y)$

Solve each equation. See Example 3.

39. ${}^-x = 32$

40. ${}^-c = 23$

41. ${}^-2 = {}^-w$

42. ${}^-75 = {}^-t$

43. ${}^-n = {}^-50$

44. ${}^-x = {}^-1$

45. $10 = {}^-p$

46. $100 = {}^-k$

47. Look again at the solutions to Exercises 39–46. Describe the pattern you see. Then write a rule for solving equations with a negative sign in front of the variable, such as $^-x = 5$.

48. Explain the division property of equality in your own words.

49. Explain and correct the error made by a student who solved this equation.

$$3x = \underbrace{16 - 1}$$

$$\frac{3x}{-3} = \frac{15}{-3}$$

$$x = {}^-5$$

50. Write two *different* equations that have $^-4$ as the solution. Be sure that you have to use the division property of equality to solve the equations. Show how to solve each equation. Use Exercises 1–14 as models.

51. The perimeter of a triangle with sides of equal length is 3 times the length of one side (s). If the perimeter is 45 ft, solving the equation $3s = 45$ will give the length of one side. Solve the equation.

52. Refer to Exercise 51. If the perimeter of the triangle is 63 inches, solve the equation $3s = 63$ to find the length of one side.

53. The perimeter of a pentagon with sides of equal length is 5 times the length of one side (s). If the perimeter is 120 meters, solve the equation $120 = 5s$ to find the length of one side.

54. Refer to Exercise 53. If the pentagon has a perimeter of 335 yards, solving the equation $335 = 5s$ will give the length of one side. Solve the equation.

Solve each equation. Show your work.

55. $89 - 116 = {}^-4({}^-4y) - 9(2y) + y$

56. $58 - 208 = {}^-b + 8({}^-3b) + 5({}^-5b)$

57. $^-37(14x) + 28(21x) = |72 - 72| + |{}^-166 + 96|$

58. $6a - 10a - 3(2a) = |{}^-25 - 25| - 5(8)$

4.5 ▶▶▶ Solving Equations with Several Steps

OBJECTIVE 1 Solve equations using the addition and division properties of equality. To solve some equations, you need to use both the addition property of equality (see **Section 4.3**) and the division property of equality (see **Section 4.4**). Here are the steps.

Solving an Equation Using the Addition and Division Properties

Step 1 *Add* the same amount to both sides of the equation so that the variable term (the variable and its coefficient) ends up by itself on one side of the equal sign.

Step 2 *Divide* both sides by the coefficient of the variable term to find the solution.

Step 3 *Check* the solution by going back to the *original* equation.

OBJECTIVES

1 Solve equations using the addition and division properties of equality.

2 Solve equations using the distributive, addition, and division properties.

EXAMPLE 1 **Solving an Equation with Several Steps**

Solve this equation and check the solution: $5m + 1 = 16$.

Step 1 Get the variable term by itself on one side of the equal sign. The variable term is $5m$. Adding $^{-}1$ to the left side of the equation will leave $5m$ by itself. To keep the balance, add $^{-}1$ to the right side also.

$$\begin{aligned} 5m + 1 &= 16 \\ \underline{-1 \quad -1} & \\ 5m + 0 &= 15 \\ 5m &= 15 \end{aligned}$$

First *add* the same thing to both sides.

Step 2 Divide both sides by the coefficient of the variable term. In $5m$, the coefficient is 5, so divide both sides by 5.

Divide both sides by the coefficient.

$$\frac{5m}{5} = \frac{15}{5}$$

$$m = 3$$

Step 3 Check the solution by going back to the *original* equation.

$$5m + 1 = 16$$

Use the *original* equation and replace m with 3.

The solution is 3, **not** 16.

$$5(3) + 1 = 16$$

$$15 + 1 = 16$$

$$16 = 16 \qquad \text{Balances}$$

When m is replaced with 3, the equation balances, so **3 is the correct solution**.

Work Problem **1** *at the Side.* ▶

So far, variable terms have appeared on just one side of the equal sign. But some equations start with variable terms on both sides. In that case, you can use the addition property of equality to add the same *variable term* to both sides of the equation, just as you have added the same *number* to both sides.

1 Solve each equation and check each solution.

(a) $2r + 7 = 13$

Check

(b) $20 = 6y - 4$

Check

(c) $^{-}10z - 9 = 11$

Check

ANSWERS

1. (a) $r = 3$
   Check $2(3) + 7 = 13$
   $6 + 7 = 13$
   Balances $13 = 13$

(b) $y = 4$
   Check $20 = 6(4) - 4$
   $20 = 24 - 4$
   Balances $20 = 20$

(c) $z = ^{-}2$
   Check $^{-}10(^{-}2) - 9 = 11$
   $20 - 9 = 11$
   Balances $11 = 11$

2 Solve each equation *two ways*. First keep the variable term on the *left* side when you solve. Then solve again, keeping the variable term on the *right* side. Compare the solutions.

(a) $3y - 1 = 2y + 7$

$3y - 1 = 2y + 7$

(b) $3p - 2 = p - 6$

$3p - 2 = p - 6$

First decide whether to keep the variable term on the left side, or to keep the variable term on the right side. It doesn't matter which one you keep; just pick one side or the other. Then use the addition property to "get rid of" the variable term on the *other* side by adding its opposite.

| EXAMPLE 2 | **Solving an Equation with Variable Terms on Both Sides** |

Solve this equation and check the solution: $2x - 2 = 5x - 11$.

First let's keep $2x$, the variable term on the *left* side. That means we need to "get rid of" $5x$ on the *right* side. We can do that by adding the opposite of $5x$, which is ^-5x.

To keep the balance, add ^-5x to the left side also. Write ^-5x under $2x$, *not* under 2.

To get ^-3x by itself, add 2 to both sides.

Divide both sides by $^-3$, the coefficient of the variable term.

$$
\begin{array}{rcl}
2x - 2 &=& 5x - 11 \\
-5x & & -5x \\
\hline
^-3x - 2 &=& 0 - 11 \\
\downarrow\ \downarrow & & \downarrow\ \downarrow \\
^-3x + {}^-2 &=& 0 + {}^-11 \\
\quad 2 & & \quad 2 \\
\hline
^-3x + 0 &=& 0 + {}^-9 \\
\dfrac{^-3x}{-3} &=& \dfrac{^-9}{-3} \\
x &=& 3
\end{array}
$$

Write ^-5x under $5x$, *not* under 11.
$5x + {}^-5x$ is $0x$, or 0.

Change subtractions to adding the opposite.

Suppose that, in the first step, we decided to keep $5x$ on the *right* side and "get rid of" $2x$ on the *left* side. Let's see what happens.

Add ^-2x to both sides.

$$
\begin{array}{rcl}
2x - 2 &=& 5x - 11 \\
-2x & & -2x \\
\hline
0 - 2 &=& 3x - 11 \\
\downarrow\ \downarrow & & \downarrow\ \downarrow \\
0 + {}^-2 &=& 3x + {}^-11 \\
\quad 11 & & \quad 11 \\
\hline
0 + 9 &=& 3x + 0 \\
\dfrac{9}{3} &=& \dfrac{3x}{3} \\
3 &=& x
\end{array}
$$

Change subtractions to adding the opposite.
To get $3x$ by itself, add 11 to both sides.

Divide both sides by 3.

The two solutions are the same. In both cases, x balances with 3.

Notice that we used the addition principle *twice:* once to "get rid of" the variable term $2x$ and once to "get rid of" the number $^-11$. We could have done those steps in the reverse order without changing the result.

> **Note**
>
> More than one sequence of steps will work to solve complicated equations. The basic approach is the following:
>
> • Simplify each side of the equation, if possible.
> • Get the variable term by itself on one side of the equal sign and a number by itself on the other side.
> • Divide both sides by the coefficient of the variable term.

ANSWERS

2. (a) $y = 8$ and $8 = y$
 (b) $p = {}^-2$ and $^-2 = p$

◀ *Work Problem* **2** *at the Side.*

OBJECTIVE **2** **Solve equations using the distributive, addition, and division properties.**   If an equation contains parentheses, check to see whether you can use the distributive property to remove them.

> **EXAMPLE 3** **Solving an Equation Using the Distributive Property**

Solve this equation and check the solution: $^-6 = 3(y - 2)$.

We can use the distributive property to simplify the right side of the equation. Recall from **Section 4.2** that

$$3(y - 2) \quad \text{can be written as} \quad \underbrace{3 \cdot y} - \underbrace{3 \cdot 2}$$
$$3y \quad - \quad 6$$

So the original equation $^-6 = 3(y - 2)$ becomes $^-6 = 3y - 6$.

$$^-6 = 3y - 6 \qquad \text{Change subtraction to adding the opposite.}$$
$$^-6 = 3y + {}^-6 \qquad \text{To get } 3y \text{ by itself, add 6 to both sides.}$$
$$\underline{\quad 6 \qquad\qquad 6 \quad}$$
$$\frac{0}{3} = \frac{3y}{3} \qquad \text{Divide both sides by 3, the coefficient of } 3y.$$
$$0 = y$$

The solution is 0.

Check $\quad ^-6 = 3(y - 2) \qquad$ Go back to the *original* equation and replace y with 0.

$^-6 = 3(0 - 2) \qquad$ Follow the order of operations: work inside parentheses first.

$^-6 = 3(0 + {}^-2) \qquad$ Change subtraction to addition.

$^-6 = \quad 3({}^-2)$

$^-6 = \quad {}^-6 \qquad$ Balances

When y is replaced with 0, the equation balances, so **0 is the correct solution.**

Work Problem **3** *at the Side.* ▶

Here is a summary of all the steps you can use to solve an equation. Sometimes you will use only two or three steps, and sometimes you will need all five steps, as in the example on the next page.

> **Solving an Equation**
>
> *Step 1* If possible, use the ***distributive property*** to remove parentheses.
>
> *Step 2* ***Combine*** any like terms on the left side of the equation. Combine any like terms on the right side of the equation.
>
> *Step 3* ***Add*** the same amount to both sides of the equation so that the variable term ends up by itself on one side of the equal sign and a number is by itself on the other side. You may have to do this step more than once.
>
> *Step 4* ***Divide*** both sides by the coefficient of the variable term to find the solution.
>
> *Step 5* ***Check*** your solution by going back to the *original* equation. Replace the variable with your solution. Follow the order of operations to complete the calculations. If the two sides of the equation balance, your solution is correct.

3 Solve each equation and check each solution.

(a) $^-12 = 4(y - 1)$

(b) $5(m + 4) = 20$

(c) $6(t - 2) = 18$

4 Solve each equation and check each solution.

(a) $3(b + 7) = 2b - 1$

EXAMPLE 4 **Solving an Equation**

Solve this equation and check the solution: $8 + 5(m + 2) = 6 + 2m$

Step 1 Use the distributive property on the left side.

$$8 + 5(m + 2) = 6 + 2m$$

Step 2 Combine like terms on the left side.

$$8 + 5m + 10 = 6 + 2m$$ No like terms on the right side.

$$5m + 18 = 6 + 2m$$

Step 3 Add ^-2m to both sides.

$$\underline{ ^-2m \quad ^-2m}$$
$$3m + 18 = 6 + 0$$
$$3m + 18 = 6$$

Step 3 To get $3m$ by itself, add $^-18$ to both sides.

$$\underline{^-18 \quad ^-18}$$
$$3m + 0 = ^-12$$

Step 4 Divide both sides by 3, the coefficient of the variable term $3m$.

$$\frac{3m}{3} = \frac{^-12}{3}$$
$$m = ^-4$$

The solution is $^-4$.

Step 5 **Check**

$$8 + 5(m + 2) = 6 + 2m$$ Replace each m with $^-4$.

$$8 + 5(^-4 + 2) = 6 + 2(^-4)$$
$$8 + 5(^-2) = 6 + ^-8$$
$$8 + ^-10 = ^-2$$
$$^-2 = ^-2$$ Balances

When m is replaced with $^-4$, the equation balances, so $^-4$ **is the correct solution** (**not** $^-2$).

(b) $6 - 2n = 14 + 4(n - 5)$

◀ *Work Problem* **4** *at the Side.*

4.5 ▶▶▶ Exercises

Solve each equation and check each solution. See Example 1.

 1. $7p + 5 = 12$ **Check** $7p + 5 = 12$

2. $6k + 3 = 15$ **Check** $6k + 3 = 15$

3. $2 = 8y - 6$ **Check**

4. $10 = 11p - 12$ **Check**

5. $^-3m + 1 = 1$ **Check**

6. $^-4k + 5 = 5$ **Check**

7. $28 = {}^-9a + 10$ **Check**

8. $75 = {}^-10w + 25$ **Check**

9. $^-5x - 4 = 16$ **Check**

10. $^-12b - 3 = 21$ **Check**

*In Exercises 11–16, solve each equation **two** ways. First keep the variable term on the left side when you solve it. Then solve it again, keeping the variable term on the right side. Finally, check your solution. See Example 2.*

11. $6p - 2 = 4p + 6$ $6p - 2 = 4p + 6$ **Check** $6p - 2 = 4p + 6$
                                                                                                    $\downarrow$ $\downarrow$

12. $5y - 5 = 2y + 10$ $5y - 5 = 2y + 10$ **Check** $5y - 5 = 2y + 10$
                                                                                                    $\downarrow$ $\downarrow$

13. $^-2k - 6 = 6k + 10$ $^-2k - 6 = 6k + 10$ **Check**

14. $5x + 4 = {}^-3x - 4$ $5x + 4 = {}^-3x - 4$ **Check**

15. $^-18 + 7a = 2a + 7$ $^-18 + 7a = 2a + 7$ **Check**

16. $^-9 + 2z = 9z + 12$ $^-9 + 2z = 9z + 12$ **Check**

Use the distributive property to help you solve each equation. Show your work.
See Example 3.

17. $8(w - 2) = 32$ **18.** $9(b - 4) = 27$ **19.** $^-10 = 2(y + 4)$

20. $^-3 = 3(x + 6)$ ⊕ **21.** $^-4(t + 2) = 12$ **22.** $^-5(k + 3) = 25$

23. $6(x - 5) = ^-30$ **24.** $7(r - 7) = ^-49$ **25.** $^-12 = 12(h - 2)$

26. $^-11 = 11(c - 3)$ **27.** $0 = ^-2(y + 2)$ **28.** $0 = ^-9(b + 1)$

Solve each equation. Show your work. See Example 4.

29. $6m + 18 = 0$

30. $8p - 40 = 0$

31. $6 = 9w - 12$

32. $8 = 8h + 24$

33. $5x = 3x + 10$

34. $7n = {}^-2n - 36$

35. $2a + 11 = 8a - 7$

36. $r - 10 = 10r + 8$

37. $7 - 5b = 28 + 2b$

38. $1 - 8t = {}^-9 - 3t$

39. ${}^-20 + 2k = k - 4k$

40. $6y - y = {}^-16 + y$

41. $10(c - 6) + 4 = 2 + c - 58$

42. $8(z + 7) - 6 = z + 60 - 10$

43. ${}^-18 + 13y + 3 = 3(5y - 1) - 2$

44. $3 + 5h - 9 = 4(3h + 4) - 1$

45. $6 - 4n + 3n = 20 - 35$

46. $^-19 + 8 = 6p - 7p - 5$

47. $6(c - 2) = 7(c - 6)$

48. $^-3(5 + x) = 4(x - 2)$

49. $^-5(2p + 2) - 7 = 3(2p + 5)$

50. $4(3m - 6) = 72 + 3(m - 8)$

51. $^-6b - 4b + 7b = 10 - b + 3b$

52. $w + 8 - 5w = ^-w - 15w + 11w$

53. Solve $^-2t - 10 = 3t + 5$. Show each step you take while solving it. Next to each step, write a sentence that explains what you did in that step. Be sure to tell when you used the addition property of equality and when you used the division property of equality.

54. Explain the distributive property in your own words. Show two examples of using the distributive property to remove parentheses in an expression.

55. Here is one student's solution to an equation. Show how to check the solution. If the solution doesn't check, explain the error and correct it.

$$
\begin{array}{rcl}
{}^-8 + 4a &=& 2a + 2 \\
\underline{{}^-2a} & & \underline{{}^-2a} \\
{}^-10 + 4a &=& \underline{0 + 2} \\
{}^-10 + 4a &=& 2 \\
\underline{10} & & \underline{10} \\
\underline{0 + 4a} &=& 12 \\
\dfrac{4a}{4} &=& \dfrac{12}{4} \\
a &=& 3
\end{array}
$$

56. Here is one student's solution to an equation. Show how to check the solution. If the solution doesn't check, explain the error and correct it.

$$
\begin{array}{rcl}
2(x + 4) &=& {}^-16 \\
2x + 4 &=& {}^-16 \\
\underline{{}^-4} & & \underline{{}^-4} \\
\underline{2x + 0} &=& {}^-20 \\
\dfrac{2x}{2} &=& \dfrac{{}^-20}{2} \\
x &=& {}^-10
\end{array}
$$

Relating Concepts (Exercises 57–60) For Individual or Group Work

Work Exercises 57–60 in order.

57. **(a)** Suppose that the sum of two numbers is negative and you know that one of the numbers is positive. What can you conclude about the other number?

(b) How can you tell, just by looking, that the solution to $x + 5 = {}^-7$ must be a negative number? Recall your answer from part (a).

58. **(a)** Suppose that the sum of two numbers is positive and you know that one of the numbers is negative. What can you conclude about the other number?

(b) How can you tell, just by looking, that the solution to ${}^-8 + d = 2$ must be a positive number? Recall your answer from part (a).

59. **(a)** Suppose the product of two numbers is negative and you know that one of the numbers is negative. What can you conclude about the other number?

(b) How can you tell, just by looking, that the solution to ${}^-15n = {}^-255$ must be positive?

60. **(a)** Suppose the product of two numbers is positive and you know that one of the numbers is negative. What can you conclude about the other number?

(b) How can you tell, just by looking, that the solution to $437 = {}^-23y$ must be negative?

Chapter 4  Summary

▶ Key Terms

4.1	**variable**	A variable is a letter that represents a number that varies or changes, depending on the situation.
	constant	A constant is a number that is added or subtracted in an expression. It does not vary. For example, 5 is the constant in the expression $c + 5$.
	expression	An expression expresses, or tells, the rule for doing something. It is a combination of operations on variables and numbers. An expression does *not* have an equal sign.
	evaluate the expression	To evaluate an expression, replace each variable with specific values (numbers) and follow the order of operations.
	coefficient	The number part in a multiplication expression is the coefficient. For example, 4 is the coefficient in the expression $4s$.
4.2	**simplifying expressions**	To simplify an expression, write it in a simpler way by combining all the like terms.
	term	Each addend in an expression is a term.
	variable term	A variable term has a number part (called the coefficient) multiplied by a variable part (a letter). An example is $4s$.
	like terms	Like terms are terms with exactly the same variable parts (the same letters and exponents). The coefficients may be different.
4.3	**equations**	An equation has an equal sign. It shows the relationship between what is known about a problem and what isn't known.
	solve the equation	To solve an equation, find a number that can replace the variable and make the equation balance.
	solution	A solution of an equation is a number that can replace the variable and make the equation balance.
	addition property of equality	The addition property of equality states that adding the same quantity to both sides of an equation will keep it balanced.
	check the solution	To check the solution of an equation, go back to the *original* equation and replace the variable with the solution. If the equation balances, the solution is correct.
4.4	**division property of equality**	The division property of equality states that dividing both sides of an equation by the same nonzero number will keep it balanced.

▶ Test Your Word Power

See how well you have learned the vocabulary in this chapter. Answers follow the Quick Review.

1. A **variable**
   A. can only be the letter x
   B. is never an addend in an expression
   C. is the solution of an equation
   D. represents a number that varies.

2. Which expression has 2 as a **coefficient?**
   A. x^2
   B. $2x$
   C. $x + 2$
   D. $2 - x$

3. Which expression has 4 as a **constant** term?
   A. $4y$
   B. y^4
   C. $4 + y$
   D. $\dfrac{y}{4}$

4. Which expression has four **terms?**
   A. $2 + 3x = {}^-6 + x$
   B. $2 + 3x - 6 + x$
   C. $(2)(3x)({}^-6)(x)$
   D. $2(3x) = {}^-6(x)$

5. **Like terms**
   A. can be multiplied but not added
   B. have the same coefficients
   C. have the same solutions
   D. have the same variable parts.

6. To **simplify an expression,**
   A. combine all the like terms
   B. multiply the exponents
   C. add all the numbers in the expression
   D. add the same quantity to both sides.

▶ Quick Review

Concepts	Examples

(4.1) Evaluating Expressions

Replace each variable with the specified value. Then follow the order of operations to simplify the expression.

The expression for ordering textbooks for two prealgebra classes is $2c + 10$, where c is the class limit. Evaluate the expression when the class limit is 24.

$$2c + 10 \qquad \text{Replace } c \text{ with 24.}$$
$$2 \cdot 24 + 10 \qquad \text{Multiply first.}$$
$$48 + 10 \qquad \text{Add last.}$$
$$58 \qquad \text{Order 58 books.}$$

(4.1) Using Exponents with Variables

An exponent next to a variable tells how many times to use the variable as a factor in multiplication.

Rewrite $^-6x^4$ without exponents.

$^-6x^4$ can be written as $^-6 \cdot x \cdot x \cdot x \cdot x$

Coefficient is $^-6$ — x is used as a factor 4 times.

(4.1) Evaluating Expressions with Exponents

Rewrite the expression without exponents, replace each variable with the specified value, and multiply all the factors.

Evaluate x^3y when x is $^-4$ and y is 5.

x^3y means $x \cdot x \cdot x \cdot y$ — Replace x with $^-4$ and y with 5.

$^-4 \cdot {}^-4 \cdot {}^-4 \cdot 5$ — Multiply two factors at a time.

$16 \cdot {}^-4 \cdot 5$

$^-64 \cdot 5$

$^-320$

(4.2) Identifying Like Terms

Like terms have *exactly* the same letters and exponents. The coefficients may be different.

List the like terms in this expression. Then identify the coefficients of the like terms.

$$^-3b + {}^-3b^2 + 3ab + b + 3$$

The like terms are ^-3b and b. The coefficient of ^-3b is $^-3$, and the coefficient of b is understood to be 1.

(4.2) Combining Like Terms

Step 1 If there are any variable terms with no coefficient, write in the understood 1.

Step 2 Change any subtractions to adding the opposite.

Step 3 Find like terms.

Step 4 Add the coefficients of like terms, keeping the variable part the same.

Simplify $4x^2 - 10 + x^2 + 15$.

Write understood 1.

$4x^2 - 10 + 1x^2 + 15$ — Change subtraction to adding the opposite.

$4x^2 + {}^-10 + 1x^2 + 15$

$4x^2 + 1x^2 + {}^-10 + 15$ — Combine $4x^2 + 1x^2$. The variable part stays the same. Also combine $^-10 + 15$.

$(4 + 1)x^2 + 5$

$5x^2 + 5$

The simplified expression is $5x^2 + 5$.

Concepts

4.2 Simplifying Multiplication Expressions

Use the associative property to rewrite the expression so that the two number parts can be multiplied. The variable part stays the same.

4.2 Using the Distributive Property

Multiplication distributes over addition and over subtraction. Be careful to multiply *every* term inside the parentheses by the number outside the parentheses.

4.3 Solving and Checking Equations Using the Addition Property of Equality

If possible, *simplify* the expression on one or both sides of the equal sign.

Next, to get the variable by itself on one side of the equal sign, *add* the same number to both sides.

Finally, *check* the solution by going back to the original equation and replacing the variable with the solution. If the equation balances, the solution is correct.

Examples

Simplify: $^-7(5k)$
Use the associative property of multiplication.

$^-7 \cdot (5 \cdot k)$ can be written as $(^-7 \cdot 5) \cdot k$

$$\underbrace{}_{^-35} \cdot k$$

$$\underbrace{}_{^-35k}$$

The simplified expression is ^-35k.

Simplify.

(a) $6(w - 4)$ can be written as $\underbrace{6 \cdot w}_{6w} - \underbrace{6 \cdot 4}_{24}$

The simplified expression is $6w - 24$.

(b) $^-3(2b + 5)$ can be written as $\underbrace{^-3 \cdot 2b}_{^-6b} + \underbrace{^-3 \cdot 5}_{^-15}$

Use the definition of subtraction "in reverse" to write $^-6b + ^-15$ as $^-6b - 15$.

The simplified expression is $^-6b - 15$.

Solve this equation and check the solution.

$$
\begin{array}{rcl}
\underbrace{^-5 + 8}_{} & = & 9 + r \\
3 & = & 9 + r \\
\underline{^-9} & & \underline{^-9} \\
^-6 & = & \underbrace{0 + r}_{} \\
^-6 & = & r
\end{array}
$$

Simplify the left side by adding $^-5 + 8$.
To get r by itself, add the opposite of 9, which is $^-9$, to both sides.

The solution is $^-6$.

Check $^-5 + 8 = 9 + r$ Use the original equation and replace r with $^-6$.

$$^-5 + 8 = 9 + {^-6}$$

$$\underbrace{}_{3} = \underbrace{}_{3}$$ Balances

When r is replaced with $^-6$, the equation balances, so $^-6$ is the correct solution (**not** 3).

Concepts

Examples

4.4 Solving and Checking Equations Using the Division Property of Equality

If possible, *simplify* the expression on one or both sides of the equal sign.

Next, to get the variable by itself on one side of the equal sign, *divide* both sides by the coefficient of the variable term.

Finally, *check* the solution by going back to the original equation and replacing the variable with the solution. If the equation balances, the solution is correct.

Solve this equation and check the solution.

Simplify the left side. Change subtraction to adding the opposite.

$$2h - 6h = 18 + 22$$

Simplify the right side; add $18 + 22$.

$$2h + {}^-6h = 40$$

Divide by ${}^-4$, the coefficient of ${}^-4h$.

$$\frac{{}^-4h}{{}^-4} = \frac{40}{{}^-4}$$

Also divide 40 by ${}^-4$ to keep the balance.

$$h = {}^-10$$

The solution is ${}^-10$.

Check

$$2h - 6h = 18 + 22$$
$$2({}^-10) - 6({}^-10) = 40$$
$${}^-20 - {}^-60 = 40$$
$${}^-20 + {}^+60$$
$$40 = 40$$

Original equation; replace h with ${}^-10$.

Balances

When h is replaced with ${}^-10$, the equation balances, so ${}^-10$ is the correct solution (**not** 40).

4.4 Solving Equations Such as ${}^-x = 5$

As the last step in solving an equation, do **not** leave a negative sign in front of the variable, such as ${}^-x = 5$, because ${}^-x$ is **not** the same as x. Divide both sides by ${}^-1$, the understood coefficient of ${}^-x$.

Solve this equation and check the solution.

$$9 = {}^-n$$

Write the understood ${}^-1$ as the coefficient of n.

$$9 = {}^-n \quad \text{can be written as} \quad 9 = {}^-1n$$

Now divide both sides by ${}^-1$.

$$\frac{9}{{}^-1} = \frac{{}^-1n}{{}^-1}$$

$${}^-9 = n$$

The solution is ${}^-9$.

Check

$$9 = {}^-n \quad \text{Original equation}$$
$$9 = {}^-1n \quad \text{Write understood } {}^-1.$$
$$9 = {}^-1({}^-9) \quad \text{Replace } n \text{ with } {}^-9.$$
$$9 = 9 \quad \text{Balances}$$

When n is replaced with ${}^-9$, the equation balances, so ${}^-9$ is the correct solution (**not** 9).

Concepts	Examples

4.5 Solving Equations with Several Steps

Solve this equation and check the solution.

Step 1   If possible, use the distributive property to remove parentheses.

Step 1 $3 + 2(y + 8) = 5y + 4$

Step 2   Combine any like terms on the left side of the equal sign. Combine any like terms on the right side of the equal sign.

Step 2 $3 + 2y + 16 = 5y + 4$

$$2y + 19 = 5y + 4$$

Step 3   Add the same amount to both sides of the equation so that the variable term ends up by itself on one side of the equal sign, and a number is by itself on the other side. You may have to do this step more than once.

Step 3
$$\begin{array}{cc} {}^{-}2y & {}^{-}2y \\ \hline 0 + 19 = & 3y + 4 \end{array}$$

Step 3
$$\begin{array}{cc} {}^{-}4 & {}^{-}4 \\ \hline 0 + 15 = & 3y + 0 \end{array}$$

Step 4   Divide both sides by the coefficient of the variable term to find the solution.

Step 4
$$\frac{15}{3} = \frac{3y}{3}$$

$$5 = y$$

The solution is 5.

Step 5   Check the solution by going back to the original equation. Replace the variable with the solution. If the equation balances, the solution is correct.

Check
Step 5
$3 + 2(y + 8) = 5y + 4$ Original equation

$3 + 2(5 + 8) = 5(5) + 4$

$3 + 2(13) = 25 + 4$

$3 + 26 = 29$

$29 = 29$ Balances

When y is replaced with 5, the equation balances, so 5 is the correct solution (**not** 29).

ANSWERS TO TEST YOUR WORD POWER

1. D; *Example:* In $c + 5$, the variable is c.
2. B; *Example:* $2y^3$ and $2n$ also have 2 as a coefficient.
3. C; *Example:* $^{-}5a^2 + 4$ also has 4 as a constant term.
4. B; *Example:* $3y^2 - 6y + 2y - 5$ also has four terms. Choices (A) and (D) are equations, not expressions; choice (C) has four *factors*.
5. D; *Example:* $7n^2$ and $^{-}3n^2$ are like terms.
6. A; *Example:* To simplify $4a - 9 + 6a$, combine $4a$ and $6a$ by adding the coefficients. The simplified expression is $10a - 9$.

Math in the Media

ALGEBRAIC EXPRESSIONS AND TUITION COSTS

Algebraic expressions are useful in the real world whenever the same set of instructions is repeated for different choices of numbers. Calculating college tuition and fees is an example. The information below is for "resident of the district" students at North Harris Montgomery Community College District (NHMCCD) in Texas.

Fees Required at NHMCCD, Spring 2008

[*Residents of the district pay*] tuition at the rate of $36 per credit hour, a $6 per credit hour technology fee, a $2 per credit hour student activity fee, a $2 per credit hour general use fee, and a registration fee of $12.

1. Calculate the tuition and fees for a student who is a resident of the district and who enrolls at NHMCCD for the number of credit hours listed in parts **(a)**, **(b)**, and **(c)** below. Then, for part **(d)**, let x represent the number of credit hours. Pay attention to the *process* you used in your calculations so that you can write the algebraic expression for x credit hours.

    (a) 3 credit hours: _____

    (b) 9 credit hours: _____

    (c) 12 credit hours: _____

    (d) x credit hours: _____ dollars

Write the algebraic expression that represents the tuition and fees for each institution for one semester. Let x represent the number of credit hours.

Institution/Web Site	Description of Tuition and Fees	Algebraic Expression
2. American River College, California Nonresident student www.arc.losrios.edu	Enrollment: $20 per credit hour Parking: $30 per semester Additional nonresident enrollment: $193 per credit hour Student representation fee: $1 per semester	
3. Austin Community College, Texas Out-of-district student www.austincc.edu	Tuition: $39 per credit hour General fee: $13 per credit hour Parking: $5 per semester Additional out-of-district tuition: $79 per credit hour Student activity fee: $2 per credit hour	
4. Valdosta State University, Georgia In-state student www.valdosta.edu	Tuition: $124 per credit hour Health fee: $87 per semester Student activity fee: $209 per semester Athletics fee: $116 per semester Technology fee: $48 per semester Parking fee: $50 per semester	

5. List the tuition and fees for your college. Then write an algebraic expression using x to represent the number of credit hours.

Source: www.nhmdd.edu

Chapter 4 ▶▶▶ Review Exercises

[4.1]

1. (a) Identify the variable, the coefficient, and the constant in this expression.

$$^-3 + 4k$$

(b) Circle the expression that has 20 as the constant term and $^-9$ as the coefficient.

$20m - 9$ $\qquad$ $^-9 + 20x$

$^-9y + 20$ $\qquad$ $20 + 9n$

3. Rewrite each expression without exponents.

(a) x^2y^4

(b) $5ab^3$

2. The expression for ordering test tubes for a chemistry lab is $4c + 10$, where c is the class limit. Evaluate the expression when

(a) the class limit is 15.

(b) the class limit is 24.

4. Evaluate each expression when m is 2, n is $^-3$, and p is 4.

(a) n^2 $\qquad$ **(b)** n^3

(c) $^-4mp^2$ $\qquad$ **(d)** $5m^4n^2$

[4.2] *Simplify.*

5. $ab + ab^2 + 2ab$

6. $^-3x + 2y - x - 7$

7. $^-8(^-2g^3)$

8. $4(3r^2t)$

9. $5(k + 2)$

10. $^-2(3b + 4)$

11. $3(2y - 4) + 12$

12. $^-4 + 6(4x + 1) - 4x$

13. Write an expression with four terms that *cannot* be simplified.

[4.3] *Solve each equation and check each solution.*

14. $16 + n = 5$ $\qquad$ **Check** $\quad 16 + \quad n \ = 5$

15. $^-4 + 2 = 2a - 6 - a$ $\qquad$ **Check**

$$^-4 + 2 = 2a \quad - \ 6 \ - \ 4$$

[4.4] *Solve each equation. Show your work.*

16. $48 = {}^-6m$

17. $k - 5k = {}^-40$

18. $^-17 + 11 + 6 = 7t$

19. $^-2p + 5p = 3 - 21$

20. $^-30 = 3(^-5r)$

21. $12 = ^-h$

[4.5] *Solve each equation. Show your work.*

22. $12w - 4 = 8w + 12$

23. $0 = ^-4(c + 2)$

24. Every Wednesday is "treat day" at the office. The person who brings the treats buys two treat items for each employee plus four extras. If Roger brings 34 doughnuts, solve the equation $34 = 2n + 4$ to find the number of employees.

> > > **Mixed Review Exercises**

Solve each equation. Show your work.

25. $12 + 7a = 4a - 3$

26. $^-2(p - 3) = ^-14$

27. $10y = 6y + 20$

28. $2m - 7m = 5 - 20$

29. $20 = 3x - 7$

30. $b + 6 = 3b - 8$

31. $z + 3 = 0$

32. $3(2n - 1) = 3(n + 3)$

33. $^-4 + 46 = 7(^-3t + 6)$

34. $6 + 10d - 19 = 2(3d + 4) - 1$

35. $^-4(3b + 9) = 24 + 3(2b - 8)$

1. Identify the parts of this expression: $^-7w + 6$
Choose from these labels: variable, constant, coefficient.

1. _____

2. The expression for buying hot dogs for the company picnic is $3a + 2c$, where a is the number of adults and c is the number of children. Evaluate the expression when there are 45 adults and 21 children.

2. _____

Rewrite each expression without exponents.

3. x^5y^3

4. $4ab^4$

3. _____

4. _____

5. Evaluate $^-2s^2t$ when s is $^-5$ and t is 4.

5. _____

Simplify each expression.

6. $3w^3 - 8w^3 + w^3$

7. $xy - xy$

6. _____

7. _____

8. $^-6c - 5 + 7c + 5$

9. $3m^2 - 3m + 3mn$

8. _____

9. _____

10. $^-10(4b^2)$

11. $^-5(^-3k)$

10. _____

11. _____

12. $7(3t + 4)$

13. $^-4(a + 6)$

12. _____

13. _____

14. $^-8 + 6(x - 2) + 5$

15. $^-9b - c - 3 + 9 + 2c$

14. _____

15. _____

Solve each equation and check each solution.

16. _____

17. _____

18. _____

19. _____

16. $^-4 = x - 9$ **Check**

17. $^-7w = 77$ **Check**

18. $^-p = 14$ **Check**

19. $^-15 = ^-3(a + 2)$ **Check**

Solve each equation. Show your work.

20. _____

21. _____

22. _____

23. _____

24. _____

25. _____

20. $6n + 8 - 5n = ^-4 + 4$

21. $5 - 20 = 2m - 3m$

22. $^-2x + 2 = 5x + 9$

23. $3m - 5 = 7m - 13$

24. $2 + 7b - 44 = ^-3b + 12 + 9b$

25. $3c - 24 = 6(c - 4)$

26. _____

26. Write an equation that requires the *addition* property of equality to solve it and has $^-4$ as its solution. Then write a different equation that requires the *division* property of equality to solve it and has $^-4$ as its solution. Show how to solve each equation.

4.6 ▶▶▶ Problem Solving: Perimeter

OBJECTIVE **1** **Use the formula for perimeter of a square to find the perimeter or the length of one side.**   If you have ever studied geometry, you probably used several different formulas such as $P = 2l + 2w$ and $A = lw$. A **formula** is just a shorthand way of writing a rule for solving a particular type of problem. A formula uses variables (letters) and it has an equal sign, so it is an equation. That means you can use the equation-solving techniques you learned in **Chapter 4** to work with formulas.

But let's start at the beginning. Geometry was developed centuries ago when people needed a way to measure land. The name *geometry* comes from the Greek words *ge,* meaning earth, and *metron,* meaning measure. Today we still use geometry to measure land. It is also important in architecture, construction, navigation, art and design, physics, chemistry, and astronomy. You can use geometry at home when you buy carpet or wallpaper, hang a picture, or do home repairs. In this chapter you'll learn about two basic ideas, perimeter and area. Other geometry concepts will appear in later chapters.

In **Section 4.1**, you found the *perimeter* of a square garden.

> **Perimeter**
> The distance around the outside edges of any flat shape is called the **perimeter** of the shape.

To review, a **square** has four sides that are all the same length. Also, the sides meet to form *right angles,* which measure 90° (90 degrees). This means that the sides form "square corners." Two examples of squares are shown below.

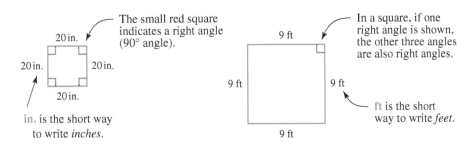

To find the *perimeter* of a square, we can "unfold" the shape so the four sides lie end-to-end, as shown below.

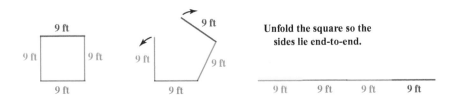

Now we can see the total length of the four sides. The total length is the *perimeter* of the square. We can find the perimeter by adding.

$$\text{Perimeter} = 9 \text{ ft} + 9 \text{ ft} + 9 \text{ ft} + 9 \text{ ft} = 36 \text{ ft}$$

A shorter way is to multiply the length of one side times 4, because all 4 sides are the same length.

OBJECTIVES

1 Use the formula for perimeter of a square to find the perimeter or the length of one side.

2 Use the formula for perimeter of a rectangle to find the perimeter, the length, or the width.

3 Find the perimeter of parallelograms, triangles, and irregular shapes.

1 Find the perimeter of each square, using the appropriate formula.

(a) The 20 in. square shown on the previous page

(b) A square measuring 14 miles (14 mi) on each side (*Hint:* Draw a sketch of the square and label each side with its length.)

2 Use the perimeter of each square and the appropriate formula to find the length of one side. Then check your solution by drawing a square, labeling each side, and finding the perimeter.

(a) Perimeter is 28 in.

(b) Perimeter is 100 ft.

(c) Perimeter is 64 cm.

ANSWERS

1. **(a)** $P = 80$ in.
   (b) $P = 56$ miles

14 mi
14 mi | 14 mi
14 mi

2. **(a)** $s = 7$ in.

7 in.
7 in. | 7 in.
7 in.

Check
$P = 7$ in. $+ 7$ in. $+ 7$ in. $+ 7$ in. $= 28$ in.

   (b) $s = 25$ ft

25 ft
25 ft | 25 ft
25 ft

Check
$P = 25$ ft $+ 25$ ft $+ 25$ ft $+ 25$ ft $= 100$ ft

   (c) $s = 16$ cm

16 cm
16 cm | 16 cm
16 cm

Check
$P = 16$ cm $+ 16$ cm $+ 16$ cm $+ 16$ cm $= 64$ cm

Finding the Perimeter of a Square

Perimeter of a square $=$ side $+$ side $+$ side $+$ side

or $\quad P = 4 \cdot$ side

$$P = 4s$$

EXAMPLE 1 **Finding the Perimeter of a Square**

Find the perimeter of the square on the previous page that measures 9 ft on each side.

Use the formula for perimeter of a square, $P = 4s$. You know that for this particular square, the value of s is 9 ft.

$P = 4s \qquad$ Formula for perimeter of a square

$P = 4 \cdot 9$ ft $\qquad$ Replace s with 9 ft. Multiply 4 times 9 ft.

$P = \quad 36$ ft $\qquad$ Write 36 ft; ft is the unit of measure.

The perimeter of the square is 36 ft. Notice that this answer matches the result obtained from adding the four sides.

◀ *Work Problem* **1** *at the Side.*

EXAMPLE 2 **Finding the Length of One Side of a Square**

If the perimeter of a square is 40 cm, find the length of one side. (Note: **cm** is the short way to write *centimeters*.)

Use the formula for perimeter of a square, $P = 4s$. This time you know that the value of P (the perimeter) is 40 cm.

$P = 4s \qquad$ Formula for perimeter of a square

40 cm $= 4s \qquad$ Replace P with 40 cm

$\dfrac{40 \text{ cm}}{4} = \dfrac{4s}{4} \qquad$ To get the variable by itself on the right side, divide both sides by 4.

10 cm $= s$

The length of one side of the square is 10 cm. Write **cm** as part of your answer.

Check Check the solution by drawing a square and labeling the length of each side as 10 cm. The perimeter is 10 cm $+ 10$ cm $+ 10$ cm $+ 10$ cm $= 40$ cm. This result matches the perimeter given in the problem.

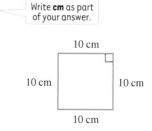

10 cm
10 cm | 10 cm
10 cm

◀ *Work Problem* **2** *at the Side.*

OBJECTIVE **2** **Use the formula for perimeter of a rectangle to find the perimeter, the length, or the width.** A **rectangle** is a figure with four sides that meet to form right angles, which measure 90°. Each set of opposite sides is parallel and congruent (has the same length). Three examples of rectangles are shown below.

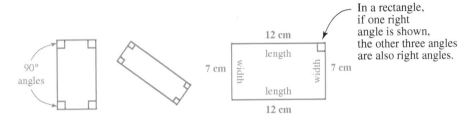

3 Find the perimeter of each rectangle using the appropriate formula. Check your solutions by adding the lengths of the four sides.

(a)

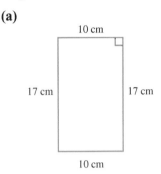

Each longer side of a rectangle is called the length (*l*) and each shorter side is called the width (*w*).

Look at the rectangle above with the lengths of the sides labeled. To find the perimeter (distance around), you could unfold the shape so the sides lie end-to-end. Then add the lengths of the sides.

$$P = 12 \text{ cm} + 7 \text{ cm} + 12 \text{ cm} + 7 \text{ cm} = 38 \text{ cm}$$

or $P = 12 \text{ cm} + 12 \text{ cm} + 7 \text{ cm} + 7 \text{ cm} = 38 \text{ cm}$ Commutative property

Because the two long sides are both 12 cm, and the two short sides are both 7 cm, you can also use the formula below.

(b) A rectangle 6 m wide and 11 m long (*Hint:* First draw a sketch of the rectangle and label the length of each side.)

Finding the Perimeter of a Rectangle

Perimeter of a rectangle = length + length + width + width

$$P = (2 \cdot \text{length}) + (2 \cdot \text{width})$$
$$P = 2l + 2w$$

EXAMPLE 3 **Finding the Perimeter of a Rectangle**

Find the perimeter of this rectangle.

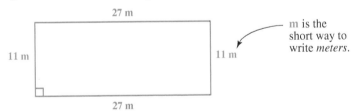

The length is **27 m**, and the width is **11 m**.

$$P = 2l + 2w \qquad \text{Replace } l \text{ with 27 m and } w \text{ with 11 m.}$$
$$P = 2 \cdot 27 \text{ m} + 2 \cdot 11 \text{ m} \qquad \text{Do the multiplications first.}$$
$$P = 54 \text{ m} + 22 \text{ m} \qquad \text{Add last.}$$
$$P = 76 \text{ m}$$

The perimeter of the rectangle (the distance you would walk around the outside edges of the rectangle) is 76 m.

Check To check the solution, add the lengths of the four sides.

$$P = 27 \text{ m} + 27 \text{ m} + 11 \text{ m} + 11 \text{ m}$$
$$P = 76 \text{ m} \qquad \text{Matches the solution above}$$

Work Problem **3** *at the Side.* ▶

(c)

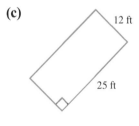

ANSWERS

3. (a) $P = 54$ cm
   Check 17 cm + 17 cm + 10 cm + 10 cm = 54 cm
(b)

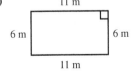

   $P = 34$ m
   Check
   11 m + 11 m + 6 m + 6 m = 34 m
(c) $P = 74$ ft
   Check
   25 ft + 25 ft + 12 ft + 12 ft = 74 ft

4   Use the perimeter of each rectangle and the appropriate formula to find the length or width. Draw a sketch of each rectangle and use it to check your solution.

(a) The perimeter of a rectangle is 36 in. and the width is 8 in. Find the length.

(b) A rectangle has a width of 4 cm. The perimeter is 32 cm. Find the length.

(c) A rectangle with a perimeter of 14 ft has a length of 6 ft. Find the width.

EXAMPLE 4   **Finding the Length or Width of a Rectangle**

If the perimeter of a rectangle is 20 ft and the width is 3 ft, find the length.

First draw a sketch of the rectangle and label the widths as 3 ft.

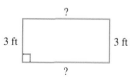

Then use the formula for perimeter of a rectangle, $P = 2l + 2w$. The value of P is 20 ft and the value of w is 3 ft.

$$P = 2l + 2w \qquad \text{Formula for perimeter of a rectangle}$$

$$20 \text{ ft} = 2l + \underline{2 \cdot 3 \text{ ft}} \qquad \begin{array}{l}\text{Replace } P \text{ with 20 ft and } w \text{ with 3 ft.}\\ \text{Simplify the right side by multiplying } 2 \cdot 3 \text{ ft.}\end{array}$$

$$\begin{array}{ll} 20 \text{ ft} = 2l + & 6 \text{ ft} \\ \underline{{}^-6 \text{ ft}} \qquad \underline{{}^-6 \text{ ft}} & \\ 14 \text{ ft} = 2l + & 0 \end{array} \qquad \begin{array}{l}\text{To get } 2l \text{ by itself, add } {}^-6 \text{ ft to both sides:}\\ 6 + {}^-6 \text{ is 0.}\end{array}$$

$$\frac{14 \text{ ft}}{2} = \frac{2l}{2} \qquad \text{To get } l \text{ by itself, divide both sides by 2.}$$

$$7 \text{ ft} = l$$

The length is 7 ft.   Write **ft** as part of your answer.

Check   To check the solution, put the length measurements on your sketch. Then add the four measurements.

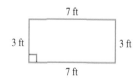

$$P = 7 \text{ ft} + 7 \text{ ft} + 3 \text{ ft} + 3 \text{ ft}$$
$$P = 20 \text{ ft}$$

A perimeter of 20 ft matches the information in the original problem, so 7 ft is the correct length of the rectangle.

◀ *Work Problem* **4** *at the Side.*

OBJECTIVE 3 Find the perimeter of parallelograms, triangles, and irregular shapes.   A **parallelogram** is a four-sided figure in which opposite sides are both parallel and equal in length. Some examples are shown below. Notice that opposite sides have the same length.

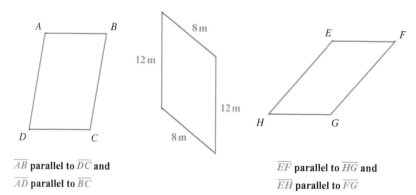

$\overline{AB}$ **parallel to** $\overline{DC}$ **and**
$\overline{AD}$ **parallel to** $\overline{BC}$

$\overline{EF}$ **parallel to** $\overline{HG}$ **and**
$\overline{EH}$ **parallel to** $\overline{FG}$

Perimeter is the distance around a flat shape, so the easiest way to find the perimeter of a parallelogram is to add the lengths of the four sides.

ANSWERS

4. **(a)** $l = 10$ in.

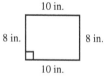

Check   10 in. + 10 in. + 8 in. + 8 in. = 36 in.

(b) $l = 12$ cm

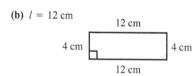

Check   12 cm + 12 cm + 4 cm + 4 cm = 32 cm

(c) $w = 1$ ft

1 ft — 6 ft — 1 ft   (6 ft)

Check   6 ft + 6 ft + 1 ft + 1 ft = 14 ft

EXAMPLE 5   **Finding the Perimeter of a Parallelogram**

Find the perimeter of the middle parallelogram on the previous page.

$$P = 12 \text{ m} + 12 \text{ m} + 8 \text{ m} + 8 \text{ m}$$
$$P = 40 \text{ m}$$

Work Problem **5** *at the Side.* ▶

A **triangle** is a figure with exactly three sides. Some examples are shown below.

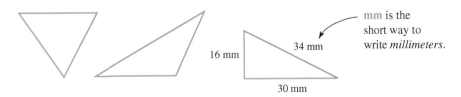

mm is the short way to write *millimeters.*

To find the perimeter of a triangle (the distance around the edges), add the lengths of the three sides.

EXAMPLE 6   **Finding the Perimeter of a Triangle**

Find the perimeter of the triangle above on the right.

To find the perimeter, add the lengths of the sides.

$$P = 16 \text{ mm} + 30 \text{ mm} + 34 \text{ mm}$$
$$P = 80 \text{ mm}$$

Work Problem **6** *at the Side.* ▶

As with any other shape, you can find the perimeter of (distance around) an irregular shape by adding the lengths of the sides.

EXAMPLE 7   **Finding the Perimeter of an Irregular Shape**

The floor of a room has the shape shown below.

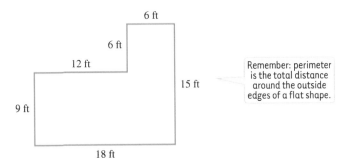

Remember: perimeter is the total distance around the outside edges of a flat shape.

Suppose you want to put a new wallpaper border along the top of all the walls. How much material do you need?

Find the perimeter of the room by adding the lengths of the sides.

$$P = 9 \text{ ft} + 12 \text{ ft} + 6 \text{ ft} + 6 \text{ ft} + 15 \text{ ft} + 18 \text{ ft}$$
$$P = 66 \text{ ft}$$

You need 66 ft of wallpaper border.

Work Problem **7** *at the Side.* ▶

---

5 Find the perimeter of each parallelogram.

(a)

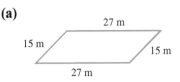

(b)

6 Find the perimeter of each triangle.

(a)

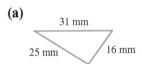

(b) A triangle with sides that each measure 5 in. Draw a sketch of the triangle and label the length of each side.

7 How much fencing will be needed to go around a flower bed with the measurements shown below?

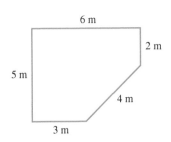

ANSWERS

5. **(a)** $P = 84$ m   **(b)** $P = 18$ ft
6. **(a)** $P = 72$ mm
   (b) $P = 15$ in.
7. 20 m of fencing are needed.

Find the perimeter of each square, using the appropriate formula. See Example 1.

1.

2.
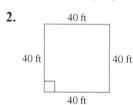

3.
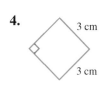

4.
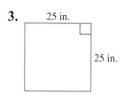

Draw a sketch of each square and label the lengths of the sides. Then find the perimeter. (Sketches may vary; show your sketches to your instructor.)

5. A square park measuring 1 mile on each side

6. A square garden measuring 4 meters on each side

7. A 22 mm square postage stamp

8. A 10 in. square piece of cardboard

For the given perimeter of each square, find the length of one side using the appropriate formula. See Example 2.

9. The perimeter is 120 ft.

10. The perimeter is 52 cm.

11. The perimeter is 4 mm.

12. The perimeter is 20 miles.

13. A square parking lot with a perimeter of 92 yards

14. A square building with a perimeter of 144 meters

15. A square closet with a perimeter of 8 ft

16. A square bedroom with a perimeter of 44 ft

Find the perimeter of each rectangle, using the appropriate formula. Check your solutions by adding the lengths of the four sides. See Example 3.

17.
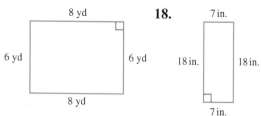

18.
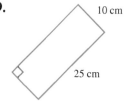

19.
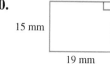

20.
15 mm
19 mm

Draw a sketch of each rectangle and label the lengths of the sides. Then find the perimeter by using the appropriate formula. (Sketches may vary; show your sketches to your instructor.)

21. A rectangular living room 20 ft long by 16 ft wide

22. A rectangular placemat 45 cm long by 30 cm wide

23. An 8 in. by 5 in. rectangular piece of paper

24. A 2 ft by 3 ft rectangular window

For each rectangle, you are given the perimeter and either the length or width. Find the unknown measurement using the appropriate formula. Draw a sketch of each rectangle and use it to check your solution. See Example 4. (Show your sketches to your instructor.)

25. The perimeter is 30 cm and the width is 6 cm.

26. The perimeter is 48 yards and the length is 14 yards.

27. The length is 4 miles and the perimeter is 10 miles.

28. The width is 8 meters and the perimeter is 34 meters.

29. A 6 ft long rectangular table has a perimeter of 16 ft.

30. A 13 in. wide rectangular picture frame has a perimeter of 56 in.

31. A rectangular door 1 meter wide has a perimeter of 6 meters.

32. A rectangular house 33 ft long has a perimeter of 118 ft.

In exercises 33–44, find the perimeter of each shape. The figures in Exercises 33–36 are parallelograms. See Examples 5–7.

33.

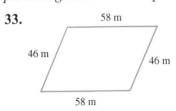

34.

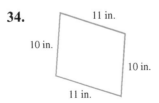

35.

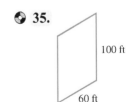

36.

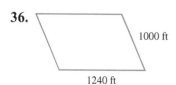

1000 ft

1240 ft

37.

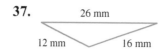

26 mm

12 mm   16 mm

38.

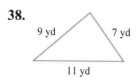

9 yd   7 yd

11 yd

39.

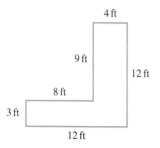

4 ft

9 ft

12 ft

8 ft

3 ft

12 ft

40.

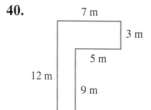

7 m

3 m

5 m

12 m

9 m

2 m

41.

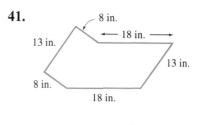

8 in.

13 in.   ←— 18 in. —→

8 in.   13 in.

18 in.

42.

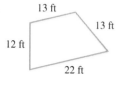

13 ft

13 ft

12 ft

22 ft

☻ 43.

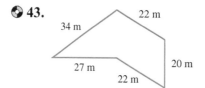

22 m

34 m

27 m   20 m

22 m

44.

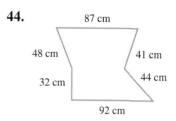

87 cm

48 cm   41 cm

32 cm   44 cm

92 cm

For each shape you are given the perimeter and the lengths of all sides except one.
Find the length of the unlabeled side.

45. The perimeter is 115 cm.

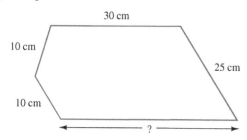

30 cm

10 cm

25 cm

10 cm

?

46. The perimeter is 63 in.

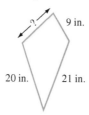

?   9 in.

20 in.   21 in.

47. The perimeter is 78 in.

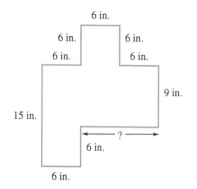

6 in.

6 in.   6 in.

6 in.   6 in.

9 in.

15 in.

?

6 in.

6 in.

48. The perimeter is 196 ft.

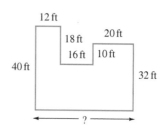

12 ft

18 ft   20 ft

16 ft   10 ft

40 ft   32 ft

?

49. In an *equilateral* triangle, all sides have the same length.

   (a) Draw sketches of four different equilateral triangles, label the lengths of the sides, and find the perimeters.

   (b) Write a "shortcut" rule (a formula) for finding the perimeter of an equilateral triangle.

   (c) Will your formula work for other kinds of triangles that are not equilateral? Explain why or why not.

50. Be sure that you have done Exercise 49 first.

   (a) Draw a sketch of a figure with five sides of equal length. Write a "shortcut" rule (a formula) for finding the perimeter of this shape.

   (b) Draw a sketch of a figure with six sides of equal length. Write a formula for finding the perimeter of the shape.

   (c) Write a formula for finding the perimeter of a shape with 10 sides of equal length.

   (d) Write a formula for finding the perimeter of a shape with *n* sides of equal length.

Relating Concepts (Exercises 51–54) For Individual or Group Work

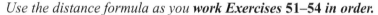

A formula that has many uses for drivers is d = rt, called the distance formula. If you are driving a car, then

        d is the *distance* you travel (how many miles)
        r is the *rate* (how fast you are driving in miles per hour)
        t is the *time* (how many hours you drive).

*Use the distance formula as you **work Exercises 51–54 in order.***

51. Suppose you are driving on Interstate highways at an average rate of 70 miles per hour. Use the distance formula to find out how far you will travel in **(a)** 2 hours; **(b)** 5 hours; **(c)** 8 hours.

52. If an ice storm slows your driving rate to 35 miles per hour, how far will you travel in **(a)** 2 hours, **(b)** 5 hours, **(c)** 8 hours? Show how to find each answer using the formula. **(d)** Explain how to find each answer using the results from Exercise 51 instead of the formula.

53. Use the distance formula to find out how many hours you would have to drive to travel the 3000 miles from Boston to San Francisco if your average rate is **(a)** 60 miles per hour; **(b)** 50 miles per hour; **(c)** 20 miles per hour (which was the speed limit 100 years ago).

54. Use the distance formula to find the average driving rate (speed) on each of these trips. (Distances are from *World Almanac.*)

   (a) It took 11 hours to drive 671 miles from Atlanta to Chicago.

   (b) Sam drove 1539 miles from New York City to Dallas in 27 hours.

   (c) Carlita drove 16 hours to travel 1040 miles from Memphis to Denver.

4.7 ▶▶▶ Problem Solving: Area

OBJECTIVE 1 Use the formula for area of a rectangle to find the area, the length, or the width.

> **Understanding the Difference between Perimeter and Area**
> **Perimeter** is the *distance around the outside edges* of a flat shape.
> **Area** is the amount of *surface inside* a flat shape.

The *perimeter* of a rectangle is the distance around the *outside edges*. Recall that we unfolded a shape and laid the sides end-to-end so we could see the total distance. The *area* of a rectangle is the amount of surface *inside* the rectangle. We measure area by finding the number of squares of a certain size needed to cover the surface inside the rectangle. Think of covering the floor of a living room with carpet. Carpet is measured in square yards, that is, square pieces that measure 1 yard along each side. Here is a drawing of a rectangular living room floor.

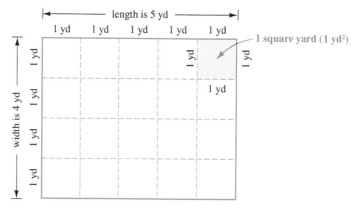

You can see from the drawing that it takes 20 squares to cover the floor. We say that the area of the floor is 20 *square yards*. A short way to write square yards is yd².

20 **square yards** can be written as 20 yd²

To find the number of squares, you can count them, or you can multiply the number of squares in the length (5) times the number of squares in the width (4) to get 20. The formula is given below.

> **Finding the Area of a Rectangle**
> Area of a rectangle = length • width
> $$A = lw$$
> Remember to use *square units* when measuring area.

Squares of many sizes can be used to measure area. For smaller areas, you might use the ones shown at the right.

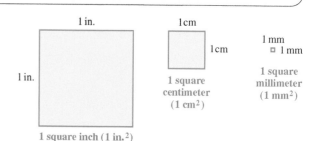

Actual-size drawings

Other sizes of squares that are often used to measure area are listed here, but they are too large to draw on this page.

1 square meter (1 m²)
1 square kilometer (1 km²)

1 square foot (1 ft²)
1 square yard (1 yd²)
1 square mile (1 mi²)

CAUTION
The raised 2 in 4² means that you multiply 4 • 4 to get 16. The raised 2 in cm² or yd² is a short way to write the word "square." It means that you multiplied cm times cm to get cm², or yd times yd to get yd². Recall that a short way to write $x \cdot x$ is x^2. Similarly, cm • cm is cm². When you see 5 cm², say "five square centimeters." Do *not* multiply 5 • 5, because the exponent applies only to the *first* thing to its immediate left. The exponent applies to cm, *not* to the number.

> **EXAMPLE 1**   **Finding the Area of Rectangles**

Find the area of each rectangle.

(a)

Each small square in this figure represents 1 square meter, written as 1 m². You could count all the squares to find the total area of 104 m².

8 m

13 m

The length of this rectangle is 13 m and the width is 8 m. Use the formula $A = lw$, which means $A = l \cdot w$.

$A = \quad l \quad \cdot \quad w$ ⟶ Replace *l* with 13 m and *w* with 8 m.

$A = 13 \text{ m} \cdot 8 \text{ m}$ Multiply 13 times 8 to get 104.

$A = 104 \text{ m}^2$ Multiply m times m to get m².

The area of the rectangle is 104 m². If you count the number of squares in the sketch, you will also get 104 m². Each square in the sketch represents 1 m by 1 m, which is 1 square meter (1 m²).

(b) A rectangle measuring 7 cm by 21 cm
First make a sketch of the rectangle. The length is 21 cm (the longer measurement) and the width is 7 cm. Then use the formula for area of a rectangle, $A = lw$.

7 cm

21 cm

$A = \quad l \quad \cdot \quad w$ Replace *l* with 21 cm and *w* with 7 cm.

$A = 21 \text{ cm} \cdot 7 \text{ cm}$ Multiply 21 • 7 to get 147.

$A = 147 \text{ cm}^2$ Multiply cm • cm to get cm².

The area of the rectangle is 147 cm².

Work Problem **1** *at the Side.* ▶

CAUTION
The units for *area* will always be *square* units (cm², m², yd², mi², and so on). The units for *perimeter* will always be *linear* units (cm, m, yd, mi, and so on), *not* square units.

1 Find the area of each rectangle, using the appropriate formula.

(a)

9 ft

4 ft   4 ft

9 ft

(b) A rectangle is 35 yd long and 20 yd wide. (First make a sketch of the rectangle and label the lengths of the sides.)

(c) A rectangular patio measures 3 m by 2 m. (First make a sketch of the patio and label the lengths of the sides.)

ANSWERS

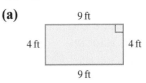

1. **(a)** $A = 36 \text{ ft}^2$

(b)

20 yd

35 yd

$A = 700 \text{ yd}^2$

(c)

2 m

3 m

$A = 6 \text{ m}^2$

2 Use the area of each rectangle and the appropriate formula to find the length or width. Draw a sketch of each rectangle and use it to check your solution.

(a) The area of a microscope slide is 12 cm², and the length is 6 cm. Find the width.

(b) A child's play lot is 10 ft wide and has an area of 160 ft². Find the length.

(c) A hallway floor is 31 m long and has an area of 93 m². Find the width of the floor.

EXAMPLE 2 **Finding the Length or Width of a Rectangle**

If the area of a rectangular rug is 12 yd² and the length is 4 yd, find the width.

First draw a sketch of the rug and label the length as 4 yd.

4 yd

Use the formula for area of a rectangle, $A = lw$.
The value of A is 12 yd² and the value of l is 4 yd.

$$A = l \cdot w \qquad \text{Replace } A \text{ with 12 yd}^2 \text{ and replace } l \text{ with 4 yd.}$$

$$12 \text{ yd}^2 = 4 \text{ yd} \cdot w \qquad \text{To get } w \text{ by itself, divide both sides by 4 yd.}$$

$$\frac{12 \text{ yd} \cdot \text{yd}}{4 \text{ yd}} = \frac{4 \text{ yd} \cdot w}{4 \text{ yd}} \qquad \text{On the left side, rewrite yd}^2 \text{ as yd} \cdot \text{yd. Then } \frac{\text{yd}}{\text{yd}} \text{ is 1, so they "cancel out."}$$

$$3 \text{ yd} = w \qquad \text{On the left side, 12 yd} \div 4 \text{ is 3 yd.}$$

The width of the rug is 3 yd.

Check To check the solution, put the width measurement on your sketch. Then use the area formula.

$$A = l \cdot w$$
$$A = 4 \text{ yd} \cdot 3 \text{ yd}$$
$$A = 12 \text{ yd}^2$$

3 yd

4 yd

An area of 12 yd² matches the information in the original problem. So 3 yd is the correct width of the rug.

◀ *Work Problem* **2** *at the Side.*

OBJECTIVE **2** **Use the formula for area of a square to find the area or the length of one side.** As with a rectangle, you can multiply length times width to find the area (surface inside) of a square. Because the length and the width are the same in a square, the formula is written as shown below.

Finding the Area of a Square

Area of a square = side • side
$$A = s \cdot s$$
$$A = s^2$$

Remember to use *square units* when measuring area.

EXAMPLE 3 **Finding the Area of a Square**

Find the area of a square highway sign that is 4 ft on each side.
Use the formula for area of a square, $A = s^2$.

$$A = s^2 \qquad \text{Remember that } s^2 \text{ means } s \cdot s.$$

$$A = s \cdot s \qquad \text{Replace } s \text{ with 4 ft.}$$

$$A = 4 \text{ ft} \cdot 4 \text{ ft} \qquad \text{Multiply } 4 \cdot 4 \text{ to get 16.}$$

$$A = 16 \text{ ft}^2 \qquad \text{Multiply ft} \cdot \text{ft to get ft}^2.$$

> **Be careful!**
> s^2 is 4 • 4 or 16
> (**not** 2 • 4).

The area of the sign is 16 ft².

Continued on Next Page

CAUTION
Be careful! s^2 means $s \cdot s$. It does *not* mean $2 \cdot s$. In this example s is 4 ft, so $(4\text{ ft})^2$ is $4\text{ ft} \cdot 4\text{ ft} = 16\text{ ft}^2$. It is *not* $2 \cdot 4\text{ ft} = 8\text{ ft}$.

Check   Check the solution by drawing a square and labeling each side as 4 ft. You can multiply length (4 ft) times width (4 ft), as you did for a rectangle. So the area is $4\text{ ft} \cdot 4\text{ ft}$, or 16 ft^2. This result matches the solution you got by using the formula $A = s^2$.

4 ft

4 ft

— *Work Problem* **3** *at the Side.* ▶

EXAMPLE 4   **Finding the Length of One Side of a Square**

If the area of a square township is 49 mi^2, what is the length of one side of the township?

Use the formula for area of a square, $A = s^2$. The value of A is 49 mi^2.

$$A = s^2 \qquad \text{Replace } A \text{ with 49 mi}^2.$$

$$49\text{ mi}^2 = s^2 \qquad \begin{array}{l}\text{To get } s \text{ by itself, we have to "undo" the}\\ \text{squaring of } s. \text{ This is called } \textit{finding the}\\ \textit{square root} \text{ (more on square roots in}\\ \textbf{Chapter 6}).\end{array}$$

$$49\text{ mi}^2 = s \cdot s \qquad \begin{array}{l}\text{For now, solve by inspection. Ask, what}\\ \text{number times itself gives 49?}\end{array}$$

$$49\text{ mi}^2 = 7\text{ mi} \cdot 7\text{ mi} \qquad 7 \cdot 7 \text{ is 49, so 7 mi} \cdot 7 \text{ mi is 49 mi}^2.$$

The value of s is 7 mi, so the length of one side of the township is 7 mi. Notice how this result matches the information about the township in Margin Problem 3(b) at the left.

— *Work Problem* **4** *at the Side.* ▶

OBJECTIVE **3** **Use the formula for area of a parallelogram to find the area, the base, or the height.**   To find the area of a parallelogram, first draw a dashed line inside the figure, as shown here.

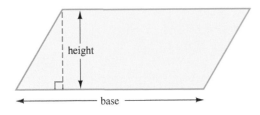
height

base

As an experiment, try this yourself by tracing this parallelogram onto a piece of paper.

The length of the dashed line is the *height* of the parallelogram. It forms a 90° angle (a right angle) with the base. The height is the shortest distance between the base and the opposite side.

(continued)

---

3 Find the area of each square, using the appropriate formula. Make a sketch of each square.

(a) A 12 in. square piece of fabric

(b) A square township 7 miles on a side

(c) A square earring measuring 20 mm on each side

4 Given the area of each square, find the length of one side by inspection.

(a) The area of a square-shaped nature center is 16 mi^2.

(b) A square floor with an area of 100 m^2

(c) A square clock face with an area of 81 in.^{2}

ANSWERS

3. (a)

12 in.

12 in.

$A = 144$ in.^{2}

(b)
7 mi

7 mi

$A = 49$ mi^2

(c)
20 mm

20 mm

$A = 400$ mm^2

4. (a) $s = 4$ mi   **(b)** $s = 10$ m   **(c)** $s = 9$ in.

5 Find the area of each parallelogram.

(a)

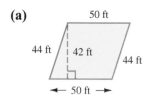

(b)

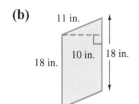

(c) A parallelogram with base 8 cm and height 1 cm.

Now cut off the triangle created on the left side of the parallelogram and move it to the right side, as shown below.

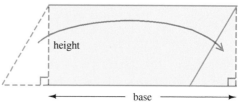

You have made the parallelogram into a rectangle. You can see that the area of the parallelogram and the rectangle are the same.

Equal areas

Area of the rectangle = length • width

Area of the parallelogram = base • height

> **Finding the Area of a Parallelogram**
>
> Area of a parallelogram = base • height
>
> $$A = bh$$
>
> Remember to use *square units* when measuring area.

EXAMPLE 5 **Finding the Area of Parallelograms**

Find the area of each parallelogram.

(a)

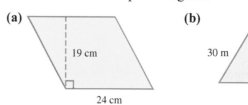

(b)

(a) The base is 24 cm and the height is 19 cm. The formula for the area of a parallelogram is $A = bh$.

$A = b \cdot h$ Replace b with 24 cm and h with 19 cm.

$A = 24 \text{ cm} \cdot 19 \text{ cm}$ Multiply 24 • 19 to get 456.

$A = 456 \text{ cm}^2$ Multiply cm • cm to get cm^2.

The area of the parallelogram is 456 cm².   Write **cm²** as part of your answer.

(b) Use the formula for area of a parallelogram, $A = bh$.

$A = b \cdot h$ Replace b with 47 m and h with 24 m.

$A = 47 \text{ m} \cdot 24 \text{ m}$ Multiply 47 • 24 to get 1128.

$A = 1128 \text{ m}^2$ Multiply m • m to get m^2.

Notice that the 30 m sides are *not* used in finding the area. But you would use them when finding the *perimeter* of the parallelogram.

◀ Work Problem **5** at the Side.

EXAMPLE 6 **Finding the Base or Height of a Parallelogram**

The area of a parallelogram is 24 ft² and the base is 6 ft. Find the height.

First draw a sketch of the parallelogram and label the base as 6 ft.

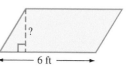

Continued on Next Page

ANSWERS

5. **(a)** $A = 2100 \text{ ft}^2$ **(b)** $A = 180 \text{ in.}^2$
 (c) $A = 8 \text{ cm}^2$

Use the formula for the area of a parallelogram, $A = bh$. The value of A is 24 ft², and the value of b is 6 ft.

$$A = b \cdot h \qquad \text{Replace } A \text{ with 24 ft}^2 \text{ and } b \text{ with 6 ft.}$$

$$24 \text{ ft}^2 = 6 \text{ ft} \cdot h \qquad \text{To get } h \text{ by itself, divide both sides by 6 ft.}$$

$$\frac{24 \text{ ft} \cdot ft}{6 \, ft} = \frac{6 \text{ ft} \cdot h}{6 \text{ ft}} \qquad \text{On the left side, rewrite ft}^2 \text{ as ft} \cdot \text{ft. Then } \frac{ft}{ft} \text{ is 1, so they "cancel out."}$$

$$4 \text{ ft} = h \qquad \text{On the left side, 24 ft} \div 6 \text{ is 4 ft.}$$

The height of the parallelogram is 4 ft.

Check To check the solution, put the height measurement on your sketch. Then use the area formula.

$$A = b \cdot h$$
$$A = 6 \text{ ft} \cdot 4 \text{ ft}$$
$$A = 24 \text{ ft}^2$$

An area of 24 ft² matches the information in the original problem. So 4 ft is the correct height of the parallelogram.

Work Problem **6** *at the Side.* ▶

OBJECTIVE **4** **Solve application problems involving perimeter and area of rectangles, squares, or parallelograms.** When you are solving problems, first decide whether you need to find the perimeter or the area.

EXAMPLE 7 **Solving an Application Problem Involving Perimeter or Area**

A group of neighbors is fixing up a playground for their children. The rectangular lot is 22 yd by 16 yd. If chain-link fencing costs $6 per yard, how much will they spend to put a fence around the lot?

First draw a sketch of the rectangular lot and label the lengths of the sides. The fence will go around the edges of the lot, so you need to find the *perimeter* of the lot.

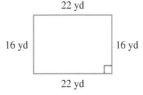

$$P = 2l + 2w \qquad \text{Formula for perimeter of a rectangle}$$
$$P = \underbrace{2 \cdot 22 \text{ yd}} + \underbrace{2 \cdot 16 \text{ yd}} \qquad \text{Replace } l \text{ with 22 yd and } w \text{ with 16 yd.}$$
$$P = 44 \text{ yd} + 32 \text{ yd}$$
$$P = 76 \text{ yd}$$

The perimeter of the lot is 76 yd, so the neighbors need to buy 76 yd of fencing. The cost of the fencing is $6 *per yard,* which means $6 *for 1 yard.* To find the cost for 76 yd, multiply $6 • 76. The neighbors will spend $456 on the fence.

An application involving the *area* of the playground is found in Margin Problem 7 at the left.

Work Problem **7** *at the Side.* ▶

---

6 Use the area of each parallelogram and the appropriate formula to find the base or height. Draw a sketch of each parallelogram and use it to check your solution.

(a) The area of a parallelogram is 140 in.² and the base is 14 in. Find the height.

(b) A parallelogram has an area of 4 yd². The height is 1 yd. Find the base.

7 If sod costs $3 per square yard, how much will the neighbors in Example 7 spend to cover the playground with grass?

ANSWERS

6. (a) $h = 10$ in.

Check $A = 14$ in. • 10 in.
$A = 140$ in.²
Matches original problem

(b) $b = 4$ yd

Check $A = 4$ yd • 1 yd
$A = 4$ yd²
Matches original problem

7. $1056 (Find the area by multiplying 22 yd • 16 yd to get 352 yd². Then multiply $3 • 352 to get $1056.)

*Find the area of each rectangle, square, or parallelogram using the appropriate formula.
See Examples 1, 3, and 5.*

1.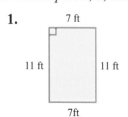

2.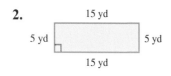

3.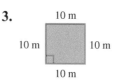

4.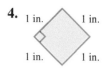

5.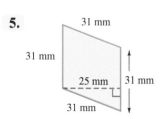

6.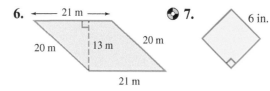

7.

8.

*In Exercises 9–16, first draw a sketch of the shape and label the lengths of the sides or base
and height. Then find the area. (Sketches may vary; show your sketches to your instructor.)*

9. A rectangular calculator that measures 15 cm by 7 cm

10. A rectangular piece of plywood that is 8 ft long and 2 ft wide

11. A parallelogram with height of 9 ft and base of 8 ft

12. A parallelogram measuring 18 mm on the base and 3 mm on the height

13. A fire burned a square-shaped forest 25 mi on a side.

14. An 11 in. square pillow

15. A square piece of window glass 1 m on each side

16. A table 12 ft long by 3 ft wide

*In Exercises 17–22, use the area of each rectangle and either its length or width, and the
appropriate formula, to find the other measurement. Draw a sketch of each rectangle and use it to
check your solution. See Example 2. (Sketches may vary; show your sketches to your instructor.)*

17. The area of a desk is 18 ft^2, and the width is 3 ft. Find its length.

18. The area of a classroom is 630 ft^2, and the length is 30 ft. Find its width.

19. A parking lot is 90 yd long and has an area of 7200 yd^2. Find its width.

20. A playground is 60 yd wide and has an area of 6000 yd^2. Find its length.

◎ 21. A 154 in.^{2} photo has a width of 11 in. Find its length.

22. A 15 in.^{2} note card has a width of 3 in. Find its length.

Given the area of each square, find the length of one side by inspection. See Example 4.

23. A square floor has an area of 36 m^2.

24. A square stamp has an area of 9 cm^2.

25. The area of a square sign is 4 ft^2.

26. The area of a square piece of metal is 64 in.^{2}.

Use the area of each parallelogram and either its base or height, and the appropriate formula, to find the other measurement. Draw a sketch of each parallelogram and use it to check your solution. See Example 6. (Sketches may vary; show your sketches to your instructor.)

27. The area is 500 cm^2, and the base is 25 cm. Find the height.

28. The area is 1500 m^2, and the height is 30 m. Find the base.

29. The height is 13 in. and the area is 221 in.^{2}. Find the base.

30. The base is 19 cm, and the area is 114 cm^2. Find the height.

31. The base is 9 m, and the area is 9 m^2. Find the height.

32. The area is 25 mm^2, and the height is 5 mm. Find the base.

*Explain and correct the **two** errors made by students in Exercises 33 and 34.*

33.

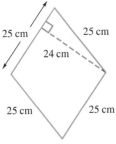

$P = 25 \text{ cm} + 24 \text{ cm} + 25 \text{ cm} + 25 \text{ cm} + 25 \text{ cm}$

$P = 124 \text{ cm}^2$

34.

7 ft

$A = s^2$

$A = 2 \cdot 7 \text{ ft}$

$A = 14 \text{ ft}$

Name each figure and find its perimeter and area.

35.
45 in.
45 in.

36.
4 m
5 m
6 m
6 m
← 4 m →

37.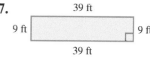
39 ft
9 ft
9 ft
39 ft

38.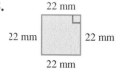
22 mm
22 mm
22 mm
22 mm

39.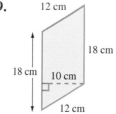
12 cm
18 cm
18 cm
10 cm
12 cm

40.
100 yd
80 yd

Solve each application problem. You may need to find the perimeter, the area, or one of the side measurements. In Exercises 41–46, draw a sketch for each problem and label the sketch with the appropriate measurements. See Example 7. (Sketches may vary; show your sketches to your instructor.)

41. Gymnastic floor exercises are performed on a square mat that is 12 meters on a side. Find the perimeter and area of a mat. (*Source:* www.nist.gov)

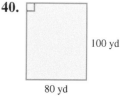

42. A regulation volleyball court is 18 meters by 9 meters. Find the perimeter and area of a regulation court. (*Source:* www.nist.gov)

43. Tyra's kitchen is 4 m wide and 5 m long. She is pasting a decorative strip that costs $6 per meter around the top edge of all the walls. How much will she spend?

44. The Wang's family room measures 20 ft by 25 ft. They are covering the floor with square tiles that measure 1 ft on a side and cost $1 each. How much will they spend on tile?

45. Mr. and Mrs. Gomez are buying carpet for their square-shaped bedroom, which measures 5 yd along each wall. The carpet is $23 per square yard and padding and installation is another $6 per square yard. How much will they spend in all?

46. A page in this book measures about 27 cm from top to bottom and 21 cm from side to side. Find the perimeter and the area of the page.

47. A regulation football field is 100 yd long (excluding end zones) and has an area of 5300 yd². Find the width of the field. (*Source:* NFL.)

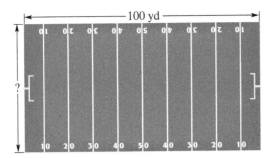

48. There are 14,790 ft² of ice in the rectangular playing area for a major league hockey game (excluding the area behind the goal lines). If the playing area is 85 ft wide, how long is it? (*Source:* NHL.)

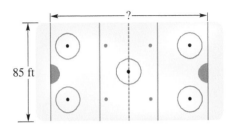

49. The table below shows information on two rectangular tents for camping.

Tents	Coleman Family Dome	Eddie Bauer Dome Tent
Dimensions	13 ft × 13 ft	12 ft × 12 ft
Sleeps	8 campers	6 campers
Sale price	$127	$99

Source: target.com

For the Coleman tent, find the perimeter, area, and number of square feet of floor space for each camper. Round to the nearest whole number if necessary.

50. Look at the table in Exercise 49. For the Eddie Bauer tent, find the perimeter, area, and number of square feet of floor space for each camper. Round to the nearest whole number if necessary.

Relating Concepts (Exercises 51–54) For Individual or Group Work

Use your knowledge of perimeter and area to **work Exercises 51–54** *in order.*

51. Suppose you have 12 ft of fencing to make a square or rectangular garden plot. Draw sketches of *all* the possible plots that use exactly 12 ft of fencing and label the lengths of the sides. Use only *whole number* lengths. (*Hint:* There are three possibilities.)

52. **(a)** Find the area of each plot in Exercise 51.

(b) Which plot has the greatest area?

53. Repeat Exercise 51 using 16 ft of fencing. Be sure to draw *all* possible square or rectangular plots that have whole number lengths for the sides.

54. **(a)** Find the area of each plot in Exercise 53.

(b) Compare your results to those from Exercise 52. What do you notice about the plots with the greatest area?

Summary Exercises on Perimeter and Area

Name each figure and find its perimeter and area using the appropriate formulas.

1.
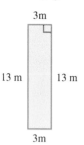
3m

13 m   13 m

3m

2.
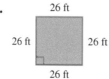
26 ft

26 ft   26 ft

26 ft

3. ←7 yd→
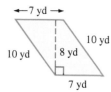
10 yd

10 yd   8 yd

7 yd

4.
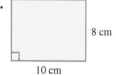
8 cm

10 cm

5.

9 in.

9 in.

6. 9 m
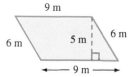
6 m   5 m   6 m

←9 m→

7.
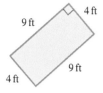
4 ft

9 ft

9 ft

4 ft

8.
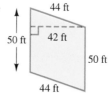
44 ft

50 ft   42 ft

50 ft

44 ft

In Exercises 9–14, use the appropriate formula to find the unknown measurement. Draw a sketch of the figure and use it to check your solution.

9. A rectangle has a length of 7 ft and a perimeter of 16 ft. Find the width.

10. A parallelogram with an area of 5 yd² has a height of 1 yd. Find the base.

11. A square photograph has an area of 36 in.² Find the length on one side.

12. A sidewalk is 42 m long and has an area of 84 m². Find the width of the sidewalk.

13. The perimeter of a square map is 64 cm. What is the length of one side?

14. A rectangular patio is 9 ft wide and has a perimeter of 48 ft. What is the patio's length?

Solve each application problem using the appropriate formula. Show your work.

15. How much fencing is needed to enclose a triangular building site that measures 168 meters on each side?

16. Regulation soccer fields can measure 50 to 100 yards wide and 100 to 130 yards long, depending upon the age and skill level of the players. Find the difference in playing room between the smallest and largest fields. (*Source:* Womenssportsnet.com)

17. A Toshiba laptop computer has a rectangular screen with a perimeter of 42 inches. The width of the screen is 12 inches. Find the height of the screen. (*Source:* Toshiba.)

18. Kari is decorating the cover of a square-shaped photo album that is 22 cm along each side. She is gluing braid along the edges of the front and back covers. How much braid will she need?

19. A school flag measures 3 feet by 5 feet. Find the amount of fabric needed to make seven flags, and the amount of binding needed to go around all the edges of all the flags.

20. The lobby floor of a new skyscraper is in the shape of a parallelogram, with an area of 3024 ft². If the base of the parallelogram measures 63 ft, what is its height?

4.8 ▶▶▶ Solving Application Problems with One Unknown Quantity

OBJECTIVES

1 Translate word phrases into algebraic expressions.

2 Translate sentences into equations.

3 Solve application problems with one unknown quantity.

1 Write each phrase as an algebraic expression. Use x as the variable.

(a) 15 less than a number

(b) 12 more than a number

(c) A number increased by 13

(d) A number minus 8

(e) 10 plus a number

(f) A number subtracted from 6

(g) 6 subtracted from a number

2 Write each phrase as an algebraic expression. Use x as the variable.

(a) Double a number

(b) The product of $^-8$ and a number

(c) The quotient of 15 and a number

(d) 5 times a number subtracted from 30

OBJECTIVE 1 Translate word phrases into algebraic expressions. In **Sections 4.5** and **4.6** you worked with applications involving perimeter and area. You were able to use well-known rules (formulas) to set up equations that could be solved. However, you will encounter many problems for which no formula is available. Then you need to analyze the problem and translate the words into an equation that fits the particular situation. We'll start by translating word phrases into algebraic expressions.

EXAMPLE 1 Translating Word Phrases into Algebraic Expressions

Write each phrase as an algebraic expression. Use x as the variable.

Words	Algebraic Expression	
A number plus 2	$x + 2$ or $2 + x$	⎫
The sum of 8 and a number	$8 + x$ or $x + 8$	*Two* correct ways to write each *addition* expression
5 more than a number	$x + 5$ or $5 + x$	
$^-35$ added to a number	$^-35 + x$ or $x + {}^-35$	
A number increased by 6	$x + 6$ or $6 + x$	⎭
9 less than a number	$x - 9$	⎫
A number subtracted from 3	$3 - x$	*Only one* correct way to write each *subtraction* expression
3 subtracted from a number	$x - 3$	
A number decreased by 4	$x - 4$	
10 minus a number	$10 - x$	⎭

> **CAUTION**
> Recall that addition can be done in any order, so $x + 2$ gives the same result as $2 + x$. This is *not* true in subtraction, so be careful. $10 - x$ does *not* give the same result as $x - 10$.

◀ *Work Problem* **1** *at the Side.*

EXAMPLE 2 Translating Word Phrases into Algebraic Expressions

Write each phrase as an algebraic expression. Use x as the variable.

Words	Algebraic Expression
8 times a number	$8x$
The product of 12 and a number	$12x$
Double a number (meaning "2 times")	$2x$
The quotient of $^-6$ and a number	$\dfrac{^-6}{x}$
A number divided by 10	$\dfrac{x}{10}$
15 subtracted from 4 times a number	$4x - 15$
The result is	$=$

◀ *Work Problem* **2** *at the Side.*

ANSWERS

1. **(a)** $x - 15$ **(b)** $x + 12$ or $12 + x$
   (c) $x + 13$ or $13 + x$ **(d)** $x - 8$
   (e) $10 + x$ or $x + 10$ **(f)** $6 - x$
   (g) $x - 6$

2. **(a)** $2x$ **(b)** ^-8x **(c)** $\dfrac{15}{x}$
   (d) $30 - 5x$ (**not** $5x - 30$)

OBJECTIVE **2** **Translate sentences into equations.**   The next example shows you how to translate a sentence into an equation that you can solve.

[**EXAMPLE 3**]   **Translating a Sentence into an Equation**

If 5 times a number is added to 11, the result is 26. Find the number.

Let x represent the unknown number. Use the information in the problem to write an equation.

$$\underbrace{5 \text{ times a number}}_{5x} \underbrace{\text{added to } 11}_{+\ 11} \underbrace{\text{is } 26}_{=\ 26}$$

Next, solve the equation.

$$
\begin{array}{rcl}
5x + 11 & = & 26 \\
-11 & & -11 \\
\hline
5x + 0 & = & 15
\end{array}
$$
To get $5x$ by itself, add $^-11$ to both sides.

$$
\begin{array}{rcl}
\dfrac{5x}{5} & = & \dfrac{15}{5} \\
x & = & 3
\end{array}
$$
To get x by itself, divide both sides by 5.

The number is 3.

Check   Go back to the words of the *original* problem.

$$\text{If } \underbrace{5 \cdot}_{5} \underbrace{\text{times a number}}_{3} \underbrace{\text{is added to}}_{+} \underbrace{11}_{11}, \underbrace{\text{the result is}}_{=} \underbrace{26}_{26}.$$

Does $5 \cdot 3 + 11$ really equal 26? Yes, $5 \cdot 3 + 11 = 15 + 11 = 26$.
So 3 is the correct solution because it "works" when you put it back into the original problem.

────────────────────────── *Work Problem* **3** *at the Side.* ▶

OBJECTIVE **3** **Solve application problems with one unknown quantity.**   Now you are ready to tackle application problems. The steps we will use are summarized below.

┌───┐
Solving an Application Problem

Step 1   **Read** the problem once to see what it is about. Read it carefully a second time. As you read, make a sketch or write word phrases that identify the known and the unknown parts of the problem.

Step 2(a)   If there is one unknown quantity, **assign a variable** to represent it. Write down what your variable represents.

Step 2(b)   If there is more than one unknown quantity, **assign a variable** to represent "the thing you know the least about." Then write variable expression(s), using the same variable, to show the relationship of the other unknown quantities to the first one.

Step 3   **Write an equation,** using your sketch or word phrases as the guide.

Step 4   **Solve** the equation.

Step 5   **State the answer** to the question in the problem and label your answer.

Step 6   **Check** whether your answer fits all the facts given in the *original* statement of the problem. If it does, you are done. If it doesn't, start again at Step 1.
└───┘

3 Translate each sentence into an equation and solve it. Check your solution by going back to the words in the original problem.

(a) If 3 times a number is added to 4, the result is 19. Find the number.

(b) If 7 is subtracted from 6 times a number, the result is $^-25$. Find the number.

ANSWERS

3. (a) $3x + 4 = 19$
$x = 5$
Check $\underbrace{3 \cdot 5}_{15} + 4$ does equal 19
$\underbrace{15 + 4}_{19}$

(b) $6x - 7 = {}^-25$
$x = {}^-3$
Check $\underbrace{6 \cdot {}^-3}_{{}^-18} - 7$ does equal $^-25$
$\underbrace{{}^-18 + {}^-7}_{{}^-25}$

4 Some people got on an empty bus at its first stop. At the second stop, 3 people got on. At the third stop, 5 more people got on. At the fourth stop, 10 people got off, but 4 people were still on the bus. How many people got on at the first stop? Show your work for each of the six problem-solving steps.

EXAMPLE 4   **Solving an Application Problem with One Unknown Quantity**

Heather put some money aside in an envelope for small household expenses. Yesterday she took out $20 for groceries. Today a friend paid back a loan and Heather put the $34 in the envelope. Now she has $43 in the envelope. How much was in the envelope at the start?

Step 1   **Read** the problem once. It is about money in an envelope. Read it a second time and write word phrases.

Unknown: amount of money in the envelope at the start
Known: took out $20; put in $34; ended up with $43

Step 2(a)   There is only one unknown quantity, so **assign a variable** to represent it. Let m represent the money at the start.

Step 3   **Write an equation,** using the phrases you wrote as a guide.

Money at the start	Took out $20	Put in $34	Ended up with $43
m	$- \$20$	$+ \$34$	$= \$43$

Step 4   **Solve** the equation.

$$m - \ 20 + 34 = \ 43 \quad \text{Change subtraction to adding the opposite.}$$
$$m + \ ^-20 + 34 = \ 43 \quad \text{Simplify the left side.}$$
$$m + \quad 14 \quad = \ 43 \quad \text{To get } m \text{ by itself.}$$
$$\underline{\qquad \ ^-14 \qquad\qquad ^-14} \quad \text{add } ^-14 \text{ to both sides.}$$
$$m + \quad 0 \quad = \ 29$$
$$m \quad = \ 29$$

Step 5   **State the answer** to the question, "How much was in the envelope at the start?" There was $29 in the envelope.

Step 6   **Check** the solution by going back to the *original* problem and inserting the solution.

Started with $29 in the envelope

Took out $20, so $29 − $20 = $9 in the envelope

Put in $34, so $9 + $34 = $43

Now has $43 ⟵ Matches ⟶

Because $29 "works" when you put it back into the original problem, you know it is the correct solution.

If your answer does **not** work in the original problem, start again at *Step 1.*

◀ *Work Problem* **4** *at the Side.*

ANSWER

4. *Step 1*   **Read.**
Unknown: number of people who got on at first stop
Known: 3 got on; 5 got on; 10 got off; 4 people still on bus

Step 2(a)   **Assign a variable.**
Let p be people who got on at first stop. (You may use any letter you like as the variable.)

Step 3   **Write an equation.**
$p + 3 + 5 - 10 = 4$

Step 4   **Solve.**
$$p + \underbrace{3 + 5 + \ ^-10} = 4$$
$$p + \qquad ^-2 \qquad = 4$$
$$\underline{\qquad\qquad +2 \qquad\qquad +2}$$
$$p + \qquad 0 \qquad = 6$$
$$\underbrace{p} \qquad\qquad = 6$$

Step 5   **State the answer.**
6 people got on at the first stop.

Step 6   **Check.**
6 got on at first stop
3 got on at 2nd stop: $6 + 3 = 9$
5 got on at 3rd stop: $9 + 5 = 14$
10 got off at 4th stop: $14 - 10 = 4$
4 people are left. ⟵ Matches ⟶

EXAMPLE 5 **Solving an Application Problem with One Unknown Quantity**

Three friends each put in the same amount of money to buy a gift. After they spent $2 for a card and $31 for the gift, they had $6 left. How much money had each friend put in originally?

Step 1 **Read** the problem. It is about 3 friends buying a gift.

Unknown: amount of money each friend contributed
Known: 3 friends put in money; spent $2 and $31; had $6 left

Step 2(a) There is only one unknown quantity. **Assign a variable**, m, to represent the amount of money each friend contributed.

Step 3 **Write an equation.**

Number of friends	Amount each friend put in	Spent on card	Spent on gift	Left over
3 •	m	− $2	− $31 =	$6

To see why this is multiplication, think of an example. If each friend put in $10, how much money would there be? 3 • $10, or $30

Step 4 **Solve.**

$3m - 2 - 31 = 6$ Change subtractions to adding the opposite.
$3m + {}^-2 + {}^-31 = 6$ Simplify the left side.

$3m + {}^-33 = 6$

${}^+33 {}^+33$ To get $3m$ by itself, add 33 to both sides.

$3m + 0 = 39$

$\dfrac{3m}{3} = \dfrac{39}{3}$ To get m by itself, divide both sides by 3.

$m = 13$

Step 5 **State the answer.** Each friend put in $13.   Write a $ as part of your answer.

Step 6 **Check** the solution by putting it back into the *original* problem.

3 friends each put in $13, so 3 • $13 = $39.

Spent $2, spent $31, so $39 − $2 − $31 = $6

Had $6 left ⟵ Matches ⟶

$13 is the correct solution because it "works."

Work Problem **5** *at the Side.* ▶

---

5 Five donors each gave the same amount of money to a college to use for scholarships. From the money, scholarships of $1250, $900, and $850 were given to students; $250 was left. How much money did each donor give to the college? Show your work for each of the six problem-solving steps.

ANSWER

5. *Step 1* **Read.**
Unknown: money given by each donor
Known: 5 donors; gave out $1250, $900, $850; $250 left

Step 2(a) **Assign a variable.**
Let m be each donor's money.

Step 3 **Write an equation.**
5 • m − $1250 − $900 − $850 = $250

Step 4 **Solve.**

$5m + {}^-1250 + {}^-900 + {}^-850 = 250$

$5m + {}^-3000 = 250$
${}^+3000 {}^+3000$

$5m + 0 = 3250$

$\dfrac{5m}{5} = \dfrac{3250}{5}$

$m = 650$

Step 5 **State the answer.**
Each donor gave $650.

Step 6 **Check.**
5 donors each gave $650, so
5 • $650 = $3250
Gave out $1250, $900, $850, so
$3250 − 1250 − 900 − 850 = $250
Had $250 left ⟵ Matches ⟶
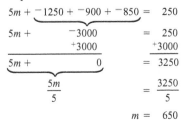

6 Susan donated $10 more than twice what LuAnn donated. If Susan donated $22, how much did LuAnn donate?

Show your work for each of the six problem-solving steps.

6. *Step 1*   Read.
Unknown: LuAnn's donation
Known: Susan donated $10 more than twice what LuAnn donated; Susan donated $22.

***Step 2(a)*   Assign a variable.**
Let d be LuAnn's donation.

***Step 3*   Write an equation.**
$2d + \$10 = \$22$
(or $\$10 + 2d = \$22$)

***Step 4*   Solve.**
$$\begin{array}{rcr} 2d + 10 &=& 22 \\ -10 &=& -10 \\ \hline 2d + 0 &=& 12 \end{array}$$

$$\frac{2d}{2} = \frac{12}{2}$$

$$d = 6$$

***Step 5*   State the answer.**
LuAnn donated $6.

***Step 6*   Check.**
$10 more than twice $6 is

$\$10 + (2 \cdot \$6) = \$10 + \$12 = \$22$

Susan donated $22. ←Matches ——↑

EXAMPLE 6   **Solving a More Complex Application Problem with One Unknown Quantity**

Michael has completed 5 less than three times as many lab experiments as David. If Michael has completed 13 experiments, how many experiments has David completed?

Step 1   **Read** the problem. It is about the number of experiments done by two students.

> Unknown: number of experiments David did
> Known: Michael did 5 less than 3 times the number David did; Michael did 13.

Step 2(a)   **Assign a variable.** Let n represent the number of experiments David did.

Step 3   **Write an equation.**

The number Michael did	is	5 less than 3 times David's number.
13	=	$3n - 5$

> Be careful with subtraction!
> $5 - 3n$ is **not** the same as $3n - 5$.

Step 4   **Solve.**

$13 = 3n - 5$ Change subtraction to adding the opposite.

$13 = 3n + {}^-5$

$$\begin{array}{rcr} & {}^+5 & {}^+5 \\ \hline 18 &=& 3n + 0 \end{array}$$ To get $3n$ by itself, add 5 to both sides.

$$\frac{18}{3} = \frac{3n}{3}$$ To get n by itself, divide both sides by 3.

$$6 = n$$

Step 5   **State the answer.** David did 6 experiments.

Step 6   **Check** the solution by putting it back into the *original* problem.

3 times David's number $3 \cdot 6 = 18$

Less 5 $18 - 5 = 13$

Michael did 13. ←———— Matches ————↑

The correct solution is: David did 6 experiments.

> Label your answer. Write 6 experiments, **not** just 6.

◀ *Work Problem* **6** *at the Side.*

Math in the Media

To estimate the number of words in a child's vocabulary, a pediatrician may use this formula.

$$V = 60A - 900$$

where V is the number of vocabulary words and A is the age of the child in months.

Source: Pediatrics.

Use the formula to find the *age* of each child.

1. The child's vocabulary is 180 words.

2. The child's vocabulary is 1440 words.

3. The child's vocabulary is 60 words.

4. Describe *in words* what you were doing as you found each child's age.

5. Find the child's age if the child's vocabulary is 0 words.

6. Refer to Problem 5 above. *Without solving an equation,* are there any other ages at which children would have a vocabulary of 0 words?

7. Is the formula useful for all ages of children? Explain your answer.

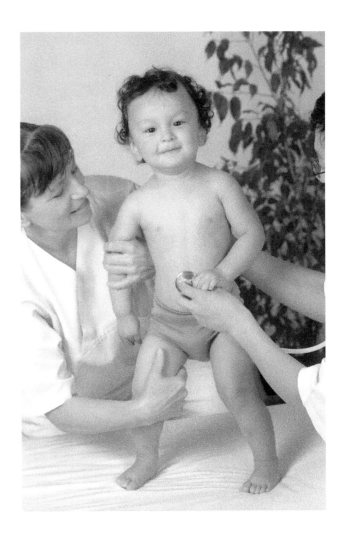

Write an algebraic expression, using x as the variable. See Examples 1 and 2.

1. 14 plus a number

2. The sum of a number and $^-8$

3. $^-5$ added to a number

4. 16 more than a number

5. 20 minus a number

6. A number decreased by 25

7. 9 less than a number

8. A number subtracted from $^-7$

9. Subtract 4 from a number.

10. 3 fewer than a number

11. $^-6$ times a number

12. The product of $^-3$ and a number

13. Double a number

14. A number times 10

15. A number divided by 2

16. 4 divided by a number

17. Twice a number added to 8

18. Five times a number plus 5

19. 10 fewer than seven times a number

20. 12 less than six times a number

21. The sum of twice a number and the number

22. Triple a number subtracted from the number

Translate each sentence into an equation and solve it. Check your solution by going back to the words in the original problem. See Example 3.

23. If four times a number is decreased by 2, the result is 26. Find the number.

24. The sum of 8 and five times a number is 53. Find the number.

25. If a number is added to twice the number, the result is ⁻15. What is the number?

26. If a number is subtracted from three times the number, the result is ⁻8. What is the number?

27. If the product of some number and 5 is increased by 12, the result is seven times the number. Find the number.

28. If eight times a number is subtracted from eleven times the number, the result is ⁻9. Find the number.

29. When three times a number is subtracted from 30, the result is 2 plus the number. What is the number?

30. When twice a number is decreased by 8, the result is the number increased by 7. Find the number.

Solve each application problem. Use the six problem-solving steps you learned in this section. See Examples 4–6.

31. Ricardo gained 15 pounds over the winter. He went on a diet and lost 28 pounds. Then he regained 5 pounds and weighed 177 pounds. How much did he weigh originally?

32. Mr. Chee deposited $80 into his checking account. Then, after writing a $23 check for gas and a $90 check for his child's day care, the balance in his account was $67. How much was in his account before he made the deposit?

33. There were 18 cookies in Magan's cookie jar. While she was busy in another room, her children ate some of the cookies. Magan bought three dozen cookies and added them to the jar. At that point she had 49 cookies in the jar. How many cookies did her children eat?

34. The Greens had a 20-pound bag of bird seed in their garage. Mice got into the bag and ate some of it. The Greens then bought an 8-pound bag of seed and put all the seed in a metal container. They now have 24 pounds of seed. How much did the mice eat?

35. A college bookstore ordered six boxes of red pens. The store sold 32 red pens last week and 35 red pens this week. Five pens were left on the shelf. How many pens were in each box?

36. A local charity received a donation of eight cartons filled with cans of soup. The charity gave out 100 cans of soup yesterday and 92 cans today before running out. How many cans were in each carton?

37. The 14 music club members each paid the same amount for dues. The club also earned $340 selling magazine subscriptions. They spent $575 to organize a jazz festival. Now their bank account, which started at $0, is overdrawn by $25. How much did each member pay in dues?

38. The manager of an apartment complex had 11 packages of lightbulbs on hand. He replaced 29 burned out bulbs in hallway lights and 7 bulbs in the party room. Eight bulbs were left. How many bulbs were in each package?

39. When 75 is subtracted from four times Tamu's age, the result is Tamu's age. How old is Tamu?

40. If three times Linda's age is decreased by 36, the result is twice Linda's age. How old is Linda?

41. While shopping for clothes, Consuelo spent $3 less than twice what Brenda spent. Consuelo spent $81. How much did Brenda spend?

42. Dennis weighs 184 pounds. His weight is 2 pounds less than six times his child's weight. How much does his child weigh?

43. Paige bought five bags of candy for Halloween. Forty-eight children visited her home and she gave each child three pieces of candy. At the end of the night she still had one bag of candy. How many pieces of candy were in each bag?

44. A restaurant ordered four packages of paper napkins. Yesterday they used up one package, and today they used up 140 napkins. Two packages plus 60 napkins remain. How many napkins are in each package?

45. The recommended daily intake of iron for an adult female is 4 mg less than twice the recommended amount for an infant. The amount for an adult female is 18 mg. How much should the infant receive? (*Source:* Food and Nutrition Board.)

46. A cheetah's sprinting speed is 61 miles per hour less than three times a zebra's running speed. A cheetah can sprint 68 miles per hour. Find the zebra's running speed. (*Source: Grolier Multimedia Encyclopedia.*)

4.9 ▶▶▶ Solving Application Problems with Two Unknown Quantities

OBJECTIVE 1 Solve application problems with two unknown quantities. In the preceding section, the problems had only one unknown quantity. As a result, we used Step 2(a) rather than Step 2(b) in the problem-solving steps. For easy reference, we repeat the steps here.

Solving an Application Problem

Step 1   **Read** the problem once to see what it is about. Read it carefully a second time. As you read, make a sketch or write word phrases that identify the known and the unknown parts of the problem.

Step 2(a)   If there is one unknown quantity, **assign a variable** to represent it. Write down what your variable represents.

Step 2(b)   If there is more than one unknown quantity, **assign a variable** to represent "the thing you know the least about." Then write variable expression(s), using the same variable, to show the relationship of the other unknown quantities to the first one.

Step 3   **Write an equation,** using your sketch or word phrases as the guide.

Step 4   **Solve** the equation.

Step 5   **State the answer** to the question in the problem and label your answer.

Step 6   **Check** whether your answer fits all the facts given in the *original* statement of the problem. If it does, you are done. If it doesn't, start again at Step 1.

Now you are ready to solve problems with two unknown quantities.

EXAMPLE 1 **Solving an Application Problem with Two Unknown Quantities**

Last month, Sheila worked 72 hours more than Russell. Together they worked a total of 232 hours. Find the number of hours each person worked last month.

Step 1   **Read** the problem. It is about the number of hours worked by Sheila and by Russell.

   Unknowns: hours worked by Sheila;
          hours worked by Russell
   Known: Sheila worked 72 hours more than Russell;
          232 hours total for Sheila and Russell

Step 2(b)   There are *two* unknowns so **assign a variable** to represent "the thing you know the least about." You know the *least* about the hours worked by Russell, so let h represent Russell's hours.

   Sheila worked 72 hours more than Russell, so her hours are $h + 72$, that is, Russell's hours (h) plus 72 more.

Step 3   **Write an equation.**

Hours worked by Russell		Hours worked by Sheila		Total hours worked
h	$+$	$h + 72$	$=$	232

Continued on Next Page

Step 4   **Solve.**

$$\underbrace{h + h} + 72 = 232 \qquad \text{Simplify the left side by combining like terms.}$$
$$2h \;\; + 72 = 232$$

$$\underline{ \;\; -72 \quad -72} \qquad \text{To get } 2h \text{ by itself, add } {}^-72 \text{ to both sides.}$$
$$\underbrace{2h \;\; + \;\; 0} = 160$$

$$\frac{2h}{2} = \frac{160}{2} \qquad \text{To get } h \text{ by itself, divide both sides by 2.}$$
$$h \;\;\; = \;\; 80$$

Step 5   **State the answer.**
Because h represents Russell's hours, and the solution of the equation is $h = 80$, Russell worked 80 hours.

h + 72 represents Sheila's hours. Replace h with 80.

$80 + 72 = 152$, so Sheila worked 152 hours.

The final answer is:
Russell worked 80 hours and
Sheila worked 152 hours.

> Write **hours** as part of both answers.

Step 6   **Check** the solution by putting both numbers back into the *original* problem.

"Sheila worked 72 hours more than Russell."
Sheila's 152 hours are 72 more than Russell's 80 hours, so the solution checks.

$$\begin{array}{r} 152 \\ -\ 72 \\ \hline 80 \end{array}$$

"Together they worked a total of 232 hours."
Sheila's 152 hours + Russell's 80 hours = 232 hours, so the solution checks.

$$\begin{array}{r} 152 \\ +\ 80 \\ \hline 232 \end{array}$$

You've answered the question correctly because 80 hours and 152 hours fit all the facts given in the problem.

CAUTION
Check the solution to an application problem by putting the numbers back in the *original* problem. If they do *not* work, recheck your work or try solving the problem in a different way.

Work Problem **1** *at the Side.* ▶

EXAMPLE 2   **Solving an Application Problem with Two Unknown Quantities**

Riley cut a cord that was 83 ft long into two pieces. One piece was 19 ft shorter than the other. How long was each piece?

Step 1   **Read** the problem. It is about a cord that is cut into two pieces.

Unknowns: length of first piece;
length of second piece
Known: Second piece is 19 ft shorter than first piece;
total length of both pieces is 83 ft

Step 2(b)   There are *two* unknowns so **assign a variable** to represent "the thing you know the least about." You know the *least* about the first piece, so let p represent the length of the first piece.

Continued on Next Page

---

1 In a day of work, Keonda made $12 more than her daughter. Together they made $182. Find the amount that each person made. (*Hint:* Which amount do you know the *least* about, Keonda's or her daughter's? Let m be that amount.) Use the six problem-solving steps.

ANSWER

1. Daughter made m.
Keonda made $m + 12$.
$m + m + 12 = 182$
Daughter made $85.
Keonda made $97.

Check $97 − $85 = $12
and $97 + $85 = $182

2 Charles had 175 yd of fishing line to put on two fishing reels. He put 25 yd less of line on one reel than on the other. How much line did he put on each reel? Use the six problem-solving steps.

The second piece is 19 ft shorter than the first piece, so its length is $p - 19$.

Step 3 **Write an equation.**

Length of first piece		Length of second piece		Total length
p	$+$	$p - 19$	$=$	83

Step 4 **Solve.**

$\underbrace{p + p}\ -\ 19 = 83$ Simplify the left side by combining like terms.

$\quad 2p\ -\ 19 = 83$ Change subtraction to adding the opposite.

$\quad 2p\ +\ {}^-19 = 83$

$\quad\quad\quad\quad\underline{{}^+19\quad\ {}^+19}$ To get $2p$ by itself, add 19 to both sides.

$\underbrace{2p\ +\ \ 0} = 102$

$\quad\dfrac{2p}{2} = \dfrac{102}{2}$ To get p by itself, divide both sides by 2.

$\quad\quad p = 51$

Step 5 **State the answer.**

p represents the length of the first piece, and $p = 51$, so the first piece is 51 ft long.

$p - 19$ represents the second piece. Replace p with 51.

$51 - 19 = 32$, so the second piece is 32 ft long.

The final answer is: One piece was 51 ft long and the other piece was 32 ft long.

Step 6 **Check** the solution by putting both numbers back into the *original* problem.

"**Riley cut a cord that was 83 ft long.**"

$51\text{ ft} + 32\text{ ft} = 83\text{ ft}$, so the solution checks.

> If your answers do **not** fit all the given facts, start over at *Step 1*.

"**One piece was 19 ft shorter than the other.**"

32 ft is 19 ft shorter than 51 ft, so the solution checks.

You've answered the question correctly because 51 ft and 32 ft fit all the facts given in the problem.

◀ *Work Problem* **2** *at the Side.*

EXAMPLE 3 **Solving a Geometry Application with Two Unknown Quantities**

The length of a rectangle is 2 cm more than the width. The perimeter is 68 cm. Find the length and width.

Step 1 **Read** the problem. It is about a rectangle. Make a sketch of a rectangle.

Unknowns: length of the rectangle; width of the rectangle
Known: The length is 2 cm more than the width; the perimeter is 68 cm.

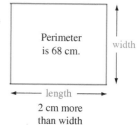

Perimeter is 68 cm. width

length

2 cm more than width

ANSWER

2. Length on first reel is r.
Length on second reel is $r - 25$.
$r + r - 25 = 175$
First reel had 100 yd of line.
Second reel had 75 yd of line.

Check $100\text{ yd} + 75\text{ yd} = 175\text{ yd}$ and
$100\text{ yd} - 75\text{ yd} = 25\text{ yd}$

Continued on Next Page

Step 2(b) There are *two* unknowns so **assign a variable** to represent "the thing you know the least about." You know the *least* about the width, so let *w* represent the width.

The length is 2 cm more than the width, so the **length** is *w* + 2.

Step 3 **Write an equation.**
Use the formula for perimeter of a rectangle, $P = 2l + 2w$, to help you write the equation.

$$P = 2 \quad l \quad + 2 \quad w$$
$$\downarrow \quad \downarrow \quad \downarrow \qquad \downarrow \quad \downarrow$$
$$68 = 2(w + 2) + 2 \cdot w$$

Replace *P* with 68.
Replace *l* with (*w* + 2).

Step 4 **Solve.**

$$68 = 2(w + 2) + 2w \qquad \text{Use the distributive property.}$$
$$68 = 2w + 4 + 2w \qquad \text{Combine like terms.}$$

$$68 = 4w + 4$$
$$\underline{ {}^{-}4 \qquad\quad {}^{-}4} \qquad \text{To get } 4w \text{ by itself, add } {}^{-}4 \text{ to both sides.}$$
$$64 = 4w + 0$$

$$\frac{64}{4} = \frac{4w}{4} \qquad \text{To get } w \text{ by itself, divide both sides by 4.}$$

$$16 = w$$

Step 5 **State the answer.**

w represents the width, and *w* = 16, so the width is 16 cm.

w + 2 represents the length. Replace *w* with 16.
$$\downarrow$$
$$16 + 2 = 18, \text{ so the length is 18 cm.}$$

Write **cm** as the label for both width and length.

The final answer is: The width is 16 cm and the length is 18 cm.

Step 6 **Check** the solution by putting the measurements on your sketch and going back to the original problem.

"The length of a rectangle is 2 cm more than the width."

18 cm is 2 cm more than 16 cm, so the solution checks.

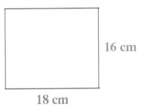
16 cm

18 cm

"The perimeter is 68 cm."

$$P = 2 \cdot 18 \text{ cm} + 2 \cdot 16 \text{ cm}$$
$$P = 36 \text{ cm} + 32 \text{ cm}$$
$$P = 68 \text{ cm} \;\leftarrow\; \text{This matches the perimeter given in the original problem, so the solution checks.}$$

Work Problem **3** *at the Side.* ▶

3 Make a sketch to help solve this problem.
The length of Ann's rectangular garden plot is 3 yd more than the width. She used 22 yd of fencing to go around the entire garden. Find the length and the width of the garden, using the six problem-solving steps.

ANSWER

3.

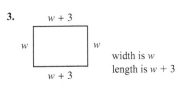

width is *w*
length is *w* + 3

$22 = 2(w + 3) + 2 \cdot w$
width is 4 yd
length is 7 yd

Check 7 yd is 3 yd more than 4 yd.
$P = 2 \cdot 7 \text{ yd} + 2 \cdot 4 \text{ yd} = 22 \text{ yd}$
Matches perimeter given in the original problem

4.9 ▶▶▶   **Exercises**

FOR
EXTRA
HELP   **MyMathLab**   Math XL
PRACTICE   WATCH   DOWNLOAD   READ   REVIEW

Solve each application problem using the six problem-solving steps you learned in this section. See Examples 1 and 2.

1. My sister is 9 years older than I am. The sum of our ages is 51. Find our ages.

2. Ed and Marge were candidates for city council. Marge won with 93 more votes than Ed. The total number of votes cast in the election was 587. Find the number of votes received by each candidate.

3. Last year, Lien earned $1500 more than her husband. Together they earned $37,500. How much did each of them earn?

4. A $149,000 estate is to be divided between two charities so that one charity receives $18,000 less than the other. How much will each charity receive?

5. Jason paid five times as much for his computer as he did for his printer. He paid a total of $1320 for both items. What did each item cost?

6. The attendance at the Saturday night baseball game was three times the attendance at Sunday's game. In all, 56,000 fans attended the games. How many fans were at each game?

7. A board is 78 cm long. Rosa cut the board into two pieces, with one piece 10 cm longer than the other. Find the length of both pieces. (*Hint:* Make a sketch of the board. Which piece do you know the least about? Let *x* represent the length of that piece.)

Longer piece ┆ Shorter piece

8. A rope is 21 yd long. Marcos cut it into two pieces so that one piece is 3 yd longer than the other. Find the length of each piece.

Longer piece ┆ Shorter piece

9. A wire is cut into two pieces, with one piece 7 ft shorter than the other. The wire was 31 ft long before it was cut. How long was each piece?

10. A 90 cm pipe is cut into two pieces so that one piece is 6 cm shorter than the other. Find the length of each piece.

11. In the U.S. Congress, the number of Representatives is 65 less than five times the number of Senators. There are a total of 535 members of Congress. Find the number of Senators and the number of Representatives. (*Source: World Almanac.*)

12. Florida's record low temperature is 68 degrees higher than Montana's record low. The sum of the two record lows is ⁻72 degrees. What is the record low for each state? (*Source*: National Climatic Data Center.)

13. A fence is 706 m long. It is to be cut into three parts. Two parts are the same length, and the third part is 25 m longer than either of the other two. Find the length of each part.

14. A wooden railing is 82 m long. It is to be divided into four pieces. Three pieces will be the same length, and the fourth piece will be 2 m longer than each of the other three. Find the length of each piece.

In Exercises 15–20, use the formula for the perimeter of a rectangle, $P = 2l + 2w$. Make a sketch to help you solve each problem. See Example 3. (Sketches may vary; show your sketches to your instructor.)

15. The perimeter of a rectangle is 48 yd. The width is 5 yd. Find the length.

16. The length of a rectangle is 27 cm, and the perimeter is 74 cm. Find the width of the rectangle.

17. A rectangular dog pen is twice as long as it is wide. The perimeter of the pen is 36 ft. Find the length and the width of the pen.

18. A new city park is a rectangular shape. The length is triple the width. It will take 240 meters of fencing to go around the park. Find the length and width of the park.

19. The length of a rectangular jewelry box is 3 in. more than twice the width. The perimeter is 36 in. Find the length and the width.

20. The perimeter of a rectangular house is 122 ft. The width is 5 ft less than the length. Find the length and the width.

21. A photograph measures 8 in. by 10 in. Earl put it in a frame that added 2 in. to every side. Find the outside perimeter and total area of the photograph and frame.

22. Barb had a 16 in. by 20 in. photograph. She cropped 3 in. off every side of the photo. What are the perimeter and the area of the cropped photo?

5

Positive and Negative Fractions

5.1 ▶▶▶ Introduction to Signed Fractions

OBJECTIVES

1. **Use a fraction to name part of a whole.**

2. **Identify numerators, denominators, proper fractions, and improper fractions.**

3. **Graph positive and negative fractions on a number line.**

4. **Find the absolute value of a fraction.**

5. **Write equivalent fractions.**

OBJECTIVE 1 Use a fraction to name part of a whole. Recall that a list of the integers can be written as follows.

$$\ldots, {}^{-}6, {}^{-}5, {}^{-}4, {}^{-}3, {}^{-}2, {}^{-}1, 0, 1, 2, 3, 4, 5, 6, \ldots$$

The dots show that the list goes on forever in both directions.

Now we will work with *fractions*.

> **Fractions**
>
> A **fraction** is a number of the form $\frac{a}{b}$ where a and b are integers and b is not 0.

One use for fractions is situations in which we need a number that is between two integers. Here is an example.

$\frac{2}{3}$ cup

A recipe uses $\frac{2}{3}$ cup of milk.

$\frac{2}{3}$ is between 0 and 1.

$\frac{2}{3}$ is a fraction because it is of the form $\frac{a}{b}$ and 2 and 3 are integers.

The number $\frac{2}{3}$ is a fraction that represents 2 of 3 equal parts. In this example, the cup is divided into 3 equal parts and we use enough milk to fill 2 of the parts.

We read $\frac{2}{3}$ as "two-thirds."

1 Write fractions for the shaded portion and the unshaded portion of each figure.

(a)

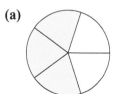

(b)

(c)

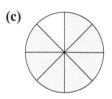

EXAMPLE 1   Using Fractions to Represent Part of One Whole

Use fractions to represent the shaded portion and the unshaded portion of each figure.

(a)

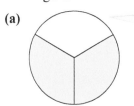

The whole circle must be divided into parts that are the *same* size.

The figure has 3 equal parts. The 2 shaded parts are represented by the fraction $\frac{2}{3}$. The *un*shaded part is $\frac{1}{3}$ of the figure.

(b)

The figure has 7 equal parts. The 4 shaded parts are represented by the fraction $\frac{4}{7}$. The *un*shaded part is $\frac{3}{7}$ of the figure.

◀ *Work Problem* **1** *at the Side.*

ANSWERS

1. (a) $\frac{3}{5}; \frac{2}{5}$ (b) $\frac{1}{6}; \frac{5}{6}$ (c) $\frac{7}{8}; \frac{1}{8}$

Fractions can also be used to represent more than one whole object.

EXAMPLE 2   Using Fractions to Represent More Than One Whole

Use a fraction to represent the shaded parts.

(a)

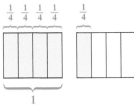

An area equal to 5 of the $\frac{1}{4}$ parts is shaded, so $\frac{5}{4}$ is shaded.

(b)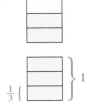

An area equal to 5 of the $\frac{1}{3}$ parts is shaded, so $\frac{5}{3}$ is shaded.

Work Problem **2** *at the Side.* ▶

OBJECTIVE 2 Identify numerators, denominators, proper fractions, and improper fractions.   In the fraction $\frac{2}{3}$, the number 2 is the *numerator* and 3 is the *denominator*. The bar between the numerator and the denominator is the *fraction bar*.

$$\text{Fraction bar} \rightarrow \frac{2}{3} \begin{array}{l} \leftarrow \text{Numerator} \\ \leftarrow \text{Denominator} \end{array}$$

Numerator and Denominator

The **denominator** of a fraction shows the number of equal parts in the whole, and the **numerator** shows how many parts are being considered.

Note

Recall that a fraction bar, —, is a symbol for division and division by 0 is *undefined*. Therefore a fraction with a denominator of 0 is also *undefined*.

EXAMPLE 3   Identifying Numerators and Denominators

Identify the numerator and denominator in each fraction. Then state the number of equal parts in the whole.

(a) $\dfrac{5}{9}$ $\dfrac{5}{9} \begin{array}{l} \leftarrow \text{Numerator} \\ \leftarrow \text{Denominator} \end{array}$

9 equal parts in the whole

(b) $\dfrac{11}{7}$ $\dfrac{11}{7} \begin{array}{l} \leftarrow \text{Numerator} \\ \leftarrow \text{Denominator} \end{array}$

7 equal parts in the whole

Work Problem **3** *at the Side.* ▶

Fractions are sometimes called *proper* or *improper* fractions.

Proper and Improper Fractions

If the numerator of a fraction is *less* than the denominator, the fraction is a **proper fraction.** A proper fraction is less than 1.

If the numerator is *greater than or equal to* the denominator, the fraction is an **improper fraction.** An improper fraction is greater than or equal to 1.

---

2 Write fractions for the shaded portions.

(a)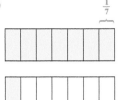

(b)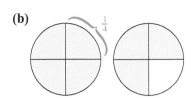

3 Identify the numerator and the denominator. Draw a picture with shaded parts to show each fraction. Your drawings may vary, but they should have the correct number of shaded parts.

(a) $\dfrac{2}{3}$

(b) $\dfrac{1}{4}$

(c) $\dfrac{8}{5}$

(d) $\dfrac{5}{2}$

ANSWERS

2. (a) $\dfrac{8}{7}$ **(b)** $\dfrac{7}{4}$

3. (a) N: 2; D: 3

(b) N: 1; D: 4

(c) N: 8; D: 5

(d) N: 5; D: 2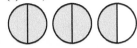

4 From this group of fractions:

$$\frac{3}{4} \quad \frac{8}{7} \quad \frac{5}{7} \quad \frac{6}{6} \quad \frac{1}{2} \quad \frac{2}{1}$$

(a) list all proper fractions.

Proper Fractions			Improper Fractions		
$\dfrac{1}{2}$	$\dfrac{5}{11}$	$\dfrac{35}{36}$	$\dfrac{9}{7}$	$\dfrac{126}{125}$	$\dfrac{7}{7}$

EXAMPLE 4 Classifying Types of Fractions

(a) Identify all proper fractions in this list.

$$\frac{3}{4} \quad \frac{5}{9} \quad \frac{17}{5} \quad \frac{9}{7} \quad \frac{3}{3} \quad \frac{12}{25} \quad \frac{1}{9} \quad \frac{5}{3}$$

Proper fractions have a numerator that is *less* than the denominator. The proper fractions in the list are shown below.

$$\frac{3}{4} \quad \leftarrow 3 \text{ is less than 4.} \qquad \frac{5}{9} \quad \frac{12}{25} \quad \frac{1}{9}$$

(b) Identify all improper fractions in the list in part (a).

Improper fractions have a numerator that is *equal to or greater* than the denominator. The improper fractions in the list are shown below.

$$\frac{17}{5} \quad \leftarrow 17 \text{ is greater than 5.} \qquad \frac{9}{7} \quad \frac{3}{3} \quad \frac{5}{3}$$

◀ *Work Problem* **4** *at the Side.*

CAUTION

In **Chapters 3–4** we used a raised negative sign to help you avoid confusion between negative numbers and subtraction. Now you are ready to start writing the negative sign in the more traditional way. In this chapter, the negative sign will still be red, but it will be centered on the number instead of raised: for example, -2 instead of $^-2$. When the negative sign might be confused with the sign for subtraction, we will write parentheses around the negative number. Here is an example.

$$3 - (-2) \quad \text{means} \quad 3 \text{ minus (negative 2)}$$

For fractions, the negative sign will be written in front of the fraction bar: for example, $-\frac{3}{4}$. As with integers, the negative sign tells you that a fraction is *less than 0;* it is to the *left* of 0 on the number line. When there is *no* sign in front of a fraction, the fraction is assumed to be positive. For example, $\frac{3}{4}$ is assumed to be $+\frac{3}{4}$. It is to the *right* of 0 on the number line.

(b) list all improper fractions.

OBJECTIVE **3** **Graph positive and negative fractions on a number line.** Sometimes we need *negative* numbers that are between two integers. For example, $-\frac{3}{4}$ is between 0 and -1. Graphing numbers on a number line helps us see the difference between $\frac{3}{4}$ and $-\frac{3}{4}$. Both represent 3 out of 4 equal parts, but they are in opposite directions from 0 on the number line. For $\frac{3}{4}$, divide the distance from 0 to 1 into 4 equal parts. Then start at 0, count over 3 parts, and make a dot. For $-\frac{3}{4}$, repeat the same process between 0 and -1.

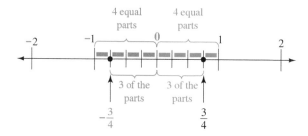

EXAMPLE 5 **Graphing Positive and Negative Fractions**

Graph each fraction on the number line.

(a) $\dfrac{2}{5}$

There is *no* sign in front of $\frac{2}{5}$, so it is *positive*. Because $\frac{2}{5}$ is between 0 and 1, we divide that space into 5 equal parts. Then we start at 0 and count to the right 2 parts.

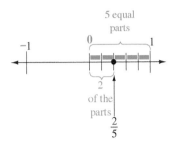

(b) $-\dfrac{4}{5}$

The fraction is *negative,* so it is between 0 and -1. We divide that space into 5 equal parts. Then we start at 0 and count to the left 4 parts.

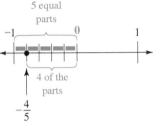

Work Problem **5** *at the Side.* ▶

OBJECTIVE **4** **Find the absolute value of a fraction.** In **Section 3.1** we said that the *absolute value* of a number was its distance from 0 on the number line. Two vertical bars indicate absolute value, as shown below.

$\left|-\dfrac{3}{4}\right|$ is read "the absolute value of negative three-fourths."

As with integers, the absolute value of fractions will *always* be positive (or 0) because it is the *distance* from 0 on the number line.

 EXAMPLE 6 **Finding the Absolute Value of Fractions**

Find each absolute value: $\left|\dfrac{1}{2}\right|$ and $\left|-\dfrac{1}{2}\right|$.

The distance from 0 to $\dfrac{1}{2}$ on the number line is $\dfrac{1}{2}$ space, so $\left|\dfrac{1}{2}\right| = \dfrac{1}{2}$.

The distance from 0 to $-\dfrac{1}{2}$ is also $\dfrac{1}{2}$ space, so $\left|-\dfrac{1}{2}\right| = \dfrac{1}{2}$.

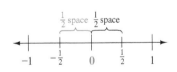

Work Problem **6** *at the Side.* ▶

5 Graph each fraction on the number line.

(a) $\dfrac{2}{4}$

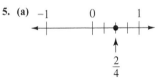

(b) $\dfrac{1}{2}$

(c) $-\dfrac{2}{3}$

6 Find each absolute value.

(a) $\left|-\dfrac{3}{4}\right|$

(b) $\left|\dfrac{5}{8}\right|$

(c) $|0|$

ANSWERS

5. (a)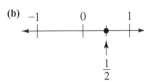

(b)

(c)

6. (a) $\dfrac{3}{4}$ **(b)** $\dfrac{5}{8}$ **(c)** 0
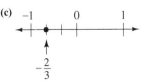

OBJECTIVE **5** **Write equivalent fractions.** You may have noticed in Margin Problems 5(a) and 5(b) on the previous page that $\frac{2}{4}$ and $\frac{1}{2}$ were at the same point on the number line. Both of them were halfway between 0 and 1. There are actually *many* different names for this point. We illustrate some of them below.

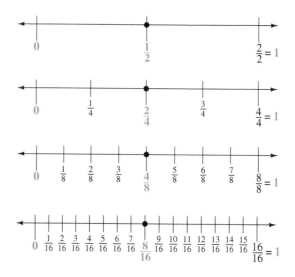

That is, $\frac{8}{16} = \frac{4}{8} = \frac{2}{4} = \frac{1}{2}$. If you have used a standard ruler with inches divided into sixteenths, you probably already noticed that these distances are the same. Although the fractions look different, they all name the same point that is halfway between 0 and 1. In other words, they have the same value. We say that they are *equivalent fractions.*

Equivalent Fractions

Fractions that represent the same number (the same point on a number line) are **equivalent fractions.**

Drawing number lines is tedious, so we usually find equivalent fractions by multiplying or dividing both the numerator and denominator by the same number. We can use some of the fractions that we just graphed to illustrate this method.

$$\frac{1}{2} = \frac{1 \cdot 2}{2 \cdot 2} = \frac{2}{4} \qquad\qquad \frac{8}{16} = \frac{8 \div 4}{16 \div 4} = \frac{2}{4}$$

Multiply both numerator   Divide both numerator
and denominator by 2.   and denominator by 4.

Writing Equivalent Fractions

If *a*, *b*, and *c* are numbers (and *b* and *c* are not 0), then:

$$\frac{a}{b} = \frac{a \cdot c}{b \cdot c} \qquad \text{or} \qquad \frac{a}{b} = \frac{a \div c}{b \div c}$$

In other words, if the numerator and denominator of a fraction are multiplied or divided by the *same* nonzero number, the result is an *equivalent* fraction.

EXAMPLE 7 **Writing Equivalent Fractions**

(a) Write $-\dfrac{1}{2}$ as an equivalent fraction with a denominator of 16.

In other words, $-\dfrac{1}{2} = -\dfrac{?}{16}$.

The original denominator is 2. *Multiplying* 2 times 8 gives 16, the new denominator. To write an equivalent fraction, multiply *both* the numerator and denominator by 8.

$$-\frac{1}{2} = -\frac{1 \cdot 8}{2 \cdot 8} = -\frac{8}{16}$$

> Multiply numerator and denominator by the *same* number.

Keep the negative sign.

So, $-\dfrac{1}{2}$ is equivalent to $-\dfrac{8}{16}$.

(b) Write $\dfrac{12}{15}$ as an equivalent fraction with a denominator of 5.

In other words, $\dfrac{12}{15} = \dfrac{?}{5}$.

The original denominator is 15. *Dividing* 15 by 3 gives 5, the new denominator. To write an equivalent fraction, divide *both* the numerator and denominator by 3.

$$\frac{12}{15} = \frac{12 \div 3}{15 \div 3} = \frac{4}{5}$$

> Divide numerator and denominator by the *same* number.

So, $\dfrac{12}{15}$ is equivalent to $\dfrac{4}{5}$.

Work Problem **7** *at the Side.* ▶

7 (a) Write $\frac{2}{5}$ as an equivalent fraction with a denominator of 20.

(b) Write $-\frac{21}{28}$ as an equivalent fraction with a denominator of 4.

Look back at the set of four number lines on the previous page. Notice that there are many different names for 1.

$$\frac{2}{2} = 1 \qquad \frac{4}{4} = 1 \qquad \frac{8}{8} = 1 \qquad \frac{16}{16} = 1$$

Because a fraction bar is a symbol for division, you can think of $\frac{2}{2}$ as $2 \div 2$, which equals 1. Similarly, $\frac{4}{4}$ is $4 \div 4$, which also is 1, and so on. These examples illustrate one of the division properties from **Section 3.6.**

Division Properties

If a is any number (except 0), then $\dfrac{a}{a} = 1$. In other words, when a nonzero number is divided by itself, the result is 1.

For example: $\dfrac{6}{6} = 1$ and $\dfrac{-4}{-4} = 1$

Also recall that when any number is divided by 1, the result is the number. That is, $\dfrac{a}{1} = a$.

For example: $\dfrac{6}{1} = 6$ and $-\dfrac{12}{1} = -12$

ANSWERS

7. **(a)** $\dfrac{2}{5} = \dfrac{2 \cdot 4}{5 \cdot 4} = \dfrac{8}{20}$

   (b) $-\dfrac{21}{28} = -\dfrac{21 \div 7}{28 \div 7} = -\dfrac{3}{4}$

8 Simplify each fraction by dividing the numerator by the denominator.

(a) $\dfrac{10}{10}$

(b) $-\dfrac{3}{1}$

(c) $\dfrac{8}{2}$

(d) $-\dfrac{25}{5}$

EXAMPLE 8 **Using Division to Simplify Fractions**

Simplify each fraction by dividing the numerator by the denominator.

(a) $\dfrac{5}{5}$ Think of $\dfrac{5}{5}$ as $5 \div 5$. The result is 1, so $\dfrac{5}{5} = 1$.

> A fraction bar is a symbol for division.

(b) $-\dfrac{12}{4}$ Think of $-\dfrac{12}{4}$ as $-12 \div 4$. The result is -3, so $-\dfrac{12}{4} = -3$.

> Keep the negative sign.

(c) $\dfrac{6}{1}$ Think of $\dfrac{6}{1}$ as $6 \div 1$. The result is 6, so $\dfrac{6}{1} = 6$.

◀ *Work Problem* **8** *at the Side.*

Note

The title of this chapter is "Rational Numbers: Positive and Negative Fractions." *Rational numbers* are numbers that can be written in the form $\dfrac{a}{b}$, where a and b are integers and b is not 0. In Example 8(c) above, you saw that an integer can be written in the form $\dfrac{a}{b}$ (6 can be written as $\frac{6}{1}$). So rational numbers include all the integers and all the fractions. In **Chapter 6** you'll work with rational numbers that are in decimal form.

5.1 ▶▶▶ **Exercises**

FOR EXTRA HELP

MyMathLab

Math XL
PRACTICE

WATCH

DOWNLOAD

READ

REVIEW

Write the fractions that represent the shaded and unshaded portions of each figure. See Examples 1 and 2.

1.

2.

3.

4.

5.

6.

7.

8.

9. What fraction of these coins are dimes? What fraction are pennies? What fraction are nickels?

10. What fraction of these recording artists are men? What fraction are women? What fraction are wearing something white?

11. Of the 71 computers in the lab, 58 are laptops. What fraction of the computers are *not* laptops? What fraction are laptops?

12. A community college basketball team has 12 members. If five of the players are sophomores and the rest are freshmen, find the fraction of the members that are sophomores and the fraction that are freshmen.

The circle graph shows the results of a survey on where women would like to have flowers delivered on Valentine's Day. Use the graph to answer Exercises 13–14.

13. **(a)** What fraction of the women would like flowers delivered at work? **(b)** Delivered at home or at work?

14. **(a)** What fraction picked a location other than home or work? **(b)** What fraction picked at home or other?

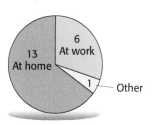

Delivering Flowers On Valentine's Day

13 At home

6 At work

1 Other

Out of every 20 women surveyed, the number who would like flowers delivered at home, at work, or elsewhere.

Source: FTD, Inc.

Identify the numerator and denominator in each fraction. Then state the number of equal parts in the whole. See Example 3.

15. $\dfrac{3}{4}$ **16.** $\dfrac{5}{8}$ **17.** $\dfrac{12}{7}$ **18.** $\dfrac{8}{3}$

List the proper and improper fractions in each group of numbers. See Example 4.

	Proper	Improper		Proper	Improper
19. $\dfrac{8}{5}, \dfrac{1}{3}, \dfrac{5}{8}, \dfrac{6}{6}, \dfrac{12}{2}, \dfrac{7}{16}$	_____	_____	**20.** $\dfrac{1}{6}, \dfrac{5}{8}, \dfrac{15}{14}, \dfrac{11}{9}, \dfrac{7}{7}, \dfrac{3}{4}$	_____	_____

Graph each pair of fractions on the number line. See Example 5.

21. $\dfrac{1}{4}, -\dfrac{1}{4}$ **22.** $-\dfrac{1}{3}, \dfrac{1}{3}$ **23.** $-\dfrac{3}{5}, \dfrac{3}{5}$

24. $\dfrac{5}{6}, -\dfrac{5}{6}$ **25.** $\dfrac{7}{8}, -\dfrac{7}{8}$ **26.** $-\dfrac{3}{4}, \dfrac{3}{4}$

Write a positive or negative fraction to describe each situation.

27. The baby lost $\frac{3}{4}$ pound in weight while she was sick.

28. Greta needed $\frac{1}{3}$ cup of brown sugar for the cookie recipe.

29. Barb Brown's driveway is $\frac{3}{10}$ mile long.

30. The oil level in my car is $\frac{1}{2}$ quart below normal.

Find each absolute value. See Example 6.

31. $\left| -\dfrac{2}{5} \right|$ **32.** $\left| -\dfrac{4}{4} \right|$ **33.** $|0|$ **34.** $\left| \dfrac{9}{10} \right|$

35. Rewrite each fraction as an equivalent fraction with a denominator of 24. See Example 7.

(a) $\dfrac{1}{2} = \dfrac{}{24}$ **(b)** $\dfrac{1}{3} = \text{---}$ **(c)** $\dfrac{2}{3} = \text{---}$ **(d)** $\dfrac{1}{4} = \text{---}$ **(e)** $\dfrac{3}{4} = \text{---}$

(f) $\dfrac{1}{6} = \text{---}$ **(g)** $\dfrac{5}{6} = \text{---}$ **(h)** $\dfrac{1}{8} = \text{---}$ **(i)** $\dfrac{3}{8} = \text{---}$ **(j)** $\dfrac{5}{8} = \text{---}$

36. Rewrite each fraction as an equivalent fraction with a denominator of 36. See Example 7.

(a) $\dfrac{1}{2} = \dfrac{}{36}$ (b) $\dfrac{1}{3} = \text{---}$ (c) $\dfrac{2}{3} = \text{---}$ (d) $\dfrac{1}{4} = \text{---}$ (e) $\dfrac{3}{4} = \text{---}$

(f) $\dfrac{1}{6} = \text{---}$ (g) $\dfrac{5}{6} = \text{---}$ (h) $\dfrac{1}{9} = \text{---}$ (i) $\dfrac{4}{9} = \text{---}$ (j) $\dfrac{8}{9} = \text{---}$

37. Rewrite each fraction as an equivalent fraction with a denominator of 3. See Example 7.

(a) $-\dfrac{2}{6} = -\dfrac{}{3}$ (b) $-\dfrac{4}{6} = \text{---}$ (c) $-\dfrac{12}{18} = \text{---}$ (d) $-\dfrac{6}{18} = \text{---}$ (e) $-\dfrac{200}{300} = \text{---}$

(f) Write two more fractions that are equivalent to $-\frac{1}{3}$ and two more fractions equivalent to $-\frac{2}{3}$.

38. Rewrite each fraction as an equivalent fraction with a denominator of 4. See Example 7.

(a) $-\dfrac{2}{8} = -\dfrac{}{4}$ (b) $-\dfrac{6}{8} = \text{---}$ (c) $-\dfrac{15}{20} = \text{---}$ (d) $-\dfrac{50}{200} = \text{---}$ (e) $-\dfrac{150}{200} = \text{---}$

(f) Write two more fractions that are equivalent to $-\frac{1}{4}$ and two more fractions equivalent to $-\frac{3}{4}$.

Relating Concepts (Exercises 39–42) For Individual or Group Work

*Use your calculator as you **work Exercises 39–42 in order.***

39. (a) Write $\frac{3}{8}$ as an equivalent fraction with a denominator of 3912.

    (b) Explain how you solved part (a).

40. (a) Write $\frac{7}{9}$ as an equivalent fraction with a denominator of 5472.

    (b) Explain how you solved part (a).

41. (a) Is $-\dfrac{697}{3485}$ equivalent to $-\dfrac{1}{2}$, $-\dfrac{1}{3}$, or $-\dfrac{1}{5}$?

    (b) Explain how you solved part (a).

42. (a) Is $-\dfrac{817}{4902}$ equivalent to $-\dfrac{1}{4}$, $-\dfrac{1}{6}$, or $-\dfrac{1}{8}$?

    (b) Explain how you solved part (a).

43. Can you write $\frac{3}{5}$ as an equivalent fraction with a denominator of 18? Explain why or why not. If not, what denominators could you use instead of 18?

44. Can you write $\frac{3}{4}$ as an equivalent fraction with a denominator of 0? Explain why or why not.

Simplify each fraction by dividing the numerator by the denominator. See Example 8.

45. $\dfrac{10}{1}$ **46.** $\dfrac{9}{9}$ **47.** $-\dfrac{16}{16}$ **48.** $-\dfrac{7}{1}$

49. $-\dfrac{18}{3}$ **50.** $-\dfrac{40}{4}$ **51.** $\dfrac{24}{8}$ **52.** $\dfrac{42}{6}$

53. $\dfrac{14}{7}$ **54.** $\dfrac{8}{2}$ **55.** $-\dfrac{90}{10}$ **56.** $-\dfrac{45}{9}$

57. $\dfrac{150}{150}$ **58.** $\dfrac{55}{5}$ **59.** $-\dfrac{32}{4}$ **60.** $-\dfrac{200}{200}$

There are many correct ways to draw the answers for Exercises 61–68, so ask your instructor to check your work.

61. Shade $\frac{3}{5}$ of this figure. What fraction is unshaded?

62. Shade $\frac{5}{6}$ of this figure. What fraction is unshaded?

63. Shade $\frac{3}{8}$ of this figure. What fraction is unshaded?

64. Shade $\frac{1}{3}$ of this figure. What fraction is unshaded?

65. Draw a group of figures. Make $\frac{1}{10}$ of the figures circles, $\frac{6}{10}$ of the figures squares, and $\frac{3}{10}$ of the figures triangles. Then shade $\frac{1}{6}$ of the squares and $\frac{2}{3}$ of the triangles.

66. Write a group of capital letters. Make $\frac{4}{9}$ of the letters A's, $\frac{2}{9}$ of the letters B's, and $\frac{3}{9}$ of the letters C's. Then draw a line under $\frac{3}{4}$ of the A's and $\frac{1}{2}$ of the B's.

67. Draw a group of punctuation marks. Make $\frac{5}{12}$ of them exclamation points, $\frac{1}{12}$ of them commas, $\frac{3}{12}$ of them periods, and add enough question marks to make a full $\frac{12}{12}$ in all. Then circle $\frac{2}{5}$ of the exclamation points.

68. Draw a group of symbols. Make $\frac{2}{15}$ of them addition signs, $\frac{4}{15}$ of them subtraction signs, $\frac{2}{15}$ of them division signs, and add enough equal signs to make a full $\frac{15}{15}$ in all. Then circle $\frac{3}{4}$ of the subtraction signs.

5.2 ▶▶▶ Writing Fractions in Lowest Terms

OBJECTIVE 1 Identify fractions written in lowest terms. You can see from these drawings that $\frac{1}{2}$ and $\frac{4}{8}$ are different names for the same amount of pizza.

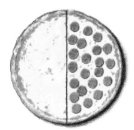

$\frac{1}{2}$ of the pizza has pepperoni on it.

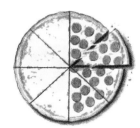

$\frac{4}{8}$ of the pizza has pepperoni on it.

You saw in the last section that $\frac{1}{2}$ and $\frac{4}{8}$ are equivalent fractions. But we say that the fraction $\frac{1}{2}$ is in *lowest terms* because the numerator and denominator have no *common factor* other than 1. That means that 1 is the only number that divides evenly into both 1 and 2. However, the fraction $\frac{4}{8}$ is *not* in lowest terms because its numerator and denominator have a common factor of 4. That means 4 will divide evenly into both 4 and 8.

> **Note**
> Recall that *factors* are numbers being multiplied to give a product. For example,
> $1 \cdot 4 = 4$, so 1 and 4 are factors of 4.
> $2 \cdot 4 = 8$, so 2 and 4 are factors of 8.
> 4 is a factor of both 4 and 8, so 4 is a *common factor* of those numbers.

> **Writing a Fraction in Lowest Terms**
> A fraction is written in **lowest terms** when the numerator and denominator have no common factor other than 1. Examples are $\frac{1}{3}$, $\frac{3}{4}$, $\frac{2}{5}$, and $\frac{7}{10}$.
>
> When you work with fractions, always write the final answer in lowest terms.

EXAMPLE 1 Identifying Fractions Written in Lowest Terms

Are the following fractions in lowest terms? If not, find a common factor of the numerator and denominator (other than 1).

(a) $\frac{3}{8}$

The numerator and denominator have no common factor other than 1, so the fraction is in lowest terms.

(b) $\frac{21}{36}$

The numerator and denominator have a common factor of 3, so the fraction is *not* in lowest terms.

Work Problem **1** *at the Side.* ▶

OBJECTIVES

1 Identify fractions written in lowest terms.

2 Write a fraction in lowest terms using common factors.

3 Write a number as a product of prime factors.

4 Write a fraction in lowest terms using prime factorization.

5 Write a fraction with variables in lowest terms.

1 Are the following fractions in lowest terms? If not, find a common factor of the numerator and denominator (other than 1).

(a) $\frac{2}{3}$

(b) $-\frac{8}{10}$

(c) $-\frac{9}{11}$

(d) $\frac{15}{20}$

ANSWERS
1. **(a)** yes **(b)** No; 2 is a common factor.
   (c) yes **(d)** No; 5 is a common factor.

2 Divide by a common factor to write each fraction in lowest terms.

(a) $\dfrac{5}{10}$

(b) $\dfrac{9}{12}$

(c) $-\dfrac{24}{30}$

(d) $\dfrac{15}{40}$

(e) $-\dfrac{50}{90}$

OBJECTIVE 2 Write a fraction in lowest terms using common factors. We will show you two methods for writing a fraction in lowest terms. The first method, dividing by a common factor, works best when the numerator and denominator are small numbers.

EXAMPLE 2 Using Common Factors to Write Fractions in Lowest Terms

Divide by a common factor to write each fraction in lowest terms.

(a) $\dfrac{20}{24}$

The *greatest* common factor of 20 and 24 is 4. Divide both numerator and denominator by 4.

$$\frac{20}{24} = \frac{20 \div 4}{24 \div 4} = \frac{5}{6}$$

(b) $\dfrac{30}{50} = \dfrac{30 \div 10}{50 \div 10} = \dfrac{3}{5}$ Divide both numerator and denominator by 10.

(c) $-\dfrac{24}{42} = -\dfrac{24 \div 6}{42 \div 6} = -\dfrac{4}{7}$ Divide both numerator and denominator by 6. Keep the negative sign.

(d) $\dfrac{60}{72}$

Suppose we made an error and thought that 4 was the greatest common factor of 60 and 72. Dividing by 4 gives the following.

$$\frac{60}{72} = \frac{60 \div 4}{72 \div 4} = \frac{15}{18}$$

But $\frac{15}{18}$ is *not* in lowest terms because 15 and 18 have a common factor of 3. Therefore, divide the numerator and denominator by 3.

$$\frac{15}{18} = \frac{15 \div 3}{18 \div 3} = \frac{5}{6} \leftarrow \text{Lowest terms}$$

The fraction $\frac{60}{72}$ could have been written in lowest terms in one step by dividing by 12, the *greatest* common factor of 60 and 72.

$$\frac{60}{72} = \frac{60 \div 12}{72 \div 12} = \frac{5}{6} \quad \left\{ \begin{array}{l}\text{Same answer} \\ \text{as above}\end{array}\right.$$

Either way works. Just keep dividing until the fraction is in lowest terms.

This method of writing a fraction in lowest terms by dividing by a common factor is summarized below.

Dividing by a Common Factor to Write a Fraction in Lowest Terms

Step 1 Find the *greatest* number that will divide evenly into both the numerator and denominator. This number is a ***common factor.***

Step 2 **Divide** both numerator and denominator by the common factor.

Step 3 **Check** to see if the new numerator and denominator have any common factors (besides 1). If they do, repeat Steps 2 and 3. If the only common factor is 1, the fraction is in lowest terms.

◀ *Work Problem* **2** *at the Side.*

OBJECTIVE 3 Write a number as a product of prime factors.
In Example 2(d) on the previous page, the greatest common factor of 60 and 72 was difficult to see quickly. You can handle a problem like that by writing the numerator and denominator as a product of *prime numbers*.

3 Label each number as *prime* or *composite* or *neither*.
1, 2, 3, 4, 7, 9, 13, 19, 25, 29

> **Prime Numbers**
>
> A **prime number** is a whole number that has exactly *two different* factors, itself and 1.

The number 3 is a prime number because it can be divided evenly only by itself and 1. The number 8 is *not* a prime number. The number 8 is a *composite number* because it can be divided evenly by 2 and 4, as well as by itself and 1.

> **Composite Numbers**
>
> A number with a factor other than itself or 1 is called a **composite number.**

> **CAUTION**
>
> A prime number has *only two* different factors, itself and 1. The number 1 is *not* a prime number because it does not have *two different* factors; the only factor of 1 is 1. Also, 0 is *not* a prime number. Therefore, 0 and 1 are *neither* prime nor composite numbers.

EXAMPLE 3 Finding Prime Numbers

Label each number as *prime* or *composite* or *neither*.

0   2   5   10   11   15

First, 0 is *neither* prime nor composite. Next, 2, 5, and 11, are *prime*. Each of these numbers is divisible only by itself and 1. The number 10 can be divided by 5 and 2, so it is *composite*. Also, 15 is a *composite* number because 15 can be divided by 5 and 3.

Work Problem **3** *at the Side.* ▶

For reference, here are the prime numbers smaller than 100.

2	3	5	7	11
13	17	19	23	29
31	37	41	43	47
53	59	61	67	71
73	79	83	89	97

> **CAUTION**
>
> All prime numbers are odd numbers except the number 2. Be careful though, because *not all odd numbers are prime numbers*. For example, 9, 15, and 21 are odd numbers but they are *not* prime numbers.

The *prime factorization* of a number can be especially useful when working with fractions.

> **Prime Factorization**
>
> A **prime factorization** of a number is a factorization in which every factor is a prime number.

ANSWERS

3. 2, 3, 7, 13, 19, and 29 are *prime*.
4, 9, and 25 are *composite*.
1 is *neither* prime nor composite.

4 Find the prime factorization of each number.

(a) 8

(b) 42

(c) 90

(d) 100

(e) 81

EXAMPLE 4   **Factoring Using the Division Method**

(a) Find the prime factorization of 48.

$2\overline{)48}$ ⟵ Divide 48 by 2 (the first prime number); quotient is 24

$2\overline{)24}$ ⟵ Divide 24 by 2; quotient is 12

All the divisors are prime factors.

$2\overline{)12}$ ⟵ Divide 12 by 2; quotient is 6

$2\overline{)6}$ ⟵ Divide 6 by 2; quotient is 3

$3\overline{)3}$ ⟵ Divide 3 by 3; quotient is 1

1 ⟵ Continue to divide until the quotient is 1

Because all the factors (divisors) are prime, the prime factorization of 48 is

$$2 \cdot 2 \cdot 2 \cdot 2 \cdot 3$$

Check by multiplying the factors to see if the product is 48.
Yes, 2 • 2 • 2 • 2 • 3 does equal 48.

> **Note**
>
> You may write the factors in any order because multiplication is commutative. So you could write the factorization of 48 as 3 • 2 • 2 • 2 • 2. We will show the factors from least to greatest in our examples.

(b) Find the prime factorization of 225.

$3\overline{)225}$ ⟵ 225 is not divisible by 2 (first prime) so use 3 (next prime)

All the divisors are prime factors.

$3\overline{)75}$ ⟵ Divide 75 by 3

$5\overline{)25}$ ⟵ 25 is not divisible by 3; use 5

$5\overline{)5}$ ⟵ Divide 5 by 5

1 ⟵ Quotient is 1

$225 = 3 \cdot 3 \cdot 5 \cdot 5$ CHECK: 3 • 3 is 9; 9 • 5 is 45; 45 • 5 is **225**

> **CAUTION**
>
> When you're using the division method of factoring, the last quotient is 1. Do **not** list 1 as a prime factor because 1 is not a prime number.

◀ *Work Problem* **4** *at the Side.*

Another method of factoring uses what is called a *factor tree*.

EXAMPLE 5   **Factoring Using a Factor Tree**

Find the prime factorization of each number.

(a) 60

Try to divide 60 by the first prime number, 2. The quotient is 30. Write the factors 2 and 30 under the 60. Circle the 2, because it is a prime.

60

Continued on Next Page

ANSWERS

4. **(a)** 2 • 2 • 2   **(b)** 2 • 3 • 7
   (c) 2 • 3 • 3 • 5   **(d)** 2 • 2 • 5 • 5
   (e) 3 • 3 • 3 • 3

Try dividing 30 by 2. The quotient is 15. Write the factors 2 and 15 under the 30.

60
② 30
② 15

Because 15 cannot be divided evenly by 2, try dividing 15 by the next prime number, 3. The quotient is 5. Write the factors 3 and 5 under the 15.

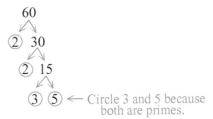

60
② 30
② 15
③ ⑤ ← Circle 3 and 5 because both are primes.

No uncircled factors remain, so you have found the prime factorization (the circled factors).

$$60 = 2 \cdot 2 \cdot 3 \cdot 5$$

CHECK: 2 • 2 is 4;
4 • 3 is 12; 12 • 5 is **60**

(b) 72

Divide 72 by 2, the first prime number.

72
② 36 ← Divide by 2 again; 36 = 2 • 18
② 18 ← Divide by 2 again; 18 = 2 • 9
② 9 ← Divide by 3; 9 = 3 • 3
③ ③

$$72 = 2 \cdot 2 \cdot 2 \cdot 3 \cdot 3$$

(c) 45

Because 45 cannot be divided evenly by 2, try dividing by the next prime, 3.

45
③ 15 ← Divide by 3 again.
③ ⑤

$$45 = 3 \cdot 3 \cdot 5$$

CHECK: 3 • 3 is 9;
9 • 5 is **45**.

Note

Here is a reminder about the quick way to see whether a number is *divisible* by 2, 3, or 5; in other words, there is no remainder when you do the division.

A number is divisible by 2 if the ones digit is 0, 2, 4, 6, or 8. For example, 30, 512, 76, and 3018 are all divisible by 2.

A number is divisible by 3 if the *sum* of the digits is divisible by 3. For example, 129 is divisible by 3 because $1 + 2 + 9 = 12$ and 12 is divisible by 3.

A number is divisible by 5 if the ones digit is 0 or 5. For example, 85, 610, and 1725 are all divisible by 5.

Work Problem **5** *at the Side.* ▶

5 Complete each factor tree and write the prime factorization.

(a)   28

28
② 14
○ ○

(b)   35

35
⑤

(c) 90

90

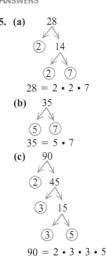

⊞ **Calculator Tip** You can use your calculator to find the prime factorization of a number. Here is an example that uses 539.

Try dividing 539 by the first prime number, 2.

539 ⊕ 2 ⊜ **269.5**   Does not divide evenly

Try dividing 539 by the next prime number, 3.

539 ⊕ 3 ⊜ **179.6666667**   Does not divide evenly

Keep trying the next prime numbers until you find one that divides evenly.

539 ⊕ 5 ⊜ **107.8**   Does not divide evenly

539 ⊕ 7 ⊜ **77**   Divides evenly

Once you have found that 7 works, try using it again on the quotient 77.

77 ⊕ 7 ⊜ **11**   Divides evenly

Because 11 is prime, you're finished. The prime factorization of 539 is $7 \cdot 7 \cdot 11$.

Now try factoring 2431 using your calculator. (The answer is at the bottom left of this page.)

OBJECTIVE 4 **Write a fraction in lowest terms using prime factorization.** Now you can use the second method for writing fractions in lowest terms: prime factorization. This is a good method to use when the numerator and denominator are larger numbers or include variables.

EXAMPLE 6 **Using Prime Factorization to Write Fractions in Lowest Terms**

(a) Write $\frac{20}{35}$ in lowest terms.

20 can be written as $2 \cdot 2 \cdot 5$ ← Prime factors
35 can be written as $5 \cdot 7$ ← Prime factors

$$\frac{20}{35} = \frac{2 \cdot 2 \cdot 5}{5 \cdot 7}$$

The numerator and denominator have 5 as a common factor. Dividing both numerator and denominator by 5 will give an equivalent fraction.

Any number divided by itself is 1

$$\frac{20}{35} = \frac{2 \cdot 2 \cdot 5}{5 \cdot 7} = \frac{2 \cdot 2 \cdot 5}{7 \cdot 5} = \frac{2 \cdot 2 \cdot \boxed{5 \div 5}}{7 \cdot \boxed{5 \div 5}} = \frac{2 \cdot 2 \cdot 1}{7 \cdot 1} = \frac{4}{7}$$

Multiplication is commutative.

$\frac{20}{35}$ is written in lowest terms as $\frac{4}{7}$.

To shorten the work, you may use slashes to indicate the divisions. For example, the work on $\frac{20}{35}$ can be shown as follows.

$$\frac{20}{35} = \frac{2 \cdot 2 \cdot \overset{1}{\cancel{5}}}{\underset{1}{\cancel{5}} \cdot 7}$$

Slashes indicate $5 \div 5$, and the result is 1

Continued on Next Page

(b) Write $\frac{60}{72}$ in lowest terms.

Use the prime factorizations of 60 and 72 from Examples 5(a) and 5(b) on pages 418–419.

$$\frac{60}{72} = \frac{2 \cdot 2 \cdot 3 \cdot 5}{2 \cdot 2 \cdot 2 \cdot 3 \cdot 3}$$

This time there are three common factors. Use slashes to show the three divisions.

$$\frac{60}{72} = \frac{\overset{1}{\cancel{2}} \cdot \overset{1}{\cancel{2}} \cdot \overset{1}{\cancel{3}} \cdot 5}{\underset{1}{\cancel{2}} \cdot \underset{1}{\cancel{2}} \cdot 2 \cdot \underset{1}{\cancel{3}} \cdot 3} = \frac{5}{6}$$ ← Multiply 1 · 1 · 1 · 5 to get 5
← Multiply 1 · 1 · 2 · 1 · 3 to get 6

2 ÷ 2 is 1   2 ÷ 2 is 1   3 ÷ 3 is 1

(c) $\dfrac{18}{90}$

$$\frac{18}{90} = \frac{\overset{1}{\cancel{2}} \cdot \overset{1}{\cancel{3}} \cdot \overset{1}{\cancel{3}}}{\underset{1}{\cancel{2}} \cdot \underset{1}{\cancel{3}} \cdot \underset{1}{\cancel{3}} \cdot 5} = \frac{1}{5}$$ ← Multiply 1 · 1 · 1 to get 1
← Multiply 1 · 1 · 1 · 5 to get 5

> **CAUTION**
> In Example 6(c) above, all factors of the numerator divided out. But 1 · 1 · 1 is still 1, so the final answer is $\frac{1}{5}$ (*not* 5).

This method of using prime factorization to write a fraction in lowest terms is summarized below.

> **Using Prime Factorization to Write a Fraction in Lowest Terms**
> **Step 1** Write the **prime factorization** of both numerator and denominator.
> **Step 2** Use slashes to show where you are **dividing** the numerator and denominator by any common factors.
> **Step 3** **Multiply** the remaining factors in the numerator and in the denominator.

Work Problem **6** *at the Side.* ▶

OBJECTIVE 5 Write a fraction with variables in lowest terms.
Fractions may have variables in the numerator or denominator. Examples are shown below.

$$\frac{6}{2x} \qquad \frac{3xy}{9xy} \qquad \frac{4b^3}{8ab} \qquad \frac{7ab^2}{n^2}$$

You can use prime factorization to write these fractions in lowest terms.

---

6 Use the method of prime factorization to write each fraction in lowest terms.

(a) $\dfrac{16}{48}$

(b) $\dfrac{28}{60}$

(c) $\dfrac{74}{111}$

(d) $\dfrac{124}{340}$

ANSWERS

6. **(a)** $\dfrac{\overset{1}{\cancel{2}} \cdot \overset{1}{\cancel{2}} \cdot \overset{1}{\cancel{2}} \cdot \overset{1}{\cancel{2}}}{\underset{1}{\cancel{2}} \cdot \underset{1}{\cancel{2}} \cdot \underset{1}{\cancel{2}} \cdot \underset{1}{\cancel{2}} \cdot 3} = \dfrac{1}{3}$

(b) $\dfrac{\overset{1}{\cancel{2}} \cdot \overset{1}{\cancel{2}} \cdot 7}{\underset{1}{\cancel{2}} \cdot \underset{1}{\cancel{2}} \cdot 3 \cdot 5} = \dfrac{7}{15}$

(c) $\dfrac{2 \cdot \overset{1}{\cancel{37}}}{3 \cdot \underset{1}{\cancel{37}}} = \dfrac{2}{3}$

(d) $\dfrac{\overset{1}{\cancel{2}} \cdot \overset{1}{\cancel{2}} \cdot 31}{\underset{1}{\cancel{2}} \cdot \underset{1}{\cancel{2}} \cdot 5 \cdot 17} = \dfrac{31}{85}$

7 Write each fraction in lowest terms.

(a) $\dfrac{5c}{15}$

(b) $\dfrac{10x^2}{8x^2}$

(c) $\dfrac{9a^3}{11b^3}$

(d) $\dfrac{6m^2n}{9n^2}$

EXAMPLE 7 **Writing Fractions with Variables in Lowest Terms**

Write each fraction in lowest terms.

(a) $\dfrac{6}{2x}$ ← Prime factors of 6 are $2 \cdot 3$
  ← $2x$ means $2 \cdot x$.

$$\frac{6}{2x} = \frac{\overset{1}{\cancel{2}} \cdot 3}{\cancel{2} \cdot x} = \frac{3}{x}$$
  ← $1 \cdot 3$ is 3
  ← $1 \cdot x$ is x

(b) $3xy$ means $3 \cdot x \cdot y$

$$\frac{3xy}{9xy} = \frac{3 \cdot x \cdot y}{3 \cdot 3 \cdot x \cdot y} = \frac{\overset{1}{\cancel{3}} \cdot \overset{1}{\cancel{x}} \cdot \overset{1}{\cancel{y}}}{\cancel{3} \cdot 3 \cdot \cancel{x} \cdot \cancel{y}} = \frac{1}{3}$$

The prime factors of 9 are $3 \cdot 3$

> Be careful! In the numerator, $1 \cdot 1 \cdot 1$ is 1. The answer is $\frac{1}{3}$ (**not** 3).

(c) b^3 means $b \cdot b \cdot b$

$$\frac{4b^3}{8ab} = \frac{2 \cdot 2 \cdot b \cdot b \cdot b}{2 \cdot 2 \cdot 2 \cdot a \cdot b} = \frac{\overset{1}{\cancel{2}} \cdot \overset{1}{\cancel{2}} \cdot \overset{1}{\cancel{b}} \cdot b \cdot b}{\cancel{2} \cdot \cancel{2} \cdot 2 \cdot a \cdot \cancel{b}} = \frac{b^2}{2a}$$
  ← $b \cdot b$ is b^2
  ← $2 \cdot a$ is $2a$

The prime factors of 8 are $2 \cdot 2 \cdot 2$

(d) $\dfrac{7ab^2}{n^2} = \dfrac{7 \cdot a \cdot b \cdot b}{n \cdot n}$ There are no common factors.

$\dfrac{7ab^2}{n^2}$ is already in lowest terms.

◀ *Work Problem* **7** *at the Side.*

ANSWERS

7. (a) $\dfrac{\overset{1}{\cancel{5}} \cdot c}{3 \cdot \cancel{5}} = \dfrac{1c}{3}$ or $\dfrac{c}{3}$

(b) $\dfrac{\overset{1}{\cancel{2}} \cdot 5 \cdot \overset{1}{\cancel{x}} \cdot \overset{1}{\cancel{x}}}{\cancel{2} \cdot 2 \cdot 2 \cdot \cancel{x} \cdot \cancel{x}} = \dfrac{5}{4}$

(c) already in lowest terms

(d) $\dfrac{2 \cdot \overset{1}{\cancel{3}} \cdot m \cdot m \cdot \overset{1}{\cancel{n}}}{\cancel{3} \cdot 3 \cdot n \cdot \cancel{n}} = \dfrac{2m^2}{3n}$

Are the following fractions in lowest terms? If not, find a common factor of the numerator and denominator (other than 1). See Example 1.

1. (a) $-\dfrac{3}{10}$ (b) $\dfrac{10}{15}$ (c) $\dfrac{9}{16}$ (d) $-\dfrac{4}{21}$ (e) $\dfrac{6}{9}$ (f) $-\dfrac{7}{28}$

2. (a) $\dfrac{10}{12}$ (b) $\dfrac{3}{18}$ (c) $-\dfrac{8}{15}$ (d) $-\dfrac{22}{33}$ (e) $\dfrac{2}{25}$ (f) $-\dfrac{14}{15}$

Write each fraction in lowest terms. Use the method of dividing by a common factor. See Example 2.

◉ 3. (a) $\dfrac{10}{15}$ (b) $\dfrac{6}{9}$ (c) $-\dfrac{7}{28}$ (d) $-\dfrac{25}{50}$ (e) $\dfrac{16}{18}$ (f) $-\dfrac{8}{20}$

4. (a) $\dfrac{10}{12}$ (b) $\dfrac{3}{18}$ (c) $-\dfrac{22}{33}$ (d) $\dfrac{12}{16}$ (e) $-\dfrac{15}{20}$ (f) $-\dfrac{9}{15}$

Label each number as prime *or* composite *or* neither. *See Example 3.*

5.   9   2   8   1   5   11   10   21

6.   12   3   7   6   0   15   13   25

Find the prime factorization of each number. See Examples 4 and 5.

7. 6   **8.** 12   **9.** 20   **10.** 30

11. 25   **12.** 18   **◉ 13.** 36   **14.** 56

15. (a) 44   **16.** (a) 45   **17.** (a) 75   **18.** (a) 80

(b) 88   (b) 135   (b) 68   (b) 64

(c) 189   (c) 385

Write each numerator and denominator as a product of prime factors. Then use the prime factorization to write the fraction in lowest terms. See Example 6.

19. $\dfrac{8}{16}$

20. $\dfrac{6}{8}$

21. $\dfrac{32}{48}$

22. $\dfrac{9}{27}$

23. $\dfrac{14}{21}$

24. $\dfrac{20}{32}$

25. $\dfrac{36}{42}$

26. $\dfrac{22}{33}$

27. $\dfrac{50}{63}$

28. $\dfrac{72}{80}$

29. $\dfrac{27}{45}$

30. $\dfrac{36}{63}$

31. $\dfrac{12}{18}$

32. $\dfrac{63}{90}$

33. $\dfrac{35}{40}$

34. $\dfrac{36}{48}$

35. $\dfrac{90}{180}$

36. $\dfrac{16}{64}$

37. $\dfrac{210}{315}$

38. $\dfrac{96}{192}$

39. $\dfrac{429}{495}$

40. $\dfrac{135}{182}$

Write your answers to Exercises 41–46 in lowest terms.

41. There are 60 minutes in an hour. What fraction of an hour is

    (a) 15 minutes?   **(b)** 30 minutes?

    (c) 6 minutes?   **(d)** 60 minutes?

42. There are 24 hours in a day. What fraction of a day is

    (a) 8 hours?   **(b)** 18 hours?

    (c) 12 hours?   **(d)** 3 hours?

43. SueLynn's monthly income is $2400.

    (a) She spends $800 on rent. What fraction of her income is spent on rent?

    (b) She spends $400 on food. What fraction of her income is spent on food?

    (c) What fraction of her income is left for other expenses?

44. There are 10,000 students at Minneapolis Community and Technical College.

    (a) 7500 of the students receive some form of financial aid. What fraction of the students receive financial aid?

    (b) 6000 of the students are women. What fraction are women?

    (c) What fraction of the students are men?

45. What fraction of the time spent on household chores is done by **(a)** husbands, **(b)** wives, **(c)** children?

> Of the typical 48 hours spent weekly on household chores, here is the amount of time spent by each family member.

Husbands	Wives	Children
10 hours	**32** hours	**6** hours

Source: *Journal of Marriage and the Family.*

46. A survey asked people whether certain types of advertising were believable. Out of every 100 people in the survey, here is the number who said the advertising was believable.

Type of Advertising	Number Who Said Advertising Was Believable
Computer software	35
Pharmaceutical companies	28
Auto manufacturers	18
Insurance companies	15

Source: Porter Novella.

What fraction of the people said each type of advertising was believable?

47. Explain the error in each of these problems and correct it.

    (a) $\dfrac{9}{36} = \dfrac{\cancel{3} \cdot \cancel{3}}{2 \cdot 2 \cdot \cancel{3} \cdot \cancel{3}} = 4$

    (b) $\dfrac{9}{16} = \dfrac{9 \div 3}{16 \div 4} = \dfrac{3}{4}$

48. **(a)** Explain how you could use your calculator to find the prime factorization of 437. Then find the prime factorization.

    (b) The text lists all the prime numbers less than 100. Use the divisibility rules and your calculator to find at least five prime numbers between 100 and 150.

Write each fraction in lowest terms. See Example 7.

49. $\dfrac{16c}{40}$

50. $\dfrac{36}{54a}$

51. $\dfrac{20x}{35x}$

52. $\dfrac{21n}{28n}$

53. $\dfrac{18r^2}{15rs}$

54. $\dfrac{18ab}{48b^2}$

55. $\dfrac{6m}{42mn^2}$

56. $\dfrac{10g^2}{90g^2h}$

57. $\dfrac{9x^2}{16y^2}$

58. $\dfrac{5rst}{8st}$

59. $\dfrac{7xz}{9xyz}$

60. $\dfrac{6a^3}{23b^3}$

61. $\dfrac{21k^3}{6k^2}$

62. $\dfrac{16x^3}{12x^4}$

63. $\dfrac{13a^2bc^3}{39a^2bc^3}$

64. $\dfrac{22m^3n^4}{55m^3n^4}$

65. $\dfrac{14c^2d}{14cd^2}$

66. $\dfrac{19rs}{19s^3}$

67. $\dfrac{210ab^3c}{35b^2c^2}$

68. $\dfrac{81w^4xy^2}{300wy^4}$

69. $\dfrac{25m^3rt^2}{36n^2s^3w^2}$

70. $\dfrac{42a^5b^4c^3}{7a^4b^3c^2}$

71. $\dfrac{33e^2fg^3}{11efg}$

72. $\dfrac{21xy^2z^3}{17ab^2c^3}$

5.3 ▶▶▶ Multiplying and Dividing Signed Fractions

OBJECTIVE 1 Multiply signed fractions. Suppose that you give $\frac{1}{3}$ of your candy bar to your friend Ann. Then Ann gives $\frac{1}{2}$ of her share to Tim. How much of the bar does Tim get to eat?

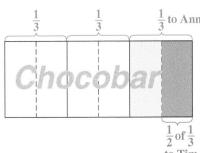

$\frac{1}{3}$ $\frac{1}{3}$ $\frac{1}{3}$ to Ann

A sketch of the candy bar shows that Tim will get $\frac{1}{6}$ of the bar.

$\frac{1}{2}$ of $\frac{1}{3}$ to Tim

OBJECTIVES

1. **Multiply signed fractions.**
2. **Multiply fractions that involve variables.**
3. **Divide signed fractions.**
4. **Divide fractions that involve variables.**
5. **Solve application problems involving multiplying and dividing fractions.**

Tim's share is $\frac{1}{2}$ of $\frac{1}{3}$ candy bar. When used with fractions, the word **of** indicates multiplication.

$$\frac{1}{2} \text{ of } \frac{1}{3} \quad \text{means} \quad \frac{1}{2} \cdot \frac{1}{3}$$

Tim's share is $\frac{1}{6}$ bar, so $\frac{1}{2} \cdot \frac{1}{3} = \frac{1}{6}$.

This example illustrates the rule for multiplying fractions.

Multiplying Fractions

If a, b, c, and d are numbers (but b and d are not 0), then

$$\frac{a}{b} \cdot \frac{c}{d} = \frac{a \cdot c}{b \cdot d}$$

In other words, multiply the numerators and multiply the denominators.

When we apply this rule to find Tim's part of the candy bar, we get

$$\frac{1}{2} \cdot \frac{1}{3} = \frac{1 \cdot 1}{2 \cdot 3} = \frac{1}{6} \quad \leftarrow \text{Multiply numerators.} \\ \leftarrow \text{Multiply denominators.}$$

EXAMPLE 1 **Multiplying Signed Fractions**

Find each product.

(a) $-\frac{5}{8} \cdot -\frac{3}{4}$ Recall that the product of two negative numbers is a positive number.

Multiply the numerators and multiply the denominators.

$$-\frac{5}{8} \cdot -\frac{3}{4} = \frac{5 \cdot 3}{8 \cdot 4} = \frac{15}{32} \quad \leftarrow \text{Lowest terms}$$

The product of two negative numbers is positive.

The answer is in lowest terms because 15 and 32 have no common factor other than 1.

Continued on Next Page

1 Find each product.

(a) $-\dfrac{3}{4} \cdot \dfrac{1}{2}$

(b) $\left(\dfrac{4}{7}\right)\left(-\dfrac{2}{5}\right) = -\dfrac{4 \cdot 2}{7 \cdot 5} = -\dfrac{8}{35}$ Recall that the product of a negative number and a positive number is negative.

◀ *Work Problem* **1** *at the Side.*

Sometimes the result won't be in lowest terms. For example, find $\frac{3}{10}$ of $\frac{5}{6}$.

$$\dfrac{3}{10} \text{ of } \dfrac{5}{6} \quad \text{means} \quad \dfrac{3}{10} \cdot \dfrac{5}{6} = \dfrac{3 \cdot 5}{10 \cdot 6} = \dfrac{15}{60} \quad \left\{ \begin{array}{l} \text{Not in lowest} \\ \text{terms} \end{array} \right.$$

Now write $\frac{15}{60}$ in lowest terms.

$$\dfrac{15}{16} = \dfrac{\overset{1}{\cancel{3}} \cdot \overset{1}{\cancel{5}}}{2 \cdot 2 \cdot \underset{1}{\cancel{3}} \cdot \underset{1}{\cancel{5}}} = \dfrac{1}{4} \leftarrow \text{Lowest terms}$$

(b) $\left(-\dfrac{2}{5}\right)\left(-\dfrac{2}{3}\right)$

You used prime factorization in **Section 5.2** to write fractions in lowest terms. You can also use it when multiplying fractions. Writing the prime factors of the original fractions and dividing out common factors *before* multiplying usually saves time. If you divide out *all* the common factors, the result will automatically be in lowest terms. Let's see how that works when finding $\frac{3}{10}$ of $\frac{5}{6}$.

3 and 5 are already prime.

$$\dfrac{3}{10} \cdot \dfrac{5}{6} = \dfrac{3 \cdot 5}{2 \cdot 5 \cdot 2 \cdot 3} = \dfrac{\overset{1}{\cancel{3}} \cdot \overset{1}{\cancel{5}}}{2 \cdot \underset{1}{\cancel{5}} \cdot 2 \cdot \underset{1}{\cancel{3}}} = \dfrac{1}{4} \quad \left\{ \begin{array}{l} \text{Same result} \\ \text{as above} \end{array} \right.$$

Write 10 as 2 • 5

Write 6 as 2 • 3

Divide out the common factors.

(c) $\dfrac{3}{4}\left(\dfrac{3}{8}\right)$

CAUTION

When you are working with fractions, always write the final result in lowest terms. Visualizing $\frac{15}{60}$ is hard to do. But when $\frac{15}{60}$ is written as $\frac{1}{4}$, working with it is much easier. A fraction is *simplified* when it is written in lowest terms.

EXAMPLE 2 **Using Prime Factorization to Multiply Fractions**

(a) $-\dfrac{8}{5}\left(\dfrac{5}{12}\right)$

Multiplying a negative number times a positive number gives a negative product.

Write 8 as 2 • 2 • 2

$$-\dfrac{8}{5}\left(\dfrac{5}{12}\right) = -\dfrac{2 \cdot 2 \cdot 2 \cdot 5}{5 \cdot 2 \cdot 2 \cdot 3} = -\dfrac{\overset{1}{\cancel{2}} \cdot \overset{1}{\cancel{2}} \cdot 2 \cdot \overset{1}{\cancel{5}}}{\underset{1}{\cancel{5}} \cdot \underset{1}{\cancel{2}} \cdot \underset{1}{\cancel{2}} \cdot 3} = -\dfrac{2}{3} \quad \left\{ \begin{array}{l} \text{Lowest} \\ \text{terms} \end{array} \right.$$

5 is already prime.

Write 12 as 2 • 2 • 3

Negative product

Continued on Next Page

ANSWERS

1. (a) $-\dfrac{3}{8}$ (b) $\dfrac{4}{15}$ (c) $\dfrac{9}{32}$

(b) Find $\frac{2}{9}$ of $\frac{15}{16}$.

Recall that, when used with fractions, *of* indicates multiplication.

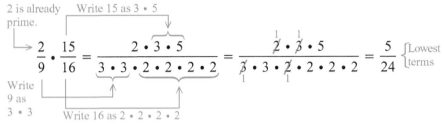

2 is already prime.

Write 15 as 3 • 5

$$\frac{2}{9} \cdot \frac{15}{16} = \frac{2 \cdot 3 \cdot 5}{3 \cdot 3 \cdot 2 \cdot 2 \cdot 2 \cdot 2} = \frac{\cancel{2} \cdot \cancel{3} \cdot 5}{\cancel{3} \cdot 3 \cdot \cancel{2} \cdot 2 \cdot 2 \cdot 2} = \frac{5}{24} \left\{ \text{Lowest terms} \right.$$

Write 9 as 3 • 3

Write 16 as 2 • 2 • 2 • 2

Work Problem **2** *at the Side.* ▶

⊞ **Calculator Tip**   If your calculator has a fraction key ⬭ᵃᵇ/꜀⬭ , you can do calculations with fractions. You'll also need the change of sign key ⬭+⊂-⬭ to enter negative fractions, as you did to enter negative integers in **Section 3.3.**

Start by entering several different fractions. Clear your calculator after each one.

To enter $\frac{3}{4}$, press 3 ⬭ᵃᵇ/꜀⬭ 4. The display will show **3⌐4**

↑
Fraction bar

To enter $-\frac{9}{10}$, press 9 ⬭ᵃᵇ/꜀⬭ 10 ⬭+⊂-⬭ . The display will show **-9⌐10**.

Try entering a fraction that is *not* in lowest terms. As soon as you press an operation key, such as ⊗ or ⊘ , most calculators will automatically show the fraction in lowest terms. Suppose that you start to enter the multiplication problem $\frac{4}{16} \cdot \frac{2}{3}$. Press 4 ⬭ᵃᵇ/꜀⬭ 16 ⊗ . The display shows **1⌐4**, or $\frac{1}{4}$, which is $\frac{4}{16}$ in lowest terms. The calculator will always show fractions in lowest terms.

Let's check the result of Example 2(a) on the previous page: Multiply $-\frac{8}{5} \left(\frac{5}{12} \right)$ by pressing the following keys.

8 ⬭ᵃᵇ/꜀⬭ 5 ⬭+⊂-⬭ ⊗ 5 ⬭ᵃᵇ/꜀⬭ 12 ⊜   The display shows **-2⌐3**.

$-\frac{8}{5}$ $\frac{5}{12}$ $-\frac{2}{3}$

Now try Example 2(b) above: Find $\frac{2}{9}$ of $\frac{15}{16}$. (Did you get $\frac{5}{24}$?)

There are some limitations to the calculations that you can do using the fraction key.

Try entering the fraction $\frac{9}{1000}$. What happens?

(You can't enter denominators >999.)

Try doing this multiplication: $\frac{7}{10} \cdot \frac{3}{100}$. The result should be $\frac{21}{1000}$. What happens?

(The answer is given in decimal form because the denominator is >999.)

---

2 Use prime factorization to multiply these fractions.

(a) $\frac{15}{28} \left(-\frac{6}{5} \right)$

(b) $\frac{12}{7} \cdot \frac{7}{24}$

(c) $\left(-\frac{11}{18} \right) \left(-\frac{9}{20} \right)$

Answers

2. (a) $-\dfrac{3 \cdot \cancel{5} \cdot \cancel{2} \cdot 3}{2 \cdot \cancel{2} \cdot 7 \cdot \cancel{5}} = -\dfrac{9}{14}$

(b) $\dfrac{\cancel{2} \cdot \cancel{2} \cdot \cancel{3} \cdot \cancel{7}}{\cancel{7} \cdot \cancel{2} \cdot \cancel{2} \cdot 2 \cdot \cancel{3}} = \dfrac{1}{2}$

(c) $\dfrac{11 \cdot \cancel{3} \cdot \cancel{3}}{2 \cdot \cancel{3} \cdot \cancel{3} \cdot 2 \cdot 5} = \dfrac{11}{40}$

3 Use prime factorization to find these products.

(a) $\dfrac{3}{4}$ of 36

(b) $-10 \cdot \dfrac{2}{5}$

(c) $\left(-\dfrac{7}{8}\right)(-24)$

4 Use prime factorization to find these products.

(a) $\dfrac{2c}{5} \cdot \dfrac{c}{4}$

(b) $\left(\dfrac{m}{6}\right)\left(\dfrac{9}{m^2}\right)$

(c) $\left(\dfrac{w^2}{y}\right)\left(\dfrac{x^2 y}{w}\right)$

ANSWERS

3. (a) $\dfrac{3 \cdot \cancel{2} \cdot \cancel{2} \cdot 3 \cdot 3}{\cancel{2} \cdot \cancel{2} \cdot 1} = \dfrac{27}{1} = 27$

(b) $-\dfrac{2 \cdot \cancel{5} \cdot 2}{1 \cdot \cancel{5}} = -\dfrac{4}{1} = -4$

(c) $\dfrac{7 \cdot \cancel{2} \cdot \cancel{2} \cdot \cancel{2} \cdot 3}{\cancel{2} \cdot \cancel{2} \cdot \cancel{2}} = \dfrac{21}{1} = 21$

4. (a) $\dfrac{\cancel{2} \cdot c \cdot c}{5 \cdot \cancel{2} \cdot 2} = \dfrac{c^2}{10}$

(b) $\dfrac{\cancel{m} \cdot \cancel{3} \cdot 3}{2 \cdot \cancel{3} \cdot \cancel{m} \cdot m} = \dfrac{3}{2m}$

(c) $\dfrac{\cancel{y} \cdot w \cdot x \cdot x \cdot \cancel{y}}{\cancel{y} \cdot \cancel{w}} = \dfrac{wx^2}{1} = wx^2$

CAUTION

The fraction key on a calculator is useful for *checking* your work. But knowing the rules for fraction computation is important because you'll need them when fractions involve variables. You *cannot* enter fractions such as $\dfrac{3x}{5}$ or $\dfrac{9}{m^2}$ on your calculator (see Example 4 below).

EXAMPLE 3 Multiplying a Fraction and an Integer

Find $\frac{2}{3}$ of 6.

We can write 6 in fraction form as $\frac{6}{1}$. Recall that $\frac{6}{1}$ means $6 \div 1$, which is 6. So we can write any integer a as $\frac{a}{1}$.

$$\underset{\frac{2}{3}\text{ of 6 means}}{\dfrac{2}{3}} \cdot \dfrac{6}{1} = \dfrac{2 \cdot 2 \cdot \overset{1}{\cancel{3}}}{\underset{1}{\cancel{3}} \cdot 1} = \overset{4 \div 1 \text{ is } 4}{\dfrac{4}{1}} = 4$$

◄ *Work Problem* **3** *at the Side.*

OBJECTIVE 2 Multiply fractions that involve variables. The multiplication method that uses prime factors also works when there are variables in the numerators and/or denominators of the fractions.

EXAMPLE 4 Multiplying Fractions with Variables

Find each product.

(a) $\dfrac{3x}{5} \cdot \dfrac{2}{9x}$

$3x$ means $3 \cdot x$.

$$\dfrac{3x}{5} \cdot \dfrac{2}{9x} = \dfrac{3 \cdot x \cdot 2}{5 \cdot 3 \cdot 3 \cdot x} = \dfrac{\overset{1}{\cancel{3}} \cdot \overset{1}{\cancel{x}} \cdot 2}{5 \cdot \underset{1}{\cancel{3}} \cdot 3 \cdot \underset{1}{\cancel{x}}} = \dfrac{2}{15}$$

$\dfrac{x}{x}$ is 1

The prime factors of 9 are $3 \cdot 3$, so $9x$ is $3 \cdot 3 \cdot x$.

(b) $\left(\dfrac{3y}{4x}\right)\left(\dfrac{2x^2}{y}\right)$

$2x^2$ means $2 \cdot x \cdot x$.

$$\left(\dfrac{3y}{4x}\right)\left(\dfrac{2x^2}{y}\right) = \dfrac{3 \cdot y \cdot 2 \cdot x \cdot x}{2 \cdot 2 \cdot x \cdot y} = \dfrac{3 \cdot \overset{1}{\cancel{y}} \cdot \overset{1}{\cancel{2}} \cdot \overset{1}{\cancel{x}} \cdot x}{2 \cdot \underset{1}{\cancel{2}} \cdot \underset{1}{\cancel{x}} \cdot \underset{1}{\cancel{y}}} = \dfrac{3x}{2}$$

The prime factors of 4 are $2 \cdot 2$, so $4x$ is $2 \cdot 2 \cdot x$.

◄ *Work Problem* **4** *at the Side.*

OBJECTIVE 3 Divide signed fractions. To divide fractions, you will rewrite division problems as multiplication problems. For division, you will leave the first number (the dividend) as it is, but change the second number (the divisor) to its *reciprocal*.

Reciprocal of a Fraction

Two numbers are **reciprocals** of each other if their product is 1.

The reciprocal of the fraction $\frac{a}{b}$ is $\frac{b}{a}$ because

$$\frac{a}{b} \cdot \frac{b}{a} = \frac{\overset{1}{\cancel{a}} \cdot \overset{1}{\cancel{b}}}{\underset{1}{\cancel{b}} \cdot \underset{1}{\cancel{a}}} = \frac{1}{1} = 1$$

Notice that you "flip" or "invert" a fraction to find its reciprocal. Here are some examples.

Number	Reciprocal	Reason
$\frac{1}{6}$	$\frac{6}{1}$	Because $\frac{1}{6} \cdot \frac{6}{1} = \frac{6}{6} = 1$
$-\frac{2}{5}$	$-\frac{5}{2}$	Because $\left(-\frac{2}{5}\right)\left(-\frac{5}{2}\right) = \frac{10}{10} = 1$
4 Think of 4 as $\frac{4}{1}$	$\frac{1}{4}$	Because $4 \cdot \frac{1}{4} = \frac{4}{1} \cdot \frac{1}{4} = \frac{4}{4} = 1$

Note

Every number has a reciprocal except 0. Why not 0? Recall that a number times its reciprocal equals 1. But that doesn't work for 0.

$$0 \cdot (\text{reciprocal}) \neq 1$$

Put any number here. When you multiply it by 0, you get 0, never 1

Dividing Fractions

If a, b, c, and d are numbers (but b, c, and d are not 0), then we have the following.

$$\frac{a}{b} \div \frac{c}{d} = \frac{a}{b} \cdot \frac{d}{c}$$

Reciprocals

In other words, change division to multiplying by the reciprocal of the divisor.

Use this method to find the quotient for $\frac{2}{3} \div \frac{1}{6}$. Rewrite it as a multiplication problem and then use the steps for multiplying fractions.

Change division to multiplication.

$$\frac{2}{3} \div \frac{1}{6} = \frac{2}{3} \cdot \frac{6}{1} = \frac{2 \cdot 2 \cdot \overset{1}{\cancel{3}}}{\underset{1}{\cancel{3}} \cdot 1} = \frac{4}{1} = 4$$

The reciprocal of $\frac{1}{6}$ is $\frac{6}{1}$

Does it make sense that $\frac{2}{3} \div \frac{1}{6} = 4$? Let's compare dividing fractions to dividing whole numbers.

$15 \div 3$ is asking, "How many 3s are in 15?"

$\frac{2}{3} \div \frac{1}{6}$ is asking, "How many $\frac{1}{6}$s are in $\frac{2}{3}$?"

The figure below illustrates $\frac{2}{3} \div \frac{1}{6}$.

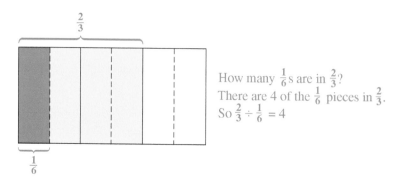

How many $\frac{1}{6}$s are in $\frac{2}{3}$?
There are 4 of the $\frac{1}{6}$ pieces in $\frac{2}{3}$.
So $\frac{2}{3} \div \frac{1}{6} = 4$

As a final check on this method of dividing, try changing $15 \div 3$ into a multiplication problem. You know that the quotient should be 5.

$$15 \div 3 = 15 \cdot \frac{1}{3} = \frac{15}{1} \cdot \frac{1}{3} = \frac{\cancel{3} \cdot 5 \cdot 1}{1 \cdot \cancel{3}} = \frac{5}{1} = 5 \quad \left\{ \begin{array}{l} \text{The quotient} \\ \text{we expected} \end{array} \right.$$

Reciprocals

So, you can see that *dividing* by a fraction is the same as *multiplying* by the *reciprocal* of the fraction.

EXAMPLE 5   **Dividing Signed Fractions**

Rewrite each division problem as a multiplication problem. Then multiply.

Change the *divisor* $\left(\frac{4}{5}\right)$ to its reciprocal, $\frac{5}{4}$. Do **not** change $\frac{3}{10}$.

(a) $\dfrac{3}{10} \div \dfrac{4}{5} = \dfrac{3}{10} \cdot \dfrac{5}{4} = \dfrac{3 \cdot \cancel{5}^{1}}{2 \cdot \cancel{5} \cdot 2 \cdot 2} = \dfrac{3}{8}$

Reciprocals

> **Note**
>
> When multiplying fractions, you don't always have to factor the numerator and denominator completely into prime numbers. In part (a) above, if you notice that 5 is a common factor of the numerator and denominator, you can write
>
> $$\frac{3}{10} \cdot \frac{5}{4} = \frac{3 \cdot \cancel{5}^{1}}{2 \cdot \cancel{5} \cdot 4} = \frac{3}{8}$$
>
> Factor 10 into $2 \cdot 5$
>
> Leave 4 as it is.
>
> If no common factors are obvious to you, then write out the complete prime factorization to help find the common factors.

Continued on Next Page

(b) $2 \div \left(-\dfrac{1}{3}\right)$

First notice that the numbers have different signs. In a division problem, different signs mean that the quotient is negative. Then write 2 in fraction form as $\frac{2}{1}$.

$$2 \div \left(-\frac{1}{3}\right) = \frac{2}{1} \cdot \left(-\frac{3}{1}\right) = -\frac{2 \cdot 3}{1 \cdot 1} = -\frac{6}{1} = -6$$

Reciprocals

Negative product

(c) $-\dfrac{3}{4} \div (-8) = -\dfrac{3}{4} \cdot \left(-\dfrac{1}{8}\right) = \dfrac{3 \cdot 1}{4 \cdot 8} = \dfrac{3}{32}$

Reciprocals

No common factor to divide out

Both numbers in the problem were negative. When signs match, the quotient is *positive*.

(d) $\dfrac{9}{16} \div 0$ Dividing by 0 **cannot** be done.

This is *undefined,* just as dividing by 0 was undefined for integers (see **Section 3.6**). Recall that 0 does *not* have a reciprocal, so you can't change the division to multiplying by the reciprocal of the divisor.

(e) $0 \div \dfrac{9}{16} = 0 \cdot \dfrac{16}{9} = 0$ Recall that 0 divided by any nonzero number gives a result of 0.

Reciprocals

Work Problem **5** *at the Side.* ▶

OBJECTIVE 4 Divide fractions that involve variables. The method for dividing fractions also works when there are variables in the numerators and/or denominators of the fractions.

EXAMPLE 6 Dividing Fractions with Variables

Divide. (Assume that none of the variables represent zero.)

(a) $\dfrac{x^2}{y} \div \dfrac{x}{3y} = \dfrac{x^2}{y} \cdot \dfrac{3y}{x} = \dfrac{x \cdot x \cdot 3 \cdot y}{y \cdot x} = \dfrac{3x}{1} = 3x$

Reciprocals

(b) $\dfrac{8b}{5} \div b^2 = \dfrac{8b}{5} \cdot \dfrac{1}{b^2} = \dfrac{8 \cdot b \cdot 1}{5 \cdot b \cdot b} = \dfrac{8}{5b}$

Think of b^2 as $\dfrac{b^2}{1}$ so the reciprocal is $\dfrac{1}{b^2}$.

Work Problem **6** *at the Side.* ▶

5 Rewrite each division problem as a multiplication problem. Then multiply.

(a) $-\dfrac{3}{4} \div \dfrac{5}{8}$

(b) $0 \div \left(-\dfrac{7}{12}\right)$

(c) $\dfrac{5}{6} \div 10$

(d) $-9 \div \left(-\dfrac{9}{16}\right)$

(e) $\dfrac{2}{5} \div 0$

6 Divide. (Assume none of the variables represent zero.)

(a) $\dfrac{c^2 d^2}{4} \div \dfrac{c^2 d}{4}$

(b) $\dfrac{20}{7h} \div \dfrac{5h}{7}$

(c) $\dfrac{n}{8} \div mn$

ANSWERS

5. (a) $-\dfrac{3}{4} \cdot \dfrac{8}{5} = -\dfrac{3 \cdot 2 \cdot 4}{4 \cdot 5} = -\dfrac{6}{5}$

(b) $0 \cdot \left(-\dfrac{12}{7}\right) = 0$

(c) $\dfrac{5}{6} \cdot \dfrac{1}{10} = \dfrac{5 \cdot 1}{6 \cdot 2 \cdot 5} = \dfrac{1}{12}$

(d) $-\dfrac{9}{1} \cdot \left(-\dfrac{16}{9}\right) = \dfrac{9 \cdot 16}{1 \cdot 9} = \dfrac{16}{1} = 16$

(e) undefined; can't be written as multiplication because 0 doesn't have a reciprocal

6. (a) d **(b)** $\dfrac{4}{h^2}$ **(c)** $\dfrac{1}{8m}$

7 Look for indicator words or draw sketches to help you with these problems.

(a) How many times can a $\frac{2}{3}$ quart spray bottle be filled before 18 quarts of window cleaner are used up?

(b) A retiring police officer will receive $\frac{5}{8}$ of her highest annual salary as retirement income. If her highest annual salary is $64,000, how much will she receive as retirement income?

OBJECTIVE 5 Solve application problems involving multiplying and dividing fractions. When you're solving application problems, some indicator words are used to suggest multiplication and some are used to suggest division.

INDICATOR WORDS FOR MULTIPLICATION	INDICATOR WORDS FOR DIVISION
product	per
double	each
triple	goes into
times	divided by
twice	divided into
of (when *of* follows a fraction)	divided equally

Look for these indicator words in the following examples. However, *you won't always find an indicator word.* Then, you need to think through the problem to decide what to do. Sometimes, drawing a sketch of the situation described in the problem will help you decide which operation to use.

EXAMPLE 7   Using Indicator Words and Sketches to Solve Application Problems

(a) Lois gives $\frac{1}{10}$ of her income to her church. Last month she earned $1980. How much of that did she give to her church?

Notice the word **of**. Because the word **of** *follows the fraction* $\frac{1}{10}$, it indicates multiplication.

$$\frac{1}{10} \text{ of } 1980 = \frac{1}{10} \cdot \frac{1980}{1} = \frac{1 \cdot \overset{1}{\cancel{10}} \cdot 198}{\underset{1}{\cancel{10}} \cdot 1} = \frac{198}{1} = 198$$

Lois gave $198 to her church.

(b) The apparel design class is making infant snowsuits to give to a local shelter. A fabric store donated a 12 yd length of fabric for the project. If one snowsuit needs $\frac{2}{3}$ yd of fabric, how many suits can the class make?

The word **of** appears in the second sentence: "A fabric store donated a 12 yd length **of** fabric." But the word **of** does *not follow a fraction,* so it is *not* an indicator to multiply. Let's try a sketch. There is a piece of fabric 12 yd long. One snowsuit will use $\frac{2}{3}$ yd. The question is, how many $\frac{2}{3}$ yd pieces can be cut from the 12 yards?

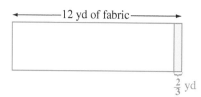

├─── 12 yd of fabric ───┤

$\frac{2}{3}$ yd

Cutting 12 yards into equal size pieces indicates division. How many $\frac{2}{3}$s are in 12?

$$12 \div \frac{2}{3} = \frac{12}{1} \cdot \frac{3}{2} = \frac{\overset{1}{\cancel{2}} \cdot 6 \cdot 3}{1 \cdot \underset{1}{\cancel{2}}} = \frac{18}{1} = 18$$

Reciprocals

The class can make 18 snowsuits.

◀ *Work Problem* **7** *at the Side.*

ANSWERS

7. (a)

$$18 \div \frac{2}{3} = \frac{18}{1} \cdot \frac{3}{2} = \frac{\overset{1}{\cancel{2}} \cdot 9 \cdot 3}{1 \cdot \underset{1}{\cancel{2}}} = \frac{27}{1} = 27$$

The bottle can be filled 27 times.

(b) $\frac{5}{8} \cdot \frac{64,000}{1} = \frac{5 \cdot \overset{1}{\cancel{8}} \cdot 8000}{\underset{1}{\cancel{8}} \cdot 1} = \frac{40,000}{1}$

$= 40,000$

The officer will receive $40,000.

FOR
EXTRA
HELP   **MyMathLab**   *Math* **XL**
PRACTICE
WATCH   DOWNLOAD   READ   REVIEW

Multiply. Write the products in lowest terms. See Examples 1–4.

1. $-\dfrac{3}{8} \cdot \dfrac{1}{2}$

2. $\left(\dfrac{2}{3}\right)\left(-\dfrac{5}{7}\right)$

3. $\left(-\dfrac{3}{8}\right)\left(-\dfrac{12}{5}\right)$

4. $\dfrac{4}{9} \cdot \dfrac{12}{7}$

5. $\dfrac{21}{30}\left(\dfrac{5}{7}\right)$

6. $\left(-\dfrac{6}{11}\right)\left(-\dfrac{22}{15}\right)$

7. $10\left(-\dfrac{3}{5}\right)$

8. $-20\left(\dfrac{3}{4}\right)$

9. $\dfrac{4}{9}$ of 81

10. $\dfrac{2}{3}$ of 48

11. $\left(\dfrac{3x}{4}\right)\left(\dfrac{5}{xy}\right)$

12. $\left(\dfrac{2}{5a^2}\right)\left(\dfrac{a}{8}\right)$

Divide. Write the quotients in lowest terms. (Assume that none of the variables represent zero.) See Examples 5 and 6.

13. $\dfrac{1}{6} \div \dfrac{1}{3}$

14. $-\dfrac{1}{2} \div \dfrac{2}{3}$

15. $-\dfrac{3}{4} \div \left(-\dfrac{5}{8}\right)$

16. $\dfrac{7}{10} \div \dfrac{2}{5}$

17. $6 \div \left(-\dfrac{2}{3}\right)$

18. $-7 \div \left(-\dfrac{1}{4}\right)$

19. $-\dfrac{2}{3} \div 4$

20. $\dfrac{5}{6} \div (-15)$

21. $\dfrac{11c}{5d} \div 3c$

22. $8x^2 \div \dfrac{4x}{7}$

23. $\dfrac{ab^2}{c} \div \dfrac{ab}{c}$

24. $\dfrac{mn}{6} \div \dfrac{n}{3m}$

25. Explain and correct the error in each of these calculations.

(a) $\dfrac{3}{14} \cdot \dfrac{7}{9} = \dfrac{\cancel{3} \cdot \cancel{7}}{2 \cdot \cancel{7} \cdot \cancel{3} \cdot 3} = 6$

(b) $8 \cdot \dfrac{2}{3} = \dfrac{8}{1} \cdot \dfrac{3}{2} = \dfrac{\overset{1}{\cancel{2}} \cdot 4 \cdot 3}{1 \cdot \underset{1}{\cancel{2}}} = \dfrac{12}{1} = 12$

26. Explain and correct the error in each of these calculations.

(a) $\dfrac{3}{4} \cdot \dfrac{8}{9} = \dfrac{3 \cdot 8}{4 \cdot 9} = \dfrac{24}{36}$

(b) $\dfrac{2}{5} \cdot \dfrac{3}{8} = \dfrac{\overset{1}{\cancel{2}}}{5} \cdot \dfrac{3}{\underset{2}{\cancel{8}}} = \dfrac{3}{10}$

27. Explain and correct the error in each of these calculations.

(a) $\dfrac{2}{3} \div 4 = \dfrac{2}{3} \cdot \dfrac{4}{1} = \dfrac{2 \cdot 4}{3 \cdot 1} = \dfrac{8}{3}$

(b) $\dfrac{5}{6} \div \dfrac{10}{9} = \dfrac{6}{5} \cdot \dfrac{10}{9} = \dfrac{2 \cdot \overset{1}{\cancel{5}} \cdot 2 \cdot \overset{1}{\cancel{5}}}{\underset{1}{\cancel{5}} \cdot \underset{1}{\cancel{5}} \cdot 3} = \dfrac{4}{3}$

28. Explain and correct the error in each of these calculations.

(a) $\dfrac{1}{2} \div 0 = 0$

(b) $\dfrac{\overset{1}{\cancel{5}}}{10} \div \dfrac{1}{\underset{1}{\cancel{5}}} = \dfrac{1}{10}$

29. Your friend missed class and is confused about how to divide fractions. Write a short explanation for your friend.

30. Mary spilled coffee on her math homework, and part of one problem is covered up.

$$\blacksquare \dfrac{3}{\blacksquare} \div \dfrac{4}{5}$$

She knows the answer given in the back of the book is $\frac{3}{4}$. Describe how to find the missing number.

Find each product or quotient. Write all answers in lowest terms. See Examples 1–6.

31. $\dfrac{4}{5} \div 3$

32. $\left(-\dfrac{20}{21}\right)\left(-\dfrac{14}{15}\right)$

33. $-\dfrac{3}{8}\left(\dfrac{3}{4}\right)$

34. $-\dfrac{8}{17} \div \dfrac{4}{5}$

35. $\dfrac{3}{5}$ of 35

36. $\dfrac{2}{3} \div (-6)$

37. $-9 \div \left(-\dfrac{3}{5}\right)$

38. $\dfrac{7}{8} \cdot \dfrac{25}{21}$

39. $\dfrac{12}{7} \div 0$

40. $\dfrac{5}{8}$ of (-48)

41. $\left(\dfrac{11}{2}\right)\left(-\dfrac{5}{6}\right)$

42. $\dfrac{3}{4} \div \dfrac{3}{16}$

43. $\dfrac{4}{7}$ of $14b$

44. $\dfrac{ab}{6} \div \dfrac{b}{9}$

45. $\dfrac{12}{5} \div 4d$

46. $\dfrac{18}{7} \div 2t$

47. $\dfrac{x^2}{y} \div \dfrac{w}{2y}$

48. $\dfrac{5}{6}$ of $18w$

Solve each application problem. See Example 7.

49. Al is helping Tim make a mahogany lamp table for Jill's birthday. Find the area of the rectangular top of the table if it is $\frac{4}{5}$ yd long by $\frac{3}{8}$ yd wide.

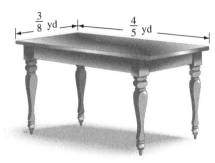

50. A rectangular dog bed is $\frac{7}{8}$ yd by $\frac{10}{9}$ yd. Find its area.

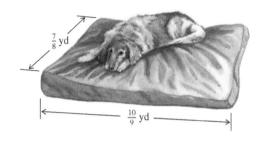

51. How many $\frac{1}{8}$-ounce eyedrop dispensers can be filled from a container that holds 10 ounces of eyedrops?

52. Ms. Shaffer has a piece of property with an area that is $\frac{9}{10}$ acre. She wishes to divide it into three equal parts for her children. How many acres of land will each child get?

53. Todd estimates that it will cost him $12,400 to attend a community college for one year. He thinks he can earn $\frac{3}{4}$ of the cost and borrow the balance. Find the amount he must earn and the amount he must borrow.

54. Joyce Chen wants to make vests to sell at a craft fair. Each vest requires $\frac{3}{4}$ yd of material. She has 36 yd of material. Find the number of vests she can make.

55. Pam Trizlia has a small pickup truck that can carry $\frac{2}{3}$ cord of firewood. Find the number of trips needed to deliver 6 cords of wood.

56. At the Garlic Festival Fun Run, $\frac{5}{12}$ of the runners are women. If there are 780 runners, how many are women? How many are men?

57. There are 234 baseball players in the Baseball Hall of Fame. About one-third of these men played at infield positions (1st base, 2nd base, 3rd base, or short stop). About how many infield players are in the Hall of Fame? (*Source:* National Baseball Hall of Fame.)

58. Parking lot A is $\frac{1}{4}$ mile long and $\frac{3}{16}$ mile wide, and parking lot B is $\frac{3}{8}$ mile long and $\frac{1}{8}$ mile wide. Which parking lot has the larger area?

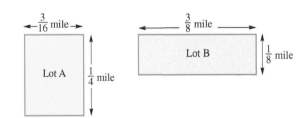

59. An adult male alligator may weigh 400 pounds. A newly hatched alligator weighs only $\frac{1}{8}$ pound. The adult weighs how many times the hatchling? (*Source:* St. Marks NWR.)

60. A female alligator lays about 35 eggs in a nest of marsh grass and mud. But $\frac{4}{5}$ of the eggs or hatchlings will fall prey to raccoons, wading birds, or larger alligators. How many of the 35 eggs will hatch and survive? (*Source:* St. Marks NWR.)

The table below shows the income for the Gomez family last year and the circle graph shows how they spent their income. Use this information to work Exercises 61–64.

Month	Income	Month	Income
January	$4575	July	$5540
February	$4312	August	$3732
March	$4988	September	$4170
April	$4530	October	$5512
May	$4320	November	$4965
June	$4898	December	$6458

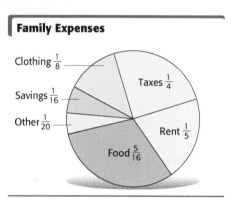

Family Expenses

Clothing $\frac{1}{8}$
Savings $\frac{1}{16}$
Other $\frac{1}{20}$
Taxes $\frac{1}{4}$
Rent $\frac{1}{5}$
Food $\frac{5}{16}$

61. **(a)** What was the family's total income for the year?

   (b) Find the amount of the family's rent for the year.

62. **(a)** How much did the family pay in taxes during the year?

   (b) How much more did the family spend on taxes than on rent?

63. How much did the family spend for food and clothing last year?

64. Find the amount the family saved during the year.

There are a total of about 175 million companion pets in the United States. This table shows the fraction of pets that are dogs, cats, birds, and horses. Use the table to answer Exercises 65–68.

COMPANION PETS IN THE UNITED STATES

Type of Pet	Fraction of All Pets
Dog	$\frac{2}{5}$
Cat	$\frac{12}{25}$
Bird	$\frac{3}{50}$
Horse	$\frac{1}{25}$

Source: American Veterinary Medical Association.

65. How many U.S. pets are horses?

66. How many U.S. pets are dogs?

67. How many dogs and cats are pets?

68. How many birds are pets?

5.4 ▶▶▶ Adding and Subtracting Signed Fractions

OBJECTIVE 1 Add and subtract like fractions. You probably remember learning something about "common denominators" in other math classes. When fractions have the *same* denominator, we say that they have a *common* denominator, which makes them **like fractions.** When fractions have different denominators, they are called **unlike fractions.** Here are some examples.

OBJECTIVES

1. **Add and subtract like fractions.**

2. **Find the lowest common denominator for unlike fractions.**

3. **Add and subtract unlike fractions.**

4. **Add and subtract unlike fractions that contain variables.**

Like Fractions

$$\frac{3}{4} \quad \text{and} \quad -\frac{7}{4}$$

Common denominator

$$\frac{6}{x} \quad \text{and} \quad \frac{y}{x}$$

Common denominator

Unlike Fractions

$$\frac{2}{9} \quad \text{and} \quad \frac{2}{8}$$

Different denominators

$$\frac{a^2}{3} \quad \text{and} \quad \frac{3}{a}$$

Different denominators

You can add or subtract fractions *only* when they have a common denominator. To see why, let's look at more pizzas.

Nathan ate $\frac{1}{2}$ of the pizza.

Amanda ate $\frac{1}{3}$ of the pizza.

What fraction of the pizza has been eaten? We can't write a fraction until the pizza is cut into pieces of *equal* size. That's what the denominator of a fraction tell us: the number of *equal* size pieces in the pizza.

Now the pizza is cut into 6 *equal* pieces, and we can find out how much was eaten.

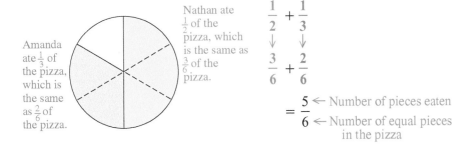

Amanda ate $\frac{1}{3}$ of the pizza, which is the same as $\frac{2}{6}$ of the pizza.

Nathan ate $\frac{1}{2}$ of the pizza, which is the same as $\frac{3}{6}$ of the pizza.

$$\frac{1}{2} + \frac{1}{3}$$
$$\downarrow \qquad \downarrow$$
$$\frac{3}{6} + \frac{2}{6}$$

$$= \frac{5}{6} \leftarrow \text{Number of pieces eaten}$$
$$ 6 \leftarrow \text{Number of equal pieces in the pizza}$$

Adding and Subtracting Like Fractions

You can add or subtract fractions ***only*** when they have a common denominator. If a, b, and c are numbers (and b is not 0), then

$$\frac{a}{b} + \frac{c}{b} = \frac{a+c}{b} \qquad \text{and} \qquad \frac{a}{b} - \frac{c}{b} = \frac{a-c}{b}$$

In other words, add or subtract the numerators and write the result over the common denominator. Then check to be sure that the answer is in lowest terms.

1 Write each sum or difference in lowest terms.

(a) $\dfrac{1}{6} + \dfrac{5}{6}$

(b) $-\dfrac{11}{12} + \dfrac{5}{12}$

(c) $-\dfrac{2}{9} - \dfrac{3}{9}$

(d) $\dfrac{8}{ab} + \dfrac{3}{ab}$

EXAMPLE 1 **Adding and Subtracting Like Fractions**

Find each sum or difference.

(a) $\dfrac{1}{8} + \dfrac{3}{8}$

These are *like* fractions because they have a *common denominator of 8*. So they are ready to be added. Add the numerators and write the sum over the common denominator.

$$\dfrac{1}{8} + \dfrac{3}{8} = \dfrac{1+3}{8} = \dfrac{4}{8}$$

Common denominator

Now write $\frac{4}{8}$ in lowest terms.

$$\dfrac{4}{8} = \dfrac{\overset{1}{\cancel{2}} \cdot \overset{1}{\cancel{2}}}{\underset{1}{\cancel{2}} \cdot \underset{1}{\cancel{2}} \cdot 2} = \dfrac{1}{2}$$

The sum, in lowest terms, is $\frac{1}{2}$.

> **CAUTION**
>
> Add *only* the numerators. ***Do not add the denominators.*** In part (a) above we **kept the common denominator.**
>
> $$\dfrac{1}{8} + \dfrac{3}{8} = \dfrac{1+3}{8} \qquad \text{not} \qquad \dfrac{1}{8} + \dfrac{3}{8} = \dfrac{1+3}{\cancel{8+8}} = \dfrac{4}{16}$$
>
> Incorrect
>
> To help you understand why we add *only* the numerators, think of $\frac{1}{8}$ as $1(\frac{1}{8})$ and $\frac{3}{8}$ as $3(\frac{1}{8})$. Then we use the distributive property.
>
> $$\dfrac{1}{8} + \dfrac{3}{8} = \underbrace{1\left(\dfrac{1}{8}\right) + 3\left(\dfrac{1}{8}\right)}_{} = \underbrace{(1+3)\left(\dfrac{1}{8}\right)}_{} = 4\left(\dfrac{1}{8}\right) = \dfrac{4}{8} = \dfrac{1}{2}$$
>
> Use the distributive property.
>
> Or think about a pie cut into 8 equal pieces. If you eat 1 piece and your friend eats 3 pieces, together you've eaten 4 of the 8 pieces or $\frac{4}{8}$ of the pie (***not*** $\frac{4}{16}$ of the pie, which would be 4 out of 16 pieces).

(b) $-\dfrac{3}{5} + \dfrac{4}{5} = \dfrac{-3+4}{5} = \dfrac{1}{5}$ ← Lowest terms

Common denominator

Rewrite subtraction as adding the opposite.

(c) $\dfrac{3}{10} - \dfrac{7}{10} = \dfrac{3-7}{10} = \dfrac{3+(-7)}{10} = \dfrac{-4}{10}$ or $-\dfrac{4}{10}$

Common denominator

Always write fraction answers in lowest terms.

Now write $-\frac{4}{10}$ in lowest terms.

$$-\dfrac{4}{10} = -\dfrac{\overset{1}{\cancel{2}} \cdot 2}{\underset{1}{\cancel{2}} \cdot 5} = -\dfrac{2}{5}$$

(d) $\dfrac{5}{x^2} - \dfrac{2}{x^2} = \dfrac{5-2}{x^2} = \dfrac{3}{x^2}$

Common denominator

◄ *Work Problem* **1** *at the Side.*

ANSWERS

1. (a) $\dfrac{6}{6} = 1$ (b) $-\dfrac{1}{2}$

   (c) $-\dfrac{5}{9}$ (d) $\dfrac{11}{ab}$

OBJECTIVE 2 Find the lowest common denominator for unlike fractions. When we first tried to add the pizza eaten by Nathan and Amanda, we could *not* do so because the pizza was *not cut into pieces of the same size.* So we rewrote $\frac{1}{2}$ and $\frac{1}{3}$ as equivalent fractions that both had 6 as the common denominator.

$$\frac{1}{2} = \frac{1 \cdot 3}{2 \cdot 3} = \frac{3}{6} \leftarrow$$
$$\frac{1}{3} = \frac{1 \cdot 2}{3 \cdot 2} = \frac{2}{6} \leftarrow$$
Common denominator of 6

Then we could add the fractions, because the pizza was cut into pieces of *equal* size.

$$\frac{1}{2} + \frac{1}{3} = \frac{3}{6} + \frac{2}{6} = \frac{3 + 2}{6} = \frac{5}{6} \leftarrow \text{Lowest terms}$$

In other words, when you want to add or subtract unlike fractions, the first thing you must do is rewrite them so that they have a common denominator.

> **A Common Denominator for Unlike Fractions**
>
> To find a common denominator for two unlike fractions, find a number that is divisible by *both* of the original denominators.
>   For example, a common denominator for $\frac{1}{2}$ and $\frac{1}{3}$ is 6 because 2 goes into 6 evenly and 3 goes into 6 evenly.

Notice that 12 is also a common denominator for $\frac{1}{2}$ and $\frac{1}{3}$ because 2 and 3 both go into 12 evenly.

$$\frac{1}{2} = \frac{1 \cdot 6}{2 \cdot 6} = \frac{6}{12} \leftarrow$$
$$\frac{1}{3} = \frac{1 \cdot 4}{3 \cdot 4} = \frac{4}{12} \leftarrow$$
Common denominator of 12

Now that the fractions have a common denominator, we can add them.

$$\frac{1}{2} + \frac{1}{3} = \frac{6}{12} + \frac{4}{12} = \frac{6 + 4}{12} = \frac{10}{12} \left\{\begin{matrix}\text{Not in} \\ \text{lowest} \\ \text{terms}\end{matrix}\right. \quad \text{but} \quad \frac{10}{12} = \frac{\cancel{2} \cdot 5}{\cancel{2} \cdot 6} = \frac{5}{6} \left\{\begin{matrix}\text{Same} \\ \text{result as} \\ \text{above}\end{matrix}\right.$$

Both 6 and 12 worked as common denominators for adding $\frac{1}{2}$ and $\frac{1}{3}$, but using the smaller number saved some work. You should always try to find the smallest common denominator. If you don't for some reason, you can still work the problem—but it may take you longer. You'll have to divide out some common factors at the end in order to write the answer in lowest terms.

> **Least Common Denominator (LCD)**
>
> The **least common denominator** (LCD) for two fractions is the *smallest* positive number divisible by both denominators of the original fractions. For example, both 6 and 12 are common denominators for $\frac{1}{2}$ and $\frac{1}{3}$, but 6 is smaller, so it is the LCD.

There are several ways to find the LCD. When the original denominators are small numbers, you can often find the LCD by inspection. *Hint:* **Always check to see if the larger denominator will work as the LCD.**

2 Find the LCD for each pair of fractions by inspection.

(a) $\dfrac{3}{5}$ and $\dfrac{3}{10}$

(b) $\dfrac{1}{2}$ and $\dfrac{2}{5}$

(c) $\dfrac{3}{4}$ and $\dfrac{1}{6}$

(d) $\dfrac{5}{6}$ and $\dfrac{7}{18}$

EXAMPLE 2 **Finding the LCD by Inspection**

(a) Find the LCD for $\frac{2}{3}$ and $\frac{1}{9}$ by inspection.

Check to see if 9 (the larger denominator) will work as the LCD. Is 9 divisible by 3 (the other denominator)? Yes, so 9 is the LCD for $\frac{2}{3}$ and $\frac{1}{9}$.

(b) Find the LCD for $\frac{5}{8}$ and $\frac{5}{6}$ by inspection.

Check to see if 8 (the larger denominator) will work. No, 8 is not divisible by 6. So start checking numbers that are multiples of 8, that is, 16, 24, and 32. Notice that 24 will work because it is divisible by 8 and by 6.

The LCD for $\frac{5}{8}$ and $\frac{5}{6}$ is 24.

◀ *Work Problem* **2** *at the Side.*

For larger denominators, you can use prime factorization to find the LCD. Factor each denominator completely into prime numbers. Then use the factors to build the LCD.

---

3 Use prime factorization to find the LCD for each pair of fractions.

(a) $\dfrac{1}{10}$ and $\dfrac{13}{14}$

(b) $\dfrac{5}{12}$ and $\dfrac{17}{20}$

(c) $\dfrac{7}{15}$ and $\dfrac{7}{9}$

EXAMPLE 3 **Using Prime Factors to Find the LCD**

(a) What is the LCD for $\frac{7}{12}$ and $\frac{13}{18}$?

Write 12 and 18 as the product of prime factors. Then use prime factors in the LCD that "cover" both 12 and 18.

$$12 = 2 \cdot 2 \cdot 3$$
$$18 = 2 \cdot 3 \cdot 3$$

Factors of 12

$$LCD = 2 \cdot 2 \cdot 3 \cdot 3 = 36$$

Factors of 18

Check whether 36 is divisible by 12 (yes) and by 18 (yes). So 36 is the LCD for $\frac{7}{12}$ and $\frac{13}{18}$.

> **CAUTION**
> When finding the LCD, notice that we did *not* have to repeat the factors that 12 and 18 have in common. If we had used *all* the 2s and 3s, we would get a common denominator, but not the *smallest* one.

(b) What is the LCD for $\frac{11}{15}$ and $\frac{9}{70}$?

$$15 = 3 \cdot 5$$
$$70 = 2 \cdot 5 \cdot 7$$

Factors of 15

$$LCD = 3 \cdot 5 \cdot 2 \cdot 7 = 210$$

Factors of 70

Check whether 210 is divisible by 15 (yes) and divisible by 70 (yes). So 210 is the LCD for $\frac{11}{15}$ and $\frac{9}{70}$.

◀ *Work Problem* **3** *at the Side.*

ANSWERS

2. (a) 10 (b) 10 (c) 12 (d) 18

3. (a) $\begin{aligned}10 &= 2 \cdot 5\\14 &= 2 \cdot 7\end{aligned}$ LCD $= 2 \cdot 5 \cdot 7 = 70$

(b) $\begin{aligned}12 &= 2 \cdot 2 \cdot 3\\20 &= 2 \cdot 2 \cdot 5\end{aligned}$ LCD $= 2 \cdot 2 \cdot 3 \cdot 5 = 60$

(c) $\begin{aligned}15 &= 3 \cdot 5\\9 &= 3 \cdot 3\end{aligned}$ LCD $= 3 \cdot 3 \cdot 5 = 45$

OBJECTIVE 3 Add and subtract unlike fractions. Here are the steps for adding or subtracting unlike fractions. The key idea is that you must rewrite the fractions so that they have a common denominator before you can add or subtract them.

Adding and Subtracting Unlike Fractions

Step 1 Find the LCD, the smallest number divisible by both denominators in the problem.

Step 2 Rewrite each original fraction as an equivalent fraction whose denominator is the LCD.

Step 3 Add or subtract the numerators of the like fractions. Keep the common denominator.

Step 4 Write the sum or difference in lowest terms.

EXAMPLE 4 **Adding and Subtracting Unlike Fractions**

Find each sum or difference.

(a) $\dfrac{1}{5} + \dfrac{3}{10}$ First check to see if the larger denominator is the LCD.

Step 1 The larger denominator (10) is the LCD.

Step 2 $\dfrac{1}{5} = \dfrac{1 \cdot 2}{5 \cdot 2} = \dfrac{2}{10} \leftarrow \text{LCD}$ and $\dfrac{3}{10}$ already has the LCD.

Step 3 Add the numerators. Write the sum over the common denominator.

$$\dfrac{1}{5} + \dfrac{3}{10} = \dfrac{2}{10} + \dfrac{3}{10} = \dfrac{2+3}{10} = \dfrac{5}{10}$$

Step 4 Write $\frac{5}{10}$ in lowest terms.

$$\dfrac{5}{10} = \dfrac{\overset{1}{\cancel{5}}}{2 \cdot \underset{1}{\cancel{5}}} = \dfrac{1}{2} \leftarrow \text{Lowest terms}$$

(b) $\dfrac{3}{4} - \dfrac{5}{6}$

Step 1 The LCD is 12.

Step 2 $\dfrac{3}{4} = \dfrac{3 \cdot 3}{4 \cdot 3} = \dfrac{9}{12} \leftarrow \text{LCD}$ and $\dfrac{5}{6} = \dfrac{5 \cdot 2}{6 \cdot 2} = \dfrac{10}{12} \leftarrow \text{LCD}$

Step 3 Subtract the numerators. Write the difference over the common denominator.

$9 + (-10)$ is -1

$$\dfrac{3}{4} - \dfrac{5}{6} = \dfrac{9}{12} - \dfrac{10}{12} = \dfrac{9-10}{12} = \dfrac{-1}{12} \quad \text{or} \quad -\dfrac{1}{12}$$

Step 4 $-\frac{1}{12}$ is in lowest terms.

Continued on Next Page

4 Find each sum or difference. Write all answers in lowest terms.

(a) $\dfrac{2}{3} + \dfrac{1}{6}$

(b) $\dfrac{1}{12} - \dfrac{5}{6}$

(c) $3 - \dfrac{4}{5}$

(d) $-\dfrac{5}{12} + \dfrac{9}{16}$

(c) $-\dfrac{5}{12} + \dfrac{5}{9}$

Step 1 Use prime factorization to find the LCD.

$$12 = 2 \cdot 2 \cdot 3$$
$$9 = 3 \cdot 3$$

Factors of 12

$$LCD = 2 \cdot 2 \cdot 3 \cdot 3 = 36$$

Factors of 9

Step 2 $-\dfrac{5}{12} = -\dfrac{5 \cdot 3}{12 \cdot 3} = -\dfrac{15}{36}$ and $\dfrac{5}{9} = \dfrac{5 \cdot 4}{9 \cdot 4} = \dfrac{20}{36}$

Step 3 Add the numerators. Keep the common denominator.

$$-\dfrac{5}{12} + \dfrac{5}{9} = -\dfrac{15}{36} + \dfrac{20}{36} = \dfrac{-15 + 20}{36} = \dfrac{5}{36}$$

Step 4 $\dfrac{5}{36}$ is in lowest terms.

(d) $4 - \dfrac{2}{3}$

Step 1 Think of 4 as $\dfrac{4}{1}$. The LCD for $\dfrac{4}{1}$ and $\dfrac{2}{3}$ is 3, the larger denominator.

Step 2 $\dfrac{4}{1} = \dfrac{4 \cdot 3}{1 \cdot 3} = \dfrac{12}{3}$ and $\dfrac{2}{3}$ already has the LCD.

Step 3 Subtract the numerators. Keep the common denominator.

$$\dfrac{4}{1} - \dfrac{2}{3} = \dfrac{12}{3} - \dfrac{2}{3} = \dfrac{12 - 2}{3} = \dfrac{10}{3}$$

Step 4 $\dfrac{10}{3}$ is in lowest terms.

◀ Work Problem **4** at the Side.

OBJECTIVE 4 Add and subtract unlike fractions that contain variables. We use the same steps to add or subtract unlike fractions with variables in the numerators or denominators.

EXAMPLE 5 **Adding and Subtracting Unlike Fractions with Variables**

Find each sum or difference.

(a) $\dfrac{1}{4} + \dfrac{b}{5}$

Step 1 The LCD is 20.

Step 2 $\dfrac{1}{4} = \dfrac{1 \cdot 5}{4 \cdot 5} = \dfrac{5}{20}$ and $\dfrac{b}{5} = \dfrac{b \cdot 4}{5 \cdot 4} = \dfrac{4b}{20}$

Continued on Next Page

Step 3 $\dfrac{1}{4} + \dfrac{b}{5} = \dfrac{5}{20} + \dfrac{4b}{20} = \dfrac{5 + 4b}{20}$ ← Add the numerators.
← Keep the common denominator.

Step 4 $\dfrac{5 + 4b}{20}$ is in lowest terms.

CAUTION
In *Step 4* above, we could **not** add $5 + 4b$ in the numerator of the answer because 5 and $4b$ are **not** like terms. We *could* add $5b + 4b$ but **not** $5 + 4b$.

Variable parts match.

(b) $\dfrac{2}{3} - \dfrac{6}{x}$

Step 1   The LCD is $3 \cdot x$, or $3x$.

Step 2 $\dfrac{2}{3} = \dfrac{2 \cdot x}{3 \cdot x} = \dfrac{2x}{3x}$ and $\dfrac{6}{x} = \dfrac{6 \cdot 3}{x \cdot 3} = \dfrac{18}{3x}$

Step 3 $\dfrac{2}{3} - \dfrac{6}{x} = \dfrac{2x}{3x} - \dfrac{18}{3x} = \dfrac{2x - 18}{3x}$ ← Subtract the numerators.
← Keep the common denominator.

Step 4 $\dfrac{2x - 18}{3x}$ is in lowest terms.

Note
Notice in part (b) above that we found the LCD for $\frac{2}{3} - \frac{6}{x}$ by multiplying the two denominators. The LCD is $3 \cdot x$ or $3x$.

Multiplying the two denominators will *always* give you a common denominator, but it may not be the *least* common denominator. Here are more examples.

$\dfrac{1}{3} - \dfrac{2}{5}$ If you multiply the denominators, $3 \cdot 5 = 15$ and 15 is the LCD.

$\dfrac{5}{6} + \dfrac{3}{4}$ If you multiply the denominators, $6 \cdot 4 = 24$ and 24 will work. But you'll save some time by using the least common denominator, which is 12.

$\dfrac{7}{y} + \dfrac{a}{4}$ If you multiply the denominators, $y \cdot 4 = 4y$ and 4y is the LCD.

Work Problem **5** *at the Side.* ▶

5 Find each sum or difference.

(a) $\dfrac{5}{6} - \dfrac{h}{2}$

(b) $\dfrac{7}{t} + \dfrac{3}{5}$

(c) $\dfrac{4}{x} - \dfrac{8}{3}$

Math in the Media

The time signature at the beginning of a piece of music looks like a fraction. Commonly used time signatures are $\frac{2}{4}$, $\frac{3}{4}$, $\frac{4}{4}$, and $\frac{6}{8}$. Musicians use the time signature to tell how long to hold each note. The values of different notes can be written as fractions:

$$\mathbf{o} = 1 \qquad \textstyle\frac{1}{2} \qquad = \frac{1}{4} \qquad = \frac{1}{8} \qquad = \frac{1}{16}$$

Music is divided into measures. In $\frac{4}{4}$ time, each measure contains notes that add up to $\frac{4}{4}$ (or 1). In $\frac{2}{4}$ time the notes in each measure add up to $\frac{2}{4}$ $\left(\text{or } \frac{1}{2}\right)$, and so on for $\frac{3}{4}$ time and $\frac{6}{8}$ time.

Write one or more notes in each measure to make it add up to its time signature. Use as many different kinds of notes as possible. Write the addition problem underneath the notes that shows how the notes add up to the time signature.

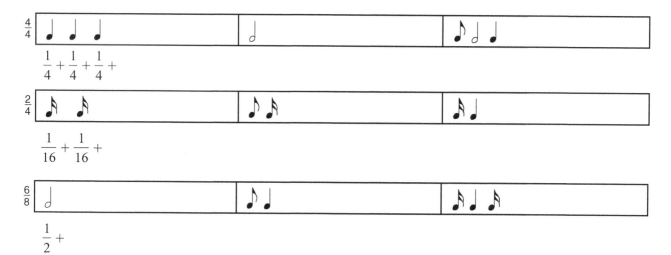

Below is an excerpt from "The Star-Spangled Banner." Divide the music into measures based on the time signature.

say   does   that   Star-span-gled   Ban-ner   yet   wave   O'er   the

446

5.4 ▶▶▶ Exercises

Find each sum or difference. Write all answers in lowest terms. See Examples 1–5.

1. $\dfrac{3}{4} + \dfrac{1}{8}$

2. $\dfrac{1}{3} + \dfrac{1}{2}$

3. $-\dfrac{1}{14} + \left(-\dfrac{3}{7}\right)$

4. $-\dfrac{2}{9} + \dfrac{2}{3}$

5. $\dfrac{2}{3} - \dfrac{1}{6}$

6. $\dfrac{5}{12} - \dfrac{1}{4}$

7. $\dfrac{3}{8} - \dfrac{3}{5}$

8. $\dfrac{1}{3} - \dfrac{3}{5}$

9. $-\dfrac{5}{8} + \dfrac{1}{12}$

10. $-\dfrac{13}{16} + \dfrac{13}{16}$

11. $-\dfrac{7}{20} - \dfrac{5}{20}$

12. $-\dfrac{7}{9} - \dfrac{5}{6}$

13. $0 - \dfrac{7}{18}$

14. $-\dfrac{7}{8} + 3$

15. $2 - \dfrac{6}{7}$

16. $5 - \dfrac{2}{5}$

17. $-\dfrac{1}{2} + \dfrac{3}{24}$

18. $\dfrac{7}{10} + \dfrac{7}{15}$

19. $\dfrac{1}{5} + \dfrac{c}{3}$

20. $\dfrac{x}{4} + \dfrac{2}{3}$

21. $\dfrac{5}{m} - \dfrac{1}{2}$

22. $\dfrac{2}{9} - \dfrac{4}{y}$

23. $\dfrac{3}{b^2} + \dfrac{5}{b^2}$

24. $\dfrac{10}{xy} - \dfrac{7}{xy}$

25. $\dfrac{c}{7} + \dfrac{3}{b}$

26. $\dfrac{2}{x} - \dfrac{y}{5}$

27. $-\dfrac{4}{c^2} - \dfrac{d}{c}$

28. $-\dfrac{1}{n} + \dfrac{m}{n^2}$

29. $-\dfrac{11}{42} - \dfrac{11}{70}$

30. $\dfrac{7}{45} - \dfrac{7}{20}$

31. A key step in adding or subtracting unlike fractions is to rewrite the fractions so that they have a common denominator. Explain why this step is necessary.

32. Explain how to write a fraction with an indicated greater denominator. As part of your explanation, show how to rewrite $\frac{3}{4}$ as an equivalent fraction with a denominator of 12.

33. Explain the error in each calculation and correct it.

   (a) $\dfrac{3}{4} + \dfrac{2}{5} = \dfrac{3+2}{4+5} = \dfrac{5}{9}$

   (b) $\dfrac{5}{6} - \dfrac{4}{9} = \dfrac{5}{18} - \dfrac{4}{18} = \dfrac{5-4}{18} = \dfrac{1}{18}$

34. Explain the error in each calculation and correct it.

   (a) $-\dfrac{1}{4} + \dfrac{7}{12} = -\dfrac{3}{12} + \dfrac{7}{12} = \dfrac{-3+7}{12} = \dfrac{4}{12}$

   (b) $\dfrac{3}{10} - \dfrac{1}{4} = \dfrac{3-1}{10-4} = \dfrac{2}{6} = \dfrac{1}{3}$

Relating Concepts (Exercises 35–36) For Individual or Group Work

*As you **work Exercises 35 and 36 in order,** think about the properties you learned when working with integers. Then explain what each pair of problems illustrates.*

35. (a) $-\dfrac{2}{3} + \dfrac{3}{4} = $ _____ $\dfrac{3}{4} + \left(-\dfrac{2}{3}\right) = $ _____

   (b) $\dfrac{5}{6} - \dfrac{1}{2} = $ _____ $\dfrac{1}{2} - \dfrac{5}{6} = $ _____

   (c) $\left(-\dfrac{2}{3}\right)\left(\dfrac{9}{10}\right) = $ _____ $\left(\dfrac{9}{10}\right)\left(-\dfrac{2}{3}\right) = $ _____

   (d) $\dfrac{2}{5} \div \dfrac{1}{15} = $ _____ $\dfrac{1}{15} \div \dfrac{2}{5} = $ _____

36. (a) $-\dfrac{7}{12} + \dfrac{7}{12} = $ _____ $\dfrac{3}{5} + \left(-\dfrac{3}{5}\right) = $ _____

   (b) $-\dfrac{13}{16} \div \left(-\dfrac{13}{16}\right) = $ _____ $\dfrac{1}{8} \div \dfrac{1}{8} = $ _____

   (c) $\dfrac{5}{6} \cdot 1 = $ _____ $1\left(-\dfrac{17}{20}\right) = $ _____

   (d) $\left(-\dfrac{4}{5}\right)\left(-\dfrac{5}{4}\right) = $ _____ $7 \cdot \dfrac{1}{7} = $ _____

Solve each application problem. Write all answers in lowest terms.

37. When assembling shelving units, Pam Phelps must use the proper type and size of hardware. Find the total length of the bolt shown.

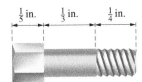

$\frac{1}{5}$ in. $\frac{1}{3}$ in. $\frac{1}{4}$ in.

38. How much fencing will be needed to enclose this rectangular wildflower preserve?

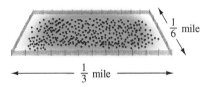

$\frac{1}{6}$ mile

$\frac{1}{3}$ mile

39. The owner of Racy's Feed Store ordered $\frac{1}{3}$ cubic yard of corn, $\frac{3}{8}$ cubic yard of oats, and $\frac{1}{4}$ cubic yard of washed medium mesh gravel. How many cubic yards of material were ordered?

40. A flower grower purchased $\frac{9}{10}$ acre of land one year and $\frac{3}{10}$ acre the next year. She then sold $\frac{7}{10}$ acre of land. How much land does she now have?

41. A forester planted $\frac{5}{12}$ acre of seedlings in the morning and $\frac{11}{12}$ acre in the afternoon. The next day, $\frac{7}{12}$ acre of seedlings were destroyed by a brush fire. How many acres of seedlings remained?

42. Adrian Ortega drives a tanker for the British Petroleum Company. He leaves the refinery with his tanker filled to $\frac{7}{8}$ of capacity. If he delivers $\frac{1}{4}$ of the tanker's capacity at the first stop and $\frac{1}{3}$ of the tanker's capacity at the second stop, find the fraction of the tanker's capacity remaining.

The circle graph shows the fraction of U.S. workers who used various methods to learn about computers. Use the graph to answer Exercises 43–46.

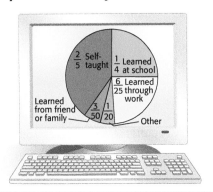

Ways To Learn Computers

$\frac{2}{5}$ Self-taught

$\frac{1}{4}$ Learned at school

$\frac{6}{25}$ Learned through work

Learned from friend or family

$\frac{3}{50}$ $\frac{1}{20}$ Other

Source: John J. Heldrich Center for Workforce Development.

43. What fraction of workers are self-taught or learned from friends or family?

44. What fraction of workers learned at school or through work?

45. What is the difference in the fraction of workers who are self-taught and those who learned at work?

46. What is the difference in the fraction of workers who are self-taught and those who learned at school?

Refer to the circle graph to answer Exercises 47–50.

47. What fraction of the day was spent in class and study? How many hours is that?

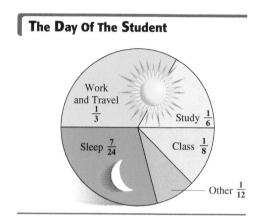

The Day Of The Student

48. What fraction of the day was spent in work and travel and sleep? How many hours is that?

49. How much more of the day was spent sleeping than studying? Write your answer as a fraction of the day.

50. How much more of the day was spent working and traveling than in class? Write your answer as a fraction of the day.

Use the photo to answer Exercises 51–52. A nut driver is like a screwdriver but is used to tighten nuts instead of screws. The ends of the drivers are sized from $\frac{3}{16}$ inch to $\frac{1}{2}$ inch to fit smaller or larger nuts. (The symbol " is for inches.)

51. The rightmost driver fits a nut that is how much larger than the nut for the leftmost driver?

52. The nut size for the yellow-handled driver is how much less than the nut size for the blue-handled driver?

$$\frac{3}{16}"\quad \frac{1}{4}"\quad \frac{5}{16}"\quad \frac{11}{32}"\quad \frac{3}{8}"\quad \frac{7}{16}"\quad \frac{1}{2}"$$

Source: Author's tool collection.

53. A hazardous waste dump site will require $\frac{7}{8}$ mile of security fencing. The site has four sides with three of the sides measuring $\frac{1}{4}$ mile, $\frac{1}{6}$ mile, and $\frac{3}{8}$ mile. Find the length of the fourth side.

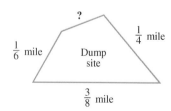

54. Chakotay is fitting a turquoise stone into a bear claw pendant. Find the diameter of the hole in the pendant. (The diameter is the distance across the center of the hole.)

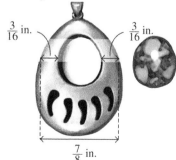

Study Skills

▶▶▶ MAKING A MIND MAP

Mind mapping is a visual way to show information that you have learned. It is an excellent way to review. Mapping is flexible and can be personalized, which is helpful for your memory. Your brain likes to see things that are **pleasing** to look at, **colorful**, and that **show connections** between ideas. Take advantage of that by creating maps that

▶ are easy to read,

▶ use color in a systematic way, and

▶ clearly show you how different concepts are related (using arrows or dotted lines, for example).

Below are some general directions for making a map. After you read them, go to the next page and work on completing the map that has been started for you. It is from **Sections 5.3** and **5.4.**

▶ To begin a mind map, write the concept in the center of a piece of paper and either circle it or draw a box around it.

▶ Make a line out from the center concept, and draw a box large enough to write the definition of the concept.

▶ Think of the other aspects (subpoints) of the concept that you have learned, such as procedures to follow or formulas. Make a separate line and box connecting each subpoint to the center.

▶ From each of the new boxes, add the information you've learned. You can continue making new lines and boxes and circles, or you can list items below the new information.

▶ Use color to highlight the major points. For example, everything related to one subpoint might be the same color. That way you can easily see related ideas.

▶ You may also use arrows, underlining, or small drawings to help yourself remember.

OBJECTIVES

1 Create mind maps for appropriate concepts.

2 Visually show how concepts relate to each other using arrows or lines.

Directions for Making a Mind Map

Why Is Mapping Brain Friendly?

Remember that your brain grows dendrites when you are **actively thinking** about and working with information. Making a map requires you to think hard about **how to place the information, how to show connections** between parts of the map, and **how color will be useful.** It also takes a lot of thinking to fill in all related details and **show how those details connect to the larger concept.** All that thinking will let your brain grow a complex, many-branched neural network of interconnected dendrites. It is time well spent.

Try this Fractions Mind Map Using Sections 5.3 and 5.4

On a separate paper, make a map that summarizes Computations with Fractions. Follow the directions below. Use the starter map below.

▶ The longest rectangles are instructions for all four operations. (The first one starts "Rewrite all numbers as fractions..." and the second one is at the bottom of the map.)

▶ Notice the wavy dividing lines that separate the map into two sides.

▶ Your job is to complete the map by writing the steps used in multiplying fractions (from **Section 5.3**) and the steps used in adding and subtracting fractions (from **Section 5.4**).

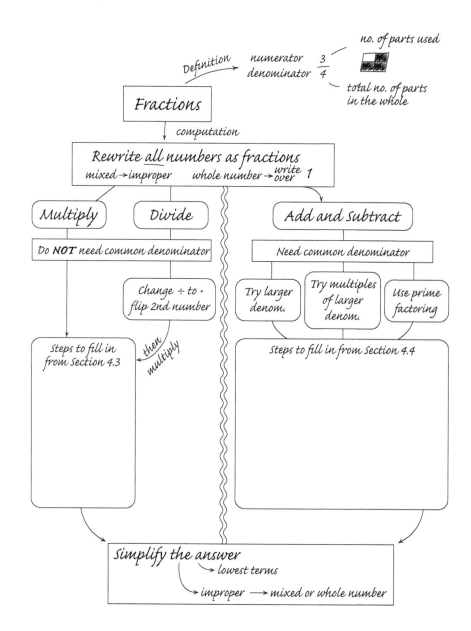

5.5 ▶▶▶ Problem Solving: Mixed Numbers and Estimating

OBJECTIVE 1 Identify mixed numbers and graph them on a number line.   When a fraction and a whole number are written together, the result is a **mixed number.** For example, the mixed number

$$3\frac{1}{2} \quad \text{represents} \quad 3 + \frac{1}{2}$$

or 3 wholes and $\frac{1}{2}$ of a whole. Read $3\frac{1}{2}$ as "three and one half."

One common use of mixed numbers is to measure things. Examples are shown below.

Juan worked $5\frac{1}{2}$ hours.   The box weighs $2\frac{3}{4}$ pounds.

The park is $1\frac{7}{10}$ miles long.   Add $1\frac{2}{3}$ cups of flour.

EXAMPLE 1   Illustrating a Mixed Number with a Diagram and a Number Line

As this diagram shows, the mixed number $3\frac{1}{2}$ is equivalent to the improper fraction $\frac{7}{2}$.

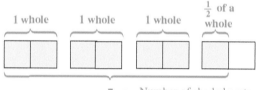

We can also use a number line to show mixed numbers, as in this graph of $3\frac{1}{2}$ and $-3\frac{1}{2}$.

The number line shows the following.

$$3\frac{1}{2} \quad \text{is equivalent to} \quad \frac{7}{2}$$

$$-3\frac{1}{2} \quad \text{is equivalent to} \quad -\frac{7}{2}$$

Note

$3\frac{1}{2}$ represents $3 + \frac{1}{2}$.

$-3\frac{1}{2}$ represents $-3 + \left(-\frac{1}{2}\right)$, which can also be written as $-3 - \frac{1}{2}$.

In algebra we usually work with the improper fraction form of mixed numbers, especially for negative mixed numbers. However, positive mixed numbers are frequently used in daily life, so it's important to know how to work with them. For example, we usually say $3\frac{1}{2}$ inches rather than $\frac{7}{2}$ inches.

Work Problem (1) *at the Side.* ▶

OBJECTIVES

1. **Identify mixed numbers and graph them on a number line.**

2. **Rewrite mixed numbers as improper fractions, or the reverse.**

3. **Estimate the answer and multiply or divide mixed numbers.**

4. **Estimate the answer and add or subtract mixed numbers.**

5. **Solve application problems containing mixed numbers.**

1 **(a)** Use this diagram to write $1\frac{2}{3}$ as an improper fraction.

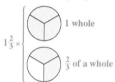

(b) Now graph $1\frac{2}{3}$ and $-1\frac{2}{3}$ on this number line.

(c) Use this diagram to write $2\frac{1}{4}$ as an improper fraction.

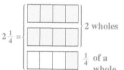

(d) Now graph $2\frac{1}{4}$ and $-2\frac{1}{4}$ on this number line.

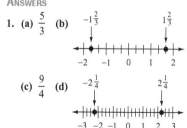

ANSWERS

1. **(a)** $\frac{5}{3}$ **(b)**

(c) $\frac{9}{4}$ **(d)**

2 Write each mixed number as an equivalent improper fraction.

(a) $3\dfrac{2}{3}$

(b) $4\dfrac{7}{10}$

(c) $5\dfrac{3}{4}$

(d) $8\dfrac{5}{6}$

OBJECTIVE **2** **Rewrite mixed numbers as improper fractions, or the reverse.** You can use the following steps to write $3\frac{1}{2}$ as an improper fraction without drawing a diagram or a number line.

Step 1 Multiply 2 times 3 and add 1 to the product.

$$3\dfrac{1}{2} \qquad 2 \cdot 3 = 6 \qquad \text{Then } 6 + 1 = 7$$

Step 2 Use 7 (from Step 1) as the numerator and 2 as the denominator.

$$3\dfrac{1}{2} = \dfrac{7}{2} \leftarrow (2 \cdot 3) + 1$$

Same denominator

To see why this method works, recall that $3\frac{1}{2}$ represents $3 + \frac{1}{2}$. Let's add $3 + \frac{1}{2}$.

$$3 + \dfrac{1}{2} = \dfrac{3}{1} + \dfrac{1}{2} = \dfrac{6}{2} + \dfrac{1}{2} = \dfrac{6+1}{2} = \dfrac{7}{2} \quad \begin{cases} \text{Same result} \\ \text{as above} \end{cases}$$

Common denominator

In summary, use the following steps to *write a mixed number as an improper fraction.*

Writing a Mixed Number as an Improper Fraction

Step 1 **Multiply** the denominator of the fraction times the whole number and **add** the numerator of the fraction to the product.

Step 2 Write the result of *Step 1* as the **numerator** and keep the original **denominator.**

EXAMPLE 2 **Writing a Mixed Number as an Improper Fraction**

Write $7\frac{2}{3}$ as an improper fraction (numerator greater than denominator).

Step 1 $7\dfrac{2}{3} \qquad 3 \cdot 7 = 21 \qquad \text{Then } 21 + 2 = 23$

Step 2 $7\dfrac{2}{3} = \dfrac{23}{3} \leftarrow (3 \cdot 7) + 2$

Keep the same denominator.

Same denominator

◀ *Work Problem* **2** *at the Side.*

We used *multiplication* for the first step in writing a mixed number as an improper fraction. To work in *reverse*, writing an improper fraction as a mixed number, we will use *division*. Recall that the fraction bar is a symbol for division.

Writing an Improper Fraction as a Mixed Number

To write an *improper fraction* as a mixed number, divide the numerator by the denominator. The quotient is the whole number part (of the mixed number), the remainder is the numerator of the fraction part, and the denominator remains the same.

Always check to be sure that the fraction part of the mixed number is in lowest terms. Then the mixed number is in *simplest form*.

EXAMPLE 3   **Writing Improper Fractions as Mixed Numbers**

Write each improper fraction as an equivalent mixed number in simplest form.

(a) $\dfrac{17}{5}$

Divide 17 by 5.

$$
\begin{array}{r}
3 \quad \leftarrow \text{Whole number part} \\
5\overline{)17} \\
\underline{15} \\
2 \quad \leftarrow \text{Remainder}
\end{array}
$$

The quotient **3** is the whole number part of the mixed number. The remainder **2** is the numerator of the fraction, and the denominator stays as **5**.

$$\frac{17}{5} = 3\frac{2}{5} \quad \leftarrow \text{Remainder}$$

Same denominator

Let's look at a drawing of $\frac{17}{5}$ to check our work.

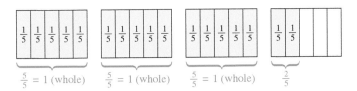

$\frac{5}{5} = 1$ (whole) $\frac{5}{5} = 1$ (whole) $\frac{5}{5} = 1$ (whole) $\frac{2}{5}$

Continued on Next Page

3 Write each improper fraction as an equivalent mixed number in simplest form.

(a) $\dfrac{5}{2}$

(b) $\dfrac{14}{4}$

(c) $\dfrac{33}{5}$

(d) $\dfrac{58}{10}$

4 Round each mixed number to the nearest whole number.

(a) $2\dfrac{3}{4}$

(b) $6\dfrac{3}{8}$

(c) $4\dfrac{2}{3}$

(d) $1\dfrac{7}{10}$

(e) $3\dfrac{1}{2}$

(f) $5\dfrac{4}{9}$

In other words,

$$\frac{17}{5} = \frac{5}{5} + \frac{5}{5} + \frac{5}{5} + \frac{2}{5}$$
$$= 1 + 1 + 1 + \frac{2}{5}$$
$$= \quad 3 \quad + \frac{2}{5}$$
$$= 3\frac{2}{5}$$

(b) $\dfrac{26}{4}$

Divide 26 by 4.

$$4\overline{)26} \quad \text{so} \quad \frac{26}{4} = 6\frac{2}{4} = 6\frac{1}{2} \quad \left\{ \begin{array}{l}\text{Simplest}\\\text{form}\end{array}\right.$$

Write $\frac{2}{4}$ in lowest terms.

You could write $\frac{26}{4}$ in lowest terms first.

$$\frac{26}{4} = \frac{\overset{1}{\cancel{2}} \cdot 13}{\underset{1}{\cancel{2}} \cdot 2} = \frac{13}{2} \quad \text{Then} \quad 2\overline{)13} \quad \text{so} \quad \frac{13}{2} = 6\frac{1}{2} \quad \left\{ \begin{array}{l}\text{Same result}\\\text{as above}\end{array}\right.$$

◀ Work Problem **3** at the Side.

OBJECTIVE 3 Estimate the answer and multiply or divide mixed numbers. Once you have rewritten mixed numbers as improper fractions, you can use the steps you learned in **Section 5.3** to multiply and divide. However, it's a good idea to estimate the answer before you start any other work.

EXAMPLE 4 **Rounding Mixed Numbers to the Nearest Whole Number**

To estimate answers, first round each mixed number to the *nearest whole number*. If the numerator is *half* of the denominator or *more*, round up the whole number part. If the numerator is *less* than half the denominator, leave the whole number as it is.

(a) Round $1\dfrac{5}{8}$ ← 5 is more than 4 $1\dfrac{5}{8}$ rounds up to 2
← Half of 8 is 4

(b) Round $3\dfrac{2}{5}$ ← 2 is less than $2\frac{1}{2}$ $3\dfrac{2}{5}$ rounds to 3
← Half of 5 is $2\frac{1}{2}$

◀ Work Problem **4** at the Side.

ANSWERS

3. (a) $2\dfrac{1}{2}$ (b) $3\dfrac{1}{2}$ (c) $6\dfrac{3}{5}$ (d) $5\dfrac{4}{5}$

4. (a) 3 (b) 6 (c) 5 (d) 2 (e) 4 (f) 5

> **Multiplying and Dividing Mixed Numbers**
>
> **Step 1**   **Rewrite** each mixed number as an improper fraction.
>
> **Step 2**   **Multiply** or **divide** the improper fractions.
>
> **Step 3**   Write the answer in lowest terms and change it to a mixed number or whole number where possible. This step gives you an answer that is in **simplest form.**

EXAMPLE 5   **Estimating the Answer and Multiplying Mixed Numbers**

First, round the numbers and estimate each answer. Then find the exact answer. Write exact answers in simplest form.

(a) $2\frac{1}{2} \cdot 3\frac{1}{5}$

Estimate the answer by rounding the mixed numbers.

$2\frac{1}{2}$ rounds to 3   and $3\frac{1}{5}$ rounds to 3

$3 \cdot 3 = 9 \leftarrow$ Estimated answer

To find the exact answer, first rewrite each mixed number as an improper fraction.

Step 1 $2\frac{1}{2} = \frac{5}{2}$ and $3\frac{1}{5} = \frac{16}{5}$

Next, multiply.

Step 2   Step 3

$$2\frac{1}{2} \cdot 3\frac{1}{5} = \frac{5}{2} \cdot \frac{16}{5} = \frac{\overset{1}{\cancel{5}} \cdot \overset{1}{2} \cdot 8}{\underset{1}{\cancel{2}} \cdot \underset{1}{\cancel{5}}} = \frac{8}{1} = 8 \; \begin{cases} \text{Simplest} \\ \text{form} \end{cases}$$

The estimate was 9, so an exact answer of 8 is reasonable.

> Estimating helps you catch errors.

(b) $\left(3\frac{5}{8}\right)\left(4\frac{4}{5}\right)$

First, round each mixed number and estimate the answer.

$3\frac{5}{8}$ rounds to 4   and $4\frac{4}{5}$ rounds to 5

$4 \cdot 5 = 20 \leftarrow$ Estimated answer

Now find the exact answer.

Step 1   Step 2   Step 3

$$\left(3\frac{5}{8}\right)\left(4\frac{4}{5}\right) = \left(\frac{29}{8}\right)\left(\frac{24}{5}\right) = \frac{29 \cdot 3 \cdot \overset{1}{\cancel{8}}}{\underset{1}{\cancel{8}} \cdot 5} = \frac{87}{5} = 17\frac{2}{5} \; \begin{cases} \text{Simplest} \\ \text{form} \end{cases}$$

The estimate was 20, so an exact answer of $17\frac{2}{5}$ is reasonable.

Work Problem **5** *at the Side.* ▶

---

5 First, round the numbers and estimate each answer. Then find the exact answer. Write exact answers in simplest form.

(a) $2\frac{1}{4} \quad \cdot \quad 7\frac{1}{3}$

⬇   ⬇

_____ • _____ = _____ *estimate*

(b) $\left(4\frac{1}{2}\right) \left(1\frac{2}{3}\right)$

⬇   ⬇

(____) (____) = ____ *estimate*

(c) $3\frac{3}{5} \quad \cdot \quad 4\frac{4}{9}$

⬇   ⬇

_____ • _____ = _____ *estimate*

(d) $\left(3\frac{1}{5}\right) \left(5\frac{3}{8}\right)$

⬇   ⬇

(____) (____) = ____ *estimate*

ANSWERS

5. (a) *Estimate:* $2 \cdot 7 = 14$; *Exact:* $16\frac{1}{2}$

(b) *Estimate:* $(5)(2) = 10$; *Exact:* $7\frac{1}{2}$

(c) *Estimate:* $4 \cdot 4 = 16$; *Exact:* 16

(d) *Estimate:* $(3)(5) = 15$; *Exact:* $17\frac{1}{5}$

6 First, round the numbers and estimate each answer. Then find the exact answer. Write exact answers in simplest form.

(a) $6\frac{1}{4} \div 3\frac{1}{3}$

$\downarrow \qquad \downarrow$

_____ ÷ _____ = _____ *estimate*

(b) $3\frac{3}{8} \div 2\frac{4}{7}$

$\downarrow \qquad \downarrow$

_____ ÷ _____ = _____ *estimate*

(c) $8 \div 5\frac{1}{3}$

$\downarrow \qquad \downarrow$

_____ ÷ _____ = _____ *estimate*

(d) $4\frac{1}{2} \div 6$

$\downarrow \qquad \downarrow$

_____ ÷ _____ = _____ *estimate*

ANSWERS

6. (a) *Estimate:* $6 \div 3 = 2$; *Exact:* $1\frac{7}{8}$

(b) *Estimate:* $3 \div 3 = 1$; *Exact:* $1\frac{5}{16}$

(c) *Estimate:* $8 \div 5 = 1\frac{3}{5}$; *Exact:* $1\frac{1}{2}$

(d) *Estimate:* $5 \div 6 = \frac{5}{6}$; *Exact:* $\frac{3}{4}$

EXAMPLE 6 **Estimating the Answer and Dividing Mixed Numbers**

First, round the numbers and estimate each answer. Then find the exact answer. Write exact answers in simplest form.

(a) $3\frac{3}{5} \div 1\frac{1}{2}$

To estimate the answer, round each mixed number to the nearest whole number.

$$3\frac{3}{5} \qquad \div \qquad 1\frac{1}{2}$$
$$\downarrow \quad \text{Rounded} \quad \downarrow$$
$$4 \quad \div \quad 2 \quad = \quad 2 \leftarrow \text{Estimate}$$

To find the exact answer, first rewrite each mixed number as an improper fraction.

$$3\frac{3}{5} \div 1\frac{1}{2} = \frac{18}{5} \div \frac{3}{2}$$

> You do **not** need a common denominator when multiplying or dividing fractions.

Now rewrite the problem as multiplying by the reciprocal of $\frac{3}{2}$.

$$\frac{18}{5} \div \frac{3}{2} = \frac{18}{5} \cdot \frac{2}{3} = \frac{\overset{1}{\cancel{3}} \cdot 6 \cdot 2}{5 \cdot \cancel{3}} = \frac{12}{5} = 2\frac{2}{5} \quad \left\{ \begin{matrix} \text{Simplest} \\ \text{form} \end{matrix} \right.$$

Reciprocals

The estimate was 2, so an exact answer of $2\frac{2}{5}$ is reasonable.

(b) $4\frac{3}{8} \div 5$

First, round the numbers and estimate the answer.

$$4\frac{3}{8} \qquad \div \qquad 5$$
$$\downarrow \quad \text{Rounded} \quad \downarrow$$
$$4 \quad \div \quad 5 \qquad \text{Write } 4 \div 5 \text{ using a fraction bar.} \left. \right\} \frac{4}{5} \leftarrow \text{Estimate}$$

Now find the exact answer.

Write 5 as $\frac{5}{1}$

$$4\frac{3}{8} \div 5 = \frac{35}{8} \div \frac{5}{1} = \frac{35}{8} \cdot \frac{1}{5} = \frac{\overset{1}{\cancel{5}} \cdot 7 \cdot 1}{8 \cdot \cancel{5}} = \frac{7}{8} \quad \left\{ \begin{matrix} \text{Simplest} \\ \text{form} \end{matrix} \right.$$

Reciprocals

The estimate was $\frac{4}{5}$, so an exact answer of $\frac{7}{8}$ is reasonable. They are both less than 1.

◀ *Work Problem* **6** *at the Side.*

OBJECTIVE 4 **Estimate the answer and add or subtract mixed numbers.** The steps you learned for adding and subtracting fractions in **Section 5.4** will also work for mixed numbers: Just rewrite the mixed numbers as equivalent improper fractions. Again, it is a good idea to estimate the answer before you start any other work.

EXAMPLE 7 **Estimating the Answer and Adding or Subtracting Mixed Numbers**

First, estimate each answer. Then add or subtract to find the exact answer. Write exact answers in simplest form.

(a) $2\frac{3}{8} + 3\frac{3}{4}$

To estimate the answer, round each mixed number to the nearest whole number.

$$2\frac{3}{8} + 3\frac{3}{4}$$
$$\downarrow \qquad \downarrow$$
$$2 + 4 = 6 \leftarrow \text{Estimate}$$

To find the exact answer, first rewrite each mixed number as an equivalent improper fraction.

$$2\frac{3}{8} + 3\frac{3}{4} = \frac{19}{8} + \frac{15}{4}$$

You **do** need a common denominator to add or subtract fractions.

You can't add fractions until they have a common denominator. The LCD for $\frac{19}{8}$ and $\frac{15}{4}$ is 8. Rewrite $\frac{15}{4}$ as an equivalent fraction with a denominator of 8.

$$\frac{19}{8} + \frac{15}{4} = \frac{19}{8} + \frac{30}{8} = \frac{19 + 30}{8} = \frac{49}{8} = 6\frac{1}{8} \begin{cases} \text{Simplest} \\ \text{form} \end{cases}$$

Common denominator

The estimate was 6, so an exact answer of $6\frac{1}{8}$ is reasonable.

(b) $4\frac{2}{3} - 2\frac{4}{5}$

Round each number and estimate the answer.

$$4\frac{2}{3} - 2\frac{4}{5}$$
$$\downarrow \qquad \downarrow$$
$$5 - 3 = 2 \leftarrow \text{Estimate}$$

To find the exact answer, rewrite the mixed numbers as improper fractions and subtract.

$$4\frac{2}{3} - 2\frac{4}{5} = \frac{14}{3} - \frac{14}{5} = \frac{70}{15} - \frac{42}{15} = \frac{70 - 42}{15} = \frac{28}{15} = 1\frac{13}{15} \begin{cases} \text{Simplest} \\ \text{form} \end{cases}$$

LCD is 15

The estimate was 2, so an exact answer of $1\frac{13}{15}$ is reasonable.

Continued on Next Page

7 First, round the numbers and estimate each answer. Then add or subtract to find the exact answer.

(a) $5\dfrac{1}{3} \;-\; 2\dfrac{5}{6}$

$\downarrow \qquad\quad \downarrow$

_____ − _____ = _____ *estimate*

(b) $\dfrac{3}{4} \;+\; 3\dfrac{1}{8}$

$\downarrow \qquad\quad \downarrow$

_____ + _____ = _____ *estimate*

(c) $6 \;-\; 3\dfrac{4}{5}$

$\downarrow \qquad\quad \downarrow$

_____ − _____ = _____ *estimate*

(c) $5 - 1\dfrac{3}{8}$

$$5 - 1\dfrac{3}{8}$$
$$\downarrow \qquad\quad \downarrow$$
$$5 \;-\; 1 \;=\; 4 \;\leftarrow \text{Estimate}$$

Write 5 as $\dfrac{5}{1}$

$$5 - 1\dfrac{3}{8} = \dfrac{5}{1} - \dfrac{11}{8} = \dfrac{40}{8} - \dfrac{11}{8} = \dfrac{29}{8} = 3\dfrac{5}{8} \quad \begin{cases}\text{Simplest}\\ \text{form}\end{cases}$$

LCD is 8

The estimate was 4, so an exact answer of $3\frac{5}{8}$ is reasonable.

◀ *Work Problem* **7** *at the Side.*

Note

In some situations the method of rewriting mixed numbers as improper fractions may result in very large numerators. Consider this example.

Last year Hue's child was $48\frac{3}{8}$ in. tall. This year the child is $51\frac{1}{4}$ in. tall. How much has the child grown?

First, estimate the answer by rounding each mixed number to the nearest whole number.

$$51\dfrac{1}{4} \;-\; 48\dfrac{3}{8}$$
$$\downarrow \qquad\qquad \downarrow$$
$$51 \;-\; 48 \;=\; 3 \text{ in.} \;\leftarrow \text{Estimate}$$

To find the exact answer, rewrite the mixed numbers as improper fractions.

Rewrite $\frac{205}{4}$ as $\frac{410}{8}$

$$51\dfrac{1}{4} - 48\dfrac{3}{8} = \dfrac{205}{4} - \dfrac{387}{8} = \dfrac{410}{8} - \dfrac{387}{8} = \dfrac{410 - 387}{8} = \dfrac{23}{8} = 2\dfrac{7}{8}\text{ in.}$$

LCD is 8

You can also use the fraction key $\boxed{a^{b/c}}$ on your *scientific* calculator to solve this problem.

To enter $51\frac{1}{4}$, press

51 $\boxed{a^{b/c}}$ 1 $\boxed{a^{b/c}}$ 4 $\boxed{a^{b/c}}$. The display shows $\boxed{\mathbf{51\_1\_4}}$.

↑   ↑   ↑

Whole   Numerator   Denominator
number

Then press $\boxed{-}$ 48 $\boxed{a^{b/c}}$ 3 $\boxed{a^{b/c}}$ 8 $\boxed{=}$. The display shows $\boxed{\mathbf{2\_7\_8}}$.

↑
Subtract. $48\dfrac{3}{8}$ $2\dfrac{7}{8}$

Either way the exact answer is $2\frac{7}{8}$ in., which is close to the estimate of 3 in.

Another efficient method for handling large mixed numbers is to rewrite them in decimal form. You will learn how to do that in **Chapter 5.**

ANSWERS

7. (a) *Estimate:* $5 - 3 = 2$; *Exact:* $2\dfrac{1}{2}$

  (b) *Estimate:* $1 + 3 = 4$; *Exact:* $3\dfrac{7}{8}$

  (c) *Estimate:* $6 - 4 = 2$; *Exact:* $2\dfrac{1}{5}$

OBJECTIVE 5 Solve application problems containing mixed numbers. Rounding mixed numbers to the nearest whole number can also help you decide whether to solve an application problem by adding, subtracting, multiplying, or dividing.

EXAMPLE 8   Solving Application Problems with Mixed Numbers

First, estimate the answer to each application problem. Then find the exact answer.

(a) Gary needs to haul $15\frac{3}{4}$ tons of sand to a construction site. His truck can carry $2\frac{1}{4}$ tons. How many trips will he need to make?
First, round each mixed number to the nearest whole number.

$$15\frac{3}{4} \quad \text{rounds to} \quad 16 \quad \text{and} \quad 2\frac{1}{4} \quad \text{rounds to} \quad 2$$

Now read the problem again, *using the rounded numbers*.
   Gary needs to haul **16 tons** of sand to a construction site. His truck can carry **2 tons**. How many trips will he need to make?
   Using the rounded numbers in the problem makes it easier to see that you need to *divide*.

$$16 \div 2 = 8 \text{ trips} \leftarrow \text{Estimate}$$

To find the exact answer, use the original mixed numbers and divide.

$$15\frac{3}{4} \div 2\frac{1}{4} = \frac{63}{4} \div \frac{9}{4} = \frac{63}{4} \cdot \frac{4}{9} = \frac{7 \cdot \cancel{9} \cdot \cancel{4}}{\cancel{4} \cdot \cancel{9}} = \frac{7}{1} = 7 \begin{cases} \text{Simplest} \\ \text{form} \end{cases}$$

Reciprocals

Gary needs to make 7 trips to haul all the sand. This result is close to the estimate of 8 trips.

(b) Zenitia worked $3\frac{5}{6}$ **hours** on Monday and $6\frac{1}{2}$ **hours** on Tuesday. How much longer did she work on Tuesday than on Monday?
First, round each mixed number to the nearest whole number.

$$3\frac{5}{6} \quad \text{rounds to} \quad 4 \quad \text{and} \quad 6\frac{1}{2} \quad \text{rounds to} \quad 7$$

Now read the problem again, *using the rounded numbers*.
   Zenitia worked **4 hours** on Monday and **7 hours** on Tuesday. How much longer did she work on Tuesday than on Monday?
   Using the rounded numbers in the problem makes it easier to see that you need to *subtract*.

$$7 - 4 = 3 \text{ hours} \leftarrow \text{Estimate}$$

To find the exact answer, use the original mixed numbers and subtract.

Write answer in simplest form.

$$6\frac{1}{2} - 3\frac{5}{6} = \frac{13}{2} - \frac{23}{6} = \frac{39}{6} - \frac{23}{6} = \frac{39 - 23}{6} = \frac{16}{6} = 2\frac{4}{6} = 2\frac{2}{3}$$

LCD is 6

Zenitia worked $2\frac{2}{3}$ hours longer on Tuesday. This result is close to the estimate of 3 hours.

Work Problem **8** *at the Side.* ▶

8 First, round the numbers and estimate the answer to each problem. Then find the exact answer.

(a) Richard's son grew $3\frac{5}{8}$ inches last year and $2\frac{1}{4}$ inches this year. How much has his height increased over the two years?

Estimate:

Exact:

(b) Ernestine used $2\frac{1}{2}$ packages of chocolate chips in her cookie recipe. Each package has $5\frac{1}{2}$ ounces of chips. How many ounces of chips did she use in the recipe?

Estimate:

Exact:

ANSWERS

8. (a) *Estimate:* $4 + 2 = 6$ inches;

   Exact: $5\frac{7}{8}$ inches

(b) *Estimate:* $3 \cdot 6 = 18$ ounces;

   Exact: $13\frac{3}{4}$ ounces

Math in the Media

Guilt-free Gravy

Makes 2 cups.

- 3 tablespoons corn starch
- $\frac{1}{4}$ cup apple cider
- 2 cups fat-free broth

- $\frac{1}{2}$ teaspoon rubbed sage
- $\frac{3}{4}$ teaspoon salt
- $\frac{1}{8}$ teaspoon pepper

To make in the microwave:

Combine corn starch, apple cider, broth, and sage in a 2-quart, microwave-safe bowl. With a whisk, stir mixture until corn starch is completely dissolved. Microwave on high power for 7 to 9 minutes or until mixture boils, stirring every minute. Boil for 1 minute. Add salt and pepper.

Source: www.argostarch.com

You decide to make gravy for Thanksgiving dinner and find this recipe through an Internet search.

1. (a) How much gravy does the recipe make?

   (b) You need 5 cups of gravy. By what factor should you multiply each ingredient in the recipe?

   (c) Find the amount of each ingredient needed to make 5 cups of gravy.

   corn starch: _____   sage: _____

   apple cider: _____   salt: _____

   fat-free broth: _____   pepper: _____

2. Most sets of measuring spoons have a spoon for each of these amounts:

   1 tablespoon, $\frac{1}{2}$ tablespoon,   1 teaspoon, $\frac{1}{2}$ teaspoon,

   $\frac{1}{4}$ teaspoon, $\frac{1}{8}$ teaspoon

   (a) How could you measure $1\frac{7}{8}$ teaspoons of salt in the fewest steps?

   (b) How might you measure the pepper from Question 1?

Graph the mixed numbers or improper fractions on the number line. See Example 1.

1. Graph $2\frac{1}{3}$ and $-2\frac{1}{3}$.

-4 -3 -2 -1 0 1 2 3 4

2. Graph $1\frac{3}{4}$ and $-1\frac{3}{4}$.

-4 -3 -2 -1 0 1 2 3 4

3. Graph $\frac{3}{2}$ and $-\frac{3}{2}$.

-4 -3 -2 -1 0 1 2 3 4

4. Graph $\frac{11}{3}$ and $-\frac{11}{3}$.

-4 -3 -2 -1 0 1 2 3 4

Write each mixed number as an improper fraction. See Example 2.

5. $4\frac{1}{2}$ **6.** $2\frac{1}{4}$ **7.** $-1\frac{3}{5}$ **8.** $-1\frac{5}{6}$ **9.** $2\frac{3}{8}$

10. $3\frac{4}{9}$ **11.** $-5\frac{7}{10}$ **12.** $-4\frac{5}{7}$ **13.** $10\frac{11}{15}$ **14.** $12\frac{9}{11}$

Write each improper fraction as a mixed number in simplest form. See Example 3.

15. $\frac{13}{3}$ **16.** $\frac{11}{2}$ **17.** $-\frac{10}{4}$ **18.** $-\frac{14}{5}$ **19.** $\frac{22}{6}$

20. $\frac{28}{8}$ **21.** $-\frac{51}{9}$ **22.** $-\frac{44}{10}$ ⊙**23.** $\frac{188}{16}$ **24.** $\frac{200}{15}$

First, round each mixed number to the nearest whole number and estimate the answer. Then find the exact answer. Write exact answers in simplest form. See Examples 4–7.

⊙**25.** *Exact:*

$2\frac{1}{4} \cdot 3\frac{1}{2}$

Estimate:

___ • ___ = ___

26. *Exact:*

$\left(1\frac{1}{2}\right)\left(3\frac{3}{4}\right)$

Estimate:

(___)(___) = ___

⊙**27.** *Exact:*

$3\frac{1}{4} \div 2\frac{5}{8}$

Estimate:

___ ÷ ___ = ___

28. *Exact:*

$2\frac{1}{4} \div 1\frac{1}{8}$

Estimate:

___ ÷ ___ = ___

⊙**29.** *Exact:*

$3\frac{2}{3} + 1\frac{5}{6}$

Estimate:

___ + ___ = ___

30. *Exact:*

$4\frac{4}{5} + 2\frac{1}{3}$

Estimate:

___ + ___ = ___

31. *Exact:*

$$4\frac{1}{4} - \frac{7}{12}$$

Estimate:

___ − ___ = ___

32. *Exact:*

$$10\frac{1}{3} - 6\frac{5}{6}$$

Estimate:

___ − ___ = ___

33. *Exact:*

$$5\frac{2}{3} \div 6$$

Estimate:

___ ÷ ___ = ___

34. *Exact:*

$$1\frac{7}{8} \div 6\frac{1}{4}$$

Estimate:

___ ÷ ___ = _____

35. *Exact:*

$$8 - 1\frac{4}{5}$$

Estimate:

_____ − ___ = _____

36. *Exact:*

$$7 - 3\frac{3}{10}$$

Estimate:

___ − ___ = _____

Find the perimeter and the area of each square or rectangle. Write all answers in simplest form.

37.

$1\frac{3}{4}$ in.

$1\frac{3}{4}$ in.

$1\frac{3}{4}$ in.

38.

$2\frac{1}{3}$ ft

$2\frac{1}{3}$ ft

39.

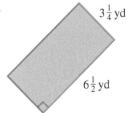

$3\frac{1}{4}$ yd

$6\frac{1}{2}$ yd

40.

$2\frac{3}{10}$ mi

$\frac{2}{5}$ mi

$\frac{2}{5}$ mi

$2\frac{3}{10}$ mi

First, estimate the answer to each application problem. Then find the exact answer. Write all answers in simplest form. See Example 8.

41. A carpenter has two pieces of oak trim. One piece of trim is $12\frac{1}{2}$ ft long and the other is $8\frac{2}{3}$ ft long. How many feet of oak trim does he have in all?

Estimate:

Exact:

42. On Monday, $5\frac{3}{4}$ tons of cans were recycled, and on Tuesday, $9\frac{3}{5}$ tons were recycled. How many tons were recycled on these two days?

Estimate:

Exact:

43. The directions for mixing an insect spray say to use $1\frac{3}{4}$ ounces of chemical in each gallon of water. How many ounces of chemical should be mixed with $5\frac{1}{2}$ gallons of water?

Estimate:

Exact:

44. Shirley Cicero wants to make 16 holiday wreaths to sell at a craft fair. Each wreath requires $2\frac{1}{4}$ yd of ribbon. How many yards does she need in all?

Estimate:

Exact:

45. The Boy Scout troop has volunteered to pick up trash along a 4-mile stretch of highway. So far they have done $1\frac{7}{10}$ miles. How much do they have left to do?

Estimate:

Exact:

46. Marv bought a 10 yd length of Italian silk fabric. He used $3\frac{7}{8}$ yd to make a jacket. What length of fabric is left for other sewing projects?

Estimate:

Exact:

47. Suppose that a bridesmaid's floor-length dress requires a piece of material $3\frac{3}{4}$ yd in length. What length of material is needed to make dresses for five bridesmaids?

Estimate:

Exact:

48. A cookie recipe uses $\frac{2}{3}$ cup brown sugar. How much brown sugar is needed to make $2\frac{1}{2}$ times the original recipe?

Estimate:

Exact:

Solve each application problem. Write all answers in simplest form. Use the information on the Oregon state park sign for Exercises 49–52. The distances on the sign are in miles.

49. What is the distance from Devils Kitchen to the beach parking?

50. How far is it from Face Rock to the beach parking?

51. Suppose you bicycle from the park sign to the picnic parking, then bicycle back to Face Rock, and finally bicycle to the beach parking. How far will you have traveled?

52. If you drive back and forth from the sign to the picnic parking each day for a week, how many miles will you drive?

53. Find the length of the arrow shaft.

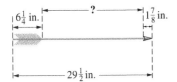

54. Find the length of the indented section on this board.

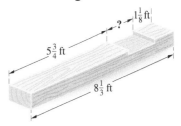

First, estimate the answer to each application problem. Then use your calculator to find the exact answer.

55. A craftsperson must attach a lead strip around all four sides of a rectangular stained glass window before it is installed. Find the length of lead stripping needed for the window shown.

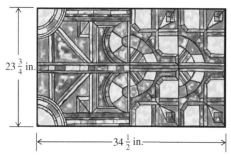

$23\frac{3}{4}$ in.

$34\frac{1}{2}$ in.

Estimate:

Exact:

56. To complete a custom order, Zak Morten of Home Depot must find the number of inches of brass trim needed to go around the four sides of the lamp base plate shown. Find the length of brass trim needed.

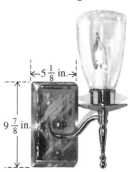

$5\frac{1}{8}$ in.

$9\frac{7}{8}$ in.

Estimate:

Exact:

57. A fishing boat anchor requires $10\frac{3}{8}$ pounds of steel. Find the number of anchors that can be manufactured with 25,730 pounds of steel.

Estimate:

Exact:

58. Each apartment requires $62\frac{1}{2}$ square yards of carpet. Find the number of apartments that can be carpeted with 6750 square yards of carpet.

Estimate:

Exact:

59. Claire and Deb create custom hat bands that people can put around the crowns of their hats. The finished bands are the lengths shown in the table. The strip of fabric for each band must include the finished length plus an extra $\frac{3}{4}$ in. for the seam.

Band Size	Finished Length
Small	$21\frac{7}{8}$ in.
Medium	$22\frac{5}{8}$ in.
Large	$23\frac{1}{2}$ in.

What length of fabric strip is needed to make 4 small bands, 5 medium bands, and 3 large bands, including the seam allowance?

Estimate:

Exact:

60. Three sides of a parking lot are $108\frac{1}{4}$ ft, $162\frac{3}{8}$ ft, and $143\frac{1}{2}$ ft. If the distance around the lot is $518\frac{3}{4}$ ft, find the length of the fourth side.

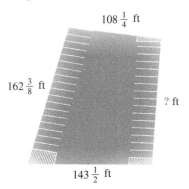

$108\frac{1}{4}$ ft

$162\frac{3}{8}$ ft

? ft

$143\frac{1}{2}$ ft

Estimate:

Exact:

Summary Exercises on Fractions

1. Write fractions that represent the shaded and unshaded portion of each figure.

(a)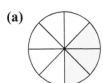

(b)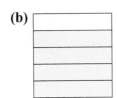

2. Graph $\dfrac{2}{3}$ and $-\dfrac{2}{3}$ on the number line.

3. Rewrite each fraction with the indicated denominator.

(a) $-\dfrac{4}{5} = -\dfrac{}{30}$ **(b)** $\dfrac{2}{7} = \dfrac{}{14}$

4. Simplify.

(a) $\dfrac{15}{15}$ **(b)** $-\dfrac{24}{6}$ **(c)** $\dfrac{9}{1}$

5. Write the prime factorization of each number.

(a) 72   **(b)** 105

6. Write each fraction in lowest terms.

(a) $\dfrac{24}{30}$ **(b)** $\dfrac{175}{200}$

Simplify.

7. $\left(-\dfrac{3}{4}\right)\left(-\dfrac{2}{3}\right)$

8. $-\dfrac{7}{8} + \dfrac{2}{3}$

9. $\dfrac{7}{16} + \dfrac{5}{8}$

10. $\dfrac{5}{8} \div \dfrac{3}{4}$

11. $\dfrac{2}{3} - \dfrac{4}{5}$

12. $\dfrac{7}{12}\left(-\dfrac{9}{14}\right)$

13. $-21 \div \left(-\dfrac{3}{8}\right)$

14. $\dfrac{7}{8} - \dfrac{5}{12}$

15. $-\dfrac{35}{45} \div \dfrac{10}{15}$

16. $-\dfrac{5}{6} - \dfrac{3}{4}$

17. $\dfrac{7}{12} + \dfrac{5}{6} + \dfrac{2}{3}$

18. $\dfrac{5}{8}$ of 56

First round the numbers and estimate each answer. Then find the exact answer.

19. *Exact:*

$4\dfrac{3}{4} + 2\dfrac{5}{6}$

Estimate:

___ + ___ = ___

20. *Exact:*

$2\dfrac{2}{9} \cdot 5\dfrac{1}{7}$

Estimate:

___ • ___ = ___

21. *Exact:*

$6 - 2\dfrac{7}{10}$

Estimate:

___ − ___ = ___

22. *Exact:*

$1\dfrac{3}{5} \div 3\dfrac{1}{2}$

Estimate:

___ ÷ ___ = ___

23. *Exact:*

$4\dfrac{2}{3} \div 1\dfrac{1}{6}$

Estimate:

___ ÷ ___ = ___

24. *Exact:*

$3\dfrac{5}{12} - \dfrac{3}{4}$

Estimate:

___ − ___ = ___

Solve each application problem. Write all answers in simplest form.

25. When installing cabinets, Cecil Feathers must be certain that the proper type and size of mounting screw is used.

(a) Find the total length of the screw shown.

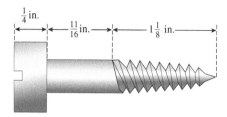

(b) If the screw is put into a board that is $1\frac{3}{4}$ in. thick, how much of the screw will stick out the back of the board?

26. Find the perimeter and the area of this postage stamp.

27. A batch of cookies requires $\frac{3}{4}$ pound of chocolate chips. If you have nine pounds of chocolate chips, how many batches of cookies can you make?

28. The Municipal Utility District says that the cost of operating a hair dryer is $\frac{1}{5}$¢ per minute. Find the cost of operating the hair dryer for a half hour.

29. A survey asked 1500 adults if UFOs (unidentified flying objects) are real. The circle graph shows the fraction of the adults who gave each answer. How many adults gave each answer?

Out Of This World?

When asked in a survey if UFOs actually exist, respondents answered:

$\frac{3}{20}$ Not sure

$\frac{9}{20}$ Real

$\frac{2}{5}$ Imaginary

Source: Yankelovich Partners for *Life* magazine.

30. Find the diameter of the hole in the rectangular mounting bracket shown. (The diameter is the distance across the center of the hole.) Then find the perimeter of the bracket.

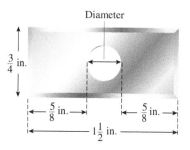

31. A bottle of contact lens daily cleaning solution holds $\frac{2}{3}$ fluid ounce. How many bottles can be filled with $15\frac{1}{3}$ fluid ounces? (*Source:* Alcon Laboratories, Inc.)

32. A home builder bought two parcels of land that were $5\frac{7}{8}$ acres and $10\frac{3}{4}$ acres. She is setting aside $2\frac{7}{8}$ acres for a park and using the rest for $1\frac{1}{4}$ acre home lots. How many lots will be in the development?

5.6 ▷▷▷ Exponents, Order of Operations, and Complex Fractions

OBJECTIVE 1 Simplify fractions with exponents. We have used exponents as a quick way to write repeated multiplication of integers and variables. Here are two examples as a review.

$$\overbrace{(-3)^2}^{\text{Exponent}} = \underbrace{(-3)(-3)}_{\text{Two factors of } -3} = 9 \quad \text{and} \quad \overbrace{x^3}^{\text{Exponent}} = \underbrace{x \cdot x \cdot x}_{\text{Three factors of } x}$$

Base Two factors of -3 Base Three factors of x

The meaning of an exponent remains the same when a fraction is the base.

OBJECTIVES

1 Simplify fractions with exponents.

2 Use the order of operations with fractions.

3 Simplify complex fractions.

EXAMPLE 1 Simplifying Fractions with Exponents

Simplify.

(a) $\left(-\dfrac{1}{2}\right)^3$

The base is $-\frac{1}{2}$. The exponent indicates that there are three factors of $-\frac{1}{2}$.

$$\left(-\frac{1}{2}\right)^3 = \overbrace{\left(-\frac{1}{2}\right)\left(-\frac{1}{2}\right)\left(-\frac{1}{2}\right)}^{\text{Three factors of } -\frac{1}{2}}$$ Multiply $\left(-\frac{1}{2}\right)\left(-\frac{1}{2}\right)$ to get $\frac{1}{4}$

Watch the signs! Multiply two factors at a time.

$$= \frac{1}{4}\left(-\frac{1}{2}\right)$$ Now multiply $\frac{1}{4}\left(-\frac{1}{2}\right)$ to get $-\frac{1}{8}$

$$= -\frac{1}{8}$$ The product is negative.

(b) $\left(\dfrac{3}{4}\right)^2 \left(\dfrac{2}{3}\right)^3$

Two factors of $\frac{3}{4}$

Three factors of $\frac{2}{3}$

$$\left(\frac{3}{4}\right)^2\left(\frac{2}{3}\right)^3 = \left(\frac{3}{4}\right)\left(\frac{3}{4}\right)\left(\frac{2}{3}\right)\left(\frac{2}{3}\right)\left(\frac{2}{3}\right)$$

$$= \frac{\overset{1}{\cancel{3}} \cdot \overset{1}{\cancel{3}} \cdot \overset{1}{\cancel{2}} \cdot \overset{1}{\cancel{2}} \cdot \overset{1}{\cancel{2}}}{\underset{1}{\cancel{2}} \cdot \underset{1}{\cancel{2}} \cdot \underset{1}{\cancel{2}} \cdot 2 \cdot \underset{1}{\cancel{3}} \cdot \underset{1}{\cancel{3}} \cdot 3}$$ Divide out all common factors.

$$= \frac{1}{6}$$

Work Problem **1** *at the Side.* ▶

1 Simplify.

(a) $\left(-\dfrac{3}{5}\right)^2$

(b) $\left(\dfrac{1}{3}\right)^4$

(c) $\left(-\dfrac{2}{3}\right)^3 \left(\dfrac{1}{2}\right)^2$

(d) $\left(-\dfrac{1}{2}\right)^2 \left(\dfrac{1}{4}\right)^2$

OBJECTIVE 2 Use the order of operations with fractions. The order of operations that you used in **Section 1.8** for integers also applies to fractions.

ANSWERS

1. (a) $\dfrac{9}{25}$ (b) $\dfrac{1}{81}$ (c) $-\dfrac{2}{27}$ (d) $\dfrac{1}{64}$

2 Simplify.

(a) $\dfrac{1}{3} - \dfrac{5}{9}\left(\dfrac{3}{4}\right)$

(b) $-\dfrac{3}{4} + \left(-\dfrac{1}{2}\right)^2 \div \dfrac{2}{3}$

(c) $\dfrac{12}{5} - \dfrac{1}{6}\left(3 - \dfrac{3}{5}\right)$

Order of Operations

Step 1 Work inside *parentheses* or *other grouping symbols*.

Step 2 Simplify expressions with *exponents*.

Step 3 Do the remaining *multiplications and divisions* as they occur from left to right.

Step 4 Do the remaining *additions and subtractions* as they occur from left to right.

EXAMPLE 2 **Using the Order of Operations with Fractions**

Simplify.

(a) $-\dfrac{1}{3} + \dfrac{1}{2}\left(\dfrac{4}{5}\right)$ There is no work to be done inside the parentheses. There are no exponents, so start with Step 3, multiplying and dividing.

$-\dfrac{1}{3} + \dfrac{1 \cdot 4}{2 \cdot 5}$ Multiply.   Multiply $\frac{1}{2} \cdot \frac{4}{5}$ first. Do **not** start by adding $-\frac{1}{3} + \frac{1}{2}$.

$-\dfrac{1}{3} + \dfrac{4}{10}$ Now add. The LCD is 30.
$-\dfrac{1}{3} = -\dfrac{10}{30}$ and $\dfrac{4}{10} = \dfrac{12}{30}$

$\dfrac{-10 + 12}{30}$ Add the numerators; keep the common denominator.

$\dfrac{2}{30}$ Write $\dfrac{2}{30}$ in lowest terms: $\dfrac{\overset{1}{\cancel{2}}}{\underset{1}{\cancel{2}} \cdot 15} = \dfrac{1}{15}$

$\dfrac{1}{15}$ The answer is in lowest terms.

(b) $-2 + \left(\dfrac{1}{4} - \dfrac{3}{2}\right)^2$ Work inside parentheses.
The LCD for $\dfrac{1}{4}$ and $\dfrac{3}{2}$ is 4

$-2 + \left(\dfrac{1 - 6}{4}\right)^2$ Rewrite $\dfrac{3}{2}$ as $\dfrac{6}{4}$ and subtract.

$-2 + \left(\dfrac{-5}{4}\right)^2$ Simplify the term with the exponent.
Multiply $\left(-\dfrac{5}{4}\right)\left(-\dfrac{5}{4}\right)$. *Signs match,* so the product is *positive.*

$-2 + \left(\dfrac{25}{16}\right)$ Add last.
Write -2 as $-\dfrac{2}{1}$

$-\dfrac{2}{1} + \dfrac{25}{16}$ The LCD is 16. Rewrite $-\dfrac{2}{1}$ as $-\dfrac{32}{16}$

$\dfrac{-32 + 25}{16}$ Add the numerators; keep the common denominator.

$-\dfrac{7}{16}$ ⟵   The answer is in lowest terms.

◀ *Work Problem* **2** *at the Side.*

ANSWERS

2. (a) $-\dfrac{1}{12}$ (b) $-\dfrac{3}{8}$ (c) 2

OBJECTIVE 3 Simplify complex fractions.   We have used both the $\div$ symbol and a fraction bar to indicate division. For example,

Indicates division $\rightarrow \dfrac{6}{2}$ can be written as $6 \div 2$ — Indicates division

That means we could write $-\frac{4}{5} \div (-\frac{3}{10})$ using a fraction bar instead of $\div$.

$-\dfrac{4}{5} \div \left(-\dfrac{3}{10}\right)$ can be written as $\dfrac{-\dfrac{4}{5}}{-\dfrac{3}{10}}$ $\leftarrow$ Indicates division

Indicates division

The result looks a bit complicated, and its name reflects that fact. We call it a *complex fraction*.

Complex Fractions

A **complex fraction** is a fraction in which the numerator and/or denominator contain one or more fractions.

To simplify a complex fraction, rewrite it in horizontal format using the $\div$ symbol for division.

EXAMPLE 3   Simplifying a Complex Fraction

Simplify: **(a)** $\dfrac{-\dfrac{4}{5}}{-\dfrac{3}{10}}$ **(b)** $\dfrac{\left(\dfrac{2}{3}\right)^2}{6}$

(a) Rewrite the complex fraction using the $\div$ symbol for division. Then follow the steps for dividing fractions.

$$\dfrac{-\dfrac{4}{5}}{-\dfrac{3}{10}} = -\dfrac{4}{5} \div -\dfrac{3}{10} = -\dfrac{4}{5} \cdot -\dfrac{10}{3} = \dfrac{4 \cdot 2 \cdot \cancel{5}}{\cancel{5} \cdot 3} = \dfrac{8}{3} \text{ or } 2\dfrac{2}{3}$$

Reciprocals

The quotient is positive because the numbers in the problem had matching signs (both were negative).

(b) Rewrite the complex fraction using the $\div$ symbol for division. Then follow the order of operations.

$$\dfrac{\left(\dfrac{2}{3}\right)^2}{6} = \left(\dfrac{2}{3}\right)^2 \div 6 = \dfrac{4}{9} \div 6 = \dfrac{4}{9} \cdot \dfrac{1}{6} = \dfrac{\cancel{2} \cdot 2 \cdot 1}{9 \cdot \cancel{2} \cdot 3} = \dfrac{2}{27}$$

Reciprocals

Work Problem **3** *at the Side.* ▶

---

3 Simplify.

(a) $\dfrac{-\dfrac{3}{5}}{\dfrac{9}{10}}$

(b) $\dfrac{6}{\dfrac{3}{4}}$ $\leftarrow$ *Hint:* Write 6 as $\frac{6}{1}$

(c) $\dfrac{-\dfrac{15}{16}}{-5}$

(d) $\dfrac{-3}{\left(-\dfrac{3}{4}\right)^2}$

ANSWERS

3. **(a)** $-\dfrac{2}{3}$ **(b)** 8   **(c)** $\dfrac{3}{16}$

(d) $-\dfrac{16}{3}$ or $-5\dfrac{1}{3}$

Math in the Media

HEART-RATE TRAINING ZONE

Performing aerobic exercise benefits your aerobic fitness and helps burn fat. For best results, you should keep your heart rate within the training zone for a minimum of 12 minutes.

Example: The Training Zone (TZ) is based on your Heart Rate (HR) for one minute. To see if you are in the training zone, measure your heart rate for 15 seconds. Compare it to the 15-second training zone. Find the exact answer, then round to the nearest whole number.

Source: www.runningforfitness.org

Instruction	Calculation	Example (age 22)
Calculate maximum heart rate (MHR)	$220 - \text{your age}$	$220 - 22 = 198$
Calculate lower limit of training zone (TZ)	$\frac{3}{5} \times (\text{MHR})$	$\frac{3}{5} \times (198) = \frac{594}{5} = 118\frac{4}{5}$
Calculate upper limit of training zone (TZ)	$\frac{4}{5} \times (\text{MHR})$	$\frac{4}{5} \times (198) = \frac{792}{5} = 158\frac{2}{5}$
Calculate the exact 15-second training zone; then round to the nearest whole number.	$\left(\frac{1}{4} \times \text{lower TZ}, \frac{1}{4} \times \text{Upper TZ} \right)$	$\frac{1}{4} \times \frac{594}{5} = 29\frac{7}{10}; \frac{1}{4} \times \frac{792}{5} = 39\frac{3}{5}$ $29\frac{7}{10} < \text{HR} < 39\frac{3}{5}$ (exact) $30 < \text{HR} < 40$ (rounded)

1. Suppose you work in a physical fitness center and decide to design a poster to remind the clients of the training zone for their age. Compute the exact 15-second training zone for people of each age below. Write fractions in lowest terms. Then round the answers to the nearest whole number.

2. Explain why the lower and upper training zones (TZ) are multiplied by $\frac{1}{4}$.

Age	MHR	Lower Limit of TZ	Upper Limit of TZ	15-Second TZ (exact)	15-Second TZ (rounded)
20					
30					
40					
50					
60					

5.6 ▶▶▶ Exercises

FOR EXTRA HELP

 MyMathLab

 Math XL
PRACTICE

WATCH

DOWNLOAD

 READ

 REVIEW

Simplify. See Example 1.

1. $\left(-\dfrac{3}{4}\right)^2$

2. $\left(-\dfrac{4}{5}\right)^2$

3. $\left(\dfrac{2}{5}\right)^3$

4. $\left(\dfrac{1}{4}\right)^3$

5. $\left(-\dfrac{1}{3}\right)^3$

6. $\left(-\dfrac{3}{5}\right)^3$

7. $\left(\dfrac{1}{2}\right)^5$

8. $\left(\dfrac{1}{3}\right)^4$

9. $\left(\dfrac{7}{10}\right)^2$

10. $\left(\dfrac{8}{9}\right)^2$

11. $\left(-\dfrac{6}{5}\right)^2$

12. $\left(-\dfrac{8}{7}\right)^2$

13. $\dfrac{15}{16}\left(\dfrac{4}{5}\right)^3$

14. $-8\left(-\dfrac{3}{8}\right)^2$

15. $\left(\dfrac{1}{3}\right)^4\left(\dfrac{9}{10}\right)^2$

16. $\left(\dfrac{4}{5}\right)^2\left(\dfrac{1}{2}\right)^6$

17. $\left(-\dfrac{3}{2}\right)^3\left(-\dfrac{2}{3}\right)^2$

18. $\left(\dfrac{5}{6}\right)^2\left(-\dfrac{2}{5}\right)^3$

Relating Concepts (Exercises 19–20) For Individual or Group Work

Use your knowledge of exponents as you work Exercises 19 and 20 in order.

19. (a) Evaluate this series of examples.

$$\left(-\frac{1}{2}\right)^2 = \underline{\hspace{1cm}} \quad \bigg| \quad \left(-\frac{1}{2}\right)^6 = \underline{\hspace{1cm}}$$

$$\left(-\frac{1}{2}\right)^3 = \underline{\hspace{1cm}} \quad \bigg| \quad \left(-\frac{1}{2}\right)^7 = \underline{\hspace{1cm}}$$

$$\left(-\frac{1}{2}\right)^4 = \underline{\hspace{1cm}} \quad \bigg| \quad \left(-\frac{1}{2}\right)^8 = \underline{\hspace{1cm}}$$

$$\left(-\frac{1}{2}\right)^5 = \underline{\hspace{1cm}} \quad \bigg| \quad \left(-\frac{1}{2}\right)^9 = \underline{\hspace{1cm}}$$

20. Several drops of ketchup fell on Ron's homework. Explain how he can figure out what real number is covered by each drop. Be careful. More than one number may work, or there may not be any real number that works.

(a) $\left(\bullet\right)^2 = \dfrac{4}{9}$ **(b)** $\left(\bullet\right)^3 = -\dfrac{1}{27}$

(c) $\left(\bullet\right)^4 = \dfrac{1}{16}$ **(d)** $\left(\bullet\right)^2 = -\dfrac{9}{16}$

(e) $\left(\bullet\right)^2\left(\bullet\right)^2 = \dfrac{1}{36}$

(b) Explain the pattern in the sign of the answers.

Simplify. See Example 2.

21. $\dfrac{1}{5} - 6\left(\dfrac{7}{10}\right)$

22. $\dfrac{2}{9} - 4\left(\dfrac{5}{6}\right)$

23. $\left(\dfrac{4}{3} \div \dfrac{8}{3}\right) + \left(-\dfrac{3}{4} \cdot \dfrac{1}{4}\right)$

24. $\left(-\dfrac{1}{3} \cdot \dfrac{3}{5}\right) + \left(\dfrac{3}{4} \div \dfrac{1}{4}\right)$

25. $-\dfrac{3}{10} \div \dfrac{3}{5}\left(-\dfrac{2}{3}\right)$

26. $5 \div \left(-\dfrac{10}{3}\right)\left(-\dfrac{4}{9}\right)$

27. $\dfrac{8}{3}\left(\dfrac{1}{4}-\dfrac{1}{2}\right)^2$

28. $\dfrac{1}{3}\left(\dfrac{4}{5}-\dfrac{3}{10}\right)^3$

29. $-\dfrac{3}{8}+\dfrac{2}{3}\left(-\dfrac{2}{3}+\dfrac{1}{6}\right)$

30. $\dfrac{1}{6}+4\left(\dfrac{2}{5}-\dfrac{7}{10}\right)$

31. $2\left(\dfrac{1}{3}\right)^3-\dfrac{2}{9}$

32. $8\left(-\dfrac{3}{4}\right)^2+\dfrac{3}{2}$

33. $\left(-\dfrac{2}{3}\right)^3\left(\dfrac{1}{8}-\dfrac{1}{2}\right)-\dfrac{2}{3}\left(\dfrac{1}{8}\right)$

34. $\left(\dfrac{3}{5}\right)^2\left(\dfrac{5}{9}-\dfrac{2}{3}\right)\div\left(-\dfrac{1}{5}\right)^2$

35. A square operation key on a calculator is $\frac{3}{8}$ inch on each side. What is the area of the key? Use the formula $A = s^2$. (*Source:* Texas Instruments.)

$\frac{3}{8}$ in.

36. A square lot for sale in the country is $\frac{3}{10}$ mile on a side. Find the area of the lot by using the formula $A = s^2$.

$\frac{3}{10}$ mi

37. A rectangular parking lot at the megamall is $\frac{7}{10}$ mile long and $\frac{1}{4}$ mile wide. How much fencing is needed to enclose the lot? Use the formula $P = 2l + 2w$.

38. A computer chip in a rectangular shape is $\frac{7}{8}$ inch long and $\frac{5}{16}$ inch wide. An insulating strip must be put around all sides of the chip. Find the length of the strip. Use the formula $P = 2l + 2w$.

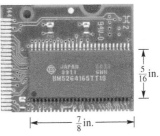

$\frac{5}{16}$ in.

$\frac{7}{8}$ in.

Simplify. See Example 3.

39. $\dfrac{-\dfrac{7}{9}}{-\dfrac{7}{36}}$

40. $\dfrac{\dfrac{15}{32}}{-\dfrac{5}{64}}$

41. $\dfrac{-15}{\dfrac{6}{5}}$

42. $\dfrac{-6}{-\dfrac{5}{8}}$

43. $\dfrac{\dfrac{4}{7}}{8}$

44. $\dfrac{-\dfrac{11}{5}}{3}$

45. $\dfrac{-\dfrac{2}{3}}{-2\dfrac{2}{5}}$

46. $\dfrac{\dfrac{1}{2}}{3\dfrac{1}{3}}$

⊕ **47.** $\dfrac{-4\dfrac{1}{2}}{\left(\dfrac{3}{4}\right)^2}$

48. $\dfrac{1\dfrac{2}{3}}{\left(-\dfrac{1}{6}\right)^2}$

49. $\dfrac{\left(\dfrac{2}{5}\right)^2}{\left(-\dfrac{4}{3}\right)^2}$

50. $\dfrac{\left(-\dfrac{5}{6}\right)^2}{\left(\dfrac{1}{2}\right)^3}$

5.7 ▶▶▶ Problem Solving: Equations Containing Fractions

OBJECTIVE 1 **Use the multiplication property of equality to solve equations containing fractions.** In **Section 4.4** you used the division property of equality to solve an equation such as $4s = 24$. The division property says that you may divide both sides of an equation by the same nonzero number and the equation will still be balanced. Now that you have some experience with fractions, let's look again at how the division property works.

$$4s \text{ means } 4 \cdot s \longrightarrow 4s = 24$$

$$\longrightarrow \frac{4 \cdot s}{4} = \frac{24}{4} \qquad \text{Divide both sides by 4}$$

Divide out the common factor of 4 $\qquad \dfrac{\overset{1}{\cancel{4}} \cdot s}{\underset{1}{\cancel{4}}} = 6$

$$s = 6$$

Because multiplication and division are related to each other, we can also *multiply* both sides of an equation by the same nonzero number and keep it balanced.

> **Multiplication and Division Properties of Equality**
>
> The **multiplication property of equality** says, if $a = b$, then $a \cdot c = b \cdot c$
>
> The **division property of equality** says, if $a = b$, then $\dfrac{a}{c} = \dfrac{b}{c}$ as long as
>
> c is not 0. In other words, you may multiply or divide both sides of an equation by the same nonzero number and it will still be balanced.

OBJECTIVES

1 Use the multiplication property of equality to solve equations containing fractions.

2 Use both the addition and multiplication properties of equality to solve equations containing fractions.

3 Solve application problems using equations containing fractions.

EXAMPLE 1 **Using the Multiplication Property of Equality**

Solve each equation and check each solution.

(a) $\dfrac{1}{2}b = 5$

As in **Chapter 4**, you want the variable by itself on one side of the equal sign. In this example, you want $1b$, not $\frac{1}{2}b$, on the left side. (Recall that $1b$ is equivalent to b.)

In **Section 5.3** you learned that the product of a number and its reciprocal is 1. Thus, multiplying $\frac{1}{2}$ by $\frac{2}{1}$ will give the desired coefficient of 1.

$$\frac{1}{2}b = 5$$

$$\frac{2}{1}\left(\frac{1}{2}b\right) = \frac{2}{1}(5) \qquad \begin{array}{l}\text{Multiply both sides by } \frac{2}{1}\\ \text{(the reciprocal of } \frac{1}{2}\text{).}\end{array}$$

On the left side, use the associative property to regroup the factors. $\qquad \left(\dfrac{2}{1} \cdot \dfrac{1}{2}\right)b = \dfrac{2}{1}\left(\dfrac{5}{1}\right) \qquad \begin{array}{l}\text{On the right side, 5 is}\\ \text{equivalent to } \frac{5}{1}\end{array}$

$$\left(\frac{\overset{1}{\cancel{2}}}{1} \cdot \frac{1}{\underset{1}{\cancel{2}}}\right)b = \frac{10}{1}$$

$1b$ is equivalent to b. $\qquad \longrightarrow 1b = 10$

$$\longrightarrow b = 10 \longleftarrow \text{The solution is 10.}$$

Continued on Next Page

Once you understand the process, you don't have to show every step. Here is a shorthand solution of the same problem.

$$\frac{1}{2}b = 5$$

$$\frac{\overset{1}{\cancel{2}}}{1}\left(\frac{1}{\cancel{2}}b\right) = \frac{2}{1}\left(\frac{5}{1}\right)$$

$$b = 10 \quad \leftarrow \text{Solution}$$

The solution is 10. Check the solution by going back to the *original* equation.

Check $\frac{1}{2}b = 5$ Replace b with 10 in the *original* equation.

$\frac{1}{2}(10) = 5$ Multiply on the left side: $\frac{1}{2}(10)$ is $\frac{1}{2} \cdot \frac{10}{1}$ or $\frac{1}{2} \cdot \frac{2 \cdot 5}{1}$

$$\frac{1 \cdot \overset{1}{\cancel{2}} \cdot 5}{\cancel{2} \cdot 1} = 5$$

$$5 = 5 \quad \text{Balances}$$

When b is 10, the equation balances, so 10 is the correct solution (***not*** 5).

(b) $12 = -\frac{3}{4}x$

$12 = -\frac{3}{4}x$ Multiply both sides by $-\frac{4}{3}$ (the reciprocal of $-\frac{3}{4}$). The reciprocal of a negative number is also negative.

$-\frac{4}{3}(12) = -\frac{\cancel{4}}{\cancel{3}}\left(-\frac{\cancel{3}}{\cancel{4}}x\right)$ On the left side $-\frac{4}{3}(12)$ is $-\frac{4}{3} \cdot \frac{12}{1}$ or $-\frac{4 \cdot \cancel{3} \cdot 4}{\cancel{3} \cdot 1} = -16$

$$-16 = x$$

The solution is -16. Check the solution by going back to the *original* equation.

Check $12 = -\frac{3}{4}x$ Replace x with -16 in the *original* equation.

$12 = -\frac{3}{4}(-16)$ The product of two negative numbers is positive. $-\frac{3}{4}(-16)$ is $\frac{3}{4} \cdot \frac{16}{1}$ or $\frac{3}{4} \cdot \frac{4 \cdot 4}{1}$

$$12 = \frac{3 \cdot \cancel{4} \cdot 4}{\cancel{4} \cdot 1}$$

$$12 = 12 \quad \text{Balances} \quad \boxed{\text{If the equation does \textbf{not} balance, your solution is wrong. Start over.}}$$

When x is -16, the equation balances, so -16 is the correct solution (***not*** 12).

Continued on Next Page

(c) $-\dfrac{2}{5}n = -\dfrac{1}{3}$

$$-\dfrac{\cancel{5}^{1}}{\cancel{2}_{1}}\left(-\dfrac{\cancel{2}^{1}}{\cancel{5}_{1}}n\right) = \left(-\dfrac{5}{2}\right)\left(-\dfrac{1}{3}\right)$$

Multiply both sides by $-\dfrac{5}{2}$ (the reciprocal of $-\dfrac{2}{5}$).

$$n = \dfrac{5 \cdot 1}{2 \cdot 3}$$

The product of two negative numbers is positive.

$$n = \dfrac{5}{6} \longleftarrow \text{The solution is } \tfrac{5}{6}.$$

Check

$-\dfrac{2}{5}n = -\dfrac{1}{3}$ Original equation

$\left(-\dfrac{2}{5}\right)\left(\dfrac{5}{6}\right) = -\dfrac{1}{3}$ Replace n with $\tfrac{5}{6}$

$-\dfrac{\cancel{2}^{1} \cdot \cancel{5}^{1}}{\cancel{5}_{1} \cdot \cancel{2}_{1} \cdot 3} = -\dfrac{1}{3}$ Multiply on the left side.

$-\dfrac{1}{3} = -\dfrac{1}{3}$ Balances

When n is $\tfrac{5}{6}$, the equation balances, so $\tfrac{5}{6}$ is the correct solution (**not** $-\tfrac{1}{3}$).

Work Problem **1** *at the Side.* ▶

OBJECTIVE 2 Use both the addition and multiplication properties of equality to solve equations containing fractions. In **Section 4.5** you used both the addition and *division* properties of equality to solve equations. Now you can use both the addition and *multiplication* properties.

EXAMPLE 2 Using the Addition and Multiplication Properties of Equality

Solve each equation and check each solution.

(a) $\dfrac{1}{3}c + 5 = 7$

The first step is to get the variable term $\tfrac{1}{3}c$ by itself on the left side of the equal sign. Recall that to "get rid of" the 5 on the left side, add the opposite of 5, which is -5, to both sides.

$$\dfrac{1}{3}c + 5 = 7$$
$$\underline{\phantom{\dfrac{1}{3}c +} -5 \quad -5} \qquad \text{Add } -5 \text{ to both sides.}$$
$$\dfrac{1}{3}c + 0 = 2$$
$$\underbrace{\dfrac{1}{3}c} = 2$$

$$\dfrac{\cancel{3}^{1}}{1}\left(\dfrac{1}{\cancel{3}_{1}}c\right) = \dfrac{3}{1}\left(\dfrac{2}{1}\right)$$

Multiply both sides by $\tfrac{3}{1}$ (the reciprocal of $\tfrac{1}{3}$).

$$c = 6$$

The solution is 6. Check the solution by going back to the *original* equation.

Continued on Next Page

---

1 Solve each equation. Check each solution.

(a) $\dfrac{1}{6}m = 3$

Check

(b) $\dfrac{3}{2}a = -9$

Check

(c) $\dfrac{3}{14} = -\dfrac{2}{7}x$

Check

ANSWERS

1. **(a)** $m = 18$ **Check** $\dfrac{1}{6}m = 3$
$\dfrac{1}{6}(18) = 3$
Balances $3 = 3$

(b) $a = -6$ **Check** $\dfrac{3}{2}a = -9$
$\dfrac{3}{2}(-6) = -9$
Balances $-9 = -9$

(c) $x = -\dfrac{3}{4}$ **Check** $\dfrac{3}{14} = -\dfrac{2}{7}x$
$\dfrac{3}{14} = -\dfrac{2}{7}\left(-\dfrac{3}{4}\right)$
Balances $\dfrac{3}{14} = \dfrac{3}{14}$

2 Solve each equation. Check each solution.

(a) $18 = \dfrac{4}{5}x + 2$

Check

(b) $\dfrac{1}{4}h - 5 = 1$

Check

(c) $\dfrac{4}{3}r + 4 = -8$

Check

Check $\dfrac{1}{3}c + 5 = 7$ Original equation

$\dfrac{1}{3}(6) + 5 = 7$ Replace c with 6.

$\underbrace{2}_{} + 5 = 7$

$7 = 7$ Balances

When c is 6, the equation balances, so 6 is the correct solution (**not** 7).

(b) $-3 = \dfrac{2}{3}y + 7$

To get the variable term $\frac{2}{3}y$ by itself on the right side, add -7 to both sides.

$$-3 = \dfrac{2}{3}y + 7$$

$$\underline{-7 \qquad\qquad -7}$$ Add -7 to both sides.

$$-10 = \underbrace{\dfrac{2}{3}y + 0}_{}$$

$$\dfrac{3}{2}(-10) = \dfrac{\cancel{3}}{\cancel{2}}\left(\dfrac{\cancel{2}}{\cancel{3}}y\right)$$ Multiply both sides by $\frac{3}{2}$ (the reciprocal of $\frac{2}{3}$).

$$-15 = y \quad\longleftarrow\quad \text{The solution is } -15.$$

Check $-3 = \dfrac{2}{3}y + 7$ Original equation

$-3 = \dfrac{2}{3}(-15) + 7$ Replace y with -15

$-3 = \underbrace{-10}_{} + 7$

$-3 = -3$ Balances

When y is -15, the equation balances, so -15 is the correct solution (**not** -3).

◀ *Work Problem* **2** *at the Side.*

ANSWERS

2. (a) $x = 20$ **Check** $18 = \dfrac{4}{5}x + 2$

$18 = \dfrac{4}{5}(20) + 2$

$18 = 16 + 2$

Balances $18 = 18$

(b) $h = 24$ **Check** $\dfrac{1}{4}h - 5 = 1$

$\dfrac{1}{4}(24) - 5 = 1$

$6 - 5 = 1$

Balances $1 = 1$

(c) $r = -9$ **Check** $\dfrac{4}{3}r + 4 = -8$

$\dfrac{4}{3}(-9) + 4 = -8$

$-12 + 4 = -8$

Balances $-8 = -8$

OBJECTIVE 3 Solve application problems using equations containing fractions. Use the six problem-solving steps from **Section 3.3** to solve application problems.

EXAMPLE 3 **Solving an Application Problem Using an Equation with Fractions**

The expression for finding a person's approximate systolic blood pressure is $100 + \dfrac{\text{age}}{2}$. Suppose your friend's systolic blood pressure is 116 (and he has normal blood pressure). Find his age.

Step 1   **Read** the problem. It is about blood pressure and age.

Unknown: friend's age

Known: Blood pressure expression is $100 + \dfrac{\text{age}}{2}$; friend's pressure is 116.

Step 2   **Assign a variable.** Let a represent the friend's age.

Step 3   **Write an equation.**

$$100 + \frac{\text{age}}{2} \text{ is blood pressure}$$

$$100 + \frac{a}{2} = 116$$

Step 4   **Solve.**

$$100 + \frac{a}{2} = 116$$

$$\underline{-100 \qquad\quad -100} \qquad \text{Add} -100 \text{ to both sides.}$$

$$0 + \frac{a}{2} = 16$$

$$\frac{a}{2} = 16$$

$\frac{1}{2}a$ is equivalent to $\frac{a}{2}$ because $\frac{1}{2}a$ is $\frac{1}{2} \cdot \frac{a}{1}$

$$\frac{1}{2}a = 16$$

$$\frac{\cancel{2}}{1}\left(\frac{1}{\cancel{2}}a\right) = \frac{2}{1}(16) \qquad \text{Multiply both sides by } \frac{2}{1} \text{ (the reciprocal of } \frac{1}{2}\text{).}$$

$$a = 32$$

Step 5   **State the answer.** Your friend is 32 years old.

Step 6   **Check** the solution by putting it back into the *original* problem.

Approximate systolic blood pressure is $100 + \dfrac{\text{age}}{2}$.

If the age is 32, then $100 + \frac{32}{2} = 100 + 16 = 116$.

Friend's blood pressure is 116. ← Matches — | Your answer must fit all the information in the original problem.

Age 32 is the correct solution because it "works" when you put it back into the original problem.

Work Problem 3 *at the Side.* ▶

---

3 A woman's systolic blood pressure is 111. Find her age, using the expression for systolic blood pressure from Example 3 and the six problem-solving steps. (Assume that the woman has normal blood pressure.)

Answer

3. Age is a.

$100 + \dfrac{a}{2} = 111$ The woman is 22 years old.

Check $100 + \dfrac{22}{2} = 100 + 11 = 111$

Math in the Media

Mathematics teachers attending a national conference in Salt Lake City, Utah, in April, 2008 found the following information about hotel rates on their organization's Web site. The rates do not include taxes, so ignore taxes when answering the problems.

Hotel (Salt Lake City)	Single	Double	Triple	Quad
Grand America (executive suite rooms)	$208	$219	$235	$248
Embassy Suites	$146	$166	$181	$196
Little America (Tower rooms)	$172	$172	$182	$202
Super 8 Airport	$105	$115	$125	$135

Source: www.nctm.org

1. **(a)** The double rate is for two people sharing a room. What fractional part does each person pay?

   (b) **Multiply** the double rate at the Super 8 Airport by $\frac{1}{2}$. What is the result?

   (c) **Divide** the double rate at the Super 8 Airport by 2. What is the result?

   (d) Explain what happened. How much money would one person owe if he or she shared a double room at the Super 8 Airport hotel?

2. **(a)** The triple rate is for three people sharing a room. What fractional part does each person pay?

   (b) How much money would one person owe if he or she shared a triple room at the Little America Hotel? Find your answer using *two different methods,* based on your observations in Problem 1.

3. **(a)** Suppose you have a travel allotment of $800 that can be spent on transportation, hotel, food, and registration fees. You and a colleague decide to attend the 3-day conference in Salt Lake City and plan to share a room for three nights at the Grand America. Conference registration is $225; the flight costs $334 round-trip; the shuttle between the airport and the hotel costs $20 per person each way; and you budget $35 per day for meals. How much out-of-pocket expense will you have to pay?

   (b) How much would you save if you could recruit a third person to share the room?

DO NOT DISTURB

NO MOLESTE

PRIÈRE DE NE PAS DÉRANGER

BITTE NICHT STÖREN

FOR EXTRA HELP

 PRACTICE   WATCH   DOWNLOAD READ REVIEW

Solve each equation and check each solution. See Examples 1 and 2.

1. $\dfrac{1}{3}a = 10$ **Check**

2. $7 = \dfrac{1}{5}y$ **Check**

3. $-20 = \dfrac{5}{6}b$ **Check**

4. $-\dfrac{4}{9}w = 16$ **Check**

5. $-\dfrac{7}{2}c = -21$ **Check**

6. $-25 = \dfrac{5}{3}x$ **Check**

7. $\dfrac{9}{16} = \dfrac{3}{4}m$ **Check**

8. $\dfrac{5}{12}k = \dfrac{15}{16}$ **Check**

9. $\dfrac{3}{10} = -\dfrac{1}{4}d$ **Check**

10. $-\dfrac{7}{8}h = -\dfrac{1}{6}$ **Check**

11. $\dfrac{1}{6}n + 7 = 9$ **Check**

12. $3 + \dfrac{1}{4}p = 5$ **Check**

13. $-10 = \dfrac{5}{3}r + 5$ **Check**

14. $0 = 6 + \dfrac{3}{2}t$ **Check**

15. $\dfrac{3}{8}x - 9 = 0$ **Check**

16. $\dfrac{1}{3}s - 10 = -5$ **Check**

Solve each equation. Show your work.

17. $7 - 2 = \dfrac{1}{5}y - 4$

18. $0 - 8 = \dfrac{1}{10}k - 3$

19. $4 + \dfrac{2}{3}n = -10 + 2$

20. $-\dfrac{2}{5}m - 3 = -9 + 0$

21. $3x + \dfrac{1}{2} = \dfrac{3}{4}$

22. $4y + \dfrac{1}{3} = \dfrac{7}{9}$

23. $\dfrac{3}{10} = -4b - \dfrac{1}{5}$

24. $\dfrac{5}{6} = -3c - \dfrac{2}{3}$

25. Check the solution given for each equation. If a solution doesn't check, show how to find the correct solution.

(a) $\frac{1}{6}x + 1 = -2$

$x = 18$

(b) $-\frac{3}{2} = \frac{9}{4}k$

$k = -\frac{2}{3}$

26. Check the solution given for each equation. If a solution doesn't check, show how to find the correct solution.

(a) $-\frac{3}{4}y = -\frac{5}{8}$

$y = \frac{5}{6}$

(b) $16 = -\frac{7}{3}w + 2$

$w = 6$

27. Write two different equations that have 8 as a solution. Write your equations with a fraction as the coefficient of the variable term. Use Exercises 1–10 as models.

28. Write two different equations that have -12 as the solution. Write your equations with a fraction as the coefficient of the variable term. Use Exercises 1–10 as models.

In Exercises 29–32, find each person's age using the six problem-solving steps and this expression for approximate systolic blood pressure: $100 + \dfrac{age}{2}$. *Assume that all the people have normal blood pressure. See Example 3.*

29. A man has systolic blood pressure of 109. How old is he?

30. A man has systolic blood pressure of 118. How old is he?

31. A woman has systolic blood pressure of 122. How old is she?

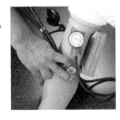

32. A woman has systolic blood pressure of 113. How old is she?

As you read at the start of this chapter, nails for home repair projects are classified by the "penny" system, which is a number that indicates the nail's length. The expression for finding the length of a nail, in inches, is $\dfrac{\text{penny size}}{4} + \dfrac{1}{2}$ inch. In Exercises 33–36, find the penny size for each nail using this expression and the six problem-solving steps. (Source: Season by Season Home Maintenance.)

33. The length of a common nail is 3 inches. What is its penny size?

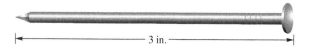

34. The length of a drywall nail is 2 inches. Find the nail's penny size.

35. The length of a box nail is $2\frac{1}{2}$ inches. What penny size would you ask for when buying these nails?

36. The length of a finishing nail is $1\frac{1}{2}$ inches. What is its penny size?

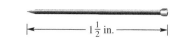

An expression for the recommended weight of an adult is $\frac{11}{2}$ (height in inches) $- 220$. In Exercises 37–40, find each person's height using this expression and the six problem-solving steps. Assume that all the people are at their recommended weight.

37. A man weighs 209 pounds. What is his height in inches?

38. A woman weighs 165 pounds. What is her height in inches?

39. A woman weighs 132 pounds. What is her height in inches?

40. A man weighs 176 pounds. What is his height in inches?

5.8 ▶▶▶ Geometry Applications: Area and Volume

OBJECTIVE 1 Find the area of a triangle. In **Section 4.5** you worked with triangles, which are flat shapes that have exactly three sides. You found the perimeter of a triangle by adding the lengths of the three sides. Now you are ready to find the area of a triangle (the amount of surface inside the triangle).

You can find the *height* of a triangle by measuring the distance from one vertex of the triangle to the opposite side (the base). The height must be *perpendicular* to the base, that is, it must form a right angle with the base. Sometimes you have to extend the base before you can draw the height perpendicular to it, as shown on the right-hand figure below.

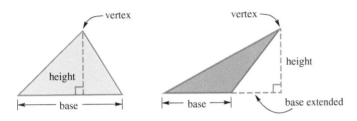

If you cut out two identical triangles and turn one upside down, you can fit them together to form a parallelogram, as shown below.

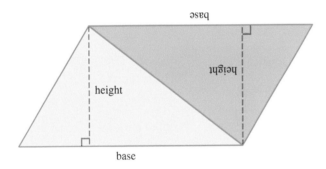

Recall from **Section 4.6** that the area of the parallelogram is *base* times *height*. Because each triangle is *half* of the parallelogram, the area of one triangle is

$$\frac{1}{2} \text{ of base times height}$$

Use the following formula to find the area of a triangle.

Finding the Area of a Triangle

$$\text{Area of triangle} = \frac{1}{2} \cdot \text{base} \cdot \text{height}$$

$$A = \frac{1}{2} bh$$

Remember to use *square units* when measuring area.

---

1 Find the area of each triangle.

(a)

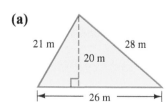

(b) |◄——— 6 yd ———►|

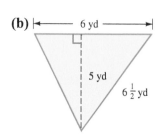

(c)

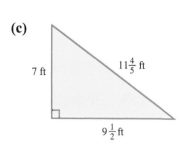

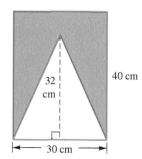

EXAMPLE 1 **Finding the Area of Triangles**

Find the area of each triangle.

(a)

26 ft   39¾ ft
    22 ft
|◄——— 47 ft ———►|

The base is 47 ft and the height is 22 ft. You do *not* need the 26 ft or $39\frac{3}{4}$ ft sides to find the area.

$$A = \frac{1}{2} \cdot b \cdot h$$

> Replace b with 47 ft and h with 22 ft.

$$A = \frac{1}{2} \cdot 47 \text{ ft} \cdot 22 \text{ ft}$$

$$A = \frac{1}{2} \cdot \frac{47 \text{ ft}}{1} \cdot \frac{22 \text{ ft}}{1}$$

> Divide out the common factor of 2

$$A = \frac{1 \cdot 47 \text{ ft} \cdot \overset{1}{\cancel{2}} \cdot 11 \text{ ft}}{\underset{1}{\cancel{2}} \cdot 1 \cdot 1}$$

> Multiply 47 • 11 to get 517

> This is *area*, so write **ft²** in the answer.

$$A = 517 \text{ ft}^2 \quad \text{Multiply ft • ft to get ft}^2.$$

(b)

$11\frac{1}{10}$ in.

$6\frac{1}{2}$ in.

9 in.

Because two sides of the triangle are perpendicular to each other, use those sides as the base and the height. (Remember that the height must be perpendicular to the base.)

$$A = \frac{1}{2} bh \qquad \text{Formula for area of a triangle}$$

$$A = \frac{1}{2} \cdot 9 \text{ in.} \cdot 6\frac{1}{2} \text{ in.} \qquad \text{Replace } b \text{ with 9 in. and } h \text{ with } 6\frac{1}{2} \text{ in.}$$

$$A = \frac{1}{2} \cdot \frac{9 \text{ in.}}{1} \cdot \frac{13 \text{ in.}}{2} \qquad \text{Write 9 in. and } 6\frac{1}{2} \text{ in. as improper fractions.}$$

$$A = \frac{1 \cdot 9 \text{ in.} \cdot 13 \text{ in.}}{2 \cdot 1 \cdot 2} \quad \longleftarrow \quad \text{Multiply 9 • 13 to get 117 and in. • in. to get in.}^2$$

$$A = \frac{117}{4} \text{ in.}^2 \text{ or } 29\frac{1}{4} \text{ in.}^2$$

◄ *Work Problem* **1** *at the Side.*

EXAMPLE 2 **Using the Concept of Area**

Find the area of the shaded part in this figure.

The *entire* figure is a rectangle.

$$A = lw$$
$$A = 30 \text{ cm} \cdot 40 \text{ cm}$$
$$A = 1200 \text{ cm}^2$$

32 cm   40 cm

|◄——— 30 cm ———►|

ANSWERS

1. (a) 260 m² **(b)** 15 yd²
  (c) $\frac{133}{4}$ ft² or $33\frac{1}{4}$ ft²

Continued on Next Page

The *un*shaded part of the figure is a triangle.

$$A = \frac{1}{2} bh$$

$$A = \frac{1}{2} \cdot \frac{30 \text{ cm}}{1} \cdot \frac{32 \text{ cm}}{1}$$

$$A = \frac{1 \cdot \overset{1}{\cancel{2}} \cdot 15 \text{ cm} \cdot 32 \text{ cm}}{\underset{1}{\cancel{2}} \cdot 1 \cdot 1}$$

$$A = 480 \text{ cm}^2$$

Subtract to find the area of the shaded part.

$$A = \overbrace{1200 \text{ cm}^2}^{\text{Entire area}} - \overbrace{480 \text{ cm}^2}^{\text{Unshaded part}} = \overbrace{720 \text{ cm}^2}^{\text{Shaded part}}$$

This is *area*, so write **cm²** in the answer.

Work Problem **2** *at the Side.* ▶

2 Find the area of the shaded part in this figure.

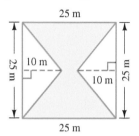

OBJECTIVE 2 Find the volume of a rectangular solid. A shoe box and a cereal box are examples of three-dimensional (or solid) figures. The three dimensions are length, width, and height. (A rectangle or square is a two-dimensional figure. The two dimensions are length and width.) If we want to know how much a shoe box will hold, we find its *volume*. We measure volume by seeing how many cubes of a certain size will fill the space inside the box. Three sizes of *cubic units* are shown here. Notice that all the edges of a cube have the same length and all sides meet at right angles.

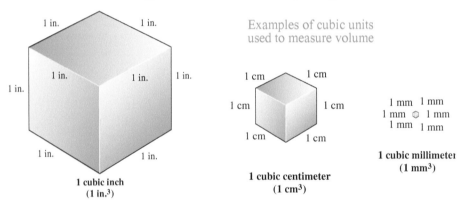

Examples of cubic units used to measure volume

1 cubic inch (1 in.³)

1 cubic centimeter (1 cm³)

1 cubic millimeter (1 mm³)

Some other sizes of cubes that are used to measure volume are 1 cubic foot (1 ft³), 1 cubic yard (1 yd³), and 1 cubic meter (1 m³).

CAUTION

The raised 3 in 4^3 means that you multiply $4 \cdot 4 \cdot 4$ to get 64. The raised 3 in cm³ or ft³ is a short way to write the word "cubic." It means that you multiplied cm times cm times cm to get cm³, or ft times ft times ft to get ft³. Recall that a short way to write $x \cdot x \cdot x$ is x^3. Similarly, cm • cm • cm is cm³. When you see 5 cm³, say "five cubic centimeters." Do *not* multiply $5 \cdot 5 \cdot 5$ because the exponent applies only to the *first* thing to its left. The exponent applies to cm, *not* to the 5.

Volume

Volume is a measure of the space inside a solid shape. The volume of a solid is the number of cubic units it takes to fill the solid.

Use the formula below to find the volume of *rectangular solids* (box-like shapes).

3 Find the volume of each rectangular solid.

(a)

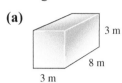

3 m
8 m
3 m

> **Finding the Volume of Rectangular Solids**
> Volume of a rectangular solid = length • width • height
> $$V = lwh$$
> Remember to use *cubic units* when measuring volume.

EXAMPLE 3   **Finding the Volume of Rectangular Solids**

Find the volume of each box.

(a)

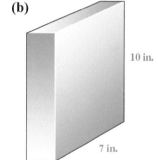

1 cm³

height
2 cm

width
3 cm

length
4 cm

Each cube that fits in the box is 1 cubic centimeter (1 cm³). To find the volume, you can count the number of cubes.

Bottom layer has 12 cubes.
Top layer has 12 cubes.
} Total of 24 cubes (24 cm³)

Or you can use the formula for rectangular solids.

$$V = l \bullet w \bullet h$$
$$V = 4 \text{ cm} \bullet 3 \text{ cm} \bullet 2 \text{ cm} \qquad \text{Multiply } 4 \bullet 3 \bullet 2 \text{ to get } 24$$
$$V = 24 \text{ cm}^3 \qquad \text{Multiply cm} \bullet \text{cm} \bullet \text{cm to get cm}^3.$$

(b) Length $6\frac{1}{4}$ ft,

width $3\frac{1}{2}$ ft, height 2 ft

(b)

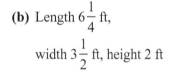

10 in.

7 in.

$2\frac{1}{2}$ in.

This is *volume* so write **in.³** in the answer.

Use the formula $V = lwh$.

$$V = 7 \text{ in.} \bullet 2\frac{1}{2} \text{ in.} \bullet 10 \text{ in.} \qquad \begin{array}{l}\text{Write each}\\ \text{measurement}\\ \text{as an improper}\\ \text{fraction.}\end{array}$$

$$V = \frac{7 \text{ in.}}{1} \bullet \frac{5 \text{ in.}}{2} \bullet \frac{10 \text{ in.}}{1}$$

$$V = \frac{7 \text{ in.} \bullet 5 \text{ in.} \bullet \overset{1}{2} \bullet 5 \text{ in.}}{1 \bullet \underset{1}{2} \bullet 1} \qquad \begin{array}{l}\text{Divide out}\\ \text{the common}\\ \text{factor of } 2\end{array}$$

$$V = 175 \text{ in.}^3 \qquad \text{Cubic units for volume}$$

◀ *Work Problem* **3** *at the Side.*

OBJECTIVE **3** **Find the volume of a pyramid.**   A pyramid is a solid shape like the one shown below. We will study pyramids with square or rectangular bases.

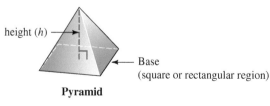

height (*h*)
Base
(square or rectangular region)
Pyramid

The height is the distance from the base to the highest point of the pyramid. The height must be perpendicular to the base.

ANSWERS

3. (a) 72 m³   (b) $\frac{175}{4}$ ft³ or $43\frac{3}{4}$ ft³

Note

In this book we will work only with pyramids that have a base with four sides that is square or rectangular. In later math courses you may work with pyramids that have a base with three sides (triangle), five sides (pentagon), six sides (hexagon), and so on.

4 Find the volume of a pyramid with a square base measuring 10 ft by 10 ft. The height of the pyramid is 6 ft.

Use this formula to find the volume of a pyramid.

Finding the Volume of a Pyramid

$$\text{Volume of a pyramid} = \frac{1}{3} \cdot B \cdot h$$

$$V = \frac{1}{3} Bh$$

where B is the area of the base of the pyramid and h is the height of the pyramid.

Remember to use *cubic units* when measuring volume.

EXAMPLE 4   **Finding the Volume of a Pyramid**

Find the volume of this pyramid with a rectangular base.

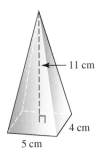

11 cm

4 cm

5 cm

First find the value of B in the formula, which is the *area of the rectangular base*. Recall that the area of a rectangle is found by multiplying length times width.

$$B = 5 \text{ cm} \cdot 4 \text{ cm}$$

$$B = 20 \text{ cm}^2$$

Now find the volume.

$$V = \frac{1}{3} Bh \qquad \text{Formula for volume of pyramid}$$

$$V = \frac{1}{3} \cdot 20 \text{ cm}^2 \cdot 11 \text{ cm} \qquad \text{Replace } B \text{ with 20 cm}^2 \text{ and } h \text{ with 11 cm.}$$

$$V = \frac{1}{3} \cdot \frac{20 \text{ cm}^2}{1} \cdot \frac{11 \text{ cm}}{1} \qquad \text{There are no common factors to divide out.}$$

$$V = \frac{1 \cdot 20 \text{ cm}^2 \cdot 11 \text{ cm}}{3 \cdot 1 \cdot 1}$$

This is *volume*, so write **cm³** in the answer.

$$V = \frac{220}{3} \text{ cm}^3 \quad \text{or} \quad 73\frac{1}{3} \text{ cm}^3 \qquad \text{Cubic units for volume}$$

Work Problem **4** *at the Side.* ▶

ANSWER

4. $V = 200 \text{ ft}^3$

Math in the Media

QUILT PATTERNS

People who make quilts often base their designs on a block that is cut into a grid of 4, 9, 16, or 25 squares. The quilter chooses various colors for the pieces. Each quilt design shown below was selected from an Archive of American Quilt Designs.

Source: Patchwork Persuasion: Quilts from Traditional Designs.

1. Identify the makeup of the block as 4, 9, 16, etc. Each color is what fractional part of the block?

(a)

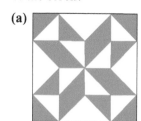

Barbara Fritchie Star

Block size: ____

Blue: ____ White: ____

(b)

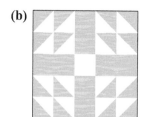

Handy Andy

Block size: ____

Blue: ____ White: ____

(c)

Peace and Plenty

Block size: ____

Blue: ____ Yellow: ____

Whitish: ____

(d)

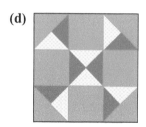

Cobwebs

Block size: ____

Mauve: ____ Purple: ____

Yellow: ____

2. Use the empty block to design and color your own quilt pattern. Tell the fractional part of the block that is represented by each color.

5.8 ▶▶▶ **Exercises**

Find the perimeter and area of each triangle. See Example 1.

1.
58 m
66 m
72 m 72 m

2.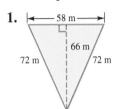
9 yd
8 yd
13 yd 12 yd

3.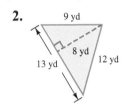
$2\frac{1}{4}$ ft
$1\frac{1}{4}$ ft $1\frac{1}{2}$ ft
$\frac{3}{4}$ ft

4.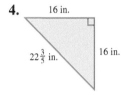
16 in.
$22\frac{3}{5}$ in. 16 in.

5.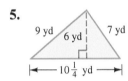
9 yd 6 yd 7 yd
$10\frac{1}{4}$ yd

6.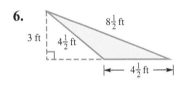
3 ft $4\frac{1}{2}$ ft $8\frac{1}{2}$ ft
$4\frac{1}{2}$ ft

7.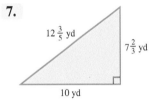
$12\frac{3}{5}$ yd
$7\frac{2}{3}$ yd
10 yd

8.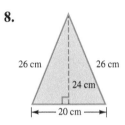
26 cm 26 cm
24 cm
20 cm

Find the shaded area in each figure. See Example 2.

9.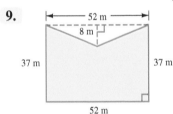
52 m
8 m
37 m 37 m
52 m

10.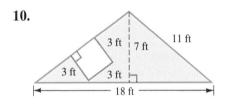
3 ft 7 ft 11 ft
3 ft 3 ft
18 ft

Solve each application problem.

11. A triangular tent flap measures $3\frac{1}{2}$ ft along the base and has a height of $4\frac{1}{2}$ ft. How much canvas is needed to make the flap?

12. A wooden sign in the shape of a right triangle has perpendicular sides measuring $1\frac{1}{2}$ yd and 1 yd. How much surface area does the front of the sign have?

13. A triangular space between three streets has the measurements shown below. How much new curbing is needed to go around the space? How much sod is needed to cover the space?

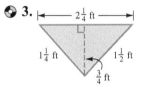
33 m 55 m
44 m

14. A city lot with an unusual shape is shown below.

(a) How much frontage (distance along streets) does the lot have?

(b) What is the area of the lot?

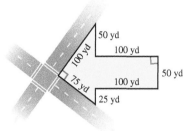
50 yd
100 yd
100 yd
75 yd 50 yd
100 yd
25 yd

In Exercises 15–20, name each solid and find its volume. See Examples 3 and 4.

15.
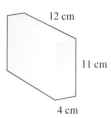
12 cm
11 cm
4 cm

16.
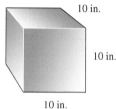
10 in.
10 in.
10 in.

17.
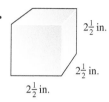
$2\frac{1}{2}$ in.
$2\frac{1}{2}$ in.
$2\frac{1}{2}$ in.

18.

$3\frac{1}{2}$ ft
8 ft
2 ft

19.
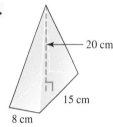
20 cm
15 cm
8 cm

20.
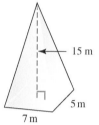
15 m
5 m
7 m

21. Find the volume of a pyramid with a height of 5 ft and a square base that is 8 ft on each side.

22. A pyramid has a height of 4 yd. The rectangular base measures 10 yd by 4 yd. What is the volume of the pyramid?

23. A box to hold pencils measures 3 in. by 8 in. by $\frac{3}{4}$ in. high. Find the volume of the box. (*Source:* Faber Castell.)

$\frac{3}{4}$ in.
8 in.
3 in.

24. A train is being loaded with shipping crates. Each crate is 12 ft long, 8 ft wide, and $2\frac{1}{4}$ ft high. How much space will each crate take?

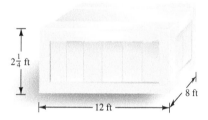
$2\frac{1}{4}$ ft
12 ft
8 ft

25. One of the ancient stone pyramids in Egypt has a square base that measures 145 m on each side. The height is 93 m. What is the volume of the pyramid? (*Source: Columbia Encyclopedia.*)

26. A cardboard model of an ancient stone pyramid has a square base that is $10\frac{3}{8}$ in. on each side. The height is $6\frac{1}{2}$ in. Find the volume of the model.

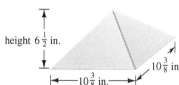
height $6\frac{1}{2}$ in.
$10\frac{3}{8}$ in.
$10\frac{3}{8}$ in

Chapter 5 ▷▷▷ Summary

▶ Key Terms

5.1   **fraction**   A fraction is a number of the form $\frac{a}{b}$, where a and b are integers and b is not 0.

numerator   The top number in a fraction is the numerator. It shows how many of the equal parts are being considered.

denominator   The bottom number in a fraction is the denominator. It shows how many equal parts are in the whole.

proper fraction   In a proper fraction, the numerator is less than the denominator. The fraction is less than 1.

improper fraction   In an improper fraction, the numerator is greater than or equal to the denominator. The fraction is greater than or equal to 1.

equivalent fractions   Equivalent fractions have the same value even though they look different. When graphed on a number line, they are names for the same point.

5.2   **lowest terms**   A fraction is written in lowest terms when its numerator and denominator have no common factor other than 1.

prime number   A prime number is a whole number that has exactly two different factors, itself and 1. The first few prime numbers are 2, 3, 5, 7, 11, 13, and 17.

composite number   A composite number has at least one factor other than itself and 1. Examples are 4, 6, 9, and 10. The numbers 0 and 1 are neither prime nor composite.

prime factorization   In a prime factorization, every factor is a prime number. For example, the prime factorization of 24 is 2 • 2 • 2 • 3.

5.3   **reciprocal**   Two numbers are reciprocals of each other if their product is 1. The reciprocal of $\frac{a}{b}$ is $\frac{b}{a}$ because $\frac{a}{b} \cdot \frac{b}{a} = 1$.

5.4   **like fractions**   Like fractions have the same denominator.

unlike fractions   Unlike fractions have different denominators.

least common denominator   The least common denominator (LCD) for two fractions is the smallest positive number that can be divided evenly by both denominators.

5.5   **mixed number**   A mixed number is a fraction and a whole number written together. It represents the sum of the whole number and the fraction. For example, $5\frac{1}{3}$ represents $5 + \frac{1}{3}$.

5.6   **complex fraction**   A complex fraction is a fraction in which the numerator and/or denominator contain one or more fractions.

5.7   **multiplication property of equality**   The multiplication property of equality states that you may multiply both sides of an equation by the same nonzero number and it will still be balanced.

division property of equality   The division property of equality states that you may divide both sides of an equation by the same nonzero number and it will still be balanced.

5.8   **volume**   Volume is a measure of the space inside a solid shape. Volume is measured in cubic units, such as in.^{3}, ft^3, yd^3, mm^3, cm^3, and so on.

▶ New Symbols

Cubic units (for measuring volume)   in.^{3} ft^3 yd^3 mm^3 cm^3 m^3

▶ New Formulas

Area of a triangle: $A = \frac{1}{2}bh$

Volume of a rectangular solid: $V = lwh$

Volume of a pyramid: $V = \frac{1}{3}Bh$

▶ Test Your Word Power

See how well you have learned the vocabulary in this chapter. Answers follow the Quick Review.

1. A **fraction** is in lowest terms if
   A. it has a value less than 1
   B. its numerator and denominator have no common factor other than 1
   C. its numerator and denominator are composite numbers
   D. it is rewritten as a mixed number.

2. The **denominator** of a fraction
   A. is written above the fraction bar
   B. is a prime number
   C. shows how many equal parts are in the whole
   D. is the smallest number divisible by the numerator.

3. The **LCD** of two fractions is the
   A. smallest number divisible by both denominators
   B. largest factor common to both denominators
   C. smallest number divisible by both numerators
   D. smallest prime number that divides evenly into both denominators.

4. Two numbers are **reciprocals** of each other if
   A. they have the same prime factorizations
   B. their sum is 0
   C. they are written in lowest terms
   D. their product is 1.

5. **Volume** is
   A. measured in square units
   B. the space inside a solid shape
   C. the sum of the lengths of the sides of a shape
   D. found by multiplying base times height.

6. A **mixed number**
   A. has a value equal to 1
   B. is the reciprocal of an improper fraction
   C. is the sum of a whole number and a fraction
   D. has a value less than 1.

7. A whole number is **prime** if
   A. it is divisible by itself and 1
   B. it has only composite factors
   C. it cannot be divided
   D. it has exactly two factors, itself and 1.

8. **Equivalent fractions**
   A. have the same denominators
   B. are written in lowest terms
   C. name the same point on a number line
   D. are reciprocals of each other.

▶ Quick Review

Concepts	Examples

5.1 Understanding Fraction Terminology

The *numerator* is the top number. The *denominator* is the bottom number.

In a *proper fraction*, the numerator is less than the denominator, so the fraction is less than 1. In an *improper fraction*, the numerator is greater than or equal to the denominator, so the fraction is greater than or equal to 1.

Proper fractions $\dfrac{2}{3}, \dfrac{3}{4}, \dfrac{15}{16}, \dfrac{1}{8}$ ← Numerator / ← Denominator

Improper fractions $\dfrac{17}{8}, \dfrac{19}{12}, \dfrac{11}{2}, \dfrac{5}{3}, \dfrac{7}{7}$

5.1 Writing Equivalent Fractions

Multiply or divide the numerator and denominator by the same nonzero number. The result is an equivalent fraction.

$$\frac{1}{2} = \frac{1 \cdot 8}{2 \cdot 8} = \frac{8}{16} \quad \leftarrow \text{Equivalent to } \tfrac{1}{2}$$

$$-\frac{12}{15} = -\frac{12 \div 3}{15 \div 3} = -\frac{4}{5} \quad \leftarrow \text{Equivalent to } -\tfrac{12}{15}$$

Concepts	Examples

5.2 Finding Prime Factorizations

A prime factorization of a number shows the number as the product of prime numbers. The first few prime numbers are 2, 3, 5, 7, 11, 13, and 17. You can use a division method or a factor tree to find the prime factorization.

Find the prime factorization of 24.

Division Method:

$2\overline{)24}$ ← Divide 24 by 2, the first prime; quotient is 12

$2\overline{)12}$ ← Divide 12 by 2; quotient is 6

$2\overline{)6}$ ← Divide 6 by 2; quotient is 3

$3\overline{)3}$ ← Divide 3 by 3; quotient is 1

1 ← Continue to divide until the quotient is 1

$24 = 2 \cdot 2 \cdot 2 \cdot 3$

Factor Tree Method:

Circle each prime number.

$$24 = 2 \cdot 2 \cdot 2 \cdot 3$$

5.2 Writing Fractions in Lowest Terms

Write the prime factorization of both numerator and denominator. Divide out all common factors, using slashes to show the division. Multiply any remaining factors in the numerator and in the denominator.

$$\frac{18}{90} = \frac{\overset{1}{\cancel{2}} \cdot \overset{1}{\cancel{3}} \cdot \overset{1}{\cancel{3}}}{\underset{1}{\cancel{2}} \cdot \underset{1}{\cancel{3}} \cdot \underset{1}{\cancel{3}} \cdot 5} = \frac{1}{5}$$

$$\frac{2b^3}{8ab} = \frac{\overset{1}{\cancel{2}} \cdot \overset{1}{\cancel{b}} \cdot b \cdot b}{\underset{1}{\cancel{2}} \cdot 2 \cdot 2 \cdot a \cdot \underset{1}{\cancel{b}}} = \frac{b^2}{4a}$$

5.3 Multiplying Fractions

Multiply the numerators and multiply the denominators. The product must be written in lowest terms. One way to do this is to write each original numerator and each original denominator as the product of primes and divide out any common factors before multiplying.

$$\left(-\frac{7}{10}\right)\left(\frac{5}{6}\right) = -\frac{7 \cdot \overset{1}{\cancel{5}}}{2 \cdot \underset{1}{\cancel{5}} \cdot 2 \cdot 3} = -\frac{7}{12}$$

$$\frac{3x^2}{5} \cdot \frac{2}{9x} = \frac{\overset{1}{\cancel{3}} \cdot \overset{1}{\cancel{x}} \cdot x \cdot 2}{5 \cdot \underset{1}{\cancel{3}} \cdot 3 \cdot \underset{1}{\cancel{x}}} = \frac{2x}{15}$$

5.3 Dividing Fractions

Rewrite the division problem as multiplying by the reciprocal of the divisor. In other words, the first number (dividend) stays the same and the second number (divisor) is changed to its reciprocal. Then use the steps for multiplying fractions. The quotient must be in lowest terms.

Division by 0 is undefined.

$$2 \div \left(-\frac{1}{3}\right) = \frac{2}{1} \cdot \left(-\frac{3}{1}\right) = -\frac{2 \cdot 3}{1 \cdot 1} = -6$$

Reciprocals

$$\frac{x^2}{y^2} \div \frac{x}{3y} = \frac{x^2}{y^2} \cdot \frac{3y}{x} = \frac{\overset{1}{\cancel{x}} \cdot x \cdot 3 \cdot \overset{1}{\cancel{y}}}{\underset{1}{\cancel{y}} \cdot y \cdot \underset{1}{\cancel{x}}} = \frac{3x}{y}$$

Reciprocals

Concepts	Examples

5.4   Adding and Subtracting Like Fractions

You can add or subtract fractions *only* when they have the *same* denominator. Add or subtract the numerators and write the result over the common denominator. Be sure that the final result is in lowest terms.

$$\frac{3}{10} - \frac{7}{10} = \frac{3-7}{10} = \frac{-4}{10} \quad \text{or} \quad -\frac{4}{10}$$

Write $-\frac{4}{10}$ in lowest terms.
$$-\frac{4}{10} = -\frac{\overset{1}{2}\cdot 2}{\underset{1}{2}\cdot 5} = -\frac{2}{5} \left\{ \begin{array}{l}\text{Lowest} \\ \text{terms}\end{array}\right.$$

$$\frac{5}{a} + \frac{7}{a} = \frac{5+7}{a} = \frac{12}{a} \left\{ \begin{array}{l}\text{Lowest} \\ \text{terms}\end{array}\right.$$

5.4   Finding the Lowest Common Denominator (LCD)

Write the prime factorization of each denominator. Then use enough prime factors in the LCD to "cover" both denominators.

What is the LCD for $\frac{5}{12}$ and $\frac{5}{18}$?

$$\begin{array}{l} 12 = 2 \cdot 2 \cdot 3 \\ 18 = 2 \cdot 3 \cdot 3 \end{array} \quad \text{LCD} = 2 \cdot 2 \cdot 3 \cdot 3 = 36$$

Factors of 12

Factors of 18

The LCD for $\frac{5}{12}$ and $\frac{5}{18}$ is 36.

5.4   Adding and Subtracting Unlike Fractions

Find the LCD. Rewrite each original fraction as an equivalent fraction whose denominator is the LCD. Then add or subtract the numerators and keep the common denominator. Be sure that the final result is in lowest terms.

$$-\frac{5}{12} + \frac{7}{9}$$

The LCD is 36.

Rewrite: $\quad -\dfrac{5}{12} = -\dfrac{5 \cdot 3}{12 \cdot 3} = -\dfrac{15}{36}$

Rewrite: $\quad \dfrac{7}{9} = \dfrac{7 \cdot 4}{9 \cdot 4} = \dfrac{28}{36}$

Add: $\quad -\dfrac{15}{36} + \dfrac{28}{36} = \dfrac{-15+28}{36} = \dfrac{13}{36} \left\{ \begin{array}{l}\text{Lowest} \\ \text{terms}\end{array}\right.$

$$\frac{2}{3} - \frac{6}{x}$$

The LCD is $3 \cdot x$ or $3x$.

Rewrite: $\quad \dfrac{2}{3} = \dfrac{2 \cdot x}{3 \cdot x} = \dfrac{2x}{3x}$

Rewrite: $\quad \dfrac{6}{x} = \dfrac{6 \cdot 3}{x \cdot 3} = \dfrac{18}{3x}$

Subtract: $\quad \dfrac{2x}{3x} - \dfrac{18}{3x} = \dfrac{2x-18}{3x} \left\{ \begin{array}{l}\text{Lowest} \\ \text{terms}\end{array}\right.$

Concepts	Examples

(5.5) Mixed Numbers and Improper Fractions

Changing Mixed Numbers to Improper Fractions
Multiply the denominator by the whole number, add the numerator, and place the result over the original denominator.

Changing Improper Fractions to Mixed Numbers
Divide the numerator by the denominator and place the remainder over the original denominator.

Mixed to improper

$$7\frac{2}{3} = \frac{23}{3} \leftarrow (3 \cdot 7) + 2$$

Same denominator

Improper to mixed

$$\frac{17}{5} = 3\frac{2}{5}$$

Same denominator

(5.5) Multiplying Mixed Numbers

First, round the numbers and estimate the answer. Then follow these steps to find the exact answer.

Step 1 Rewrite each mixed number as an improper fraction.
Step 2 Multiply.
Step 3 Write the answer in lowest terms and change the answer to a mixed number if desired. Then the answer is in simplest form.

Estimate:

$$1\frac{3}{5} \cdot 3\frac{1}{3}$$

$$\downarrow \text{ Rounded } \downarrow$$

$$2 \cdot 3 = 6$$

Exact:

$$1\frac{3}{5} \cdot 3\frac{1}{3} = \frac{8}{5} \cdot \frac{10}{3}$$

$$= \frac{8 \cdot 2 \cdot \cancel{5}}{\cancel{5} \cdot 3}$$

$$= \frac{16}{3} = 5\frac{1}{3} \leftarrow$$

Close to estimate

(5.5) Dividing Mixed Numbers

First, round the numbers and estimate the answer. Then follow these steps to find the exact answer.

Step 1 Rewrite each mixed number as an improper fraction.
Step 2 Divide. (Rewrite as multiplication using the reciprocal of the divisor.)
Step 3 Write the answer in lowest terms and change the answer to a mixed number if desired. Then the answer is in simplest form.

Estimate:

$$3\frac{3}{4} \div 2\frac{2}{5}$$

$$\downarrow \text{ Rounded } \downarrow$$

$$4 \div 2 = 2$$

Exact:

$$3\frac{3}{4} \div 2\frac{2}{5} = \frac{15}{4} \div \frac{12}{5} \leftarrow$$

Reciprocal of $\frac{12}{5}$ is $\frac{5}{12}$

$$= \frac{15}{4} \cdot \frac{5}{12} \leftarrow$$

$$= \frac{\cancel{3} \cdot 5 \cdot 5}{4 \cdot \cancel{3} \cdot 4}$$

$$= \frac{25}{16} = 1\frac{9}{16} \leftarrow$$

Close to estimate

(5.5) Adding and Subtracting Mixed Numbers

First round the numbers and estimate the answer. Then rewrite the mixed numbers as improper fractions and follow the steps for adding and subtracting fractions. Write the answer in simplest form.

Estimate:

$$2\frac{3}{8} + 3\frac{3}{4}$$

$$\downarrow \qquad \downarrow$$

$$2 + 4 = 6 \leftarrow \text{Estimate}$$

Exact:

$$2\frac{3}{8} + 3\frac{3}{4} = \frac{19}{8} + \frac{15}{4} = \frac{19}{8} + \frac{30}{8} = \frac{19 + 30}{8}$$

$$= \frac{49}{8} = 6\frac{1}{8} \leftarrow \text{Close to estimate}$$

Concepts	Examples

5.6 Simplifying Fractions with Exponents

The meaning of an exponent is the same for fractions as it is for integers. An exponent is a way to write repeated multiplication.

$$\left(-\frac{2}{3}\right)^2 \text{ means } \left(-\frac{2}{3}\right)\left(-\frac{2}{3}\right) = \frac{2 \cdot 2}{3 \cdot 3} = \frac{4}{9}$$

The product of two negative numbers is positive.

5.6 Order of Operations

The order of operations is the same for fractions as for integers.

1. Work inside *parentheses* or *other grouping symbols*.

2. Simplify expressions with *exponents*.

3. Do the remaining *multiplications and divisions* as they occur from left to right.

4. Do the remaining *additions and subtractions* as they occur from left to right.

Simplify.

$$-\frac{2}{3} + 3\left(\frac{1}{4}\right)^2$$ Cannot work inside parentheses. Apply the exponent: $\frac{1}{4} \cdot \frac{1}{4}$ is $\frac{1}{16}$

$$-\frac{2}{3} + 3\left(\frac{1}{16}\right)$$ Multiply next: $3\left(\frac{1}{16}\right)$ is $\frac{3}{1} \cdot \frac{1}{16} = \frac{3}{16}$

$$-\frac{2}{3} + \frac{3}{16}$$ Add last. The LCD is 48

$$-\frac{32}{48} + \frac{9}{48}$$ Rewrite $-\frac{2}{3}$ as $-\frac{32}{48}$
Rewrite $\frac{3}{16}$ as $\frac{9}{48}$

$$\frac{-32 + 9}{48}$$ Add the numerators. Keep the common denominator.

$$-\frac{23}{48}$$ The answer is in lowest terms.

5.6 Simplifying Complex Fractions

Recall that the fraction bar indicates division. Rewrite the complex fraction using the ÷ symbol for division. Then follow the steps for dividing fractions.

Simplify. $$\dfrac{-\dfrac{4}{5}}{10}$$

Rewrite as $-\dfrac{4}{5} \div 10$.

$$-\frac{4}{5} \div 10 = -\frac{4}{5} \cdot \frac{1}{10} = -\frac{\overset{1}{\cancel{2}} \cdot 2 \cdot 1}{5 \cdot \underset{1}{\cancel{2}} \cdot 5} = -\frac{2}{25}$$

Reciprocals

Concepts	Examples

5.7 Solving Equations Containing Fractions

Solve the equation. Check the solution.

$$\frac{1}{3}b + 6 = 10$$
$$\underline{\quad -6 \quad -6 \quad}$$ Add -6 to both sides.
$$\frac{1}{3}b + 0 = 4$$

$$\frac{1}{3}b = 4$$

Step 1 If necessary, add the same number to both sides of the equation so that the variable term is by itself on one side of the equal sign.

Step 2 Multiply both sides by the reciprocal of the coefficient of the variable term.

$$\frac{3}{1}\left(\frac{1}{3}b\right) = \frac{3}{1}(4)$$ Multiply both sides by $\frac{3}{1}$ (the reciprocal of $\frac{1}{3}$).

$$b = 12$$

The solution is 12.

Step 3 To check your solution, go back to the *original* equation and replace the variable with your solution. If the equation balances, your solution is correct. If it does not balance, rework the problem.

Check $\frac{1}{3}b + 6 = 10$ Original equation

$$\frac{1}{3}(12) + 6 = 10$$ Replace b with 12

$$4 + 6 = 10$$

$$10 = 10$$ Balances

When b is 12, the equation balances, so 12 is the correct solution (**not** 10).

5.8 Finding the Area of a Triangle

Use this formula to find the area of a triangle.

$$\text{Area} = \frac{1}{2} \cdot \text{base} \cdot \text{height}$$

$$A = \frac{1}{2}bh$$

Remember that area is measured in square units.

Find the area of this triangle.

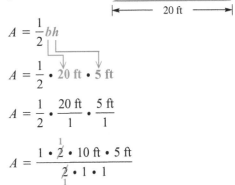

$$A = \frac{1}{2}bh$$

$$A = \frac{1}{2} \cdot 20 \text{ ft} \cdot 5 \text{ ft}$$

$$A = \frac{1}{2} \cdot \frac{20 \text{ ft}}{1} \cdot \frac{5 \text{ ft}}{1}$$

$$A = \frac{1 \cdot 2 \cdot 10 \text{ ft} \cdot 5 \text{ ft}}{2 \cdot 1 \cdot 1}$$

$$A = 50 \text{ ft}^2$$ Measure area in square units.

5.8 Finding the Volume of a Rectangular Solid

Use this formula to find the volume of box-like solids.

$$\text{Volume} = \text{length} \cdot \text{width} \cdot \text{height}$$

$$V = lwh$$

Volume is measured in cubic units.

Find the volume of this box.

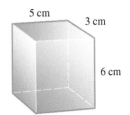

$$V = l \cdot w \cdot h$$
$$V = 5 \text{ cm} \cdot 3 \text{ cm} \cdot 6 \text{ cm}$$
$$V = 90 \text{ cm}^3$$
Measure volume in cubic units.

Concepts	Examples

(5.8) Finding the Volume of a Pyramid

Use this formula to find the volume of a pyramid.

$$\text{Volume} = \frac{1}{3} \cdot B \cdot h$$

$$V = \frac{1}{3}Bh$$

where B is the area of the base and h is the height of the pyramid.

Volume is measured in **cubic units**.

Find the volume of a pyramid with a square base 2 cm by 2 cm and a height of 6 cm.

$$\text{Area of square base} = 2 \text{ cm} \cdot 2 \text{ cm}$$
$$B = 4 \text{ cm}^2$$

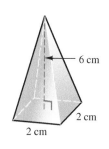

$$V = \frac{1}{3} \cdot B \cdot h$$

$$V = \frac{1}{3} \cdot 4 \text{ cm}^2 \cdot 6 \text{ cm}$$

$$V = \frac{1}{3} \cdot \frac{4 \text{ cm}^2}{1} \cdot \frac{6 \text{ cm}}{1}$$

$$V = \frac{1 \cdot 4 \text{ cm}^2 \cdot \overset{1}{\cancel{3}} \cdot 2 \text{ cm}}{\underset{1}{\cancel{3}} \cdot 1 \cdot 1}$$

$$V = 8 \text{ cm}^3 \qquad \text{Measure volume in cubic units.}$$

ANSWERS TO TEST YOUR WORD POWER

1. B; *Example:* $\frac{2}{5}$ is in lowest terms, but $\frac{4}{10}$ is not.

2. C; *Example:* In $\frac{3}{4}$ the denominator, 4, shows that the whole is divided into 4 equal parts.

3. A; *Example:* The LCD of $\frac{1}{4}$ and $\frac{5}{6}$ is 12, because 12 is the smallest number that can be divided evenly by 4 and by 6.

4. D; *Example:* The reciprocal of $\frac{3}{8}$ is $\frac{8}{3}$ because $\frac{3}{8} \cdot \frac{8}{3} = \frac{24}{24} = 1$.

5. B; *Example:* The volume of a rectangular solid (box-like shape) is the space inside the box, measured in cubic units.

6. C; *Example:* The mixed number $2\frac{3}{4}$ represents $2 + \frac{3}{4}$.

7. D; *Example:* 7 is prime because it has exactly two factors, 7 and 1.

8. C; *Example:* $\frac{1}{2}$ and $\frac{2}{4}$ are equivalent fractions because they both name the point halfway between 0 and 1.

Chapter 5 Review Exercises

[5.1] **1.** What fraction of these figures are squares? What fraction are circles?

2. Write fractions to represent the shaded and unshaded portions of this figure.

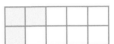

3. Graph $-\frac{1}{2}$ and $1\frac{1}{2}$ on the number line.

4. Simplify each fraction.

(a) $-\dfrac{20}{5}$ (b) $\dfrac{8}{1}$ (c) $-\dfrac{3}{3}$

[5.2] *Write each fraction in lowest terms.*

5. $\dfrac{28}{32}$

6. $\dfrac{54}{90}$

7. $\dfrac{16}{25}$

8. $\dfrac{15x^2}{40x}$

9. $\dfrac{7a^3}{35a^3b}$

10. $\dfrac{12mn^2}{21m^3n}$

[5.3] *Multiply or divide. Write all answers in lowest terms.*

11. $-\dfrac{3}{8} \div (-6)$

12. $\dfrac{2}{5}$ of (-30)

13. $\dfrac{4}{9}\left(\dfrac{2}{3}\right)$

14. $\left(\dfrac{7}{3x^3}\right)\left(\dfrac{x^2}{14}\right)$

15. $\dfrac{ab}{5} \div \dfrac{b}{10a}$

16. $\dfrac{18}{7} \div 3k$

[5.4] *Add or subtract. Write all answers in lowest terms.*

17. $-\dfrac{5}{12} + \dfrac{5}{8}$

18. $\dfrac{2}{3} - \dfrac{4}{5}$

19. $4 - \dfrac{5}{6}$

20. $\dfrac{7}{9} + \dfrac{13}{18}$

21. $\dfrac{n}{5} + \dfrac{3}{4}$

22. $\dfrac{3}{10} - \dfrac{7}{y}$

[5.5] First, round each mixed number to the nearest whole number and estimate the answer. Then find the exact answer.

23. *Exact:*

$$2\frac{1}{4} \div 1\frac{5}{8}$$

Estimate:

____ ÷ ____ = ____

24. *Exact:*

$$7\frac{1}{3} - 4\frac{5}{6}$$

Estimate:

____ − ____ = ____

25. *Exact:*

$$1\frac{3}{4} + 2\frac{3}{10}$$

Estimate:

____ + ____ = ____

[5.6] Simplify.

26. $\left(-\dfrac{3}{4}\right)^3$

27. $\left(\dfrac{2}{3}\right)^2\left(-\dfrac{1}{2}\right)^4$

28. $\dfrac{2}{5} + \dfrac{3}{10}(-4)$

29. $-\dfrac{5}{8} \div \left(-\dfrac{1}{2}\right)\left(\dfrac{14}{15}\right)$

30. $\dfrac{\frac{5}{8}}{\frac{1}{16}}$

31. $\dfrac{\frac{8}{9}}{-6}$

[5.7] Solve each equation. Show your work.

32. $-12 = -\dfrac{3}{5}w$

33. $18 + \dfrac{6}{5}r = 0$

34. $3x - \dfrac{2}{3} = \dfrac{5}{6}$

[5.8] Find the area of the triangle. Name each solid and find its volume.

35.

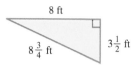

8 ft

$8\frac{3}{4}$ ft $3\frac{1}{2}$ ft

36.

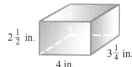

$2\frac{1}{2}$ in.

4 in. $3\frac{1}{4}$ in.

37.

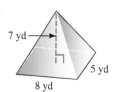

7 yd

8 yd   5 yd

>>> Mixed Review Exercises

Solve each application problem.

38. A chili recipe that makes 10 servings uses $2\frac{1}{2}$ pounds of meat. How much meat will be in each serving? How much meat would be needed to make 30 servings?

39. Yanli worked as a math tutor for $4\frac{1}{2}$ hours on Monday, $2\frac{3}{4}$ hours on Tuesday, and $3\frac{2}{3}$ hours on Friday. How much longer did she work on Monday than on Friday? How many hours did she work in all?

40. There are 60 children in the day care center. If $\frac{1}{5}$ of the children are preschoolers, $\frac{2}{3}$ of the children are toddlers, and the rest are infants, find the number of children in each age group.

41. A rectangular city park is $\frac{3}{4}$ mile long and $\frac{3}{10}$ mile wide. Find the perimeter and area of the park.

Chapter 5 ▶▶▶ **Test**  Use the Chapter Test Prep Video CD to see fully worked-out solutions to any of the exercises you want to review.

1. Write fractions to represent the shaded and unshaded portions of the figure.

2. Graph $-\frac{2}{3}$ and $2\frac{1}{3}$ on the number line at the right.

Write each fraction in lowest terms.

3. $\dfrac{21}{84}$

4. $\dfrac{25}{54}$

5. $\dfrac{6a^2b}{9b^2}$

Add, subtract, multiply, or divide, as indicated. Write all answers in lowest terms.

6. $\dfrac{1}{6} + \dfrac{7}{10}$

7. $-\dfrac{3}{4} \div \dfrac{3}{8}$

8. $\dfrac{5}{8} - \dfrac{4}{5}$

9. $(-20)\left(-\dfrac{7}{10}\right)$

10. $\dfrac{\frac{4}{9}}{-6}$

11. $4 - \dfrac{7}{8}$

12. $-\dfrac{2}{9} + \dfrac{2}{3}$

13. $\dfrac{21}{24}\left(\dfrac{9}{14}\right)$

14. $\dfrac{12x}{7y} \div 3x$

15. $\dfrac{6}{n} - \dfrac{1}{4}$

16. $\dfrac{2}{3} + \dfrac{a}{5}$

17. $\left(\dfrac{5}{9b^2}\right)\left(\dfrac{b}{10}\right)$

18. Simplify.

$$\left(-\dfrac{1}{2}\right)^3\left(\dfrac{2}{3}\right)^2$$

19. Simplify.

$$\dfrac{1}{6} + 4\left(\dfrac{2}{5} - \dfrac{7}{10}\right)$$

1. _____

2.

3. _____

4. _____

5. _____

6. _____

7. _____

8. _____

9. _____

10. _____

11. _____

12. _____

13. _____

14. _____

15. _____

16. _____

17. _____

18. _____

19. _____

First, round the numbers and estimate each answer. Then find the exact answer. Write exact answers in simplest form.

20. Estimate: _____

Exact: _____

20. $4\frac{4}{5} \div 1\frac{1}{8}$

21. $3\frac{2}{5} - 1\frac{9}{10}$

21. Estimate: _____

Exact: _____

Solve each equation. Show your work.

22. $7 = \frac{1}{5}d$

23. $-\frac{3}{10}t = \frac{9}{14}$

22. _____

23. _____

24. _____

24. $0 = \frac{1}{4}b - 2$

25. $\frac{4}{3}x + 7 = -13$

25. _____

Find the area of each triangle.

26. _____

26.

12 m   8 m   9 m

13 m

27.

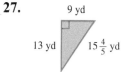

9 yd

13 yd $15\frac{4}{5}$ yd

27. _____

Name each solid and find its volume.

28. _____

28.

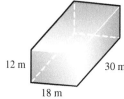

12 m   30 m

18 m

29.

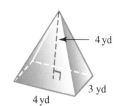

4 yd

3 yd

4 yd

29. _____

Solve each application problem.

30. _____

30. Ann-Marie Sargent is training for an upcoming wheelchair race. She rides $4\frac{5}{6}$ hours on Monday, $6\frac{2}{3}$ hours on Tuesday, and $3\frac{1}{4}$ hours on Wednesday. How many hours did she spend in all? How many more hours did she train on Tuesday than on Monday?

31. _____

31. A new vaccine is synthesized at the rate of $2\frac{1}{2}$ ounces per day. How long will it take to synthesize $8\frac{3}{4}$ ounces?

32. _____

32. There are 8448 students at the Metro Community College campus. If $\frac{7}{8}$ of the students work either full time or part time, find the total number of students who work.

6

Positive and Negative Decimals/Statistics

6.1 ▶▶▶ Reading and Writing Decimal Numbers

OBJECTIVES

1. **Write parts of a whole using decimals.**
2. **Identify the place value of a digit.**
3. **Read decimal numbers.**
4. **Write decimals as fractions or mixed numbers.**

In **Chapter 5,** you worked with rational numbers written in fraction form to represent parts of a whole. In this chapter, we will use rational numbers written as **decimals** to show parts of a whole. For example, our money system is based on decimals. One dollar is divided into 100 equivalent parts. One cent ($0.01) is one of the parts, and a dime ($0.10) is 10 of the parts. Metric measurement is also based on decimals.

 1 There are 10 dimes in one dollar. Each dime is $\frac{1}{10}$ of a dollar. Write a fraction, a decimal, and the words that name the yellow shaded portion of each dollar.

(a)

(b)

(c)

OBJECTIVE 1 Write parts of a whole using decimals. Decimals are used when a whole is divided into 10 equivalent parts or into 100 or 1000 or 10,000 equivalent parts. In other words, decimals are fractions with denominators that are a power of 10. For example, the square at the right is cut into 10 equivalent parts. Written as a fraction, each part is $\frac{1}{10}$ of the whole. Written as a decimal, each part is **0.1**. Both $\frac{1}{10}$ and 0.1 are read as "*one tenth.*"

One tenth of the square is shaded.

The dot in 0.1 is called the **decimal point.**

$$0.1$$
$$\uparrow$$
Decimal point

The square at the right has **7** of its 10 parts shaded.
Written as a *fraction,* $\frac{7}{10}$ of the square is shaded.
Written as a *decimal,* **0.7** of the square is shaded.
Both $\frac{7}{10}$ and 0.7 are read as "*seven tenths.*"

0.7

Seven tenths of the square is shaded.

◀ *Work Problem* **1** *at the Side.*

Each square below is cut into 100 equivalent parts.
Written as a fraction, each part is $\frac{1}{100}$ of the whole.
Written as a decimal, each part is **0.01** of the whole.
Both $\frac{1}{100}$ and 0.01 are read as "*one hundredth.*"

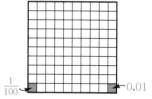 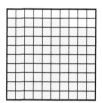

$\frac{1}{100}$ 0.01

Eighty-seven hundredths of the square is shaded.

ANSWERS

1. (a) $\frac{1}{10}$; 0.1; one tenth

   (b) $\frac{3}{10}$; 0.3; three tenths

   (c) $\frac{9}{10}$; 0.9; nine tenths

The square above on the right has 87 of its 100 parts shaded.
Written as a fraction, $\frac{87}{100}$ of the total area is shaded.
Written as a decimal, **0.87** of the total area is shaded.
Both $\frac{87}{100}$ and 0.87 are read as "*eighty-seven hundredths.*"

Work Problem **2** *at the Side.* ▶

The example below shows several numbers written as fractions, as decimals, and in words.

2 Write the portion of each square that is shaded as a fraction, as a decimal, and in words.

EXAMPLE 1   **Using the Decimal Forms of Fractions**

Fraction	Decimal	Read As
(a) $\dfrac{4}{10}$	0.4	four tenths
(b) $-\dfrac{9}{100}$	−0.09	negative nine hundredths
(c) $\dfrac{71}{100}$	0.71	seventy-one hundredths
(d) $\dfrac{8}{1000}$	0.008	eight thousandths
(e) $-\dfrac{45}{1000}$	−0.045	negative forty-five thousandths
(f) $\dfrac{832}{1000}$	0.832	eight hundred thirty-two thousandths

(a)

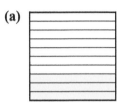

(b)

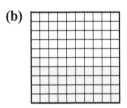

Work Problem **3** *at the Side.* ▶

OBJECTIVE **2** **Identify the place value of a digit.** The decimal point separates the *whole number part* from the *fractional part* in a decimal number. In the chart below, you see that the **place value** names for fractional parts are similar to those on the whole number side but end in "*ths.*"

3 Write each decimal as a fraction.

(a) −0.7

(b) 0.2

(c) −0.03

(d) 0.69

(e) 0.047

(f) −0.351

Decimal Place Value Chart

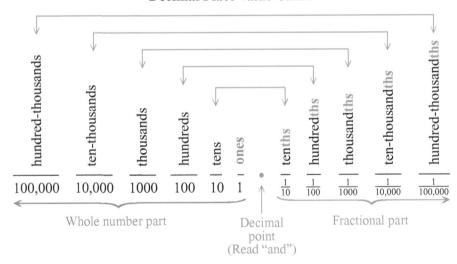

Note

Notice that the **ones** place is at the center of the place value chart above. There is no "oneths" place.

Also notice that each place is 10 times the value of the place to its right.

Finally, be sure to write a hyphen (dash) in ten-thousand**ths** and hundred-thousand**ths**.

ANSWERS

2. (a) $\dfrac{3}{10}$; 0.3; three tenths

(b) $\dfrac{41}{100}$; 0.41; forty-one hundredths

3. (a) $-\dfrac{7}{10}$ (b) $\dfrac{2}{10}$ (c) $-\dfrac{3}{100}$

(d) $\dfrac{69}{100}$ (e) $\dfrac{47}{1000}$ (f) $-\dfrac{351}{1000}$

4 Identify the place value of each digit.

(a) 971.54

(b) 0.4

(c) 5.60

(d) 0.0835

5 Tell how to read each decimal in words.

(a) 0.6

(b) 0.46

(c) 0.05

(d) 0.409

(e) 0.0003

(f) 0.2703

(g) 0.088

CAUTION

If a number does *not* have a decimal point, it is an *integer*. An integer has no fractional part. If you want to show the decimal point in an integer, it is just to the **right** of the digit in the ones place. Here are three examples.

$$8 = 8. \qquad 306 = 306. \qquad -42 = -42.$$

Decimal point   Decimal point   Decimal point

EXAMPLE 2 Identifying the Place Value of a Digit

Identify the place value of each digit.

(a) 178.36

hundreds, tens, ones, tenths, hundredths

1 7 8 . 3 6

(b) 0.00935

ones, tenths, hundredths, thousandths, ten-thousandths, hundred-thousandths

0 . 0 0 9 3 5

Notice in Example 2(b) that we do *not* use commas on the right side of the decimal point.

◀ *Work Problem* **4** *at the Side.*

OBJECTIVE **3** **Read decimal numbers.** A decimal number is read according to its form as a fraction.

ones, tenths

0 . 9

We read 0.9 as "nine tenths" because 0.9 is the same as $\frac{9}{10}$. Notice that 0.9 ends in the tenths place.

ones, tenths, hundredths

0 . 0 2

We read 0.02 as "two hundredths" because 0.02 is the same as $\frac{2}{100}$. Notice that 0.02 ends in the hundredths place.

EXAMPLE 3 Reading Decimal Numbers

Tell how to read each decimal in words.

(a) 0.3

   Because $0.3 = \frac{3}{10}$, read the decimal as: three <u>tenths</u>.

(b) 0.49   Read it as: forty-nine <u>hundredths</u>.

(c) 0.08   Read it as: eight <u>hundredths</u>.

   Think: $0.08 = \frac{8}{100}$ so write *hundredths*.

(d) 0.918   Read it as: nine hundred eighteen <u>thousandths</u>.

(e) 0.0106   Read it as: one hundred six <u>ten-thousandths</u>.

   Think: $0.0106 = \frac{106}{10,000}$

◀ *Work Problem* **5** *at the Side.*

ANSWERS

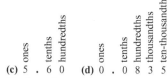

4. (a) hundreds, tens, ones, tenths, hundredths   9 7 1 . 5 4   (b) ones, tenths   0 . 4

(c) ones, tenths, hundredths   5 . 6 0   (d) ones, tenths, hundredths, thousandths, ten-thousandths   0 . 0 8 3 5

5. (a) six tenths
   (b) forty-six hundredths
   (c) five hundredths
   (d) four hundred nine thousandths
   (e) three ten-thousandths
   (f) two thousand seven hundred three ten-thousandths
   (g) eighty-eight thousandths

Reading a Decimal Number

Step 1 Read any whole number part to the *left* of the decimal point as you normally would.

Step 2 Read the decimal point as "*and.*"

Step 3 Read the part of the number to the *right* of the decimal point as if it were an ordinary whole number.

Step 4 Finish with the place value name of the rightmost digit; these names all end in "*ths.*"

Note

If there is *no whole number part,* you will use only Steps 3 and 4.

EXAMPLE 4 **Reading Decimal Numbers**

Read each decimal.

(a)

9 is in tenths place.

16.9

sixteen and nine tenths

Remember to say or write "and" **only** when you see a decimal point.

16.9 is read "sixteen and nine tenths."

(b)

5 is in hundredths place.

482.35

four hundred eighty-two and thirty-five hundredths

482.35 is read "four hundred eighty-two and thirty-five hundredths."

3 is in thousandths place.

(c) 0.063 is "sixty-three thousandths." (No whole number part)

(d) 11.1085 is "eleven and one thousand eighty-five ten-thousandths."

CAUTION

Use "and" *only* when reading a decimal point. A common mistake is to read the whole number 405 as "four hundred *and* five." But there is *no decimal point* shown in 405, so it is read "four hundred five."

Work Problem **6** *at the Side.* ▶

OBJECTIVE 4 Write decimals as fractions or mixed numbers.
Knowing how to read decimals will help you when writing decimals as fractions or mixed numbers.

Writing a Decimal as a Fraction or Mixed Number

Step 1 The digits to the right of the decimal point are the numerator of the fraction.

Step 2 The denominator is 10 for tenths, 100 for hundredths, 1000 for thousandths, 10,000 for ten-thousandths, and so on.

Step 3 If the decimal has a whole number part, it is written as a mixed number with the same whole number part.

6 Tell how to read each decimal in words.

(a) 3.8

(b) 15.001

(c) 0.0073

(d) 764.309

7 Write each decimal as a fraction or mixed number.

(a) 0.7

(b) 12.21

(c) 0.101

(d) 0.007

(e) 1.3717

8 Write each decimal as a fraction or mixed number in lowest terms.

(a) 0.5

(b) 12.6

(c) 0.85

(d) 3.05

(e) 0.225

(f) 420.0802

EXAMPLE 5 **Writing Decimals as Fractions or Mixed Numbers**

Write each decimal as a fraction or mixed number.

(a) 0.19

The digits to the right of the decimal point, 19, are the numerator of the fraction. The denominator is 100 for hundredths because the rightmost digit is in the hundredths place.

$$0.19 = \frac{19}{100} \leftarrow 100 \text{ for hundredths}$$

Hundredths place

(b) 0.863

$$0.863 = \frac{863}{1000} \leftarrow 1000 \text{ for thousandths}$$

Thousandths place

(c) 4.0099

The whole number part stays the same.

$$4.0099 = 4\frac{99}{10,000} \leftarrow 10,000 \text{ for ten-thousandths}$$

Ten-thousandths place

◀ Work Problem **7** at the Side.

EXAMPLE 6 **Writing Decimals as Fractions or Mixed Numbers**

Write each decimal as a fraction or mixed number in lowest terms.

(a) $0.4 = \frac{4}{10} \leftarrow 10$ for tenths

Write $\frac{4}{10}$ in lowest terms. $\frac{4}{10} = \frac{4 \div 2}{10 \div 2} = \frac{2}{5} \leftarrow$ Lowest terms

(b) $0.75 = \frac{75}{100} = \frac{75 \div 25}{100 \div 25} = \frac{3}{4} \leftarrow$ Lowest terms

The whole number part stays the same.

(c) $18.105 = 18\frac{105}{1000} = 18\frac{105 \div 5}{1000 \div 5} = 18\frac{21}{200} \leftarrow$ Lowest terms

(d) $42.8085 = 42\frac{8085}{10,000} = 42\frac{8085 \div 5}{10,000 \div 5} = 42\frac{1617}{2000} \leftarrow$ Lowest terms

CAUTION
Always check that your fraction answers are in lowest terms.

◀ Work Problem **8** at the Side.

ANSWERS

7. (a) $\frac{7}{10}$ (b) $12\frac{21}{100}$ (c) $\frac{101}{1000}$
 (d) $\frac{7}{1000}$ (e) $1\frac{3717}{10,000}$

8. (a) $\frac{1}{2}$ (b) $12\frac{3}{5}$ (c) $\frac{17}{20}$ (d) $3\frac{1}{20}$
 (e) $\frac{9}{40}$ (f) $420\frac{401}{5000}$

📱 **Calculator Tip**   In this book, we will write 0.45 instead of just .45, to emphasize that there is no whole number. Your *scientific* calculator shows these zeros also. Enter ⊙ ④ ⑤ and notice that the display automatically shows 0.45 even though you did not press 0. For comparison, enter the whole number 45 by pressing ④ ⑤ ⊕ and notice that the decimal point automatically appears to the *right* of the 5. (*Graphing* calculators may not automatically show a 0 in the ones place.)

Identify the digit that has the given place value. See Example 2.

1. 70.489
 tens
 ones
 tenths

2. 135.296
 ones
 tenths
 tens

3. 0.2518
 hundredths
 thousandths
 ten-thousandths

4. 0.9347
 hundredths
 thousandths
 ten-thousandths

5. 93.01472
 thousandths
 ten-thousandths
 tenths

6. 0.51968
 tenths
 ten-thousandths
 hundredths

🌐 **7.** 314.658
 tens
 tenths
 hundreds

8. 51.325
 tens
 tenths
 hundredths

9. 149.0832
 hundreds
 hundredths
 ones

10. 3458.712
 hundreds
 hundredths
 tenths

11. 6285.7125
 thousands
 thousandths
 hundredths

12. 5417.6832
 thousands
 thousandths
 ones

Write the decimal number that has the specified place values. See Example 2.

13. 0 ones, 5 hundredths, 1 ten, 4 hundreds, 2 tenths

14. 7 tens, 9 tenths, 3 ones, 6 hundredths, 8 hundreds

15. 3 thousandths, 4 hundredths, 6 ones, 2 ten-thousandths, 5 tenths

16. 8 ten-thousandths, 4 hundredths, 0 ones, 2 tenths, 6 thousandths

17. 4 hundredths, 4 hundreds, 0 tens, 0 tenths, 5 thousandths, 5 thousands, 6 ones

18. 7 tens, 7 tenths, 6 thousands, 6 thousandths, 3 hundreds, 3 hundredths, 2 ones

Write each decimal as a fraction or mixed number in lowest terms. See Examples 5 and 6.

19. 0.7   **20.** 0.1   ● **21.** 13.4   **22.** 9.8   **23.** 0.35

24. 0.85   **25.** 0.66   **26.** 0.33   **27.** 10.17   **28.** 31.99

29. 0.06   **30.** 0.08   **31.** 0.205   **32.** 0.805

33. 5.002   **34.** 4.008   **35.** 0.686   **36.** 0.492

Tell how to read each decimal in words. See Examples 1, 3, and 4.

37. 0.5   **38.** 0.2

39. 0.78   **40.** 0.55

41. 0.105   **42.** 0.609

43. 12.04   **44.** 86.09

45. 1.075   **46.** 4.025

Write each decimal in numbers. See Examples 3 and 4.

47. Six and seven tenths

48. Eight and twelve hundredths

49. Thirty-two hundredths

50. One hundred eleven thousandths

51. Four hundred twenty and eight thousandths

52. Two hundred and twenty-four thousandths

53. Seven hundred three ten-thousandths

54. Eight hundred and six hundredths

55. Seventy-five and thirty thousandths

56. Sixty and fifty hundredths

57. Anne read the number 4302 as "four thousand three hundred and two." Explain what is wrong with the way Anne read the number.

58. Jerry read the number 9.0106 as "nine and one hundred and six ten-thousandths." Explain the error he made.

The father on the first page of this chapter needs to select the correct fishing line for his daughter's reel. Fishing line is sold according to how many pounds of "pull" the line can withstand before breaking. Use the table to answer Exercises 59–62. Write all fractions in lowest terms. (Note: The diameter of the fishing line is its thickness.)

FISHING LINE

Test Strength (pounds)	Average Diameter (inches)
4	0.008
8	0.010
12	0.013
14	0.014
17	0.015
20	0.016

Source: Berkley Outdoor Technologies Group.

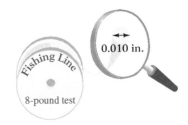

The diameter is the distance across the end of the line (or its thickness).

59. Write the diameter of 8-pound test line in words and as a fraction.

60. Write the diameter of 17-pound test line in words and as a fraction.

61. What is the test strength of the line with a diameter of $\frac{13}{1000}$ inch?

62. What is the test strength of the line with a diameter of sixteen thousandths inch?

Suppose your job is to take phone orders for precision parts. Use the table below. In Exercises 63–66, write the correct part number that matches what you hear the customer say over the phone. In Exercises 67–68, write the words you would say to the customer.

Part Number	Size in Centimeters
3-A	0.06
3-B	0.26
3-C	0.6
3-D	0.86
4-A	1.006
4-B	1.026
4-C	1.06
4-D	1.6
4-E	1.602

63. "Please send the six tenths centimeter bolt."

Part number _____

64. "The part missing from our order was the one and six hundredths size."

Part number _____

65. "The size we need is one and six thousandths centimeters."

Part number _____

66. "Do you still stock the twenty-six hundredths centimeter bolt?"

Part number _____

67. "What size is part number 4-E?" Write your answer in words.

68. "What size is part number 4-B?" Write your answer in words.

Relating Concepts (Exercises 69–76) For Individual or Group Work

*Use your knowledge of place value to **work Exercises 69–76 in order.***

69. Look back at the decimal place value chart on page 329 of this section. What do you think would be the names of the next four places to the *right* of hundred-thousandths? What information did you use to come up with these names?

70. A common mistake is to think that the first place to the right of the decimal point is "oneths" and the second place is "tenths." Why might someone make that mistake? How would you explain why there is no "oneths" place?

71. Use your answer from Exercise 69 to write 0.72436955 in words.

72. Use your answer from Exercise 69 to write 0.000678554 in words.

73. Write 8006.500001 in words.

74. Write 20,060.000505 in words.

75. Write this decimal using digits.
three hundred two thousand forty ten-millionths

76. Write this decimal using digits.
nine billion, eight hundred seventy-six million, five hundred forty-three thousand, two hundred ten and one hundred million two hundred thousand three hundred billionths

6.2 ▶▶▶ Rounding Decimal Numbers

Section 3.4 showed how to round integers. For example, 89 rounded to the nearest ten is 90, and 8512 rounded to the nearest hundred is 8500.

OBJECTIVE 1 Learn the rules for rounding decimals. It is also important to be able to **round** decimals. For example, a store is selling 2 candy mints for $0.75 but you want only one mint. The price of each mint is $0.75 ÷ 2, which is $0.375, but you cannot pay part of a cent. Is $0.375 closer to $0.37 or to $0.38? Actually, it's exactly halfway between. When this happens in everyday situations, the rule is to round *up*. The store will charge you $0.38 for the mint.

OBJECTIVES

1. **Learn the rules for rounding decimals.**

2. **Round decimals to any given place.**

3. **Round money amounts to the nearest cent or nearest dollar.**

Rounding a Decimal Number

Step 1 Find the place to which the rounding is being done. Draw a "cut-off" line *after* that place to show that you are cutting off and dropping the rest of the digits.

Step 2 Look *only* at the *first* digit you are cutting off.

Step 3A If this digit is *4 or less,* the part of the number you are keeping *stays the same.*

Step 3B If this digit is *5 or more,* you must *round up* the part of the number you are keeping.

Step 4 You can use the ≈ symbol or the ≐ symbol to indicate that the rounded number is now an approximation (close, but *not exact*). Both symbols mean "is approximately equal to." (In this book we will use the ≈ symbol.)

CAUTION
Do *not* move the decimal point when rounding.

OBJECTIVE 2 Round decimals to any given place. These examples show you how to round decimals.

EXAMPLE 1 Rounding a Decimal Number

Round 14.39652 to the nearest thousandth. (Is it closer to 14.396 or to 14.397?)

Step 1 Draw a "cut-off" line after the thousandths place.

$$1\ 4\ .\ 3\ 9\ 6\ |\ 5\ 2$$

You are cutting off the 5 and 2
They will be dropped.

Thousandths ⬏

Step 2 Look *only* at the *first* digit you are cutting off. Ignore the other digits you are cutting off.

Look *only* at the 5
Ignore the 2

$$1\ 4\ .\ 3\ 9\ 6\ |\ 5\ 2$$

Continued on Next Page

1 Round to the nearest thousandth.

(a) 0.33492

(b) 8.00851

(c) 265.42068

(d) 10.70180

Step 3 If the first digit you are cutting off is *5 or more,* round up the part of the number you are keeping.

First digit cut is 5 *or more,* so round up by adding 1 thousandth to the part you are keeping.

$$1\ 4\ .\ 3\ 9\ 6\ |\ 5\ 2$$
$$+\ \ 0\ .\ 0\ 0\ 1$$
$$\overline{1\ 4\ .\ 3\ 9\ 7}$$

Rounding to **thousandths** means **three** decimal places.

So, **14.39652** rounded to the nearest thousandth is **14.397**
You can write 14.39652 ≈ 14.397

> **CAUTION**
> When rounding integers in **Section 3.4,** you kept all the digits but changed some to zeros. With decimals, you cut off and *drop the extra digits.* In the example above, 14.39652 rounds to 14.397 (*not* 14.39700).

◀ *Work Problem* **1** *at the Side.*

In Example 1 above, the rounded number 14.397 had *three decimal places.* **Decimal places** are the number of digits to the *right* of the decimal point. The first decimal place is tenths, the second is hundredths, the third is thousandths, and so on.

EXAMPLE 2 **Rounding Decimals to Different Places**

Round to the place indicated.

(a) Round 5.3496 to the nearest tenth. (Is it closer to 5.3 or to 5.4?)

Step 1 Draw a cut-off line after the tenths place. — **Tenths is one** decimal place.

$$5\ .\ 3\ |\ 4\ 9\ 6$$

You are cutting off the 4, 9, and 6

Tenths

Step 2 Look *only* at the 4

$$5\ .\ 3\ |\ 4\ \underline{9\ 6}$$

Ignore these digits.

Step 3 First digit cut is 4 *or less,* so the part you are keeping stays the same.

$$\underline{5\ .\ 3}\ |\ 4\ 9\ 6$$

$$5\ .\ 3\ \leftarrow \text{Stays the same}$$

5.3496 rounded to the nearest tenth is 5.3 (*one* decimal place for *tenths*).
You can write 5.3496 ≈ 5.3
Notice: 5.3496 does *not* round to 5.3000 (which would be ten-thousandths instead of tenths).

(b) Round 0.69738 to the nearest hundredth. (Is it closer to 0.69 or to 0.70?)

Step 1
$$0\ .\ 6\ 9\ |\ 7\ 3\ 8$$

Draw a cut-off line after the hundredths place.

Hundredths

Look *only* at the 7

Step 2
$$0\ .\ 6\ 9\ |\ 7\ 3\ 8$$

Continued on Next Page

Step 3   0 . 6 9 | 7 3 8 ⟵ First digit cut is *5 or more,* so round up by adding 1 hundredth to the part you are keeping.

1
0 . 6 9 ⟵ Keep this part.
+ 0 . 0 1 ⟵ To round up, add 1 hundredth.
0 . 7 0 ⟵ 9 + 1 is 10; write 0 and regroup 1 to the tenths place.

So, 0.69738 rounded to the nearest hundredth is 0.70. Hundredths is *two* decimal places so you *must* write the 0 in the hundredths place.
You can write $0.69738 \approx 0.70$

> **CAUTION**
> If a *rounded* number has a 0 in the rightmost place, you *must* keep the 0. As shown above, 0.69738 rounded to the nearest hundredth is 0.70. Do *not* write 0.7, which is rounded to tenths instead of hundredths.

(c) Round 0.01806 to the nearest thousandth. (Is it closer to 0.018 or to 0.019?)

0 . 0 1 8 | 0 6 ⟵ First digit cut is *4 or less,* so the part you are keeping stays the same.

0 . 0 1 8 ⟵ Stays the same

So, 0.01806 rounded to the nearest thousandth is 0.018 (three decimal places for thousandths).
You can write $0.01806 \approx 0.018$

(d) Round 57.976 to the nearest tenth. (Is it closer to 57.9 or to 58.0?)

57.9 | 76 ⟵ First digit cut is *5 or more,* so round up by adding 1 tenth to the part you are keeping.

1
57.9
+ 0.1
58.0 ⟵ 9 + 1 is 10; write 0 and regroup 1 to the ones place.

> Be sure to write the 0 in the *tenths* place.

So, 57.976 rounded to the nearest tenth is 58.0. You can write $57.976 \approx 58.0$
You *must* write the 0 in the tenths place to show that the number was rounded to the nearest tenth.

> **CAUTION**
> Check that your rounded answer shows *exactly* the number of decimal places asked for in the problem. Be sure your answer shows *one decimal place* if you rounded to *tenths, two decimal places* for *hundredths, three decimal places* for *thousandths,* and so on.

Work Problem **2** *at the Side.* ▶

OBJECTIVE **3** **Round money amounts to the nearest cent or nearest dollar.** When you are shopping in a store, money amounts are usually rounded to the nearest cent. There are 100 cents in a dollar.

$$\text{Each cent is } \frac{1}{100} \text{ of a dollar.}$$

Another way to write $\frac{1}{100}$ is 0.01. So rounding to the *nearest cent* is the same as rounding to the *nearest hundredth of a dollar.*

2 Round to the place indicated.

(a) 0.8988 to the nearest hundredth

(b) 5.8903 to the nearest hundredth

(c) 11.0299 to the nearest thousandth

(d) 0.545 to the nearest tenth

3 Round each money amount to the nearest cent.

(a) $14.595

You pay _____.

(b) $578.0663

You pay _____.

(c) $0.849

You pay _____.

(d) $0.0548

You pay _____.

EXAMPLE 3 **Rounding to the Nearest Cent**

Round each money amount to the nearest cent.

(a) $2.4238 (Is it closer to $2.42 or to $2.43?)

First digit cut is *4 or less*, so the part you are keeping stays the same.

$2.42|38

$2.42 ⟵ You pay $2.42

$2.4238 rounded to the nearest cent is $2.42.

Rounding to the *nearest cent* is rounding to *hundredths*.

(b) $0.695 (Is it closer to $0.69 or to $0.70?)

5 or more; round up.

$0.69|5

$0.69
+ $0.01 ⟵ To round up, add 1 hundredth (1 cent).
$0.70 ⟵ You pay $0.70

$0.695 rounded to the nearest cent is $0.70.

◀ *Work Problem* **3** *at the Side.*

Note

Some stores round *all* money amounts up to the next higher cent, even if the next digit is *4 or less*. In Example 3(a) above, some stores would round $2.4238 *up* to $2.43, even though it is closer to $2.42.

It is also common to round money amounts to the nearest dollar. For example, you can do that on your federal and state income tax returns to make the calculations easier.

EXAMPLE 4 **Rounding to the Nearest Dollar**

Round to the nearest dollar.

(a) $48.69 (Is it closer to $48 or to $49?)

First digit cut is *5 or more,* so round up by adding $1

$48.|69

$48
+ 1
$49

Write $49 **not** $49.00

$48.69 rounded to the nearest dollar is $49

CAUTION

$48.69 rounded to the nearest dollar is $49. Be careful to write the answer as **$49** to show that the rounding is to the *nearest dollar*. Writing $49.00 would show rounding to the *nearest cent*.

Continued on Next Page

(b) $594.36 (Is it closer to $594 or to $595?)

First digit cut is *4 or less*, so the part you are keeping stays the same.

$594.|36

$594

$594.36 rounded to the nearest dollar is $594 — Write $594 **not** $594.00

(c) $399.88 (Is it closer to $399 or to $400?)

5 or more so round up by adding $1

$399.|88

$399
+   1
$400

You are rounding to the nearest whole number, so do *not* show any decimal places.

$399.88 rounded to the nearest dollar is $400

(d) $2689.50 (Is it closer to $2689 or to $2690?)

5 or more, so round up by adding $1

$2689.|50

$2689
+   1
$2690

$2689.50 rounded to the nearest dollar is $2690

> **Note**
> When rounding $2689.50 to the nearest dollar, above, notice that it is exactly halfway between $2689 and $2690. When this happens in everyday situations, the rule is to round *up*. (Scientists working with technical data may use a more complicated rule when rounding numbers that are exactly in the middle.)

(e) $0.61 (Is it closer to $0 or to $1?)

5 or more, so round up.

$0.|61

$0.61 rounded to the nearest dollar is $1 — Write $1 **not** $1.00

 Calculator Tip Accountants and other people who work with money amounts often set their calculators to automatically round to two decimal places (nearest cent) or to round to zero decimal places (nearest dollar). Your calculator may have this feature.

────── *Work Problem* (4) *at the Side.* ▶

4 Round to the nearest dollar.

(a) $29.10

(b) $136.49

(c) $990.91

(d) $5999.88

(e) $49.60

(f) $0.55

(g) $1.08

Math in the Media

LAWN FERTILIZER

Gotta Be Green

A lot's being written about personal responsibility these days, and the idea seems to be ending up on the front lawn—literally! Each spring, homeowners across the country gear up to green up their lawns, and the increased use of fertilizer has a lot of environmentalists concerned about the potential effects of chemical runoff into nearby rivers and streams.

Every year, according to a study conducted by the University of Minnesota's Department of Agriculture, each household in the Minneapolis/St. Paul metro area uses an average of 36 pounds of lawn fertilizer. That adds up to 25,529,295 pounds, or 12,765 tons. Add to that another 193,000 pounds of weed killer and you're looking at the total picture for keeping it green in the Twin Cities.

Source: Minneapolis Star Tribune.

1. According to the article,

   (a) How many pounds of lawn fertilizer are used each year in the *entire metro area?*

   (b) Do a division on your calculator to find the number of *households* in the metro area.

   (c) Why does it make sense to round your answer to part (b)? If so, how would you round it?

2. There are 2000 pounds in one ton.

   (a) Find the number of tons equivalent to 25,529,295 pounds of fertilizer.

   (b) Does your answer match the figure given in the article? If not, what did the author of the article do to get 12,765 tons?

   (c) Is the author's figure accurate? Why or why not?

3. According to the article, "each household in the Minneapolis/St. Paul metro area uses an average of 36 pounds of lawn fertilizer" each year. When the calculations were done to find the average, the answer was probably not *exactly* 36 pounds.

   (a) List three different values that are *less than* 36 that would round to 36. List a value with one decimal place, a value with two decimal places, and a value with three decimal places.

   (b) List three different values that are *greater than* 36 that would round to 36. List one value each with one, two, and three decimal places.

6.2 ▶▶▶ **Exercises**

FOR
EXTRA
HELP  Math XL
PRACTICE   WATCH   DOWNLOAD   READ   REVIEW

Round each number to the place indicated. See Examples 1 and 2.

1. 16.8974 to the nearest tenth

2. 193.845 to the nearest hundredth

3. 0.95647 to the nearest thousandth

4. 96.81584 to the nearest ten-thousandth

5. 0.799 to the nearest hundredth

6. 0.952 to the nearest tenth

7. 3.66062 to the nearest thousandth

8. 1.5074 to the nearest hundredth

9. 793.988 to the nearest tenth

10. 476.1196 to the nearest thousandth

11. 0.09804 to the nearest ten-thousandth

12. 176.004 to the nearest tenth

13. 48.512 to the nearest one

14. 3.385 to the nearest one

15. 9.0906 to the nearest hundredth

16. 30.1290 to the nearest thousandth

17. 82.000151 to the nearest ten-thousandth

18. 0.400594 to the nearest ten-thousandth

Nardos is grocery shopping. The store will round the amount she pays for each item to the nearest cent. Write the rounded amounts. See Example 3.

19. Soup is three cans for $2.45, so one can is $0.81666. Nardos pays _____.

20. Orange juice is two cartons for $3.89, so one carton is $1.945. Nardos pays _____.

21. Facial tissue is four boxes for $4.89, so one box is $1.2225. Nardos pays _____.

22. Muffin mix is three packages for $1.75, so one package is $0.58333. Nardos pays _____.

23. Candy bars are six for $2.99, so one bar is $0.4983. Nardos pays _____.

24. Boxes of spaghetti are four for $4.39, so one box is $1.0975. Nardos pays _____.

As she gets ready to do her income tax return, Ms. Chen rounds each amount to the nearest dollar. Write the rounded amounts. See Example 4.

25. Income from job, $48,649.60

26. Income from interest on bank account, $69.58

27. Union dues, $310.08

28. Federal withholding, $6064.49

29. Donations to charity, $848.91

30. Medical expenses, $609.38

Round each money amount as indicated.

31. $499.98 to the nearest dollar

32. $9899.59 to the nearest dollar

33. $0.996 to the nearest cent

34. $0.09929 to the nearest cent

35. $999.73 to the nearest dollar

36. $9999.80 to the nearest dollar

The table lists speed records for various types of transportation. Use the table to answer Exercises 37–40.

Record	Speed (miles per hour)
Land speed record (specially built car)	763.04
Motorcycle speed record (specially adapted motorcycle)	322.16
Fastest rollercoaster	106.9
Fastest military jet	2193.167
Boeing 737-300 airplane (regular passenger service)	495
Indianapolis 500 auto race (fastest average winning speed)	185.981
Daytona 500 auto race (fastest average winning speed)	177.602

Sources: Guinness World Records and The World Almanac.

37. Round these speed records to the nearest whole number.

(a) Motorcycle

(b) Rollercoaster

38. Round these speed records to the nearest hundredth.

(a) Daytona 500 average winning speed

(b) Indianapolis 500 average winning speed

39. Round these speed records to the nearest tenth.

(a) Indianapolis 500 average winning speed

(b) Land speed record

40. Round these speed records to the nearest hundred.

(a) military jet

(b) Boeing 737-300 airplane

Relating Concepts (Exercises 41–44) For Individual or Group Work

*Use your knowledge about rounding money amounts to **work Exercises 41–44 in order.***

41. Explain what happens when you round $0.499 to the nearest dollar. Why does this happen?

42. Look again at Exercise 41. How else could you round $0.499 that would be more helpful? What kind of guideline does this suggest about rounding to the nearest dollar?

43. Explain what happens when you round $0.0015 to the nearest cent. Why does this happen?

44. Suppose you want to know which of these amounts is less, so you round them both to the nearest cent.

$0.5968 $0.6014

Explain what happens. Describe what you could do instead of rounding to the nearest cent.

6.3 ▶▶▶ Adding and Subtracting Signed Decimal Numbers

OBJECTIVE 1 Add and subtract positive decimals. When adding or subtracting *whole* numbers, you line up the numbers in columns so that you are adding ones to ones, tens to tens, and so on. A similar idea applies to adding or subtracting *decimal* numbers. With decimals, you line up the decimal points to be sure that you are adding tenths to tenths, hundredths to hundredths, and so on.

OBJECTIVES

1 Add and subtract positive decimals.

2 Add and subtract negative decimals.

3 Estimate the answer when adding or subtracting decimals.

Adding and Subtracting Decimal Numbers

Step 1 Write the numbers in columns with the decimal points lined up.

Step 2 If necessary, write in zeros so both numbers have the same number of decimal places. Then add or subtract as if they were whole numbers.

Step 3 Line up the decimal point in the answer directly below the decimal points in the problem.

EXAMPLE 1 Adding Decimal Numbers

Find each sum.

(a) 16.92 and 48.34

Step 1 Write the numbers in columns with the decimal points lined up.

```
   tens
   ones
       tenths
       hundredths
    1 6 . 9 2
 + 4 8 . 3 4
        ↑
        └──── Decimal points are lined up.
```

Step 2 Add as if these were whole numbers.

```
   1 1
   16 . 92
 + 48 . 34
   ─────────
   65 . 26
      ↑
      └──── Decimal point in answer is lined up under
            decimal points in problem.
```
Step 3

(b) 5.897 + 4.632 + 12.174

Write the numbers in columns with the decimal points lined up. Then add.

```
   11   21
    5 . 897
    4 . 632
 + 12 . 174
   ─────────
   22 . 703
       ↑
       └──── Decimal points are lined up.
```

Work Problem **1** *at the Side.* ▶

In Example 1(a) above, both numbers had *two* decimal places (two digits to the right of the decimal point). In Example 1(b), all the numbers had *three decimal places* (three digits to the right of the decimal point). That made it easy to add tenths to tenths, hundredths to hundredths, and so on.

1 Find each sum.

(a) 2.86 + 7.09

(b) 13.761 + 8.325

(c) 0.319 + 56.007 + 8.252

(d) 39.4 + 0.4 + 177.2

ANSWERS

1. (a) 9.95 **(b)** 22.086 **(c)** 64.578
(d) 217.0

If the numbers of decimal places do *not* match, you can write in zeros as placeholders to make them match. This is shown in Example 2 below.

2 Find each sum.

(a) $6.54 + 9.8$

EXAMPLE 2   **Writing Zeros as Placeholders before Adding**

Find each sum.

(a) $7.3 + 0.85$

There are two decimal places in 0.85 (tenths and hundredths), so write a 0 in the hundredths place in 7.3 so that it has two decimal places also.

$$\begin{array}{r} 7.30 \\ + \ 0.85 \\ \hline 8.15 \end{array}$$ ← One 0 is written in.

7.30 is equivalent to 7.3 because

$7\dfrac{30}{100}$ in lowest terms is $7\dfrac{3}{10}$

(b) $0.831 + 222.2 + 10$

(b) $6.42 + 9 + 2.576$

Write in zeros so that all the addends have three decimal places. Notice how the whole number 9 is written with the decimal point on the *right* side. (If you put the decimal point on the *left* side of the 9, you would turn it into the decimal fraction 0.9.)

Write the decimal point on the *right* side of the 9.

$$\begin{array}{r} 6.420 \\ 9.000 \\ + \ 2.576 \\ \hline 17.996 \end{array}$$

← One 0 is written in.
← 9 is a whole number; decimal point and three zeros are written in.
← No zeros are needed.

Note

Writing zeros to the right of a *decimal* number does *not* change the value of the number, as shown in Example 2(a) above.

(c) $8.64 + 39.115 + 3.0076$

◀ *Work Problem* **2** *at the Side.*

EXAMPLE 3   **Subtracting Decimal Numbers**

Find each difference.

(a) 15.82 from 28.93

Step 1

$$\begin{array}{r} 28.93 \\ - \ 15.82 \end{array}$$

Line up decimal points. Then you will be subtracting hundredths from hundredths and tenths from tenths.

(d) $5 + 429.823 + 0.76$

Step 2

$$\begin{array}{r} 28.93 \\ - \ 15.82 \\ \hline 13 \ 11 \end{array}$$

Both numbers have two decimal places; no need to write in zeros.
Subtract as if they were whole numbers.

Step 3

$$\begin{array}{r} 28.93 \\ - \ 15.82 \\ \hline 13.11 \end{array}$$

Decimal point in answer is lined up.

Continued on Next Page

ANSWERS

2. (a) 16.34 **(b)** 233.031 **(c)** 50.7626
   (d) 435.583

(b) 146.35 minus 58.98

Regrouping is needed here.

⎯⎯ Line up decimal points.

$$
\begin{array}{r}
{\scriptstyle 0\ \ 13\ \ 15\ \ \ 12\ \ 15} \\
\not{1}\ \not{4}\ \not{6}\ .\ \not{3}\ \not{5} \\
-\ \ 5\ \ 8\ .\ 9\ \ 8 \\
\hline
8\ \ 7\ .\ 3\ \ 7
\end{array}
$$

Work Problem **3** *at the Side.* ▶

⎯⎯⎯⎯⎯⎯⎯⎯⎯⎯⎯⎯⎯⎯⎯

EXAMPLE 4 **Writing Zeros as Placeholders before Subtracting**

Find each difference.

(a) 16.5 from 28.362

Use the same steps as in Example 3 above. Remember to write in zeros so both numbers have three decimal places.

⎯⎯ Line up decimal points.

16.500 is equivalent to 16.5

$$
\begin{array}{r}
28.362 \\
-\ 16.500 \quad \leftarrow \text{Write two zeros.} \\
\hline
11.862 \quad \leftarrow \text{Subtract as usual.}
\end{array}
$$

(b) 59.7 − 38.914

$$
\begin{array}{r}
59.700 \quad \leftarrow \text{Write two zeros.} \\
-\ 38.914 \\
\hline
20.786 \quad \leftarrow \text{Subtract as usual.}
\end{array}
$$

(c) 12 less 5.83

12.00 is equivalent to 12

$$
\begin{array}{r}
12.00 \quad \leftarrow \text{Write a decimal point and two zeros.} \\
-\ 5.83 \\
\hline
6.17 \quad \leftarrow \text{Subtract as usual.}
\end{array}
$$

Work Problem **4** *at the Side.* ▶

⎯⎯⎯⎯⎯⎯⎯⎯⎯⎯⎯⎯⎯⎯⎯

🔲 **Calculator Tip** If you are *adding* decimal numbers, you can enter them in any order on your calculator. Try these; jot down the answers.

9.82 ⊕ 1.86 ⊜ ⎯⎯⎯⎯⎯   1.86 ⊕ 9.82 ⊜ ⎯⎯⎯⎯⎯

The answers are the same because addition is *commutative* (see **Section 1.3**). But subtraction is *not* commutative. It *does* matter which number you enter first. Try these:

9.82 ⊖ 1.86 ⊜ ⎯⎯⎯⎯⎯   1.86 ⊖ 9.82 ⊜ ⎯⎯⎯⎯⎯

The answers are 7.96 and −7.96. As you know, positive numbers are *greater* than 0, but negative numbers are *less* than 0. So it is important to do subtraction in the correct order, particularly if it is in your checkbook!

OBJECTIVE 2 Add and subtract negative decimals. The rules that you used to add integers in **Section 3.2** will also work for positive and negative decimal numbers.

⎯⎯⎯⎯⎯⎯⎯⎯⎯⎯⎯⎯⎯⎯⎯

Adding Signed Numbers

To add two numbers with the *same* sign, add the absolute values of the numbers. Use the common sign as the sign of the sum.

To add two numbers with *unlike* signs, subtract the smaller absolute value from the larger absolute value. Use the sign of the number with the larger absolute value as the sign of the sum.

---

3 Find each difference.

(a) 22.7 from 72.9

(b) 6.425 from 11.813

(c) $20.15 − $19.67

4 Find each difference.

(a) 18.651 from 25.3

(b) 5.816 − 4.98

(c) 40 less 3.66

(d) 1 − 0.325

ANSWERS

3. (a) 50.2 **(b)** 5.388 **(c)** $0.48
4. (a) 6.649 **(b)** 0.836 **(c)** 36.34
 (d) 0.675

5 Find each sum.

(a) $13.245 + (-18)$

(b) $-0.7 + (-0.33)$

(c) $-6.02 + 100.5$

EXAMPLE 5 **Adding Positive and Negative Decimal Numbers**

Find each sum.

(a) $-3.7 + (-16)$

Both addends are negative, so the sum will be negative. To begin, $|-3.7|$ is 3.7 and $|-16|$ is 16. Then add the absolute values.

$$\begin{array}{r} 3.7 \\ + \; 16.\mathbf{0} \leftarrow \text{Write a decimal point and one 0} \\ \hline 19.7 \end{array}$$

$$-3.7 + (-16) = -19.7$$

Both negative   Negative sum

Note

In **Chapters 3–5,** the negative sign was **red** to help you distinguish it from the subtraction symbol. From now on it will be **black.** We will continue to write parentheses around negative numbers when the negative sign might be confused with other symbols. Thus in part (a) above,

$$-3.7 + (-16) \quad \text{means} \quad \text{negative } 3.7 \quad \text{plus} \quad \text{negative } 16$$

(b) $-5.23 + 0.792$

The addends have different signs. To begin, $|-5.23|$ is 5.23 and $|0.792|$ is 0.792. Then subtract the smaller absolute value from the larger.

$$\begin{array}{r} 5.23\mathbf{0} \leftarrow \text{Write one 0} \\ - \; 0.792 \\ \hline 4.438 \end{array}$$

$$-5.23 + 0.792 = -4.438$$

Number with larger absolute value is negative.   Answer is negative.

◀ *Work Problem* **5** *at the Side.*

In **Section 3.3** you rewrote subtraction of integers as addition of the first number to the opposite of the second number. This same strategy works with positive and negative decimal numbers.

EXAMPLE 6 **Subtracting Positive and Negative Decimal Numbers**

Find each difference.

(a) $4.3 - 12.73$

Rewrite subtraction as adding the opposite.

$$4.3 - 12.73 \qquad \text{The opposite of 12.73 is}$$
$$\downarrow \quad \downarrow \qquad \qquad -12.73$$
$$4.3 + (-12.73)$$

-12.73 has the larger absolute value and is negative, so the answer will be negative.

$$4.3 + (-12.73) = -8.43 \qquad \text{Subtract the absolute values:}$$
$$\begin{array}{r} 12.73 \\ - \; 4.30 \\ \hline 8.43 \end{array}$$

Answer is negative.

Continued on Next Page

(b) $-3.65 - (-4.8)$

Rewrite subtraction as adding the opposite.

$$-3.65 - (-4.8) \qquad \text{The opposite of } -4.8 \text{ is } 4.8$$
$$\qquad\quad \downarrow \quad \downarrow$$
$$-3.65 + 4.8$$

4.8 has the larger absolute value and is positive, so the answer will be positive.

$$-3.65 + 4.8 = 1.15 \qquad \text{Subtract the absolute values:}$$
$$\qquad\qquad \uparrow \qquad\qquad\qquad 4.80$$
$$\qquad \text{Answer is} \qquad\quad -3.65$$
$$\qquad \text{positive.} \qquad\qquad \overline{1.15}$$

(c) $14.2 - (1.69 + 0.48)$ Work inside parentheses first.

$14.2 - \quad (2.17)$ Change subtraction to adding the opposite.

$\underbrace{14.2 + \quad (-2.17)}$ 14.2 has the larger absolute value and is positive,
so the answer will be positive.

$\qquad 12.03$

Work Problem **6** *at the Side.* ▶

OBJECTIVE 3 Estimate the answer when adding or subtracting decimals. A common error when working decimal problems by hand is to misplace the decimal point in the answer. Or, when using a calculator, you may accidentally press the wrong key. Using *front end rounding* to estimate the answer will help you avoid these mistakes. Start by rounding each number to the highest possible place (as you did in **Section 3.4**). Here are several examples. Notice that in the rounded numbers, only the leftmost digit is something other than 0.

3.25	rounds to	3	6.812	rounds to	7
532.6	rounds to	500	26.397	rounds to	30
7094.2	rounds to	7000	351.24	rounds to	400

EXAMPLE 7 Estimating Decimal Answers

First, use front end rounding to round each number. Then add or subtract the rounded numbers to get an estimated answer. Finally, find the exact answer.

(a) Find the sum of 194.2 and 6.825

$$
\begin{array}{ccc}
\textit{Estimate:} & & \textit{Exact:} \\
200 \;\xleftarrow{\text{Rounds to}} & & 194.200 \\
\underline{+\quad 7} \;\xleftarrow{\text{Rounds to}} & & \underline{+\quad 6.825} \\
207 & & 201.025
\end{array}
$$

The estimate goes out to the hundreds place (three places to the *left* of the decimal point), and so does the exact answer. Therefore, the decimal point is probably in the correct place in the exact answer.

(b) Subtract $13.78 from $69.42

$$
\begin{array}{ccc}
\textit{Estimate:} & & \textit{Exact:} \\
\$70 \;\xleftarrow{\text{Rounds to}} & & \$69.42 \\
\underline{-\;10} \;\xleftarrow{\text{Rounds to}} & & \underline{-\;13.78} \\
\$60 & & \$55.64
\end{array}
$$
← Exact answer is close to estimate, so it is probably correct.

Continued on Next Page

---

6 Find each difference.

(a) $-0.37 - (-6)$

(b) $5.8 - 10.03$

(c) $-312.72 - 65.7$

(d) $0.8 - (6 - 7.2)$

7   Use front end rounding to estimate each answer. Then find the exact answer.

(a) $2.83 + 5.009 + 76.1$

Estimate:

Exact:

(b) $19.28 less $1.53

Estimate:

Exact:

(c) $11.365 - 38$

Estimate:

Exact:

(d) $-214.6 + 300.72$

Estimate:

Exact:

(c) $-1.861 - 7.3$

Rewrite subtraction as adding the opposite. Then use front end rounding to get an estimated answer.

$$-1.861 \quad - \quad 7.3$$
$$\downarrow \qquad\qquad \downarrow$$
$$-1.861 \quad + \quad (-7.3)$$
$$\downarrow \qquad\qquad \downarrow$$
Rounded $\quad -2 \quad + \quad (-7) \quad = -9 \leftarrow$ Estimate

To find the exact answer, add the absolute values.

$$1.861 \leftarrow \text{Absolute value of } -1.861$$
$$\underline{+\ 7.300} \leftarrow \text{Absolute value of } -7.3 \text{ with two zeros written in}$$
$$9.161$$

The answer will be negative because both numbers are negative.

$$-1.861 + (-7.3) = -9.161 \leftarrow \text{Exact}$$

The exact answer of -9.161 is reasonable because it is close to the estimated answer of -9.

◀ *Work Problem* **7** *at the Side.*

ANSWERS

7. (a) *Estimate:* $3 + 5 + 80 = 88$;
     Exact: 83.939
   (b) *Estimate:* $20 - $2 = 18;
     Exact: 17.75
   (c) *Estimate:* $10 + (-40) = -30$;
     Exact: -26.635
   (d) *Estimate:* $-200 + 300 = 100$;
     Exact: 86.12

Find each sum. See Examples 1 and 2.

1. $\begin{array}{r} 5.69 \\ 0.24 \\ + 11.79 \\ \hline \end{array}$ **2.** $\begin{array}{r} 372.1 \\ 33.7 \\ + 42.3 \\ \hline \end{array}$ **3.** $\begin{array}{r} 0.38 \\ 7 \\ + 4.6 \\ \hline \end{array}$ **4.** $\begin{array}{r} 3.7 \\ 0.812 \\ + 55 \\ \hline \end{array}$

5. $14.23 + 8 + 74.63 + 18.715 + 0.286$ **6.** $197.4 + 0.72 + 17.43 + 25 + 1.4$

7. $27.65 + 18.714 + 9.749 + 3.21$ **8.** $58.546 + 19.2 + 8.735 + 14.58$

9. Explain and correct
the error that a student
made when he added
$0.72 + 6 + 39.5$ this way:
$\begin{array}{r} 0.72 \\ 6 \\ + 39.50 \\ \hline 40.28 \end{array}$

10. Explain and correct the
error that a student made
when she added
$7.21 + 65 + 13.15$ this way:
$\begin{array}{r} 7.21 \\ .65 \\ + 13.15 \\ \hline 21.01 \end{array}$

11. Show why 0.3 is equivalent to 0.3000.

12. Explain why 7 may be written as 7.0 but not as 0.7.

Find each difference. See Examples 3 and 4.

13. $90.5 - 0.8$ **14.** $303.72 - 0.68$ **15.** 0.4 less 0.291   **16.** 0.35 less 0.088

17. 6 minus 5.09   **18.** 80 minus 16.3   **19.** Subtract 8.339 from 15   **20.** Subtract 0.08 from 44

21. Explain and correct
the error that a student
made when he subtracted
7.45 from 15.32 this way:
$\begin{array}{r} 7.45 \\ - 15.32 \\ \hline 12.13 \end{array}$

22. Explain the difference between saying
"subtract 2.9 from 8" and saying
"2.9 minus 8."

This drawing of a human skeleton shows the average length of the longest bones, in inches. Use the drawing to answer Exercises 23–26.

7th rib
9.45 in.

Humerus 14.35 in.

8th rib
9.06 in.

Radius 10.4 in.

Ulna 11.1 in.

Femur 19.88 in.

Tibia 16.94 in.

Fibula 15.94 in.

Source: *The Top 10 of Everything.*

23. (a) What is the combined length of the humerus and radius bones?

(b) What is the difference in the lengths of these two bones?

24. (a) What is the total length of the femur and tibia bones?

(b) How much longer is the femur than the tibia?

25. (a) Find the sum of the lengths of the humerus, ulna, femur, and tibia.

(b) How much shorter is the 8th rib than the 7th rib?

26. (a) What is the difference in the lengths of the two bones in the lower arm?

(b) What is the difference in the lengths of the two bones in the lower leg?

Find each sum or difference. See Examples 5 and 6.

27. $24.008 + (-0.995)$

28. $0.77 - 3.06$

29. $-6.05 + (-39.7)$

30. $-6.409 + 8.224$

31. $0.9 - 7.59$

32. $-489.7 - 38$

33. $-2 - 4.99$

34. $2.068 - (-32.7)$

35. $-5.009 + 0.73$

36. $-0.33 - 65$

37. $-1.7035 - (5 - 6.7)$

38. $60 + (-0.9345 + 1.4)$

39. $8000 - (8002.63 - 8)$

40. $-210 - (-0.7306 + 0.5)$

Use front end rounding to estimate each answer. Then use your estimate to select the correct exact answer. Circle your choice. See Example 7.

41. $18 - 11.725$

Estimate:

Exact: 29.725   6.275   −11.545

42. $20 - 1.37$

Estimate:

Exact: −21.37   −1.863   18.63

43. $-6.5 + 0.7$

Estimate:

Exact: −5.8   7.2   −0.58

44. $-9.67 + 3.09$

Estimate:

Exact: −12.76   −6.58   6.58

45. $-42.671 - 194.9$

Estimate:

Exact: −152.229   −23.7571
−237.571

46. $-803.25 - 0.6$

Estimate:

Exact: −803.85   80.385
803.85

47. $8.4 - (-50.83)$

Estimate:

Exact: −42.43   −59.23   59.23

48. $14.98 - (-6.506)$

Estimate:

Exact: −8.474   21.486   8.004

Use front end rounding to estimate each sum or difference. Then find the exact answer to each application problem. Use the information in the table for Exercises 49–52.

INTERNET USERS IN SELECTED COUNTRIES

Country	Number of Users
United States	197.8 million
China	119.5 million
Japan	86.3 million
India	50.6 million
South Korea	34 million
Canada	21.9 million
Mexico	16.9 million
World total	**1081.1 million**

Source: Computer Industry Almanac.

49. How many fewer Internet users are there in Canada compared to South Korea?

Estimate:

Exact:

50. How many more users are there in China compared to India?

Estimate:

Exact:

51. How many Internet users are there in all the countries listed in the table?

Estimate:

Exact:

52. Using the answer from Exercise 51, calculate the number of world-wide Internet users in countries other than the ones in the table.

Estimate:

Exact:

53. The tallest known land mammal is a prehistoric ancestor of the rhino, measuring 6.4 m. Compare the rhino's height to the combined heights of these NBA basketball stars: Kevin Garnett at 2.1 m, Allen Iverson at 1.83 m, and Shaquille O'Neal at 2.16 m. Is their combined height greater or less than the prehistoric rhino's? By how much? (*Source:* www.NBA.com/players)

6.4 m

Estimate:

Exact:

54. Sammy works in a veterinarian's office. He weighed two kittens. One was 3.9 ounces and the other was 4.05 ounces. What was the difference in the weight of the two kittens?

Estimate:

Exact:

55. Steven One Feather gave the cashier a $20 bill to pay for $9.12 worth of groceries. How much change did he get?

Estimate:

Exact:

56. The cost of Julie's tennis racket, with tax, was $41.09. She gave the clerk two $20 bills and a $10 bill. What amount of change did Julie receive?

Estimate:

Exact:

When buying fishing equipment, the father and daughter on the first page of this chapter brought along the store's sale insert from the Sunday paper. Use the information below on sale prices to answer Exercises 57–60. **When estimating, round to the nearest whole number.**

☆ **Fishing Opener Sale** ☆
Catch your limit of savings!

Bobbers 3 for 87¢

Environmentally safe
tin split shot
$2.07

Leaded split shot
94¢

8-pound test fishing line
regular $4.84
invisible $7.47   No-
fluorescent $5.14   See
                     Line

Tackle boxes

Two trays   Three trays
$7.96 $9.96

Spinning reels: $9.88, $12.54, $18.84, $24.96
Spinning rods: $9.97, $18.97, $22.96, $28.94

Source: Wal-Mart.

57. What is the difference in price between the fluorescent and regular fishing line?

Estimate:

Exact:

58. How much more does the least expensive spinning rod cost than the least expensive spinning reel?

Estimate:

Exact:

59. Find the total cost of the second-highest-priced spinning reel, two packages of tin split shot, and a three-tray tackle box. Sales tax for all the items is $2.31.

Estimate:

Exact:

60. The father bought three bobbers on sale. He also bought some SPF15 sunscreen for $7.53 and a flotation vest for $44.96. Sales tax was $3.74. How much did he spend in all?

Estimate:

Exact:

Olivia Sanchez kept track of her expenses for one month. Use her list to answer Exercises 61–64.

61. What were Olivia's total expenses for the month?

62. How much did Olivia pay for her cell phone, cable TV, and Internet access?

63. What was the difference in the amounts spent for groceries and for the car payment?

64. How much more did Olivia spend on rent than on all her car expenses?

Monthly Expenses	
Rent	$994
Car payment	$190.78
Car repairs, gas	$205
Cable TV	$39.95
Internet access	$19.95
Electricity	$40.80
Cell phone	$57.32
Groceries	$186.81
Entertainment	$97.75
Clothing, laundry	$107

Find the length of the dashed line in each rectangle or circle.

65.

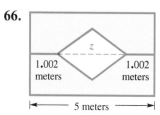

0.91 cm   0.7 cm b

3 cm

66.

1.002 meters   1.002 meters

z

5 meters

67.

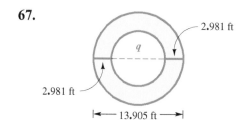

2.981 ft

q

2.981 ft

13.905 ft

6.4 ▶▶▶ Multiplying Signed Decimal Numbers

OBJECTIVE 1 Multiply positive and negative decimals. The decimals 0.3 and 0.07 can be multiplied by writing them as fractions.

$$0.3 \times 0.07 = \frac{3}{10} \times \frac{7}{100} = \frac{3 \times 7}{10 \times 100} = \frac{21}{1000} = 0.021$$

1 decimal place + 2 decimal places → 3 decimal places

Can you see a way to multiply decimals without writing them as fractions? Try these steps. Remember that each number in a multiplication problem is called a *factor,* and the answer is called the *product.*

OBJECTIVES

1 Multiply positive and negative decimals.

2 Estimate the answer when multiplying decimals.

Multiplying Two Decimal Numbers

Step 1 Multiply the factors (the numbers being multiplied) as if they were whole numbers.

Step 2 Find the *total* number of decimal places in *both* factors.

Step 3 Write the decimal point in the product (the answer) so it has the same number of decimal places as the total from Step 2. You may need to write in extra zeros on the left side of the product in order to get the correct number of decimal places.

Step 4 If two factors have the *same sign,* the product is *positive.* If two factors have *different signs,* the product is *negative.*

Note

When multiplying decimals, you do ***not*** need to line up decimal points. (You ***do*** need to line up decimal points when adding or subtracting.)

EXAMPLE 1 **Multiplying Decimal Numbers**

Find the product of 8.34 and (−4.2)

Step 1 Multiply the numbers as if they were whole numbers.

$$
\begin{array}{r}
8.34 \\
\times\ 4.2 \\
\hline
1668 \\
3336 \\
\hline
35028
\end{array}
$$

You do *not* have to line up decimal points when multiplying.

Step 2 Count the total number of decimal places in both factors.

$$
\begin{array}{r}
8.34 \leftarrow 2 \text{ decimal places} \\
\times\ 4.2 \leftarrow 1 \text{ decimal place} \\
\hline
1668 \qquad 3 \text{ total decimal places} \\
3336 \\
\hline
35028
\end{array}
$$

Continued on Next Page

1 Find each product.

(a) $-2.6\,(0.4)$

(b) $(45.2)\,(0.25)$

(c)
$$
\begin{array}{r}
0.104 \quad \leftarrow \text{3 decimal places} \\
\times \qquad 7 \quad \leftarrow \text{0 decimal places} \\
\hline
\qquad \leftarrow \text{3 decimal places} \\
\text{in the product}
\end{array}
$$

(d) $(-3.18)^2$

Hint: Recall that squaring a number means multiplying the number by itself, so this is $(-3.18)\,(-3.18)$.

2 Find each product.

(a) $0.04\,(-0.09)$

(b) $(0.2)\,(0.008)$

(c) $(-0.063)\,(-0.04)$

(d) $(0.003)^2$

Step 3 Count over 3 places in the product and write the decimal point. Count from *right to left*.

$$
\begin{array}{r}
8.3\,4 \quad \leftarrow \text{2 decimal places} \\
\times \quad 4.2 \quad \leftarrow \text{1 decimal place} \\
\hline
1\,6\,6\,8 \quad \text{3 total decimal places} \\
3\,3\,3\,6 \quad\ \\
\hline
3\,5.0\,2\,8 \quad \leftarrow \text{3 decimal places in product}
\end{array}
$$

Count over 3 places from right to left to position the decimal point.

Step 4 The factors have *different* signs, so the product is *negative:*
8.34 times (-4.2) is -35.028

◀ *Work Problem* **1** *at the Side.*

<u>EXAMPLE 2</u> **Writing Zeros as Placeholders in the Product**

Find the product: $(-0.042)\,(-0.03)$

Start by multiplying, then count decimal places.

$$
\begin{array}{r}
0.0\,4\,2 \quad \leftarrow \text{3 decimal places} \\
\times \quad 0.0\,3 \quad \leftarrow \text{2 decimal places} \\
\hline
1\,2\,6 \quad \leftarrow \text{5 decimal places needed in product}
\end{array}
$$

After multiplying, the answer has only three decimal places, but five are needed. So write two zeros on the *left* side of the answer.

$$
\begin{array}{r}
0.0\,4\,2 \\
\times \quad 0.0\,3 \\
\hline
0\,0\,1\,2\,6
\end{array}
\qquad
\begin{array}{r}
0.0\,4\,2 \quad \leftarrow \text{3 decimal places} \\
\times \quad 0.0\,3 \quad \leftarrow \text{2 decimal places} \\
\hline
.0\,0\,1\,2\,6 \quad \leftarrow \text{5 decimal places}
\end{array}
$$

Write two zeros on *left* side of answer.   Now count over 5 places and write in the decimal point.

The final product is 0.00126, which has five decimal places. The product is *positive* because the factors have the *same* sign (both factors are negative).

◀ *Work Problem* **2** *at the Side.*

▦ **Calculator Tip** When working with money amounts, you may need to write a 0 in your answer. For example, try multiplying $\$3.54 \times 5$ on your calculator. Write down the result.

$$3.54 \ \textcircled{\times}\ 5 \ \textcircled{=} \ \underline{\qquad}$$

Notice that the result is 17.7, which is *not* the way to write a money amount. You have to write the 0 in the hundredths place: $\$17.70$ is correct. The calculator does not show the "extra" 0 because:

$$17.70 \text{ or } 17\frac{70}{100} \quad \text{simplifies to} \quad 17\frac{7}{10} \text{ or } 17.7$$

So keep an eye on your calculator—it doesn't know when you're working with money amounts.

ANSWERS

1. **(a)** -1.04 **(b)** 11.300 or 11.3 **(c)** 0.728
   (d) 10.1124
2. **(a)** -0.0036 **(b)** 0.0016 **(c)** 0.00252
   (d) 0.000009

OBJECTIVE 2 Estimate the answer when multiplying decimals.
If you are doing multiplication problems by hand, estimating the answer helps you check that the decimal point is in the right place. When you are using a calculator, estimating helps you catch an error like pressing the ⊝ key instead of the ⊗ key.

EXAMPLE 3 Estimating before Multiplying

First, use front end rounding to estimate (76.34) (12.5). Then find the exact answer.

Estimate: *Exact:*

```
    80  ←Rounds to    7 6.3 4  ← 2 decimal places
  × 10  ←Rounds to  ×   1 2.5  ← 1 decimal place
   800               3 8 1 7 0    3 decimal places are
                     1 5 2 6 8      in the product.
                     7 6 3 4
                     9 5 4.2 5 0
```

Both the estimate and the exact answer go out to the hundreds place, so the decimal point in 954.250 is probably in the correct place.

Work Problem **3** *at the Side.* ▶

3 First, use front end rounding to estimate the answer. Then find the exact answer.

(a) (11.62) (4.01)

Estimate:

Exact:

(b) (−5.986) (−33)

Estimate:

Exact:

(c) 8 ($4.35)

Estimate:

Exact:

(d) 58.6 (−17.4)

Estimate:

Exact:

ANSWERS

3. **(a)** *Estimate:* (10) (4) = 40;
   Exact: 46.5962
   (b) *Estimate:* (−6) (−30) = 180;
   Exact: 197.538
   (c) *Estimate:* 8 ($4) = $32;
   Exact: $34.80
   (d) *Estimate:* 60 (−20) = −1200;
   Exact: −1019.64

Math in the Media

Many Americans complain about being "too busy." Yet, according to surveys, they find time to watch television. Use the information in the table to answer the questions on TV viewing.

Time Spent by American Men Watching TV
2.5 hours on an average weekday
3.59 hours on an average weekend day
Time Spent by American Women Watching TV
2.22 hours on an average weekday
2.7 hours on an average weekend day

Sources: American Time Use Survey, Bureau of Labor Statistics and Americans' Use of Time Project.

1. **(a)** How many more hours do men spend than women watching TV on an average weekend day? How many minutes is this, to the nearest whole minute?

   (b) Who spends less time watching TV on an average weekday, men or women? How much less time in hours? How many minutes is this, to the nearest whole minute?

2. **(a)** How many hours would a man spend watching TV during one week with five weekdays and two weekend days? How many hours in one year, to the nearest whole hour? (Use 1 year = 52 weeks.)

   (b) How many more or fewer hours would a woman spend than a man watching TV in the same week as part (a)? How many more or fewer hours in one year, to the nearest whole hour?

3. **(a)** How many hours do you spend watching TV on an average weekday? On an average weekend day?

   (b) Using your answers from part (a), how many hours do you watch TV during an average week? During one year?

6.4 ▶▶▶ **Exercises**

Find each product. See Example 1.

1. 0.042
    $\times$ 3.2

2. 0.571
    $\times$ 2.9

3. $-21.5\,(7.4)$

4. $-85.4\,(-3.5)$

5. $(-23.4)\,(-0.66)$

6. $0.896\,(-0.7)$

7. $51.88
    $\times$ 665

8. $736.75
    $\times$ 118

Use the fact that $(72)\,(6) = 432$ *to solve Exercises 9–16 by simply counting decimal places and writing the decimal point in the correct location. Be sure to indicate the sign of the product.*

9. $72\,(-0.6) =$ 4 3 2

10. $7.2\,(-6) =$ 4 3 2

11. $(7.2)\,(0.06) =$ 4 3 2

12. $(0.72)\,(0.6) =$ 4 3 2

13. $-0.72\,(-0.06) =$ 4 3 2

14. $-72\,(-0.0006) =$ 4 3 2

15. $(0.0072)\,(0.6) =$ 4 3 2

16. $(0.072)\,(0.006) =$ 4 3 2

Find each product. See Example 2.

17. $(0.006)\,(0.0052)$

18. $(0.0052)\,(0.009)$

19. $(-0.003)^2$

20. $(0.0004)^2$

Relating Concepts (Exercises 21–22) For Individual or Group Work

*Look for patterns as you **work Exercises 21 and 22 in order.***

21. Do these multiplications:

$(5.96)\,(10) =$ _____ $(3.2)\,(10) =$ _____
$(0.476)\,(10) =$ _____ $(80.35)\,(10) =$ _____
$(722.6)\,(10) =$ _____ $(0.9)\,(10) =$ _____

What pattern do you see? Write a "rule" for multiplying by 10. What do you think the rule is for multiplying by 100? by 1000? Write the rules and try them out on the numbers above.

22. Do these multiplications:

$(59.6)\,(0.1) =$ _____ $(3.2)\,(0.1) =$ _____
$(0.476)\,(0.1) =$ _____ $(80.35)\,(0.1) =$ _____
$(65)\,(0.1) =$ _____ $(523)\,(0.1) =$ _____

What pattern do you see? Write a "rule" for multiplying by 0.1. What do you think the rule is for multiplying by 0.01? by 0.001? Write the rules and try them out on the numbers above.

First, use front end rounding to estimate the answer. Then find the exact answer.
See Example 3.

23. Estimate: Exact:
          Rounds to   39.6
    ×   Rounds to   × 4.8
    ‾‾‾‾‾‾‾‾‾‾‾   ‾‾‾‾‾‾‾‾

24. Estimate: Exact:
                          18.7
    ×   × 2.3
    ‾‾‾‾‾‾   ‾‾‾‾‾‾‾‾

25. Estimate: Exact:
                          37.1
    ×   × 42
    ‾‾‾‾‾‾   ‾‾‾‾‾‾‾‾

26. Estimate: Exact:
                          5.08
    ×   × 71
    ‾‾‾‾‾‾   ‾‾‾‾‾‾‾‾

27. Estimate: Exact:
                          6.53
    ×   × 4.6
    ‾‾‾‾‾‾   ‾‾‾‾‾‾‾‾

28. Estimate: Exact:
                          7.51
    ×   × 8.2
    ‾‾‾‾‾‾   ‾‾‾‾‾‾‾‾

29. Estimate: Exact:
                          2.809
    ×   × 6.85
    ‾‾‾‾‾‾   ‾‾‾‾‾‾‾‾

30. Estimate: Exact:
                          73.52
    ×   × 22.34
    ‾‾‾‾‾‾   ‾‾‾‾‾‾‾‾

Even with most of the problem missing, you can tell whether or not these answers are
reasonable. Circle reasonable *or* unreasonable. *If the answer is unreasonable, move the*
decimal point or insert a decimal point to make the answer reasonable.

31. How much was his car payment? $28.90

reasonable

unreasonable, should be _____

32. How many hours did she work today? 25 hours

reasonable

unreasonable, should be _____

33. How tall is her son? 60.5 inches

reasonable

unreasonable, should be _____

34. How much does he pay for rent now? $6.92

reasonable

unreasonable, should be _____

35. What is the price of one gallon of milk? $419

reasonable

unreasonable, should be _____

36. How long is the living room? 16.8 feet

reasonable

unreasonable, should be _____

37. How much did the baby weigh? 0.095 pound

reasonable

unreasonable, should be _____

38. What was the sale price of the jacket? $1.49

reasonable

unreasonable, should be _____

Solve each application problem. Round money answers to the nearest cent when necessary.

39. LaTasha worked 50.5 hours over the last two weeks. She earns $18.73 per hour. How much did she make?

40. Michael's time card shows 42.2 hours at $10.03 per hour. What are his earnings?

41. Sid needs a piece of canvas material 0.6 meter in length to make a carry-all bag that fits on his wheelchair. If canvas is $4.09 per meter, how much will Sid spend? (*Note:* $4.09 *per* meter means $4.09 for *one* meter.)

42. How much will Mrs. Nguyen pay for 3.5 yards of lace trim that costs $0.87 per yard?

43. Michelle filled the tank of her SUV with regular unleaded gas. Use the information shown on the pump to find how much she paid for gas.

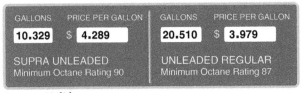

GALLONS	PRICE PER GALLON	GALLONS	PRICE PER GALLON
10.329	$ 4.289	20.510	$ 3.979
SUPRA UNLEADED		UNLEADED REGULAR	
Minimum Octane Rating 90		Minimum Octane Rating 87	

Source: Holiday.

44. Ground beef and chicken legs are on sale. Juma bought 1.7 pounds of legs. Use the information in the ad to find the amount she paid.

BIG ONE FOODS   Sale

Ground Beef $2.09 per pound   For juicy burgers

Chicken Legs $0.98 per pound

PRICES GOOD THROUGH SUNDAY!

45. Ms. Rolack is a real estate broker who helps people sell their homes. Her fee is 0.07 times the price of the home. What was her fee for selling a $289,500 home?

46. Manny Ramirez of the Boston Red Sox had a batting average of 0.296 in the 2007 season. He went to bat 483 times. How many hits did he make? (*Hint:* Multiply the number of times at bat by his batting average.) Round to the nearest whole number. (*Source: World Almanac.*)

Paper money in the United States has not always been the same size. Shown below are the measurements of bills printed before 1929 and the measurements from 1929 on. Use this information to answer Exercises 47–50. Recall that perimeter is the total distance around the edges of a figure (see **Section 4.6***). The area of a rectangle is found by multiplying the length by the width (see* **Section 4.7***). (Source:* www.moneyfactory.com)

Before 1929

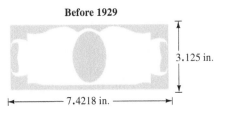

3.125 in.

7.4218 in.

From 1929 on

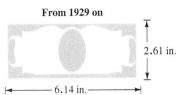

2.61 in.

6.14 in.

47. (a) Find the area of each bill, rounded to the nearest tenth.

(b) What is the difference in the rounded areas?

48. (a) Find the perimeter of each bill, to the nearest hundredth.

(b) How much less is the perimeter of today's bills than the bills printed before 1929?

49. The thickness of one piece of today's paper money is 0.0043 inch.

(a) If you had a pile of 100 bills, how high would it be?

(b) How high would a pile of 1000 bills be?

50. (a) Use your answers from Exercise 49 to find the number of bills in a pile that is 43 inches high.

(b) How much money would you have if the pile is all $20 bills?

51. Judy Lewis pays $38.96 per month for basic cable TV. The one-time installation fee was $49. How much will she pay for cable over two years? How much would she pay in two years for the deluxe cable package that costs $89.95 per month?

52. Chuck's car payment is $420.27 per month for four years. He also made a down payment of $5000 at the time he bought the car. How much will he pay altogether?

53. Paper for the copy machine at the library costs $0.015 per sheet. How much will the library pay for 5100 sheets?

54. A student group collected 2200 pounds of plastic as a fund-raiser. How much will they make if the recycling center pays $0.142 per pound?

55. Barry bought 16.5 meters of rope at $0.47 per meter and three meters of wire at $1.05 per meter. How much change did he get from three $5 bills?

56. Susan bought a 42-inch plasma HDTV that cost $1999.99. She paid $68.83 per month for 36 months. How much could she have saved by paying for the HDTV when she bought it?

Use the information below from the Look Smart mail order catalog to answer Exercises 57–60.

Knit Shirt Ordering Information				Total Price of Items (excluding monograms and gift boxes)	Shipping, Packing, and Handling
43–2A	short sleeved, solid colors	$14.75 each		$0–25.00	$3.50
43–2B	short sleeved, stripes	$16.75 each		$25.01–75.00	$5.95
43–3A	long sleeved, solid colors	$18.95 each		$75.01–125.00	$7.95
43–3B	long sleeved, stripes	$21.95 each		$125.01+	$9.95
XXL size, add $2 per shirt.					
Monogram, $4.95 each. Gift box, $5 each.				Shipping to each additional address, add $4.25.	

57. Find the total cost of ordering four long-sleeved, solid-color shirts and two short-sleeved, striped shirts, all in the XXL size, and all shipped to your home.

58. What is the total cost of eight long-sleeved shirts, five in solid colors and three striped? None of the shirts are the XXL size. Include the cost of shipping the solid shirts to your home and the striped shirts to your brother's home.

59. (a) What is the total cost, including shipping, of sending three short-sleeved, solid-color shirts, size M, with monograms, in a gift box to your aunt for her birthday?

(b) How much did the monograms, gift box, and shipping add to the cost of your gift?

60. (a) Suppose you order one of each type of shirt for yourself, adding a monogram on each of the solid-color shirts. At the same time, you order three long-sleeved striped shirts, in the XXL size, shipped to your dad in a gift box. Find the total cost of your order.

(b) What is the difference in total cost (excluding shipping) between the shirts for yourself and the gift for your dad?

6.5 ▶▶▶ Dividing Signed Decimal Numbers

There are two kinds of decimal division problems: those in which a decimal is divided by an integer, and those in which a number is divided by a decimal. First recall the parts of a division problem.

$$\text{Divisor} \rightarrow 2)\overline{16} \begin{array}{l} \leftarrow \text{Quotient} \\ \leftarrow \text{Dividend} \end{array} \qquad \overset{\text{Dividend}}{16} \div \overset{\text{Divisor}}{2} = \underset{\text{Quotient}}{8} \qquad \text{Dividend} \rightarrow \frac{16}{2} = 8 \\ \text{Divisor} \rightarrow \qquad \uparrow \text{Quotient}$$

OBJECTIVE 1 Divide a decimal by an integer. When the divisor is an integer, use these steps.

> **Dividing a Decimal Number by an Integer**
>
> *Step 1* Write the decimal point in the quotient (answer) directly above the decimal point in the dividend.
>
> *Step 2* Divide as if both numbers were whole numbers.
>
> *Step 3* If both numbers have the *same sign*, the quotient is *positive*. If they have *different signs*, the quotient is *negative*.

EXAMPLE 1 **Dividing Decimals by Integers**

Find each quotient. Check the quotients by multiplying.

(a) $21.93 \div (-3)$

Dividend ⌒   Divisor ↑

First consider $21.93 \div 3$.

$3)\overline{21.93}$

Step 1 Write the decimal point in the quotient directly above the decimal point in the dividend.

Decimal points lined up
$3)\overline{21.93}^{\,\cdot}$

Step 2 Divide as if the numbers were whole numbers.

Check by multiplying the quotient times the divisor.

$3)\overline{21.93}^{\;7.31}$

Check

$$\begin{array}{r} 7.31 \\ \times\ \ 3 \\ \hline 21.93 \end{array}$$

Matches, so 7.31 is correct.

Step 3 The quotient is -7.31 because the numbers have *different* signs.

$$21.93 \div (-3) = -7.31$$

Different signs ↑   ↑ Negative quotient

Different signs, negative quotient.

Continued on Next Page

1 Divide. Check the quotients by multiplying.

(a) $4\overline{)93.6}$

(b) $6\overline{)6.804}$

(c) $\dfrac{278.3}{11}$

(d) $-0.51835 \div 5$

(e) $-213.45 \div (-15)$

(b)

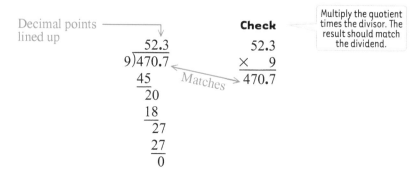

$9\overline{)470.7}$

Divisor ──┘ └── Dividend

Write the decimal point in the quotient directly above the decimal point in the dividend. Then divide as if they were whole numbers.

Decimal points lined up

$$\begin{array}{r} 52.3 \\ 9\overline{)470.7} \\ 45 \\ \hline 20 \\ 18 \\ \hline 27 \\ 27 \\ \hline 0 \end{array}$$

Matches

Check

Multiply the quotient times the divisor. The result should match the dividend.

$$\begin{array}{r} 52.3 \\ \times\quad 9 \\ \hline 470.7 \end{array}$$

The quotient is 52.3 and is *positive* because both numbers have the *same* sign.

◀ *Work Problem* **1** *at the Side.*

EXAMPLE 2 **Writing Extra Zeros to Complete a Division**

Divide 1.5 by 8. Use multiplying to check the quotient.

Keep dividing until the remainder is 0, or until the digits in the quotient begin to repeat in a pattern. In Example 1(b) above, you ended up with a remainder of 0. But sometimes you run out of digits in the dividend before that happens. If so, write extra zeros on the right side of the dividend so you can continue dividing.

$$\begin{array}{r} 0.1 \\ 8\overline{)1.5} \\ 8 \\ \hline 7 \end{array}$$

← All digits have been used.

← Remainder is not yet 0.

Write a 0 after the 5 in the dividend so you can continue dividing. Keep writing more zeros in the dividend if needed. Recall that writing zeros to the *right* of a decimal number does *not* change its value.

$$\begin{array}{r} 0.1\,8\,7\,5 \\ 8\overline{)1.5\,0\,0\,0} \\ 8 \\ \hline 7\,0 \\ 6\,4 \\ \hline 6\,0 \\ 5\,6 \\ \hline 4\,0 \\ 4\,0 \\ \hline 0 \end{array}$$

← Three zeros needed to complete the division

← Stop dividing when the remainder is 0.

Check

$$\begin{array}{r} 0.1875 \\ \times\qquad 8 \\ \hline 1.5000 \end{array}$$

Matches dividend, so 0.1875 is correct.

> **CAUTION**
> Notice that in decimals the dividend might *not* be the larger number. In Example 2 above, the dividend is 1.5, which is *smaller* than 8.

Continued on Next Page

▦ **Calculator Tip**   When *multiplying* numbers, you can enter them in any order because multiplication is commutative (see **Section 3.5**). But division is *not* commutative. It *does* matter which number you enter first. Try Example 2 on the previous page both ways; jot down your answers.

$$1.5 \;⊕\; 8 \;⊜\; \underline{\hspace{2cm}} \qquad 8 \;⊕\; 1.5 \;⊜\; \underline{\hspace{2cm}}$$

Notice that the first answer, 0.1875, matches the result from Example 2. But the second answer is much different: 5.333333333. Be careful to enter the dividend first.

Work Problem ② *at the Side.* ▶

In the next example the remainder is never 0, even if we keep dividing.

┌─ **EXAMPLE 3**   **Rounding a Decimal Quotient**

Divide 4.7 by 3. Round the quotient to the nearest thousandth.

Write extra zeros in the dividend so that you can continue dividing.

```
        1.5 6 6 6
     3)4.7 0 0 0   ← Three zeros added so far
       3 |
       ‾ ↓
       1 7 |
       1 5 ↓
       ‾ ‾
         2 0
         1 8 ↓
         ‾ ‾
           2 0
           1 8 ↓
           ‾ ‾
             2 0
             1 8
             ‾ ‾
               2   ← Remainder is still not 0.
```

Notice that the digit 6 in the quotient is repeating. It will continue to do so. The remainder will *never be 0*. There are two ways to show that an answer is a **repeating decimal** that goes on forever. You can write three dots after the answer, or you can write a bar above the digits that repeat (in this case, the 6).

$$\underbrace{1.5666\ldots}_{\text{Three dots}} \quad \text{or} \quad 1.5\overline{6} \;\; \substack{\leftarrow \text{Bar above} \\ \text{repeating digit}}$$

┌───┐
│ **CAUTION**   │
│ Do not use *both* the dots *and* the bar at the same time. Use three dots *or* the bar. │
└───┘

When repeating decimals occur, round the quotient according to the directions in the problem. In this example, to round to thousandths, divide out one *more* place, to ten-thousandths.

$$4.7 ÷ 3 = 1.5666\ldots \quad \text{rounds to} \quad 1.567 \;\; \boxed{\substack{\text{Nearest \textbf{thousandth} is} \\ \textbf{three} \text{ decimal places.}}}$$

Check the answer by multiplying 1.567 by 3. Because 1.567 is a rounded answer, the check will *not* give exactly 4.7, but it should be very close.

$$(1.567)\,(3) = 4.701 \;\; \substack{\leftarrow \text{Does not equal exactly 4.7} \\ \text{because 1.567 was rounded}}$$

Continued on Next Page

② Divide. Check the quotients by multiplying.

(a) $\dfrac{6.4}{5}$

(b) $30.87 ÷ (-14)$

(c) $\dfrac{-259.5}{-30}$

(d) $0.3 ÷ 8$

ANSWERS

2. (a) 1.28;
   Check (1.28) (5) = 6.40 or 6.4
 (b) −2.205;
   Check (−2.205) (−14) = 30.870
   or 30.87
 (c) 8.65;
   Check (8.65) (−30) = −259.50
   or −259.5
 (d) 0.0375;
   Check (0.0375) (8) = 0.3000 or 0.3

3 Divide. Round quotients to the nearest thousandth. If it is a repeating decimal, also write the answer using a bar. Check your answers by multiplying.

(a) $13\overline{)267.01}$

(b) $6\overline{)20.5}$

(c) $\dfrac{10.22}{9}$

(d) $16.15 \div 3$

(e) $116.3 \div 11$

> **CAUTION**
> When checking quotients that you've rounded, the check will *not* match the dividend exactly, but it should be very close.

◀ *Work Problem* **3** *at the Side.*

OBJECTIVE **2** **Divide a number by a decimal.** To divide by a *decimal* divisor, first change the divisor to a whole number. Then divide as before. To see how this is done, write the problem in fraction form. Here is an example.

$$1.2\overline{)6.36} \quad \text{can be written} \quad \frac{6.36}{1.2}$$

In **Section 4.1** you learned that multiplying the numerator and denominator by the same number gives an equivalent fraction. We want the divisor (1.2) to be a whole number. Multiplying by 10 will accomplish that.

$$\text{Decimal divisor} \rightarrow \frac{6.36}{1.2} = \frac{(6.36)\,(10)}{(1.2)\,(10)} = \frac{63.6}{12} \leftarrow \text{Whole number divisor}$$

The short way to multiply by 10 is to move the decimal point *one place* to the *right* in both the divisor and the dividend.

$$1.2\overline{)6.36} \quad \text{is equivalent to} \quad 12\overline{)63.6}$$

> **Note**
> Moving the decimal points the *same* number of places to the right in *both* the divisor and dividend will *not* change the answer.

Dividing by a Decimal Number

Step 1 Count the number of decimal places in the divisor and move the decimal point that many places to the *right*. (This changes the divisor to a whole number.)

Step 2 Move the decimal point in the dividend the *same* number of places to the *right*. (Write in extra zeros if needed.)

Step 3 Write the decimal point in the quotient directly above the decimal point in the dividend. Then divide as usual.

Step 4 If both numbers have the *same sign,* the quotient is *positive.* If they have *different signs,* the quotient is *negative.*

ANSWERS

3. **(a)** 20.539; no repeating digits visible on calculator;
   Check (20.539) (13) = 267.007
   (b) 3.417; $3.41\overline{6}$;
   Check (3.417) (6) = 20.502
   (c) 1.136; $1.13\overline{5}$;
   Check (1.136) (9) = 10.224
   (d) 5.383; $5.38\overline{3}$;
   Check (5.383) (3) = 16.149
   (e) 10.573; $10.5\overline{72}$;
   Check (10.573) (11) = 116.303

EXAMPLE 4 **Dividing by Decimal Numbers**

(a) $\dfrac{27.69}{0.003}$

Move the decimal point in the divisor *three* places to the *right* so that 0.003 becomes the whole number 3. In order to move the decimal point in the dividend the same number of places, write in an extra 0.

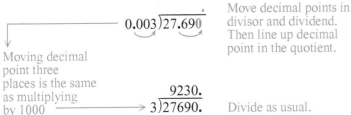

Move decimal points in divisor and dividend. Then line up decimal point in the quotient.

Moving decimal point three places is the same as multiplying by 1000

$$3\overline{)27690.}$$ Divide as usual.

(b) Divide -5 by -4.2 and round the quotient to the nearest hundredth.

First consider $5 \div 4.2$. Move the decimal point in the divisor one place to the right so that 4.2 becomes the whole number 42. The decimal point in the dividend starts on the right side of 5 and is also moved one place to the right.

Move both decimal points the *same* number of places.

$$
\begin{array}{r}
1.190 \\
4.2\overline{)5.0000} \\
\underline{42} \\
80 \\
\underline{42} \\
380 \\
\underline{378} \\
20
\end{array}
$$

← In order to round to hundredths, divide out one *more* place, to thousandths.

Rounding the quotient to the nearest hundredth gives 1.19. The quotient is *positive* because both the divisor and dividend have the *same* sign (both are negative).

$$-5 \div (-4.2) \approx 1.19$$

Same sign   Positive quotient

Work Problem **4** *at the Side.* ▶

OBJECTIVE 3 Estimate the answer when dividing decimals.
Estimating the answer to a division problem helps you catch errors. Compare the estimate to your exact answer. If they are very different, do the division again.

4 Divide. If the quotient does not come out even, round to the nearest hundredth.

(a) $0.2\overline{)1.04}$

(b) $0.06\overline{)1.8072}$

(c) $0.005\overline{)32}$

(d) $-8.1 \div 0.025$

(e) $\dfrac{7}{1.3}$

(f) $-5.3091 \div (-6.2)$

5 Decide whether each answer is reasonable by using front end rounding to estimate the answer. If the exact answer is *not* reasonable, find and correct the error.

(a) $42.75 \div 3.8 = 1.125$

Estimate:

(b) $807.1 \div 1.76 = 458.580$
to nearest thousandth

Estimate:

(c) $48.63 \div 52 = 93.519$
to nearest thousandth

Estimate:

(d) $9.0584 \div 2.68 = 0.338$

Estimate:

ANSWERS

5. (a) Estimate is $40 \div 4 = 10$;
exact answer is not reasonable,
should be 11.25
(b) Estimate is $800 \div 2 = 400$;
exact answer is reasonable.
(c) Estimate is $50 \div 50 = 1$;
exact answer is not reasonable,
should be 0.935
(d) Estimate is $9 \div 3 = 3$;
exact answer is not reasonable,
should be 3.38

EXAMPLE 5 **Estimating before Dividing**

First, use front end rounding to estimate the answer. Then divide to find the exact answer.

$$580.44 \div 2.8$$

Here is how one student solved this problem. She rounded 580.44 to 600 and 2.8 to 3 to estimate the answer.

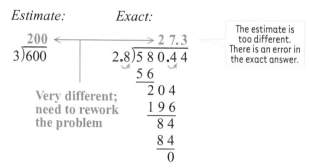

Estimate: *Exact:*

The estimate is too different. There is an error in the exact answer.

Notice that the estimate, which is in the hundreds, is very different from the exact answer, which is only in the tens. This tells the student that she needs to rework the problem. Can you find the error?
(The exact answer should be 207.3, which fits with the estimate of 200.)

◀ *Work Problem* **5** *at the Side.*

OBJECTIVE **4** **Use the order of operations with decimals.** Use the order of operations from **Section 3.7** when a decimal problem involves more than one operation.

Order of Operations

Step 1 Work inside *parentheses* or *other grouping symbols.*

Step 2 Simplify expressions with *exponents.*

Step 3 Do the remaining *multiplications and divisions* as they occur from left to right.

Step 4 Do the remaining *additions and subtractions* as they occur from left to right.

EXAMPLE 6 **Using the Order of Operations**

Simplify by using the order of operations.

(a) $2.5 + (-6.3)^2 + 9.62$ Apply the exponent: $(-6.3)(-6.3)$ is 39.69

$2.5 + 39.69 + 9.62$ Add from left to right.

$42.19 + 9.62$

51.81

(b) $1.82 + (5.2 - 6.7)(5.8)$ Work inside parentheses.

$1.82 + (-1.5)(5.8)$ Multiply next.

$1.82 + (-8.7)$ Add last.

-6.88

Continued on Next Page

(c) $\underbrace{3.7^2}$ $- 1.8 \div 5(1.5)$ Apply the exponent.

$13.69 - \underbrace{1.8 \div 5}(1.5)$ Multiply and divide from *left to right*, so first divide 1.8 by 5

$13.69 - \underbrace{0.36\ (1.5)}$ Multiply 0.36 by 1.5

$\underbrace{13.69 - \hspace{1cm} 0.54}$ Subtract last.

13.15

Work Problem **6** *at the Side.* ▶

⊞ **Calculator Tip**   Most calculators that have parentheses keys ⒪ ⒫ can handle calculations like those in Example 6(b) on the previous page just by entering the numbers in the order given. For example, the keystrokes for Example 6(b) are:

Parentheses

1.82 ⊕ ⒪ 5.2 ⊖ 6.7 ⒫ ⊗ 5.8 ⊜   Answer is −6.88

Standard, four-function calculators generally do *not* give the correct answer if you enter the numbers in the order given. Check the instruction manual that came with your calculator for information on "order of calculations" to see if your model has the rules for order of operations built into it. For a quick check, try entering this problem:

2 ⊕ 2 ⊗ 2 ⊜

If the result is 6, the calculator follows the order of operations. If the result is 8, it does *not* have the rules built into it. Use the space below to explain how this test works.

Answer: The test works because a calculator that follows the order of operations will automatically do the multiplication first. If the calculator does *not* have the rules built into it, it will work from left to right.

Following Order of Operations		**Working from Left to Right**
$2 + \underbrace{2 \times 2}$	Multiply before adding.	$\underbrace{2 + 2} \times 2$
$\underbrace{2 + \hspace{0.5cm} 4}$		$\underbrace{4 \hspace{0.5cm} \times 2}$
6 ← Correct		8 ✗ ← Incorrect

6 Simplify.

(a) $-4.6 - 0.79 + 1.5^2$

(b) $3.64 \div 1.3(3.6)$

(c) $0.08 + 0.6(2.99 - 3)$

(d) $10.85 - 2.3(5.2) \div 3.2$

ANSWERS

6. (a) -3.14 **(b)** 10.08 **(c)** 0.074
    (d) 7.1125

Math in the Media

DOLLAR-COST AVERAGING

Making money in the stock market can be difficult. You want to buy shares of stock when the price is low and sell them when the price is high. Predicting the right time to buy is tricky. One strategy is dollar-cost averaging. You invest the same amount at regular intervals, like the first of each month. Over time you will usually buy more shares at lower prices, though there is no guarantee of making a profit.

The table below shows Microsoft's closing share price on the first day of each month in 2007. See what happens if you invest $100 each month rather than buying a lot of shares at one time.

Microsoft Corp. (MSFT)	Amount Invested	Price Per Share	Number of Shares Bought
January	$100	30.86	($100 ÷ 30.86) ≈ 3.2404 shares
February	$100	28.17	
March	$100	27.87	
April	$100	29.94	
May	$100	30.69	
June	$100	29.47	
July	$100	28.99	
August	$100	28.73	
September	$100	29.46	
October	$100	36.81	
November	$100	34.74	
December	$100	33.60	
Total investment			

Source: http://finance.yahoo.com

Use a calculator to help answer these questions.

1. Calculate the total amount invested and enter the value in the table.

2. Calculate the number of shares bought each month. Round the number of shares to the nearest ten-thousandth. The calculation for January is shown.

3. Calculate the average market price per share. (*Hint:* Add the monthly prices per share and divide by 12.)

4. Calculate the average price based on *dollar-cost averaging*. (*Hint:* Divide the total amount invested by the total number of shares.)

5. Rank the following scenarios in order of which was the best investment (most profit or least loss). Show the value of each investment in December 2007 as a basis for your answer.

   (a) $1200 invested in Microsoft in January 2007

   (b) $1200 invested in Microsoft using *dollar-cost averaging*

   (c) $1200 invested in Microsoft in October 2007

Find each quotient. See Examples 1, 2, and 4.

1. $27.3 \div (-7)$

2. $-50.4 \div 8$

3. $\dfrac{4.23}{9}$

4. $\dfrac{1.62}{6}$

5. $-20.01 \div (-0.05)$

6. $-16.04 \div (-0.08)$

7. $1.5\overline{)54}$

8. $2.4\overline{)132}$

Use the fact that $108 \div 18 = 6$ *to work Exercises 9–16 simply by moving decimal points. See Examples 1, 2, and 4.*

9. $1.8\overline{)0.108}$

10. $18\overline{)10.8}$

11. $0.018\overline{)108}$

12. $0.18\overline{)1.08}$

13. $0.18\overline{)10.8}$

14. $0.18\overline{)108}$

15. $18\overline{)0.0108}$

16. $1.8\overline{)0.0108}$

Divide. Round quotients to the nearest hundredth when necessary. See Examples 3 and 4.

17. $4.6\overline{)116.38}$

18. $2.6\overline{)4.992}$

19. $\dfrac{-3.1}{-0.006}$

20. $\dfrac{-1.7}{0.09}$

Divide. Round quotients to the nearest thousandth. See Examples 3 and 4.

21. $-240.8 \div 9$

22. $-76.43 \div (-7)$

23. $0.034\overline{)342.81}$

24. $0.043\overline{)1748.4}$

Relating Concepts (Exercises 25–26) For Individual or Group Work

*First, look back at your work in **Section 6.4**, Exercises 21 and 22. Then look for patterns as you **work Exercises 25 and 26 in order.***

25. Do these division problems.

$3.77 \div 10 =$ _____ $9.1 \div 10 =$ _____

$0.886 \div 10 =$ _____ $30.19 \div 10 =$ _____

$406.5 \div 10 =$ _____ $6625.7 \div 10 =$ _____

(a) What pattern do you see? Write a "rule" for dividing by 10. What do you think the rule is for dividing by 100? by 1000? Write the rules and try them out on the numbers above.

(b) Compare your rules to the ones you wrote in **Section 6.4**, Exercise 21.

26. Do these division problems.

$40.2 \div 0.1 =$ _____ $7.1 \div 0.1 =$ _____

$0.339 \div 0.1 =$ _____ $15.77 \div 0.1 =$ _____

$46 \div 0.1 =$ _____ $873 \div 0.1 =$ _____

(a) What pattern do you see? Write a "rule" for dividing by 0.1. What do you think the rule is for dividing by 0.01? by 0.001? Write the rules and try them out on the numbers above.

(b) Compare your rules to the ones you wrote in **Section 6.4**, Exercise 22.

Decide whether each answer is reasonable *or* unreasonable *by using front end rounding to estimate the answer. If the exact answer is not reasonable, find and correct the error. See Example 5.*

27. 37.8 ÷ 8 = 47.25

   Estimate:

28. 345.6 ÷ 3 = 11.52

   Estimate:

29. 54.6 ÷ 48.1 ≈ 1.135

   Estimate:

30. 2428.8 ÷ 4.8 = 56

   Estimate:

31. 307.02 ÷ 5.1 = 6.2

   Estimate:

32. 395.415 ÷ 5.05 = 78.3

   Estimate:

33. 9.3 ÷ 1.25 = 0.744

   Estimate:

34. 78 ÷ 14.2 = 0.182

   Estimate:

Solve each application problem. Round money answers to the nearest cent when necessary.

35. Rob has discovered that his daughter's favorite brand of tights are on sale. He decided to buy one pair as a surprise for her. How much did he pay?

36. The bookstore has a special price on notepads. How much did Randall pay for one notepad?

37. It will take 21 months for Aimee to pay off her credit card balance of $1408.68. How much is she paying each month?

38. Marcella Anderson bought a 2.6 meter length of microfiber woven suede fabric for $33.77. How much did she pay per meter?

39. Adrian Webb bought 619 bricks to build a barbecue pit, paying $185.70. Find the cost per brick. (*Hint:* Cost *per* brick means the cost for *one* brick.)

40. Lupe Wilson is a newspaper distributor. Last week she paid the newspaper $130.51 for 842 copies. Find the cost per copy.

41. Darren Jackson earned $476.80 for 40 hours of work. Find his earnings per hour.

42. At a CD manufacturing company, 400 CDs cost $289. Find the cost per CD.

43. It took 16.35 gallons of gas to fill the gas tank of Kim's car. She had driven 346.2 miles since her last fill-up. How many miles per gallon did she get? Round to the nearest tenth.

44. Mr. Rodriquez pays $53.19 each month to Household Finance. How many months will it take him to pay off $1436.13?

Use the table of women's longest long jumps (through the year 2007) to answer Exercises 45–50. To find an average, add up the values you are interested in and then divide the sum by the number of values. Round your answers to the nearest hundredth.

Athlete	Country	Year	Length (meters)
Galina Christyakova	USSR	1988	7.52
Jackie Joyner-Kersee	U.S.	1994	7.49
Heike Drechsler	Germany	1992	7.48
Jackie Joyner-Kersee	U.S.	1987	7.45
Jackie Joyner-Kersee	U.S.	1988	7.40
Jackie Joyner-Kersee	U.S.	1991	7.32
Jackie Joyner-Kersee	U.S.	1996	7.20
Chioma Ajunwa	Nigeria	1996	7.12
Fiona May	Italy	2000	7.09
Tatyana Lebedeva	Russia	2004	7.07

Source: CNNSI.com

45. Find the average length of the long jumps made by Jackie Joyner-Kersee.

46. Find the average length of all the long jumps listed in the table.

47. How much longer was the fifth-longest jump than the sixth-longest jump?

48. If the first-place athlete made five jumps of the same length, what would be the total distance jumped?

49. What was the total length jumped by the top three athletes in the table?

50. How much less was the last-place jump than the next-to-last-place jump?

Simplify. See Example 6.

51. $7.2 - 5.2 + 3.5^2$

52. $6.2 + 4.3^2 - 9.72$

53. $38.6 + 11.6(10.4 - 13.4)$

54. $2.25 - 1.06(0.85 - 3.95)$

55. $-8.68 - 4.6(10.4) \div 6.4$

56. $25.1 + 11.4 \div 7.5(-3.75)$

57. $33 - 3.2(0.68 + 9) + (-1.3)^2$

58. $0.6 + (-1.89 + 0.11) \div 0.004(0.5)$

Solve each application problem.

59. Soup is on sale at six cans for \$3.25, or you can purchase individual cans for \$0.57. How much will you save per can if you buy six cans? Round to the nearest cent.

60. Nadia's diet says she can eat 3.5 ounces of chicken nuggets. The package weighs 10.5 ounces and contains 15 nuggets. How many nuggets can Nadia eat?

61. The U.S. Treasury prints about 38,000,000 pieces of paper money each day. The printing presses run 24 hours a day. How many pieces of money are printed, to the nearest whole number:

(a) each hour

38,000,000 pieces of paper money are printed each day

(b) each minute

(c) each second

(*Source:* www.moneyfactory.com)

62. Mach 1 is the speed of sound. Dividing a vehicle's speed by the speed of sound gives its speed on the Mach scale. In 1997, a specially built car with two 110,000-horsepower engines broke the world land speed record by traveling 763.035 miles per hour. The speed of sound changes slightly with the weather. That day it was 748.11 miles per hour. What was the car's Mach speed, to the nearest hundredth? (*Source:* Associated Press.)

General Mills will give a school 10¢ for each box top logo from its cereals and other products. A school can earn up to \$10,000 per year. Use this information to answer Exercises 63–66. Round answers to the nearest whole number. (Source: General Mills.)

63. How many box tops would a school need to collect in one year to earn the maximum amount?

64. (Complete Exercise 63 first.) If a school has 550 children, how many box tops would each child need to collect to reach the maximum?

65. How many box tops would need to be collected during each of the 38 weeks in the school year to reach the maximum amount?

66. How many box tops would each of the 550 children need to collect during each of the 38 weeks of school to reach the maximum amount?

Summary Exercises on Decimals

Write each decimal as a fraction or mixed number in lowest terms.

1. 0.8

2. 6.004

3. 0.35

Write each decimal in words.

4. 94.5

5. 2.0003

6. 0.706

Write each decimal in numbers.

7. five hundredths

8. three hundred nine ten-thousandths

9. ten and seven tenths

Round to the place indicated.

10. 6.1873 to the nearest hundredth

11. 0.95 to the nearest tenth

12. 0.42025 to the nearest thousandth

13. $0.893 to the nearest cent

14. $3.0017 to the nearest cent

15. $99.64 to the nearest dollar

Simplify.

16. $-0.27\,(3.5)$

17. $50 - 0.3801$

18. $0.35 \div (-0.007)$

19. $\dfrac{-90.18}{-6}$

20. $(0.004)\,(1.22)$

21. $1.55 - 3.7$

22. $-0.95 + 10.005$

23. $3.6 + 0.718 + 9 + 5.0829$

24. $32.305 - 40 + 0.7$

25. $-8.9 + 4^2 \div (-0.02)$

26. $(-0.18 + 2.5) + 4\,(-0.05)$

27. $0.64 \div 16.3$ Round your answer to the nearest hundredth.

Find the perimeter of each figure.

28.

19.75 in.

6.3 in.   6.3 in.

19.75 in.

29.

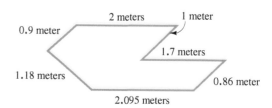

2 meters   1 meter

0.9 meter

1.7 meters

1.18 meters   0.86 meter

2.095 meters

Solve each application problem.

30. At a bakery, Sue Chee bought $7.42 worth of muffins and $10.09 worth of croissants for a staff party and a $0.69 cookie for herself. How much change did she receive from two $10 bills?

31. A craft cooperative paid $40.32 for enough fabric to make eight baby blankets for their store. They sold the blankets for $15.95 each. How much profit was made on the blankets?

The table below shows information on two tents for camping. Use the table to answer Exercises 32 and 33.

Tents	Coleman Family Dome	Eddie Bauer Dome Tent
Dimensions	13 ft × 13 ft	12 ft × 12 ft
Sleeps	8 campers	6 campers
Sale price	$127	$99

Source: target.com

32. For the Coleman tent, find:
   (a) the area of the tent floor

   (b) the cost per square foot of floor space, to the nearest cent.

33. Find the same information for the Eddie Bauer tent as you did for the Coleman tent.

Use the information in the table to answer Exercises 34–36.

Animal	Average Weight of Animal (ounces)	Average Weight of Food Eaten Each Day (ounces)
Hamster	3.5	0.4
Queen bee	0.004	?
Hummingbird	?	0.07

Source: NCTM News Bulletin.

34. (a) In how many days will a hamster eat enough food to equal its body weight? Round to the nearest whole number of days.

   (b) If a 140-pound woman ate her body weight of food in the same number of days as the hamster, how much would she eat each day? Round to the nearest tenth.

35. While laying eggs, a queen bee eats eighty times her weight each day. Use this information to fill in one of the missing values in the table.

36. A hummingbird's body weight is about 1.6 times the weight of its daily food intake. Find its body weight.

6.6 ▶▶▶ Fractions and Decimals

Writing fractions as equivalent decimals can help you do calculations or compare the size of two numbers more easily.

OBJECTIVE 1 Write fractions as equivalent decimals. Recall that a fraction is one way to show division (see **Section 3.6**). For example, $\frac{3}{4}$ means $3 \div 4$. If you are doing the division by hand, write it as $4\overline{)3}$. When you do the division, the result is 0.75, the decimal equivalent of $\frac{3}{4}$.

> **Writing a Fraction as an Equivalent Decimal**
>
> **Step 1** Divide the numerator of the fraction by the denominator.
>
> **Step 2** If necessary, round the answer to the place indicated.

Work Problem **1** *at the Side.* ▶

EXAMPLE 1 Writing Fractions or Mixed Numbers as Decimals

(a) Write $\frac{1}{8}$ as a decimal.

$\frac{1}{8}$ means $1 \div 8$. Write it as $8\overline{)1}$. The decimal point in the dividend is on the *right* side of the 1. Write extra zeros in the dividend so you can continue dividing until the remainder is 0.

Decimal points lined up

$$\frac{1}{8} \implies 1 \div 8 \implies 8\overline{)1} \implies \begin{array}{r} 0.125 \\ 8\overline{)1.000} \\ \underline{8} \\ 20 \\ \underline{16} \\ 40 \\ \underline{40} \\ 0 \end{array}$$

Be careful to divide $8\overline{)1}$, **not** $1\overline{)8}$

Three extra zeros needed

← Remainder is 0

Therefore, $\frac{1}{8} = 0.125$

To check, write 0.125 as a fraction, then write it in lowest terms.

$$0.125 = \frac{125}{1000} \quad \text{In lowest terms: } \frac{125 \div 125}{1000 \div 125} = \frac{1}{8} \quad \left\{ \begin{array}{l} \text{Original} \\ \text{fraction} \end{array} \right.$$

▦ **Calculator Tip** When using your calculator to write fractions as decimals, enter the numbers from the top down. Remember that the *order* in which you enter the numbers *does* matter in division. Example 1(a) above works like this:

$$\frac{1}{8} \downarrow \text{ Top down} \quad \text{Enter 1 } ⊝ \text{ 8 } ⊜ \quad \text{Answer is 0.125}$$

What happens if you enter 8 ⊝ 1 ⊜? Do you see why that cannot possibly be correct? (Answer: $8 \div 1 = 8$. A proper fraction like $\frac{1}{8}$ *cannot* be equivalent to a whole number.)

Continued on Next Page

OBJECTIVES

1 Write fractions as equivalent decimals.

2 Compare the size of fractions and decimals.

1 Rewrite each fraction so you could do the division by hand. Do *not* complete the division.

(a) $\frac{1}{9}$ is written $\quad 9\overline{}$

(b) $\frac{2}{3}$ is written $\quad \overline{}$

(c) $\frac{5}{4}$ is written $\quad \overline{}$

(d) $\frac{3}{10}$ is written $\quad \overline{}$

(e) $\frac{21}{16}$ is written $\quad \overline{}$

(f) $\frac{1}{50}$ is written $\quad \overline{}$

ANSWERS

1. **(a)** $9\overline{)1}$ **(b)** $3\overline{)2}$ **(c)** $4\overline{)5}$
   (d) $10\overline{)3}$ **(e)** $16\overline{)21}$ **(f)** $50\overline{)1}$

2 Write each fraction or mixed number as a decimal.

(a) $\dfrac{1}{4}$

(b) $2\dfrac{1}{2}$

(c) $\dfrac{5}{8}$

(d) $4\dfrac{3}{5}$

(e) $\dfrac{7}{8}$

(b) Write $2\frac{3}{4}$ as a decimal.

One method is to divide 3 by 4 to get 0.75 for the fraction part. Then add the whole number part to 0.75.

$$\dfrac{3}{4} \;\Longrightarrow\; 4\overline{)3.00} \quad \begin{array}{r} 0.75 \\ \underline{2\,8} \\ 20 \\ \underline{20} \\ 0 \end{array}$$

Fraction part $\longrightarrow$

$$\begin{array}{r} 2.00 \leftarrow \text{Whole number part} \\ +\;0.75 \\ \hline 2.75 \end{array}$$

So, $2\frac{3}{4} = 2.75$ **Check** $2.75 = 2\frac{75}{100} = 2\frac{3}{4}$ ←Lowest terms

Whole number parts match.

A second method is to write $2\frac{3}{4}$ as an improper fraction before dividing numerator by denominator.

$$2\dfrac{3}{4} = \dfrac{11}{4}$$

$$\dfrac{11}{4} \;\Longrightarrow\; 11 \div 4 \;\Longrightarrow\; 4\overline{)11} \;\Longrightarrow\; 4\overline{)11.0\,0} \;\begin{array}{r} 2.7\,5 \\ \underline{8} \\ 3\,0 \\ \underline{2\,8} \\ 2\,0 \\ \underline{2\,0} \\ 0 \end{array}$$

← Two extra zeros needed

Whole number parts match.

So, $2\dfrac{3}{4} = 2.75$

$\frac{3}{4}$ is equivalent to $\frac{75}{100}$ or 0.75

◀ *Work Problem* **2** *at the Side.*

EXAMPLE 2 **Writing a Fraction as a Decimal with Rounding**

Write $\frac{2}{3}$ as a decimal and round to the nearest thousandth.

$\frac{2}{3}$ means $2 \div 3$. To round to thousandths, divide out one *more* place, to ten-thousandths.

$$\dfrac{2}{3} \;\Longrightarrow\; 2 \div 3 \;\Longrightarrow\; 3\overline{)2} \;\Longrightarrow\; 3\overline{)2.0000} \;\begin{array}{r} 0.6666 \\ \underline{1\,8} \\ 20 \\ \underline{18} \\ 20 \\ \underline{18} \\ 20 \\ \underline{18} \\ 2 \end{array}$$

$\left\{\begin{array}{l}\text{Four zeros needed} \\ \text{for ten-thousandths}\end{array}\right.$

Be careful to divide $3\overline{)2}$, **not** $2\overline{)3}$

Written as a repeating decimal, $\dfrac{2}{3} = 0.\overline{6}$ ← Bar above repeating digit

Rounded to the nearest thousandth, $\dfrac{2}{3} \approx 0.667$

ANSWERS

2. **(a)** 0.25 **(b)** 2.5 **(c)** 0.625
   (d) 4.6 **(e)** 0.875

Continued on Next Page

⊞ **Calculator Tip**   Try Example 2 on the previous page on your calculator. Enter 2 ÷ 3. Which answer do you get?

| **0.666666667** | or | **0.666666666** |

Most *scientific* and *graphing* calculators will show a 7 as the last digit. Because the 6s keep on repeating forever, the calculator automatically rounds in the last decimal place it has room to show. If you have a 10-digit display space, the calculator is rounding as shown below.

0.6666666666 (11 digits)   rounds to   0.66666666**7**

Next digit is 5 *or more,* so 6 rounds to 7

Other calculators, especially standard, four-function ones, may *not* round. They just cut off, or *truncate,* the extra digits. Such a calculator would show 0.6666666 in the display.

   Would this difference in calculators show up when changing $\frac{1}{3}$ to a decimal? Why not? (Answer: The repeating digit is a 3, which is *4 or less,* so it stays as a 3 whether it's rounded or not.)

Work Problem **3** *at the Side.* ▶

OBJECTIVE **2** **Compare the size of fractions and decimals.**
You can use a number line to compare fractions and decimals. For example, the number line below shows the space between 0 and 1. The locations of some commonly used fractions are marked, along with their decimal equivalents.

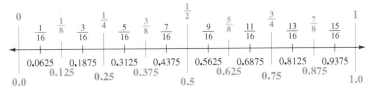

   The next number line shows the locations of some commonly used fractions between 0 and 1 that are equivalent to repeating decimals. The decimal equivalents use a bar above repeating digits.

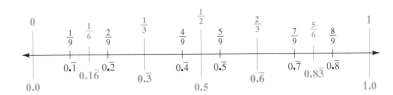

EXAMPLE 3   **Using a Number Line to Compare Numbers**

Use the number lines above to decide whether to write >, <, or = in the blank between each pair of numbers.

(a) 0.6875 _____ 0.625
   You learned in **Section 1.2** that the number farther to the right on the number line is the greater number. On the first number line, 0.6875 is to the *right* of 0.625, so use the > symbol.

0.6875   is greater than   0.625   0.6875 > 0.625

Continued on Next Page

---

3 Write as decimals. Round to the nearest thousandth.

(a) $\frac{1}{3}$

(b) $2\frac{7}{9}$

(c) $\frac{10}{11}$

(d) $\frac{3}{7}$

(e) $3\frac{5}{6}$

ANSWERS
3. **(a)** $\frac{1}{3} \approx 0.333$ **(b)** $2\frac{7}{9} \approx 2.778$

   (c) $\frac{10}{11} \approx 0.909$ **(d)** $\frac{3}{7} \approx 0.429$

   (e) $3\frac{5}{6} \approx 3.833$

4 Use the number lines on the previous page to help you decide whether to write $<$, $>$, or $=$ in each blank.

(a) 0.4375 _____ 0.5

(b) 0.75 _____ 0.6875

(c) 0.625 _____ 0.0625

(d) $\dfrac{2}{8}$ _____ 0.375

(e) $0.8\overline{3}$ _____ $\dfrac{5}{6}$

(f) $\dfrac{1}{2}$ _____ $0.\overline{5}$

(g) $0.\overline{1}$ _____ $0.1\overline{6}$

(h) $\dfrac{8}{9}$ _____ $0.\overline{8}$

(i) $0.\overline{7}$ _____ $\dfrac{4}{6}$

(j) $\dfrac{1}{4}$ _____ 0.25

5 Arrange each group in order from least to greatest.

(a) 0.7, 0.703, 0.7029

(b) 6.39, 6.309, 6.401, 6.4

(c) 1.085, $1\dfrac{3}{4}$, 0.9

(d) $\dfrac{1}{4}, \dfrac{2}{5}, \dfrac{3}{7}$, 0.428

ANSWERS

4. (a) $<$ (b) $>$ (c) $>$ (d) $<$ (e) $=$
   (f) $<$ (g) $<$ (h) $=$ (i) $>$ (j) $=$
5. (a) 0.7, 0.7029, 0.703
   (b) 6.309, 6.39, 6.4, 6.401
   (c) 0.9, 1.085, $1\dfrac{3}{4}$
   (d) $\dfrac{1}{4}, \dfrac{2}{5}, 0.428, \dfrac{3}{7}$

(b) $\dfrac{3}{4}$ _____ 0.75

On the first number line, $\frac{3}{4}$ and 0.75 are at the same point on the number line. They are equivalent, so use the $=$ symbol.

$$\frac{3}{4} = 0.75$$

(c) 0.5 _____ $0.\overline{5}$

On the second number line, 0.5 is to the *left* of $0.\overline{5}$ (which is actually $0.555\ldots$), so use the $<$ symbol.

$$0.5 \underset{\text{is less than}}{} 0.\overline{5} \qquad 0.5 < 0.\overline{5}$$

(d) $\dfrac{2}{6}$ _____ $0.\overline{3}$

Write $\frac{2}{6}$ in lowest terms as $\frac{1}{3}$.
On the second number line you can see that $\frac{1}{3}$ and $0.\overline{3}$ are equivalent.

$$\frac{1}{3} = 0.\overline{3}$$

◀ Work Problem **4** at the Side.

You can also compare fractions by first writing each one as a decimal. You can then compare the decimals by writing each one with the same number of decimal places.

EXAMPLE 4 **Arranging Numbers in Order**

Write each group of numbers in order, from least to greatest.

(a) 0.49   0.487   0.4903

It is easier to compare decimals if they are all tenths, or all hundredths, and so on. Because 0.4903 has four decimal places (ten-thousandths), write zeros to the right of 0.49 and 0.487 so they also have four decimal places. Writing zeros to the right of a decimal number does *not* change its value (see **Section 6.3**). Then find the least and greatest number of ten-thousandths.

$0.49 = 0.4900 = \mathbf{4900}$ ten-thousandths ← 4900 is in the middle.

$0.487 = 0.4870 = \mathbf{4870}$ ten-thousandths ← 4870 is the least.

$0.4903 = \mathbf{4903}$ ten-thousandths ← 4903 is the greatest.

From least to greatest, the correct order is shown below.

$$0.487 \qquad 0.49 \qquad 0.4903$$

(b) $2\dfrac{5}{8}$ 2.63   2.6

Write $2\frac{5}{8}$ as $\frac{21}{8}$ and divide $8)\overline{21}$ to get the decimal form, 2.625. Then, because 2.625 has three decimal places, write zeros so all the numbers have three decimal places.

$2\dfrac{5}{8} = 2.625 = 2$ and $\mathbf{625}$ thousandths ← 625 is in the middle.

$2.63 = 2.630 = 2$ and $\mathbf{630}$ thousandths ← 630 is the greatest.

$2.6 = 2.600 = 2$ and $\mathbf{600}$ thousandths ← 600 is the least.

From least to greatest, the correct order is shown below.

$$2.6 \qquad 2\dfrac{5}{8} \qquad 2.63$$

◀ Work Problem **5** at the Side.

6.6 ▶▶▶ Exercises

Write each fraction or mixed number as a decimal. Round to the nearest thousandth when necessary. See Examples 1 and 2.

1. $\dfrac{1}{2}$ **2.** $\dfrac{1}{4}$ **3.** $\dfrac{3}{4}$ **4.** $\dfrac{1}{10}$ **5.** $\dfrac{3}{10}$

6. $\dfrac{7}{10}$ **7.** $\dfrac{9}{10}$ **8.** $\dfrac{4}{5}$ **9.** $\dfrac{3}{5}$ **10.** $\dfrac{2}{5}$

11. $\dfrac{7}{8}$ **12.** $\dfrac{3}{8}$ **13.** $2\dfrac{1}{4}$ **14.** $1\dfrac{1}{2}$ **15.** $14\dfrac{7}{10}$

16. $23\dfrac{3}{5}$ **17.** $3\dfrac{5}{8}$ **18.** $2\dfrac{7}{8}$ **19.** $6\dfrac{1}{3}$ **20.** $5\dfrac{2}{3}$

 21. $\dfrac{5}{6}$ **22.** $\dfrac{1}{6}$ **23.** $1\dfrac{8}{9}$ **24.** $5\dfrac{4}{7}$

Relating Concepts (Exercises 25–28) For Individual or Group Work

*Use your knowledge of fractions and decimals as you **work Exercises 25–28 in order.***

25. (a) Explain how you can tell that Keith made an error *just by looking at his final answer*. Here is his work.

$$\frac{5}{9} \qquad 5\overline{)9.0}^{\,1.8} \quad \text{so} \quad \frac{5}{9} = 1.8$$

(b) Show the correct way to change $\frac{5}{9}$ to a decimal. Explain why your answer makes sense.

26. (a) How can you prove to Sandra that $2\frac{7}{20}$ is *not* equivalent to 2.035? Here is her work.

$$2\frac{7}{20} \qquad 20\overline{)7.00}^{\,0.35} \quad \text{so} \quad 2\frac{7}{20} = 2.035$$

(b) What is the correct answer? Show how to prove that it is correct.

27. Ving knows that $\frac{3}{8} = 0.375$. How can he write $1\frac{3}{8}$ as a decimal *without* having to do a division? How can he write $3\frac{3}{8}$ as a decimal? $295\frac{3}{8}$ as a decimal? Explain your answer.

28. Iris has found a shortcut for writing mixed numbers as decimals.

$$2\frac{7}{10} = 2.7 \qquad 1\frac{13}{100} = 1.13$$

Does her shortcut work for all mixed numbers? Explain when it works and why it works.

Find the decimal or fraction equivalent for each number. Write fractions in lowest terms.

Fraction	Decimal	Fraction	Decimal
29. _____	0.4	**30.** _____	0.75
31. _____	0.625	**32.** _____	0.111
33. _____	0.35	**34.** _____	0.9
35. $\dfrac{7}{20}$	_____	**36.** $\dfrac{1}{40}$	_____
37. _____	0.04	**38.** _____	0.52
39. _____	0.15	**40.** _____	0.85
41. $\dfrac{1}{5}$	_____	**42.** $\dfrac{1}{8}$	_____
43. _____	0.09	**44.** _____	0.02

Solve each application problem.

45. The average length of a newborn baby is 20.8 inches. Charlene's baby is 20.08 inches long. Is her baby longer or shorter than the average? By how much?

46. The patient in room 830 is supposed to get 8.3 milligrams of medicine. She was actually given 8.03 milligrams. Did she get too much or too little medicine? What was the difference?

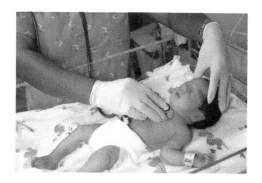

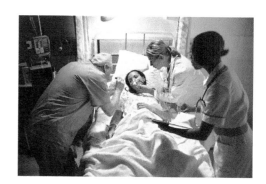

47. The label on the bottle of vitamins says that each capsule contains 0.5 gram of calcium. When checked, each capsule had 0.505 gram of calcium. Was there too much or too little calcium? What was the difference?

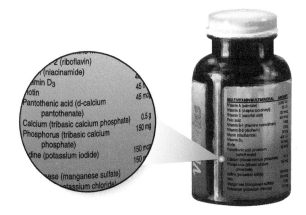

48. The glass mirror of the Hubble telescope had to be repaired in space because it would not focus properly. The problem was that the mirror's outer edge had a thickness of 0.6248 cm when it was supposed to be 0.625 cm. Was the edge too thick or too thin? By how much? (*Source:* NASA.)

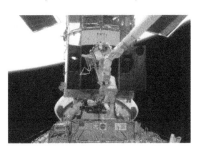

49. Precision Medical Parts makes an artificial heart valve that must measure between 0.998 centimeter and 1.002 centimeters. Circle the lengths that are acceptable.

1.01 cm   0.9991 cm   1.0007 cm   0.99 cm

50. The white rats in a medical experiment must start out weighing between 2.95 ounces and 3.05 ounces. Circle the weights that can be used.

3.0 ounces   2.995 ounces   3.055 ounces

3.005 ounces

51. Ginny Brown had hoped her crops would get $3\frac{3}{4}$ inches of rain this month. The newspaper said the area received 3.8 inches of rain. Was that more or less than Ginny had hoped for? By how much?

52. The rats in the experiment in Exercise 50 gained $\frac{3}{8}$ ounce. They were expected to gain 0.3 ounce. Was their actual gain more or less than expected? By how much?

*Use the number lines near Example 3 in the text to decide whether to write >, <, or =
between each pair of numbers. See Example 3.*

53. (a) 0.3125 ____ 0.375   **(b)** $\frac{6}{8}$ ____ 0.75   **(c)** $0.\overline{8}$ ____ $0.8\overline{3}$ **(d)** 0.5 ____ $\frac{5}{9}$

54. (a) 0.125 ____ 0.0625   **(b)** $\frac{4}{9}$ ____ $\frac{3}{6}$ **(c)** 1.0 ____ $\frac{4}{4}$ **(d)** $\frac{1}{6}$ ____ $0.\overline{1}$

Arrange each group of numbers in order from least to greatest. See Example 4.

55. 0.54, 0.5455, 0.5399

56. 0.76, 0.7, 0.7006

57. 5.8, 5.79, 5.0079, 5.804

58. 12.99, 12.5, 13.0001, 12.77

59. 0.628, 0.62812, 0.609, 0.6009

60. 0.27, 0.281, 0.296, 0.3

61. 5.8751, 4.876, 2.8902, 3.88

62. 0.98, 0.89, 0.904, 0.9

63. 0.043, 0.051, 0.006, $\frac{1}{20}$

64. 0.629, $\frac{5}{8}$, 0.65, $\frac{7}{10}$

65. $\frac{3}{8}$, $\frac{2}{5}$, 0.37, 0.4001

66. 0.1501, 0.25, $\frac{1}{10}$, $\frac{1}{5}$

Four boxes of fishing line are in a sale bin. The thicker the line, the stronger it is. The diameter of the fishing line is its thickness. Use the information on the boxes to answer Exercises 67–68.

67. (a) Which color box has the strongest line? The weakest line?

(b) What is the difference in line diameter between the weakest and strongest lines?

68. (a) Which color box has the line that is $\frac{1}{125}$ inch in diameter?

(b) What is the difference in line diameter between the blue and purple boxes?

Fishing Line 0.018 in. diameter
Fishing Line 0.01 in. diameter
Fishing Line
Fishing Line 0.010 in. diameter

Some rulers for technical drawings show each inch divided into tenths. Use this scale drawing for Exercises 69–74. Change the measurements on the drawing to decimals and round them to the nearest tenth of an inch.

69. Length **(a)** is _____

70. Length **(b)** is _____

71. Length **(c)** is _____

72. Length **(d)** is _____

73. Length **(e)** is _____

74. Length **(f)** is _____

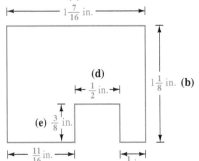

(a) $1\frac{7}{16}$ in.

(d) $\frac{1}{2}$ in.

(b) $1\frac{1}{8}$ in.

(e) $\frac{3}{8}$ in.

(f) $\frac{11}{16}$ in.

(c) $\frac{1}{4}$ in.

6.7 ▶▶▶ Geometry Applications: Pythagorean Theorem and Square Roots

In **Section 4.7,** you used this formula for area of a square, $A = s^2$. The blue square below has an area of 25 cm² because $(5 \text{ cm})(5 \text{ cm}) = 25 \text{ cm}^2$.

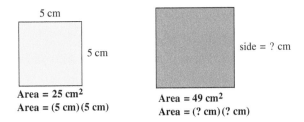

5 cm

5 cm

Area = 25 cm²
Area = (5 cm)(5 cm)

side = ? cm

Area = 49 cm²
Area = (? cm)(? cm)

The red square above has an area of 49 cm². To find the length of a side, ask yourself, "What number can be multiplied by itself to give 49?" Because $(7)(7) = 49$, the length of each side is 7 cm. Also, because $(7)(7) = 49$ we say that 7 is the *square root* of 49, or $\sqrt{49} = 7$.

> **Square Root**
>
> The positive **square root** of a positive number is one of two identical positive factors of that number.
>   For example, $\sqrt{36} = 6$ because $(6)(6) = 36$.

> **Note**
> There is another square root for 36. We know that
>
> $$(6)(6) = 36 \quad \text{and} \quad (-6)(-6) = 36$$
>
> so the *positive* square root of 36 is 6 and the *negative* square root of 36 is -6. In this section we will work only with positive square roots.

Work Problem **1** *at the Side.* ▶

A number that has a whole number as its square root is called a *perfect square*. For example, 9 is a perfect square because $\sqrt{9} = 3$, and 3 is a whole number. The first few perfect squares are listed below.

> **The First Twelve Perfect Squares**
>
> | | | | |
> |---|---|---|---|
> | $\sqrt{1} = 1$ | $\sqrt{16} = 4$ | $\sqrt{49} = 7$ | $\sqrt{100} = 10$ |
> | $\sqrt{4} = 2$ | $\sqrt{25} = 5$ | $\sqrt{64} = 8$ | $\sqrt{121} = 11$ |
> | $\sqrt{9} = 3$ | $\sqrt{36} = 6$ | $\sqrt{81} = 9$ | $\sqrt{144} = 12$ |

OBJECTIVE 1 Find square roots using the square root key on a calculator.   If a number is *not* a perfect square, then you can find its *approximate* square root by using a calculator with a square root key.

1 Find each square root.

(a) $\sqrt{36}$

(b) $\sqrt{25}$

(c) $\sqrt{9}$

(d) $\sqrt{100}$

(e) $\sqrt{121}$

ANSWERS

1. (a) 6   **(b)** 5   **(c)** 3   **(d)** 10   **(e)** 11

2 Use a calculator with a square root key to find each square root. Round to the nearest thousandth when necessary.

(a) $\sqrt{11}$

(b) $\sqrt{40}$

(c) $\sqrt{56}$

(d) $\sqrt{196}$

(e) $\sqrt{147}$

▦ **Calculator Tip**   To find a square root on a *scientific* calculator, use the ⓥ or the ⓥ̄ₓ key. (On some models you may have to press the ⓦ key to access the square root function.) You do *not* need to use the ⓔ key. Try these.

To find $\sqrt{16}$ press: 16 ⓥ̄ₓ   Answer is 4

To find $\sqrt{7}$ press: 7 ⓥ̄ₓ   Answer is 2.645751311

For $\sqrt{7}$, your calculator shows 2.645751311, which is an *approximate* answer. (Some calculators may show more or fewer digits.) We will round to the nearest thousandth, so $\sqrt{7} \approx 2.646$. To check, multiply 2.646 times 2.646. Do you get 7 as the result? No, you get 7.001316, which is very close to 7. The difference is due to rounding.

EXAMPLE 1   **Finding the Square Root of Numbers**

▦ Use a calculator to find each square root. Round to the nearest thousandth.

(a) $\sqrt{35}$ Calculator shows 5.916079783; round to 5.916

(b) $\sqrt{124}$ Calculator shows 11.13552873; round to 11.136

◀ *Work Problem* **2** *at the Side.*

OBJECTIVE **2** **Find the unknown length in a right triangle.**   One place you will use square roots is when working with the *Pythagorean Theorem*. This theorem applies only to *right* triangles (triangles with a 90° angle). The longest side of a right triangle is called the **hypotenuse.** It is opposite the right angle. The other two sides are called *legs*. The legs form the right angle. Here are some right triangles.

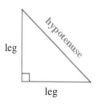
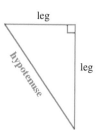
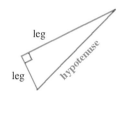

Examples of right triangles

Pythagorean Theorem

$$(\text{hypotenuse})^2 = (\text{leg})^2 + (\text{leg})^2$$

In other words, square the length of each side. After you have squared all the sides, the sum of the squares of the two legs will equal the square of the hypotenuse. An example is shown below.

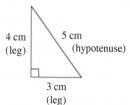

$$(\text{hypotenuse})^2 = (\text{leg})^2 + (\text{leg})^2$$
$$5^2 = 4^2 + 3^2$$
$$25 = 16 + 9$$
$$25 = 25$$

ANSWERS

2. (a) $\sqrt{11} \approx 3.317$ **(b)** $\sqrt{40} \approx 6.325$
  (c) $\sqrt{56} \approx 7.483$ **(d)** $\sqrt{196} = 14$
  (e) $\sqrt{147} \approx 12.124$

The theorem is named after Pythagoras, a Greek mathematician who lived about 2500 years ago. He and his followers may have used floor tiles to prove the theorem, as shown on the next page.

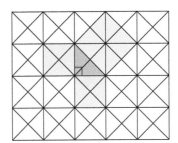

Right triangle

The green right triangle in the center of the floor tiles has sides a, b, and c. The pink square drawn on side a contains four triangular tiles. The pink square on side b contains four tiles. The blue square on side c contains eight tiles. The number of tiles in the square on side c equals the sum of the number of tiles in the squares on sides a and b, that is, 8 tiles = 4 tiles + 4 tiles. As a result, you often see the Pythagorean Theorem written as $c^2 = a^2 + b^2$.

If you know the lengths of any two sides in a right triangle, you can use the Pythagorean Theorem to find the length of the third side.

> **Formulas Based on the Pythagorean Theorem**
>
> To find the hypotenuse: **hypotenuse $= \sqrt{(\text{leg})^2 + (\text{leg})^2}$**
>
> To find a leg: **leg $= \sqrt{(\text{hypotenuse})^2 - (\text{leg})^2}$**

EXAMPLE 2 Finding the Unknown Length in Right Triangles

Find the unknown length in each right triangle. Round your answers to the nearest tenth when necessary.

(a)

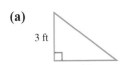

The unknown length is the side opposite the right angle, which is the hypotenuse. Use the formula for finding the hypotenuse.

$$\text{hypotenuse} = \sqrt{(\text{leg})^2 + (\text{leg})^2} \quad \text{Find the hypotenuse.}$$
$$\text{hypotenuse} = \sqrt{(3)^2 + (4)^2} \quad \text{Legs are 3 and 4}$$
$$= \sqrt{9 + 16} \quad (3)\,(3)\text{ is 9 and } (4)\,(4)\text{ is 16}$$
$$= \sqrt{25}$$
$$= 5$$

The hypotenuse is 5 ft long. Write **ft** in the answer (**not** ft²).

(b)

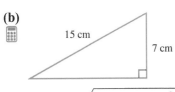

You *do* know the length of the hypotenuse (15 cm), so it is the length of one of the legs that is unknown. Use the formula for finding a leg.

$$\text{leg} = \sqrt{(\text{hypotenuse})^2 - (\text{leg})^2} \quad \text{Find a leg.}$$
$$\text{leg} = \sqrt{(15)^2 - (7)^2} \quad \text{Hypotenuse is 15; one leg is 7}$$
$$= \sqrt{225 - 49} \quad (15)\,(15)\text{ is 225 and } (7)\,(7)\text{ is 49}$$
$$= \sqrt{176} \quad \text{Use a calculator to find } \sqrt{176}$$
$$\approx 13.3 \quad \text{Round } 13.26649916 \text{ to } 13.3$$

The length of the leg is approximately 13.3 cm.

Work Problem **3** at the Side. ▶

3 Find the unknown length in each right triangle. Round your answers to the nearest tenth when necessary.

(a)

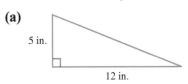

5 in.

12 in.

(b)

7 cm   25 cm   90°

(c)

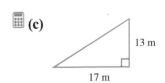

13 m

17 m

(d)

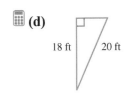

18 ft   20 ft

(e)

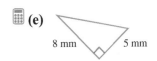

8 mm   5 mm

ANSWERS

3. (a) $\sqrt{169} = 13$ in. **(b)** $\sqrt{576} = 24$ cm
  (c) $\sqrt{458} \approx 21.4$ m **(d)** $\sqrt{76} \approx 8.7$ ft
  (e) $\sqrt{89} \approx 9.4$ mm

4 These problems show ladders leaning against buildings. Find the unknown lengths. Round answers to the nearest tenth of a foot when necessary.

(a)

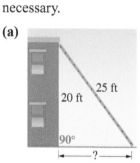

How far away from the building is the bottom of the ladder?

(b)

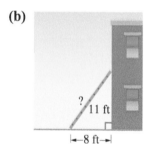

How long is the ladder?

(c) A 17 ft ladder is leaning against a building. The bottom of the ladder is 10 ft from the building. How high up on the building will the ladder reach? (*Hint:* Start by drawing a sketch of the building and the ladder.)

CAUTION

Remember: A small square drawn in one angle of a triangle indicates a right angle (90°). You can use the Pythagorean Theorem *only* on triangles that have a right angle.

OBJECTIVE 3 **Solve application problems involving right triangles.** This example is an application of the Pythagorean Theorem.

EXAMPLE 3 **Using the Pythagorean Theorem**

A television antenna is on the roof of a house, as shown. Find the length of the support wire. Round your answer to the nearest tenth of a meter if necessary.

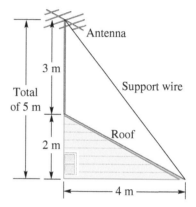

A right triangle is formed. The total length of the leg on the left is 3 m + 2 m = 5 m.

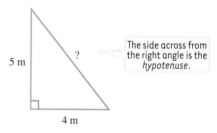

The side across from the right angle is the *hypotenuse.*

Notice that the support wire is opposite the right angle, so it is the *hypotenuse* of the right triangle.

$$\text{hypotenuse} = \sqrt{(\text{leg})^2 + (\text{leg})^2} \quad \text{Find the hypotenuse.}$$
$$\text{hypotenuse} = \sqrt{(5)^2 + (4)^2} \quad \text{Legs are 5 and 4}$$
$$= \sqrt{25 + 16} \quad 5^2 \text{ is } 25 \quad \text{and} \quad 4^2 \text{ is } 16$$
$$= \sqrt{41} \quad \text{Use a calculator to find } \sqrt{41}$$
$$\approx 6.4 \leftarrow \text{Rounded}$$

The length of the support wire is approximately 6.4 m. Write **m** in the answer (**not** m²).

CAUTION

You use the Pythagorean Theorem to find the *length* of one side, *not* the area of the triangle. Your answer will be in linear units, such as ft, yd, cm, m, and so on (*not* ft², yd², cm², m²).

ANSWERS

4. (a) leg = $\sqrt{225}$ = 15 ft

   (b) hypotenuse = $\sqrt{185}$ ≈ 13.6 ft

   (c) leg = $\sqrt{189}$ ≈ 13.7 ft

◀ *Work Problem* **4** *at the Side.*

6.7 ▶▶▶ Exercises

Find each square root. Starting with Exercise 5, find the square root using a calculator.
Round your answers to the nearest thousandth when necessary. See Example 1.

1. $\sqrt{16}$

2. $\sqrt{4}$

3. $\sqrt{64}$

4. $\sqrt{81}$

5. $\sqrt{11}$

6. $\sqrt{23}$

7. $\sqrt{5}$

8. $\sqrt{2}$

9. $\sqrt{73}$

10. $\sqrt{80}$

11. $\sqrt{101}$

12. $\sqrt{125}$

13. $\sqrt{361}$

14. $\sqrt{729}$

15. $\sqrt{1000}$

16. $\sqrt{2000}$

17. You know that $\sqrt{25} = 5$ and $\sqrt{36} = 6$. Using just that information (no calculator), describe how you could *estimate* $\sqrt{30}$. How would you estimate $\sqrt{26}$ or $\sqrt{35}$? Now check your estimates using a calculator.

18. Explain the relationship between *squaring* a number and finding the *square root* of a number. Include two examples to illustrate your explanation.

Find the unknown length in each right triangle. Use a calculator to find square roots.
Round your answers to the nearest tenth when necessary. See Example 2.

19.

15 ft | 90° | 36 ft

20.
9 cm | 12 cm

21.
8 in. | 90° | 15 in.

22.

30 in. | 72 in.

23.
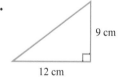
16 mm | 20 mm

24.
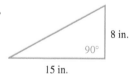
13 m | 5 m

25.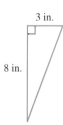
3 in.
8 in.

26.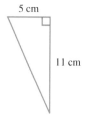
5 cm
11 cm

27.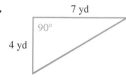
7 yd
90°
4 yd

28.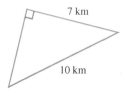
7 km
10 km

29.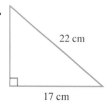
22 cm
17 cm

30.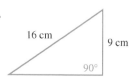
16 cm
9 cm
90°

31.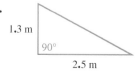
1.3 m
90°
2.5 m

32.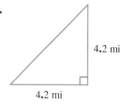
4.2 mi
4.2 mi

33.
11.5 cm
8.2 cm

34.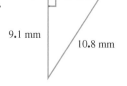
9.1 mm
10.8 mm

35.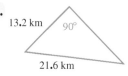
13.2 km
90°
21.6 km

36.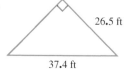
26.5 ft
37.4 ft

Solve each application problem. Round your answers to the nearest tenth when necessary. See Example 3.

37. Find the length of this loading ramp.

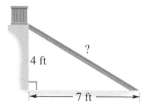
?
4 ft
7 ft

38. Find the unknown length in this window frame.

39. How high is the airplane above the ground?

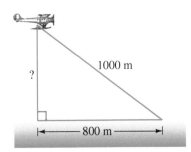

40. Find the height of this farm silo.

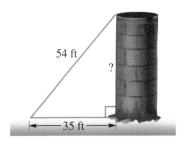

41. How long is the diagonal brace on this storage shed door?

42. Find the height of this rectangular television screen. (*Source:* Sears.)

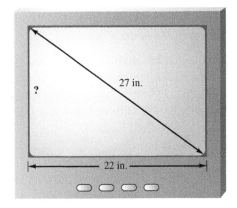

43. To reach his ladylove, a knight placed a 12 ft ladder against the castle wall. If the base of the ladder is 3 ft from the building, how high on the castle will the top of the ladder reach? Draw a sketch of the castle and ladder and solve the problem.

44. William drove his car 15 miles north, then made a right turn and drove 7 miles east. How far is he, in a straight line, from his starting point? Draw a sketch to illustrate the problem and then solve it.

45. Explain the *two* errors made by a student in solving this problem. Also find the correct answer. Round to the nearest tenth.

$? = \sqrt{(13)^2 + (20)^2}$

$= \sqrt{169 + 400}$

$= \sqrt{569} \approx 23.9 \text{ m}^2$

?   13 m

20 m

46. Explain the *two* errors made by a student in solving this problem. Also find the correct answer. Round to the nearest tenth.

$? = \sqrt{(9)^2 + (7)^2}$

$= \sqrt{18 + 14}$

$= \sqrt{32} \approx 5.657 \text{ in.}$

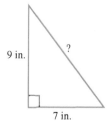

9 in.   ?

7 in.

Relating Concepts (Exercises 47–50) For Individual or Group Work

Use your knowledge of the Pythagorean Theorem to **work Exercises 47–50 in order.** *Round answers to the nearest tenth.*

47. A major league baseball diamond is a square shape measuring 90 ft on each side. If the catcher throws a ball from home plate to second base, how far is he throwing the ball? (*Source:* American League of Professional Baseball Clubs.)

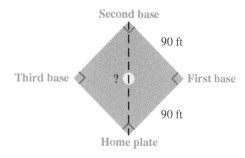

Second base

90 ft

Third base   ?   First base

90 ft

Home plate

48. A softball diamond is only 60 ft on each side. (*Source:* Amateur Softball Association.)

(a) Draw a sketch of the softball diamond and label the bases and the lengths of the sides.

(b) How far is it to throw a ball from home plate to second base?

49. Look back at your answer to Exercise 47. Explain how you can tell the distance from third base to first base without doing any further calculations.

50. (a) Look back at your answer to Exercise 48. Suppose you measured the distance from home plate to second base on a softball diamond and found it was 80 ft. What would this tell you about the length of each side of the diamond? (Assume the diamond is still a square.)

(b) Bonus question: For the diamond in part (a), find the length of each side, to the nearest tenth.

6.8 ▶▶▶ Problem Solving: Equations Containing Decimals

OBJECTIVE ■**1** **Solve equations containing decimals using the addition property of equality.** In **Section 4.3** you used the addition property of equality to solve an equation like $c + 5 = 30$. The addition property says that you can add the *same* number to *both* sides of an equation and still keep it balanced. You can also use this property when an equation contains decimal numbers.

EXAMPLE 1 **Using the Addition Property of Equality**

Solve each equation and check each solution.

(a) $w + 2.9 = -0.6$

The first step is to get the variable term (w) by itself on the left side of the equal sign. Use the addition property to "get rid of" the 2.9 on the left side by adding its opposite, -2.9, to both sides.

$$w + 2.9 = -0.6$$
$$\underline{-2.9 \qquad -2.9} \qquad \text{Add } -2.9 \text{ to both sides.}$$
$$\underbrace{w + 0}_{w} = -3.5$$
$$w = -3.5$$

The solution is -3.5. To check the solution, go back to the *original* equation.

Check $w + 2.9 = -0.6$ Original equation
$$\underbrace{-3.5 + 2.9}_{-0.6} = -0.6 \qquad \text{Replace } w \text{ with } -3.5$$
$$-0.6 = -0.6 \qquad \text{Balances}$$

When w is replaced with -3.5, the equation balances, so -3.5 is the correct solution (*not* -0.6).

(b) $7 = -4.3 + x$

To get x by itself on the right side of the equal sign, add 4.3 to both sides.

$$7 = -4.3 + x$$
$$\underline{+4.3 \qquad +4.3} \qquad \text{Add 4.3 to both sides.}$$
$$11.3 = \underbrace{0 + x}_{x}$$
$$11.3 = x$$

The solution is 11.3. To check the solution, go back to the *original* equation.

Check $7 = -4.3 + x$ Original equation
$$7 = \underbrace{-4.3 + 11.3}_{7} \qquad \text{Replace } x \text{ with } 11.3 \quad \boxed{\text{The solution is 11.3} \text{ (not 7).}}$$
$$7 = 7 \qquad \text{Balances}$$

When x is replaced with 11.3, the equation balances, so 11.3 is the correct solution (*not* 7).

Work Problem ① *at the Side.* ▶

OBJECTIVES

■**1** Solve equations containing decimals using the addition property of equality.

■**2** Solve equations containing decimals using the division property of equality.

■**3** Solve equations containing decimals using both properties of equality.

■**4** Solve application problems involving equations with decimals.

---

1 Solve each equation and check each solution.

(a) $8.1 = h + 9$ **Check**

(b) $-0.75 + y = 0$ **Check**

(c) $c - 6.8 = -4.8$ **Check**

---

2 Solve each equation and check each solution.

(a) $-3y = -0.63$

Check

(b) $2.25r = -18$

Check

(c) $1.7 = 0.5n$

Check

2. **(a)** $y = 0.21$ **Check** $-3y = -0.63$

$-3(0.21) = -0.63$

Balances $-0.63 = -0.63$

(b) $r = -8$ **Check** $2.25r = -18$

$2.25(-8) = -18$

Balances $-18 = -18$

(c) $n = 3.4$ **Check** $1.7 = 0.5n$

$1.7 = 0.5(3.4)$

Balances $1.7 = 1.7$

OBJECTIVE **2** **Solve equations containing decimals using the division property of equality.** You can also use the division property of equality (from **Section 4.4**) when an equation contains decimals.

EXAMPLE 2 **Using the Division Property of Equality**

Solve each equation and check each solution.

(a) $5x = 12.4$

On the left side of the equation, the variable is multiplied by 5. To undo the multiplication, divide both sides by 5.

$5x$ means $5 \cdot x$. $\qquad\longrightarrow 5x = 12.4$

$$\frac{5 \cdot x}{5} = \frac{12.4}{5} \qquad \text{Divide both sides by 5}$$

On the left side, divide out the common factor of 5

$$\frac{\overset{1}{\cancel{5}} \cdot x}{\underset{1}{\cancel{5}}} = 2.48 \qquad \text{On the right side, } 12.4 \div 5 \text{ is } 2.48$$

$$x = 2.48$$

The solution is 2.48. To check the solution, go back to the original equation.

Check $\qquad 5x = 12.4 \qquad$ Original equation

$$5(\mathbf{2.48}) = 12.4 \qquad \text{Replace } x \text{ with } 2.48 \quad \boxed{\text{The solution is } 2.48 \text{ (not } 12.4)}$$

$$12.4 = 12.4 \qquad \text{Balances}$$

When x is replaced with 2.48, the equation balances, so 2.48 is the correct solution (**not** 12.4).

(b) $-9.3 = 1.5t$

Signs are different, so quotient is negative.

$$\frac{-9.3}{1.5} = \frac{\overset{1}{\cancel{1.5}}t}{\underset{1}{\cancel{1.5}}} \qquad \text{Divide both sides by the coefficient of the variable term, 1.5}$$

$$-6.2 = t$$

The solution is -6.2. To check the solution, go back to the original equation.

Check $\qquad -9.3 = 1.5\,t \qquad$ Original equation

$$-9.3 = 1.5(-6.2) \qquad \text{Replace } t \text{ with } -6.2$$

$$-9.3 = -9.3 \qquad \text{Balances}$$

When t is replaced with -6.2, the equation balances, so -6.2 is the correct solution (**not** -9.3).

◀ *Work Problem* **2** *at the Side.*

OBJECTIVE **3** **Solve equations containing decimals using both properties of equality.** Sometimes you need to use both the addition and division properties to solve an equation, as shown in Example 3.

EXAMPLE 3 **Solving Equations with Several Steps**

(a) $2.5b + 0.35 = -2.65$

The first step is to get the variable term, $2.5b$, by itself on the left side of the equal sign.

$$
\begin{array}{rl}
2.5b + 0.35 &= -2.65 \\
\underline{-0.35 \quad -0.35} & \quad \text{Add } -0.35 \text{ to both sides.} \\
2.5b + \quad 0 &= -3.00 \\
2.5b \quad &= -3
\end{array}
$$

The next step is to divide both sides by the coefficient of the variable term. In $2.5b$, the coefficient is 2.5.

$$
\frac{\overset{1}{\cancel{2.5}}b}{\underset{1}{\cancel{2.5}}} = \frac{-3}{2.5}
$$

On the right side, signs do *not* match, so the quotient is *negative*.

$$b = -1.2$$

The solution is -1.2. To check the solution, go back to the original equation.

Check

$$
\begin{array}{rl}
2.5b + 0.35 &= -2.65 \qquad \text{Original equation} \\
2.5\,(-1.2) + 0.35 &= -2.65 \qquad \text{Replace } b \text{ with } -1.2 \\
-3 \quad + 0.35 &= -2.65 \\
-2.65 \quad &= -2.65 \qquad \text{Balances, so } -1.2 \text{ is the correct solution.}
\end{array}
$$

(b) $5x - 0.98 = 2x + 0.4$

There is a variable term on both sides of the equation. You can choose to keep the variable term on the left side, or to keep the variable term on the right side. Either way will work. Just pick the left side or the right side.

Suppose that you decide to keep the variable term, $5x$, on the left side. Use the addition property to "get rid of" $2x$ on the right side by adding its opposite, $-2x$, to both sides.

$$
\begin{array}{rl}
5x - 0.98 = & \ 2x + 0.4 \\
\underline{-2x} \qquad & \ \underline{-2x} \qquad \text{Add } -2x \text{ to both sides.} \\
3x - 0.98 = & \ 0 + 0.4 \\
3x + (-0.98) = & \quad 0.4 \\
\underline{+0.98} & \ \underline{+0.98} \qquad \text{Add } 0.98 \text{ to both sides.} \\
3x + \quad 0 \ = & \quad 1.38
\end{array}
$$

Change subtraction to adding the opposite.

$$
\frac{\overset{1}{\cancel{3}}x}{\underset{1}{\cancel{3}}} = \frac{1.38}{3} \qquad \text{Divide both sides by 3}
$$

$$x = 0.46$$

The solution is 0.46. To check the solution, go back to the original equation.

Check

$$
\begin{array}{rl}
5x - 0.98 = 2x + 0.4 & \qquad \text{Original equation} \\
5\,(0.46) - 0.98 = 2\,(0.46) + 0.4 & \qquad \text{Replace } x \text{ with } 0.46 \\
2.3 \ - 0.98 = \ 0.92 + 0.4 & \\
1.32 \quad = \quad 1.32 & \qquad \text{Balances, so } 0.46 \text{ is the correct solution.}
\end{array}
$$

Work Problem **3** *at the Side.* ▶

3 Solve each equation and check each solution.

(a) $4 = 0.2c - 2.6$

Check

(b) $3.1k - 4 = 0.5k + 13.42$

Check

(c) $-2y + 3 = 3y - 6$

Check

ANSWERS

3. (a) $c = 33$ **Check** $4 = 0.2c - 2.6$
$$4 = 0.2\,(33) - 2.6$$
$$4 = \ 6.6 \ - 2.6$$
Balances $4 = 4$

(b) $k = 6.7$ **Check**
$$3.1k - 4 = 0.5k + 13.42$$
$$3.1\,(6.7) - 4 = 0.5\,(6.7) + 13.42$$
$$20.77 - 4 = \ 3.35 \ + 13.42$$
Balances $16.77 = 16.77$

(c) $y = 1.8$ **Check**
$$-2y + 3 = 3y - 6$$
$$-2\,(1.8) + 3 = 3\,(1.8) - 6$$
$$-3.6 \ + 3 = \ 5.4 \ - 6$$
Balances $-0.6 = -0.6$

4 During April, a special rate was offered on air-to-ground cell phone calls. The connection fee was $1.34 and the cost per minute was $2.69. Maureen made a call that cost $39. How long did the call last? Use the six problem-solving steps.

OBJECTIVE **4** **Solve application problems involving equations with decimals.**   Use the six problem-solving steps from **Section 4.8.**

EXAMPLE 4 **Solving an Application Problem**

Many larger airplanes have phones that can be used to call people on the ground. In January 2004, the cost of using the air-to-ground cell phone was $3.28 per minute plus a $2.99 connection charge. (*Source:* AT&T.) Hernando was billed $19.39 for one call. How many minutes did the call last?

Step 1 **Read** the problem. It is about the cost of a telephone call.

Unknown: number of minutes the call lasted
Known: Costs are $3.28 per minute plus $2.99; total cost was $19.39.

Step 2 **Assign a variable:** There is only one unknown, so let m be the number of minutes.

Step 3 **Write an equation.**

Cost per minute		Number of minutes		Connection charge		Total cost
3.28	•	m	+	2.99	=	19.39

Step 4 **Solve** the equation.

$$3.28m + 2.99 = 19.39$$

$$\underline{\qquad -2.99 \qquad -2.99} \qquad \text{Add } -2.99 \text{ to both sides.}$$

$$3.28m + \quad 0 = 16.40$$

$$\frac{3.28m}{3.28} = \frac{16.40}{3.28} \qquad \text{Divide both sides by 3.28}$$

$$m = 5$$

Write **minutes** as part of your answer.

Step 5 **State the answer.** The call lasted 5 minutes.

Step 6 **Check** the solution by putting it back into the original problem.

$3.28 per minute times 5 minutes = $16.40
$16.40 plus $2.99 connection charge = $19.39
Hernando was billed $19.39. ← Matches

Because 5 minutes "works" when you put it back into the *original* problem, it is the correct solution.

If your answer does **not** work in the original problem, start again at Step 1.

◀ *Work Problem* **4** *at the Side.*

Solve each equation and check each solution. See Examples 1 and 2.

1. $h + 0.63 = 5.1$ **Check**

2. $-0.2 = k - 0.7$ **Check**

3. $-20.6 + n = -22$ **Check**

4. $g - 5 = 6.03$ **Check**

5. $0 = b - 0.008$ **Check**

6. $0.18 + m = -4.5$ **Check**

7. $2.03 = 7a$ **Check**

8. $-6.2c = 0$ **Check**

9. $0.8p = -96$ **Check**

10. $-10.16 = -4r$ **Check**

11. $-3.3t = -2.31$ **Check**

12. $8.3w = -49.8$ **Check**

Solve each equation. Show your work. See Example 3.

13. $7.5x + 0.15 = -6$

14. $0.8 = 0.2y + 3.4$

15. $-7.38 = 2.05z - 7.38$

16. $6.2h - 0.4 = 2.7$

17. $3c + 10 = 6c + 8.65$

18. $2.1b + 5 = 1.6b + 10$

19. $0.8w - 0.4 = -6 + w$

20. $7r + 9.64 = -2.32 + 5r$ **21.** $-10.9 + 0.5p = 0.9p + 5.3$ **22.** $0.7x - 4.38 = x - 2.16$

Solve each application problem using the six problem-solving steps. See Example 4.

23. Most adult medication doses are for a person weighing 150 pounds. For a 45-pound child, the adult dose should be multiplied by 0.3. If the child's dose of a decongestant is 9 milligrams, what is the adult dose?

24. For a 30-pound child, an adult dose of medication should be multiplied by 0.2. If the child's dose of a cough suppressant is 3 milliliters, find the adult dose.

25. A storm blew down many trees. Several neighbors rented a chain saw for $275.80 and helped each other cut up and stack the wood. The rental company charges $65.95 per day plus a $12 sharpening fee. How many days was the saw rented? (*Source:* Central Rental.)

26. A 20-inch chain saw can be rented for $29.95 for the first two hours, and $9 for each additional hour. Steve's rental charge was $56.95. How many hours did he rent the saw? (*Source:* Central Rental.)

Relating Concepts (Exercises 27–30) For Individual or Group Work

When doing aerobic exercises, it is important to increase your heart rate (the number of beats per minute) so that you get the maximum benefit from the exercise. But you don't want your heart rate to be so fast that it is dangerous. Here is an expression for finding a safe maximum heart rate for a healthy person with no heart disease: $0.7(220 - a)$ *where a is the person's age.* **Work Exercises 27–30** *in order: Write an equation and solve it to find each person's age. Assume all the people are healthy.*

27. How old is a person who has a maximum safe heart rate of 140 beats per minute? *Hint:* Use the distributive property to simplify $0.7(220 - a)$.

28. How old is a person who has a maximum safe heart rate of 126 beats per minute?

29. If a person's maximum safe heart rate is 134 (rounded to the nearest whole number), how old is the person, to the nearest whole year?

30. If a person's maximum safe heart rate is 117 (rounded to the nearest whole number), how old is the person, to the nearest whole year?

7

Ratio/Percent

7.1 ▶▶▶ Ratios

OBJECTIVES

1 Write ratios as fractions.

2 Solve ratio problems involving decimals or mixed numbers.

3 Solve ratio problems after converting units.

A **ratio** compares two quantities. You can compare two numbers, such as 8 and 4, or two measurements that have the *same* type of units, such as 3 days and 12 days. (*Rates* compare measurements with different types of units and are covered in the next section.)

Ratios can help you see important relationships. For example, if the ratio of your monthly expenses to your monthly income is 10 to 9, then you are spending $10 for every $9 you earn and going deeper into debt.

OBJECTIVE 1 Write ratios as fractions. A ratio can be written in three ways.

Writing a Ratio

The ratio of $7 **to** $3 can be written as follows.

$$7 \text{ to } 3 \quad \text{or} \quad 7{:}3 \quad \text{or} \quad \frac{7}{3} \leftarrow \text{Fraction bar indicates "\textbf{to}."}$$

"**:**" indicates "**to**."

Writing a ratio as a fraction is the most common method, and the one we will use here. All three ways are read, "the ratio of 7 to 3." The word **to** separates the quantities being compared.

Writing a Ratio as a Fraction

Order is important when you're writing a ratio. The quantity mentioned **first** is the **numerator**. The quantity mentioned **second** is the **denominator**. For example:

$$\text{The ratio of } 5 \text{ to } 12 \quad \text{is written} \quad \frac{5}{12}$$

EXAMPLE 1 Writing Ratios

Ancestors of the Pueblo Indians built multistory apartment towns in New Mexico about 1100 years ago. A room might measure 14 feet long, 11 feet wide, and 15 feet high.

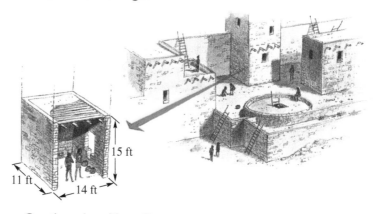

15 ft
11 ft
14 ft

Continued on Next Page

Write each ratio as a fraction, using the room measurements.

(a) Ratio of length to width

The ratio of *length to width* is $\dfrac{14 \text{ feet}}{11 \text{ feet}} = \dfrac{14}{11}$

> Do **not** rewrite the ratio as $1\frac{3}{11}$.

Numerator (mentioned first)   Denominator (mentioned second)

You can divide out common *units* just as you divided out common *factors* when writing fractions in lowest terms. (See **Section 5.2**.) However, do *not* rewrite the fraction as a mixed number. Keep it as the ratio of 14 to 11.

(b) Ratio of width to height

The ratio of *width* to *height* is $\dfrac{11 \text{ feet}}{15 \text{ feet}} = \dfrac{11}{15}$

> Divide out the common units (ft).

CAUTION

Remember, the *order* of the numbers is important in a ratio. Look for the words "ratio of *a* to *b*." Write the ratio as $\dfrac{a}{b}$, *not* $\dfrac{b}{a}$. The quantity mentioned first is the numerator.

Work Problem **1** *at the Side.* ▶

Any ratio can be written as a fraction. Therefore, you can write a ratio in *lowest terms,* just as you do with any fraction.

EXAMPLE 2   Writing Ratios in Lowest Terms

Write each ratio as a fraction in lowest terms.

(a) 60 days to 20 days

The ratio is $\frac{60}{20}$. Write this ratio in lowest terms by dividing the numerator and the denominator by 20.

$$\frac{60}{20} = \frac{60 \div 20}{20 \div 20} = \frac{3}{1} \quad \left\{\begin{array}{l}\text{Ratio in}\\\text{lowest terms}\end{array}\right.$$

So, the ratio of 60 days to 20 days is 3 to 1, or, written as a fraction, $\frac{3}{1}$.

CAUTION

In the fractions chapter (**Chapter 5**), you would have rewritten $\frac{3}{1}$ as 3. But a *ratio* compares *two* quantities, so you need to keep both parts of the ratio and write it as $\frac{3}{1}$.

(b) 50 ounces of medicine to 120 ounces of medicine

The ratio is $\frac{50}{120}$. Divide the numerator and the denominator by 10.

$$\frac{50}{120} = \frac{50 \div 10}{120 \div 10} = \frac{5}{12} \quad \left\{\begin{array}{l}\text{Ratio in}\\\text{lowest terms}\end{array}\right.$$

So, the ratio of 50 ounces to 120 ounces is $\frac{5}{12}$.

Continued on Next Page

1 Shane spent $14 on meat, $5 on milk, and $7 on fresh fruit. Write the following ratios as fractions.

(a) The ratio of amount spent on fruit to amount spent on milk

(b) The ratio of amount spent on milk to amount spent on meat

(c) The ratio of amount spent on meat to amount spent on milk

ANSWERS

1. **(a)** $\frac{7}{5}$ **(b)** $\frac{5}{14}$ **(c)** $\frac{14}{5}$

2 Write each ratio as a fraction in lowest terms.

(a) 9 hours to 12 hours

(b) 100 meters to 50 meters

(c) The ratio of width to length for this rectangle

Length
48 ft

Width
24 ft

3 Write each ratio as a ratio of whole numbers in lowest terms.

(a) The price of Tamar's favorite brand of lipstick increased from $5.50 to $7.00. Find the ratio of the increase in price to the original price.

(b) Last week, Lance worked 4.5 hours each day. This week he cut back to 3 hours each day. Find the ratio of the decrease in hours to the original number of hours.

(c) 15 people in a large van to 6 people in a small van

The ratio is $\dfrac{15}{6} = \dfrac{15 \div 3}{6 \div 3} = \dfrac{5}{2}$ ← $\begin{cases}\text{Ratio in} \\ \text{lowest terms}\end{cases}$

> **Note**
>
> Although $\frac{5}{2} = 2\frac{1}{2}$, ratios are *not* written as mixed numbers. Nevertheless, in Example 2(c) above, the ratio $\frac{5}{2}$ does mean the large van holds $2\frac{1}{2}$ times as many people as the small van.

◀ Work Problem **2** at the Side.

OBJECTIVE 2 Solve ratio problems involving decimals or mixed numbers. Sometimes a ratio compares two decimal numbers or two fractions. It is easier to understand if we rewrite the ratio as a ratio of two whole numbers.

EXAMPLE 3 Using Decimal Numbers in a Ratio

The price of a Sunday newspaper increased from $1.50 to $1.75. Find the ratio of the increase in price to the original price.

The words increase in price are mentioned first, so the increase will be the numerator. How much did the price go up? Use subtraction.

new price − original price = increase
$1.75 − $1.50 = $0.25

The words original price are mentioned second, so the original price of $1.50 is the denominator.

The ratio of increase in price to original price is shown below.

$\dfrac{0.25}{1.50}$ ← increase in price
← original price

Now rewrite the ratio as a ratio of whole numbers. Recall that if you multiply both the numerator and denominator of a fraction by the same number, you get an equivalent fraction. The decimals in this example are hundredths, so multiply by 100 to get whole numbers. (If the decimals are tenths, multiply by 10. If thousandths, multiply by 1000.) Then write the ratio in lowest terms.

$\dfrac{0.25}{1.50} = \dfrac{(0.25)(100)}{(1.50)(100)} = \dfrac{25}{150} = \dfrac{25 \div 25}{150 \div 25} = \dfrac{1}{6}$ ← $\begin{cases}\text{Ratio in} \\ \text{lowest terms}\end{cases}$

Ratio as two
whole numbers

◀ Work Problem **3** at the Side.

EXAMPLE 4 Using Mixed Numbers in Ratios

Write each ratio as a comparison of whole numbers in lowest terms.

(a) 2 days to $2\frac{1}{4}$ days
Write the ratio as follows. Divide out the common units.

$$\dfrac{2 \text{ days}}{2\frac{1}{4} \text{ days}} = \dfrac{2}{2\frac{1}{4}}$$

Continued on Next Page

Next, write 2 as $\frac{2}{1}$ and $2\frac{1}{4}$ as the improper fraction $\frac{9}{4}$.

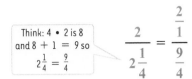

Think: 4 • 2 is 8
and 8 + 1 = 9 so
$2\frac{1}{4} = \frac{9}{4}$

$$\frac{\frac{2}{1}}{2\frac{1}{4}} = \frac{\frac{2}{1}}{\frac{9}{4}}$$

Now rewrite the problem in horizontal format, using the "÷" symbol for division. Finally, multiply by the reciprocal of the divisor, as you did in **Section 5.3.**

$$\frac{\frac{2}{1}}{\frac{9}{4}} = \frac{2}{1} \div \frac{9}{4} = \frac{2}{1} \cdot \frac{4}{9} = \frac{8}{9}$$

Reciprocals

The ratio, in lowest terms, is $\frac{8}{9}$.

(b) $3\frac{1}{4}$ to $1\frac{1}{2}$

Write the ratio as $\dfrac{3\frac{1}{4}}{1\frac{1}{2}}$. Then write $3\frac{1}{4}$ and $1\frac{1}{2}$ as improper fractions.

$$3\frac{1}{4} = \frac{13}{4} \quad \text{and} \quad 1\frac{1}{2} = \frac{3}{2}$$

The ratio is shown below.

$$\frac{3\frac{1}{4}}{1\frac{1}{2}} = \frac{\frac{13}{4}}{\frac{3}{2}}$$

Rewrite as a division problem in horizontal format, using the "÷" symbol. Then multiply by the reciprocal of the divisor.

$$\frac{13}{4} \div \frac{3}{2} = \frac{13}{4} \cdot \frac{2}{3} = \frac{13 \cdot \cancel{2}^{1}}{\cancel{2}_{1} \cdot 2 \cdot 3} = \frac{13}{6} \quad \left\{ \begin{array}{l}\text{Ratio in} \\ \text{lowest terms}\end{array}\right.$$

Reciprocals

> **Note**
> We can also work Examples 4(a) and 4(b) above by using decimals.
> **(a)** $2\frac{1}{4}$ is equivalent to 2.25, so we have the ratio shown below.
> $$\frac{2}{2\frac{1}{4}} = \frac{2}{2.25} = \frac{(2)\,(100)}{(2.25)(100)} = \frac{200}{225} = \frac{200 \div 25}{225 \div 25} = \frac{8}{9} \leftarrow \text{Same result}$$
>
> **(b)** $3\frac{1}{4}$ is equivalent to 3.25 and $1\frac{1}{2}$ is equivalent to 1.5.
> $$\frac{3\frac{1}{4}}{1\frac{1}{2}} = \frac{3.25}{1.5} = \frac{(3.25)(100)}{(1.5)\,(100)} = \frac{325}{150} = \frac{325 \div 25}{150 \div 25} = \frac{13}{6} \leftarrow \text{Same result}$$
>
> This method would *not* work for fractions that are repeating decimals, such as $\frac{1}{3}$ or $\frac{5}{6}$.

4 Write each ratio as a ratio of whole numbers in lowest terms.

(a) $3\frac{1}{2}$ to 4

(b) $5\frac{5}{8}$ pounds to $3\frac{3}{4}$ pounds

(c) $3\frac{1}{3}$ inches to $\frac{5}{6}$ inch

Work Problem **4** *at the Side.* ▶

ANSWERS

4. **(a)** $\frac{7}{8}$ **(b)** $\frac{3}{2}$ **(c)** $\frac{4}{1}$

5 Write each ratio as a fraction in lowest terms. (*Hint:* Recall that it is usually easier to write the ratio using the smaller measurement unit.)

(a) 9 inches to 6 feet

(b) 2 days to 8 hours

(c) 7 yards to 14 feet

(d) 3 quarts to 3 gallons

(e) 25 minutes to 2 hours

(f) 4 pounds to 12 ounces

OBJECTIVE 3 Solve ratio problems after converting units. When a ratio compares measurements, both measurements must be in the *same* units. For example, *feet* must be compared to *feet, hours* to *hours,* and so on.

EXAMPLE 5 Ratio Applications Using Measurement

(a) Write the ratio of the length of the shorter board on the left to the length of the longer board on the right. Compare in inches.

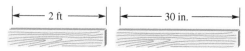

First, express 2 feet in inches. Because 1 foot has 12 inches, 2 feet is

$$2 \cdot 12 \text{ inches} = 24 \text{ inches}$$

The length of the board on the left is 24 inches, so the ratio of the lengths is shown below. The common units divide out.

> Once the units match, you can divide them out.

$$\frac{2 \text{ ft}}{30 \text{ in.}} = \frac{24 \text{ inches}}{30 \text{ inches}} = \frac{24}{30}$$

Write the ratio in lowest terms.

$$\frac{24}{30} = \frac{24 \div 6}{30 \div 6} = \frac{4}{5} \left\{ \begin{array}{l} \text{Ratio in} \\ \text{lowest terms} \end{array} \right.$$

The shorter board on the left is $\frac{4}{5}$ the length of the longer board on the right.

> **Note**
> Notice in the example above that we wrote the ratio using the smaller unit (inches are smaller than feet). Using the smaller unit will help you avoid working with fractions.

(b) Write the ratio of 28 days to 3 weeks.

Since it is usually easier to write the ratio using the smaller measurement, compare in *days* because days are shorter than weeks.

First express 3 weeks in days. Because 1 week has 7 days, 3 weeks is

$$3 \cdot 7 \text{ days} = 21 \text{ days}$$

So the ratio in days is shown below.

$$\frac{28 \text{ days}}{3 \text{ weeks}} = \frac{28 \text{ days}}{21 \text{ days}} = \frac{28}{21} = \frac{28 \div 7}{21 \div 7} = \frac{4}{3} \leftarrow \left\{ \begin{array}{l} \text{Ratio in} \\ \text{lowest terms} \end{array} \right.$$

Use the table below to help set up ratios that compare measurements.

Measurement Comparisons

Length	Weight
12 inches = 1 foot	16 ounces = 1 pound
3 feet = 1 yard	2000 pounds = 1 ton
5280 feet = 1 mile	**Time**
Capacity (Volume)	60 seconds = 1 minute
2 cups = 1 pint	60 minutes = 1 hour
2 pints = 1 quart	24 hours = 1 day
4 quarts = 1 gallon	7 days = 1 week

ANSWERS

5. (a) $\frac{1}{8}$ (b) $\frac{6}{1}$ (c) $\frac{3}{2}$ (d) $\frac{1}{4}$

(e) $\frac{5}{24}$ (f) $\frac{16}{3}$

◀ *Work Problem* **5** *at the Side.*

7.1 ▶▶▶ Exercises

Write each ratio as a fraction in lowest terms. See Examples 1 and 2.

1. 8 days to 9 days

2. $11 to $15

3. $100 to $50

4. 35¢ to 7¢

5. 30 minutes to 90 minutes

6. 9 pounds to 36 pounds

Write each ratio as a ratio of whole numbers in lowest terms. See Examples 3 and 4.

7. $4.50 to $3.50

8. $0.08 to $0.06

9. $1\frac{1}{4}$ to $1\frac{1}{2}$

10. $2\frac{1}{3}$ to $2\frac{2}{3}$

Write each ratio as a fraction in lowest terms. For help, use the table of measurement relationships on page 584. See Example 5.

11. 4 feet to 30 inches

12. 8 feet to 4 yards

13. 5 minutes to 1 hour

14. 3 pounds to 6 ounces

15. 5 gallons to 5 quarts

16. 3 cups to 3 pints

The table shows the number of greeting cards that Americans buy for various occasions. Use the information to answer Exercises 17–22. Write each ratio as a fraction in lowest terms.

Holiday/Event	Cards Sold
Valentine's Day	900 million
Mother's Day	150 million
Father's Day	95 million
Graduation	60 million
Thanksgiving	30 million
Halloween	25 million

Source: Hallmark Cards.

17. Find the ratio of Thanksgiving cards to graduation cards.

18. Find the ratio of Halloween cards to Mother's Day cards.

19. Find the ratio of Valentine's Day cards to Halloween cards.

20. Find the ratio of Mother's Day cards to Father's Day cards.

21. Explain how you might use the information in the table if you owned a shop selling gifts and greeting cards.

22. Why is the ratio of Valentine's Day cards to graduation cards $\frac{15}{1}$? Give two possible reasons.

The bar graph shows worldwide sales of the most popular songs of all time. Use the graph to complete Exercises 23–24. Write each ratio as a fraction in lowest terms.

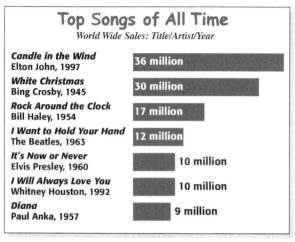

Top Songs of All Time
World Wide Sales: Title/Artist/Year

Candle in the Wind
Elton John, 1997 — 36 million

White Christmas
Bing Crosby, 1945 — 30 million

Rock Around the Clock
Bill Haley, 1954 — 17 million

I Want to Hold Your Hand
The Beatles, 1963 — 12 million

It's Now or Never
Elvis Presley, 1960 — 10 million

I Will Always Love You
Whitney Houston, 1992 — 10 million

Diana
Paul Anka, 1957 — 9 million

Sources: The Music Information Database, www.songfacts.com

23. Sales of which two songs give a ratio of $\frac{3}{1}$? There may be more than one correct answer.

24. Sales of which two songs give a ratio of $\frac{5}{6}$? There may be more than one correct answer.

For each figure in Exercises 25–28, find the ratio of the length of the longest side to the length of the shortest side. Write each ratio as a fraction in lowest terms. See Examples 2–4.

25.

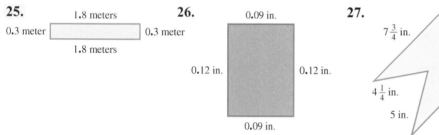

1.8 meters
0.3 meter ☐ 0.3 meter
1.8 meters

26.

0.09 in.
0.12 in. ☐ 0.12 in.
0.09 in.

27.

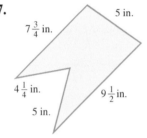

5 in.
$7\frac{3}{4}$ in.
$4\frac{1}{4}$ in.
$9\frac{1}{2}$ in.
5 in.

28.

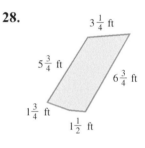

$3\frac{1}{4}$ ft
$5\frac{3}{4}$ ft
$6\frac{3}{4}$ ft
$1\frac{3}{4}$ ft
$1\frac{1}{2}$ ft

Write each ratio as a fraction in lowest terms.

29. The price of automobile engine oil has gone from $10 to $12.50 for the 5 quarts needed for an oil change. Find the ratio of the increase in price to the original price.

30. The price of an antibiotic decreased from $8.80 to $5.60 for 10 tablets. Find the ratio of the decrease in price to the original price.

31. The first time a movie was made in Minnesota, the cast and crew spent $59\frac{1}{2}$ days filming winter scenes. The next year, another movie was filmed in $8\frac{3}{4}$ weeks. Find the ratio of the first movie's filming time to the second movie's time. Compare in weeks.

32. The percheron, a large draft horse, measures about $5\frac{3}{4}$ feet at the shoulder. The prehistoric ancestor of the horse measured only $15\frac{3}{4}$ inches at the shoulder. Find the ratio of the percheron's height to its prehistoric ancestor's height. Compare in inches. (*Source: Eyewitness Books: Horse.*)

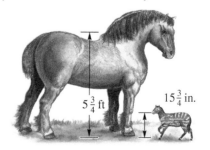

$5\frac{3}{4}$ ft $15\frac{3}{4}$ in.

7.2 ▶▶▶ Rates

A *ratio* compares two measurements with the same type of units, such as 9 feet to 12 feet (both length measurements). But many of the comparisons we make use measurements with different types of units, such as shown here.

160 <u>dollars</u> for 8 <u>hours</u> (money to time)

450 <u>miles</u> on 15 <u>gallons</u> (distance to capacity)

This type of comparison is called a **rate.**

OBJECTIVE 1 Write rates as fractions.   Suppose that yesterday you hiked 18 <u>miles</u> in 4 <u>hours</u>. The *rate* at which you hiked can be written as a fraction in lowest terms.

$$\frac{18 \text{ miles}}{4 \text{ hours}} = \frac{18 \text{ miles} \div 2}{4 \text{ hours} \div 2} = \frac{9 \text{ miles}}{2 \text{ hours}} \leftarrow \text{Rate in lowest terms}$$

In a rate, you often find one of these words separating the quantities you are comparing.

in   for   on   per   from

> **CAUTION**
> When writing a rate, always include the units, such as miles, hours, dollars, and so on. Because the units in a rate are different, the units do *not* divide out.

EXAMPLE 1   Writing Rates in Lowest Terms

Write each rate as a fraction in lowest terms.

(a) 5 gallons of chemical for $60

$$\frac{5 \text{ gallons} \div 5}{60 \text{ dollars} \div 5} = \frac{1 \text{ gallon}}{12 \text{ dollars}}$$ Write the units: gallons and dollars.

(b) $1500 wages in 10 weeks

$$\frac{1500 \text{ dollars} \div 10}{10 \text{ weeks} \div 10} = \frac{150 \text{ dollars}}{1 \text{ week}}$$

Be sure to write the units in a *rate*: dollars, miles, gallons, etc.

(c) 2225 miles on 75 gallons of gas

$$\frac{2225 \text{ miles} \div 25}{75 \text{ gallons} \div 25} = \frac{89 \text{ miles}}{3 \text{ gallons}}$$

Work Problem **1** *at the Side.* ▶

OBJECTIVE 2 Find unit rates.   When the *denominator* of a rate is 1, it is called a **unit rate.** We use unit rates frequently. For example, you earn $12.75 for *1 hour* of work. This unit rate is written:

$12.75 **per** hour   or $12.75 / hour.

You drive 28 miles on *1 gallon* of gas. This unit rate is written

28 miles **per** gallon   or   28 miles / gallon.

Use **per** or a / mark when writing unit rates.

OBJECTIVES

1 Write rates as fractions.

2 Find unit rates.

3 Find the best buy based on cost per unit.

1 Write each rate as a fraction in lowest terms.

(a) $6 for 30 packages

(b) 500 miles in 10 hours

(c) 4 teachers for 90 students

(d) 1270 bushels from 30 acres

ANSWERS

1. **(a)** $\frac{1 \text{ dollar}}{5 \text{ packages}}$ **(b)** $\frac{50 \text{ miles}}{1 \text{ hour}}$

   (c) $\frac{2 \text{ teachers}}{45 \text{ students}}$ **(d)** $\frac{127 \text{ bushels}}{3 \text{ acres}}$

2 Find each unit rate.

(a) $4.35 for 3 pounds of cheese

(b) 304 miles on 9.5 gallons of gas

(c) $850 in 5 days

(d) 24-pound turkey for 15 people

EXAMPLE 2 **Finding Unit Rates**

Find each unit rate.

(a) 337.5 miles on 13.5 gallons of gas
Write the rate as a fraction.

$$\frac{337.5 \text{ miles}}{13.5 \text{ gallons}} \leftarrow \text{The fraction bar indicates division.}$$

Divide 337.5 by 13.5 to find the unit rate.

$$13.5\overline{)337.5} \quad \overset{2\ 5.}{}$$

$$\frac{337.5 \text{ miles} \div 13.5}{13.5 \text{ gallons} \div 13.5} = \frac{25 \text{ miles}}{1 \text{ gallon}}$$

The unit rate is 25 miles **per** gallon, or 25 miles/gallon.

(b) 549 miles in 18 hours

$$\frac{549 \text{ miles}}{18 \text{ hours}} \quad \text{Divide.} \quad 18\overline{)549.0} \quad \overset{30.5}{}$$

The unit rate is 30.5 miles **per** hour, or 30.5 miles/hour.

(c) $810 in 6 days

$$\frac{810 \text{ dollars}}{6 \text{ days}} \quad \text{Divide.} \quad 6\overline{)810} \quad \overset{135}{}$$

> Use *per* or a slash mark to write unit rates.

The unit rate is $135 **per** day, or $135/day.

◀ *Work Problem* **2** *at the Side.*

OBJECTIVE 3 Find the best buy based on cost per unit. When shopping for groceries, household supplies, and health and beauty items, you will find many different brands and package sizes. You can save money by finding the lowest *cost per unit*.

Cost per Unit

Cost per unit is a rate that tells how much you pay for *one* item or *one* unit. Examples are $3.25 per gallon, $47 per shirt, and $2.98 per pound.

EXAMPLE 3 **Determining the Best Buy**

The local store charges the following prices for pancake syrup. Find the best buy.

Continued on Next Page

The best buy is the container with the *lowest* cost per unit. All the containers are measured in *ounces* (oz), so you first need to find the *cost per ounce* for each one. Divide the price of the container by the number of ounces in it. Round to the nearest thousandth if necessary.

Let the *order* of the *words* help you set up the rate.

cost ————————→ $1.28
per (means divide) → ————————
ounce ————————→ 12 ounces

Size	Cost per Unit (Rounded)
12 ounces	$\dfrac{\$1.28}{12\text{ ounces}} \approx \$0.107$ per ounce (highest)
24 ounces	$\dfrac{\$1.81}{24\text{ ounces}} \approx \$0.075$ per ounce (lowest)
36 ounces	$\dfrac{\$2.73}{36\text{ ounces}} \approx \$0.076$ per ounce

The lowest cost per ounce is $0.075, so the 24-ounce container is the best buy.

Note

Earlier we rounded money amounts to the nearest hundredth (nearest cent). But when comparing unit costs, rounding to the nearest thousandth will help you see the difference between very similar unit costs. Notice that the 24-ounce and 36-ounce syrup containers above would both have rounded to $0.08 per ounce if we had rounded to hundredths.

Work Problem **3** *at the Side.* ▶

▦ Calculator Tip   When using a calculator to find unit prices, remember that division is *not* commutative. In Example 3 above you wanted to find cost per ounce. Let the *order* of the *words* help you enter the numbers in the correct order.

cost   per   ounce
  ↓   ↓   ↓
Enter   Per means   Enter
the cost.   divide.   number
                         of ounces.
  ↓   ↓   ↓
$2.73   ÷   36   =   0.076 (rounded)

If you reversed the order and entered 36 ÷ 2.73 = , the result is the number of *ounces* per *dollar*. How could you use that information to find the best buy? (*Answer:* The best buy would be the greatest number of ounces per dollar.)

Finding the best buy is sometimes a complicated process. Things that affect the cost per unit can include "cents off" coupons and differences in how much use you'll get out of each unit.

3 Find the best buy (lowest cost per unit) for each purchase.

(a) 2 quarts for $3.25
    3 quarts for $4.95
    4 quarts for $6.48

(b) 6 cans of cola for $1.99
    12 cans of cola for $3.49
    24 cans of cola for $7

4 Solve each problem.

(a) Some batteries claim to last longer than others. If you believe these claims, which brand is the best buy?

Four-pack of AA-size batteries for $2.79

One AA-size battery for $1.19; lasts twice as long

(b) Which tube of toothpaste is the best buy? You have a coupon for 85¢ off Brand C and a coupon for 20¢ off Brand D.

Brand C is $3.89 for 6 ounces.

Brand D is $1.59 for 2.5 ounces.

EXAMPLE 4 **Solving Best Buy Applications**

Solve each application problem.

(a) There are many brands of liquid laundry detergent. If you feel they all do a good job of cleaning your clothes, you can base your purchase on cost per unit. But some brands are "concentrated" so you can use less detergent for each load of clothes. Which of the choices shown below is the best buy?

50 fluid ounces for $3.99
Does same number of washloads as the old 64-ounce bottle!

One gallon (128 ounces) for $9.89
Does twice the washloads of the old gallon bottle!

To find Sudzy's unit cost, divide $3.99 by 64 ounces, not 50 ounces. You're getting as many clothes washed as if you bought 64 ounces. Similarly, to find White-O's unit cost, divide $9.89 by 256 ounces (twice 128 ounces, or 2 • 128 ounces = 256 ounces).

Sudzy $\dfrac{\$3.99}{64 \text{ ounces}} \approx \$0.062$ per ounce

> The best buy is the *lower* cost per ounce.

White-O $\dfrac{\$9.89}{256 \text{ ounces}} \approx \$0.039$ per ounce

White-O has the lower cost per ounce and is the best buy. (However, if you try it and it doesn't get out all the stains, Sudzy may be worth the extra cost.)

(b) "Cents-off" coupons also affect the best buy. Suppose you are looking at these choices for "extra-strength" pain reliever. Both brands have the same amount of pain reliever in each tablet.

Brand X is $2.29 for 50 tablets.

Brand Y is $10.75 for 200 tablets.

You have a 40¢ coupon for Brand X and a 75¢ coupon for Brand Y. Which choice is the best buy?

To find the best buy, first subtract the coupon amounts, then divide to find the lowest cost per ounce.

Brand X costs $2.29 − $0.40 = $1.89

$\dfrac{\$1.89}{50 \text{ tablets}} \approx \$0.038$ per tablet

Brand Y costs $10.75 − $0.75 = $10.00

$\dfrac{\$10.00}{200 \text{ tablets}} = \$0.05$ per tablet

> Look for the *lower* cost per tablet.

Brand X has the lower cost per tablet and is the best buy.

◀ *Work Problem* **4** *at the Side.*

ANSWERS

4. (a) One battery that lasts twice as long (like getting two) is the best buy. The cost per unit is $0.595 per battery. The four-pack is about $0.698 per battery.

(b) Brand C with the 85¢ coupon is the best buy at about $0.507 per ounce. Brand D with the 20¢ coupon is $0.556 per ounce.

7.2 ▶▶▶ Exercises

Write each rate as a fraction in lowest terms. See Example 1.

1. 10 cups for 6 people

2. $12 for 30 pens

3. 15 feet in 35 seconds

4. 100 miles in 30 hours

5. 14 people for 28 dresses

6. 12 wagons for 48 horses

7. 25 letters in 5 minutes

8. 68 pills for 17 people

9. $63 for 6 visits

10. 25 doctors for 310 patients

11. 72 miles on 4 gallons

12. 132 miles on 8 gallons

Find each unit rate. See Example 2.

13. $60 in 5 hours

14. $2500 in 20 days

15. 50 eggs from 10 chickens

16. 36 children from 12 families

17. 7.5 pounds for 6 people

18. 44 bushels from 8 trees

19. $413.20 for 4 days

20. $74.25 for 9 hours

Earl kept the following record of the gas he bought for his car. For each entry, find the number of miles he traveled and the unit rate. Round your answers to the nearest tenth.

	Date	Odometer at Start	Odometer at End	Miles Traveled	Gallons Purchased	Miles per Gallon
21.	2/4	27,432.3	27,758.2		15.5	
22.	2/9	27,758.2	28,058.1		13.4	
23.	2/16	28,058.1	28,396.7		16.2	
24.	2/20	28,396.7	28,704.5		13.3	

Source: Author's car records.

Find the best buy (based on the cost per unit) for each item. See Example 3.
(Sources: Cub Foods, Target, Rainbow Foods.)

25. Black pepper

26. Shampoo

27. Cereal
    12 ounces for $2.49
    14 ounces for $2.89
    18 ounces for $3.96

28. Soup (same size cans)
    2 cans for $2.18
    3 cans for $3.57
    5 cans for $5.29

29. Chunky peanut butter
    12 ounces for $1.29
    18 ounces for $1.79
    28 ounces for $3.39
    40 ounces for $4.39

30. Baked beans
    8 ounces for $0.59
    16 ounces for $0.99
    21 ounces for $1.29
    28 ounces for $1.89

31. Suppose you are choosing between two brands of chicken noodle soup. Brand A is $0.88 per can and Brand B is $0.98 per can. The cans are the same size, but Brand B has more chunks of chicken in it. Which soup is the best buy? Explain your choice.

32. A small bag of potatoes costs $0.19 per pound. A large bag costs $0.15 per pound. But there are only two people in your family, so half the large bag would probably spoil before you used it up. Which bag is the best buy? Explain.

Solve each application problem. See Examples 2–4.

33. Makesha lost 10.5 pounds in six weeks. What was her rate of loss in pounds per week?

34. Enrique's taco recipe uses three pounds of meat to feed 10 people. Give the rate in pounds per person.

35. Russ works 7 hours to earn $85.82. What is his pay rate per hour?

36. Find the cost of 1 gallon of Hawaiian Punch beverage if 18 gallons for a graduation party cost $55.62.

The table lists information about three long-distance calling cards. The connection fee is charged each time you make a call, no matter how long the call lasts. Use the information in the table to answer Exercises 37–40. Round answers to the nearest thousandth when necessary.

LONG-DISTANCE CALLING CARDS (U.S.)

Card Name	Cost per Minute	Connection Fee
Radiant Penny	$0.01	$0.39
IDT Special	$0.022	$0.14
Access America	$0.047	$0.00

Source: www.1callcard.com

37. (a) Find the *actual* total cost, including the connection charge, for a five-minute call using each card.

   (b) Find the cost per minute for this call using each card and select the best buy.

38. (a) Find the *actual* total cost, including the connection charge, for a 30-minute call using each card.

   (b) Find the cost per minute for this call using each card and select the best buy.

39. Find the *actual* total cost per minute for a 15-minute call and a 20-minute call using each card. Then select the best buy for each call.

40. All the cards round calls up to the next full minute.

   (a) Suppose you call the wrong number. How much would you pay for this 40-*second* call on each card?

   (b) How much would you save on this call by using Access America instead of Radiant Penny?

41. In the 2000 Olympics, Michael Johnson ran the 400-meter event in a record time of approximately 44 seconds (actually 43.84 seconds). Give his rate in seconds per meter and in meters per second. Use 44 seconds as the time. (*Source:* www.Olympics.com)

42. Sofia can clean and adjust five hearing aids in four hours. Give her rate in hearing aids per hour and in hours per hearing aid.

🖩 **43.** If you believe the claims that some batteries last longer, which is the best buy?

🖩 **44.** Which is the best buy, assuming these laundry detergents both clean equally well?

45. Three brands of cornflakes are available. Brand G is priced at $2.39 for 10 ounces. Brand K is $3.99 for 20.3 ounces and Brand P is $3.39 for 16.5 ounces. You have a coupon for 50¢ off Brand P and a coupon for 60¢ off Brand G. Which cereal is the best buy based on cost per unit?

46. Two brands of facial tissue are available. Brand K has a special price of $5 for three boxes of 175 tissues each. Brand S is priced at $1.29 per box of 125 tissues. You have a coupon for 20¢ off one box of Brand S and a coupon for 45¢ off one box of Brand K. How can you get the best buy on one box of tissue?

Relating Concepts (Exercises 47–50) For Individual or Group Work

*On the first page of this chapter, we said that unit rates can help you get the best deal on cell phone service. Use the information in the table to **work Exercises 47–50 in order.***

CELL PHONE SERVICE PLANS

Company	Anytime Minutes	One-Time Activation Fee	Monthly Charge	Termination Fee
Verizon	400	$35	$59.99	$175
T-Mobile	600	$35	$39.99	$200
Nextel	500	$35	$45.99	$200
Sprint	500	$36	$55	$150

Source: Advertisements appearing in *Minneapolis Star Tribune.*

Notes:

1. All companies require that you sign a contract for one year of service and charge a one-time termination fee if you quit early.

2. Unused minutes cannot be carried over to the next month.

47. How much will each company's activation fee cost you on a monthly basis during the one-year contract?

48. All the plans allow unlimited calls on nights and weekends, so you would be using the "anytime minutes" on weekdays. Figure out the average number of weekdays per month. Then, for each plan, how many minutes could you use per weekday? Round to the nearest whole minute.

49. Find the actual average cost per "anytime minute" during the one-year contract for each company, including the activation fee. Assume you use all the minutes and no more. Decide how to round your answers so you can find the best buy.

50. Suppose that after two months you canceled your service because you found that you only used 100 "anytime minutes" per month. Under those conditions, find the actual cost per "anytime minute" for each company, to the nearest cent.

7.3 ▶▶▶ Proportions

OBJECTIVE 1 Write proportions. A **proportion** states that two ratios (or rates) are equivalent. For example,

$$\frac{\$20}{4 \text{ hours}} = \frac{\$40}{8 \text{ hours}}$$

is a proportion that says the rate $\frac{\$20}{4 \text{ hours}}$ is equivalent to the rate $\frac{\$40}{8 \text{ hours}}$. As the amount of money doubles, the number of hours also doubles. This proportion is read:

20 dollars **is to** 4 hours **as** 40 dollars **is to** 8 hours

EXAMPLE 1 Writing Proportions

Write each proportion.

(a) 6 feet is to 11 feet **as** 18 feet is to 33 feet.

$$\frac{6 \text{ feet}}{11 \text{ feet}} = \frac{18 \text{ feet}}{33 \text{ feet}} \quad \text{so} \quad \frac{6}{11} = \frac{18}{33}$$

The common units (feet) divide out and are not written.

(b) \$9 is to 6 liters **as** \$3 is to 2 liters.

$$\frac{\$9}{6 \text{ liters}} = \frac{\$3}{2 \text{ liters}}$$

The units do *not* match so you must write them in the proportion.

Work Problem 1 at the Side. ▶

OBJECTIVE 2 Determine whether proportions are true or false. There are two ways to see whether a proportion is true. One way is to *write both of the ratios in lowest terms.*

EXAMPLE 2 Writing Both Ratios in Lowest Terms

Determine whether each proportion is true or false by writing both ratios in lowest terms.

(a) $\frac{5}{9} = \frac{18}{27}$

Write each ratio in lowest terms.

$$\frac{5}{9} \leftarrow \text{Already in lowest terms} \qquad \frac{18 \div 9}{27 \div 9} = \frac{2}{3} \leftarrow \text{Lowest terms}$$

Because $\frac{5}{9}$ is *not* equivalent to $\frac{2}{3}$, the proportion is *false*. The ratios are *not* proportional.

(b) $\frac{16}{12} = \frac{28}{21}$

Write each ratio in lowest terms.

$$\frac{16 \div 4}{12 \div 4} = \frac{4}{3} \quad \text{and} \quad \frac{28 \div 7}{21 \div 7} = \frac{4}{3}$$

Both ratios are equivalent to $\frac{4}{3}$, so the proportion is *true*. The ratios are proportional.

Work Problem 2 at the Side. ▶

OBJECTIVES

1 Write proportions.

2 Determine whether proportions are true or false.

3 Find the unknown number in a proportion.

1 Write each proportion.

(a) \$7 is to 3 cans as \$28 is to 12 cans.

(b) 9 meters is to 16 meters as 18 meters is to 32 meters.

(c) 5 is to 7 as 35 is to 49.

(d) 10 is to 30 as 60 is to 180.

2 Determine whether each proportion is true or false by writing both ratios in lowest terms.

(a) $\frac{6}{12} = \frac{15}{30}$

(b) $\frac{20}{24} = \frac{3}{4}$

(c) $\frac{25}{40} = \frac{30}{48}$

(d) $\frac{35}{45} = \frac{12}{18}$

ANSWERS

1. **(a)** $\frac{\$7}{3 \text{ cans}} = \frac{\$28}{12 \text{ cans}}$ **(b)** $\frac{9}{16} = \frac{18}{32}$ **(c)** $\frac{5}{7} = \frac{35}{49}$ **(d)** $\frac{10}{30} = \frac{60}{180}$

2. **(a)** $\frac{1}{2} = \frac{1}{2}$; true **(b)** $\frac{5}{6} \neq \frac{3}{4}$; false **(c)** $\frac{5}{8} = \frac{5}{8}$; true **(d)** $\frac{7}{9} \neq \frac{2}{3}$; false

A second way to see whether a proportion is true is to find *cross products*.

Using Cross Products to Determine Whether a Proportion Is True

To see whether a proportion is true, first multiply along one diagonal, then multiply along the other diagonal, as shown here.

$$5 \cdot 4 = 20$$

$$\frac{2}{5} = \frac{4}{10}$$

Cross products are equal.

$$2 \cdot 10 = 20$$

In this case the **cross products** are both 20. When cross products are *equal*, the proportion is *true*. If the cross products are *unequal*, the proportion is *false*.

Note

Why does the cross products test work? It is based on rewriting both fractions with a common denominator of $5 \cdot 10$ or 50. (We do not search for the *lowest* common denominator. We simply use the product of the two given denominators.)

$$\frac{2 \cdot 10}{5 \cdot 10} = \frac{20}{50} \quad \text{and} \quad \frac{4 \cdot 5}{10 \cdot 5} = \frac{20}{50}$$

We see that $\frac{2}{5}$ and $\frac{4}{10}$ are equivalent because both can be rewritten as $\frac{20}{50}$. The cross products test takes a shortcut by comparing only the two numerators ($20 = 20$).

EXAMPLE 3 **Using Cross Products**

Use cross products to see whether each proportion is true or false.

(a) $\dfrac{3}{5} = \dfrac{12}{20}$ Multiply along one diagonal and then multiply along the other diagonal.

$$5 \cdot 12 = 60$$

$$\frac{3}{5} = \frac{12}{20}$$

Equal — When cross products are equal, the proportion is true.

$$3 \cdot 20 = 60$$

The cross products are *equal,* so the proportion is *true.*

CAUTION

Use cross products *only* when working with *proportions.* Do ***not*** use cross products when multiplying fractions, adding fractions, or writing fractions in lowest terms.

Continued on Next Page

(b) $\dfrac{2\frac{1}{3}}{3\frac{1}{3}} = \dfrac{9}{16}$ Find the cross products.

Write $3\frac{1}{3}$ as $\frac{10}{3}$ and write 9 as $\frac{9}{1}$.

$$3\frac{1}{3} \cdot 9 = \frac{10}{3} \cdot \frac{\overset{3}{\cancel{9}}}{1} = \frac{30}{1} = 30 \longleftarrow$$

$$\dfrac{2\frac{1}{3}}{3\frac{1}{3}} = \dfrac{9}{16}$$

Unequal; proportion is false.

$$2\frac{1}{3} \cdot 16 = \frac{7}{3} \cdot \frac{16}{1} = \frac{112}{3} = 37\frac{1}{3} \longleftarrow$$

The cross products are *unequal,* so the proportion is *false.*

> **Note**
>
> The numbers in a proportion do *not* have to be whole numbers. They may be fractions, mixed numbers, decimal numbers, and so on.

Work Problem **3** *at the Side.* ▶

OBJECTIVE 3 Find the unknown number in a proportion. Four numbers are used in a proportion. If any three of these numbers are known, the fourth can be found. For example, find the unknown number that will make this proportion true.

$$\frac{3}{5} = \frac{x}{40}$$

The variable x represents the unknown number. First find the cross products.

$$\frac{3}{5} = \frac{x}{40} \quad \left.\begin{array}{c} 5 \cdot x \\[4pt] 3 \cdot 40 \end{array}\right\} \text{Cross products}$$

To make the proportion true, the cross products must be equal. This gives us the following equation.

$$\underbrace{5 \cdot x}_{} = \underbrace{3 \cdot 40}_{}$$
$$5x = 120$$

Recall from **Section 2.4** that we can solve an equation of this type by dividing both sides by the coefficient of the variable term. In this case, the coefficient of $5x$ is 5.

$$\frac{5x}{5} = \frac{120}{5} \quad \leftarrow \text{Divide both sides by 5}$$

On the left side, divide out the common factor of 5; slashes indicate the division.

$$\frac{\overset{1}{\cancel{5}} \cdot x}{\underset{1}{\cancel{5}}} = 24 \quad \text{On the right side, divide 120 by 5 to get 24}$$

$$x = 24$$

3 Find the cross products to see whether each proportion is true or false.

(a) $\dfrac{5}{9} = \dfrac{10}{18}$

(b) $\dfrac{32}{15} = \dfrac{16}{8}$

(c) $\dfrac{10}{17} = \dfrac{20}{34}$

(d) $\dfrac{2.4}{6} = \dfrac{5}{12}$

$(6)(5) =$

$(2.4)(12) =$

(e) $\dfrac{3}{4.25} = \dfrac{24}{34}$

(f) $\dfrac{1\frac{1}{6}}{2\frac{1}{3}} = \dfrac{4}{8}$

ANSWERS

3. **(a)** $90 = 90$; true
   (b) $240 \neq 256$; false
   (c) $340 = 340$; true
   (d) $(6)(5) = 30$; $(2.4)(12) = 28.8$; false
   (e) $102 = 102$; true
   (f) $9\frac{1}{3} = 9\frac{1}{3}$; true

The unknown number in the proportion is 24. The complete proportion is shown below.

$$\frac{3}{5} = \frac{24}{40} \leftarrow x \text{ is } 24$$

Check by finding the cross products. If they are equal, you solved the problem correctly. If they are unequal, rework the problem.

$$5 \cdot 24 = 120 \leftarrow$$
$$\frac{3}{5} = \frac{24}{40}$$
$$3 \cdot 40 = 120 \leftarrow$$

Equal; proportion is true.

The solution is 24, **not** 120.

The cross products are equal, so the solution, $x = 24$, is correct.

CAUTION

The solution is 24, which is the unknown number in the proportion. 120 is *not* the solution; it is the cross product you get when *checking* the solution.

Solve a proportion for an unknown number by using the following steps.

Solving a Proportion to Find an Unknown Number

Step 1 Find the cross products.

Step 2 Show that the cross products are equivalent.

Step 3 Divide both sides of the equation by the coefficient of the variable term.

Step 4 Check by writing the solution in the *original* proportion and finding the cross products.

EXAMPLE 4 **Solving Proportions**

Find the unknown number in each proportion. Round answers to the nearest hundredth when necessary.

(a) $\dfrac{16}{x} = \dfrac{32}{20}$

You can write $\frac{32}{20}$ in lowest terms as $\frac{8}{5}$

Recall that ratios can be rewritten in lowest terms. If desired, you can do that *before* finding the cross products. In this example, write $\frac{32}{20}$ in lowest terms as $\frac{8}{5}$, which gives the proportion $\dfrac{16}{x} = \dfrac{8}{5}$.

Step 1 $\dfrac{16}{x} = \dfrac{8}{5}$

$$x \cdot 8 \leftarrow$$
$$16 \cdot 5 \leftarrow$$

Find the cross products.

Continued on Next Page

Step 2 $x \cdot 8 = 16 \cdot 5$ Show that the cross products are equivalent.

$x \cdot 8 = \quad 80$

Step 3 $\dfrac{x \cdot \cancel{8}^{1}}{\cancel{8}_{1}} = \dfrac{80}{8}$ ← Divide both sides by 8

$x = 10$ ← Find x. (No rounding is necessary.)

Step 4 Write the solution in the *original* proportion and check by finding the cross products.

$10 \cdot 32 = 320$

x is 10 → $\dfrac{16}{10} = \dfrac{32}{20}$ Equal; proportion is true.

$16 \cdot 20 = 320$

The cross products are equal, so 10 is the correct solution.

The solution is 10, **not** 320.

> **Note**
>
> It is not necessary to write the ratios in lowest terms before solving. However, if you do, you will have smaller numbers to work with.

(b) $\dfrac{7}{12} = \dfrac{15}{x}$

Step 1 $\dfrac{7}{12} = \dfrac{15}{x}$ Find the cross products.

$12 \cdot 15 = 180$

$7 \cdot x$

Step 2 $7 \cdot x = 180$ ← Show that cross products are equivalent.

Step 3 $\dfrac{\cancel{7}^{1} \cdot x}{\cancel{7}_{1}} = \dfrac{180}{7}$ ← Divide both sides by 7

$x \approx 25.71$ ← Rounded to nearest hundredth

When the division does not come out even, check for directions on how to round your answer. Divide out one more place, then round.

$$7)\overline{180.000} \quad \dfrac{25.714}{}$$ ← Divide out to thousandths so you can round to hundredths.

Step 4 Write the solution in the original proportion and check by finding the cross products.

$(12)(15) = 180$

$\dfrac{7}{12} \approx \dfrac{15}{25.71}$ Very close, but *not* equal due to rounding the solution

$(7)(25.71) = 179.97$

The cross products are slightly different because you rounded the value of x. However, they are close enough to see that the problem was done correctly and 25.71 is the approximate solution (**not** 179.97).

Work Problem ④ *at the Side.* ▶

---

④ Find the unknown numbers. Round to hundredths when necessary. Check your answers by finding the cross products.

(a) $\dfrac{1}{2} = \dfrac{x}{12}$

(b) $\dfrac{6}{10} = \dfrac{15}{x}$

(c) $\dfrac{28}{x} = \dfrac{21}{9}$

(d) $\dfrac{x}{8} = \dfrac{3}{5}$

(e) $\dfrac{14}{11} = \dfrac{x}{3}$

ANSWERS

4. **(a)** $x = 6$ **(b)** $x = 25$
   (c) $x = 12$ **(d)** $x = 4.8$
   (e) $x \approx 3.82$ (rounded to nearest hundredth)

The next example shows how to solve for the unknown number in a proportion with fractions or decimals.

EXAMPLE 5 **Solving Proportions with Mixed Numbers and Decimals**

Find the unknown number in each proportion.

(a) $\dfrac{2\frac{1}{5}}{6} = \dfrac{x}{10}$

Step 1 $\qquad \dfrac{2\frac{1}{5}}{6} = \dfrac{x}{10} \qquad$ $\begin{array}{l} 6 \cdot x \\[4pt] 2\frac{1}{5} \cdot 10 \end{array}$ $\leftarrow$ Find the cross products.

Find $2\frac{1}{5} \cdot 10$.

$$2\frac{1}{5} \cdot 10 = \frac{11}{5} \cdot \frac{10}{1} = \frac{11 \cdot 2 \cdot \cancel{5}^{1}}{\cancel{5} \cdot 1} = \frac{22}{1} = 22$$

Changed to improper fraction

Step 2 $\qquad 6 \cdot x = 22 \quad \leftarrow$ Show that cross products are equivalent.

Step 3 $\qquad \dfrac{\cancel{6}^{1} \cdot x}{\cancel{6}_{1}} = \dfrac{22}{6} \quad \leftarrow$ Divide both sides by 6.

Write the solution as a mixed number in lowest terms.

$$x = \frac{22 \div 2}{6 \div 2} = \frac{11}{3} = 3\frac{2}{3}$$

Step 4 Write the solution in the original proportion and check by finding the cross products.

$$6 \cdot 3\frac{2}{3} = \frac{2 \cdot \cancel{3}^{1}}{1} \cdot \frac{11}{\cancel{3}} = \frac{22}{1} = 22$$

$$\frac{2\frac{1}{5}}{6} = \frac{3\frac{2}{3}}{10} \qquad \text{Equal}$$

$$2\frac{1}{5} \cdot 10 = \frac{11}{\cancel{5}} \cdot \frac{2 \cdot \cancel{5}^{1}}{1} = \frac{22}{1} = 22$$

The cross products are equal, so $3\frac{2}{3}$ is the correct solution.

The solution is $3\frac{2}{3}$, **not** 22.

Continued on Next Page

Note

You can use decimal numbers and your calculator to solve Example 5(a) on the previous page. $2\frac{1}{5}$ is equivalent to 2.2, so the cross products are

$$6 \cdot x = (2.2)(10)$$

$$\frac{\overset{1}{\cancel{6}} \cdot x}{\underset{1}{\cancel{6}}} = \frac{22}{6}$$

When you divide 22 by 6 on your calculator, it shows 3.666666667. Write the answer using a bar to show the repeating digit: $3.\overline{6}$. Or round the answer to 3.67 (nearest hundredth).

(b) $\dfrac{1.5}{0.6} = \dfrac{2}{x}$

$\quad(1.5)(x) = (0.6)(2)$ ← Show that cross products are equivalent.

$\quad(1.5)(x) = 1.2$

$\quad\dfrac{(\overset{1}{\cancel{1.5}})(x)}{\underset{1}{\cancel{1.5}}} = \dfrac{1.2}{1.5}$ ←——— Divide both sides by 1.5.

$\qquad x = \dfrac{1.2}{1.5}\qquad$ Complete the division. $\quad 1.5\,\overline{)1.20}^{\,.8}$

$\qquad x = 0.8$

So the solution is 0.8.

Write the solution in the original equation, and check by finding the cross products.

$$(0.6)(2) = 1.2$$

$$\frac{1.5}{0.6} = \frac{2}{0.8}\qquad \text{Equal}$$

$$(1.5)(0.8) = 1.2$$

The cross products are equal, so 0.8 is the correct solution.

The solution is 0.8 (**not** 1.2)

———————— Work Problem **5** at the Side. ▶

5 Find the unknown numbers. Round to hundredths on the decimal problems when necessary. Check your solutions by finding the cross products.

(a) $\dfrac{3\frac{1}{4}}{2} = \dfrac{x}{8}$

(b) $\dfrac{x}{3} = \dfrac{1\frac{2}{3}}{5}$

(c) $\dfrac{0.06}{x} = \dfrac{0.3}{0.4}$

(d) $\dfrac{2.2}{5} = \dfrac{13}{x}$

(e) $\dfrac{x}{6} = \dfrac{0.5}{1.2}$

(f) $\dfrac{0}{2} = \dfrac{x}{7.092}$

Math in the Media

FEEDING HUMMINGBIRDS

Filling Your Feeder

After getting a hummingbird feeder, the next step is to fill it! You have two choices at this point: you can either buy one of the commercial mixtures or you can make your own solution, shown at the right.

The concentration of the sugar is important. The 1 to 4 ratio of sugar to water is recommended because it approximates the ratio of sugar to water found in the nectar of many hummingbird flowers.

Boiling the solution helps retard fermentation. Sugar-and-water solutions are subject to rapid spoiling, especially in hot weather.

Source: The Hummingbird Book.

> **Recipe for Homemade Mixture:**
> 1 part sugar (not honey)
> 4 parts water
> Boil for 1 to 2 minutes. Cool.
> Store extra in refrigerator.

A recipe can be used to make as much of a mixture as you need as long as the ingredients are kept proportional. Use the recipe for a homemade mixture of sugar water for hummingbird feeders to answer these problems.

1. What is the ratio of sugar to water in the recipe?

   What is the ratio of water to sugar in the recipe?

2. Complete each table.

Sugar	Water
1 cup	4 cups
	5 cups
	6 cups
	7 cups
2 cups	8 cups

Sugar	Water
1 cup	4 cups
	3 cups
	2 cups
	1 cup

3. How much water would you need if you used
   (a) 3 cups of sugar?
   (b) 4 cups of sugar?
   (c) $\frac{1}{3}$ cup of sugar?

4. As you change the amounts of water and sugar, should you change the length of time that you boil the mixture? Explain your answer.

7.3 ▶▶▶ **Exercises**

FOR
EXTRA
HELP      Math XL
PRACTICE
WATCH   DOWNLOAD   READ
REVIEW

Write each proportion. See Example 1.

🌐 **1.** $9 is to 12 cans as $18 is to 24 cans.

2. 28 people is to 7 cars as 16 people is to 4 cars.

🌐 **3.** 200 adults is to 450 children as 4 adults is to 9 children.

4. 150 trees is to 1 acre as 1500 trees is to 10 acres.

🌐 **5.** 120 feet is to 150 feet as 8 feet is to 10 feet.

6. $6 is to $9 as $10 is to $15.

7. 2.2 hours is to 3.3 hours as 3.2 hours is to 4.8 hours.

8. 4 meters is to 4.75 meters as 6 meters is to 7.125 meters.

Determine whether each proportion is true *or* false *by writing the ratios in lowest terms. Show the simplified ratios and then write* true *or* false. *See Example 2.*

9. $\dfrac{6}{10} = \dfrac{3}{5}$

10. $\dfrac{1}{4} \quad \dfrac{9}{36}$

🌐 **11.** $\dfrac{5}{8} \quad \dfrac{25}{40}$

12. $\dfrac{2}{3} = \dfrac{20}{27}$

🌐 **13.** $\dfrac{150}{200} = \dfrac{200}{300}$

14. $\dfrac{100}{120} \quad \dfrac{75}{100}$

In Exercises 15–26, use cross products to determine whether each proportion is true *or* false. *Show the cross products and then circle* True *or* False. *See Example 3.*

🌐 **15.** $\dfrac{2}{9} = \dfrac{6}{27}$

   True   False

16. $\dfrac{20}{25} = \dfrac{4}{5}$

   True   False

17. $\dfrac{20}{28} \quad \dfrac{12}{16}$

   True   False

18. $\dfrac{16}{40} = \dfrac{22}{55}$

True   False

19. $\dfrac{110}{18} = \dfrac{160}{27}$

True   False

20. $\dfrac{600}{420} = \dfrac{20}{14}$

True   False

21. $\dfrac{3.5}{4} = \dfrac{7}{8}$

True   False

22. $\dfrac{36}{23} = \dfrac{9}{5.75}$

True   False

23. $\dfrac{18}{15} = \dfrac{2\frac{5}{6}}{2\frac{1}{2}}$

True   False

24. $\dfrac{1\frac{3}{10}}{3\frac{1}{5}} = \dfrac{4}{9}$

True   False

⊙ **25.** $\dfrac{6}{3\frac{2}{3}} = \dfrac{18}{11}$

True   False

⊙ **26.** $\dfrac{16}{13} = \dfrac{2}{1\frac{5}{8}}$

True   False

27. Suppose Joe Mauer of the Minnesota Twins had 17 hits in 50 times at bat, and Freddy Sanchez of the Pittsburgh Pirates was at bat 450 times and got 153 hits. Paul is trying to convince Jamie that the two men hit equally well. Show how you could use a proportion and cross products to see whether Paul is correct.

28. Jay worked 3.5 hours and packed 91 cartons. Craig packed 126 cartons in 5.25 hours. To see if the men worked equally fast, Barry set up this proportion:

$$\dfrac{3.5}{91} = \dfrac{126}{5.25}$$

Explain what is wrong with Barry's proportion and write a correct one. Is the correct proportion true or false?

Solve each proportion to find the unknown number. Round your answers to hundredths when necessary. Check your answers by finding cross products. See Examples 4 and 5.

29. $\dfrac{1}{3} = \dfrac{x}{12}$

30. $\dfrac{x}{6} = \dfrac{15}{18}$

31. $\dfrac{15}{10} = \dfrac{3}{x}$

32. $\dfrac{5}{x} = \dfrac{20}{8}$

33. $\dfrac{x}{11} = \dfrac{32}{4}$

34. $\dfrac{12}{9} = \dfrac{8}{x}$

35. $\dfrac{42}{x} = \dfrac{18}{39}$

36. $\dfrac{49}{x} = \dfrac{14}{18}$

37. $\dfrac{x}{25} = \dfrac{4}{20}$

38. $\dfrac{6}{x} = \dfrac{4}{8}$

39. $\dfrac{8}{x} = \dfrac{24}{30}$

40. $\dfrac{32}{5} = \dfrac{x}{10}$

41. $\dfrac{99}{55} = \dfrac{44}{x}$

42. $\dfrac{x}{12} = \dfrac{101}{147}$

43. $\dfrac{0.7}{9.8} = \dfrac{3.6}{x}$

44. $\dfrac{x}{3.6} = \dfrac{4.5}{6}$

45. $\dfrac{250}{24.8} = \dfrac{x}{1.75}$

46. $\dfrac{4.75}{17} = \dfrac{43}{x}$

Find the unknown number in each proportion. Write your answers as whole or mixed numbers when possible. See Example 5.

47. $\dfrac{\dfrac{15}{1\frac{2}{3}}}{} = \dfrac{9}{x}$

48. $\dfrac{x}{\dfrac{3}{10}} = \dfrac{2\frac{2}{9}}{1}$

49. $\dfrac{2\frac{1}{3}}{1\frac{1}{2}} = \dfrac{x}{2\frac{1}{4}}$

50. $\dfrac{1\frac{5}{6}}{x} = \dfrac{\frac{3}{14}}{\frac{6}{7}}$

Solve each proportion two different ways. First change all the numbers to decimal form and solve. Then change all the numbers to fraction form and solve; write your answers in lowest terms.

51. $\dfrac{\frac{1}{2}}{x} = \dfrac{2}{0.8}$

52. $\dfrac{\frac{3}{20}}{0.1} = \dfrac{0.03}{x}$

53. $\dfrac{x}{\frac{3}{50}} = \dfrac{0.15}{1\frac{4}{5}}$

54. $\dfrac{8\frac{4}{5}}{1\frac{1}{10}} = \dfrac{x}{0.4}$

Relating Concepts (Exercises 55–56) For Individual or Group Work

Work Exercises 55–56 in order. *First prove that the proportions are* **not** *true. Then create four true proportions for each exercise by changing only one number at a time.*

55. $\dfrac{10}{4} = \dfrac{5}{3}$

56. $\dfrac{6}{8} = \dfrac{24}{30}$

Summary Exercises on Ratios, Rates, and Proportions

Use the circle graph of one college's enrollment to complete Exercises 1–4. Write each ratio as a fraction in lowest terms.

1. Write the ratio of freshmen to juniors.

2. What is the ratio of freshmen to the total college enrollment?

3. Find the ratio of seniors and sophomores to juniors.

4. Write the ratio of freshmen and sophomores to juniors and seniors.

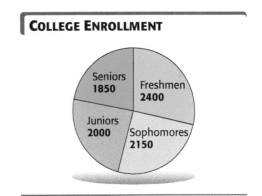

COLLEGE ENROLLMENT

Seniors 1850
Freshmen 2400
Juniors 2000
Sophomores 2150

The bar graph shows the number of Americans who play various instruments. Use the graph to complete Exercises 5 and 6. Write each ratio as a fraction in lowest terms.

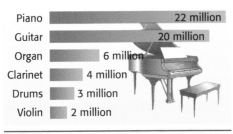

AMERICANS MAKE MUSIC BY THE MILLIONS

How many people play each type of instrument?

Piano	22 million
Guitar	20 million
Organ	6 million
Clarinet	4 million
Drums	3 million
Violin	2 million

Source: America by the Numbers.

5. Write six ratios that compare the least popular instrument to each of the other instruments.

6. Which two instruments give each of these ratios: **(a)** $\frac{5}{1}$; **(b)** $\frac{2}{1}$? There may be more than one correct answer.

The table lists data on the top three individual scoring NBA basketball games of all time. Use the data to answer Exercises 7 and 8. Round answers to the nearest tenth.

7. What was Wilt Chamberlain's scoring rate in points per minute and in minutes per point?

Player	Date	Points	Min
Wilt Chamberlain	3/2/62	100	48
David Thompson	4/9/78	73	43
David Robinson	4/24/94	71	44

Source: www.NBA.com

8. Find David Robinson's scoring rate in points per minute and minutes per point.

Wilt Chamberlain (#13)

9. Lucinda's paycheck showed gross pay of $652.80 for 40 hours of work and $195.84 for 8 hours of overtime work. Find her regular hourly pay rate and her overtime rate.

10. Satellite TV is being offered to new subscribers at $25 per month for 50 channels, $39 per month for 100 channels, or $48 per month for 150 channels. What is the monthly cost per channel under each plan? (*Source:* Dish1Up Satellites.)

11. Find the best buy on gourmet coffee beans.

   11 ounces for $6.79

   12 ounces for $7.24

   16 ounces for $10.99

   (*Source:* Cub Foods.)

12. Which brand of cat food is the best buy? You have a coupon for $2 off on Brand P, and another for $1 off on Brand N.

   Brand N is $3.75 for 3.5 pounds

   Brand P is $5.99 for 7 pounds

   Brand R is $10.79 for 18 pounds

Use either the method of writing in lowest terms or the method of finding cross products to decide whether each proportion is true *or* false. *Show your work and then write* true *or* false.

13. $\dfrac{28}{21} = \dfrac{44}{33}$

14. $\dfrac{2.3}{8.05} = \dfrac{0.25}{0.9}$

15. $\dfrac{2\frac{5}{8}}{3\frac{1}{4}} = \dfrac{21}{26}$

Solve each proportion to find the unknown number. Round your answers to hundredths when necessary.

16. $\dfrac{7}{x} = \dfrac{25}{100}$

17. $\dfrac{15}{8} = \dfrac{6}{x}$

18. $\dfrac{x}{84} = \dfrac{78}{36}$

19. $\dfrac{10}{11} = \dfrac{x}{4}$

20. $\dfrac{x}{17} = \dfrac{3}{55}$

21. $\dfrac{2.6}{x} = \dfrac{13}{7.8}$

22. $\dfrac{0.14}{1.8} = \dfrac{x}{0.63}$

23. $\dfrac{\frac{1}{3}}{8} = \dfrac{x}{24}$

24. $\dfrac{6\frac{2}{3}}{4\frac{1}{6}} = \dfrac{\frac{6}{5}}{x}$

7.4 ▶▶▶ Problem Solving with Proportions

OBJECTIVE 1 Use proportions to solve application problems.
Proportions can be used to solve a wide variety of problems. Watch for problems in which you are given a ratio or rate and then asked to find part of a corresponding ratio or rate. Remember that a ratio or rate compares two quantities and often includes one of these indicator words.

in   for   on   per   from   to

Use the six problem-solving steps from **Section 4.8.** When setting up the proportion, use a variable to represent the unknown number. We have used the letter x, but you may use any letter you like.

EXAMPLE 1 Solving a Proportion Application

Mike's car can travel 163 miles **on** 6.4 gallons of gas. How far can it travel on a full tank of 14 gallons of gas? Round to the nearest mile.

Step 1 Read the problem. It is about how far a car can travel on a certain amount of gas.

> Unknown: miles traveled on 14 gallons of gas
> Known: 163 miles traveled on 6.4 gallons of gas

Step 2 Assign a variable. There is only one unknown, so let x be the number of miles traveled on 14 gallons.

Step 3 Write an equation. The equation is in the form of a proportion. Decide what is being compared. This problem compares miles to gallons. Write the two rates described in the problem. Be sure that *both* rates compare miles to gallons in the same order. In other words, miles is in both numerators and gallons is in both denominators.

Matching units

This rate compares miles to gallons. $$\frac{163 \text{ miles}}{6.4 \text{ gallons}} = \frac{x \text{ miles}}{14 \text{ gallons}}$$ This rate compares miles to gallons.

Matching units

Step 4 Solve the equation. Ignore the units while finding the cross products.

$$\frac{163 \text{ miles}}{6.4 \text{ gallons}} = \frac{x \text{ miles}}{14 \text{ gallons}}$$

$(6.4)(x) = (163)(14)$ Show that cross products are equivalent.

$(6.4)(x) = 2282$

$$\frac{(6.4)(x)}{6.4} = \frac{2282}{6.4}$$ Divide both sides by 6.4

$x = 356.5625$ Round to 357   Always check the problem for rounding directions.

Step 5 State the answer. Mike's car can travel 357 miles, rounded to the nearest mile, on a full tank of gas.

Continued on Next Page

1 Set up and solve a proportion for each problem using the six problem-solving steps.

(a) If 2 pounds of fertilizer will cover 50 square feet of garden, how many pounds are needed for 225 square feet?

(b) A U.S. map has a scale of 1 inch to 75 miles. Lake Superior is 4.75 inches long on the map. What is the lake's actual length, to the nearest whole mile?

(c) Cough syrup is to be given at the rate of 30 milliliters for each 100 pounds of body weight. How much should be given to a 34-pound child? Round to the nearest whole milliliter.

ANSWERS

1. (a) $\dfrac{2 \text{ pounds}}{50 \text{ sq. feet}} = \dfrac{x \text{ pounds}}{225 \text{ sq. feet}}$
$x = 9$ pounds

(b) $\dfrac{1 \text{ inch}}{75 \text{ miles}} = \dfrac{4.75 \text{ inches}}{x \text{ miles}}$
$x = 356.25$ miles, rounds to 356 miles

(c) $\dfrac{30 \text{ milliliters}}{100 \text{ pounds}} = \dfrac{x \text{ milliliters}}{34 \text{ pounds}}$
$x \approx 10$ milliliters (rounded)

Step 6 **Check** that the solution is reasonable and fits the facts given in the original statement of the problem. The car traveled 163 miles on 6.4 gallons of gas; 14 gallons is a little more than *twice as much* gas, so the car should travel a little more than *twice as far*.

$$(2)(163 \text{ miles}) = 326 \text{ miles} \leftarrow \text{Estimate}$$

The solution, 357 miles, is a little more than the estimate of 326 miles, so it is reasonable.

CAUTION

When setting up the proportion, do *not* mix up the units in the rates.

$\left.\begin{array}{c}\text{compares miles} \\ \text{to gallons}\end{array}\right\} \quad \dfrac{163 \text{ miles}}{6.4 \text{ gallons}} \neq \dfrac{14 \text{ gallons}}{x \text{ miles}} \quad \left\{\begin{array}{c}\text{compares gallons} \\ \text{to miles}\end{array}\right.$

These rates do *not* compare things in the same order and *cannot* be set up as a proportion.

◀ *Work Problem* **1** *at the Side.*

EXAMPLE 2 **Solving a Proportion Application**

A newspaper report says that 7 out of 10 people surveyed watch the news on TV. At that rate, how many of the 3200 people in town would you expect to watch the news?

Step 1 **Read** the problem. It is about people watching the news on TV.

> Unknown: how many people in town are expected to watch the news on TV
> Known: 7 out of 10 people surveyed watched the news on TV.

Step 2 **Assign a variable.** There is only one unknown, so let x be the number of people in town who watch the news on TV.

Step 3 **Write an equation.** Set up the two rates as a proportion. You are comparing people who watch the news to people surveyed. Write the two rates described in the example. Be sure that both rates make the same comparison. "People who watch the news" is mentioned first, so it should be in the numerator of *both* rates.

$\begin{array}{ccc} \text{People who watch the news} \rightarrow & \dfrac{7}{10} = \dfrac{x}{3200} & \leftarrow \text{People who watch the news} \\ \text{Total group} \rightarrow & & \leftarrow \text{Total group} \\ \text{(people surveyed)} & & \text{(people in town)} \end{array}$

Step 4 **Solve** the equation.

$$\frac{7}{10} = \frac{x}{3200}$$

$(10)(x) = (7)(3200)$ Show that cross products are equivalent.

$(10)(x) = 22{,}400$

$\dfrac{\overset{1}{\cancel{10}}(x)}{\underset{1}{\cancel{10}}} = \dfrac{22{,}400}{10}$ Divide both sides by 10

$x = 2240$ No rounding is needed here.

Continued on Next Page

Step 5   **State the answer.** You would expect 2240 people in town to watch the news on TV.

Step 6   **Check** that the solution is reasonable by putting it back into the original statement of the problem.

Notice that 7 out of 10 people is more than half the people, but less than all the people. Half of the 3200 people in town is $3200 \div 2 = 1600$, so between 1600 and 3200 people would be expected to watch the news on TV. The solution, 2240 people, is between 1600 and 3200, so it is reasonable.

CAUTION

Always check that your answer is reasonable. If it isn't, look at the way your proportion is set up. Be sure you have matching units in the numerators and matching units in the denominators.

For example, suppose you set up the last proportion *incorrectly,* as shown below.

$$\frac{7}{10} = \frac{3200}{x} \quad \leftarrow \text{Incorrect setup}$$

$$(7)(x) = (10)(3200)$$

$$\frac{\overset{1}{\cancel{(7)}}(x)}{\underset{1}{\cancel{7}}} = \frac{32{,}000}{7}$$

$$x \approx 4571 \text{ people} \quad \leftarrow \text{Unreasonable answer}$$

This answer is *unreasonable* because there are only 3200 people in the town; it is *not* possible for 4571 people to watch the news.

Work Problem ▶ 2 *at the Side.* ▶

2 Solve each problem to find a reasonable answer. Then flip one side of your proportion to see what answer you get with an **incorrect** setup. Explain why the second answer is **unreasonable.**

(a) A survey showed that 2 out of 3 people would like to lose weight. At this rate, how many people in a group of 150 want to lose weight?

(b) In one state, 3 out of 5 college students receive financial aid. At this rate, how many of the 4500 students at Central Community College receive financial aid?

(c) An advertisement says that 9 out of 10 dentists recommend sugarless gum. If the ad is true, how many of the 60 dentists in our city would recommend sugarless gum?

ANSWERS

2. (a) 100 people (reasonable); incorrect setup gives 225 people (only 150 people in the group).
(b) 2700 students (reasonable); incorrect setup gives 7500 students (only 4500 students at the college).
(c) 54 dentists (reasonable); incorrect setup gives $\approx$ 67 dentists (only 60 dentists in the city).

Math in the Media

CURRENCY EXCHANGE

When you travel between countries, you will exchange U.S. dollars for the local currency. The exchange rate between currencies changes daily, and you can easily find the updated rates using the Internet or any major newspaper. The table below has been extracted from the Oanda Web page, www.oanda.com. It shows how much of each country's currency was equivalent to 1 U.S. dollar on April 16, 2008.

NORTH AMERICA/CARIBBEAN CURRENCY RATES
(APRIL 16, 2008)

Currency	Symbol	Value
Canadian dollar	CAD	1.0198
Cayman Islands dollar	KYD	0.833
Jamaican dollar	JMD	74.75
Mexican peso	MXN	10.5
United States dollar	USD	1.00

From the table, $1.00 U.S. was equivalent to 10.5 Mexican pesos. You can set up a proportion to convert dollars to pesos. For example, suppose you want to determine the number of pesos that is equivalent to $50.00.

$$\frac{\$1}{10.5 \text{ pesos}} = \frac{\$50}{x \text{ pesos}} \quad \text{or} \quad \frac{1}{10.5} = \frac{50}{x}$$
$$(1)(x) = (10.5)(50)$$
$$x = 525.0 \text{ pesos}$$

So $50 buys 525 pesos.

1. Based on the currency exchange rates for April 16, 2008, find the amount of each local currency that is equivalent to $50 U.S. and find the number of U.S. dollars that is equivalent to 200 units of each local currency. Round your answers to the nearest hundredth.

   (a) $50 = _____ Canadian dollars, and
   200 Canadian dollars = _____ U.S. dollars.

   (b) $50 = _____ Cayman Islands dollars, and
   200 Cayman Islands dollars = _____ U.S. dollars.

   (c) $50 = _____ Jamaican dollars, and
   200 Jamaican dollars = _____ U.S. dollars.

2. Set up a proportion to find the number of U.S. dollars that was equivalent to 1 Mexican Peso. Round your answer to the nearest cent.
   1 Mexican peso was equivalent to $_____ (U.S.).

3. From Problem 2, you should recognize the conversion rate based on 1 Mexican peso as the expression $\frac{1}{10.5}$. What is the mathematical word that describes the relationship between the conversion rates 10.5 and $\frac{1}{10.5}$?

Set up and solve a proportion for each application problem. See Example 1.

1. Caroline can sketch four cartoon strips in five hours. How long will it take her to sketch 18 strips?

2. The Cosmic Toads recorded eight songs on their first CD in 26 hours. How long will it take them to record 14 songs for their second CD?

3. Sixty newspapers cost $27. Find the cost of 16 newspapers.

4. Twenty-two guitar lessons cost $528. Find the cost of 12 lessons.

5. If three pounds of fescue grass seed cover about 350 square feet of ground, how many pounds are needed for 4900 square feet?

6. Anna earns $1242.08 in 14 days. How much does she earn in 260 days?

7. Tom makes $672.80 in five days. How much does he make in three days?

8. If 5 ounces of a medicine must be mixed with 8 ounces of water, how many ounces of medicine would be mixed with 20 ounces of water?

9. The bag of rice noodles shown below makes 7 servings. At that rate, how many ounces of noodles do you need for 12 servings, to the nearest ounce?

10. This can of sweet potatoes is enough for four servings. How many ounces are needed for nine servings, to the nearest ounce?

RICE NOODLES
Net Weight 6 ounces

SWEET POTATOES
23 ounces

11. Three quarts of a latex enamel paint will cover about 270 square feet of wall surface. How many quarts will you need to cover 350 square feet of wall surface in your kitchen and 100 square feet of wall surface in your bathroom?

12. One gallon of clear gloss wood finish covers about 550 square feet of surface. If you need to apply three coats of finish to 400 square feet of surface, how many gallons do you need, to the nearest tenth?

Use the floor plan shown to answer Exercises 13–16. On the plan, one inch represents four feet.

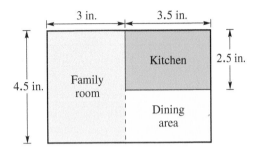

3 in.   3.5 in.

Kitchen   2.5 in.

4.5 in.   Family room

Dining area

13. What is the actual length and width of the kitchen?

14. What is the actual length and width of the family room?

15. What is the actual length and width of the dining area?

16. What is the actual length and width of the entire floor plan?

The table below lists recommended amounts of food to order for 25 party guests. Use the table to answer Exercises 17 and 18. (Source: Cub Foods.)

FOOD FOR 25 GUESTS	
Item	Amount
Fried chicken	40 pieces
Lasagna	14 pounds
Deli meats	4.5 pounds
Sliced cheese	$2\frac{1}{3}$ pounds
Bakery buns	3 dozen
Potato salad	6 pounds

17. How much of each food item should Nathan and Amanda order for a graduation party with 60 guests?

18. Taisha is having 20 neighbors over for a Fourth of July picnic. How much food should she buy?

In Exercises 19–24, set up a proportion to solve each problem. Check to see whether your answer is reasonable. Then flip one side of your proportion to see what answer you get with an incorrect setup. Explain why the second answer is unreasonable. See Example 2.

19. About 7 out of 10 people entering our community college need to take a refresher math course. If we have 2950 entering students, how many will probably need refresher math? (*Source:* Minneapolis Community and Technical College.)

20. In a survey, only 3 out of 100 people like their eggs poached. At that rate, how many of the 60 customers who ordered eggs at Soon-Won's restaurant this morning asked to have them poached? Round to the nearest whole person.

21. About 1 out of 3 people choose vanilla as their favorite ice cream flavor. If 238 people attend an ice cream social, how many would you expect to choose vanilla? Round to the nearest whole person.

22. In a test of 200 sewing machines, only one had a defect. At that rate, how many of the 5600 machines shipped from the factory have defects?

23. About 98 out of 100 U.S. households have at least one TV set. There were 113,100,000 U.S. households in 2005. How many households had one or more TVs? (*Source:* Nielsen Media Research.)

24. In a survey, 3 out of 100 dog owners washed their pets by having the dogs go into the shower with them. If the survey is accurate, how many of the 31,200,000 dog owners in the United States use this method? (*Source:* Teledyne Water Pik; American Veterinary Medical Association.)

Set up and solve a proportion for each problem.

25. The stock market report says that five stocks went up for every six stocks that went down. If 750 stocks went down yesterday, how many went up?

26. The human body contains 90 pounds of water for every 100 pounds of body weight. How many pounds of water are in a child who weighs 80 pounds?

27. The ratio of the length of an airplane wing to its width is 8 to 1. If the length of a wing is 32.5 meters, how wide must it be? Round to the nearest hundredth.

28. The Rosebud School District wants a student-to-teacher ratio of 19 to 1. How many teachers are needed for 1850 students? Round to the nearest whole number.

29. The number of calories you burn is proportional to your weight. A 150-pound person burns 222 calories during 30 minutes of tennis. How many calories would a 210-pound person burn, to the nearest whole number? (*Source: Wellness Encyclopedia.*)

30. (Complete Exercise 29 first.) A 150-pound person burns 189 calories during 45 minutes of grocery shopping. How many calories would a 115-pound person burn, to the nearest whole number? (*Source: Wellness Encyclopedia.*)

31. At 3 P.M., Coretta's shadow is 1.05 meters long. Her height is 1.68 meters. At the same time, a tree's shadow is 6.58 meters long. How tall is the tree? Round to the nearest hundredth.

32. (Complete Exercise 31 first.) Later in the day, Coretta's shadow was 2.95 meters long. How long a shadow did the tree have at that time? Round to the nearest hundredth.

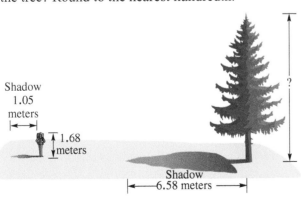

Shadow
1.05
meters

1.68
meters

Shadow
6.58 meters

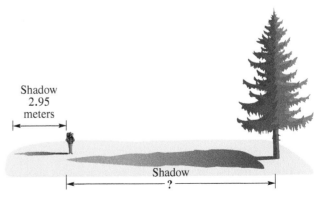

Shadow
2.95
meters

Shadow
?

33. Can you set up a proportion to solve this problem? Explain why or why not. Jim is 25 years old and weighs 180 pounds. How much will he weigh when he is 50 years old?

34. Write your own application problem that can be solved by setting up a proportion. Also show the proportion and the steps needed to solve your problem.

35. A survey of college students shows that 4 out of 5 drink coffee. Of the students who drink coffee, 1 out of 8 adds cream to it. How many of the 50,500 students at Ohio State University would be expected to use cream in their coffee?

36. About 9 out of 10 adults think it is a good idea to exercise regularly. But of the ones who think it is a good idea, only 1 in 6 actually exercises at least three times a week. At this rate, how many of the 300 employees in our company exercise regularly?

37. The nutrition information on a bran cereal box says that a $\frac{1}{3}$ cup serving provides 80 calories and 8 grams of dietary fiber. At that rate, how many calories and grams of fiber are in a $\frac{1}{2}$ cup serving? (*Source:* Kraft Foods, Inc.)

38. A $\frac{2}{3}$ cup serving of penne pasta has 210 calories and 2 grams of dietary fiber. How many calories and grams of fiber would be in a 1 cup serving? (*Source:* Borden Foods.)

Relating Concepts (Exercises 39–42) For Individual or Group Work

A box of instant mashed potatoes has the list of ingredients shown in the table. Use this information to **work Exercises 39–42 in order.**

Ingredient	For 12 Servings
Water	$3\frac{1}{2}$ cups
Margarine	6 tablespoons
Milk	$1\frac{1}{2}$ cups
Potato flakes	4 cups

Source: General Mills.

39. Find the amount of each ingredient needed for six servings. Show *two* different methods for finding the amounts. One method should use proportions.

40. Find the amount of each ingredient needed for 18 servings. Show *two* different methods for finding the amounts, one using proportions and one using your answers from Exercise 39.

41. Find the amount of each ingredient needed for three servings, using your answers from either Exercise 39 or Exercise 40.

42. Find the amount of each ingredient needed for nine servings, using your answers from either Exercise 40 or Exercise 41.

7.5 ▶▶▶ Geometry: Lines and Angles

Geometry starts with the idea of a point. A **point** can be described as a location in space. It has no length or width. A point is represented by a dot and is named by writing a capital letter next to the dot.

Point *P*

OBJECTIVE 1 Identify and name lines, line segments, and rays.
A **line** is a straight row of points that goes on forever in both directions. A line is drawn by using arrowheads to show that it never ends. The line is named by using the letters of any two points on the line.

Line *AB*, written $\overleftrightarrow{AB}$

A piece of a line that has two endpoints is called a **line segment.** A line segment is named for its endpoints. The segment with endpoints *P* and *Q* is shown below. It can be named $\overline{PQ}$ or $\overline{QP}$.

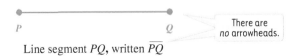

Line segment *PQ*, written $\overline{PQ}$

A **ray** is a part of a line that has only one endpoint and goes on forever in one direction. A ray is named by using the endpoint and some other point on the ray. The endpoint is always mentioned first.

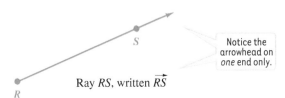

Ray *RS*, written $\overrightarrow{RS}$

EXAMPLE 1 Identifying and Naming Lines, Rays, and Line Segments

Identify each figure below as a line, line segment, or ray and name it using the appropriate symbol.

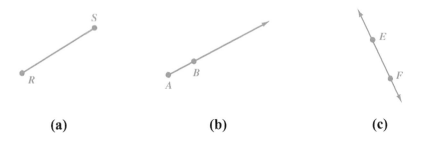

(a) **(b)** **(c)**

Figure **(a)** has two endpoints, so it is a *line segment* named $\overline{RS}$ or $\overline{SR}$.
Figure **(b)** starts at point *A* and goes on forever in one direction, so it is a *ray* named $\overrightarrow{AB}$.
Figure **(c)** goes on forever in both directions, so it is a *line* named $\overleftrightarrow{EF}$ or $\overleftrightarrow{FE}$.

Work Problem **1** *at the Side.* ▶

OBJECTIVES

1 Identify and name lines, line segments, and rays.

2 Identify parallel and intersecting lines.

3 Identify and name angles.

4 Classify angles as right, acute, straight, or obtuse.

5 Identify perpendicular lines.

6 Identify complementary angles and supplementary angles and find the measure of a complement or supplement of a given angle.

7 Identify congruent angles and vertical angles and use this knowledge to find the measures of angles.

8 Identify corresponding angles and alternate interior angles and use this knowledge to find the measures of angles.

1 Identify each figure as a line, line segment, or ray, and name it.

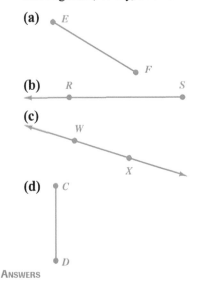

(a)
(b)
(c)
(d)

ANSWERS

1. **(a)** line segment named $\overline{EF}$ or $\overline{FE}$
   (b) ray named $\overrightarrow{SR}$ **(c)** line named $\overleftrightarrow{WX}$ or $\overleftrightarrow{XW}$
   (d) line segment named $\overline{CD}$ or $\overline{DC}$

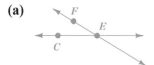

2 Label each pair of lines as appearing to be parallel or as intersecting.

(a)

(b)

(c)

OBJECTIVE **2** **Identify parallel and intersecting lines.** A *plane* is an infinitely large, flat surface. A floor or a wall is part of a plane. Lines that are in the *same plane,* but that never intersect (never cross), are called **parallel lines,** while lines that cross are called **intersecting lines.** (Think of an intersection, where two streets cross each other.)

EXAMPLE 2 **Identifying Parallel and Intersecting Lines**

Label each pair of lines as appearing to be parallel or as intersecting.

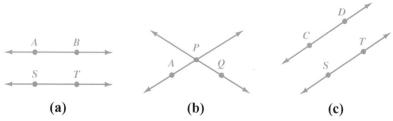

(a) **(b)** **(c)**

The lines in Figures **(a)** and **(c)** do not intersect; they appear to be *parallel lines.*

The lines in Figure **(b)** cross at *P*, so they are *intersecting lines.*

CAUTION
Appearances may be deceiving! Do not assume that lines are parallel unless it is stated that they are parallel.

◀ *Work Problem* **2** *at the Side.*

OBJECTIVE **3** **Identify and name angles.** An **angle** is made up of two rays that start at a common endpoint. This common endpoint is called the *vertex.*

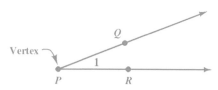

$\overrightarrow{PQ}$ and $\overrightarrow{PR}$ are called the *sides* of the angle. The angle can be named in four different ways, as shown below.

$\angle 1$ $\angle P$ $\angle QPR$ $\angle RPQ$

Vertex alone   Vertex in the middle

Naming an Angle
To name an angle, write the vertex alone or write the vertex in the middle of two other points, one from each side. If two or more angles have the *same vertex,* as in Example 3 on the next page, do *not* use the vertex alone to name an angle.

EXAMPLE 3   **Identifying and Naming an Angle**

Name the highlighted angle in three different ways.

In this situation, do **not** use the *vertex alone* to name the angle.

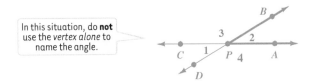

The angle can be named ∠*BPA*, ∠*APB*, or ∠2. It *cannot* be named ∠*P*, using the vertex alone, because four different angles have *P* as their vertex.

Work Problem **3** *at the Side.* ▶

OBJECTIVE 4 **Classify angles as right, acute, straight, or obtuse.** Angles can be measured in **degrees.** The symbol for degrees is a small, raised circle °. Think of the minute hand on a clock as a ray of an angle. Suppose it is at 12:00. During one hour of time, the minute hand moves around in a complete circle. It moves 360 *degrees*, or 360°. In half an hour, at 12:30, the minute hand has moved halfway around the circle, or 180°. An angle of 180° is called a **straight angle.** When two rays go in opposite directions and form a straight line, then the rays form a straight angle.

Complete circle
360°

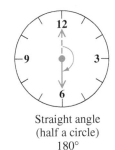

Straight angle
(half a circle)
180°

In a quarter of an hour, at 12:15, the minute hand has moved $\frac{1}{4}$ of the way around the circle, or 90°. An angle of 90° is called a **right angle.** The rays of a right angle form one corner of a square. So, to show that an angle is a right angle, we draw a small square at the vertex.

Right angle
($\frac{1}{4}$ of a circle)
90°

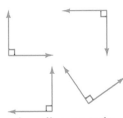

A small square at the vertex identifies right angles.

An angle that measures 1° is shown below. You can see that an angle of 1° is very small.

1° angle

3 **(a)** Name the highlighted angle in three different ways.

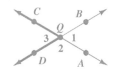

(b) Darken the rays that make up ∠*ZTW*.

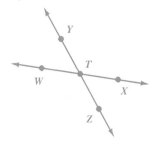

(c) Name this angle in four different ways.

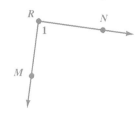

ANSWERS

3. (a) ∠3, ∠*CQD*, ∠*DQC*
(b)

(c) ∠1, ∠*R*, ∠*MRN*, ∠*NRM*

4 Label each angle as acute, right, obtuse, or straight. State the number of degrees in the right angle and in the straight angle.

(a)

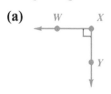

(b)

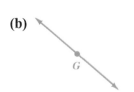

(c)

(d)

Some other terms used to describe angles are shown below.

Acute angles measure less than 90°.

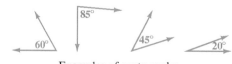

Examples of acute angles

Obtuse angles measure more than 90° but less than 180°.

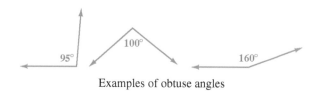

Examples of obtuse angles

Section 9.2 shows you how to use a tool called a *protractor* to measure the number of degrees in an angle.

Classifying Angles

Acute angles measure less than 90°.

Right angles measure *exactly* 90°.

Obtuse angles measure more than 90° but less than 180°.

Straight angles measure *exactly* 180°.

Note

Angles can also be measured in radians, which you will learn about in a later math course.

EXAMPLE 4 **Classifying an Angle**

Label each angle as acute, right, obtuse, or straight.

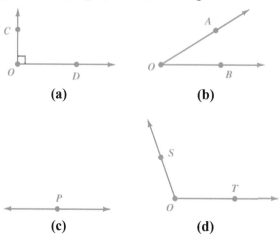

Figure **(a)** shows a *right angle* (exactly 90° and identified by a small square at the vertex).

Figure **(b)** shows an *acute angle* (less than 90°).

Figure **(c)** shows a *straight angle* (exactly 180°).

Figure **(d)** shows an *obtuse angle* (more than 90° but less than 180°).

◀ *Work Problem* **4** *at the Side.*

ANSWERS

4. **(a)** right; 90° **(b)** straight; 180°
   (c) obtuse **(d)** acute

OBJECTIVE 5 Identify perpendicular lines. Two lines are called **perpendicular lines** if they intersect to form a right angle.

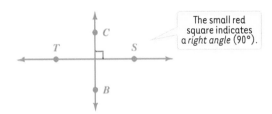

The small red square indicates a *right angle* (90°).

$\overleftrightarrow{CB}$ and $\overleftrightarrow{ST}$ are perpendicular lines because they intersect at right angles, as indicated by the small red square in the figure.
   Perpendicular lines can be written in the following way: $\overleftrightarrow{CB} \perp \overleftrightarrow{ST}$.

EXAMPLE 5   Identifying Perpendicular Lines

Which pairs of lines are perpendicular?

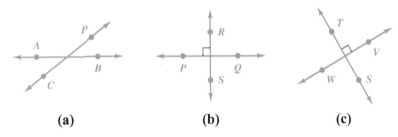

(a)   **(b)**   **(c)**

   The lines in Figures **(b)** and **(c)** are *perpendicular* to each other, because they intersect at right angles.
   The lines in Figure **(a)** are *intersecting lines,* but they are *not* perpendicular because they do *not* form a right angle.

Work Problem **5** *at the Side.* ▶

OBJECTIVE 6 Identify complementary angles and supplementary angles and find the measure of a complement or supplement of a given angle. Two angles are called **complementary angles** if the sum of their measures is 90°. If two angles are complementary, each angle is the *complement* of the other.

EXAMPLE 6   Identifying Complementary Angles

Identify each pair of complementary angles.

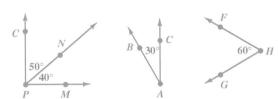

$\angle MPN$ (40°) and $\angle NPC$ (50°) are complementary angles because

$$40° + 50° = 90°$$

$\angle CAB$ (30°) and $\angle FHG$ (60°) are complementary angles because

$$30° + 60° = 90°$$

Work Problem **6** *at the Side.* ▶

---

5 Which pair of lines is perpendicular? How can you describe the other pair of lines?

(a)

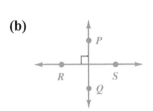

(b)

6 Identify each pair of complementary angles.

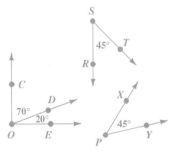

ANSWERS

5. Figure **(b)** shows perpendicular lines; Figure **(a)** shows intersecting lines.
6. $\angle COD$ and $\angle DOE$; $\angle RST$ and $\angle XPY$

7 Find the complement of each angle.

(a) 35°

(b) 80°

8 Identify each pair of supplementary angles. (*Hint:* There are four pairs.)

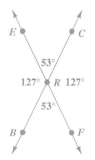

9 Find the supplement of each angle.

(a) 175°

(b) 30°

> **EXAMPLE 7** **Finding the Complement of Angles**
>
> Find the complement of each angle.
>
> **(a)** 30°
> Find the complement of 30° by subtracting. 90° − 30° = **60°** ← Complement
>
> **(b)** 75°
> Find the complement of 75° by subtracting. 90° − 75° = **15°** ← Complement

◀ *Work Problem* **7** *at the Side.*

Two angles are called **supplementary angles** if the sum of their measures is 180°. If two angles are supplementary, each angle is the *supplement* of the other.

> **EXAMPLE 8** **Identifying Supplementary Angles**
>
> Identify each pair of supplementary angles.
>
>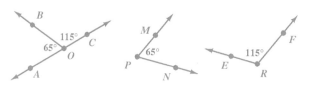
>
> ∠*BOA* and ∠*BOC*, because 65° + 115° = 180°
> ∠*BOA* and ∠*ERF*, because 65° + 115° = 180°
> ∠*BOC* and ∠*MPN*, because 115° + 65° = 180°
> ∠*MPN* and ∠*ERF*, because 65° + 115° = 180°

◀ *Work Problem* **8** *at the Side.*

> **EXAMPLE 9** **Finding the Supplement of Angles**
>
> Find the supplement of each angle.
>
> **(a)** 70°
> Find the supplement of 70° by subtracting. 180° − 70° = **110°** ← Supplement
>
> **(b)** 140°
> Find the supplement of 140° by subtracting. 180° − 140° = **40°** ← Supplement

◀ *Work Problem* **9** *at the Side.*

OBJECTIVE 7 Identify congruent angles and vertical angles and use this knowledge to find the measures of angles. Two angles are called **congruent angles** if they measure the same number of degrees. If two angles are congruent, this is written as ∠*A* ≅ ∠*B* and read as, "angle *A* is congruent to angle *B*." Here is an example.

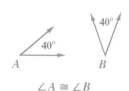

∠*A* ≅ ∠*B*

Example of congruent angles

EXAMPLE 10 **Identifying Congruent Angles**

Identify the angles that are congruent.

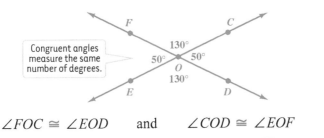

Congruent angles measure the same number of degrees.

$$\angle FOC \cong \angle EOD \quad \text{and} \quad \angle COD \cong \angle EOF$$

Work Problem 10 *at the Side.* ▶

10 Identify the angles that are congruent.

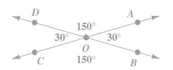

Angles that share a common side and a common vertex are called *adjacent* angles, such as $\angle FOC$ and $\angle COD$ in Example 10 above. Angles that do *not* share a common side are called *nonadjacent* angles. Two nonadjacent angles formed by two intersecting lines are called **vertical angles.**

EXAMPLE 11 **Identifying Vertical Angles**

Identify the vertical angles in this figure.

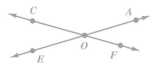

$\angle AOF$ and $\angle COE$ are vertical angles because they do *not* share a common side and they are formed by two intersecting lines ($\overleftrightarrow{CF}$ and $\overleftrightarrow{EA}$).

$\angle COA$ and $\angle EOF$ are also vertical angles.

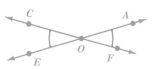 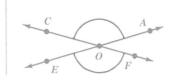

11 Identify the vertical angles. What is special about vertical angles?

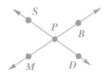

Work Problem 11 *at the Side.* ▶

Look back at Example 10 at the top of the page. Notice that the two *congruent* angles that measure 130° are also *vertical* angles. Also, the two congruent angles that measure 50° are vertical angles. This illustrates the following property.

Vertical Angles Are Congruent
If two angles are *vertical* angles, they are *congruent;* that is, they measure the same number of degrees.

ANSWERS

10. $\angle BOC \cong \angle AOD$; $\angle AOB \cong \angle DOC$
11. $\angle SPB$ and $\angle MPD$; $\angle BPD$ and $\angle SPM$; vertical angles are congruent (they measure the same number of degrees).

12 In the figure below, find the measure of each unlabeled angle. Write the angle measures on the figure.

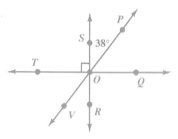

(a) ∠TOS

(b) ∠QOR

(c) ∠VOR

(d) ∠POQ

(e) ∠TOV

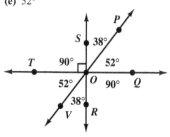

EXAMPLE 12 **Finding the Measures of Vertical Angles**

In the figure below, find the measure of each unlabeled angle.

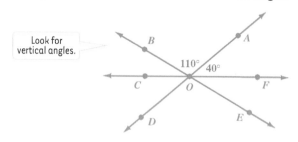

Look for vertical angles.

(a) ∠COD
 ∠COD and ∠AOF are vertical angles, so they are congruent. This means they measure the same number of degrees.

 The measure of ∠AOF is 40°   so   the measure of ∠COD is **40°** also.

(b) ∠DOE
 ∠DOE and ∠BOA are vertical angles, so they are congruent.

 The measure of ∠BOA is 110°   so   the measure of ∠DOE is **110°** also.

(c) ∠COB
 Look at ∠COB, ∠BOA, and ∠AOF. Notice that $\overrightarrow{OC}$ and $\overrightarrow{OF}$ go in opposite directions. Therefore, ∠COF is a straight angle and measures 180°. To find the measure of ∠COB, subtract the sum of the other two angles from 180°.

$$180° - (110° + 40°) = 180° - (150°) = 30°$$

The measure of ∠COB is **30°.**

(d) ∠EOF
 ∠EOF and ∠COB are vertical angles, so they are congruent. We know from part (c) above that the measure of ∠COB is 30° so the measure of ∠EOF is **30°** also.

◀ *Work Problem* **12** *at the Side.*

OBJECTIVE **8** **Identify corresponding angles and alternate interior angles and use this knowledge to find the measures of angles.**   We can also find congruent angles (angles with the same measure) when two *parallel lines* are crossed by a third line, called a *transversal.* When a transversal crosses two *parallel* lines, eight angles are formed, as shown below. There are special names for certain pairs of angles.

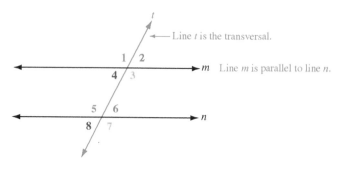

∠1 and ∠5 are called **corresponding angles.** Notice that they are both on the same side of the transversal (line *t*) and in the same relative position. *Corresponding angles are congruent,* so ∠1 and ∠5 measure the same number of degrees. There are four pairs of corresponding angles.

∠1 and ∠5 are corresponding angles, so ∠1 ≅ ∠5.

∠2 and ∠6 are corresponding angles, so ∠2 ≅ ∠6.

∠3 and ∠7 are corresponding angles, so ∠3 ≅ ∠7.

∠4 and ∠8 are corresponding angles, so ∠4 ≅ ∠8.

13 In each figure below, line *m* is parallel to line *n*. Identify all pairs of corresponding angles and all pairs of alternate interior angles.

(a)

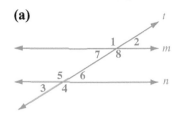

When a transversal crosses two parallel lines, angles 3, 4, 5, and 6 are called *interior angles*. You can see that they are "inside" the *parallel* lines.

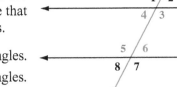

∠3 and ∠5 are alternate interior angles.

∠4 and ∠6 are alternate interior angles.

When two lines are *parallel,* then **alternate interior angles** *are congruent* (they have the same measure). Notice that alternate interior angles are on opposite sides of the transversal.

$$\angle 3 \cong \angle 5 \quad \text{and} \quad \angle 4 \cong \angle 6$$

Angles Formed by Parallel Lines and a Transversal

When two parallel lines are crossed by a transversal:
1. Corresponding angles are congruent, and
2. Alternate interior angles are congruent.

(b)

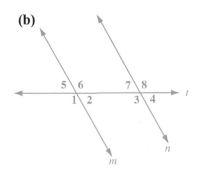

EXAMPLE 13 **Identifying Corresponding Angles and Alternate Interior Angles**

In each figure, line *m* is parallel to line *n*. Identify all pairs of corresponding angles and all pairs of alternate interior angles.

(a)

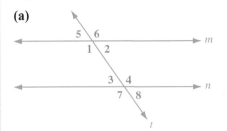

(b)

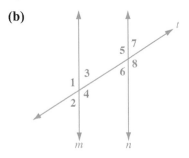

There are four pairs of corresponding angles:

∠5 and ∠3   ∠6 and ∠4

∠1 and ∠7   ∠2 and ∠8

Alternate interior angles:

∠1 and ∠4   ∠2 and ∠3

Corresponding angles:

∠1 and ∠5   ∠3 and ∠7

∠2 and ∠6   ∠4 and ∠8

Alternate interior angles:

∠3 and ∠6   ∠4 and ∠5

Work Problem **13** *at the Side.* ▶

ANSWERS

13. **(a)** corresponding angles: ∠1 and ∠5; ∠2 and ∠6; ∠7 and ∠3; ∠8 and ∠4 alternate interior angles: ∠7 and ∠6; ∠8 and ∠5

(b) corresponding angles: ∠5 and ∠7; ∠6 and ∠8; ∠1 and ∠3; ∠2 and ∠4 alternate interior angles: ∠6 and ∠3; ∠2 and ∠7

14 In each figure below, line *m* is parallel to line *n*.

(a) The measure of ∠6 is 150°. Find the measures of the other angles.

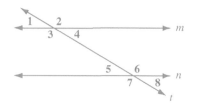

(b) The measure of ∠1 is 45°. Find the measures of the other angles.

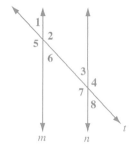

Recall that two angles are supplementary angles if the sum of their measures is 180°. Also remember that two rays that form a 180° angle form a straight line. Now you can combine your knowledge about supplementary angles with the information on parallel lines.

EXAMPLE 14 **Working with Parallel Lines**

In the figure at the right, line *m* is parallel to line *n* and the measure of ∠4 is 70°. Find the measures of the other angles.

> Look for corresponding angles and for alternate interior angles.

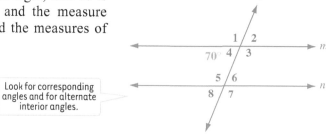

As you find the measure of each angle, write it on the figure.

∠4 ≅ ∠8 (corresponding angles), so the measure of ∠8 is also 70°.
∠4 ≅ ∠6 (alternate interior angles), so the measure of ∠6 is also 70°.
∠6 ≅ ∠2 (corresponding angles), so the measure of ∠2 is also 70°.

Notice that the exterior sides of ∠4 and ∠3 form a straight line, that is, a straight angle of 180°. Therefore, ∠4 and ∠3 are supplementary angles and the sum of their measures is 180°. If ∠4 is 70° then ∠3 must be 110° because 180° − 70° = 110°. So the measure of ∠3 is 110°.

∠3 ≅ ∠7 (corresponding angles), so the measure of ∠7 is also 110°.
∠3 ≅ ∠5 (alternate interior angles), so the measure of ∠5 is also 110°.
∠5 ≅ ∠1 (corresponding angles), so the measure of ∠1 is also 110°.

With the measures of all the angles labeled, you can double-check that each pair of angles that forms a straight angle also adds up to 180°.

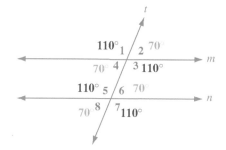

◀ *Work Problem* **14** *at the Side.*

ANSWERS

14. (a)

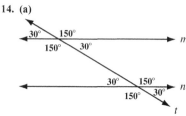

(b)

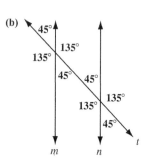

 **7.5** ▶▶▶ **Exercises**

Identify each figure as a line, line segment, *or* ray *and name it using the appropriate symbol. See Example 1.*

1.
C
D

2.
B
A

3.
F
G

4.
E   F

5.
Q
P

6.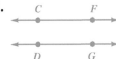
S
T

Label each pair of lines as appearing to be parallel, *as* perpendicular, *or as* intersecting. *See Examples 2 and 5.*

7.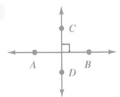
C
A   B
D

8.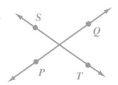
S   Q
P   T

9.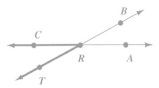
C   F
D   G

10.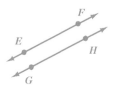
F
E   H
G

11.
K
N
M
L

12.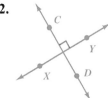
C
Y
X   D

Name each highlighted angle by using the three-letter form of identification. See Example 3.

 13.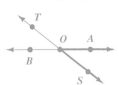
T
O   A
B
S

14.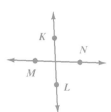
C   A
O
B   D

15.
B
C
R   A
T

16.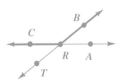
B
C
R   A
T

17.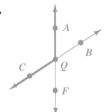
A
B
C   Q
F

18.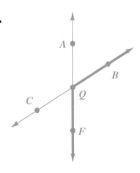
A
B
C   Q
F

Label each angle as acute, right, obtuse, *or* straight. *For right angles and straight angles, indicate the number of degrees in the angle. See Example 4.*

19.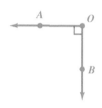

20.

21.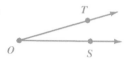

22.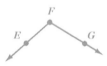

23.

24.

Identify each pair of complementary angles. See Example 6.

25.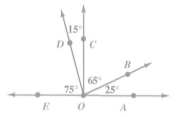

26.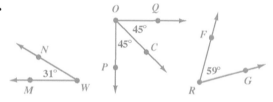

Identify each pair of supplementary angles. See Example 8.

27.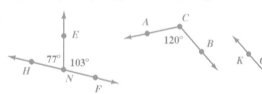

28.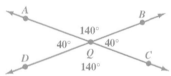

Find the complement of each angle. See Example 7.

29. 40°   **30.** 35°   **31.** 86°   **32.** 59°

Find the supplement of each angle. See Example 9.

33. 130°   **34.** 75°   **35.** 90°   **36.** 5°

In Exercises 37 and 38, identify the angles that are congruent. See Examples 10 and 11.

37.

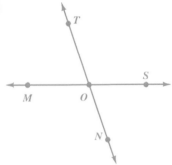

38.

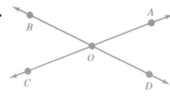

In Exercises 39 and 40, find the measure of each of the angles. See Example 12.

39. In the figure below, ∠*AOH* measures 37° and ∠*COE* measures 63°.

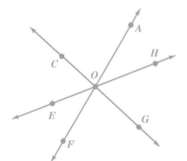

40. In the figure below, ∠*POU* measures 105° and ∠*UOT* measures 40°.

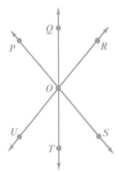

Relating Concepts (Exercises 41–46)   For Individual or Group Work

Use the figure to **work Exercises 41–46 in order.** *Decide whether each statement is* true *or* false. *If it is true, explain why. If it is false, rewrite it to make a true statement.*

41. ∠*UST* is 90°.

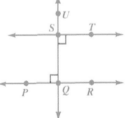

42. $\overleftrightarrow{SQ}$ and $\overleftrightarrow{PQ}$ are perpendicular.

43. The measure of ∠*USQ* is less than the measure of ∠*PQR*.

44. $\overleftrightarrow{ST}$ and $\overleftrightarrow{PR}$ are intersecting.

45. $\overleftrightarrow{QU}$ and $\overleftrightarrow{TS}$ are parallel.

46. ∠*UST* and ∠*UQR* measure the same number of degrees.

In each figure, line m is parallel to line n. Identify all pairs of corresponding angles and all pairs of alternate interior angles. See Example 13.

47.

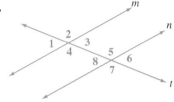

48.

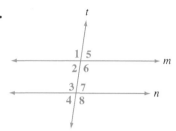

In each figure, line m is parallel to line n. Find the measure of each angle. See Example 14.

49. ∠8 measures 130°.

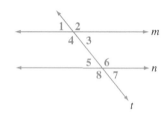

50. ∠2 measures 80°.

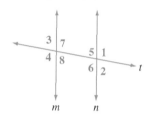

51. ∠6 measures 47°.

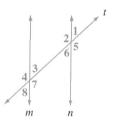

52. ∠2 measures 108°.

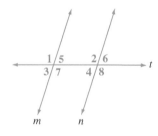

53. ∠6 measures 114°.

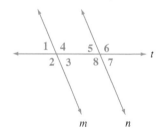

54. ∠3 measures 59°.

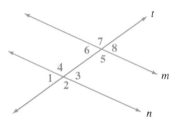

In each figure, $\overrightarrow{BA}$ is parallel to $\overrightarrow{CD}$. Find the measure of each numbered angle.

55.

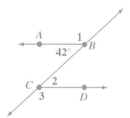

56.

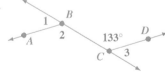

7.6 ▶▶▶ The Basics of Percent

OBJECTIVE 1 Learn the meaning of percent. You have probably seen percents frequently in daily life. The symbol for percent is %. For example, during one day you may leave a 15% tip for the waitress at dinner, pay 7% sales tax on a CD player, and buy shoes at 25% off the regular price. The next day your score on a math test may be 89% correct.

> **The Meaning of Percent**
>
> A **percent** is a ratio with a denominator of 100. So percent means "per 100" or "how many out of 100." The symbol for percent is %. Read 15% as "fifteen percent."

> **EXAMPLE 1   Understanding Percent**
>
> Write a percent to describe each situation.
>
> **(a)** If you left a $15 tip when the restaurant bill was $100, then you left $15 per $100 or $\frac{15}{100}$ or 15%.
>
> **(b)** If you pay $7 in tax on a $100 CD player, then the tax rate is $7 per $100 or $\frac{7}{100}$ or 7%.
>
> **(c)** If you earn 89 points on a 100-point math test, then your score is 89 out of 100 or $\frac{89}{100}$ or 89%.

Work Problem **1** *at the Side.* ▶

OBJECTIVE 2 Write percents as decimals. In order to work with percents, you will need to write them as decimals or as fractions. We'll start by writing percents as equivalent decimal numbers. Twenty-five percent, or 25%, means 25 parts out of 100 parts, or $\frac{25}{100}$. Remember that the fraction bar indicates division. So we can write $\frac{25}{100}$ as $25 \div 100$. When you do the division, $25 \div 100$ is 0.25.

$$\text{Indicates division} \longrightarrow \frac{25}{100} \quad \text{can be written as} \quad 25 \div 100 = 0.25$$
$$\underset{\text{Indicates division}}{\uparrow}$$

Another way to remember how to write a percent as a decimal is to use the meaning of the word *percent*. The first part of the word, *per*, is an indicator word for *division*. The last part of the word, *cent*, comes from the Latin word for *hundred*. (Recall that there are 100 *cent*s in a dollar, and 100 years in a *cent*ury.)

$$25\% \quad \text{is} \quad 25 \text{ percent}$$
$$25 \div 100 = 0.25$$

> **Writing a Percent as an Equivalent Decimal**
>
> To write a percent as a decimal, drop the % symbol and divide by 100.

OBJECTIVES

1. **Learn the meaning of percent.**
2. **Write percents as decimals.**
3. **Write decimals as percents.**
4. **Write percents as fractions.**
5. **Write fractions as percents.**
6. **Use 100% and 50%.**

---

1 Write a percent to describe each situation.

(a) You leave a $20 tip for a restaurant bill of $100. What percent tip did you leave?

(b) The tax on a $100 graphing calculator is $5. What is the tax rate?

(c) You earn 94 points on a 100 point test. What percent of the points did you earn?

ANSWERS

1. **(a)** 20%   **(b)** 5%   **(c)** 94%

2 Write each percent as a decimal.

(a) 68%

(b) 5%

(c) 40.6%

(d) 200%

(e) 350%

EXAMPLE 2 **Writing Percents as Decimals**

Write each percent as a decimal.

(a) 47%   47% =   47   ÷ 100 = 0.47   Decimal form

(b) 3%   3% =   3   ÷ 100 = 0.03   Decimal form

(c) 28.2%   28.2% = 28.2 ÷ 100 = 0.282   Decimal form

(d) 100%   100% = 100   ÷ 100 = 1.00   Decimal form

(e) 135%   135% = 135   ÷ 100 = 1.35   Decimal form

> **CAUTION**
> In Example 2(d) above, notice that 100% is 1.00, or 1, which is a whole number. Whenever you have a percent that is *100% or greater,* the equivalent decimal number will be *1 or greater.* Notice in Example 2(e) above that 135% is 1.35 (greater than 1).

◀ Work Problem **2** at the Side.

In the exercise set for **Section 6.5,** you discovered a shortcut for *dividing* by 100: Move the decimal point *two* places to the *left.* You can use this shortcut when writing percents as decimals.

EXAMPLE 3 **Changing Percents to Decimals by Moving the Decimal Point**

Write each percent as a decimal by dropping the percent symbol and moving the decimal point two places to the left.

(a) 17%

Decimal point starts at far right side.

17% = 17.%

.17 ← Percent symbol is dropped.

Decimal point is moved
two places to the *left.* | Moving the decimal point *two places* to the *left* is a quick way to *divide by 100.*

17% = 0.17

(b) 160%

160% = 160.% = 1.60 or 1.6   Decimal point starts at far right side.
1.60 is equivalent to 1.6

(c) 4.9%

04.9%   0 is attached so the decimal point can be moved
two places to the *left.*

4.9% = 0.049

(d) 0.6%

00.6% = 0.006   0 is attached so the decimal point can be
moved *two places* to the *left.*

Continued on Next Page

Note

In Example 3(d) on the previous page, notice that 0.6% is less than 1%. Because 1% is equivalent to 0.01 or $\frac{1}{100}$, any fraction of a percent smaller than 1% is less than 0.01. The decimal equivalent of 0.6% is 0.006, which is less than 0.01.

Work Problem **3** *at the Side.* ▶

OBJECTIVE 3 Write decimals as percents. You can write a decimal as a percent. For example, the decimal 0.25 is the same as the fraction $\frac{25}{100}$.

This fraction means 25 out of 100 parts, or 25%. Notice that multiplying 0.25 by 100 gives the same result.

$$(0.25)(100) = 25 \quad \text{so} \quad 0.25 = 25\%$$

This result makes sense because we are doing the opposite of what we did to change a percent to a decimal.

To change a percent to a decimal, we *drop* the % symbol and *divide* by 100. So, to *reverse* the process and change a decimal to a percent, we *multiply* by 100 and *attach* a % symbol.

Writing a Decimal as a Percent

To write a decimal as a percent, multiply by 100 and attach a % symbol.

Note

A quick way to *multiply* a number by 100 is to move the decimal point *two* places to the *right*. Notice that this is the opposite of the shortcut for *dividing* by 100.

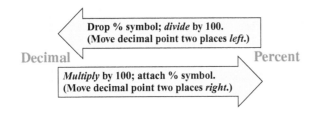

Decimal ◀ **Drop % symbol; *divide* by 100.** (Move decimal point two places *left*.) | **Percent** ▶ *Multiply* **by 100; attach % symbol.** (Move decimal point two places *right*.)

EXAMPLE 4   Changing Decimals to Percents by Moving the Decimal Point

Write each decimal as a percent.

(a) 0.21

0.21   *Moving the decimal point two places to the right is a quick way to multiply by 100.*

0.21 = 21% ◀── Percent symbol is attached after decimal point is moved.

↑──────── Decimal point is *not* written with whole number percents.

(b) 0.529 = 52.9% ◀── Percent symbol is attached after decimal point is moved.

(c) 1.92 = 192% ◀── Percent symbol is attached after decimal point is moved.

Continued on Next Page

---

3 Write each percent as a decimal by moving the decimal point.

(a) 90%

(b) 9%

(c) 900%

(d) 9.9%

(e) 0.9%

ANSWERS

3. **(a)** 0.90 or 0.9   **(b)** 0.09   **(c)** 9.00 or 9
   (d) 0.099   **(e)** 0.009

4 Write each number as a percent.

(a) 0.95

(b) 0.16

(c) 0.09

(d) 0.617

(e) 0.4

(f) 5.34

(g) 2.8

(h) 4

(d) 2.5

2.50   0 is attached so the decimal point can be moved two places to the right.

2.5 = 250%

(e) 3

3. = 3.00   so   3.00 = 300%

Hint:
1 = 100%
2 = 200%
3 = 300%
and so on.

CAUTION

In Examples 4(c), 4(d), and 4(e) above, notice that 1.92, 2.5, and 3 are greater than 1. Because the number 1 is equivalent to 100%, all *numbers greater than 1* will be equivalent to *percents greater than 100%*.

◀ Work Problem 4 at the Side.

OBJECTIVE 4 Write percents as fractions. Percents can also be written as fractions. Recall that a percent is a ratio with a denominator of 100. For example, 89% is $\frac{89}{100}$. Because the fraction bar indicates division, we are dividing by 100, just as we did when writing a percent as a decimal.

Writing a Percent as a Fraction

To write a percent as a fraction, drop the % symbol and write the number over 100. Then write the fraction in lowest terms.

EXAMPLE 5 Writing Percents as Fractions

Write each percent as a fraction or mixed number in lowest terms or as a whole number.

(a) 25%   Drop the % symbol and write 25 over 100.

$$25\% = \frac{25}{100} \leftarrow 25 \text{ per } 100$$

$$= \frac{25 \div 25}{100 \div 25} = \frac{1}{4} \leftarrow \text{Lowest terms}$$

As a check, write 25% as a decimal.

$$25\% = 25 \div 100 = 0.25 \leftarrow \text{Percent sign dropped}$$

Recall that 0.25 means 25 hundredths.

$$0.25 = \frac{25}{100} = \frac{25 \div 25}{100 \div 25} = \frac{1}{4} \leftarrow \text{Same result as above}$$

(b) 76%   Drop the % symbol and write 76 over 100.

This number becomes the numerator.

$$76\% = \frac{76}{100} \leftarrow \text{The } denominator \text{ is always 100 because percent means } parts\ per\ 100$$

Write $\frac{76}{100}$ in lowest terms. $\frac{76 \div 4}{100 \div 4} = \frac{19}{25} \leftarrow \text{Lowest terms}$

Continued on Next Page

(c) 150%

$$150\% = \frac{150}{100} = \frac{150 \div 50}{100 \div 50} = \frac{3}{2} = 1\frac{1}{2} \leftarrow \text{Mixed number}$$

(d) $100\% = \dfrac{100}{100} = 1 \leftarrow$ Whole number

> Always simplify fraction answers.

> **Note**
> Remember that percent means *per 100.*

Work Problem **5** *at the Side.* ▶

Example 6 below shows how to write decimal percents and fraction percents as fractions.

EXAMPLE 6   Writing Decimal Percents or Fraction Percents as Fractions

Write each percent as a fraction in lowest terms.

(a) 15.5%

Drop the % symbol and write 15.5 over 100.

$$15.5\% = \frac{15.5}{100}$$

To get a whole number in the numerator, multiply the numerator and denominator by 10. (Multiplying by $\frac{10}{10}$ is the same as multiplying by 1.)

$$\frac{15.5}{100} = \frac{(15.5)(10)}{(100)(10)} = \frac{155}{1000}$$

Write the fraction in lowest terms.

$$\frac{155 \div 5}{1000 \div 5} = \frac{31}{200} \leftarrow \text{Lowest terms}$$

(b) $33\frac{1}{3}\%$

Drop the % symbol and write $33\frac{1}{3}$ over 100.

$$33\frac{1}{3}\% = \frac{33\frac{1}{3}}{100}$$

When there is a mixed number in the numerator, write it as an improper fraction. So $33\frac{1}{3}$ is $\frac{100}{3}$.

Think:
3 • 33 is 99
and 99 + 1 is 100
so $33\frac{1}{3}$ is $\frac{100}{3}$

$$\frac{33\frac{1}{3}}{100} = \frac{\frac{100}{3}}{100}$$

Continued on Next Page

---

5 Write each percent as a fraction or mixed number in lowest terms or as a whole number.

(a) 50%

(b) 19%

(c) 80%

(d) 6%

(e) 125%

(f) 300%

6 Write each percent as a fraction in lowest terms.

(a) 18.5%

(b) 87.5%

(c) 6.5%

(d) $66\dfrac{2}{3}\%$

(e) $12\dfrac{1}{3}\%$

(f) $62\dfrac{1}{2}\%$

Now you have a complex fraction (see **Section 5.6**). Rewrite the complex fraction using the $\div$ symbol for division. Then follow the steps for dividing fractions.

$$\dfrac{\tfrac{100}{3}}{100} = \dfrac{100}{3} \div 100 = \dfrac{100}{3} \div \dfrac{100}{1} = \dfrac{100}{3} \cdot \dfrac{1}{100} = \dfrac{\overset{1}{\cancel{100}} \cdot 1}{3 \cdot \underset{1}{\cancel{100}}} = \dfrac{1}{3}$$

Reciprocals

> **Note**
>
> In Example 6(a) on the previous page, we could have changed 15.5% to $15\tfrac{1}{2}\%$ and then written it as the improper fraction $\tfrac{31}{2}$ over 100. But it is usually easier to work with decimal percents as they are.

◀ *Work Problem* **6** *at the Side.*

OBJECTIVE 5 Write fractions as percents. Recall that to write a percent as a fraction, you *drop* the percent symbol and *divide* by 100. So, to reverse the process and change a fraction to a percent, you *multiply* by 100 and *attach* a percent symbol.

> **Writing a Fraction as a Percent**
>
> To write a fraction as a percent, multiply by 100 and attach a % symbol. This is the same as multiplying by 100%.

> **Note**
>
> Look back at Example 5(d) near the top of the previous page to see that 100% = 1. Recall that multiplying a number by 1 does *not* change the value of the number. So multiplying by 100% does not change the value of a number; it just gives us an *equivalent percent*.

EXAMPLE 7   Writing Fractions as Percents

Write each fraction as a percent. Round to the nearest tenth of a percent when necessary.

(a) $\dfrac{2}{5}$ Multiply $\tfrac{2}{5}$ by 100%.

$$\dfrac{2}{5} = \left(\dfrac{2}{5}\right)(100\%) = \left(\dfrac{2}{5}\right)\left(\dfrac{100}{1}\%\right) = \left(\dfrac{2}{5}\right)\left(\dfrac{5 \cdot 20}{1}\%\right) = \dfrac{2 \cdot \overset{1}{\cancel{5}} \cdot 20}{\underset{1}{\cancel{5}} \cdot 1}\%$$

$$= \dfrac{40}{1}\% = 40\%$$

To check the result, write 40% as $\tfrac{40}{100}$ and simplify the fraction.

$$40\% = \dfrac{40}{100} = \dfrac{40 \div 20}{100 \div 20} = \dfrac{2}{5} \leftarrow \text{Original fraction}$$

Continued on Next Page

(b) $\dfrac{5}{8}$ Multiply $\frac{5}{8}$ by 100%.

$$\frac{5}{8} = \left(\frac{5}{8}\right)(100\%) = \left(\frac{5}{8}\right)\left(\frac{100}{1}\%\right) = \left(\frac{5}{2 \cdot 4}\right)\left(\frac{\overset{1}{\overbrace{4 \cdot 25}}}{1}\%\right) = \frac{5 \cdot \overset{1}{\cancel{4}} \cdot 25}{2 \cdot \underset{1}{\cancel{4}} \cdot 1}\%$$

$$= \frac{125}{2}\% = 62\frac{1}{2}\%$$

You can also do the last step of simplifying $\frac{125}{2}$ on your calculator. Enter $\frac{125}{2}$ as 125 ÷ 2 =. The result is 62.5,   so $\frac{5}{8} = 62\frac{1}{2}\%$ or $\frac{5}{8} = 62.5\%$.

(c) $\dfrac{1}{6}$ Multiply $\frac{1}{6}$ by 100%.

$$\frac{1}{6} = \left(\frac{1}{6}\right)(100\%) = \left(\frac{1}{6}\right)\left(\frac{100}{1}\%\right) = \left(\frac{1}{2 \cdot 3}\right)\left(\frac{\overset{1}{\overbrace{2 \cdot 50}}}{1}\%\right) = \frac{1 \cdot \overset{1}{\cancel{2}} \cdot 50}{\underset{1}{\cancel{2}} \cdot 3 \cdot 1}\%$$

$$= \frac{50}{3}\% = 16\frac{2}{3}\%$$

To simplify $\frac{50}{3}$ on your calculator, enter 50 ÷ 3 =. The result is 16.66666666, with the 6 continuing to repeat. The directions say to round to the nearest *tenth* of a percent.

┌─ Next digit is *5 or more*.

> When the next digit is *5 or more*, round up.

16.**6**6666666%   rounds to   16.**7**%

↑ Tenths place

So $\frac{1}{6} = 16\frac{2}{3}\%$ (exact answer)   or $\frac{1}{6} \approx 16.7\%$ (rounded answer).

▦ **Calculator Tip**

In Example 7(a) on the previous page, you can use your calculator to write $\frac{2}{5}$ as a percent.

Step 1   Enter $\frac{2}{5}$ as 2 ÷ 5 =. Your calculator shows   **0.4**

↑ Decimal equivalent of $\frac{2}{5}$

Step 2   Change the decimal number 0.4 to a percent by moving the decimal point two places to the right (multiply by 100%).

0.4**0** = 40% ← Attach % symbol.

Try this technique on Examples 7(b) and 7(c) on this page.

For $\frac{5}{8}$, enter 5 ÷ 8 =. Your calculator shows   **0.625**

Move the decimal point in 0.625 two places to the right.

0.**625** = 62.5% ← Attach % symbol.

Continued on Next Page

---

7 Write each fraction as a percent. If you're using a calculator, first work each one by hand. Then use your calculator and round to the nearest tenth of a percent when necessary.

(a) $\dfrac{1}{2}$

(b) $\dfrac{3}{4}$

(c) $\dfrac{1}{10}$

(d) $\dfrac{7}{8}$

(e) $\dfrac{5}{6}$

(f) $\dfrac{2}{3}$

ANSWERS

7. **(a)** 50%   **(b)** 75%   **(c)** 10%

(d) $87\frac{1}{2}\%$ or 87.5% (Both are exact answers.)

(e) exactly $83\frac{1}{3}\%$, or 83.3% (rounded)

(f) exactly $66\frac{2}{3}\%$, or 66.7% (rounded)

8 Fill in the blanks.

(a) 100% of $4.60 is _____.

(b) 100% of 3000 students is _____.

(c) 100% of 7 pages is _____.

(d) 100% of 272 miles is _____.

(e) 100% of $10\frac{1}{2}$ hours is _____.

9 Fill in the blanks.

(a) 50% of $4.60 is _____.

(b) 50% of 3000 students is _____.

(c) 50% of 7 pages is _____.

(d) 50% of 272 miles is _____.

(e) 50% of $10\frac{1}{2}$ hours is _____.

For $\frac{1}{6}$, enter 1 ⊕ 6 ⊜. Your calculator shows

| 0.166666666 |

Some calculators show 7 in the last place. ⟶

Move the decimal point two places to the right. Then round to the nearest tenth.

$$0.166666666 = 16.66666666\% \approx 16.7\% \leftarrow \text{Attach \% symbol.}$$

With a fraction such as $\frac{1}{6}$, your calculator gives only an *approximate* answer. You can't get the exact answer of $16\frac{2}{3}\%$ by using your calculator.

◀ *Work Problem* **7** *on the Previous Page at the Side.*

OBJECTIVE **6** **Use 100% and 50%.** When working with percents, it is helpful to have several reference points. 100% and 50% are two helpful reference points.

100% means 100 parts out of 100 parts. That's *all* of the parts. If you pay 100% of a $245 dentist bill, you pay $245 (*all* of it).

EXAMPLE 8 **Finding 100% of a Number**

Fill in the blanks.

(a) 100% of $42 is _____.
100% is *all* of the money.
So 100% of $42 is $42_____.

(b) 100% of 9 miles is _____.
100% is *all* of the miles.
So 100% of 9 miles is 9 miles_____.

◀ *Work Problem* **8** *at the Side.*

50% means 50 parts out of 100 parts, which is *half* of the parts because $\frac{50}{100} = \frac{1}{2}$. So 50% of $12 is $6 (*half* of the money).

EXAMPLE 9 **Finding 50% of a Number**

Fill in the blanks.

(a) 50% of $42 is _____.
50% is *half* of the money.
So 50% of $42 is $21_____.

(b) 50% of 9 miles is _____.
50% is *half* of the miles.
So 50% of 9 miles is $4\frac{1}{2}$ miles_____.

◀ *Work Problem* **9** *at the Side.*

ANSWERS

8. (a) $4.60 (b) 3000 students (c) 7 pages
   (d) 272 miles (e) $10\frac{1}{2}$ hours

9. (a) $2.30 (b) 1500 students
   (c) $3\frac{1}{2}$ pages (d) 136 miles
   (e) $5\frac{1}{4}$ hours

Math in the Media

DECIMALS, PERCENTS, AND QUILT PATTERNS

Please complete the Quilt Patterns activity in Section 5.8 before starting this activity.

Two of the quilt patterns you worked with in **Section 5.8** are repeated here. For each pattern, complete the table by copying the fractions you found and then changing the fractions to decimals and to percents. Use your calculator and round decimals to the nearest thousandth and percents to the nearest tenth when necessary. In the last row of the table, add the fractions. Then add the decimals, and finally, add the percents.

Source: Patchwork Persuasions: Quilts from Traditional Designs.

1.

Peace and Plenty

Color	Fraction	Decimal	Percent
Blue			
Yellow			
Whitish			
Total			

2.

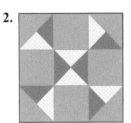

Cobwebs

Color	Fraction	Decimal	Percent
Mauve			
Purple			
Yellow			
Total			

3. What pattern do you notice in the Total row in each table?

4. Explain why some of the totals in the Cobwebs' table don't quite fit the pattern.

5. If you created a quilt pattern for the quilt activity in **Section 5.8**, make a table like the ones in Questions 1 and 2 for your design.

FOR EXTRA HELP *MyMathLab*   Math XL PRACTICE   WATCH   DOWNLOAD READ   REVIEW

Write each percent as a decimal. See Examples 2 and 3.

1. 25%   **2.** 35%   **3.** 30%   **4.** 20%

5. 6%   **6.** 3%   **7.** 140%   **8.** 250%

9. 7.8%   **10.** 6.7%   **11.** 100%   **12.** 600%

13. 0.5%   **14.** 0.2%   **15.** 0.35%   **16.** 0.076%

Write each decimal as a percent. See Example 4.

17. 0.5   **18.** 0.6   **19.** 0.62   **20.** 0.18

21. 0.03   **22.** 0.07   **23.** 0.125   **24.** 0.875

25. 0.629   **26.** 0.494   **27.** 2   **28.** 5

29. 2.6   **30.** 1.8   **31.** 0.0312   **32.** 0.0625

Write each percent as a fraction or mixed number in lowest terms. See Examples 5 and 6.

33. 20%   **34.** 40%   **35.** 50%   **36.** 75%

37. 55%   **38.** 35%   **39.** 37.5%   **40.** 87.5%

41. 6.25%   **42.** 43.75%   **43.** $16\frac{2}{3}\%$ **44.** $83\frac{1}{3}\%$

45. 130%   **46.** 175%   **47.** 250%   **48.** 325%

Write each fraction as a percent. If you're using a calculator, first work each one by hand. Then use your calculator and round to the nearest tenth of a percent when necessary. See Example 7.

49. $\dfrac{1}{4}$

50. $\dfrac{1}{5}$

51. $\dfrac{3}{10}$

52. $\dfrac{9}{10}$

53. $\dfrac{3}{5}$

54. $\dfrac{3}{4}$

55. $\dfrac{37}{100}$

56. $\dfrac{63}{100}$

57. $\dfrac{3}{8}$

58. $\dfrac{1}{8}$

59. $\dfrac{1}{20}$

60. $\dfrac{1}{50}$

61. $\dfrac{5}{9}$

62. $\dfrac{7}{9}$

63. $\dfrac{1}{7}$

64. $\dfrac{5}{7}$

In each statement, write percents as decimals and decimals as percents. See Examples 2–4.

65. In 1900, only 8% of U.S. homes had a telephone. (*Source: Harper's Index.*)

66. In 1900, only 14% of homes in the United States had a bathtub. (*Source: Harper's Index.*)

67. Tornadoes can occur on any day of the year, but 42% of them appear in May and June. (*Source: National Severe Storms Laboratory.*)

68. Only 2.1% of tornadoes occur in December, making it the least likely month for twisters. (*Source: National Severe Storms Laboratory.*)

69. The property tax rate in Alpine County is 0.035.

70. A church building fund has 0.49 of the money needed.

71. The number of people taking CPR training this session is 2 times that of the last session.

72. Attendance at this year's company picnic is 3 times last year's attendance.

Write a fraction and a percent for the shaded part of each figure. Then write a fraction and a percent for the unshaded part of each figure.

73.

74.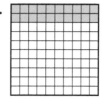

75.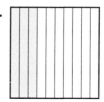

76.

77.

78.

Complete this table. Write fractions and mixed numbers in lowest terms.

	Fraction	Decimal	Percent
79.	$\frac{1}{100}$	_____	_____
80.	$\frac{1}{10}$	_____	_____
81.	_____	0.2	_____
82.	_____	0.25	_____
83.	_____	_____	30%
84.	_____	_____	40%
85.	$\frac{1}{2}$	_____	_____
86.	$\frac{3}{4}$	_____	_____
87.	_____	_____	90%
88.	_____	_____	100%
89.	_____	1.5	_____
90.	_____	2.25	_____

The road signs in Exercises 91–92 tell drivers that they are approaching a steep, downward hill. For example, the 8% sign means that for every 100 ft of roadway length, the road will drop a total of 8 ft in elevation.

91. Write the percent on the sign as a decimal and as a fraction in lowest terms.

92. Write the percent on the sign as a decimal and as a fraction in lowest terms.

93. Suppose the roadway dropped 5 ft in elevation for every 100 ft of length. Write a percent, a decimal, and a fraction in lowest terms to describe this situation.

94. Suppose the roadway dropped 7 ft in elevation for every 100 ft of length. Write a percent, a decimal, and a fraction in lowest terms to describe this situation.

The diagram shows the different types of teeth in an adult's mouth. Use the diagram to answer Exercises 95–100. Write each answer in Exercises 95–98 as a fraction in lowest terms, as a decimal, and as a percent.

95. What portion of an adult's teeth are incisors, designed to bite and cut?

96. The pointy canine teeth tear and rip food. They are what portion of an adult's teeth?

97. The molars, which grind up food, are what portion of an adult's teeth?

98. What portion of an adult's teeth are premolars?

99. Some people have four fewer molars than shown in the tooth diagram. For these people, the canines are what portion of their teeth? Write your answer as a fraction in lowest terms and as a percent.

100. For the adults who have four fewer molars than shown, the incisors are what portion of their teeth? Write your answer as a fraction in lowest terms and as a percent.

Incisors
Canines
Premolars
Molars
Upper teeth
Lower teeth
Molars
Premolars
Canines
Incisors

Source: Time-Life *Human Body.*

101. Explain and correct the errors made by students when they used their calculators on these problems.

(a) Write $\frac{7}{20}$ as a percent.

Student entered 7 ⊕ 20 ⊜, and the result was 0.35, so $\frac{7}{20} = 0.35\%$

(b) Write $\frac{16}{25}$ as a percent.

Student entered 25 ⊕ 16 ⊜, and the result was 1.5625, so $\frac{16}{25} = 156.25\%$

102. Explain and correct the errors made by students who moved decimal points to solve these problems.

(a) Write 3.2 as a percent.

$03.2 = 0.032$ so $3.2 = 0.032\%$

(b) Write 60% as a decimal.

$00.60 = 0.0060$ so $60\% = 0.0060$

Fill in the blanks in Exercises 103–118. Remember that 100% *is all of something and* 50% *is half of it. See Examples 8 and 9.*

103. (a) 100% of $78 is _____.

(b) 50% of $78 is _____.

104. (a) 100% of 5 hours is _____.

(b) 50% of 5 hours is _____.

105. (a) 100% of 15 inches is _____.

(b) 50% of 15 inches is _____.

106. (a) 100% of $6000 is _____.

(b) 50% of $6000 is _____.

107. (a) 100% of 2.8 miles is _____.

(b) 50% of 2.8 miles is _____.

108. (a) 100% of $2.50 is _____.

(b) 50% of $2.50 is _____.

109. There are 20 children in the preschool class. 100% of the children are served breakfast and lunch. How many children are served both meals?

_____

110. The Speedy Delivery company owns 345 vans. 100% of the vans are painted white with blue lettering. How many company vans are painted white with blue lettering?

_____

111. Alyssa needs 120 credits to graduate. She has earned 50% of the credits. How many credits has she earned?

_____

112. Ian has a limit of $1500 on his credit card. He has used 50% of the limit. How many dollars of credit has he used?

_____

113. (a) John owes $285 for tuition. Financial aid will pay 50% of the cost. Financial aid will pay

_____.

(b) What *percent* of the tuition will John have to pay?

_____

(c) How much *money* will John have to pay?

_____

115. (a) About 50% of the 8200 students at our college work more than 20 hours per week. How many *students* is this?

_____

(b) What *percent* of the students work 20 hours or less per week?

_____

117. (a) Dylan's test score was 100%. How many of the 35 problems did he work correctly?

_____

(b) How many *problems* did Dylan miss?

_____

119. Describe a shortcut way to find 50% of a number. Include two examples to illustrate the shortcut.

114. (a) The Animal Humane Society took in 20,000 animals last year. About 50% of them were dogs. The number of dogs taken in was about how many?

_____

(b) What *percent* of the animals were *not* dogs?

_____

(c) How many *animals* were not dogs?

_____

116. (a) Shalayna's cell phone plan includes 1600 minutes of "off-peak" calling time per month. Last month she used 50% of her "off-peak" minutes. How many *minutes* did she use?

_____

(b) What *percent* of her "off-peak" minutes were *not* used?

_____

118. (a) Latrell made 100% of his 12 free throws during a practice game today. How many free throws did he make?

_____

(b) How many *free throws* did Latrell miss?

_____

120. Describe a shortcut way to find 100% of a number. Include two examples to illustrate the shortcut.

7.7 ▶▶▶ The Percent Proportion

OBJECTIVES

1 Identify the percent, whole, and part.

2 Solve percent problems using the percent proportion.

We will show you two ways to solve percent problems. One is the proportion method, which we discuss in this section. The other is the percent equation method, which we explain in **Section 7.8.**

OBJECTIVE 1 Identify the percent, whole, and part.   You have learned that a statement of two equivalent ratios is called a proportion (see **Section 7.3**). For example, the fraction $\frac{3}{5}$ is the same as the ratio 3 to 5, and 60% is the ratio 60 to 100. As the figure below shows, these two ratios are equivalent and make a proportion.

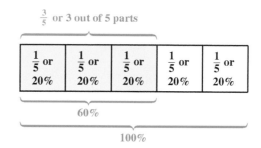

The **percent proportion** can be used to solve percent problems.

> **The Percent Proportion**
>
> *Percent* is to *100*   **as**   *part* is to *whole.*
>
> $$\frac{\text{percent}}{100} = \frac{\text{part}}{\text{whole}}$$
>
> Always 100 ⟶ because percent means "per 100"
>
> In some textbooks the percent proportion is written using the words *amount* and *base.*
>
> $$\frac{\text{percent}}{100} = \frac{\text{amount}}{\text{base}}$$

Here is the proportion for the figure at the top of the page.

60% means 60 parts out of 100 parts. } $\frac{60}{100} = \frac{3}{5}$ ← Shaded (3 parts) ← Whole (5 parts)

If we write $\frac{60}{100}$ in lowest terms, it is equal to $\frac{3}{5}$, so the proportion is true.

$$\frac{60}{100} = \frac{60 \div 20}{100 \div 20} = \frac{3}{5} \quad \left\{ \begin{array}{l} \text{Matches ratio on} \\ \text{right side of proportion} \end{array} \right.$$

In order to use the percent proportion to solve problems, you must be able to pick out the *percent*, the *whole*, and the *part*. Look for the percent first, because it is the easiest to identify.

> **Identifying the Percent**
>
> The **percent** is a ratio of a part to a whole, with 100 as the denominator. In a problem, the percent appears with the word *percent* or with the symbol % after it.

EXAMPLE 1 **Identifying the Percent in Percent Problems**

Identify the percent in each problem.

(a) 32% of the 900 women were retired. How many were retired?
↓
Percent

The percent is 32. The number 32 appears with the symbol %.

(b) $150 is 25 percent of what number?
↓
Percent

The percent is 25 because 25 appears with the word *percent*.

(c) If 7 students failed, what percent of the 350 students failed?
↓
Percent (unknown)

The word *percent* has no number with it, so the percent is the unknown part of the problem.

Work Problem **1** *at the Side.* ▶

The second thing to look for in a percent problem is the *whole* (sometimes called the *base*).

Identifying the Whole
The **whole** is the entire quantity. In a problem, the *whole* often appears after the word **of.**

EXAMPLE 2 **Identifying the Whole in Percent Problems**

These problems are the same as those in Example 1 above. Now identify the *whole*.

(a) 32% of the 900 women were retired. How many were retired?
↓   ↓
Percent   Whole

The whole is 900 women. The number 900 appears after the word *of*.

(b) $150 is 25 percent of what number?
↓   ↓
Percent   Whole (unknown; follows *of*)

The whole is unknown.

(c) If 7 students failed, what percent of the 350 students failed?
↓   ↓
Percent (unknown)   Whole (follows *of*)

The whole is 350 students. The number 350 appears after the word *of*.

Work Problem **2** *at the Side.* ▶

The third and final thing to identify in a percent problem is the *part* (sometimes called the *amount*).

Identifying the Part
The **part** is the number being compared to the whole.

1 Identify the percent.

(a) Of the $2000, 15% will be spent on a washing machine.

(b) 60 employees is what percent of 750 employees?

(c) The state sales tax is $6\frac{1}{2}$ percent of the $590 price.

(d) $30 is 48% of what amount of money?

(e) 75 of the 110 rental cars were rented today. What percent were rented?

2 Identify the whole.

(a) Of the $2000, 15% will be spent on a washing machine.

(b) 60 employees is what percent of 750 employees?

(c) The state sales tax is $6\frac{1}{2}$ percent of the $590 price.

(d) $30 is 48% of what amount of money?

(e) 75 of the 110 rental cars were rented today. What percent were rented?

ANSWERS
1. **(a)** 15% **(b)** unknown **(c)** $6\frac{1}{2}$ percent
   (d) 48% **(e)** unknown
2. **(a)** $2000 **(b)** 750 employees **(c)** $590
   (d) unknown **(e)** 110 cars

3 Identify the part.

(a) Of the $2000, 15% will be spent on a washing machine.

(b) 60 employees is what percent of 750 employees?

(c) The state sales tax is $6\frac{1}{2}$ percent of the $590 price.

(d) $30 is 48% of what amount of money?

(e) 75 of the 110 rental cars were rented today. What percent were rented?

> **Note**
> If you have trouble identifying the *part,* find the *whole* and the *percent* first. The remaining number is the *part.*

EXAMPLE 3 Identifying the Part in Percent Problems

These problems are the same as those in Examples 1 and 2 on the previous page. Identify the *part.*

(a) 32% of the 900 women were retired. How many were retired?

    Percent   Whole   Part (unknown)

The part of the women who were retired is unknown. In other words, some part of 900 women were retired.

(b) $150 is 25 percent of what number?

    Part   Percent   Whole (unknown)

$150 is the remaining number, so $150 is the part.

(c) If 7 students failed, what percent of 350 students failed?

    Part   Percent (unknown)   Whole

The part of the students who failed is 7 students.

— ◀ *Work Problem* **3** *at the Side.*

OBJECTIVE **2** Solve percent problems using the percent proportion.

EXAMPLE 4 Using the Percent Proportion to Find the Part

Use the percent proportion to answer this question.

$$15\% \text{ of } \$165 \text{ is how much money?}$$

Recall that the percent proportion is $\dfrac{\text{percent}}{100} = \dfrac{\text{part}}{\text{whole}}$. First identify the percent by looking for the % symbol or the word *percent.* Then look for the *whole* (usually follows the word *of*). Finally, identify the *part.*

$$15\% \text{ of } \$165 \text{ is how much money?}$$

    Percent   Whole   Part (unknown)
            (follows *of*)

Set up the percent proportion. Here we use *n* as the variable representing the unknown part. You may use any letter you like.

$$\text{Percent} \to \dfrac{15}{100} = \dfrac{n}{165} \leftarrow \text{Part (unknown)}$$
$$\text{Always 100} \to \qquad\qquad \leftarrow \text{Whole}$$

Recall from **Section 7.3** that the first step in solving a proportion is to find the cross products.

$$\textit{Step 1} \quad \dfrac{15}{100} = \dfrac{n}{165}$$

$$\left.\begin{array}{l} 100 \cdot n \\[4pt] 15 \cdot 165 \end{array}\right\} \text{Find the cross products.}$$

Continued on Next Page

Step 2 $100 \cdot n = \underbrace{15 \cdot 165}$ Show that the cross products are equivalent.

$100 \cdot n = \quad 2475$

Step 3 $\dfrac{\overset{1}{\cancel{100}} \cdot n}{\cancel{100}_{1}} = \dfrac{2475}{100}$ Divide both sides by 100, the coefficient of the variable term. On the left side, divide out the common factor of 100.

$n = 24.75$ On the right side, $2475 \div 100$ is 24.75

The part is $24.75, so 15% of $165 is **$24.75**.   [Write a $ in your answer.]

> **CAUTION**
> When you use the percent proportion, do **not** move the decimal point in the percent or in the answer.

——————— *Work Problem* **4** *at the Side.* ▶

Work Problem 4 at the Side.

EXAMPLE 5   **Using the Percent Proportion to Find the Percent**

Use the percent proportion to answer this question.

8 pounds is what percent of 160 pounds?

   Part   Percent   Whole
              (unknown)   (follows of)

The percent proportion is $\dfrac{\text{percent}}{100} = \dfrac{\text{part}}{\text{whole}}$. Set up the proportion using p as the variable representing the unknown percent. Then find the cross products.

Percent (unknown) → $\dfrac{p}{100} = \dfrac{8}{160}$ ← Part
Always 100 →   ← Whole

$\dfrac{p}{100} = \dfrac{8}{160}$ $100 \cdot 8 = 800$ ⟵ }Cross products
                    $p \cdot 160$ ⟵

$p \cdot 160 = 800$ Show that the cross products are equivalent.

$\dfrac{p \cdot \overset{1}{\cancel{160}}}{\cancel{160}_{1}} = \dfrac{800}{160}$ Divide both sides by 160

$p = 5$ [The *percent* was unknown. Write **%** in your answer.]

The percent is **5%**. So 8 pounds is **5%** of 160 pounds.

> **CAUTION**
> When you're finding an unknown percent, as in Example 5 above, be careful to label your answer with the % symbol. Do **not** add a decimal point or move the decimal point in your answer.

——————— *Work Problem* **5** *at the Side.* ▶

Work Problem 5 at the Side.

4 Use the percent proportion to answer these questions.

(a) 9% of 3250 miles is how many miles?

(b) What is 20% of 180 calories?

(c) 78% of $5.50 is how much?

(d) What is $12\frac{1}{2}\%$ of 400 homes? (*Hint:* Write $12\frac{1}{2}\%$ as **12.5%**.)

5 Use the percent proportion to answer these questions.

(a) 1200 books is what percent of 5000 books?

(b) What percent of $6.50 is $0.52?

(c) 20 athletes is what percent of 32 athletes?

ANSWERS

4. (a) $\dfrac{9}{100} = \dfrac{n}{3250}$ The part is 292.5 miles.

 (b) $\dfrac{20}{100} = \dfrac{n}{180}$ The part is 36 calories.

 (c) $\dfrac{78}{100} = \dfrac{n}{5.50}$ The part is $4.29.

 (d) $\dfrac{12.5}{100} = \dfrac{n}{400}$ The part is 50 homes.

5. (a) $\dfrac{p}{100} = \dfrac{1200}{5000}$;   24%

 (b) $\dfrac{p}{100} = \dfrac{0.52}{6.50}$;   8%

 (c) $\dfrac{p}{100} = \dfrac{20}{32}$;   62.5% or $62\frac{1}{2}\%$

6 Use the percent proportion to answer these questions.

(a) 37 cars is 74% of how many cars?

EXAMPLE 6 **Using the Percent Proportion to Find the Whole**

Use the percent proportion to answer this question.

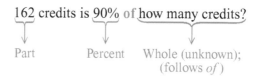

162 credits is 90% of how many credits?

Part   Percent   Whole (unknown);
                      (follows *of*)

Percent → $\dfrac{90}{100}$ = $\dfrac{162}{n}$ ← Part

Always 100 → 100   n ← Whole (unknown)

$\dfrac{90}{100} = \dfrac{162}{n}$ $\begin{matrix}100 \cdot 162 = 16{,}200 \\ 90 \cdot n\end{matrix}$ ⎤ Cross products

$90 \cdot n = 16{,}200$ Show that the cross products are equivalent.

$\dfrac{\overset{1}{\cancel{90}} \cdot n}{\underset{1}{\cancel{90}}} = \dfrac{16{,}200}{90}$ Divide both sides by 90

$n = 180$

Write **credits** in your answer.

(b) 45% of how much money is $139.59?

The whole is **180 credits.** So 162 credits is 90% of **180 credits.**

◀ *Work Problem* **6** *at the Side.*

So far in all the examples, the part has been *less* than the whole. This is because all the percents have been less than 100%. Recall that 100% of something is *all* of it. When the percent is *less* than 100%, you have *less* than all of it.

Now let's look at percents *greater* than 100%. For example,

100% of $20 is all of the money, or $20.

(c) 1.2 tons is $2\frac{1}{2}$% of how many tons?

150% of $20 is *greater* than $20.

100%	+	50%	=	150%
of the		of the		of the
money is		money is		money is
$20	+	$10	=	$30

So 150% of $20 is $30.

When the percent is *greater* than 100%, the part is *greater* than the whole, as you'll see in Example 7 on the next page.

ANSWERS

6. (a) $\dfrac{74}{100} = \dfrac{37}{n}$;   50 cars

(b) $\dfrac{45}{100} = \dfrac{139.59}{n}$; $310.20

(c) $\dfrac{2.5}{100} = \dfrac{1.2}{n}$;   48 tons

EXAMPLE 7 · **Working with Percents Greater Than 100%**

Use the percent proportion to answer each question.

(a) How many students is 210% of 40 students?

Part (unknown)   Percent   Whole (follows *of*)

Percent → $\frac{210}{100} = \frac{n}{40}$ ← Part (unknown)
Always 100 →   ← Whole

$$\frac{210}{100} = \frac{n}{40}$$ $100 \cdot n$
                                       $210 \cdot 40 = 8400$ } Cross products

$100 \cdot n = 8400$ Show that the cross products are equivalent.

$$\frac{\overset{1}{\cancel{100}} \cdot n}{\underset{1}{\cancel{100}}} = \frac{8400}{100}$$ Divide both sides by 100

$$n = 84$$

The part is **84 students**, which is *greater* than the whole of 40 students. This result makes sense because the percent is 210%. If it was exactly 200%, we would have *2 times the whole,* and 2 times 40 students is 80 students. So 210% should be even a little more than 80 students. Our answer of 84 students is reasonable.

(b) What percent of $50 is $68?

Percent   Whole   Part
(unknown) (follows *of*)

Percent (unknown) → $\frac{p}{100} = \frac{68}{50}$ ← Part
Always 100 →   ← Whole

$$\frac{p}{100} = \frac{68}{50}$$ $100 \cdot 68 = 6800$
                                      $p \cdot 50$ } Cross products

$p \cdot 50 = 6800$ Show that the cross products are equivalent.

$$\frac{p \cdot \overset{1}{\cancel{50}}}{\underset{1}{\cancel{50}}} = \frac{6800}{50}$$ Divide both sides by 50

> Write **%** in your answer.

$$p = 136$$

The percent is **136%**. This result makes sense because $68 is *greater* than $50, so $68 has to be *greater than 100%* of $50.

Work Problem **7** *at the Side.* ▶

---

7 Use the percent proportion to answer each question.

(a) 350% of $6 is how much?

(b) 23 hours is what percent of 20 hours?

▦ **(c)** What percent of $47.32 is $106.47?

ANSWERS

7. (a) $\frac{350}{100} = \frac{n}{6}$; $21

(b) $\frac{p}{100} = \frac{23}{20}$; 115%

(c) $\frac{p}{100} = \frac{106.47}{47.32}$; 225%

7.7 ▶▶▶ **Exercises**

FOR EXTRA HELP
MyMathLab
Math XL
PRACTICE
WATCH
DOWNLOAD
READ
REVIEW

In Exercises 1–12, (a) identify the percent; (b) identify the whole; (c) identify the part; (d) write a percent proportion, and solve it to answer the question. See Examples 1–6.

1. What is 10% of 3000 runners?

2. What is 35% of 2340 volunteers?

3. 4% of 120 feet is how many feet?

4. 9% of $150 is how much money?

5. 16 pepperoni pizzas is what percent of 32 pizzas?

6. 35 hours is what percent of 140 hours?

7. What percent of 200 calories is 16 calories?

8. What percent of 350 parking spaces is 7 handicapped parking spaces?

9. 495 successful students is 90% of what number of students?

10. 84 e-mails is 28% of what number of e-mails?

11. $12\frac{1}{2}$% of what amount is $3.50?

12. $5\frac{1}{2}$% of what amount is $17.60?

Write a percent proportion and solve it to answer Exercises 13–24. If necessary, round money answers to the nearest cent and percent answers to the nearest tenth of a percent. See Examples 4–7.

13. 250% of 7 hours is how long?

14. What is 130% of 60 trees?

15. What percent of $172 is $32?

16. $14 is what percent of $398?

17. 748 books is 110% of what number of books?

18. 145% of what number of inches is 11.6 inches?

19. What is 14.7% of $274?

20. 8.3% of $43 is how much?

21. 105 employees is what percent of 54 employees?

22. What percent of 46 animals is 100 animals?

23. $0.33 is 4% of what amount?

24. 6% of what amount is $0.03?

25. A student turned in the following answers on a test. You can see that *two* of the answers are incorrect *without working the problems*. Find the incorrect answers and explain how you identified them (without actually solving the problems).

$$50\% \text{ of } \$84 \quad \text{is } \underline{\quad \$42 \quad}$$
$$150\% \text{ of } \$30 \quad \text{is } \underline{\quad \$20 \quad}$$
$$25\% \text{ of } \$16 \quad \text{is } \underline{\quad \$32 \quad}$$
$$100\% \text{ of } \$217 \text{ is } \underline{\quad \$217 \quad}$$

26. Name the three parts in a percent problem. For each of these three parts, write a sentence telling how you identify it.

27. Explain and correct the *two* errors that a student made when solving this problem: $14 is what percent of $8?

$$\frac{p}{100} = \frac{8}{14} \qquad p \cdot 14 = 100 \cdot 8$$

$$\frac{p \cdot \cancel{14}^{1}}{\cancel{14}_{1}} = \frac{800}{14}$$

$$p \approx 57.1$$

The answer is 57.1 (rounded).

28. Explain and correct the *two* errors that a student made when solving this problem: 9 children is 30% of what number of children?

$$\frac{30}{100} = \frac{n}{9} \qquad 100 \cdot n = 30 \cdot 9$$

$$\frac{\cancel{100}^{1} \cdot n}{\cancel{100}_{1}} = \frac{270}{100}$$

$$n = 2.7$$

The answer is 2.7%.

7.8 ▶▶▶ The Percent Equation

OBJECTIVES

1 Estimate answers to percent problems involving 25%.

2 Find 10% and 1% of a number by moving the decimal point.

3 Solve basic percent problems using the percent equation.

OBJECTIVE **1** **Estimate answers to percent problems involving 25%.** Before showing you the percent equation, we need to do some more estimation. As you have learned when working with integers, fractions, and decimals, it is always a good idea to estimate the answer. Doing so helps you catch mistakes. Also, when you're out shopping or eating in a restaurant, you will be able to estimate the sales tax, discount, or tip.

In **Section 7.6** we used shortcuts for 100% of a number (all of the number) and 50% of a number (divide the number by 2). Now let's look at a quick way to work with 25%.

25% means 25 parts out of 100 parts, or $\frac{25}{100}$, which is the same as $\frac{1}{4}$

25% of $40 would be $\frac{1}{4}$ of $40, or $10

A quick way to find $\frac{1}{4}$ of a number is to *divide it by 4*. Recall that the denominator, 4, tells you that the whole is divided into 4 equal parts.

EXAMPLE 1 **Estimating 25% of a Number**

Estimate the answer to each question.

(a) What is 25% of $817?
Use front end rounding to round $817 to $800.
Then divide $800 by 4. The estimate is **$200**.

> 25% is $\frac{1}{4}$, so to find 25% of a number, divide it by 4.

(b) Find 25% of 19.7 miles.
Use front end rounding to round 19.7 miles to 20 miles.
Then divide 20 miles by 4. The estimate is **5 miles**.

(c) 25% of 49 days is how long?
You could round 49 days to 50 days, using front end rounding.
Then divide 50 by 4 to get an estimate of **12.5 days**.
However, the division step is simpler if you notice that 48 is a multiple of 4. You can round 49 days to 48 days and divide by 4 to get an estimate of **12 days**. Either way gives you a fairly good idea of the correct answer.

◀ *Work Problem* **1** *at the Side.*

OBJECTIVE **2** **Find 10% and 1% of a number by moving the decimal point.** There are also helpful shortcuts for finding 10% or 1% of a number.

Ten percent, or 10%, means 10 parts out of 100 parts or $\frac{10}{100}$, which is the same as $\frac{1}{10}$. A quick way to find $\frac{1}{10}$ of a number is to *divide it by 10*. The denominator, 10, tells you that the whole is divided into 10 equal parts. The shortcut for dividing by 10 is to move the decimal point *one* place to the *left*.

EXAMPLE 2 **Finding 10% of a Number by Moving the Decimal Point**

Find the *exact* answer to each question by moving the decimal point.

(a) What is 10% of $817?
To find 10% of $817, divide $817 by 10. Do the division by moving the decimal point *one* place to the *left*. The decimal point starts at the far right side of $817.

10% of $81\underset{\curvearrowleft}{7.}$ = $81.70 ← Exact answer

↑
Write this 0 because it's money.

> Do **not** leave it as $81.7

So 10% of $817 is **$81.70**.

1 Estimate the answer to each question.

(a) What is 25% of $110.38?

(b) Find 25% of 7.6 hours.

(c) 25% of 34 pounds is how many pounds?

ANSWERS

1. **(a)** $100 ÷ 4 gives an estimate of $25.
   (b) 8 hours ÷ 4 gives an estimate of 2 hours.
   (c) 30 pounds ÷ 4 gives an estimate of 7.5 pounds, or 32 pounds ÷ 4 gives an estimate of 8 pounds.

Continued on Next Page

(b) Find 10% of 19.7 miles.
To find 10% of 19.7 miles, divide 19.7 by 10.
Move the decimal point *one* place to the *left*.

$$10\% \text{ of } 19.7 \text{ miles } = 1.97 \text{ miles } \longleftarrow \text{ Exact answer}$$

So 10% of 19.7 miles is **1.97 miles**.

Work Problem **2** *at the Side.* ▶

One percent, or 1%, is 1 part out of 100 parts or $\frac{1}{100}$. This time the denominator of 100 tells you that the whole is divided into 100 parts. Recall that a quick way to divide by 100 is to move the decimal point *two* places to the *left*.

EXAMPLE 3 **Finding 1% of a Number by Moving the Decimal Point**

Find the *exact* answer to each question by moving the decimal point.

(a) What is 1% of $817?
To find 1% of $817, divide $817 by 100. Do the division by moving the decimal point *two* places to the *left*.

$$1\% \text{ of } \$817. = \$8.17 \longleftarrow \text{ Exact answer}$$

So 1% of $817 is **$8.17**.

(b) Find 1% of 19.7 miles.
To find 1% of 19.7 miles, divide 19.7 by 100.
Move the decimal point *two* places to the *left*.

$$1\% \text{ of } 19.7 \text{ miles } = 0.197 \text{ mile } \longleftarrow \text{ Exact answer}$$

So 1% of 19.7 miles is **0.197 mile**.

Work Problem **3** *at the Side.* ▶

Here is a summary of some of the shortcuts you can use with percents.

Percent Shortcuts

200% of a number is 2 times the number; **300% of a number** is 3 times the number; and so on.

100% of a number is the entire number.

To find **50% of a number,** divide the number by 2.

To find **25% of a number,** divide the number by 4.

To find **10% of a number,** divide the number by 10. To do the division, move the decimal point in the number *one* place to the *left*.

To find **1% of a number,** divide the number by 100. To do the division, move the decimal point in the number *two* places to the *left*.

2 Find the *exact* answer to each question by moving the decimal point.

(a) What is 10% of $110.38?

(b) Find 10% of 7.6 hours.

(c) 10% of 34 pounds is how many pounds?

3 Find the *exact* answer to each question by moving the decimal point.

(a) What is 1% of $110.38?

(b) Find 1% of 7.6 hours.

(c) 1% of 34 pounds is how many pounds?

ANSWERS
2. (a) $110.38 = $11.038 or $11.04 to the nearest cent
   (b) 7.6 hours = 0.76 hour
   (c) 34. pounds = 3.4 pounds
3. (a) $110.38 = $1.1038 or $1.10 to the nearest cent
   (b) 07.6 hours = 0.076 hour
   (c) 34. pounds = 0.34 pound

OBJECTIVE 3 Solve basic percent problems using the percent equation. In **Section 7.7** you used a proportion to solve percent problems. Now you will learn how to solve these problems using the percent equation.

Percent Equation

$$\text{percent } of \text{ whole} = \text{part}$$

The word *of* indicates multiplication, so the **percent equation** becomes

$$\text{percent} \cdot \text{whole} = \text{part}$$

Be sure to write the percent as a decimal or fraction before using the equation.

The percent equation is just a rearrangement of the percent proportion. Recall that in the proportion you wrote the percent over 100. Because there is no 100 in the equation, you have to change the percent to a decimal or fraction by dividing by 100 *before* using the equation.

Note

Once you have set up a percent equation, we encourage you to use your calculator to do the multiplying or dividing needed to solve the equation. For this reason, we will always write the percent as a decimal. If you're doing the problems by hand, changing the percent to a fraction may be easier at times. Either method will work.

Examples 4, 5, and 6 below are the same percent questions that were in the examples in **Section 7.7.** There we used a proportion to answer each question. Now we will use an equation to answer them. You can then compare the equation method with the proportion method.

EXAMPLE 4 Using the Percent Equation to Find the Part

Write and solve a percent equation to answer each question.

(a) 15% of $165 is how much money?

Translate the sentence into an equation. Recall that *of* indicates multiplication and *is* translates to the equal sign. The percent must be written in decimal form. Use any letter you like to represent the unknown quantity. (We will use n for an unknown number and p for an unknown percent.)

Write 15% as the decimal 0.15

15.% of $165 is how much money?

$$0.15 \quad \cdot \quad 165 = \quad n$$

To solve the equation, simplify the left side, multiplying 0.15 by 165.

$$(0.15)(165) = n$$
$$24.75 \quad = n$$

So 15% of $165 is $24.75, which matches the answer obtained using a proportion (see Example 4 in **Section 7.7**).

Continued on Next Page

Check Use estimation to check that the solution is reasonable. First find 10% of $165 by moving the decimal point.

$$10\% \text{ of } 165. \text{ is } \$16.50 \quad \text{and}$$

5% of $165 would be half as much, that is, half of $16.50 or about $8.

So the *estimate* for 15% of $165 is $16.50 + $8 = $24.50. The exact answer of $24.75 is very close to this estimate, so it is reasonable.

(b) How many students is 210% of 40 students?
Translate the sentence into an equation. Write the percent in decimal form.

How many students is 210.% of 40 students?

> Write 210% as the decimal 2.10

$$n \qquad = 2.10 \quad \cdot \quad 40$$

This time the two sides of the percent equation are reversed, so

$$\text{part} = \text{percent} \cdot \text{whole}$$

Recall that the variable may be on either side of the equal sign. To solve the equation, simplify the right side, multiplying 2.10 by 40.

$$n = (2.10)(40)$$
$$n = \qquad 84$$

So 84 students is 210% of 40 students. This matches the answer obtained by using a proportion (see Example 7(a) in **Section 7.7**).

Check Use estimation to check that the solution is reasonable. 210% is close to 200%.

$$200\% \text{ of } 40 \text{ students is } 2 \text{ times } 40 \text{ students} = 80 \text{ students} \leftarrow \text{Estimate}$$

The exact answer of 84 students is close to the estimate, so it is reasonable.

Work Problem **4** *at the Side.* ▶

EXAMPLE 5 **Using the Percent Equation to Find the Percent**

Write and solve a percent equation to answer each question.

(a) 8 pounds is what percent of 160 pounds?
Translate the sentence into an equation. This time the percent is unknown. Do *not* move the decimal point in the other numbers.

8 pounds is what percent of 160 pounds?

$$8 \quad = \quad p \quad \cdot \quad 160$$

To solve the equation, divide both sides by 160.

On the left side, divide 8 by 160 $\quad \dfrac{8}{160} = \dfrac{p \cdot \overset{1}{\cancel{160}}}{\underset{1}{\cancel{160}}} \quad$ On the right side, divide out the common factor of 160

Solution in *decimal* form $\quad 0.05 = p \quad$ **Multiply the solution by 100%** to change it from a *decimal* to a *percent*.

$$0.05 = 5\%$$

So 8 pounds is 5% of 160 pounds. This matches the answer obtained by using a proportion (see Example 5 in **Section 7.7**).

Continued on Next Page

---

4 Write and solve an equation to answer each question.

(a) 9% of 3250 miles is how many miles?

(b) 78% of $5.50 is how much?

(c) What is $12\frac{1}{2}\%$ of 400 homes? (*Hint:* Write $12\frac{1}{2}\%$ as 12.5%. Then move the decimal point two places to the left.)

(d) How much is 350% of $6?

ANSWERS

4. **(a)** $(0.09)(3250) = n$; 292.5 miles
   (b) $(0.78)(5.50) = n$; $4.29
   (c) $n = (0.125)(400)$; 50 homes
   (d) $n = (3.5)(6)$; $21

5 Write and solve an equation to answer each question.

(a) 1200 books is what percent of 5000 books?

Check The solution makes sense because 10% of 160 pounds would be 16 pounds.

10% of 160, pounds is 16 pounds   so

5% of 160 pounds is half as much, that is, half of 16 pounds, or 8 pounds.

8 pounds matches the number given in the original problem, so 5% is the correct solution.

(b) What percent of $50 is $68?
Translate the sentence into an equation and solve it.

$$\underbrace{\text{What percent}}_{p} \text{ of } \overset{\downarrow}{\$50} \overset{\downarrow}{\text{ is }} \overset{\downarrow}{\$68}?$$

$$p \quad \cdot \quad 50 = 68$$

$$\frac{p \cdot \cancel{50}^{1}}{\cancel{50}_{1}} = \frac{68}{50} \qquad \text{Divide both sides by 50}$$

$$p = 1.36 \leftarrow \text{Solution in } decimal \text{ form}$$

(b) 23 hours is what percent of 20 hours?

| **Multiply the solution by 100%** to change it from a *decimal* to a *percent*. | $1.36 = 136\%$ |

So **136%** of $50 is $68. This matches the answer obtained by using a proportion (see Example 7(b) in **Section 7.7**).

Check The solution makes sense because 100% of $50 would be $50 (all of it), and 200% of $50 would be 2 times $50, or $100. So $68 has to be between 100% and 200%.

136% is between 100% and 200%. → 100% of $50 = $50   ← $68 is between $50 and $100
                                      200% of $50 = $100

The solution of 136% fits the conditions.

(c) What percent of $6.50 is $0.52?

> **CAUTION**
> When you use an equation to solve for an unknown percent, *the solution will be in decimal form.* Remember to **multiply the solution by 100%** to change it from decimal form to a percent. The shortcut is to move the decimal point in the solution *two* places to the *right* and attach the % symbol.
>
> Recall that 100% = 1, and multiplying a number by 1 does *not* change the value of the number; it just gives us an *equivalent percent.*

◄ *Work Problem* **5** *at the Side.*

EXAMPLE 6 **Using the Percent Equation to Find the Whole**

Write and solve a percent equation to answer each question.

(a) 162 credits is 90% of how many credits?

Translate the sentence into an equation. Write the percent in decimal form.

$$\underbrace{162 \text{ credits}}_{162} \; \underbrace{\text{is}}_{=} \; \underbrace{90.\%}_{0.90} \; \underbrace{\text{of}}_{\bullet} \; \underbrace{\text{how many credits?}}_{n}$$

Write 90% as the decimal 0.90

Recall that 0.90 is equivalent to 0.9, so use 0.9 in the equation.

$$\frac{162}{0.9} = \frac{(0.9)\,(n)}{0.9}$$ Divide both sides by 0.9

$$180 = n$$

> Write **credits** in your answer.

So 162 credits is 90% of **180 credits**.

Check The solution makes sense because 90% of 180 credits should be 10% less than 100% of the credits, and 10% of 180. credits is 18 credits.

$$\underset{\text{of 180 credits}}{100\%} \; - \; \underset{\text{of 180. credits}}{10\%} \; = \; \underset{\text{of 180 credits}}{90\%}$$

$$180 \text{ credits} \; - \; 18 \text{ credits} \; = \; 162 \text{ credits} \leftarrow \text{Matches the number given in the original problem}$$

(b) 250% of what amount is $75?

Translate the sentence into an equation. Write the percent in decimal form.

$$\underbrace{250.\%}_{2.5} \; \underbrace{\text{of}}_{\bullet} \; \underbrace{\text{what amount}}_{n} \; \underbrace{\text{is}}_{=} \; \underbrace{\$75?}_{75}$$

> Write 250% as the decimal 2.5

$$\frac{(2.5)\,(n)}{2.5} = \frac{75}{2.5}$$ Divide both sides by 2.5

$$n = 30$$

> Write a **$** in your answer.

So 250% of **$30** is $75.

Check The solution makes sense because 200% of $30 is 2 times $30 = $60, and 50% of $30 is $30 ÷ 2 = $15.

$$\underset{\text{of }\$30}{200\%} \; + \; \underset{\text{of }\$30}{50\%} \; = \; \underset{\text{of }\$30}{250\%}$$

$$(2)(\$30) \quad\quad \$30 \div 2$$

$$\$60 \; + \; \$15 \; = \; \$75 \leftarrow \text{Matches the number given in the original problem}$$

Work Problem **6** *at the Side.* ▶

---

6 Write and solve an equation to answer each question.

(a) 74% of how many cars is 37 cars?

(b) 1.2 tons is $2\frac{1}{2}$% of how many tons?

(c) 216 calculators is 160% of how many calculators?

ANSWERS

6. (a) $0.74 \cdot n = 37$;   50 cars
  (b) $1.2 = 0.025 \cdot n$;   48 tons
  (c) $216 = 1.6 \cdot n$;   135 calculators

7.8 ▶▶▶ **Exercises**

FOR EXTRA HELP

 *MyMathLab*

 Math XL PRACTICE

 WATCH

 DOWNLOAD

READ

 REVIEW

*Use your estimation skills and the percent shortcuts to select the most reasonable answers. Circle your choices. Do **not** write an equation or proportion and solve it. See Examples 1–3.*

1. Find 50% of 3000 patients.

   150 patients   1500 patients   300 patients

2. What is 50% of 192 pages?

   48 pages   384 pages   96 pages

3. 25% of $60 is how much?

   $15 $6 $30

4. Find 25% of $2840.

   $28.40 $710 $284

5. What is 10% of 45 pounds?

   0.45 pound   22.5 pounds   4.5 pounds

6. 10% of 7 feet is how many feet?

   0.7 foot   3.5 feet   14 feet

7. Find 200% of $3.50.

   $0.35 $1.75 $7.00

8. What is 300% of $12?

   $4 $36 $1.20

9. 1% of 5200 students is how many students?

   520 students   52 students   2600 students

10. Find 1% of 460 miles.

   0.46 mile   46 miles   4.6 miles

11. Find 10% of 8700 cell phones.

   8700 phones   4350 phones   870 phones

12. 25% of 128 CDs is how many CDs?

   64 CDs   32 CDs   1280 CDs

13. What is 25% of 19 hours?

   4.75 hours   1.9 hours   2.5 hours

14. What is 1% of $37?

   $370 $3.70 $0.37

15. **(a)** Describe a shortcut for finding 10% of a number and explain *why* your shortcut works.

16. **(a)** Describe a shortcut for finding 1% of a number and explain *why* it works.

15. **(b)** Once you know 10% of a certain number, explain how you could use that information to find 20% and 30% of the same number.

16. **(b)** Once you know 1% of a certain number, explain how you could use that information to find 2% and 3% of the same number.

Write and solve an equation to answer each question in Exercises 17–48. See Examples 4–6.

17. 35% of 660 programs is how many programs?

18. 55% of 740 canisters is how many canisters?

19. 70 truckloads is what percent of 140 truckloads?

20. 30 crew members is what percent of 75 crew members?

21. 476 circuits is 70% of what number of circuits?

22. 621 tons is 45% of what number of tons?

23. $12\frac{1}{2}$% of what number of people is 135 people?

24. $6\frac{1}{2}$% of what number of bottles is 130 bottles?

25. What is 65% of 1300 species?

26. What is 75% of 360 dosages?

27. 4% of $520 is how much?

28. 7% of $480 is how much?

29. 38 styles is what percent of 50 styles?

30. 75 offices is what percent of 125 offices?

31. What percent of $264 is $330?

32. What percent of $480 is $696?

33. 141 employees is 3% of what number of employees?

34. 16 books is 8% of what number of books?

35. 32% of 260 quarts is how many quarts?

36. 44% of 430 liters is how many liters?

37. $1.48 is what percent of $74?

38. $0.51 is what percent of $8.50?

39. How many tablets is 140% of 500 tablets?

40. How many patients is 175% of 540 patients?

41. 40% of what number of salads is 130 salads?

42. 75% of what number of wrenches is 675 wrenches?

43. What percent of 160 liters is 2.4 liters?

44. What percent of 600 miles is 7.5 miles?

45. 225% of what number of gallons is 11.25 gallons?

46. 180% of what number of ounces is 6.3 ounces?

47. What is 12.4% of 8300 meters?

48. What is 13.2% of 9400 acres?

49. Explain and correct the error in each of these solutions.

    (a) 3 hours is what percent of 15 hours?

$$3 = p \cdot 15$$

$$\frac{3}{15} = \frac{p \cdot \cancel{15}^{1}}{\cancel{15}_{1}}$$

$$0.2 = p$$

The answer is 0.2%.

    (b) $50 is what percent of $20?

$$50 \cdot p = 20$$

$$\frac{\cancel{50}^{1} \cdot p}{\cancel{50}_{1}} = \frac{20}{50}$$

$$p = 0.40 = 40\%$$

The answer is 40%.

50. Explain and correct the error in each of these solutions.

    (a) 12 inches is 5% of what number of inches?

$$(12)(0.05) = n$$

$$0.6 = n$$

The answer is 0.6 inch.

    (b) What is 4% of 30 pounds?

$$n = (4)(30)$$

$$n = 120$$

The answer is 120 pounds.

Relating Concepts (Exercises 51–52) For Individual or Group Work

Use your knowledge of fractions to **work Exercises 51 and 52 in order.**

51. Suppose that you have this problem: $33\frac{1}{3}\%$ of $162 is how much?

    (a) First, change $33\frac{1}{3}\%$ to a fraction. (See **Section 7.6** for help.) Then, write an equation and solve it.

    (b) Now solve the problem by changing $33\frac{1}{3}\%$ to a decimal. (*Hint:* Look at part (a) to see what fraction is equivalent to $33\frac{1}{3}\%$. Change the fraction to a decimal, using your calculator. Keep *all* the decimal places shown in the calculator's display window. Now write the equation and solve it, using your calculator.)

    (c) Compare your answers from part (a) and part (b). How different are they?

52. Now suppose that you have this problem: 22 cans is $66\frac{2}{3}\%$ of what number of cans?

    (a) First, change $66\frac{2}{3}\%$ to a fraction. (See **Section 7.6** for help.) Then, write an equation and solve it. (See **Section 5.7** for help.)

    (b) Now solve the problem by changing $66\frac{2}{3}\%$ to a decimal. Use your calculator and keep all the decimal places shown. Now write the equation and solve it.

    (c) Compare your answers from part (a) and part (b). How different are they?

Summary Exercises on Percent

1. Complete this table. Write fractions in lowest terms and as whole or mixed numbers when possible.

	Fraction	Decimal	Percent
(a)	$\dfrac{3}{100}$		
(b)			30%
(c)		0.375	
(d)			160%
(e)	$\dfrac{1}{16}$		
(f)			5%
(g)		2.0	
(h)	$\dfrac{4}{5}$		
(i)		0.072	

2. Use percent shortcuts to answer these questions.

(a) 10% of 35 ft is _____.

(b) 100% of 19 miles is _____.

(c) 50% of 210 cows is _____.

(d) 1% of $8 is _____.

(e) 25% of 2000 women is _____.

(f) 300% of $15 is _____.

(g) 10% of $875 is _____.

(h) 25% of 48 pounds is _____.

(i) 1% of 9500 students is _____.

Use the percent proportion or percent equation to answer each question. If necessary, round money answers to the nearest cent and percent answers to the nearest tenth of a percent.

3. 9 Web sites is what percent of 72 Web sites?

4. 30 DVDs is 40% of what number of DVDs?

5. 6% of $8.79 is how much?

6. 945 students is what percent of 540 students?

7. $3\frac{1}{2}$% of 168 pounds is how much, to the nearest tenth of a pound?

8. 1.25% of what number of hours is 7.5 hours?

9. What percent of 80,000 deer is 40,000 deer?

10. 465 camp sites is 93% of what number of camp sites?

11. What number of golf balls is 280% of 35 golf balls?

12. What percent of $66 is $1.80?

13. 9% of what number of apartments is 207 apartments?

14. What weight is 84% of 0.75 ounce?

15. $1160 is what percent of $800?

16. Find 3.75% of 6500 voters, to the nearest whole number.

17. What is 300% of 0.007 inch?

18. 24 minutes is what percent of 6 minutes?

19. What percent of 60 yards is 4.8 yards?

20. $0.17 is 25% of what amount?

The circle graph shows the average costs for various wedding expenses. Use the graph to answer Exercises 21–24. Round money answers to the nearest cent, if necessary.

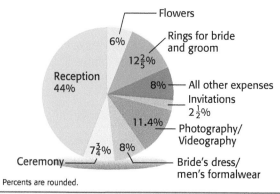

WHAT IT COSTS TO RING THE WEDDING BELLS
The average wedding has 165 guests and costs $33,600. Here is how couples are spending the money.

Flowers 6%
Rings for bride and groom $12\frac{2}{5}$%
All other expenses 8%
Invitations $2\frac{1}{2}$%
Photography/Videography 11.4%
Bride's dress/men's formalwear 8%
Ceremony $7\frac{3}{4}$%
Reception 44%

Percents are rounded.

Source: Bride's magazine.

21. Which item in the graph is least expensive, and how much is spent on it?

22. What amount is spent on the ceremony?

23. (a) Find the cost of photography and videography.

(b) What amount is spent on rings for the bride and groom?

24. (a) How much is spent on the reception?

(b) On average, what is the cost for each guest at the reception?

7.9 ▶▶▶ Problem Solving with Percent

OBJECTIVES

1 Solve percent application problems.

2 Solve problems involving percent of increase or decrease.

1 About 65% of the students at City Center College receive some form of financial aid. How many of the 9280 students enrolled this year are receiving aid? Use the six problem-solving steps.

OBJECTIVE 1 Solve percent application problems. Solving percent problems involves identifying three items: the *percent*, the *whole*, and the *part*. Then you can write a percent equation or percent proportion and solve it to answer the question in the problem. Use the six problem-solving steps from **Section 4.8**.

EXAMPLE 1 Finding the Part

A new low-income housing project charges 30% of a family's income as rent. The Smiths' family income is $1260 per month. How much will the Smiths pay for rent?

Step 1 **Read the problem.** It is about a family paying part of its income for rent.

> Unknown: amount of rent
> Known: 30% of income paid for rent; $1260 monthly income

Step 2 **Assign a variable.** There is only one unknown, so let n be the amount paid for rent.

Step 3 **Write an equation.** Use the percent equation.

$$\text{percent} \cdot \text{whole} = \text{part}$$

Recall that the *whole* often follows the word *of*.

The percent is given in the problem: 30%. The key word of appears *right after* 30%, which means that you can use the phrase "30% of a family's income" to help you write one side of the equation. Write 30% as the decimal 0.30.

30.% of a family's income is the rent.

$$0.30 \quad \cdot \quad \$1260 \quad = \quad n$$

Step 4 **Solve the equation.** Simplify the left side, multiplying 0.30 by 1260.

$$(0.30)(1260) = n$$
$$378 = n$$

> Write a $ in your answer.

Step 5 **State the answer.** The Smith family will pay $378 for rent.

Step 6 **Check** the solution. The solution of $378 makes sense because 10% of $1260 is $126, so 30% would be 3 times $126, or $378.

> **Note**
> You could also use the percent proportion in *Step 3* above.
>
> $$\text{Percent} \longrightarrow \frac{30}{100} = \frac{n}{1260} \longleftarrow \text{Part (unknown)}$$
> $$\text{Always } 100 \longrightarrow \qquad \qquad \longleftarrow \text{Whole}$$
>
> The answer will be the same, $378.
>
> Throughout the rest of this chapter, we will use the percent equation. You may, if you wish, use the percent proportion instead. The final answers will be the same.

◀ *Work Problem* **1** *at the Side.*

ANSWER

1. Let n be number of students receiving aid.
   $(0.65)(9280) = n$
   6032 students receive aid.
   Check: 10% of 9280 students is 928, which rounds to 900 students. So 60% would be 6 times 900 students = 5400 students, and 70% would be 7 • 900 = 6300. The solution falls between 5400 and 6300 students, so it is reasonable.

EXAMPLE 2 **Finding the Part**

When Britta received her first $180 paycheck as a math tutor, $12\frac{1}{2}\%$ was withheld for federal income tax. How much was withheld?

Step 1 **Read** the problem. It is about part of Britta's pay being withheld for taxes.

Unknown: amount withheld for taxes
Known: $12\frac{1}{2}\%$ of earnings withheld; $180 in pay

Step 2 **Assign a variable.** There is only one unknown, so let n be the amount withheld for taxes.

Step 3 **Write an equation.** Use the percent equation. The *percent* is given: $12\frac{1}{2}\%$. Write $12\frac{1}{2}\%$ as 12.5% and then move the decimal point two places to the left. So 12.5% becomes the decimal 0.125.

The key word *of* doesn't appear after $12\frac{1}{2}\%$. Instead, think about whether you know the *whole* or the *part*. You know Britta's *whole* paycheck is $180, but you do *not* know what *part* of it was withheld.

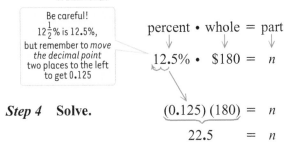

| Be careful! $12\frac{1}{2}\%$ is 12.5%, but remember to *move the decimal point two places to the left* to get 0.125 |

$$\text{percent} \cdot \text{whole} = \text{part}$$
$$12.5\% \cdot \$180 = n$$

Step 4 **Solve.**
$$(0.125)(180) = n$$
$$22.5 = n$$

Step 5 **State the answer.** $22.50 was withheld from Britta's paycheck.

Step 6 **Check the solution.** The solution of $22.50 makes sense because 10% of $180 is $18, so a little more than $18 should be withheld.

Work Problem **2** *at the Side.* ▶

EXAMPLE 3 **Finding the Percent**

On a 15-point quiz, Zenitia earned 13 points. What percent correct is this, to the nearest whole percent?

Step 1 **Read** the problem. It is about points earned on a quiz.

Unknown: percent correct
Known: earned 13 out of 15 points

Step 2 **Assign a variable.** Let p be the unknown percent.

Step 3 **Write an equation.** Use the percent equation. There is no number with a % symbol in the problem. The question, "What percent is this?" tells you that the *percent* is unknown. The *whole* is all the points on the quiz (15 points), and 13 points is the *part* of the quiz that Zenitia did correctly.

$$\text{percent} \cdot \text{whole} = \text{part}$$
$$p \cdot 15 \text{ points} = 13 \text{ points}$$

Continued on Next Page

2 There were 50 points on the first math test. Hue's score was 83% correct. How many points did Hue earn? Use the six problem-solving steps.

ANSWER

2. Let n be the points earned.
$(0.83)(50) = n$
Hue earned 41.5 points.
Check: 10% of 50 points is 5 points, so 80% would be 8 times 5 points = 40 points. Hue earned a little more than 80%, so 41.5 points is reasonable.

3 The Los Angeles Lakers made 47 of 80 field goal attempts in one game. What percent is this, to the nearest whole percent? Use the six problem-solving steps.

Step 4 **Solve** the equation.

$$\frac{p \cdot \overset{1}{\cancel{15}}}{\underset{1}{\cancel{15}}} = \frac{13}{15} \qquad \text{Divide both sides by 15}$$

> CAUTION! **Multiply the solution by 100%** to change it from a *decimal* to a *percent*.

$$p = 0.8\overline{6} \leftarrow \text{The solution is a repeating decimal.}$$

$$0.866666667 \approx 86.6666667\% \approx 87\% \leftarrow \text{Rounded}$$

Step 5 **State the answer.** Zenitia had **87%** correct, rounded to the nearest whole percent.

Step 6 **Check the solution.** The solution of 87% makes sense because she earned most of the possible points, so the percent should be fairly close to 100%.

◀ *Work Problem* **3** *at the Side.*

EXAMPLE 4 **Finding the Percent**

The rainfall in the Red River Valley was 33 inches this year. The average rainfall is 30 inches. This year's rainfall is what percent of the average rainfall?

Step 1 **Read the problem.** It is about comparing this year's rainfall to the average rainfall.

> Unknown: This year's rain is what percent of the average?
> Known: 33 inches this year; 30 inches is average

Step 2 **Assign a variable.** Let p be the unknown percent.

Step 3 **Write an equation.** The percent is unknown. The key word of appears *right after* the word *percent,* so you can use that sentence to help you write the equation.

This year's rainfall is what percent of the average rainfall?

$$\text{33 inches} \quad = \quad p \quad \cdot \quad \text{30 inches}$$

Step 4 **Solve the equation.**

$$33 = p \cdot 30$$

$$\frac{33}{30} = \frac{p \cdot \overset{1}{\cancel{30}}}{\underset{1}{\cancel{30}}} \qquad \text{Divide both sides by 30}$$

Solution in *decimal* form → $1.1 = p$

> **Multiply the solution by 100%** to change it from a *decimal* to a *percent*.

$$1.10 = 110\%$$

Step 5 **State the answer.** This year's rainfall is **110%** of the average rainfall.

Step 6 **Check the solution.** The solution of 110% makes sense because 33 inches is *more* than 30 inches (more than 100% of the average rainfall), so 33 inches must be *more* than 100% of 30 inches.

◀ *Work Problem* **4** *at the Side.*

---

4 Valley College predicted that 1200 new students would enroll in the fall. It actually had 1620 new students enroll. The actual enrollment is what percent of the predicted number? Use the six problem-solving steps.

ANSWERS

3. Let p be the unknown percent.
$p \cdot 80 = 47$
$p = 0.5875$
$0.5875 = 58.75\% \approx 59\%$
The Lakers made 59% of their field goals, to the nearest whole percent.
Check: The Lakers made a little more than half of their field goals. $\frac{1}{2} = 50\%$, so the solution of 59% is reasonable.

4. Let p be the unknown percent.
$p \cdot 1200 = 1620$
$p = 1.35$
$1.35 = 135\%$
Enrollment is 135% of the predicted number.
Check: More than 1200 students enrolled (more than 100%), so 1620 students must be more than 100% of the predicted number. The solution of 135% is reasonable.

EXAMPLE 5   **Finding the Whole**

A newspaper article stated that 648 pints of blood were donated at the blood bank last month, which was only 72% of the number of pints needed. How many pints of blood were needed?

Step 1   **Read the problem.** It is about blood donations.

   Unknown: number of pints needed

   Known: 648 pints were donated;
   648 pints is 72% of the number needed.

Step 2   **Assign a variable.** Let n be the number of pints needed.

Step 3   **Write an equation.** The percent is given in the problem: 72%. The key word **of** appears *right after* 72%, so you can use the phrase "72% **of** the number of pints needed" to help you write one side of the equation.

   72.% of the number of pints needed is 648 pints.

   $$0.72 \cdot n = 648$$

Step 4   **Solve.**

$$\frac{(0.72)(n)}{0.72} = \frac{648}{0.72} \quad \text{Divide both sides by 0.72}$$

$$n = 900$$

   Write **pints** in your answer.

Step 5   **State the answer.** 900 pints of blood were needed.

Step 6   **Check the solution.** The solution of 900 pints makes sense because 10% of 900 pints is 90 pints, so 70% would be 7 times 90 pints, or 630 pints, which is close to the number given in the problem (648 pints).

───────────────────────   *Work Problem* ⑤ *at the Side.* ▶

OBJECTIVE ② **Solve problems involving percent of increase or decrease.**   We are often interested in looking at increases or decreases in prices, earnings, population, and many other numbers. This type of problem involves finding the percent of change. Use the following steps to find the **percent of increase.**

┌───┐
Finding the Percent of Increase

Step 1   Use subtraction to find the *amount* of increase.

Step 2   Use a form of the percent equation to find the *percent* of increase.

   percent of   whole   =   part

   percent of original value = amount of increase
└───┘

⑤ Use the six problem-solving steps to answer each question.

(a) Ezra did 15 problems correctly on a test, giving him a score of $62\frac{1}{2}$%. How many problems were on the test?

(b) A frozen dinner advertises that only 18% of its calories are from fat. If the dinner contains 55 calories from fat, what is the total number of calories in the dinner? Round to the nearest whole number.

ANSWERS

5. **(a)** Let n be number of problems on the test.
   $0.625 \cdot n = 15$
   There were 24 problems on the test.
   Check: 50% of 24 problems is
   $24 \div 2 = 12$ problems correct, so it is reasonable that $62\frac{1}{2}$% would be 15 problems correct.

   (b) Let n be total number of calories.
   $0.18 \cdot n = 55$
   There were 306 calories (rounded) in the dinner. *Check:* 10% of 306 calories is about 30 calories, so 20% would be $2 \cdot 30 = 60$ calories, which is close to the number given (55 calories).

6 Use the six problem-solving steps to answer each question.

(a) Over the last two years, Duyen's rent has increased from $650 per month to $767. What is the percent increase?

(b) A shopping mall increased the number of handicapped parking spaces from 8 to 20. What is the percent increase?

EXAMPLE 6   **Finding the Percent of Increase**

Brad's hourly wage as assistant manager of a fast-food restaurant was raised from $9.40 to $9.87. What was the percent of increase?

Step 1   **Read the problem.** It is about an increase in wages.

> Unknown: percent of increase
> Known: Original hourly wage was $9.40; new hourly wage is $9.87.

Step 2   **Assign a variable.** Let *p* be the percent of increase.

Step 3   **Write an equation.** First subtract $9.87 − $9.40 to find how much Brad's wage went up. That is the *amount* of increase. Then write an equation to find the unknown *percent* of increase. Be sure to use his *original* wage ($9.40) in the equation because we are looking for the change from his *original* wage. Do **not** use the new wage of $9.87 in the equation.

$$\$9.87 - 9.40 = \$0.47 \leftarrow Amount \text{ of increase}$$

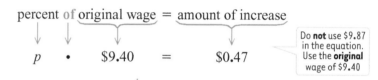

percent of original wage = amount of increase

$$p \quad \cdot \quad \$9.40 \quad = \quad \$0.47$$

> Do **not** use $9.87 in the equation. Use the **original** wage of $9.40

Step 4   **Solve.** $\dfrac{(p)\,\overset{1}{\cancel{(9.40)}}}{\underset{1}{\cancel{9.40}}} = \dfrac{0.47}{9.40}$ Divide both sides by 9.40

$$p = 0.05 \leftarrow \text{Solution in } decimal \text{ form}$$

Multiply the solution by 100% to change it from a *decimal* to a *percent*.

$$0.05 = 5\%$$

Step 5   **State the answer.** Brad's hourly wage increased **5%**.

Step 6   **Check the solution.** 10% of $9.40 would be a $0.94 raise. A raise of $0.47 is half as much, and half of 10% is 5%, so the solution checks.

> **CAUTION**
> When writing the percent equation in *Step 3* above, be sure to multiply the percent (*p*) by the **original** wage. Do **not** use the *new* wage in the percent equation.

◀ *Work Problem* 6 *at the Side.*

Use a similar procedure to find the **percent of decrease.**

> **Finding the Percent of Decrease**
>
> *Step 1*   Use subtraction to find the *amount* of decrease.
>
> *Step 2*   Use a form of the percent equation to find the *percent* of decrease.
>
> percent of   whole   =   part
>
> percent of original value = amount of decrease

EXAMPLE 7 **Finding the Percent of Decrease**

Rozenia trained for six months to run in a marathon. Her weight dropped from 137 pounds to 122 pounds. Find the percent of decrease. Round to the nearest whole percent.

Step 1 **Read the problem.** It is about a decrease in weight.

> Unknown: percent of decrease
> Known: Original weight was 137 pounds; new weight is 122 pounds.

Step 2 **Assign a variable.** Let p be the percent of decrease.

Step 3 **Write an equation.** First subtract 137 pounds − 122 pounds to find how much Rozenia's weight went down. That is the *amount* of decrease. Then write an equation to find the unknown *percent* of decrease. Be sure to use her *original* weight (137 pounds) in the equation because we are looking for the change from her *original* weight. Do *not* use the new weight of 122 pounds in the equation.

137 pounds − 122 pounds = 15 pounds ← *Amount* of decrease

$$\underbrace{\text{percent}}_{p} \text{ of } \underbrace{\text{original weight}}_{137 \text{ pounds}} = \underbrace{\text{amount of decrease}}_{15 \text{ pounds}}$$

> Do **not** use 122 pounds in the equation. Use the **original** weight of 137 pounds.

Step 4 **Solve.**
$$\frac{p \cdot \cancel{137}}{\cancel{137}} = \frac{15}{137} \quad \text{Divide both sides by 137}$$

$$p = 0.109489051 \leftarrow \text{Solution in } decimal \text{ form}$$

Multiply the solution by 100% to change it from a *decimal* to a *percent*.

$$0.109489051 = 10.9489051\% \approx 11\%$$

> Rounded to nearest whole percent

Step 5 **State the answer.** Rozenia's weight decreased approximately 11%.

Step 6 **Check the solution.** A 10% decrease would be 13.7. = 13.7 pounds, so an 11% decrease is a reasonable solution.

> **CAUTION**
> When writing the percent equation in *Step 3* above, be sure to multiply the percent (p) by the **original** weight. Do **not** use the *new* weight in the percent equation.

Work Problem 7 *at the Side.* ▶

7 Use the six problem-solving steps to answer each question. Round answers to the nearest whole percent.

(a) During a severe winter storm, average daily attendance at an elementary school fell from 425 students to 200 students. What was the percent decrease?

(b) The makers of a brand of spaghetti sauce claim that the number of calories from fat in each serving has been reduced by 20%. Is the claim correct if the number of calories from fat dropped from 70 calories to 60 calories per serving? Explain your answer.

ANSWERS

7. (a) 425 − 200 = 225 student decrease
Let p be percent of decrease.
$$p \cdot 425 = 225$$
$$p \approx 0.529 \approx 53\% \text{ (rounded)}$$
Daily attendance decreased 53%.
Check: A 50% decrease would be 425 ÷ 2 ≈ 212, so a 53% decrease is reasonable.

(b) 70 − 60 = 10 calorie decrease
Let p be percent of decrease.
$$p \cdot 70 = 10$$
$$p \approx 0.143 \approx 14\% \text{ (rounded)}$$
The claim of a 20% decrease is not true; the decrease in calories is about 14%.
Check: A 10% decrease would be 70. = 7 calories; a 20% decrease would be 2 · 7 = 14 calories, so a 14% decrease is reasonable.

FOR
EXTRA
HELP
 Math XL
PRACTICE
 WATCH
 DOWNLOAD
READ
 REVIEW

Use the six problem-solving steps in Exercises 1–22. Round percent answers to the nearest tenth of a percent when necessary. See Examples 1–5.

1. Robert Garrett, who works part-time, earns $210 per week and has 18% of this amount withheld for taxes, Social Security, and Medicare. Find the amount withheld.

2. Most shampoos contain 75% to 90% water. If a 16-ounce bottle of shampoo contains 78% water, find the number of ounces of water in the bottle, to the nearest tenth. (*Source: Consumer Reports.*)

3. An ATM machine charges $2 for any size cash withdrawal. The $2 fee is what percent of a

(a) $20 withdrawal

(b) $40 withdrawal

(c) $100 withdrawal

(d) $200 withdrawal.

4. An Internet (on-line) company charges $8 for shipping and handling on any order of $50 or less. The $8 shipping charge is what percent of a

(a) $10 order

(b) $16 order

(c) $25 order

(d) $50 order.

The figure below shows, on average, what portion of the human body is made up of water, protein, fat, and so on. Use the figure to answer Exercises 5 and 6. Round answers to the nearest tenth.

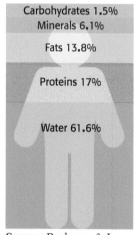

Carbohydrates 1.5%
Minerals 6.1%
Fats 13.8%
Proteins 17%
Water 61.6%

Source: Beakman & Jax, Universal Press Syndicate.

5. If an adult weighs 165 pounds, how much of that weight is

(a) water

(b) minerals.

6. If a teenager weighs 92 pounds, how much of that weight is

(a) fat

(b) carbohydrates.

7. The guided-missile destroyer USS *Sullivans* has a 335-person crew of which 44 are female. What percent of the crew is female? What percent of the crew is male? (*Source:* U.S. Navy.)

8. In a test by *Consumer Reports,* 6 of the 123 cans of tuna analyzed contained more than the 30-microgram intake limit of mercury. What percent of the cans contained an excessive level of mercury? What percent of the cans contained less than or equal to 30 micrograms of mercury?

9. The U.S. Census Bureau reported that Americans who are 65 years of age or older made up 14.2% of the total population in 2006. It said that there were 42.6 million Americans in this group. Find the total U.S. population for that year.

10. Julie Ward has 8.5% of her earnings deposited into the credit union. If this amounts to $263.50 per month, find her monthly and annual earnings.

11. The campus honor society hoped to raise $50,000 in donations from businesses for scholarships. It actually raised $69,000. This amount was what percent of the goal?

12. Doug had budgeted $220 for textbooks but ended up spending $316.80. The amount he spent was what percent of his budget?

13. Alfonso earned a score of 85% on his test. He did 34 problems correctly. How many problems were on the test?

14. In a telephone survey, 467 U.S. women said they had done a home improvement project in the past two years. This was 45% of the women in the survey. How many women were surveyed, to the nearest whole number? (*Source:* Opinion Research Corp.)

15. During the 2006–2007 NBA season, Kevin Garnett made 638 field goals, which was 47.6% of the shots he tried. How many shots did he try, to the nearest whole number? (*Source:* www.NBA.com)

16. Ray Allen, who plays basketball in the NBA, attempted 309 free throws during the 2006–2007 season. He made 90.3% of his shots. How many free throws did Ray make, to the nearest whole number? (*Source:* www.NBA.com)

17. An ad for steel-belted radial tires promises 15% better mileage. If Sheera's SUV has gotten 20.6 miles per gallon in the past, what mileage can she expect after the new tires are installed? (Round to the nearest tenth of a mile.)

18. Chris Chike set a world record for the highest score for the video game "Guitar Hero III: Legends of Rock." Chris earned 870,647 points, which is 97% of the possible points for a single song on the Expert Level. How many points were possible, to the nearest whole number? (*Source: Rochester Post-Bulletin.*)

The graph (pictograph) shows the percent of chicken noodle soup sold during the cold and flu season. Use this information to answer Exercises 19–22.

SOUP'S ON

350 million cans of chicken noodle soup are sold each year. More than half are bought during cold-and-flu season, with January being the number one month. The percent sold during each flu-season month is shown.

October November December January February March

Source: *USA Today.*

19. Which of the flu season months had the lowest sales of chicken noodle soup? How many cans were bought that month?

20. What percent of the chicken noodle soup sales take place during the flu months of October through March? What percent of sales take place in the *non-flu* season months?

21. Find the number of cans of soup sold in the highest sales month and in the second-highest sales month.

22. How many more cans of soup were sold in October than in November? How many more were sold in November than December?

Use the six problem-solving steps to find the percent increase or decrease. Round your answers to the nearest tenth of a percent. See Examples 6 and 7.

23. Henry Ford started the Ford Motor Company. The Model T first appeared in 1908 and cost $825. In 1913, Ford started using an assembly line and the price of the Model T dropped to $290. What was the percent of decrease? (*Source:* Kenneth C. Davis.)

24. In 1914, Henry Ford became a hero to his workers because he doubled the daily minimum wage. He also cut the workday from nine hours to eight hours. Find the percent of decrease in the number of hours in the workday. (*Source:* Kenneth C. Davis.)

25. Students at Lane College were charged $1449 as tuition this semester. If the tuition was $1328 last semester, find the percent of increase.

26. Americans are eating more fish. This year the average American will eat 16.1 pounds compared to only 11.7 pounds per year in 1970. Find the percent of increase. (*Source:* USDA/Economic Research Service.)

27. Jordan's part-time work schedule has been reduced to 18 hours per week. He had been working 30 hours per week. What is the percent decrease?

28. Janis works as a hair stylist. During January, she cut her price on haircuts from $28 to $25.50 to try to get more customers. By what percent did she decrease the price?

29. In 1967 there were 78 animal species listed as threatened with extinction in the United States. In 2007 there were 607 animals on the list. What was the percent increase, to the nearest whole percent? (*Source:* U.S. Fish and Wildlife Service.)

Condor with wing tag   Florida panther   Bighorn sheep

30. The world population was estimated at 6,602,275,000 people in 2007. It is projected to reach 7,985,550,000 people by 2025. By what percent will the world's population increase in those 18 years? (*Source:* United Nations.)

31. You can have an *increase* of 150% in the price of something. Could there be a 150% *decrease* in its price? Explain why or why not.

32. Show how to use a shortcut to find 25% of $80. Then explain how to use the result to find 75% of $80 and 125% of $80 *without* solving a proportion or equation.

Relating Concepts (Exercises 33–36) For Individual or Group Work

As you **work Exercises 33–36 in order,** *explain why each solution does* **not** *make sense. Then find and correct the error.*

33. The recommended maximum daily amount of dietary fat is 65 grams. George ate 78 grams of fat today. He ate what percent of the recommended amount?

$$p \cdot 78 = 65$$

$$\frac{p \cdot \cancel{78}^{1}}{\cancel{78}_{1}} = \frac{65}{78}$$

$$p = 0.833 = 83.3\%$$

34. The Goblers soccer team won 18 of its 25 games this season. What percent did the team win?

$$p \cdot 25 = 18$$

$$\frac{p \cdot \cancel{25}^{1}}{\cancel{25}_{1}} = \frac{18}{25}$$

$$p = 0.72\%$$

35. The human brain is $2\frac{1}{2}\%$ of total body weight. How much would the brain of a 150-pound person weigh?

$$2\tfrac{1}{2}\% \text{ of } 150 = n$$

$$(2.5)(150) = n$$

$$375 = n$$

36. Yesterday, because of an ice storm, 80% of the students were absent. How many of the 800 students made it to class?

$$80\% \text{ of } 800 = n$$

$$(0.80)(800) = n$$

$$640 = n$$

The answer is 640 students.

7.10 ▶▶▶ Consumer Applications: Sales Tax, Tips, Discounts, and Simple Interest

OBJECTIVES

1 **Find sales tax and total cost.**

2 **Estimate and calculate restaurant tips.**

3 **Find the discount and sale price.**

4 **Calculate simple interest and the total amount due on a loan.**

Four of the more common uses of percent in daily life are sales taxes, tips, discounts, and simple interest on loans.

OBJECTIVE 1 **Find sales tax and total cost.** Most states collect **sales taxes** on the purchases you make in stores. Your county or city may also add on a small amount of sales tax. For example, your state may charge $6\frac{1}{2}\%$ on purchases and your city may add on another $\frac{1}{2}\%$ for a total of 7%. The exact percent varies from place to place but is usually from 4% to 8%. The stores collect the tax and send it to the city or state government where it is used to pay for things like road repair, public schools, parks, police and fire protection, and so on.

You can use a form of the percent equation to calculate sales tax. The **tax rate** is the *percent*. The cost of the item(s) you are buying is the *whole*. The amount of tax you pay is the *part*.

Finding Sales Tax and Total Cost

Use a form of the percent equation to find sales tax.

$$\text{percent} \quad \bullet \quad \text{whole} \quad = \quad \text{part}$$

$$\text{tax rate} \quad \bullet \quad \text{cost of item} \quad = \quad \text{amount you pay in sales tax}$$

Then add to find how much you will pay in all.

$$\text{cost of item} + \text{sales tax} = \text{total cost paid by you}$$

EXAMPLE 1 **Finding Sales Tax and Total Cost**

Suppose that you buy a DVD player for $289 from A-1 Electronics. The sales tax rate in your state is $6\frac{1}{2}\%$. How much is the tax? What is the total cost of the DVD player?

Step 1 **Read the problem.** It asks for the sales tax on a DVD player and the total cost.

Step 2 **Assign a variable.** Let n be the amount of tax.

Step 3 **Write an equation.** Use the sales tax equation. Write $6\frac{1}{2}\%$ as 6.5% and then move the decimal point two places to the left.

Write $6\frac{1}{2}\%$ as 6.5%; then **move the decimal point** to get 0.065

$$\text{tax rate} \bullet \text{cost of item} = \text{sales tax}$$

$$06.5\% \bullet \quad \$289 \quad = \quad n$$

Step 4 **Solve.**
$$(0.065)(289) = n$$
$$18.785 = n$$

The store will round the tax to the nearest cent, so $18.785 rounds to $18.79.

Now add the sales tax to the cost of the DVD player to find your total cost.

$$\text{cost of item} + \text{sales tax} = \text{total cost}$$

$$\$289 \quad + \quad \$18.79 \quad = \quad \$307.79$$

Continued on Next Page

Step 5   **State the answer.** The tax is $18.79 and the total cost of the DVD player, including tax, is $307.79.

Step 6   **Check:** Use estimation to check that the amount of sales tax is reasonable. Round $289 to $300. Then 1% of $300. is $3. Round $6\frac{1}{2}\%$ to 7%. Then 7% would be 7 times $3 or $21 for sales tax. Our solution of $18.79 is close to $21, so it is reasonable.

Work Problem **1** *at the Side.* ▶

EXAMPLE 2   **Finding the Sales Tax Rate**

Ms. Ortiz bought a $21,950 hybrid car. She paid an additional $1646.25 in sales tax. What was the sales tax rate?

Step 1   **Read** the problem. It asks for the sales tax rate on a car purchase.

Step 2   **Assign a variable.** Let p be the tax rate (the percent).

Step 3   **Write an equation.** Use the sales tax equation.

$$\text{tax rate} \cdot \text{cost of item} = \text{sales tax}$$
$$\downarrow \qquad\qquad \downarrow \qquad\qquad \downarrow$$
$$p \quad \cdot \quad \$21{,}950 \quad = \$1646.25$$

Step 4   **Solve.**

$$\frac{(p)\overset{1}{\cancel{(21{,}950)}}}{\underset{1}{\cancel{21{,}950}}} = \frac{1646.25}{21{,}950} \qquad \text{Divide both sides by 21,950}$$

Multiply the solution by 100% → $p = 0.075$ ← Solution in *decimal* form

Change the solution from a decimal to a percent: $0.075 = 7.5\%$.

Step 5   **State the answer.** The sales tax rate is **7.5%** (or $7\frac{1}{2}\%$).

Step 6   **Check.** Use estimation to check that the solution is reasonable. If the tax rate was 1%, then 1% of $21950. = $219.50, or about $200.

Round 7.5% to 8%. Then 8% would be 8 times $200, or $1600.

The tax amount given in the original problem, $1646.25, is close to the estimate, so our solution of 7.5% is reasonable.

Work Problem **2** *at the Side.* ▶

OBJECTIVE **2** **Estimate and calculate restaurant tips.**   Waiters and waitresses rely on tips as a major part of their income. The general rule of thumb is to leave 15% of your bill for food and beverages as a tip for the server. If you receive exceptional service or are eating in an upscale restaurant, consider leaving a 20% tip.

EXAMPLE 3   **Estimating 15% and 20% Tips**

First estimate each tip. Then calculate the exact amount.

(a) Kirby took his wife to dinner at a nice restaurant to celebrate her promotion at work. The bill came to $77.85. How much should he leave for a 20% tip?

   Estimate: Round $77.85 to $80. Then 10% of $80. is $8.

20% would be 2 times $8, or $16. ← Estimate

Continued on Next Page

---

1 Find the sales tax and the total cost. Round the sales tax to the nearest cent when necessary. Check your answer by estimating the sales tax.

   (a) $495 camcorder; $5\frac{1}{2}\%$ sales tax

   (b) $29.98 watch; 7% sales tax

   (c) $1.19 candy bar; 4% sales tax

2 Find the sales tax rate on each purchase. Then use estimation to check your solution.

   (a) The tax on a $57 textbook is $3.42.

   (b) The tax on a $4 notebook is $0.18.

   (c) The tax on a $998 sofa is $49.90.

ANSWERS

1. **(a)** sales tax = $27.23 (rounded)
   total cost = $522.23
   Check: 1% of $500. is $5;

   6% is 6 times $5 = $30
   (b) sales tax = $2.10 (rounded)
   total cost = $32.08
   Check: 1% of $30. is $0.30;

   7% is 7 times $0.30 = $2.10
   (c) Sales tax = $0.05 (rounded)
   total cost = $1.24
   Check: 1% of $1 is $0.01;
   4% is 4 times $0.01 = $0.04
2. **(a)** 6%   *Check:* 1% of $60. is $0.60;
   6% would be 6 times $0.60, or $3.60
   (which is close to $3.42 given in the problem).
   (b) 4.5%   *Check:* 1% of $4 is $0.04; round
   4.5% to 5%; 5% of $4 is 5 times $0.04,
   or $0.20 (which is close to $0.18 given
   in the problem).
   (c) 5%   *Check:* 10% of $1000. is $100;

   5% is half of that, or $50 (which is close
   to $49.90 given in the problem).

3 First estimate each tip. Then calculate the exact tip.

(a) 20% tip on a bill of $58.37

Exact: Use the percent equation. Write 20% as a decimal. The bill for food and beverages is the *whole* and the tip is the *part*.

$$\text{percent} \cdot \text{whole} = \text{part}$$
$$20.\% \cdot \$77.85 = n$$

20.% = 0.20
$$(0.20)(77.85) = n$$
$$15.57 = n$$

20% of $77.85 is $15.57, which is close to the estimate of $16.

A tip is usually rounded off to a convenient amount, such as the nearest quarter or nearest dollar, so Kirby left $16.

(b) Linda, Peggy, and Mary ordered similarly priced lunches and agreed to split the bill plus a 15% tip. How much should each woman pay if the bill is $21.63?

(b) 15% tip on a bill of $11.93

Estimate: Round $21.63 to $20. Then 10% of $20, is $2.

5% of $20 would be half as much, that is, half of $2, or $1.

So an estimate of the 15% tip is $2 + $1 = $3. ← Estimates

An estimate of the amount each woman should pay is ($20 + $3) ÷ 3 ≈ $8.

Exact: Use the percent equation to calculate the 15% tip. Add the tip to the bill. Then divide the total by 3 to find the amount each woman should pay.

$$\text{percent} \cdot \text{whole} = \text{part}$$
$$15.\% \cdot \$21.63 = n$$

15.% = 0.15
$$(0.15)(21.63) = n$$
$$3.2445 = n$$

(c) A bill of $89.02 plus a 15% tip shared equally by four friends. How much will each friend pay?

Round $3.2445 to $3.24 (nearest cent), which is close to the estimate of $3 for the tip.

Add: $21.63 + $3.24 = $24.87 ← Total cost of lunch and tip

Divide: $24.87 ÷ 3 = $8.29 ← Amount paid by each woman

◀ *Work Problem* **3** *at the Side.*

OBJECTIVE **3** **Find the discount and sale price.** Most people prefer buying things when they are on sale. A store will reduce prices, or **discount,** to attract additional customers. You can use a form of the percent equation to calculate the discount. The *rate* of discount is the *percent*. The original price is the *whole*. The amount that will be discounted (subtracted from the original price) is the *part*.

Finding the Discount and Sale Price

Use a form of the percent equation to find the discount.

$$\text{percent} \cdot \text{whole} = \text{part}$$

rate of discount · original price = amount of discount

Then subtract to find the sale price.

original price − amount of discount = sale price

EXAMPLE 4   **Finding the Discount and Sale Price**

The Oak Mill Furniture Store has an oak dining room set with an original price of $840 on sale at 15% off. Find the sale price.

Step 1   **Read** the problem. It asks for the sale price on a dining room set.

Step 2   **Assign a variable.** Let *n* be the amount of discount.

Step 3   **Write an equation.** Use a form of the percent equation to find the discount. Write 15% as the decimal 0.15.

rate of discount • original price = amount of discount

Step 4   **Solve.**   (0.15)(840)   =   *n*

126   =   *n*

The amount of discount is $126. Find the sale price by subtracting the amount of the discount ($126) from the original price.

original price − amount of discount = sale price | Remember to subtract the discount.

$840   − $126   = $714

Step 5   **State the answer.** During the sale, you can buy the dining room set for $714.

Step 6   **Check.** Round $840 to $800. Then 10% of $800 is $80 and 5% is half as much, or $40. So 15% of $800 is $80 + $40 = $120. An estimate of the sale price is $800 − $120 = $680, so the exact answer of $714 is reasonable.

Work Problem **4** *at the Side.* ▶

---

4 Find the amount of the discount and the sale price for each item.

(a) An Easy-Boy leather recliner originally priced at $950 is offered at a 35% discount.

(b) In August, Eastside Boutique has women's swimsuits on sale at 40% off. One swimsuit was originally priced at $68. Another suit was originally priced at $97.

▦ **Calculator Tip**   In Example 4 above, you can use a *scientific* calculator to find the amount of discount and subtract the discount from the original price.

840 ⊖ .15 ⊗ 840 ⊜ 714

Original price   Amount of discount   Sale price

Your *scientific* calculator observes the order of operations, so it will automatically do the multiplication before the subtraction. (Recall that simple, four-function calculators *may not* follow the order of operations; they might give an incorrect result.)

OBJECTIVE **4** **Calculate simple interest and the total amount due on a loan.**   **Interest** is a fee paid, or a charge made, for lending or borrowing money. The amount of money borrowed is called the **principal**. The charge for interest is usually given as a percent, called the **interest rate**. The interest rate is assumed to be *per year* (for *one* year) unless stated otherwise.

In most cases, interest is calculated on the original principal and is called **simple interest.** Use the following **interest formula** to find simple interest.

ANSWERS

4. (a) Discount is $332.50; sale price is $617.50.

   (b) Discount is $27.20, sale price is $40.80; discount is $38.80, sale price is $58.20.

5 Find the simple interest and total amount due on each loan.

(a) $500 at 4% for 1 year

Formula for Simple Interest

Interest = principal • rate • time

The formula is usually written using variables.

$$I = p \cdot r \cdot t \quad \text{or} \quad I = prt$$

When you repay a loan, the interest is added to the original principal to find the total amount due.

Finding the Total Amount Due

amount due = principal + interest

Note

Simple interest calculations are used for most short-term business loans, automobile loans, and consumer loans.

EXAMPLE 5   **Finding Simple Interest and Total Amount Due for 1 Year**

Find the simple interest and total amount due on a $2000 loan at 6% for 1 year.

The amount borrowed, or principal (p), is $2000. The interest rate (r) is 6%, which is 0.06 as a decimal, and the time of the loan (t) is 1 year. Use the interest formula.

$$I = \quad p \quad \cdot \quad r \quad \cdot t$$
$$I = (2000)(0.06)(1)$$
$$I = 120 \quad \boxed{\text{Don't stop here. Add the interest to the principal.}}$$

(b) $1850 at $9\frac{1}{2}$% for 1 year (*Hint:* Write $9\frac{1}{2}$% as 9.5%. Then *move the decimal point* two places to the left to change 9.5% to a decimal.)

The interest is $120.

Now add the principal and the interest to find the total amount due.

$$\text{amount due} = \text{principal} + \text{interest}$$
$$= \quad \$2000 \quad + \quad \$120$$
$$= \$2120$$

The total amount due is $2120.

◄ Work Problem **5** *at the Side.*

EXAMPLE 6   **Finding Simple Interest and Total Amount Due for More Than 1 Year**

Find the simple interest and total amount due on a $4200 loan at $8\frac{1}{2}$% for $3\frac{1}{2}$ years.

The principal (p) is $4200. The rate ($r$) is $8\frac{1}{2}$%, which is the same as 8.5%. Move the decimal point two places to the left to change 8.5% to a decimal.

$$8\tfrac{1}{2}\% = 8.5\% = 08.5 = 0.085 \quad \boxed{\text{Remember to move the decimal point in 8.5% to get 0.085}}$$

The time (t) is $3\frac{1}{2}$ or 3.5 years. Use the formula.

$$I = \quad p \quad \cdot \quad r \quad \cdot \quad t$$
$$I = (4200)(0.085)(3.5)$$
$$I = 1249.50$$

The interest is $1249.50.

Continued on Next Page

ANSWERS

5. (a) $20; $520   **(b)** $175.75; $2025.75

Now add the principal and the interest to find the total amount due.

$$\text{amount due} = \text{principal} + \text{interest}$$
$$= \$4200 + \$1249.50$$
$$= \$5449.50$$

The total amount due is $5449.50.

> **CAUTION**
> Be careful when changing a mixed number percent, like $8\frac{1}{2}\%$, to a decimal. Writing $8\frac{1}{2}\%$ as 8.5% is only the first step. There is a decimal point in 8.5% but there is still a % sign. You must divide by 100 before dropping the % sign. **_Remember to move the decimal point two places to the left_**, as shown in Example 6 on the previous page.
> $$8\tfrac{1}{2}\% = 8.5\% = 0.085$$

Work Problem **6** *at the Side.* ▶

Interest rates are given *per year*. For loan periods of less than one year, be careful to express the time as a fraction of a year.

If the time is given in months, use a denominator of 12, because there are 12 months in a year. A loan of 9 months would be for $\frac{9}{12}$ of a year, a loan of 7 months would be for $\frac{7}{12}$ of a year, and so on.

EXAMPLE 7   **Finding Simple Interest and Total Amount Due for Less Than 1 Year**

Find the simple interest and total amount due on $840 at $9\frac{3}{4}\%$ for 7 months. The principal is $840. The rate is $9\frac{3}{4}\%$ or 0.0975.

$$9\frac{3}{4}\% = 9.75\% = 09.75 = 0.0975$$

The time is $\frac{7}{12}$ of a year. Use the formula $I = prt$.

$$I = (840)(0.0975)\left(\frac{7}{12}\right) \qquad \text{7 months is } \tfrac{7}{12} \text{ of a year.}$$
$$= (81.9)\left(\frac{7}{12}\right)$$
$$= \left(\frac{81.9}{1}\right)\left(\frac{7}{12}\right) \qquad \begin{array}{l}\text{Multiply numerators.}\\\text{Multiply denominators.}\end{array}$$
$$= \frac{573.3}{12} = 47.775 \qquad \text{Divide 573.3 by 12}$$

The interest is $47.78, rounded to the nearest cent.

The total amount due is $840 + $47.78 = $887.78

> ▦ **Calculator Tip**   The calculator solution for finding the interest in Example 7 above uses chain calculations.
>
> 840 ⊗ .0975 ⊗ 7 ⊘ 12 ⊜ 47.775 ← Round to $47.78

Work Problem **7** *at the Side.* ▶

---

6 Find the simple interest and total amount due for each loan.

(a) $340 at 5% for $3\frac{1}{2}$ years

(b) $2450 at 8% for $3\frac{1}{4}$ years (*Hint:* Write $3\frac{1}{4}$ years as 3.25 years.)

(c) $14,200 at $7\frac{1}{2}\%$ for $2\frac{3}{4}$ years

7 Find the simple interest and total amount due for each loan.

(a) $1600 at 7% for 4 months

(b) $25,000 at $10\frac{1}{2}\%$ for 3 months

(c) $4350 at $12\frac{1}{4}\%$ for 9 months

ANSWERS

6. **(a)** $59.50; $399.50   **(b)** $637; $3087
   (c) $2928.75; $17,128.75
7. **(a)** $37.33 (rounded); $1637.33
   (b) $656.25; $25,656.25
   (c) $399.66 (rounded); $4749.66

7.10 ▶▶▶ **Exercises**

Find the amount of the sales tax or the tax rate and the total cost. Round money answers to the nearest cent. See Examples 1 and 2.

	Cost of Item	Tax Rate	Amount of Tax	Total Cost
1.	$100	6%	_____	_____
2.	$200	4%	_____	_____
3.	$68	_____	$2.04	_____
4.	$185	_____	$9.25	_____
5.	$365.98	8%	_____	_____
6.	$28.49	7%	_____	_____
7.	$2.10	$5\frac{1}{2}\%$	_____	_____
8.	$7.00	$7\frac{1}{2}\%$	_____	_____
9.	$12,600	_____	$567	_____
10.	$21,800	_____	$1417	_____

For each restaurant bill, estimate a 15% tip and a 20% tip. Then find the exact amounts for a 15% tip and a 20% tip. Round exact amounts to the nearest cent when necessary. See Example 3.

Bill	Estimate of 15% Tip	Exact 15% Tip	Estimate of 20% Tip	Exact 20% Tip
11. $32.17	_____	_____	_____	_____
12. $21.94	_____	_____	_____	_____
13. $78.33	_____	_____	_____	_____
14. $67.85	_____	_____	_____	_____
15. $9.55	_____	_____	_____	_____
16. $52.61	_____	_____	_____	_____

Find the amount or rate of discount and the sale price. Round money answers to the nearest cent when necessary. See Example 4.

Original Price	Rate of Discount	Amount of Discount	Sale Price
17. $100	15%	_____	_____
18. $200	20%	_____	_____
19. $180	_____	$54	_____
20. $38	_____	$9.50	_____
21. $17.50	25%	_____	_____
22. $76	60%	_____	_____
23. $37.88	10%	_____	_____
24. $59.99	40%	_____	_____

Find the simple interest and total amount due on each loan. See Examples 5–7.
Round answers to the nearest cent when necessary.

	Principal	Rate	Time	Interest	Total Amount Due
25.	$300	14%	1 year	_____	_____
26.	$600	11%	6 months	_____	_____
27.	$740	6%	9 months	_____	_____
28.	$1180	9%	2 years	_____	_____
29.	$1500	$9\frac{1}{2}$%	$1\frac{1}{2}$ years	_____	_____
30.	$3000	$6\frac{1}{2}$%	$2\frac{1}{2}$ years	_____	_____
31.	$17,800	$7\frac{3}{4}$%	8 months	_____	_____
32.	$20,500	$8\frac{1}{4}$%	5 months	_____	_____

Solve each application problem. Round money answers to the nearest cent when necessary.

33. Diamonds at Discounts sells diamond engagement rings at 40% off the regular price. Find the sale price of a $\frac{1}{2}$-carat diamond ring normally priced at $1950.

34. An 80 GB iPOD classic originally priced at $249 is marked down 8%. Find the price of the iPOD after the markdown.

35. Evelina Jones lent $7500 to her son Rick, the owner of Rick's Limousine Service. He repaid the loan at the end of 9 months at $8\frac{1}{2}\%$ simple interest. What total amount did Rick pay his mother?

36. The owners of Delta Trucking purchased four diesel-powered tractors for cross-country hauling at a cost of $87,500 per tractor. If they borrowed the purchase price for $1\frac{1}{2}$ years at 11% simple interest, find the total amount due.

37. A Motorola H350 Bluetooth headset is sale priced at $24.99. The sales tax rate is $6\frac{1}{2}\%$. Find the total cost of the headset. (*Source:* www.BestBuy.com)

38. A weekday "golf/breakfast special" includes breakfast, 18 holes of golf, and use of a cart for $47.95 plus tax per person. If the sales tax rate is $7\frac{1}{2}\%$, find the total cost per person. How much will three friends pay to play golf?

39. An Anderson wood frame French door is priced at $1980 with a sales tax of $99. Find the sales tax rate.

40. Textbooks for two classes cost $185 plus sales tax of $11.10. Find the sales tax rate.

41. A "super 45% off sale" begins today. What is the sale price of a ski parka normally priced at $135?

42. A discontinued Whirlpool model side-by-side refrigerator with in-door icemaker originally sold for $1197. What is the sale price with a 35% discount?

43. Ricia and Seitu split a $43.70 dinner bill plus 15% tip. How much did each person pay?

44. Marvette took her brother out to dinner for his birthday. The bill for food was $58.36 and for wine was $15.44. How much was her 20% tip, rounded to the nearest dollar?

45. A 50" slim depth projection HDTV normally priced at $1199.99 is on sale for 18% off. Find the discount and the sale price.

46. This week, Honda CRVs are offered at 15% off the manufacturer's suggested price. Find the discount and the sale price of a CRV originally priced at $23,500.

47. Ms. Henderson owes $1900 in taxes. She is charged a penalty of $12\frac{1}{4}\%$ annual interest and pays the taxes and penalty after 6 months. Find the total amount she must pay.

48. Norell Di Loreto, owner of Sunset Realtors, borrowed $27,000 to update her office computer system. If the loan is for 24 months at $7\frac{3}{4}\%$, find the total amount due on the loan.

49. Vincente and Samuel ordered a large deep-dish pizza for $17.98. How much did they give the delivery person to pay for the pizza and a 15% tip, rounded to the nearest dollar?

50. Cher, Maya, and Adara shared a $28.50 bill for a buffet lunch. Because the server only brought their beverages, they left a 10% tip instead of the usual 15%. How much did each person pay?

Use the information in the store ad to answer Exercises 51–54. Round sale prices and sales tax to the nearest cent when necessary.

STORE CLOSE-OUT!

All clothing is now 45% off!

All jewelry is now 30% off!

All electronics are now 65% off!

6% sales tax added to jewelry and electronics purchases.

CASH ONLY! ALL SALES ARE FINAL!

51. Danika bought a computer modem originally priced at $129 and a $60 pair of earrings. What was her bill for the two items?

52. Find David's total bill for a $189 jacket and a $75 graphing calculator.

53. Sergei purchased a camcorder originally priced at $287.95, two pairs of $48 jeans, and a $95 ring. Find his total bill.

54. Richard picked out three pairs of $15 running shorts, two $28 shirts, and a digital camera originally priced at $99.99. How much did he pay in all?

Relating Concepts (Exercises 55–56) For Individual or Group Work

*Use your knowledge of percent to **work Exercises 55 and 56 in order.***

55. (a) College students are offered a 6% discount on a dictionary that sells for $18.50. If the sales tax is 6%, find the cost of the dictionary, including the sales tax, to the nearest cent.

(b) In part (a) the rate of discount and the sales tax rate are the same percent. Explain why the answer did *not* end up back at $18.50.

56. (a) A combination printer, scanner, copier, and FAX machine priced at $398 is marked down 7% to promote the new model. If the sales tax is also 7%, find the cost of the machine, including sales tax, to the nearest cent.

(b) What rate of sales tax would have made the final answer in part (a) end up back at $398? Round to the nearest hundredth of a percent.

Math in the Media

Simple interest is paid only on the original principal. But savings accounts and most investments earn *compound interest*. In that case, interest is paid on the principal *and* the interest earned. Let's see the difference made by compounding the interest.

If you invest $10,000 at 8% simple interest for 3 years, here is what you get.

$$I = (\$10,000)(0.08)(3) = \$2400 \leftarrow \text{Interest earned}$$

$$\text{Total amount you have} = \$10,000 + \$2400 = \$12,400$$

But suppose you invest $10,000 in an account that earns 8% *compounded annually,* and you leave the initial investment and the interest in the account for 3 years. The diagram below shows the compounded amount in your account at the end of each year, to the nearest dollar.

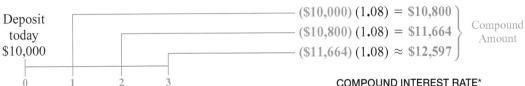

Deposit today $10,000

$$(\$10,000)(1.08) = \$10,800$$
$$(\$10,800)(1.08) = \$11,664$$
$$(\$11,664)(1.08) \approx \$12,597$$

Compound Amount

Year 0 1 2 3

You made an extra $197 with compounding ($12,597 − $12,400 = $197).

However, compound interest *really* makes a tremendous difference when you invest money over 10 or 20 or more years. The table at the right shows how a $10,000 investment, plus the interest it earns, grows. Amounts are rounded to the nearest dollar.

COMPOUND INTEREST RATE*

Years	5%	8%	10%
10	$16,289	$21,589	$25,937
20	26,533	46,610	67,275
30	43,219	100,627	174,494
40	70,400	217,245	452,593
50	114,674	469,016	1,173,909

*Interest compounded annually
Source: www.moneychimp.com/calculator

Each investment in Questions 1–3 is $10,000.

1. **(a)** Calculate the amount you would have after 10 years with a 5% *simple* interest investment.

   (b) How much more would you have with *compound* interest?

2. **(a)** Calculate the amount you would have after 30 years with an 8% simple interest investment.

   (b) How much more would you have with compound interest?

3. **(a)** Repeat the calculations you did in Questions 1 and 2 for a 10% simple interest account after 50 years.

   (b) The compounded amount is how many *times* greater than the simple interest amount?

8

Measurement

8.1 ▶▶▶ Problem Solving with U.S. Customary Measurements

OBJECTIVES

1 Learn the basic U.S. customary measurement units.

2 Convert among measurement units using multiplication or division.

3 Convert among measurement units using unit fractions.

4 Solve application problems using U.S. customary measurement units.

We measure things all the time: the distance traveled on vacation, the floor area we want to cover with carpet, the amount of milk in a recipe, the weight of the bananas we buy at the store, the number of hours we work, and many more.

In the United States, we still use **U.S. customary measurement units** for many everyday activities. Examples are inches, feet, quarts, ounces, and pounds. However, science, medicine, sports, and manufacturing use the **metric system** (meters, liters, and grams). And, because the rest of the world uses *only* the metric system, U.S. businesses have been changing to the metric system in order to compete internationally.

OBJECTIVE 1 Learn the basic U.S. customary measurement units. Until the switch to the metric system is complete, we still need to know how to use U.S. customary measurement units. The table below lists the relationships you should memorize. The time relationships are used in both the U.S. customary and metric systems.

1 After memorizing the measurement conversions, answer these questions.

(a) 1 c = _____ fl oz

(b) _____ qt = 1 gal

(c) 1 wk = _____ days

(d) _____ ft = 1 yd

(e) 1 ft = _____ in.

(f) _____ oz = 1 lb

(g) 1 ton = _____ lb

(h) _____ min = 1 hr

(i) 1 pt = _____ c

(j) _____ hr = 1 day

(k) 1 min = _____ sec

(l) 1 qt = _____ pt

(m) _____ ft = 1 mi

U.S. Customary Measurement Relationships	
Length	**Weight**
12 inches (in.) = 1 foot (ft)	16 ounces (oz) = 1 pound (lb)
3 feet (ft) = 1 yard (yd)	2000 pounds (lb) = 1 ton
5280 feet (ft) = 1 mile (mi)	
Capacity	**Time**
8 fluid ounces (fl oz) = 1 cup (c)	60 seconds (sec) = 1 minute (min)
2 cups (c) = 1 pint (pt)	60 minutes (min) = 1 hour (hr)
2 pints (pt) = 1 quart (qt)	24 hours (hr) = 1 day
4 quarts (qt) = 1 gallon (gal)	7 days = 1 week (wk)

As you can see, there is no simple way to convert among these various measures. The units evolved over hundreds of years and were based on a variety of "standards." For example, one yard was the distance from the tip of a king's nose to his thumb when his arm was outstretched. An inch was three dried barleycorns laid end to end.

EXAMPLE 1 **Knowing U.S. Customary Measurement Units**

Memorize the U.S. customary measurement conversions shown above. Then answer these questions.

(a) 24 hr = _____ day   Answer: 1 day

(b) 1 yd = _____ ft   Answer: 3 ft

◀ *Work Problem* **1** *at the Side.*

OBJECTIVE 2 Convert among measurement units using multiplication or division. You often need to convert from one unit of measure to another. Two methods of converting measurements are shown here. Study each way and use the method you prefer. The first method involves deciding whether to multiply or divide.

> **Converting among Measurement Units**
> 1. *Multiply* when converting from a larger unit to a smaller unit.
> 2. *Divide* when converting from a smaller unit to a larger unit.

2 Convert each measurement using multiplication or division.

(a) $5\frac{1}{2}$ ft to inches

EXAMPLE 2 **Converting from One Unit of Measure to Another**

Convert each measurement.

(a) 7 ft to inches
   You are converting from a *larger* unit to a *smaller* unit (a *foot* is longer than an *inch*), so multiply.
   Because *1 ft = 12 in.,* multiply by 12.
$$7 \text{ ft} = 7 \cdot 12 = 84 \text{ in.}$$

(b) 64 oz to pounds

(b) $3\frac{1}{2}$ lb to ounces
   You are converting from a *larger* unit to a *smaller* unit (a *pound* is heavier than an *ounce*), so multiply.
   Because *1 lb = 16 oz,* multiply by 16.

> Divide 16 and 2 by their common factor of 2.
> $16 \div 2$ is 8 and $2 \div 2$ is 1.

$$3\frac{1}{2} \text{ lb} = 3\frac{1}{2} \cdot 16 = \frac{7}{\overset{}{2}} \cdot \frac{\overset{8}{\cancel{16}}}{1} = \frac{56}{1} = 56 \text{ oz}$$

(c) 6 yd to feet

(c) 20 qt to gallons
   You are converting from a *smaller* unit to a *larger* unit (a *quart* is smaller than a *gallon*) so divide.
   Because *4 qt = 1 gal,* divide by 4.
$$20 \text{ qt} = \frac{20}{4} = 5 \text{ gal}$$
   Divide by 4. ⬏

(d) 2 tons to pounds

(d) 45 min to hours
   You are converting from a *smaller* unit to a *larger* unit (a *minute* is less than an *hour*), so divide.
   Because *60 min = 1 hr,* divide by 60 and write the fraction in lowest terms.

$$45 \text{ min} = \frac{45}{60} = \frac{45 \div 15}{60 \div 15} = \frac{3}{4} \text{ hr} \quad \leftarrow \text{Lowest terms}$$

Divide by 60. ⬏

(e) 35 pt to quarts

Work Problem **2** *at the Side.* ▶

(f) 20 min to hours

OBJECTIVE **3** **Convert among measurement units using unit fractions.** If you have trouble deciding whether to multiply or divide when converting measurements, use *unit fractions* to solve the problem. You'll also use this method in science courses. A **unit fraction** is equivalent to 1. Here is an example.

$$\frac{12 \text{ in.}}{12 \text{ in.}} = \frac{\cancel{12} \text{ in.}}{\cancel{12} \text{ in.}} = 1$$

(g) 4 wk to days

Use the table of measurement relationships on the previous page to find that 12 in. is the same as 1 ft. So you can substitute 1 ft for 12 in. in the numerator, or you can substitute 1 ft for 12 in. in the denominator. This makes two useful unit fractions.

Answers

2. (a) 66 in. **(b)** 4 lb **(c)** 18 ft

$$\frac{1 \text{ ft}}{12 \text{ in.}} = 1 \quad \text{or} \quad \frac{12 \text{ in.}}{1 \text{ ft}} = 1$$

  (d) 4000 lb **(e)** $17\frac{1}{2}$ qt **(f)** $\frac{1}{3}$ hr

  (g) 28 days

3 First write the unit fraction needed to make each conversion. Then complete the conversion.

(a) 36 in. to feet

$\text{unit fraction}\Big\} \dfrac{1\ \text{ft}}{12\ \text{in.}}$

(b) 14 ft to inches

$\text{unit fraction}\Big\} \dfrac{\text{in.}}{\text{ft}}$

(c) 60 in. to feet

$\text{unit fraction}\Big\}$ _____

(d) 4 yd to feet

$\text{unit fraction}\Big\}$ _____

(e) 39 ft to yards

$\text{unit fraction}\Big\}$ _____

(f) 2 mi to feet

$\text{unit fraction}\Big\}$ _____

To convert from one measurement unit to another, just multiply by the appropriate unit fraction. Remember, a unit fraction is equivalent to 1. Multiplying something by 1 does *not* change its value.

Use these guidelines to choose the correct unit fraction.

> **Choosing a Unit Fraction**
>
> The ***numerator*** should use the measurement unit you want in the *answer*.
> The ***denominator*** should use the measurement unit you want to *change*.

EXAMPLE 3 **Using Unit Fractions with Length Measurements**

(a) Convert 60 in. to feet.

Use a unit fraction with feet (the unit for your answer) in the numerator, and inches (the unit being changed) in the denominator. Because *1 ft = 12 in.,* the necessary unit fraction is

$$\dfrac{1\ \text{ft}}{12\ \text{in.}} \quad \begin{array}{l} \leftarrow \text{Unit for your answer is feet.} \\ \leftarrow \text{Unit being changed is inches.} \end{array}$$

Next, multiply 60 in. times this unit fraction. Write 60 in. as the fraction $\dfrac{60\ \text{in.}}{1}$ and divide out common units and factors wherever possible.

$$60\ \text{in.} \cdot \dfrac{1\ \text{ft}}{12\ \text{in.}} = \dfrac{\overset{5}{\cancel{60\ \text{in.}}}}{1} \cdot \dfrac{1\ \text{ft}}{\underset{1}{\cancel{12\ \text{in.}}}} = \dfrac{5 \cdot 1\text{ft}}{1} = 5\ \text{ft}$$

These units should match. —Divide out inches. —Divide 60 and 12 by 12.

(b) Convert 9 ft to inches.

Select the correct unit fraction to change 9 ft to inches.

$$\dfrac{12\ \text{in.}}{1\ \text{ft}} \quad \begin{array}{l} \leftarrow \text{Unit for your answer is inches.} \\ \leftarrow \text{Unit being changed is feet.} \end{array}$$

Multiply 9 ft times the unit fraction.

$$9\ \text{ft} \cdot \dfrac{12\ \text{in.}}{1\ \text{ft}} = \dfrac{9\ \cancel{\text{ft}}}{1} \cdot \dfrac{12\ \text{in.}}{1\ \cancel{\text{ft}}} = \dfrac{9 \cdot 12\ \text{in.}}{1} = 108\ \text{in.}$$

These units should match. —Divide out feet.

> **CAUTION**
> If no units will divide out, you made a mistake in choosing the unit fraction.

◀ *Work Problem* **3** *at the Side.*

EXAMPLE 4 **Using Unit Fractions with Capacity and Weight Measurements**

(a) Convert 9 pt to quarts.

First select the correct unit fraction.

$$\dfrac{1\ \text{qt}}{2\ \text{pt}} \quad \begin{array}{l} \leftarrow \text{Unit for your answer is quarts.} \\ \leftarrow \text{Unit being changed is pints.} \end{array}$$

Continued on Next Page

ANSWERS

3. **(a)** 3 ft **(b)** $\dfrac{12\ \text{in.}}{1\ \text{ft}}$; 168 in.

(c) $\dfrac{1\ \text{ft}}{12\ \text{in.}}$; 5 ft **(d)** $\dfrac{3\ \text{ft}}{1\ \text{yd}}$; 12 ft

(e) $\dfrac{1\ \text{yd}}{3\ \text{ft}}$; 13 yd **(f)** $\dfrac{5280\ \text{ft}}{1\ \text{mi}}$; 10,560 ft

Next multiply.

Write as a mixed number.

$$9 \text{ pt} \cdot \frac{1 \text{ qt}}{2 \text{ pt}} = \frac{9 \cancel{\text{pt}}}{1} \cdot \frac{1 \text{ qt}}{2 \cancel{\text{pt}}} = \frac{9}{2} \text{ qt} = 4\frac{1}{2} \text{ qt}$$

These units
should match.

Divide out pints.

(b) Convert $7\frac{1}{2}$ gal to quarts.

Write as an improper fraction.

$$\frac{7\frac{1}{2} \cancel{\text{gal}}}{1} \cdot \frac{4 \text{ qt}}{1 \cancel{\text{gal}}} = \frac{15}{2} \cdot \frac{4}{1} \text{ qt}$$

Divide out gallons.

Divide 4 and 2
by their common
factor of 2.
$4 \div 2$ is 2.
$2 \div 2$ is 1.

$$= \frac{15}{\cancel{2}_1} \cdot \frac{\cancel{4}^2}{1} \text{ qt}$$

$$= 30 \text{ qt}$$

(c) Convert 36 oz to pounds.

Notice that **oz**
divides out,
leaving **lb**, the
unit you want for
the answer.

$$\frac{\cancel{36}^9 \cancel{\text{oz}}}{1} \cdot \frac{1 \text{ lb}}{\cancel{16}_4 \cancel{\text{oz}}} = \frac{9}{4} \text{ lb} = 2\frac{1}{4} \text{ lb}$$

Note

In Example 4(c) above you get $\frac{9}{4}$ lb. Recall that $\frac{9}{4}$ means $9 \div 4$. If you do $9 \div 4$ on your calculator, you get 2.25 lb. U.S. customary measurements usually use fractions or mixed numbers, like $2\frac{1}{4}$ lb. However, 2.25 lb is also correct and is the way grocery stores often show weights of produce, meat, and cheese.

Work Problem **4** *at the Side.* ▶

EXAMPLE 5   Using Several Unit Fractions

Sometimes you may need to use two or three unit fractions to complete a conversion.

(a) Convert 63 in. to yards.

Use the unit fraction $\frac{1 \text{ ft}}{12 \text{ in.}}$ to change inches to feet and the unit fraction $\frac{1 \text{ yd}}{3 \text{ ft}}$ to change feet to yards. Notice how all the units divide out except yards, which is the unit you want in the answer.

$$\frac{63 \cancel{\text{in.}}}{1} \cdot \frac{1 \cancel{\text{ft}}}{12 \cancel{\text{in.}}} \cdot \frac{1 \text{ yd}}{3 \cancel{\text{ft}}} = \frac{63}{36} \text{ yd} = \frac{63 \div 9}{36 \div 9} \text{ yd} = \frac{7}{4} \text{ yd} = 1\frac{3}{4} \text{ yd}$$

Continued on Next Page

4 Convert using unit fractions.

(a) 16 qt to gallons

(b) 3 c to pints

(c) $3\frac{1}{2}$ tons to pounds

(d) $1\frac{3}{4}$ lb to ounces

(e) 4 oz to pounds

ANSWERS

4. **(a)** 4 gal   **(b)** $1\frac{1}{2}$ pt or 1.5 pt   **(c)** 7000 lb

(d) 28 oz   **(e)** $\frac{1}{4}$ lb or 0.25 lb

You can also divide out common factors in the numbers.

$$\frac{\overset{7}{\cancel{\overset{21}{\cancel{63}}}}}{1} \cdot \frac{1}{\underset{4}{\cancel{12}}} \cdot \frac{1}{\underset{1}{\cancel{3}}} = \frac{7}{4} = 1\frac{3}{4} \text{ yd}$$

Instead of changing $\frac{7}{4}$ to $1\frac{3}{4}$, you can enter $7 \div 4$ on your calculator to get 1.75 yd. Both answers are correct because 1.75 is equivalent to $1\frac{3}{4}$.

(b) Convert 2 days to seconds.

Use three unit fractions. The first one changes days to hours, the next one changes hours to minutes, and the last one changes minutes to seconds. All the units divide out except seconds, which is the unit you want in your answer.

$$\frac{2 \text{ d\cancel{ays}}}{1} \cdot \frac{24 \text{ h\cancel{r}}}{1 \text{ d\cancel{ay}}} \cdot \frac{60 \text{ m\cancel{in}}}{1 \text{ h\cancel{r}}} \cdot \frac{60 \text{ sec}}{1 \text{ m\cancel{in}}} = 172{,}800 \text{ sec}$$

Divide out **days**.
Divide out **hr**.
Divide out **min**.

◀ *Work Problem* **5** *at the Side.*

OBJECTIVE **4** **Solve application problems using U.S. customary measurement units.** To solve measurement application problems, we will use the steps summarized here.

Step 1 **Read** the problem.

Step 2 **Work out a plan.**

Step 3 **Estimate** a reasonable answer.

Step 4 **Solve** the problem.

Step 5 **State the answer.**

Step 6 **Check** your work.

Because measurement applications often involve conversions, writing an equation may not be the best way to solve the problem. Therefore, Steps 2 and 3 are different from the ones you learned in **Chapter 4;** the rest are the same.

EXAMPLE 6 **Solving U.S. Customary Measurement Applications**

(a) A 36-oz can of coffee is on sale at Jerry's Foods for $7.89. What is the cost per pound, to the nearest cent? (*Source:* Jerry's Foods.)

Step 1 **Read** the problem. The problem asks for the cost per *pound* of coffee.

Step 2 **Work out a plan.** The weight of the coffee is given in *ounces,* but the answer must be cost *per pound*. Convert ounces to pounds. The word *per* indicates division. You need to divide the cost by the number of pounds.

Step 3 **Estimate** a reasonable answer. To estimate, round $7.89 to $8. Then, there are 16 oz in a pound, so 36 oz are a little more than 2 pounds. So, $8 \div 2 =$ $4 per pound as our estimate.

Continued on Next Page

---

5 Convert using two or three unit fractions.

(a) 4 tons to ounces

(b) 3 mi to inches

(c) 36 pt to gallons

(d) 2 wk to minutes

Step 4   **Solve** the problem. Use a unit fraction to convert 36 oz to pounds.

Notice that **oz** divides out, leaving **lb** for the answer.

On your calculator,
$9 \div 4 = 2.25$

$$\frac{\overset{9}{\cancel{36}} \cancel{oz}}{1} \cdot \frac{1 \text{ lb}}{\underset{4}{\cancel{16}} \cancel{oz}} = \frac{9}{4} \text{ lb} = 2.25 \text{ lb}$$

Then divide to find the *cost* per *pound*.

Cost → per → pound →
$$\frac{\$7.89}{2.25 \text{ lb}} = 3.50\overline{6} \approx 3.51 \quad \text{(rounded)}$$

Step 5   **State the answer.** The coffee costs $3.51 per pound (to the nearest cent).

Step 6   **Check** your work. The exact answer of $3.51 is close to our estimate of $4.

(b) Bilal's favorite cake recipe uses $1\frac{2}{3}$ cups of milk. If he makes six cakes for a bake sale at his son's school, how many quarts of milk will he need?

Step 1   **Read** the problem. The problem asks for the number of *quarts* of milk needed for six cakes.

Step 2   **Work out a plan.** Multiply to find the number of *cups* of milk for six cakes. Then convert *cups* to *quarts* (the unit required in the answer).

Step 3   **Estimate** a reasonable answer. To estimate, round $1\frac{2}{3}$ cups to 2 cups. Then, 2 cups times 6 = 12 cups. There are 4 cups in a quart, so 12 cups ÷ 4 = 3 quarts as our estimate.

Step 4   **Solve** the problem. First multiply. Then use unit fractions to convert.

$$1\frac{2}{3} \cdot 6 = \frac{5}{\cancel{3}} \cdot \frac{\overset{2}{\cancel{6}}}{1} = \frac{10}{1} = 10 \text{ cups} \qquad \left\{ \begin{array}{l} \text{Milk needed for} \\ \text{six cakes} \end{array} \right.$$

$$\frac{\overset{5}{\cancel{10} \cancel{cups}}}{1} \cdot \frac{1 \cancel{pt}}{\underset{1}{\cancel{2} \cancel{cups}}} \cdot \frac{1 \text{ qt}}{2 \cancel{pt}} = \frac{5}{2} \text{ qt} = 2\frac{1}{2} \text{ qt}$$

Both **cups** and **pt** divide out, leaving **qt**, the unit you want for the answer.

Step 5   **State the answer.** Bilal needs $2\frac{1}{2}$ qt (or 2.5 qt) of milk.

Step 6   **Check** your work. The exact answer of $2\frac{1}{2}$ qt is close to our estimate of 3 qt.

Note
In Step 2 above, we *first multiplied* $1\frac{2}{3}$ cups by 6 to find the number of cups needed, then *converted* 10 cups to $2\frac{1}{2}$ quarts. It would also work to *first convert* $1\frac{2}{3}$ cups to $\frac{5}{12}$ qt, then *multiply* $\frac{5}{12}$ qt by 6 to get $2\frac{1}{2}$ qt.

Work Problem **6** *at the Side.* ▶

6 Solve each application problem using the six problem-solving steps.

(a) Kristin paid $3.29 for 12 oz of extra sharp cheddar cheese. What is the price per pound, to the nearest cent?

(b) A moving company estimates 11,000 lb of furnishings for an average 3-bedroom house. If the company made five such moves last week, how many tons of furnishings did they move? (*Source:* North American Van Lines.)

ANSWERS

6. **(a)** $4.39 per pound (rounded)

   (b) 27.5 tons or $27\frac{1}{2}$ tons

Math in the Media

The front and back of a seed packet for sunflowers are shown at the right. Look at the top of the packet first. (Ignore sales tax in Questions 1 and 2.)

1. There were 42 seeds in the packet. If 40 of the seeds sprouted, what was the cost per sprout, to the nearest cent?

2. If vegetable and flower seeds were on sale at 30% off, what was the cost per sprout, to the nearest cent?

3. What percent of the seeds sprouted, to the nearest whole percent?

4. How many seeds would add up to a weight of 1 gram?

5. The table at the bottom of the packet uses the symbol (′) for feet, and the symbol (″) for inches.

   (a) How tall will the plants grow, in feet?

   (b) How tall will they grow in inches?

   (c) How tall will they grow in yards?

6. If you plant all 42 seeds in one long row, using the spacing given on the package, how long will your row be in feet?

7. How many inches tall should the plants be when you thin them (remove less vigorous plants to give others room to grow)? How tall is that in feet?

8. What is the range in the diameter of the flowers, in inches, and in feet? Diameter is the distance across the circular flower.

Sunflower, Mammoth Grey Stripe

Tall Plants, Huge Flowers

Net Wt. 3.5 g $1.19

Sunflower, Mammoth Grey Stripe

The stalk of this sunflower will grow to 12′/4 m. Flowers will range from 6″/15 cm to 15″/38 cm in diameter. Sunflowers can thrive in poor soil with little moisture.

Type	Height	Planting Depth	Seed Spacing	Thinning Height	Spacing After Thinning	Days to Germination
Annual	8-10′ 2.4-3 m	1/2″ 13 mm	6″ 15 cm	3″ 8 cm	2′ 61 cm	10-20

Select a sunny or lightly shaded location and plant outdoors, where plants are to remain, after all danger of frost is past. For tallest plants, sow in good soil with moderate moisture.

Stock #1185

7 18964 98119 7

Source: Olds Seed Solutions.

696

8.1 ▶▶▶ Exercises

MyMathLab | Math XL PRACTICE | WATCH | DOWNLOAD | READ | REVIEW

Fill in the blanks with the measurement relationships you have memorized. See Example 1.

1. 1 yd = _____ ft;   _____ in. = 1 ft

2. 1 ft = _____ in.;   _____ ft = 1 mi

3. _____ fl oz = 1 c;   1 qt = _____ pt

4. _____ qt = 1 gal;   1 pt = _____ c

5. 1 mi = _____ ft;   _____ ft = 1 yd

6. 1 wk = _____ days;   _____ sec = 1 min

7. _____ lb = 1 ton;   1 lb = _____ oz

8. _____ oz = 1 lb;   1 ton = _____ lb

9. 1 min = _____ sec;   _____ min = 1 hr

10. 1 day = _____ hr;   _____ sec = 1 min

Convert each measurement by multiplying or dividing. See Example 2.

11. (a) 120 sec = _____ min

   (b) 4 hr = _____ min

12. (a) 180 min = _____ hr

   (b) 5 min = _____ sec

13. (a) 2 qt = _____ gal

   (b) $6\frac{1}{2}$ ft = _____ in.

14. (a) $4\frac{1}{2}$ gal = _____ qt

   (b) 12 oz = _____ lb

15. An adult African elephant could weigh 7 to 8 tons. How many pounds could it weigh? (*Source: The Top 10 of Everything.*)

16. A reticulated python snake is the world's longest snake. It grows to a length of 18 to 33 feet. How many yards long can the snake be? (*Source: The Top 10 of Everything.*)

Convert each measurement in Exercises 17–38 using unit fractions. See Examples 3 and 4.

17. 9 yd = _____ ft

18. 20,000 lb = _____ tons

19. 7 lb = _____ oz

20. 96 oz = _____ lb

21. 5 qt = _____ pt

22. 26 pt = _____ qt

23. 90 min = _____ hr

24. 45 sec = _____ min

25. 3 in. = _____ ft

26. 30 in. = _____ ft

27. 24 oz = _____ lb

28. 36 oz = _____ lb

29. 5 c = _____ pt

30. 15 qt = _____ gal

Use the information in the bar graph below to answer Exercises 31–32.

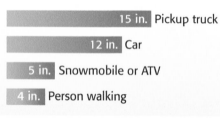

Thickness of Lake Ice Needed for Safe Walking/Driving

15 in. Pickup truck
12 in. Car
5 in. Snowmobile or ATV
4 in. Person walking

Source: Wisconsin DNR.

31. If the ice on a lake is $\frac{1}{2}$ ft thick, what will it safely support?

32. How many feet of ice are needed to safely drive a pickup truck on a lake?

33. $2\frac{1}{2}$ tons = _____ lb

34. $4\frac{1}{2}$ pt = _____ c

35. $4\frac{1}{4}$ gal = _____ qt

36. $2\frac{1}{4}$ hr = _____ min

37. After 15 years, a saguaro cactus is still only one-third to two-thirds of a foot tall, depending upon rainfall. How tall could the cactus be in inches? (*Source: Ecology of the Saguaro III.*)

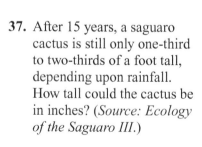

38. Yao Ming, an NBA basketball player from China, is $7\frac{1}{2}$ ft tall. What is his height in inches? (*Source:* www.NBA.com)

Use two or three unit fractions to make each conversion. See Example 5.

⊙ **39.** 6 yd = _____ in.

40. 2 tons = _____ oz

41. 112 c = _____ qt

42. 336 hr = _____ wk

43. 6 days = _____ sec

44. 5 gal = _____ c

45. $1\frac{1}{2}$ tons = _____ oz

46. $3\frac{1}{3}$ yd = _____ in.

47. The statement $8 = 2$ is *not* true. But with appropriate measurement units, it *is* true.

$$8 \; quarts = 2 \; gallons$$

Attach measurement units to these numbers to make the statement true.

(a) 1 _____ = 16 _____

(b) 10 _____ = 20 _____

(c) 120 _____ = 2 _____

(d) 2 _____ = 24 _____

(e) 6000 _____ = 3 _____

(f) 35 _____ = 5 _____

48. Explain in your own words why you can add 2 feet + 12 inches to get 3 feet, but you cannot add 2 feet + 12 pounds.

Convert each measurement. See Example 5.

49. $2\frac{3}{4}$ mi = _____ in.

50. $5\frac{3}{4}$ tons = _____ oz

51. $6\frac{1}{4}$ gal = _____ fl oz

52. $3\frac{1}{2}$ days = _____ sec

53. 24,000 oz = _____ ton

54. 57,024 in. = _____ mi

Solve each application problem. Show your work. See Example 6.

55. Geralyn bought 20 oz of strawberries for $2.29. What was the price per pound for the strawberries, to the nearest cent?

56. Zach paid $0.90 for a 0.8 oz candy bar. What was the cost per pound?

⊙ **57.** Dan orders supplies for the science labs. Each of the 24 stations in the chemistry lab needs 2 ft of rubber tubing. If rubber tubing sells for $8.75 per yard, how much will it cost to equip all the stations?

58. In 2006, Marquette, Michigan, had 170 inches of snowfall, while Detroit, Michigan, had 15 inches. What was the difference in snowfall between the two cities, in feet? Round to the nearest tenth. (*Source: World Almanac.*)

59. Tropical cockroaches are the fastest land insects. They can run about 5 feet per second. At this rate, how long would it take the cockroach to travel one mile? (*Source: Guinness World Records.*)

Give your answer

(a) in seconds;

(b) in minutes.

60. A snail moves at an average speed of 2 feet every 3 minutes. At that rate, how long would it take the snail to travel one mile? (*Source: Beakman and Jax.*)

Give your answer

(a) in hours;

(b) in days.

61. At the day care center, each of the 15 toddlers drinks about $\frac{2}{3}$ cup of milk with lunch. The center is open 5 days a week.

(a) How many quarts of milk will the center need for one week of lunches?

(b) If the center buys milk in gallon containers, how many containers should be ordered for one week?

62. Bob's Candies in Albany, Georgia, makes 135,000 pounds of candy canes each day. (*Source:* Bob's Candies, Inc.)

(a) How many tons of candy canes are produced during a 5-day workweek?

(b) The plant operates 24 hours per day. How many tons of candy canes are produced each hour, to the nearest tenth?

Relating Concepts (Exercises 63–66) For Individual or Group Work

On the first page of this chapter, we said that the bowl-shaped crater in northern Arizona made by a meteor crash was sixty stories deep and 4150 ft across. Use this information as you **work Exercises 63–66 in order.** (*Source: The Meteor Crater Story.*)

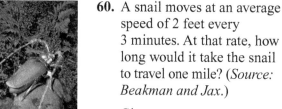

63. (a) The distance across the crater is what part of a mile, to the nearest tenth?

(b) The crater is nearly circular. In a circle, the distance around the outside edge is about 3.14 times the distance across the circle. How far is it to walk around the edge of the crater in feet?

(c) How far is it to walk around the edge of the crater in miles, to the nearest tenth?

64. (a) The crater is 550 ft deep. The depth is how many yards, to the nearest whole number?

(b) How many inches deep is the crater?

(c) The depth of the crater is what part of a mile, to the nearest tenth?

(d) When we say that the crater is as deep as a sixty-story building, we are assuming that each story is how many feet tall, to the nearest foot?

65. On one side of the crater there are a few small juniper trees. The trees are 700 years old but only 18 inches to 30 inches tall because of the strong winds and lack of rain.

(a) How tall are the trees in feet?

(b) How many months old are the trees?

(c) At this rate of growth, how long would it take a 30-inch tree to reach a height of three feet?

66. Evidence of two huge meteor crashes has been found on the floor of the Caribbean Sea. One giant circular crater is 90 miles across and the other is 120 miles across.

(a) Using the information about circles in Exercise 63, what is the approximate distance around the edge of the smaller crater, to the nearest mile?

(b) Around the larger crater?

8.2 ▶▶▶ The Metric System—Length

Around 1790, a group of French scientists developed the metric system of measurement. It is an organized system based on multiples of 10, like our number system and our money. After you are familiar with metric units, you will see that they are easier to use than the hodgepodge of U.S. customary measurement relationships you used in **Section 8.1.**

> **Note**
>
> The metric system information in this text is consistent with usage guidelines from the National Institute of Standards and Technology, www.nist.gov/metric.

OBJECTIVES

1 Learn the basic metric units of length.

2 Use unit fractions to convert among units.

3 Move the decimal point to convert among units.

OBJECTIVE 1 Learn the basic metric units of length.   The basic unit of length in the metric system is the **meter** (also spelled *metre*). Use the symbol **m** for meter; do not put a period after it. If you put five of the pages from this textbook side by side, they would measure about 1 meter. Or, look at a yardstick—a meter is just a little longer. A yard is 36 inches long; a meter is about 39 inches long.

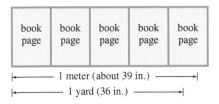

In the metric system, you use meters for things like measuring the length of your living room, talking about heights of buildings, or describing track and field athletic events.

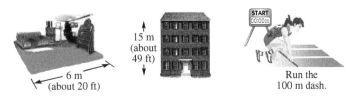

Work Problem 1 at the Side. ▶

To make longer or shorter length units in the metric system, **prefixes** are written in front of the word *meter*. For example, the prefix *kilo* means 1000, so a *kilo*meter is 1000 meters. The table below shows how to use the prefixes for length measurements. It is helpful to memorize the prefixes because they are also used with weight and capacity measurements. The purple boxes are the units you will use most often in daily life.

1 Circle the items that measure about 1 meter.

Length of a pencil

Length of a baseball bat

Height of doorknob from the floor

Height of a house

Basketball player's arm length

Length of a paper clip

Prefix	kilo-meter	hecto-meter	deka-meter	meter	deci-meter	centi-meter	milli-meter
Meaning	1000 meters	100 meters	10 meters	1 meter	$\frac{1}{10}$ of a meter	$\frac{1}{100}$ of a meter	$\frac{1}{1000}$ of a meter
Symbol	km	hm	dam	m	dm	cm	mm

Length units that are used most often

ANSWER

1. baseball bat, height of doorknob, basketball player's arm length

Here are some comparisons to help you get acquainted with the commonly used length units: km, m, cm, mm.

*Kilo*meters are used instead of miles. A kilometer is **1000** meters. It is about 0.6 mile (a little more than half a mile) or about 5 to 6 city blocks. If you participate in a 10 km run, you'll run about 6 miles.

A meter is divided into 100 smaller pieces called *centi*meters. Each centimeter is $\frac{1}{100}$ of a meter. Centimeters are used instead of inches. A centimeter is a little shorter than $\frac{1}{2}$ inch. The cover of this textbook is about 21 cm wide. A nickel is about 2 cm across. Measure the width and length of your little finger on this centimeter ruler. The width of your little finger is probably about 1 cm, or a little more.

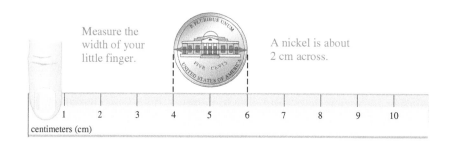

A meter is divided into 1000 smaller pieces called *milli*meters. Each millimeter is $\frac{1}{1000}$ of a meter. It takes 10 mm to equal 1 cm, so it is a very small length. The thickness of a dime is about 1 mm. Measure the width of your pen or pencil and the width of your little finger on this millimeter ruler.

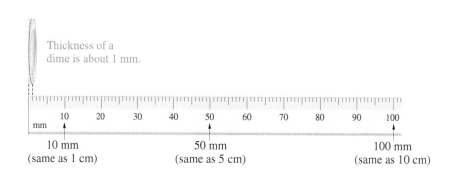

2 Write the most reasonable metric unit in each blank. Choose from km, m, cm, and mm.

(a) The woman's height is 168 _____ .

(b) The man's waist is 90 _____ around.

(c) Louise ran the 100 _____ dash in the track meet.

(d) A postage stamp is 22 _____ wide.

(e) Michael paddled his canoe 2 _____ down the river.

(f) The pencil lead is 1 _____ thick.

(g) A stick of gum is 7 _____ long.

(h) The highway speed limit is 90 _____ per hour.

(i) The classroom was 12 _____ long.

(j) A penny is about 18 _____ across.

EXAMPLE 1 | **Using Metric Length Units**

Write the most reasonable metric unit in each blank. Choose from km, m, cm, and mm.

(a) The distance from home to work is 20 _____.

20 **km** because kilometers are used instead of miles. 20 km is about 12 miles.

(b) My wedding ring is 4 _____ wide.

4 **mm** because the width of a ring is very small.

(c) The newborn baby is 50 _____ long.

50 **cm**; which is half of a meter; a meter is about 39 inches so half a meter is around 20 inches.

◀ *Work Problem* **2** *at the Side.*

OBJECTIVE **2** **Use unit fractions to convert among units.** You can convert among metric length units using unit fractions. Keep these relationships in mind when setting up the unit fractions.

Metric Length Relationships

1 km = 1000 m so the unit fractions are:	**1 m = 1000 mm** so the unit fractions are:
$\dfrac{1 \text{ km}}{1000 \text{ m}}$ or $\dfrac{1000 \text{ m}}{1 \text{ km}}$	$\dfrac{1 \text{ m}}{1000 \text{ mm}}$ or $\dfrac{1000 \text{ mm}}{1 \text{ m}}$
1 m = 100 cm so the unit fractions are:	**1 cm = 10 mm** so the unit fractions are:
$\dfrac{1 \text{ m}}{100 \text{ cm}}$ or $\dfrac{100 \text{ cm}}{1 \text{ m}}$	$\dfrac{1 \text{ cm}}{10 \text{ mm}}$ or $\dfrac{10 \text{ mm}}{1 \text{ cm}}$

EXAMPLE 2 **Using Unit Fractions to Convert Length Measurements**

Convert each measurement using unit fractions.

(a) 5 km to m
Put the unit for the answer (meters) in the numerator of the unit fraction; put the unit you want to change (km) in the denominator.

$$\begin{array}{l} \text{Unit fraction} \\ \text{equivalent to 1} \end{array} \left\{ \begin{array}{l} \dfrac{1000 \text{ m}}{1 \text{ km}} \quad \leftarrow \text{Unit for answer} \\ \phantom{\dfrac{1000 \text{ m}}{1 \text{ km}}} \leftarrow \text{Unit being changed} \end{array} \right.$$

Multiply. Divide out common units where possible.

$$5 \text{ km} \cdot \frac{1000 \text{ m}}{1 \text{ km}} = \frac{5 \text{ km}}{1} \cdot \frac{1000 \text{ m}}{1 \text{ km}} = \frac{5 \cdot 1000 \text{ m}}{1} = 5000 \text{ m}$$

These units should match.

Here, **km** divides out leaving **m**, the unit you want for your answer.

5 km = 5000 m

The answer makes sense because a kilometer is much longer than a meter, so 5 km will contain many meters.

(b) 18.6 cm to m
Multiply by a unit fraction that allows you to divide out centimeters.

Unit fraction

$$\frac{18.6 \text{ cm}}{1} \cdot \frac{1 \text{ m}}{100 \text{ cm}} = \frac{18.6}{100} \text{ m} = 0.186 \text{ m}$$

Do **not** write a period here.

18.6 cm = 0.186 m

There are 100 cm in a meter, so 18.6 cm will be a small part of a meter. The answer makes sense.

Work Problem **3** *at the Side.* ▶

3 First write the unit fraction needed to make each conversion. Then complete the conversion.

(a) 3.67 m to cm

$\left. \begin{array}{l} \text{unit} \\ \text{fraction} \end{array} \right\} \dfrac{100 \text{ cm}}{1 \text{ m}}$

(b) 92 cm to m

$\left. \begin{array}{l} \text{unit} \\ \text{fraction} \end{array} \right\} \dfrac{\text{m}}{\text{cm}}$

(c) 432.7 cm to m

$\left. \begin{array}{l} \text{unit} \\ \text{fraction} \end{array} \right\} \underline{\hspace{2cm}}$

(d) 65 mm to cm

$\left. \begin{array}{l} \text{unit} \\ \text{fraction} \end{array} \right\} \underline{\hspace{2cm}}$

(e) 0.9 m to mm

$\left. \begin{array}{l} \text{unit} \\ \text{fraction} \end{array} \right\} \underline{\hspace{2cm}}$

(f) 2.5 cm to mm

$\left. \begin{array}{l} \text{unit} \\ \text{fraction} \end{array} \right\} \underline{\hspace{2cm}}$

ANSWERS

3. **(a)** 367 cm   **(b)** $\dfrac{1 \text{ m}}{100 \text{ cm}}$; 0.92 m

(c) $\dfrac{1 \text{ m}}{100 \text{ cm}}$; 4.327 m

(d) $\dfrac{1 \text{ cm}}{10 \text{ mm}}$; 6.5 cm

(e) $\dfrac{1000 \text{ mm}}{1 \text{ m}}$; 900 mm

(f) $\dfrac{10 \text{ mm}}{1 \text{ cm}}$; 25 mm

4 Do each multiplication or division by hand or on a calculator. Compare your answer to the one you get by moving the decimal point.

(a) $(43.5)(10) =$ _____

43.5 gives 435

(b) $43.5 \div 10 =$ _____

43.5 gives _____

(c) $(28)(100) =$ _____

28.00 gives _____

(d) $28 \div 100 =$ _____

28. gives _____

(e) $(0.7)(1000) =$ _____

0.700 gives _____

(f) $0.7 \div 1000 =$ _____

000.7 gives _____

OBJECTIVE 3 Move the decimal point to convert among units.
By now you have probably noticed that conversions among metric units are made by multiplying or dividing by 10, by 100, or by 1000. A quick way to *multiply* by 10 is to move the decimal point one place to the *right*. Move it two places to the right to multiply by 100, three places to multiply by 1000. *Dividing* is done by moving the decimal point to the *left* in the same manner.

◀ *Work Problem* **4** *at the Side.*

An alternate conversion method to unit fractions is moving the decimal point using this **metric conversion line.**

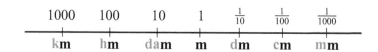

Here are the steps for using the conversion line.

Using the Metric Conversion Line

Step 1 Find the unit you are given on the metric conversion line.

Step 2 Count the number of places to get from the unit you are given to the unit you want in the answer.

Step 3 Move the decimal point the **same number of places** and in the **same direction** as you did on the conversion line.

EXAMPLE 3 Using the Metric Conversion Line

Use the metric conversion line to make the following conversions.

(a) 5.702 km to m

Find **km** on the metric conversion line. To get to **m**, you move *three places* to the *right*. So move the decimal point in 5.702 *three places* to the *right*.

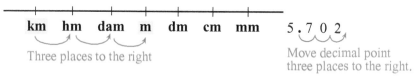

5.702 km = 5702 m

(b) 69.5 cm to m

Find **cm** on the conversion line. To get to **m**, move *two places* to the *left*.

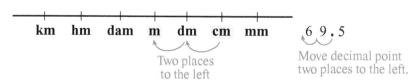

69.5 cm = 0.695 m

Continued on Next Page

(c) 8.1 cm to mm

From **cm** to **mm** is *one place* to the *right*.

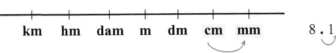

| km | hm | dam | m | dm | **cm** | **mm** |

One place to the right   Move decimal point one place to the right.

8.1 cm = 81 mm

Work Problem **5** *at the Side.* ▶

EXAMPLE 4 **Practicing Length Conversions**

Convert using the metric conversion line.

(a) 1.28 m to mm

Moving from **m** to **mm** is going *three places to the right*. In order to move the decimal point in 1.28 three places to the right, you must write a 0 as a placeholder.

1.280   Zero is written in as a placeholder.

Move decimal point three places to the right.

> The answer is a *whole number*, so you do not need to write the decimal point.

1.28 m = 1280 mm

(b) 60 cm to m

From **cm** to **m** is two places to the left. The decimal point in 60 starts at the *far right side* because 60 is a whole number. Then move it two places to the left.

60.   60.
↑
Decimal point starts here.   Move decimal point two places to the left.

60 cm = 0.60 m, and 0.60 m is equivalent to 0.6 m.

(c) 8 m to km

From **m** to **km** is three places to the left. The decimal point in 8 starts at the far right side. In order to move it three places to the left, you must write two zeros as placeholders.

━━ Two zeros are written in as placeholders.

8.   008.
↑
Decimal point starts here. Move decimal point three places to the left.

8 m = 0.008 km

Work Problem **6** *at the Side.* ▶

---

5 Convert using the metric conversion line.

(a) 12.008 km to m

(b) 561.4 m to km

(c) 20.7 cm to m

(d) 20.7 cm to mm

(e) 4.66 m to cm

(f) 85.6 mm to cm

6 Convert using the metric conversion line.

(a) 9 m to mm

(b) 3 cm to m

(c) 14.6 km to m

(d) 5 mm to cm

(e) 70 m to km

(f) 0.8 m to cm

ANSWERS

5. **(a)** 12,008 m **(b)** 0.5614 km
(c) 0.207 m **(d)** 207 mm
(e) 466 cm **(f)** 8.56 cm
6. **(a)** 9000 mm **(b)** 0.03 m
(c) 14,600 m **(d)** 0.5 cm
(e) 0.07 km **(f)** 80 cm

Math in the Media

MEASURING UP

Hair and Nail Growth

Q: How fast do hair and nails grow? Do they grow faster in the summer?

A: Fingernails grow, on average, about one-tenth of a millimeter per day, although there is considerable variation among individuals. Fingernails grow faster than toenails, and nails on the longest fingers appear to grow the fastest.

Fingernails, as well as hair and skin, grow faster in the summer, presumably under the influence of sunlight, which expands blood vessels, bringing more oxygen and nutrients to the area and allowing for faster growth.

The rate the scalp hair grows is 0.3 to 0.4 millimeter per day, or about 6 inches a year.

Source: Minneapolis Star Tribune.

1. **(a)** How much do fingernails grow in one week?

   (b) In one month?

   (c) In one year?

2. **(a)** Using metric units, how much does hair grow in one week?

   (b) In one month?

   (c) In one year?

3. When you have finished **Section 8.5,** come back to this article. Is the statement about hair growing 6 inches a year accurate? Explain your answer.

4. **(a)** According to *Guinness World Records,* the longest toenails measure 15.2 cm. How many millimeters is that length? How many meters?

   (b) The longest eyelash is listed as 5.08 cm. How long is the eyelash in millimeters? In meters?

Use your knowledge of the meaning of metric prefixes to fill in the blanks.

1. *kilo* means _____ so

1 km = _____ m

2. *deka* means _____ so

1 dam = _____ m

3. *milli* means _____ so

1 mm = _____ m

4. *deci* means _____ so

1 dm = _____ m

5. *centi* means _____ so

1 cm = _____ m

6. *hecto* means _____ so

1 hm = _____ m

Use this ruler to measure the width of your thumb and hand for Exercises 7–10.

7. The width of your hand in centimeters

8. The width of your hand in millimeters

9. The width of your thumb in millimeters

10. The width of your thumb in centimeters

Write the most reasonable metric length unit in each blank. Choose from km, m, cm, and mm.
See Example 1.

11. The child was 91 _____ tall.

12. The cardboard was 3 _____ thick.

13. Ming-Na swam in the 200 _____ backstroke race.

14. The bookcase is 75 _____ wide.

15. Adriana drove 400 _____ on her vacation.

16. The door is 2 _____ high.

17. An aspirin tablet is 10 _____ across.

18. Lamard jogs 4 _____ every morning.

19. A paper clip is about 3 _____ long.

20. My pen is 145 _____ long.

21. Dave's truck is 5 _____ long.

22. Wheelchairs need doorways that are at least 80 _____ wide.

23. Describe at least three examples of metric length units that you have come across in your daily life.

24. Explain one reason the metric system would be easier for a child to learn than the U.S. customary system.

Convert each measurement. Use unit fractions or the metric conversion line. See Examples 2–4.

25. 7 m to cm

26. 18 m to cm

27. 40 mm to m

28. 6 mm to m

29. 9.4 km to m

30. 0.7 km to m

31. 509 cm to m

32. 30 cm to m

33. 400 mm to cm

34. 25 mm to cm

35. 0.91 m to mm

36. 4 m to mm

37. Is 82 cm greater than or less than 1 m? What is the difference in the lengths?

38. Is 1022 m greater than or less than 1 km? What is the difference in the lengths?

39. On the first page of this chapter, we said that computer microchips may be only 5 mm long and 1 mm wide. Using the ruler on the previous page, draw a rectangle that measures 5 mm by 1 mm. Then convert each measurement to centimeters.

A greatly enlarged photo of a computer microchip.

40. The world's smallest butterfly has a wingspan of 15 mm. The smallest mouse is 50 mm long. Using the ruler on the previous page, draw a line that is 15 mm long and a line 50 mm long. Then convert each measurement to centimeters. (*Source: Top 10 of Everything.*)

41. The Roe River near Great Falls, Montana, is the shortest river in the world, with a north fork that is just under 18 m long. How many kilometers long is the north fork of the river? (*Source: Guinness Book of Amazing Nature.*)

42. There are 60,000 km of blood vessels in the human body. How many meters of blood vessels are in the body? (*Source: Big Book of Knowledge.*)

43. The median height for U.S. females who are 20 to 29 years old is about 1.64 m. Convert this height to centimeters and to millimeters. (*Source: U.S. National Center for Health Statistics.*)

44. The median height for 20- to 29-year-old males in the United States is about 177 cm. Convert this height to meters and to millimeters. (*Source: U.S. National Center for Health Statistics.*)

45. Use two unit fractions to convert 5.6 mm to km.

46. Use two unit fractions to convert 16.5 km to mm.

8.3 ▷▷▷ The Metric System—Capacity and Weight (Mass)

We use capacity units to measure liquids, such as the amount of milk in a recipe, the gasoline in our car tank, and the water in an aquarium. (The capacity units in the U.S. customary system are cups, pints, quarts, and gallons.) The basic metric unit for capacity is the **liter** (also spelled *litre*). The capital letter L is the symbol for liter, to avoid confusion with the numeral 1.

OBJECTIVE 1 **Learn the basic metric units of capacity.** The liter is related to metric length in this way: a box that measures 10 cm on every side holds exactly one liter. (The volume of the box is 10 cm • 10 cm • 10 cm = 1000 cubic centimeters. Volume was discussed in **Section 5.8.**) A liter is just a little more than 1 quart.

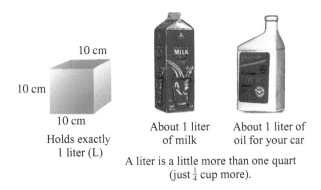

10 cm
10 cm
10 cm
Holds exactly
1 liter (L)

About 1 liter
of milk

About 1 liter of
oil for your car

A liter is a little more than one quart
(just ¼ cup more).

In the metric system you use liters for things like buying shampoo and soda at the store, filling a pail with water, and describing the size of your home aquarium.

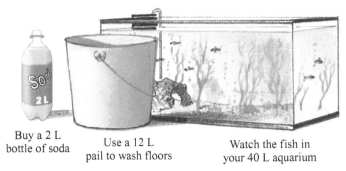

Buy a 2 L
bottle of soda

Use a 12 L
pail to wash floors

Watch the fish in
your 40 L aquarium

Work Problem 1 *at the Side.* ▶

To make larger or smaller capacity units, we use the same **prefixes** as we did with length units. For example, *kilo* means 1000 so a *kilo*meter is 1000 meters. In the same way, a *kilo*liter is 1000 liters.

Prefix	kilo-liter	hecto-liter	deka-liter	liter	deci-liter	centi-liter	milli-liter
Meaning	1000 liters	100 liters	10 liters	1 liter	$\frac{1}{10}$ of a liter	$\frac{1}{100}$ of a liter	$\frac{1}{1000}$ of a liter
Symbol	kL	hL	daL	L	dL	cL	mL

↑   ↑
Capacity units used most often

1 Which things can be measured in liters?

Amount of water in the bathtub

Length of the bathtub

Width of your car

Amount of gasoline you buy for your car

Weight of your car

Height of a pail

Amount of water in a pail

ANSWER

1. water in bathtub, gasoline, water in a pail

2 Write the most reasonable metric unit in each blank. Choose from L and mL.

(a) I bought 8 _____ of soda at the store.

(b) The nurse gave me 10 _____ of cough syrup.

(c) This is a 100 _____ garbage can.

(d) It took 10 _____ of paint to cover the bedroom walls.

(e) My car's gas tank holds 50 _____.

(f) I added 15 _____ of oil to the pancake mix.

(g) The can of orange soda holds 350 _____.

(h) My friend gave me a 30 _____ bottle of expensive perfume.

The capacity units you will use most often in daily life are liters (L) and *milli*liters (mL). A tiny box that measures 1 cm on every side holds exactly one milliliter. (In medicine, this small amount is also called 1 cubic centimeter, or 1 cc for short.) It takes 1000 mL to make 1 L. Here are some useful comparisons.

| Holds exactly 1 milliliter (mL) | Teaspoon holds 5 mL | One cup holds about 250 mL |

EXAMPLE 1 **Using Metric Capacity Units**

Write the most reasonable metric unit in each blank. Choose from L and mL.

(a) The bottle of shampoo held 500 _____.
500 **mL** because 500 L would be about 500 quarts, which is too much.

(b) I bought a 2 _____ carton of orange juice.
2 **L** because 2 mL would be less than a teaspoon.

◀ *Work Problem* **2** *at the Side.*

OBJECTIVE **2** **Convert among metric capacity units.** Just as with length units, you can convert between milliliters and liters using unit fractions.

Metric Capacity Relationships

1 L = 1000 mL, so the unit fractions are:

$$\frac{1 \text{ L}}{1000 \text{ mL}} \quad \text{or} \quad \frac{1000 \text{ mL}}{1 \text{ L}}$$

Or you can use a metric conversion line to decide how to move the decimal point.

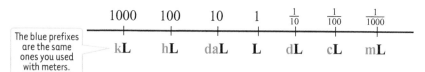

The blue prefixes are the same ones you used with meters.

EXAMPLE 2 **Converting among Metric Capacity Units**

Convert using the metric conversion line or unit fractions.

(a) 2.5 L to mL

Using the metric conversion line:
From **L** to **mL** is *three places* to the *right*.

2.5 0 0   Write two zeros as placeholders.

2.5 L = 2500 mL

Using unit fractions:

Multiply by a unit fraction that allows you to divide out liters.

$$\frac{2.5 \text{ L}}{1} \cdot \frac{1000 \text{ mL}}{1 \text{ L}} = 2500 \text{ mL}$$

L divides out, leaving mL for your answer.

Continued on Next Page

(b) 80 mL to L

Using the metric conversion line:

From **mL** to **L** is *three places* to the *left*.

80.

Decimal point starts here.

080.

Move decimal point three places to the left.

80 mL = 0.080 L or 0.08 L

Using unit fractions:

Multiply by a unit fraction that allows you to divide out mL.

$$\frac{80 \text{ mL}}{1} \cdot \frac{1 \text{ L}}{1000 \text{ mL}}$$

$$= \frac{80}{1000} \text{ L} = 0.08 \text{ L}$$

Do **not** write a period here.

Work Problem **3** *at the Side.* ▶

OBJECTIVE **3** **Learn the basic metric units of weight (mass).**
The **gram** is the basic metric unit for *mass*. Although we often call it "weight," there is a difference. Weight is a measure of the pull of gravity; the farther you are from the center of Earth, the less you weigh. In outer space you become weightless, but your mass, the amount of matter in your body, stays the same regardless of where you are. In science courses, it will be important to distinguish between the weight of an object and its mass. But for everyday purposes, we will use the word *weight*.

The gram is related to metric length in this way: The weight of the water in a box measuring 1 cm on every side is 1 gram. This is a very tiny amount of water (1 mL) and a very small weight. One gram is also the weight of a dollar bill or a single raisin. A nickel weighs 5 grams. A plain, regular-sized hamburger and bun weighs from 175 to 200 grams.

The 1 mL of water
in this tiny box weighs
1 gram.

A nickel weighs
5 grams.

A dollar bill weighs
1 gram.

A plain hamburger weighs
175 to 200 grams.

Work Problem **4** *at the Side.* ▶

---

3 Convert.

(a) 9 L to mL

(b) 0.75 L to mL

(c) 500 mL to L

(d) 5 mL to L

(e) 2.07 L to mL

(f) 3275 mL to L

4 Which things would weigh about 1 gram?

A small paper clip

A pair of scissors

One playing card from a deck of cards

A calculator

An average-sized apple

The check you wrote to the cable company

ANSWERS

3. (a) 9000 mL **(b)** 750 mL **(c)** 0.5 L
    (d) 0.005 L **(e)** 2070 mL **(f)** 3.275 L
4. paper clip, playing card, check

5 Write the most reasonable metric unit in each blank. Choose from kg, g, and mg.

(a) A thumbtack weighs

800 _____ .

(b) A teenager weighs

50 _____ .

(c) This large cast-iron frying pan weighs

1 _____ .

(d) Jerry's basketball weighed 600 _____ .

(e) Tamlyn takes a

500 _____ calcium tablet every morning.

(f) On his diet, Greg can eat

90 _____ of meat for lunch.

(g) One strand of hair weighs

2 _____ .

(h) One banana might weigh

150 _____ .

To make larger or smaller weight units, we use the same **prefixes** as we did with length and capacity units. For example, *kilo* means 1000 so a *kilo*meter is 1000 meters, a *kilo*liter is 1000 liters, and a *kilo*gram is 1000 grams.

Prefix	kilo-gram	hecto-gram	deka-gram	gram	deci-gram	centi-gram	milli-gram
Meaning	1000 grams	100 grams	10 grams	1 gram	$\frac{1}{10}$ of a gram	$\frac{1}{100}$ of a gram	$\frac{1}{1000}$ of a gram
Symbol	kg	hg	dag	g	dg	cg	mg

Weight (mass) units that are used most often

The units you will use most often in daily life are kilograms (kg), grams (g), and milligrams (mg). *Kilo*grams are used instead of pounds. A kilogram is 1000 grams. It is about 2.2 pounds. Two packages of butter plus one stick of butter weigh about 1 kg. An average newborn baby weighs 3 to 4 kg; a college football player might weigh 100 to 130 kg.

1 kilogram is about 2.2 pounds   100 to 130 kg   3 to 4 kg

Extremely small weights are measured in *milli*grams. It takes 1000 mg to make 1 g. Recall that a dollar bill weighs about 1 g. Imagine cutting it into 1000 pieces; the weight of one tiny piece would be 1 mg. Dosages of medicine and vitamins are given in milligrams. You will also use milligrams in science classes.

Cut a dollar bill into 1000 pieces. One tiny piece weighs 1 milligram.

EXAMPLE 3   Using Metric Weight Units

Write the most reasonable metric unit in each blank. Choose from kg, g, and mg.

(a) Ramon's suitcase weighed 20 _____ .
20 **kg** because kilograms are used instead of pounds. 20 kg is about 44 pounds.

(b) LeTia took a 350 _____ aspirin tablet.
350 **mg** because 350 g would be more than the weight of a hamburger, which is too much.

(c) Jenny mailed a letter that weighed 30 _____ .
30 **g** because 30 kg would be much too heavy and 30 mg is less than the weight of a dollar bill.

◀ *Work Problem* **5** *at the Side.*

OBJECTIVE **4** **Convert among metric weight (mass) units.** As with length and capacity, you can convert among metric weight units by using unit fractions. The unit fractions you need are shown here.

Metric Weight (Mass) Relationships

$1\ kg = 1000\ g$ so the unit fractions are:	$1\ g = 1000\ mg$ so the unit fractions are:
$\dfrac{1\ kg}{1000\ g}$ or $\dfrac{1000\ g}{1\ kg}$	$\dfrac{1\ g}{1000\ mg}$ or $\dfrac{1000\ mg}{1\ g}$

Or you can use a metric conversion line to decide how to move the decimal point.

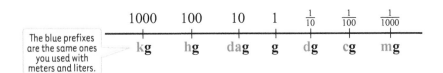

The blue prefixes are the same ones you used with meters and liters.

$$
\begin{array}{ccccccc}
1000 & 100 & 10 & 1 & \frac{1}{10} & \frac{1}{100} & \frac{1}{1000} \\
\text{kg} & \text{hg} & \text{dag} & \text{g} & \text{dg} & \text{cg} & \text{mg}
\end{array}
$$

EXAMPLE 4   **Converting among Metric Weight Units**

Convert using the metric conversion line or unit fractions.

(a) 7 mg to g

Using the metric conversion line:

From **mg** to **g** is *three places* to the *left*.

7.   007.
↑   ⌣⌣⌣
Decimal point   Move decimal
starts here.   point three places
                 to the left.

7 mg = 0.007 g

Using unit fractions:

Multiply by a unit fraction that allows you to divide out mg.

$$\frac{7\ \cancel{mg}}{1} \cdot \frac{1\ g}{1000\ \cancel{mg}} = \frac{7}{1000}\ g$$

$$= 0.007\ g$$

Three decimal places for thousandths.

(b) 13.72 kg to g

Using the metric conversion line:

From **kg** to **g** is *three places* to the *right*.

13.720   Decimal point moves
  ⌣⌣⌣   three places to
               the right.

13.72 kg = 13,720 g
                ↑
           A comma
      (not a decimal point)

Using unit fractions:

Multiply by a unit fraction that allows you to divide out kg.

$$\frac{13.72\ \cancel{kg}}{1} \cdot \frac{1000\ g}{1\ \cancel{kg}} = 13,720\ g$$
                                                        ↑
                                              A comma
                                        (not a decimal point)

6 Convert.

(a) 10 kg to g

(b) 45 mg to g

(c) 6.3 kg to g

(d) 0.077 g to mg

(e) 5630 g to kg

(f) 90 g to kg

Work Problem **6** *at the Side.* ▶

7 First decide which type of units are needed: length, capacity, or weight. Then write the most appropriate unit in the blank. Choose from km, m, cm, mm, L, mL, kg, g, and mg.

(a) Gail bought a 4 _____ can of paint.

Use _____ units.

(b) The bag of chips weighed 450 _____.

Use _____ units.

(c) Give the child 5 _____ of cough syrup.

Use _____ units.

(d) The width of the window is 55 _____.

Use _____ units.

(e) Akbar drives 18 _____ to work.

Use _____ units.

(f) The laptop computer weighs 2 _____.

Use _____ units.

(g) A credit card is 55 _____ wide.

Use _____ units.

OBJECTIVE 5 Distinguish among basic metric units of length, capacity, and weight (mass). As you encounter things to be measured at home, on the job, or in your classes at school, be careful to use the correct type of measurement unit.

Use *length units* (kilometers, meters, centimeters, millimeters) to measure:

how long	how high	how far away
how wide	how tall	how far around (perimeter)
how deep	distance	

Use *capacity units* (liters, milliliters) to measure liquids (things that can be poured) such as:

water	shampoo	gasoline
milk	perfume	oil
soft drinks	cough syrup	paint

Also use liters and milliliters to describe how much liquid something can hold, such as an eyedropper, measuring cup, pail, or bathtub.

Use *weight units* (kilograms, grams, milligrams) to measure:

the weight of something   how heavy something is

In **Chapters 4–6** you used square units (such as cm^2 and m^2) to measure area, and cubic units (such as cm^3 and m^3) to measure volume.

EXAMPLE 5 **Using a Variety of Metric Units**

First decide which type of units are needed: length, capacity, or weight. Then write the most appropriate metric unit in the blank. Choose from km, m, cm, mm, L, mL, kg, g, and mg.

(a) The letter needs another stamp because it weighs 40 _____.

Use _____ units.

The letter weighs 40 **g** because 40 mg is less than the weight of a dollar bill and 40 kg would be about 88 pounds.

Use **weight** units because of the word "weighs."

(b) The swimming pool is 3 _____ deep at the deep end.

Use _____ units.

The pool is 3 **m** deep because 3 cm is only about an inch and 3 km is more than a mile.

Use **length** units because of the word "deep."

(c) This is a 340 _____ can of juice.

Use _____ units.

It is a 340 **mL** can because 340 liters would be more than 340 quarts.

Use **capacity** units because juice is a liquid.

◄ *Work Problem* **7** *at the Side.*

FOR EXTRA HELP   **MyMathLab**    Math XL PRACTICE   WATCH   DOWNLOAD   READ   REVIEW

Write the most reasonable metric unit in each blank. Choose from L, mL, kg, g, and mg.
See Examples 1 and 3.

1. The glass held

250 _____ of water.

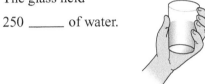

2. Hiromi used 12 _____ of water to wash the kitchen floor.

3. Dolores can make 10 _____ of soup in that pot.

4. Jay gave 2 _____ of vitamin drops to the baby.

5. Our yellow Labrador dog grew up to weigh 40 _____.

6. A small safety pin weighs 750 _____.

7. Lori caught a small sunfish weighing 150 _____.

8. One dime weighs 2 _____.

9. Andre donated 500 _____ of blood today.

10. Barbara bought the 2 _____ bottle of cola.

11. The patient received a 250 _____ tablet of medication each hour.

12. The 8 people on the elevator weighed a total of 500 _____.

13. The gas can for the lawn mower holds 4 _____.

14. Kevin poured 10 _____ of vanilla into the mixing bowl.

15. Pam's backpack weighs 5 _____ when it is full of books.

16. One grain of salt weighs 2 _____.

Today, medical measurements are usually given in the metric system. Since we convert among metric units of measure by moving the decimal point, it is possible that mistakes can be made. Examine the following dosages and indicate whether they are reasonable or unreasonable. If a dose is unreasonable, indicate whether it is too much or too little.

17. Drink 4.1 L of Kaopectate after each meal.

18. Drop 1 mL of solution into the eye twice a day.

19. Soak your feet in 5 kg of Epsom salts per liter of water.

20. Inject 0.5 L of insulin each morning.

21. Take 15 mL of cough syrup every four hours.

22. Take 200 mg of vitamin C each day.

23. Take 350 mg of aspirin three times a day.

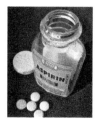

24. Buy a tube of ointment weighing 0.002 g.

25. Describe at least two examples of metric capacity units and two examples of metric weight units that you have come across in your daily life.

26. Explain in your own words how the meter, liter, and gram are related.

27. Describe how you decide which unit fraction to use when converting 6.5 kg to grams.

28. Write an explanation of each step you would use to convert 20 mg to grams using the metric conversion line.

Convert each measurement. Use unit fractions or the metric conversion line. See Examples 2 and 4.

29. 15 L to mL

30. 6 L to mL

31. 3000 mL to L

32. 18,000 mL to L

33. 925 mL to L

34. 200 mL to L

35. 8 mL to L

36. 25 mL to L

37. 4.15 L to mL

38. 11.7 L to mL

39. 8000 g to kg

40. 25,000 g to kg

41. 5.2 kg to g

42. 12.42 kg to g

43. 0.85 g to mg

44. 0.2 g to mg

45. 30,000 mg to g

46. 7500 mg to g

47. 598 mg to g

48. 900 mg to g

49. 60 mL to L

50. 6.007 kg to g

51. 3 g to kg

52. 12 mg to g

53. 0.99 L to mL

54. 13,700 mL to L

Write the most appropriate metric unit in each blank. Choose from km, m, cm, mm, L, mL, kg, g, and mg. See Example 5.

55. The masking tape is 19 _____ wide.

56. The roll has 55 _____ of tape on it.

🌐 **57.** Buy a 60 _____ jar of acrylic paint for art class.

58. One onion weighs 200 _____.

59. My waist measurement is 65 _____.

60. Add 2 _____ of windshield washer fluid to your car.

🌐 **61.** A single postage stamp weighs 90 _____.

62. The hallway is 10 _____ long.

Solve each application problem. Show your work. (Source for Exercises 63–68: Top 10 of Everything.)

63. Human skin has about 3 million sweat glands, which release an average of 300 mL of sweat per day. How many liters of sweat are released each day?

64. In hot climates, the sweat glands in a person's skin may release up to 3.5 L of sweat in one day. How many milliliters is that?

65. The average weight of a human brain is 1.34 kg. How many grams is that?

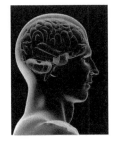

66. A healthy human heart pumps about 70 mL of blood per beat. How many liters of blood does it pump per beat?

67. On average, we breathe in and out roughly 900 mL of air every 10 seconds. How many liters of air is that?

68. In the Victorian era, people believed that heavier brains meant greater intelligence. They were impressed that Otto von Bismarck's brain weighed 1907 g, which is how many kilograms?

69. A small adult cat weighs from 3000 g to 4000 g. How many kilograms is that? (*Source:* Lyndale Animal Hospital.)

70. If the letter you are mailing weighs 29 g, you must put additional postage on it. How many kilograms does the letter weigh? (*Source:* U.S. Postal Service.)

71. Is 1005 mg greater than or less than 1 g? What is the difference in the weights?

72. Is 990 mL greater than or less than 1 L? What is the difference in the amounts?

73. One nickel weighs 5 g. How many nickels are in 1 kg of nickels?

74. The ratio of the total length of all the fish to the amount of water in an aquarium can be 3 cm of fish for every 4 L of water. What is the total length of all fish you can put in a 40 L aquarium? (*Source:* Tropical Aquarium Fish.)

Relating Concepts (Exercises 75–78) For Individual or Group Work

*Recall that the prefix **kilo** means 1000, so a **kilo**meter is 1000 meters. You'll learn about other prefixes for numbers greater than 1000 as you **work Exercises 75–78 in order.***

75. (a) The prefix *mega* means one million. Use the symbol M (capitalized) for *mega*. So a megameter (Mm) is how many meters?

1 Mm = _____ m

(b) Figure out a unit fraction that you can use to convert megameters to meters. Then use it to convert 3.5 Mm to meters.

76. (a) The prefix *giga* means one billion. Use the symbol G (capitalized) for *giga*. So a gigameter (Gm) is how many meters?

1 Gm = _____ m

(b) Figure out a unit fraction you can use to convert meters to gigameters. Then use it to convert 2500 m to gigameters.

77. (a) The prefix *tera* means one trillion. Use the symbol T (capitalized) for *tera*. So a *tera*meter (Tm) is how many meters?

1 Tm = _____ m.

(b) Think carefully before you fill in the blanks:

1 Tm = _____ Gm

1 Tm = _____ Mm

78. A computer's memory is measured in *bytes*. A byte can represent a single letter, a digit, or a punctuation mark. The memory for a desktop computer may be measured in megabytes (abbreviated MB) or gigabytes (abbreviated GB). Using the meanings of *mega* and *giga*, it would seem that

1 MB = _____ bytes and

1 GB = _____ bytes.

However, because computers use a base 2 or binary system, 1 MB is actually 2^{20} and 1 GB is 2^{30}. Use your calculator to find the actual values.

2^{20} = _____ 2^{30} = _____

Summary Exercises on U.S. Customary and Metric Units

The most commonly used U.S. customary and metric system units are listed in mixed-up order.
Write each unit in the correct box in the table below. Within each box, write the units in order from smallest to largest.

pound	yard	liter	kilogram	ton	gallon	pint
millimeter	gram	quart	meter	inch	cup	centimeter
milliliter	mile	foot	milligram	kilometer	ounce	fluid ounce

1. U.S. Customary Units			2. Metric System Units		
Length	Weight	Capacity	Length	Weight	Capacity

Fill in the blanks with the measurement relationships that you memorized.

3. (a) 1 _____ = 12 in.

    (b) 3 ft = 1 _____

    (c) 1 mi = _____ ft

4. (a) 60 sec = 1 _____

    (b) 1 hr = _____ min

    (c) _____ hr = 1 day

5. (a) 1 cup = _____ fl oz

    (b) 4 qt = 1 _____

    (c) _____ pt = 1 qt

6. (a) 16 oz = 1 _____

    (b) _____ lb = 1 ton

    (c) 1 lb = _____ oz

Write the most reasonable metric unit in each blank. Choose from km, m, cm, mm, L, mL, kg, g, and mg.

7. My water bottle holds 450 _____ .

8. Michael won the 200 _____ race today.

9. The child weighed 23 _____ .

10. Jifar took a 375 _____ aspirin tablet.

11. The red pen is 14 _____ long.

12. A quarter is about 25 _____ across.

13. Merlene made 12 _____ of fruit punch for her daughter's birthday party.

14. This cereal has 4 _____ of protein in each serving.

Convert each measurement using unit fractions or the metric conversion line. Show your work.

15. 45 cm to meters

16. $\frac{3}{4}$ min to seconds

17. 0.6 L to milliliters

18. 8 g to milligrams

19. 300 mm to centimeters

20. 45 in. to feet

21. 50 mL to liters

22. 18 qt to gallons

23. 7.28 kg to grams

24. $2\frac{1}{4}$ lb to ounces

25. 9 g to kilograms

26. 5 yd to inches

Solve Exercises 27–30 using the data in the table at the right on some of the world's tallest people.
(Source: Top 10 of Everything.)

27. What is the height of the tallest person in centimeters? In millimeters?

28. Find the 4th tallest person's height in meters and in kilometers.

Robert Wadlow was 2.72 m tall.

WORLD'S TALLEST PEOPLE

Rank	Name/Dates/Country	Height
1st	Robert Wadlow (1918–1940) USA	2.72 m
2nd	John Rogan (1868–1905) USA	268 cm
4th	John Carroll (1932–1969) USA	264 cm
7th	Edouard Beaupré (1881–1904) Canada	2.5 m
10th	Jeng Jinlian (1964–1982) China	248 cm

29. How much taller is the tallest person than the second tallest, in meters? Convert this difference to centimeters and millimeters.

30. What is the difference in height between the 7th tallest and 4th tallest people, in centimeters? Convert the height difference to meters and millimeters.

Solve each application problem. Show your work.

31. Vernice bought a 12 oz bag of chips for $3.49 today. What was the price per pound to the nearest cent?

32. In 2006, Miami, Florida, received about 64 in. of rain. In 2005, about 59 in. of rain fell. How many feet of rain did Miami get in all during the two years, to the nearest tenth?

8.4 ▶▶▶ Problem Solving with Metric Measurement

OBJECTIVE 1 Solve application problems involving metric measurements. One advantage of the metric system is the ease of comparing measurements in application situations. Just be sure that you are comparing similar units: mg to mg, km to km, and so on.

We will use the same problem-solving steps that you used for U.S. customary measurement applications in **Section 8.1.**

EXAMPLE 1 Solving a Metric Application

Cheddar cheese is on sale at $8.99 per kilogram. Jake bought 350 g of the cheese. How much did he pay, to the nearest cent?

Step 1 **Read** the problem. The problem asks for the cost of 350 g of cheese.

Step 2 **Work out a plan.** The price is $8.99 per *kilogram,* but the amount Jake bought is given in *grams.* Convert grams to kilograms (the unit in the price). Then multiply the weight by the cost per kilogram.

Step 3 **Estimate** a reasonable answer. Round the cost of 1 kg from $8.99 to $9. There are 1000 g in a kilogram, so 350 g is about $\frac{1}{3}$ of a kilogram. Jake is buying about $\frac{1}{3}$ of a kilogram, so $\frac{1}{3}$ of $9 = $3 as our estimate.

Step 4 **Solve** the problem. Use a unit fraction to convert 350 g to kilograms.

g divides out, leaving **kg** for your answer.

$$\frac{350\text{ g}}{1}\cdot\frac{1\text{ kg}}{1000\text{ g}}=\frac{350}{1000}\text{ kg}=0.35\text{ kg}$$

Now multiply 0.35 kg times the cost per kilogram.

$$\frac{\$8.99}{1\text{ kg}}\cdot\frac{0.35\text{ kg}}{1}=\$3.1465\approx\$3.15\ \text{(rounded)}$$

Nearest cent is the nearest hundredth.

Step 5 **State the answer.** Jake paid $3.15, rounded to the nearest cent.

Step 6 **Check** your work. The exact answer of $3.15 is close to our estimate of $3.

Work Problem **1** *at the Side.* ▶

1 Solve this problem using the six problem-solving steps.

Satin ribbon is on sale at $0.89 per meter. How much will 75 cm cost, to the nearest cent?

EXAMPLE 2 Solving a Metric Application

Olivia has 2.6 m of lace. How many centimeters of lace can she use to trim each of six hair ornaments? Round to the nearest tenth of a centimeter.

Step 1 **Read** the problem. The problem asks for the number of centimeters of lace for each of six hair ornaments.

Step 2 **Work out a plan.** The given amount of lace is in *meters,* but the answer must be in *centimeters.* Convert meters to centimeters, then divide by 6 (the number of hair ornaments).

Continued on Next Page

ANSWER

1. $0.67 (rounded)

2 Lucinda's doctor wants her to take 1.2 g of medication each day in three equal doses. How many milligrams should be in each dose? Use the six problem-solving steps.

Step 3 **Estimate** a reasonable answer. To estimate, round 2.6 m of lace to 3 m. Then, 3 m = 300 cm, and 300 cm ÷ 6 = 50 cm as our estimate.

Step 4 **Solve** the problem. On the metric conversion line, moving from **m** to **cm** is two places to the right, so move the decimal point in 2.6 m two places to the right. Then divide by 6.

$$2.60\,\text{m} = 260\text{ cm} \qquad \frac{260\text{ cm}}{6\text{ ornaments}} \approx 43.3\text{ cm per ornament}$$

Step 5 **State the answer.** Olivia can use about 43.3 cm of lace on each ornament.

Step 6 **Check** your work. The exact answer of 43.3 cm is close to our estimate of 50 cm.

◀ *Work Problem* **2** *at the Side.*

> **Note**
>
> In Example 1 we used a unit fraction to convert the measurement, and in Example 2 we moved the decimal point. Use whichever method you prefer. Also, there is more than one way to solve an application problem. Another way to solve Example 2 is to divide 2.6 m by 6 to get 0.4333 m of lace for each ornament. Then convert 0.4333 m to 43.3 cm (rounded to the nearest tenth).

3 Andrea has two pieces of fabric. One measures 2 m 35 cm and the other measures 1 m 85 cm. How many meters of fabric does she have in all? Use the six problem-solving steps.

EXAMPLE 3 **Solving a Metric Application**

Rubin measured a board and found that the length was 3 m plus an additional 5 cm. He cut off a piece measuring 1 m 40 cm for a shelf. Find the length in meters of the remaining piece of board.

Step 1 **Read** the problem. Part of a board is cut off. The problem asks what length of board, in meters, is left over. It may help to make a drawing of the board and label the lengths given in the problem.

Step 2 **Work out a plan.** The lengths involve two units, m and cm. Rewrite both lengths in meters (the unit called for in the answer), and then subtract.

Step 3 **Estimate** a reasonable answer. To estimate, 3 m 5 cm can be rounded to 3 m, because 5 cm is less than half of a meter (less than 50 cm). Round 1 m 40 cm down to 1 m. Then, 3 m − 1 m = 2 m as our estimate.

Step 4 **Solve** the problem. Rewrite the lengths in meters. Then subtract.

3 m ⟶	3.00 m		1 m ⟶	1.0 m
plus 5 cm ⟶	+ 0.05 m	40.	plus 40 cm ⟶	+ 0.4 m
05.	3.05 m			1.4 m

Subtract to find leftover length.

$$\begin{array}{r} 3.05\text{ m} \leftarrow \text{Board} \\ -\ 1.40\text{ m} \leftarrow \text{Shelf} \\ \hline 1.65\text{ m} \leftarrow \text{Leftover piece} \end{array}$$

Step 5 **State the answer.** The length of the remaining piece is 1.65 m.

Step 6 **Check** your work. The exact answer of 1.65 m is close to our estimate of 2 m.

◀ *Work Problem* **3** *at the Side.*

ANSWERS

2. 400 mg per dose
3. 4.2 m

8.4 ▶▶▶ **Exercises**

FOR EXTRA HELP *MyMathLab* Math XL PRACTICE WATCH DOWNLOAD READ REVIEW

Solve each application problem. Show your work. Round money answers to the nearest cent. See Examples 1–3.

1. Bulk rice at the food co-op is on special at $0.98 per kilogram. Pam scooped some rice into a bag and put it on the scale. How much will she pay for 850 g of rice?

2. Lanh is buying a piece of plastic tubing measuring 315 cm for the science lab. The price is $4.75 per meter. How much will Lanh pay?

3. A miniature Yorkshire terrier, one of the smallest dogs, may weigh only 500 g. But a St. Bernard, the heaviest dog, could easily weigh 90 kg. What is the difference in the weights of the two dogs, in kilograms? (*Source: Big Book of Knowledge.*)

4. The world's longest insect is the giant stick insect of Indonesia, measuring 33 cm. The fairy fly, the smallest insect, is just 0.2 mm long. How much longer is the giant stick insect, in millimeters? (*Source: Big Book of Knowledge.*)

5. An adult human body contains about 5 L of blood. If each beat of the heart pumps 70 mL of blood, how many times must the heart beat to pass all the blood through the heart? Round to the nearest whole number of beats. (*Source: Harper's Index.*)

6. A floor tile measures 30 cm by 30 cm and weighs 185 g. How many kilograms would a stack of 24 tiles weigh? How much would five stacks of tiles weigh? (*Source:* The Tile Shop.)

7. Each piece of lead for a mechanical pencil has a thickness of 0.5 mm and is 60 mm long. Find the total length in centimeters of the lead in a package with 30 pieces. If the price of the package is $3.29, find the cost per centimeter for the lead. (*Source:* Pentel.)

8. The apartment building caretaker puts 750 mL of chlorine into the swimming pool every day. How many liters should he order to have a one-month (30-day) supply on hand? If chlorine is sold in containers that hold 4 L, how many containers should be ordered for one month? How much chlorine will be left over at the end of the month?

9. Rosa is building a bookcase. She has one board that is 2 m 8 cm long and another that is 2 m 95 cm long. What is the total length of the two boards in meters?

10. Janet has a piece of fabric that is 10 m 30 cm in length. She wants to make curtains for three windows that are all the same size. What length of fabric is available for each window, to the nearest tenth of a meter?

11. In a chemistry lab, each of the 45 students needs 85 mL of acid. How many 1 L bottles of acid need to be ordered? How much acid will be left over?

12. James needs two 1.3 m pieces and two 85 cm pieces of wood molding to frame a picture. The price is $5.89 per meter plus 7% sales tax. How much will James pay?

Use the bar graph below to answer Exercises 13 and 14.

Caffeine Meter
Average milligrams of caffeine
per 8 oz cup or equivalent

Double espresso 160 mg

Drip coffee 90 mg

Cola 45 mg

25 mg Chocolate bar

5 mg Decaffeinated coffee

Source: Celestial Seasonings.

13. If Agnete usually drinks three 8 oz cups of drip coffee each day, how many grams of caffeine will she consume in one week?

14. Lorenzo's doctor has suggested that he cut down on caffeine. So Lorenzo switched from drinking four 8 oz cups of cola every day to drinking two 8 oz cups of decaffeinated coffee. How many fewer grams of caffeine is he consuming each week?

15. During August 2003, Mars moved closer to Earth at a rate of about 10,000 meters per second. How much closer, in kilometers, did Mars get to Earth:

(a) in one second,

(b) in one minute,

(c) in one hour?

(*Source:* NASA.)

16. Some of the newest football stadiums have Field Turf instead of grass. Use the drawing below to find the total thickness in centimeters of the top two layers of Field Turf.

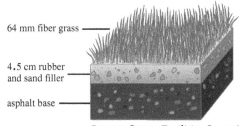

64 mm fiber grass

4.5 cm rubber and sand filler

asphalt base

Source: Sports Facilities Commission.

Relating Concepts (Exercises 17–20) For Individual or Group Work

It is difficult to weigh very light objects, such as a single sheet of paper or a single staple (unless you have an expensive scientific scale). But you can weigh a large number of the items and then divide to find the weight of one item. Before dividing, subtract the weight of the box or wrapper that the items are packaged in to find the net weight. **Work Exercises 17–20 in order** *and complete the table.*

	Item	Total Weight in Grams	Weight of Packaging	Net Weight	Weight of One Item in Grams	Weight of One Item in Milligrams
17.	Box of 50 envelopes	255 g	40 g	_____	_____	_____
18.	Box of 1000 staples	350 g	20 g	_____	_____	_____
19.	Ream of paper (500 sheets)	_____	50 g	_____	_____	3000 mg
20.	Box of 100 small paper clips	_____	5 g	_____	_____	500 mg

8.5 ▶▶▶ Metric–U.S. Customary Conversions and Temperature

OBJECTIVE **1** **Use unit fractions to convert between metric and U.S. customary units.** Until the United States has switched completely from customary units to the metric system, it will be necessary to make conversions from one system to the other. *Approximate* conversions can be made with the help of the table below, in which the values have been rounded to the nearest hundredth or thousandth. (The only value that is exact, not rounded, is 1 inch = 2.54 cm.)

Metric to U.S. Customary	U.S. Customary to Metric
1 kilometer $\approx$ 0.62 mile	1 mile $\approx$ 1.61 kilometers
1 meter $\approx$ 1.09 yards	1 yard $\approx$ 0.91 meter
1 meter $\approx$ 3.28 feet	1 foot $\approx$ 0.30 meter
1 centimeter $\approx$ 0.39 inch	1 inch = 2.54 centimeters
1 liter $\approx$ 0.26 gallon	1 gallon $\approx$ 3.79 liters
1 liter $\approx$ 1.06 quarts	1 quart $\approx$ 0.95 liter
1 kilogram $\approx$ 2.20 pounds	1 pound $\approx$ 0.45 kilogram
1 gram $\approx$ 0.035 ounce	1 ounce $\approx$ 28.35 grams

OBJECTIVES

1 Use unit fractions to convert between metric and U.S. customary units.

2 Learn common temperatures on the Celsius scale.

3 Use formulas to convert between Celsius and Fahrenheit temperatures.

EXAMPLE 1 **Converting between Metric and U.S. Customary Length Units**

Convert 10 m to yards using unit fractions. Round your answer to the nearest tenth if necessary.

We're changing from a *metric* unit to a *U.S. customary* unit. In the "Metric to U.S. Customary" side of the table above, you see that 1 meter $\approx$ 1.09 yards. Two unit fractions can be written using that information.

$$\frac{1 \text{ m}}{1.09 \text{ yd}} \quad \text{or} \quad \frac{1.09 \text{ yd}}{1 \text{ m}}$$

Multiply by the unit fraction that allows you to divide out meters (that is, meters is in the denominator).

$$10 \text{ m} \cdot \frac{1.09 \text{ yd}}{1 \text{ m}} = \frac{10 \text{ m}}{1} \cdot \frac{1.09 \text{ yd}}{1 \text{ m}} = \frac{(10)(1.09 \text{ yd})}{1} = 10.9 \text{ yd}$$

These units should match.

Meters (**m**) divide out leaving **yd**, the unit you want for the answer.

$10 \text{ m} \approx 10.9 \text{ yd}$

> **Note**
>
> In Example 1 above, you could also use the numbers from the "U.S. Customary to Metric" side of the table that involve meters and yards: 1 yard $\approx$ 0.91 meter.
>
> $$\frac{10 \text{ m}}{1} \cdot \frac{1 \text{ yd}}{0.91 \text{ m}} = \frac{10}{0.91} \text{ yd} \approx 10.99 \text{ yd}$$
>
> The answer is slightly different because the values in the table are rounded. Also, you have to divide instead of multiply, which is usually more difficult to do without a calculator. We will use the first method in this chapter.

1 Convert using unit fractions. Round your answers to the nearest tenth.

(a) 23 m to yards

(b) 40 cm to inches

(c) 5 mi to kilometers (Look at the "U.S. Customary to Metric" side of the table.)

(d) 12 in. to centimeters

ANSWERS

1. (a) 23 m $\approx$ 25.1 yd   **(b)** 40 cm $\approx$ 15.6 in.
(c) 5 mi $\approx$ 8.1 km   **(d)** 12 in. $\approx$ 30.5 cm

Work Problem **1** *at the Side.* ▶

2 Convert. Use the values from the table on the previous page to make unit fractions. Round answers to the nearest tenth.

(a) 17 kg to pounds

(b) 5 L to quarts

(c) 90 g to ounces

(d) 3.5 gal to liters

(e) 145 lb to kilograms

(f) 8 oz to grams

> **EXAMPLE 2** **Converting between Metric and U.S. Customary Weight and Capacity Units**
>
> Convert using unit fractions. Round your answers to the nearest tenth.
>
> **(a)** 3.5 kg to pounds
> Look in the "Metric to U.S. Customary" side of the table on the previous page to see that 1 kilogram ≈ 2.20 pounds. Use this information to write a unit fraction that allows you to divide out kilograms.
>
> $$\frac{3.5 \ \cancel{kg}}{1} \cdot \frac{2.20 \ lb}{1 \ \cancel{kg}} = \frac{(3.5)\,(2.20 \ lb)}{1} = 7.7 \ lb$$
>
> 3.5 kg ≈ 7.7 lb — The conversion value is approximate, so use the ≈ symbol in your answer.
>
> **(b)** 18 gal to liters
> Look in the "U.S. Customary to Metric" side of the table to see that 1 gallon ≈ 3.79 liters. Write a unit fraction that allows you to divide out gallons.
>
> **gal** divides out, leaving **L** for your answer.
>
> $$\frac{18 \ \cancel{gal}}{1} \cdot \frac{3.79 \ L}{1 \ \cancel{gal}} = \frac{(18)(3.79 \ L)}{1} = 68.22 \ L$$
>
> 68.22 rounded to the nearest tenth is 68.2
> 18 gal ≈ 68.2 L
>
> **(c)** 300 g to ounces
> In the "Metric to U.S. Customary" side of the table, 1 gram ≈ 0.035 ounce.
>
> $$\frac{300 \ \cancel{g}}{1} \cdot \frac{0.035 \ oz}{1 \ \cancel{g}} = \frac{(300)(0.035 \ oz)}{1} = 10.5 \ oz$$
>
> 300 g ≈ 10.5 oz
>
> ---
>
> **CAUTION**
> Because the metric and U.S. customary systems were developed independently, almost all comparisons are approximate. Your answers should be written with the "≈" symbol to show they are approximate.

◀ *Work Problem* **2** *at the Side.*

OBJECTIVE 2 Learn common temperatures on the Celsius scale. In the metric system, temperature is measured on the **Celsius** scale. On the Celsius scale, water freezes at 0 °C and boils at 100 °C. The small raised circle stands for "degrees" and the capital **C** is for Celsius. Read the temperatures like this:

Water freezes at 0 degrees Celsius (0 °C).

Water boils at 100 degrees Celsius (100 °C).

The U.S. customary temperature system, used only in the United States, is measured on the **Fahrenheit** scale. On this scale:

Water freezes at 32 degrees Fahrenheit (32 °F).

Water boils at 212 degrees Fahrenheit (212 °F).

ANSWERS
2. **(a)** 17 kg ≈ 37.4 lb **(b)** 5 L ≈ 5.3 qt
(c) 90 g ≈ 3.2 oz **(d)** 3.5 gal ≈ 13.3 L
(e) 145 lb ≈ 65.3 kg **(f)** 8 oz ≈ 226.8 g

The thermometer below shows some typical temperatures in both Celsius and Fahrenheit. For example, comfortable room temperature is about 20 °C or 68 °F, and normal body temperature is about 37 °C or 98.6 °F.

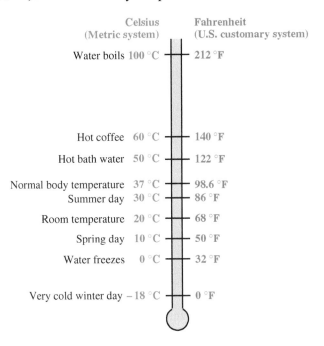

Note

The freezing and boiling temperatures are exact. The other temperatures are approximate. Even normal body temperature varies slightly from person to person.

EXAMPLE 3 **Using Celsius Temperatures**

Circle the Celsius temperature that is most reasonable for each situation.

(a) Warm summer day   29 °C   64 °C   90 °C

29 °C is reasonable. 64 °C and 90 °C are too hot; they're both above the temperature of hot bath water (above 122 °F).

(b) Inside a freezer   −10 °C   3 °C   25 °C

−10 °C is the reasonable temperature because it is the only one below the freezing point of water (0 °C). Your frozen foods would start thawing at 3 °C or 25 °C.

Work Problem ③ *at the Side.* ▶

OBJECTIVE ③ **Use formulas to convert between Celsius and Fahrenheit temperatures.** You can use these formulas to convert between Celsius and Fahrenheit temperatures.

Celsius–Fahrenheit Conversion Formulas

Converting from Fahrenheit (F)
to Celsius (C)

$$C = \frac{5(F - 32)}{9}$$

Converting from Celsius (C)
to Fahrenheit (F)

$$F = \frac{9C}{5} + 32$$

③ Circle the Celsius temperature that is *most* reasonable for each situation.

(a) Set the living room thermostat at:
11 °C   21 °C   71 °C

(b) The baby has a fever of:
29 °C   39 °C   49 °C

(c) Wear a sweater outside because it's:
15 °C   25 °C   50 °C

(d) My iced tea is:
−5 °C   5 °C   30 °C

(e) Time to go swimming! It's:
95 °C   65 °C   35 °C

(f) Inside a refrigerator (not the freezer) it's:
−15 °C   0 °C   3 °C

(g) There's a blizzard outside. It's:
12 °C   4 °C   −20 °C

(h) I need hot water to get these clothes clean. It should be:
55 °C   105 °C   200 °C

As you use these formulas, be sure to follow the order of operations from **Section 3.7**.

4 Convert to Celsius. Round your answers to the nearest degree if necessary.

(a) 72 °F

(b) 20 °F

(c) 212 °F

(d) 98.6 °F

> **Order of Operations**
> *Step 1* Work inside *parentheses* or *other grouping symbols*.
> *Step 2* Simplify any expressions with *exponents*.
> *Step 3* Do the remaining *multiplications and divisions* as they occur from left to right.
> *Step 4* Do the remaining *additions and subtractions* as they occur from left to right.

EXAMPLE 4 **Converting Fahrenheit to Celsius**

Convert 10 °F to Celsius. Round your answer to the nearest degree.

Use the correct formula and follow the order of operations.

$$C = \frac{5(F - 32)}{9}$$ Fahrenheit to Celsius formula.

$$= \frac{5(10 - 32)}{9}$$ Replace F with 10. Work inside parentheses first. $10 - 32$ becomes $10 + (-32)$.

$$= \frac{5(-22)}{9}$$ Multiply in the numerator; positive times negative gives a negative product.

$$= \frac{-110}{9}$$ Divide; negative divided by positive gives a negative quotient.

$$= -12.\overline{2}$$ Round to -12 (nearest degree).

Thus, $10\,°C \approx -12\,°F$.

◀ *Work Problem* **4** *at the Side.*

---

5 Convert to Fahrenheit. Round your answers to the nearest degree if necessary.

(a) 100 °C

(b) −25 °C

(c) 32 °C

(d) −18 °C

EXAMPLE 5 **Converting Celsius to Fahrenheit**

Convert 15 °C to Fahrenheit.

Use the correct formula and follow the order of operations.

$$F = \frac{9C}{5} + 32$$ Celsius to Fahrenheit formula.

$$= \frac{9 \cdot 15}{5} + 32$$ Replace C with 15.

$$= \frac{9 \cdot 3 \cdot \overset{1}{\cancel{5}}}{\underset{1}{\cancel{5}}} + 32$$ Divide out the common factor. Multiply in the numerator.

$$= 27 + 32$$ Add.

$$= 59$$

Thus, $15\,°C = 59\,°F$.

◀ *Work Problem* **5** *at the Side.*

FOR EXTRA HELP

MyMathLab

Math XL
PRACTICE

WATCH

DOWNLOAD

READ

REVIEW

Use the table on the first page of this section and unit fractions to make approximate conversions from metric to U.S. customary or U.S. customary to metric. Round your answers to the nearest tenth. See Examples 1 and 2.

1. 20 m to yards

2. 8 km to miles

3. 80 m to feet

4. 85 cm to inches

5. 16 ft to meters

6. 3.2 yd to meters

7. 150 g to ounces

8. 2.5 oz to grams

9. 248 lb to kilograms

10. 7.68 kg to pounds

11. 28.6 L to quarts

12. 15.75 L to gallons

13. For the 2000 Olympics, the 3M Company used 5 g of pure gold to coat Michael Johnson's track shoes. (*Source:* 3M Company.)

(a) How many ounces of gold were used, to the nearest tenth?

(b) Was this enough extra weight to slow him down?

14. The label on a Van Ness auto feeder for cats and dogs says it holds 1.4 kg of dry food. How many pounds of food does it hold, to the nearest tenth? (*Source:* Van Ness Plastics.)

15. The heavy-duty wash cycle in a dishwater uses 8.4 gal of water. How many liters does it use, to the nearest tenth? (*Source:* Frigidaire.)

16. The rinse-and-hold cycle in a dishwasher uses only 4.5 L of water. How many gallons does it use, to the nearest tenth? (*Source:* Frigidaire.)

17. The smallest pet fish are dwarf gobies, which are half an inch long. How many centimeters long is a dwarf gobie, to the nearest tenth? (*Hint:* Write half an inch in decimal form.)

18. The fastest nerve signals in the human body travel 120 meters per second. How many feet per second do the signals travel? (*Source: Big Book of Knowledge.*)

The BabyBjörn is a popular baby carrier imported from Sweden. Use the information from the instruction sheet that comes with the carrier to answer Exercises 19–20. (*Source:* BabyBjörn, Sweden.)

Infant facing adult position

Minimum baby size:
53 cm and 3.5 kg

Maximum baby size: 15 kg

19. Can the carrier be safely used for a newborn infant who weighs 8 lb and is 19.5 in. long? Explain your answer.

20. Can the carrier be safely used for a baby who weighs 30 lb? Explain your answer.

Circle the most reasonable Celsius temperature for each situation. See Example 3.

21. A snowy day

   12 °C   28 °C   −8 °C

22. Brewing coffee

   80 °C   180 °C   15 °C

23. A high fever

   21 °C   40 °C   103 °C

24. Swimming pool water

   90 °C   78 °C   25 °C

25. Oven temperature

   150 °C   50 °C   30 °C

26. Light jacket weather

   0 °C   10 °C   −10 °C

Use the conversion formulas from this section to convert Fahrenheit temperatures to Celsius and Celsius temperatures to Fahrenheit. Round your answers to the nearest degree if necessary. See Examples 4 and 5.

27. 60 °F

28. 80 °F

29. −4 °F

30. 15 °F

31. 8 °C

32. 18 °C

33. −5 °C

34. 0 °C

Solve each application problem. Round your answers to the nearest degree, if necessary.

35. The highest temperature ever recorded on Earth was 136 °F at El Azizia, Libya, in 1922. The lowest was −129 °F in Antarctica. Convert these temperatures to Celsius. (*Source: The World Almanac.*)

36. Hummingbirds have a normal body temperature of 107 °F. But on cold nights they go into a state of torpor where their body temperature drops to 39 °F. What are these temperatures in Celsius? (*Source: Wildbird.*)

37. The directions for a self-stick clothes hook with adhesive on the back are as follows: "Apply to surfaces above 50 °F. Adhesive could soften and lose adhesion above 105 °F." What are these temperatures in the metric system? (*Source: 3M Company.*)

38. A box of imported Belgian chocolates carries a warning to keep the box dry and at <18 °C. Translate this warning into the U.S. Customary system. (*Source: Chocolaterie Guylian N.V.*)

39. The tag on a pair of hiking boots is shown below.

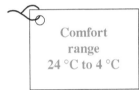
Comfort range 24 °C to 4 °C

Source: Sorel.

(a) In what kind of weather would you be most comfortable wearing these boots?

(b) For what Fahrenheit temperatures are the boots designed?

(c) What range of metric temperatures do you have in January where you live? Would you be comfortable in these boots?

40. Sleeping bags made by Eddie Bauer are sold around the world. Each type of sleeping bag is designed for outdoor camping in certain temperatures.

OUTDOOR SLEEPING BAGS	
Junior bag	5 °C or warmer
Removable liner bag	0 °C to 15 °C
Conversion bag	−7 °C to 0 °C

Source: Eddie Bauer.

(a) At what Fahrenheit temperatures should you use the Junior bag?

(b) What Fahrenheit temperatures is the Removable liner bag designed for?

(c) What are the Fahrenheit temperatures for the Conversion bag?

The article below appeared in American newspapers. However, both Newfoundland (part of Canada) and Ireland use the metric system. Their newspapers would have reported all the measurements in metric units. Complete the conversions to metric, rounding answers to the nearest tenth when necessary.

Q: **A recent news brief reported on some men who flew a model airplane from Newfoundland to Ireland. Can you provide some details of the flight?**

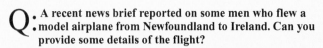

A: The model plane is 6 feet long and weighs 11 pounds. Made of balsa wood and mylar, it crossed the Atlantic—the flight path took it 1,888.3 miles—in 38 hours, 23 minutes. It soared at a cruising altitude of 1,000 feet. The plane used a souped-up piston engine and carried less than a gallon of fuel, as mandated by rules of the Federation Aeronautique Internationale, the governing body of model airplane building. When it landed in County Galway, Ireland, it had less than 2 fluid ounces of fuel left. The plane was built by Maynard Hill of Silver Spring, Maryland.

(*Source: New York Times.*)

41. Length of model plane

42. Weight of plane

43. Length of flight path

44. Time of flight

45. Cruising altitude

46. Fuel at the start, in milliliters

47. Fuel left after landing, in milliliters
(*Hint:* First convert 2 fl oz to quarts.)

48. What *percent* of the fuel was left at the end of the flight?

9

Graphs

OBJECTIVES

1 **Read and interpret data presented in a table.**

2 **Read and interpret data from a pictograph.**

Throughout this book you have used numbers, expressions, formulas, and equations to communicate rules or information. In this chapter you'll see how *tables, pictographs, circle graphs, bar graphs,* and *line graphs* are also used to communicate information.

OBJECTIVE **1** **Read and interpret data presented in a table.** A **table** presents data organized into rows and columns. The advantage of a table is that you can find very specific, exact values. The disadvantages are that you may have to spend some time searching through the table to find what you want, and it may not be easy to see trends or patterns.

The table below shows information about the performance of eight U.S. airlines during the year 2007 (January–December).

PERFORMANCE DATA FOR SELECTED U.S. AIRLINES
JANUARY–DECEMBER 2007

Airline	On-Time Performance	Luggage Handling*
Airtran	77%	4.1
American	69%	7.3
Continental	74%	5.3
Delta	77%	7.6
Northwest	70%	5.0
Southwest	80%	5.9
United	70%	5.8
US Airways	69%	8.5

*Luggage problems per 1000 passengers.
Source: Department of Transportation Air Travel Consumer Report.

For example, by reading from left to right along the row marked United, you first see that 70% of United's flights were on time during 2007. The next number is 5.8 and the heading at the top of that column is *Luggage Handling**. The little star (asterisk) tells you to look below the table for more information. Next to the asterisk below the table it says "Luggage problems per 1000 passengers." So, almost 6 passengers out of every 1000 passengers on United flights had some sort of problem with their luggage.

EXAMPLE 1 **Reading and Interpreting Data from a Table**

Use the table above on airline performance to answer these questions.

(a) What percent of American's flights were on time?
Look across the row labeled American to see that 69% of its flights were on time.

(b) Which airline had the worst luggage handling record?
Look down the column headed Luggage Handling. To find the *worst* record, look for the *highest* number of luggage problems. The highest number is 8.5. Then look to the left to find the airline, which is US Airways.

(c) What was the average percent of on-time flights for the three airlines with the best performance, to the nearest whole percent?
Look down the column headed On-Time Performance to find the three highest numbers: 80%, 77%, and 77%. To find the average, add the values and divide by 3.

Continued on Next Page

$$\frac{80 + 77 + 77}{3} = \frac{234}{3} = 78$$

The average on-time performance for the three best airlines was 78%.

Work Problem **1** *at the Side.* ▶

EXAMPLE 2 **Interpreting Data from a Table**

The table below shows the maximum cab fares in five different cities in 2006. The "flag drop" charge is made when the driver starts the meter. "Wait time" is the charge for having to wait in the middle of a ride.

MAXIMUM TAXICAB FARES ALLOWED IN SELECTED CITIES IN 2006

City	Flag Drop	Price per Mile	Wait Time (per Hour)
Chicago	$2.25	$1.80	$20
Denver	$1.60	$2	$22.50
Miami	$2.50	$2.40	$24
New York	$2.50	$2	$12
San Francisco	$2.85	$2.25	$27

Source: www.schallerconsult.com

Use the table to answer these questions.

(a) What is the maximum fare for a 9-mile ride in New York that includes having the cab wait 15 minutes while you pick up a package at a store?

The price per mile in New York is $2, so the cost for 9 miles is 9($2) = $18. Then, add the flag drop charge of $2.50. Finally, figure out the cost of the wait time. One way to do that is to set up a proportion. Recall that 1 hour is 60 minutes, so each side of the proportion compares the cost to the number of minutes of wait time.

$$\text{Cost} \rightarrow \frac{\$12}{60 \text{ min}} = \frac{\$x}{15 \text{ min}} \leftarrow \text{Cost} \atop \leftarrow \text{Wait time}$$

Show that cross products are equivalent. $60 \cdot x = 12 \cdot 15$

$$\frac{60x}{60} = \frac{180}{60} \quad \text{Divide both sides by 60}$$

$$x = \$3 \longleftarrow \text{Charge for waiting 15 minutes}$$

Total fare = $18 + $2.50 + $3 = $23.50

(b) It is customary to give the cab driver a tip. Find the total cost of the cab ride in part (a) above if the passenger added a 15% tip, rounded to the nearest quarter (nearest $0.25).

Use the percent equation to find the exact tip.

percent • whole = part   Percent equation
(15.%) ($23.50) = n   Write 15% as a decimal.
Write 15% as 0.15   (0.15) ($23.50) = n
$3.525 = n   Round to $3.50 (nearest $0.25).

The total cost of the cab ride is $23.50 + $3.50 tip = $27.00.

Work Problem **2** *at the Side.* ▶

1 Use the table of airline performance on the previous page to answer these questions.

(a) What percent of Continental's flights were on time?

(b) Which airline had the best on-time performance?

(c) Which airline had the best record for luggage handling?

(d) Which airline(s) had 5 or fewer luggage handling problems per 1000 passengers?

(e) What was the average number of luggage problems for all eight airlines, to the nearest tenth?

2 Use the table of cab fares at the left to answer these questions.

(a) What is the difference in the maximum fare for a cab ride of 6.5 miles in Chicago compared to New York? Assume there is no wait time.

(b) What is the maximum fare for a 12-mile cab ride in Miami that includes 10 minutes of wait time?

(c) Find the total cost for a cab ride of 4.5 miles in Denver, including 30 minutes of wait time and a 15% tip. Round the tip to the nearest $0.25.

ANSWERS

1. **(a)** 74% **(b)** Southwest
(c) Airtran **(d)** Airtran, Northwest
(e) 49.5 ÷ 8 ≈ 6.2 (rounded)
2. **(a)** Chicago $13.95; New York $15.50;
New York fare is $1.55 higher. **(b)** $35.30
(c) $21.85 + $3.25 tip = $25.10

3 Use the pictograph in Example 3 to answer these questions.

(a) What is the approximate population of Chicago?

(b) What is the approximate population of Atlanta?

(c) Approximately how much less is the population of Los Angeles than New York?

(d) The population of Dallas is approximately how much greater than Atlanta?

OBJECTIVE 2 **Read and interpret data from a pictograph.**
Tables show numbers in rows and columns. Graphs, on the other hand, are a *visual* way to communicate data; that is, they show a *picture* of the information rather than a list of numbers. In this section you'll work with one type of graph, *pictographs,* and in the next two sections you'll learn about circle graphs, bar graphs, and line graphs.

The advantage of a graph is that you can easily make comparisons or see trends just by looking. The disadvantage is that the graph may not give you the specific, more exact numbers you need in some situations.

EXAMPLE 3 **Reading and Interpreting a Pictograph**

A **pictograph** uses symbols or pictures to represent various amounts. The pictograph below shows the population of five U.S. metropolitan areas (cities with their surrounding suburbs) in 2005. The *key* at the bottom of the graph tells you that each symbol of a person represents 2 million people. Half of a symbol represents half of 2 million people.

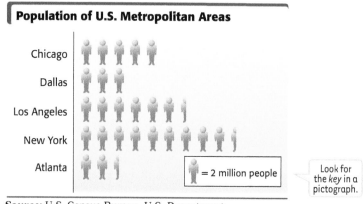

Population of U.S. Metropolitan Areas

Source: U.S. Census Bureau, U.S. Department of Commerce.

Use the pictograph to answer these questions.

(a) What is the approximate population of Los Angeles?

The population of Los Angeles is represented by 6 whole symbols ($6 \cdot 2$ million $= 12$ million) plus half of a symbol ($\frac{1}{2}$ of 2 million is 1 million) for a total of 13 million people.

Recall that 2 million can be written as 2,000,000, so another way to get the answer is to multiply 6.5 (the number of symbols) times 2,000,000 people for a total of 13,000,000 people.

(b) How much greater is the population of New York than Atlanta?

New York shows $9\frac{1}{2}$ symbols and Atlanta shows $2\frac{1}{2}$ symbols. So New York has 7 more symbols than Atlanta, and $7 \cdot 2$ million $= 14$ million. Thus, New York has about 14 million (or 14,000,000) more people than Atlanta.

Note

One disadvantage of a pictograph is that you often have to round numbers a great deal; in this case, to the nearest *million* people. The actual population of the Dallas area is 5,819,000 but the graph shows 3 symbols (6,000,000 people) so it is off by about 181,000 people.

◀ *Work Problem* **3** *at the Side.*

This table lists the basketball players in the NBA with the highest scoring average at the end of the 2006–2007 season. (Players must have a minimum of 10,000 points or 400 games.) Use the table to answer Exercises 1–10. See Examples 1 and 2.

ALL-TIME NBA STATISTICAL LEADERS—SCORING AVERAGE
(AT THE END OF THE 2006–2007 SEASON)

Player	Games	Points	Average Points Per Game
Michael Jordan	1072	32,292	30.1
Wilt Chamberlain	1045	31,419	30.1
Allen Iverson*	747	20,824	27.9
Elgin Baylor	846	23,149	27.4
Jerry West	932	25,192	
Bob Pettit	792	20,880	
Shaquille O'Neal*	981	25,454	

*Player still actively playing in the NBA.
Source: National Basketball Association.

1. (a) How many points did Wilt Chamberlain score during his NBA career?

   (b) Which player(s) scored more points than Chamberlain?

2. (a) How many games did Elgin Baylor play in during his career in the NBA?

   (b) Which player is closest to Baylor in number of games?

3. (a) Which player has been in the greatest number of games?

   (b) Which player has been in the fewest number of games?

4. Which players have scored more than 25,000 points? List them in order, starting with the player with the greatest number of points.

🌐 5. What is the difference in points scored between the player with the greatest number of points and the player with the least number of points?

6. How many fewer games has Shaquille O'Neal played in than Michael Jordan?

▦ 7. Complete the table by finding the average number of points scored per game by Jerry West, by Bob Pettit, and by Shaquille O'Neal. Look at the other averages in the table to decide how to round your answers.

▦ 8. Find the overall scoring average (points per game) for all seven players listed in the table. Use the numbers in the *Games* column and the *Points* column to calculate your answer.

9. According to the table, what is different about Iverson and O'Neal from the rest of the players? (Hint: Look at the note below the table.)

▦ 10. Michael Jordan and Wilt Chamberlain are tied in first place for average points per game. Explain what happens if you round their average points per game to the nearest hundredth instead of the nearest tenth.

This table shows the number of calories burned during 30 minutes of various types of exercise. The table also shows how the number of calories burned varies according to the weight of the person doing the exercise. Use the table to answer Exercises 11–20. See Examples 1 and 2.

CALORIES BURNED DURING 30 MINUTES OF EXERCISE BY PEOPLE
OF DIFFERENT WEIGHTS

Activity	Calories Burned in 30 Minutes		
	110 Pounds	140 Pounds	170 Pounds
Moderate jogging	322	410	495
Moderate walking	110	140	170
Moderate bicycling	140	180	220
Aerobic dance	200	255	310
Racquetball	210	268	325
Tennis	160	205	250

Source: Fairview Health Services.

11. A person weighing 140 pounds is looking at the table.

   (a) How many calories will be burned during 30 minutes of aerobic dance?

   (b) Which activity burns the most calories?

12. A person weighing 170 pounds is looking at the table.

   (a) How many calories are burned during 30 minutes of tennis?

   (b) Which activity burns the fewest calories?

13. (a) Which activities can a 110-pound person do to burn at least 200 calories in 30 minutes?

   (b) Which activities can a 170-pound person do to burn at least 200 calories in 30 minutes?

14. (a) Which activities would burn fewer than 200 calories in 30 minutes for a 140-pound person?

   (b) Which activities would burn fewer than 300 calories in 30 minutes for a 170-pound person?

15. How many total calories will a 140-pound person burn during 15 minutes of bicycling and 60 minutes of moderate walking?

16. How many total calories will a 110-pound person burn during 90 minutes of tennis and 15 minutes of aerobic dance?

Set up and solve proportions to answer Exercises 17–20.

17. How many calories would you expect a 125-pound person to burn

   (a) during 30 minutes of moderate jogging?

   (b) during 30 minutes of racquetball? Round to the nearest whole number.

18. How many calories would you expect a 185-pound person to burn

   (a) during 30 minutes of walking?

   (b) during 30 minutes of bicycling? Round to the nearest ten.

19. How many more calories would a 158-pound person burn during 15 minutes of aerobic dance than during 20 minutes of walking? Round to the nearest whole number.

20. How many fewer calories would a 196-pound person burn during 25 minutes of walking than during 20 minutes of tennis? Round to the nearest whole number.

This pictograph shows the approximate number of passenger arrivals and departures at selected U.S. airports in 2006. Use the pictograph to answer Exercises 21–28. See Example 3.

PASSENGER ARRIVALS AND DEPARTURES AT SELECTED U.S. AIRPORTS

= 10 million passenger arrivals and departures

Source: Airports Council International—North America.

21. Approximately how many passenger arrivals and departures took place at the

　(a) Chicago airport?

　(b) San Francisco airport?

22. Approximately how many passenger arrivals and departures took place at the

　(a) Dallas airport?

　(b) Las Vegas airport?

23. What is the approximate total number of arrivals and departures at the two busiest airports?

24. What is the difference in the number of arrivals and departures at the busiest airport and the least-busy airport?

25. How many fewer arrivals and departures did Chicago's airport have compared to Atlanta's airport?

26. Find the approximate total number of arrivals and departures for the three least-busy airports.

27. What is the approximate total number of arrivals and departures for all five airports?

28. Find the average number of arrivals and departures for the five airports.

Relating Concepts (Exercises 29–34) For Individual or Group Work

Look back at the first table in this section, Performance Data for Selected U.S. Airlines. Use the table as you **work Exercises 29–34 in order.**

29. Suppose you are planning a business trip where you will fly to a new city each day on a tight schedule. You'll travel light, carrying one small bag on the plane rather than checking it. If you can choose any one of the airlines in the table, which one would you pick? Explain why.

30. Suppose you are planning the business trip described in Exercise 29 and the only airline that goes to the cities you want is American. What could you do to minimize the problems caused by the possibility of late flights?

31. Now you are planning a two-week vacation trip to a beachfront resort. You'll be checking several bags and your expensive golf clubs. If you can choose any one of the airlines in the table, which one would you pick? Explain why.

32. Suppose you are planning the vacation trip described in Exercise 31 and US Airways is the only airline that goes to the city you want. What could you do to minimize possible luggage handling problems?

33. Think of three possible reasons an airline might have a lower percentage of on-time flights during a particular month than they usually do. What, if anything, could the airline do to resolve each of the problems you listed?

34. Describe three other factors you might consider when selecting an airline, other than on-time performance and luggage handling problems.

9.2 ▶▶▶ Reading and Constructing Circle Graphs

A *circle graph* is another way to show a *picture* of a set of data. This picture can often be understood faster and more easily than a formula or a list of numbers.

OBJECTIVE 1 Read a circle graph. A **circle graph** is used to show how a total amount is divided into parts. The circle graph below shows you how 24 hours in the life of a college student are divided among different activities.

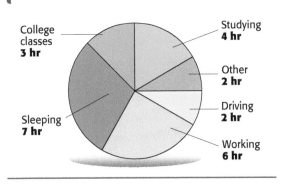

THE DAY OF A COLLEGE STUDENT

College classes 3 hr
Studying 4 hr
Other 2 hr
Driving 2 hr
Sleeping 7 hr
Working 6 hr

Work Problem **1** *at the Side.* ▶

OBJECTIVE 2 Use a circle graph. The circle graph above uses pie-shaped pieces called *sectors* to show the amount of time spent on each activity (the total must be 24 hours). The circle graph can therefore be used to compare the time spent on one activity to the total number of hours in the day.

EXAMPLE 1 Using a Circle Graph

Find the ratio of time spent in college classes to the total number of hours in a day. Write the ratio as a fraction in lowest terms. (See **Section 6.1.**)

The circle graph shows that 3 of the 24 hours in a day are spent in class. The ratio of class time to the hours in a day is shown below.

$$\frac{3 \text{ hours (college classes)}}{24 \text{ hours (whole day)}} = \frac{3 \text{ hours}}{24 \text{ hours}} = \frac{\overset{1}{\cancel{3}}}{\underset{1}{\cancel{3} \cdot 8}} = \frac{1}{8} \left\{ \begin{array}{l} \text{Ratio in} \\ \text{lowest terms} \end{array} \right.$$

Work Problem **2** *at the Side.* ▶

The circle graph above can also be used to find the ratio of the time spent on one activity to the time spent on any other activity. See the next example.

EXAMPLE 2 Finding a Ratio from a Circle Graph

Find the ratio of working time to class time.

The circle graph shows 6 hours spent working and 3 hours spent in class. The ratio of working time to class time is shown below.

$$\frac{6 \text{ hours (working)}}{3 \text{ hours (class)}} = \frac{6 \text{ hours}}{3 \text{ hours}} = \frac{\overset{1}{\cancel{3}} \cdot 2}{\underset{1}{\cancel{3}}} = \frac{2}{1} \leftarrow \text{Ratio in lowest terms}$$

Work Problem **3** *at the Side.* ▶

OBJECTIVES

1 Read a circle graph.

2 Use a circle graph.

3 Use a protractor to draw a circle graph.

---

1 Use the circle graph at the left to answer each question.

(a) The greatest number of hours is spent in which activity?

(b) How many more hours are spent working than studying?

(c) Find the total number of hours spent studying, working, and attending classes.

2 Use the circle graph to find each ratio. Write the ratios as fractions in lowest terms.

(a) Hours spent driving to whole day

(b) Hours spent studying to whole day

(c) Hours spent sleeping and doing other to whole day

3 Use the circle graph to find each ratio. Write the ratios as fractions in lowest terms.

(a) Hours spent studying to hours spent working

(b) Hours spent working to hours spent sleeping

(c) Hours spent studying to hours spent driving

ANSWERS

1. (a) sleeping (b) 2 hours (c) 13 hours
2. (a) $\frac{1}{12}$ (b) $\frac{1}{6}$ (c) $\frac{3}{8}$
3. (a) $\frac{2}{3}$ (b) $\frac{6}{7}$ (c) $\frac{2}{1}$

4 Use the circle graph on frozen pizza sales to find the amount of sales for each company.

(a) Kraft

A circle graph often shows data as percents. For example, total U.S. sales of frozen pizza are $2 billion each year. The circle graph below shows how sales are divided among various companies that make frozen pizza. The entire circle represents $2 billion in sales. Each sector represents the sales of one company as a percent of the total sales. The total in a circle graph must be 100%, although it may be slightly more or less due to rounding the percent for each sector.

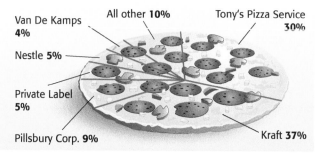

HOT SALES OF FROZEN PIZZA

Americans eat $2 billion worth of frozen pizzas each year. The percent of total sales for each company is rounded to the nearest whole percent.

All other **10%**
Van De Kamps **4%**
Tony's Pizza Service **30%**
Nestle **5%**
Private Label **5%**
Pillsbury Corp. **9%**
Kraft **37%**

Source: Information Resources, Inc.

(b) Van De Kamps

(c) Tony's Pizza Service

EXAMPLE 3 **Calculating an Amount Using a Circle Graph**

Use the circle graph above on frozen pizza sales to find the amount of sales for Nestle.

Recall the percent equation.

$$\text{percent} \cdot \text{whole} = \text{part}$$

The percent for Nestle is 5%. Rewrite 5% as the decimal 0.05. The *whole* is the total sales of $2 billion (the entire circle).

percent $\cdot$ whole $=$ part

$05.\% \cdot \$2 \text{ billion} = n$

Write 5% as 0.05

Write $2 billion as $2,000,000,000

$(0.05)(\$2,000,000,000) = n$

$\$100,000,000 = n$

The sales for Nestle are $100,000,000.

(d) Pillsbury Corp.

◀ *Work Problem* **4** *at the Side.*

OBJECTIVE 3 Use a protractor to draw a circle graph. The coordinator of the Fair Oaks Youth Soccer League organizes teams in five age groups. She counts the number of registered players in each age group as shown in the table on the next page. Then she calculates what percent of the total each group represents. For example, there are 59 players in the "Under 8" group, out of 298 total players.

$$\text{percent} \cdot \text{whole} = \text{part}$$
$$p \quad \cdot \quad 298 \quad = \quad 59$$
$$\frac{p \cdot 298}{298} = \frac{59}{298}$$

Multiply the decimal answer by 100% to get the percent.

$$p \approx 0.198 \approx 19.8\% \quad \text{rounds to } 20\%$$

ANSWERS

4. **(a)** $740,000,000 **(b)** $80,000,000
   (c) $600,000,000 **(d)** $180,000,000

FAIR OAKS YOUTH SOCCER LEAGUE

Age Group	Number of Players	Percent of Total (rounded to nearest whole percent)
Under 8 years	59	20% ← 59 players ≈ 20% of 298
Ages 8–9	46	15%
Ages 10–11	75	25%
Ages 12–13	74	25%
Ages 14–15	44	15%
Total	**298**	**100%**

You can show these percents in a circle graph. Recall that a circle has 360 degrees (written 360°). The 360° represents the entire league, or 100% of the soccer players.

EXAMPLE 4   **Drawing a Circle Graph**

Using the data on *age groups,* find the number of degrees in the sector that would represent the "Under 8" group, and begin constructing a circle graph.

A complete circle has 360°. Because the "Under 8" group makes up 20% of the total number of players, the number of degrees needed for the "Under 8" sector of the circle graph is 20% of 360°.

$$20.\% \text{ of } 360° = n$$

Write 20% as 0.20

$$(0.20)(360°) = n$$

$$72° = n$$

Use the circle drawn below and a tool called a **protractor** to make a circle graph. First, using a ruler or straightedge, draw a line from the center of the circle to the left edge. Place the hole in the protractor over the center of the circle, making sure that the 0 mark and the black line on the protractor are right over the line you drew. Find 72° and make a mark as shown in the illustration. Then remove the protractor and use the straightedge to draw a line from the 72° mark to the center of the circle. This sector is 72° and represents the "Under 8" group.

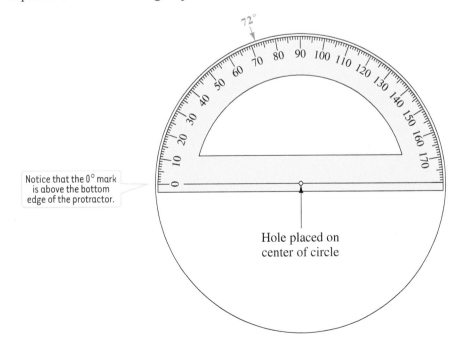

Notice that the 0° mark is above the bottom edge of the protractor.

Hole placed on center of circle

Continued on Next Page

5 Using the information on the soccer age groups in the table on the previous page, find the number of degrees needed for each sector. Then complete the circle graph at the bottom right on this page.

(a) "Ages 10–11" sector

(b) "Ages 12–13" sector

(c) "Ages 14–15" sector

To draw the "Ages 8–9" sector, begin by finding the number of degrees in the sector, which is 15% of the total circle, or 15% of 360°.

$$15.\% \text{ of } 360° = n$$
$$(0.15)(360°) = n$$
$$54° = n$$

Again, place the hole of the protractor over the center of the circle, but this time align 0 with the previous 72° mark. Make a mark at 54° and draw a line from the mark to the center of the circle. This sector is 54° and represents the "Ages 8–9" group.

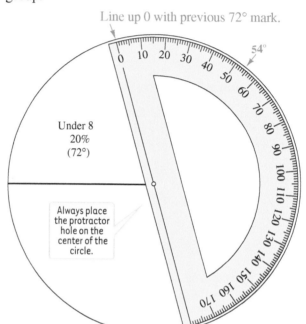

CAUTION
You must be certain that the hole in the protractor is placed on the exact center of the circle each time you measure the size of a sector.

◀ *Work Problem* **5** *at the Side.*

Use this circle for Problem 5 in the margin.

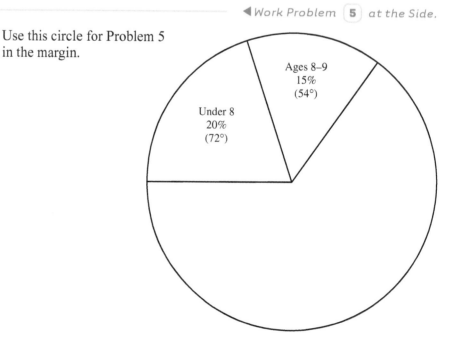

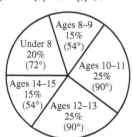

This circle graph shows the budget for adding a family room to an existing home. Use the graph to answer Exercises 1–6. Write ratios as fractions in lowest terms. See Examples 1 and 2.

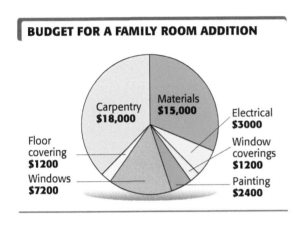

BUDGET FOR A FAMILY ROOM ADDITION

Carpentry $18,000
Materials $15,000
Electrical $3000
Floor covering $1200
Window coverings $1200
Windows $7200
Painting $2400

1. **(a)** Find the total budget for adding the family room.

   (b) What is the greatest single expense, and how much is it?

2. **(a)** What is the second-greatest expense in adding the family room, and how much is it?

   (b) What is least expensive?

3. **(a)** Find the ratio of the amount for carpentry to the total remodeling budget.

   (b) What is the ratio of the amount for materials to the amount for electrical.

4. **(a)** Find the ratio of the amount for painting to the total remodeling budget.

   (b) Find the ratio of the amount for windows to the amount for window coverings.

5. **(a)** Find the ratio of the amount for floor covering, painting, and window coverings to the total remodeling budget.

   (b) If the actual expenses for adding the family room amounted to $57,600, what is the ratio of the actual total to the budget total?

6. **(a)** Find the ratio of the amount for carpentry and electrical to the amount for materials.

   (b) The homeowner found a sale on carpet and spent only $900 to cover the floor. What is the ratio of the carpet cost to the budget amount for floor covering?

This circle graph, adapted from USA Today, *shows the number of people in a survey who gave various reasons for eating dinner at restaurants. Each person could pick only one reason. Use the graph to answer Exercises 7–14. See Examples 1 and 2.*

ON THE TOWN

When asked in a survey why they ate dinner in restaurants, a group of people gave these reasons.

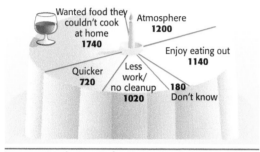

Wanted food they couldn't cook at home **1740**

Atmosphere **1200**

Enjoy eating out **1140**

Quicker **720**

Less work/ no cleanup **1020**

180 Don't know

Source: Market Facts for Tyson Foods.

7. (a) Which reason was given by the least number of people?

(b) Which reason was given by the second-fewest number of people?

8. (a) Which reason was given by the greatest number of people?

(b) Which reason was given by the second-greatest number of people?

Find each ratio in Exercises 9–14. Write the ratios as fractions in lowest terms.

9. Those who said dining out is "Quicker" to total people in the survey

10. Those who said "Enjoy eating out" to the total people in the survey

11. Those who said "Less work/no cleanup" to those who said "Atmosphere"

12. Those who said "Don't know" to those who said "Quicker"

13. Those who said "Wanted food they couldn't cook at home" to those who said "Don't know"

14. Those who said "Atmosphere" to those who said "Enjoy eating out"

This circle graph shows the results of an on-line survey of 400 people who have a cat as a pet. They answered the question, "How does your cat react when you entertain?" The responses are expressed as percents of the 400 people in the survey. Use the graph to answer Exercises 15–20. See Example 3.

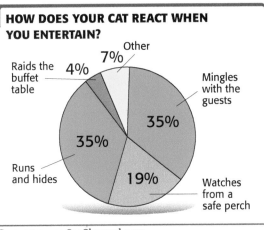

HOW DOES YOUR CAT REACT WHEN YOU ENTERTAIN?

Other 7%
Raids the buffet table 4%
Mingles with the guests 35%
Runs and hides 35%
Watches from a safe perch 19%

Source: www.CatChannel.com

15. How many people said their cat mingles with the guests?

16. How many cat owners said their cats watch from a safe perch?

17. Which response was given least often and by how many people?

18. Which response category represented 7% of the people surveyed? How many people were in this category?

19. How many fewer people said "watches from a safe perch" than said "runs and hides"?

20. How many more people said "mingles with the guests" than said "raids the buffet table"?

This circle graph shows the results of a survey on favorite hot dog toppings in the United States. Each topping is expressed as a percent of the 3200 people in the survey. Use the graph to find the number of people favoring each of the toppings in Exercises 21–26.

FAVORITE HOT DOG TOPPINGS

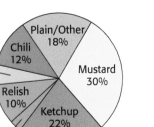

Plain/Other 18%
Chili 12%
Onions 5%
Relish 10%
Mustard 30%
Ketchup 22%
Sauerkraut 3%

Source: National Hot Dog and Sausage Council.

🌐 **21.** Onions

22. Sauerkraut

🌐 **23.** The most popular topping

24. The second-most-popular topping

25. How many more people chose chili than chose relish?

26. How many fewer people chose onions than chose mustard?

27. Describe the steps for calculating the size of the sector for each item in a circle graph.

28. A protractor is the tool used to draw a circle graph. Give a brief explanation of what the protractor does and how you would use it to measure and draw each sector in the circle graph.

29. During one semester Kara Diano spent $10,920 for school expenses as shown in this table. Find all numbers missing from the table.

Item	Dollar Amount	Percent of Total	Degrees of a Circle
(a) Rent	$2730	25%	_____
(b) Food	$2184	_____	72°
(c) Clothing	$1092	_____	_____
(d) Books and supplies	$1092	_____	_____
(e) Tuition and fees	$1638	_____	_____
(f) Savings	$ 546	_____	_____
(g) Entertainment	$1638	_____	_____

(h) Draw a circle graph using the budget information from the table. Label each sector with the budget item and the percent of total for that item. See Example 4.

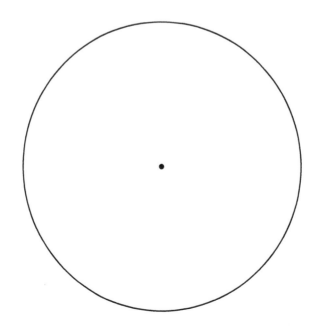

30. The Pathfinder Research Group asked 4488 Americans how they fall asleep. The results are shown in the figure on the right.

Use this information to complete the table. Round to the nearest whole percent and to the nearest degree.

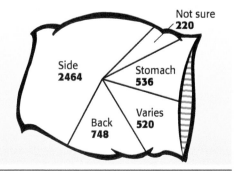

SET TO SLEEP

Number of Americans surveyed who fall asleep on their:

Source: Pathfinder Research Group.

	Sleeping Position	Number of Americans	Percent of Total	Number of Degrees
(a)	Side	____	____	____
(b)	Back	____	____	____
(c)	Stomach	____	____	____
(d)	Varies	____	____	____
(e)	Not sure	____	____	____

(f) Add up the percents. Is the total 100%? Explain why or why not.

(g) Add up the degrees. Is the total 360°? Explain why or why not.

(h) Draw a circle graph using the information from the table above. Label each sector with the sleeping position and the percent of total for that position.

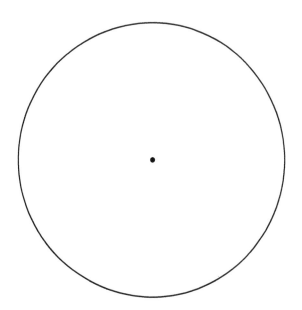

31. White Water Rafting Company divides its annual sales into five categories as shown in the table below.

Category	Annual Sales	Percent of Total
Adventure classes	$12,500	_____
Grocery/provision sales	$40,000	_____
Equipment rentals	$60,000	_____
Rafting tours	$50,000	_____
Equipment sales	$37,500	_____

(a) Find the total sales for the year.

(b) Find the percent of the total for each category and write it in the table.

(c) Find the number of degrees in a circle graph for each item.

(d) Make a circle graph showing the sales information. Label each sector with the category and the percent of total for that category.

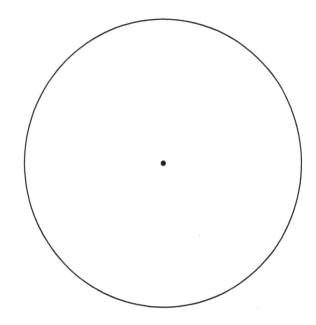

32. A book publisher had 25% of total sales in mysteries, 10% in biographies, 15% in cookbooks, 15% in romance novels, 20% in science, and the rest in travel books.

(a) Find the number of degrees in a circle graph for each type of book.

(b) Draw a circle graph, using the information given. Label each sector with the type of book and the percent of total for that type.

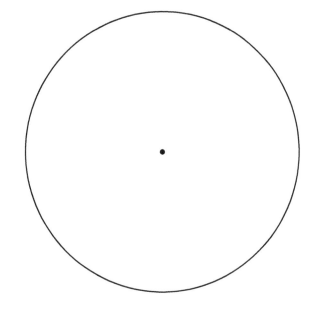

9.3 ⟩⟩⟩ Bar Graphs and Line Graphs

OBJECTIVE 1 Read and understand a bar graph. A **bar graph** is useful for showing comparisons. For example, the bar graph below compares the number of college graduates who continued taking advanced courses in their major field during each of five years.

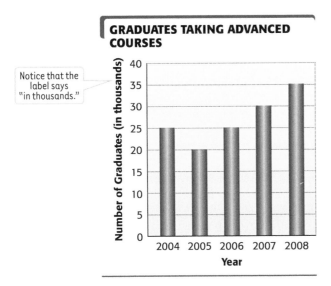

Notice that the label says "in thousands."

GRADUATES TAKING ADVANCED COURSES

OBJECTIVES

Read and understand

1 **a bar graph;**

2 **a double-bar graph;**

3 **a line graph;**

4 **a comparison line graph.**

---

1 Use the bar graph at the left to find the number of college graduates who took advanced courses in their major field in each of these years.

(a) 2004

EXAMPLE 1 Using a Bar Graph

How many college graduates took advanced courses in their major field in 2006?

The bar for 2006 rises to 25. Notice the label along the left side of the graph that says "Number of Graduates (in thousands)." The phrase *in thousands* means you have to **multiply 25 by 1000** to get 25,000. So, 25,000 (**not** 25) graduates took advanced courses in their major field in 2006.

(b) 2005

Work Problem 1 *at the Side.* ▶

OBJECTIVE 2 Read and understand a double-bar graph. A **double-bar graph** can be used to compare two sets of data. The graph below shows the number of DSL (digital subscriber line) installations each quarter for two different years.

(c) 2007

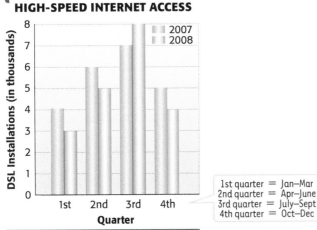

DSL INSTALLATIONS FOR HIGH-SPEED INTERNET ACCESS

1st quarter = Jan–Mar
2nd quarter = Apr–June
3rd quarter = July–Sept
4th quarter = Oct–Dec

(d) 2008

2 Use the double-bar graph on the previous page to find the number of DSL installations in 2007 and 2008 for each quarter.

(a) 1st quarter

(b) 3rd quarter

(c) 4th quarter

(d) Identify the quarter and year with the greatest number of installations. How many installations were made?

3 Use the line graph at the right to answer these questions.

(a) How many trout were stocked in June?

(b) How many fewer trout were stocked in May than in April?

(c) Find the total number of trout stocked during the five months.

(d) In which month were the most trout stocked? How many were stocked?

EXAMPLE 2 **Reading a Double-Bar Graph**

Use the double-bar graph on the previous page to find the following.

(a) The number of DSL installations in the second quarter of 2007.

There are two bars for the second quarter. The color code in the upper right-hand corner of the graph tells you that the red bars represent 2007. So the red bar on the *left* is for the 2nd quarter of 2007. It rises to 6. Multiply 6 by 1000 because the label on the left side of the graph says *in thousands*. So there were 6000 DSL installations for the second quarter in 2007.

(b) The number of DSL installations in the second quarter of 2008.

The green bar for the second quarter rises to 5 and 5 times 1000 is 5000. So, in the second quarter of 2008, there were 5000 DSL installations.

◀ *Work Problem* **2** *at the Side.*

OBJECTIVE 3 Read and understand a line graph. A **line graph** is often useful for showing a trend. The line graph below shows the number of trout stocked along the Feather River during five months. Each dot indicates the number of trout stocked during the month directly below that dot.

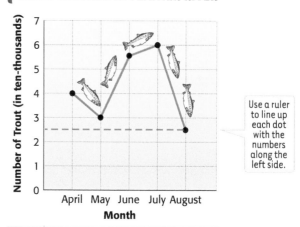

TROUT STOCKED IN FEATHER RIVER

Use a ruler to line up each dot with the numbers along the left side.

EXAMPLE 3 **Understanding a Line Graph**

Use the line graph above to answer each question.

(a) In which month were the least number of trout stocked?

The lowest point on the graph is the dot directly above August, so the least number of trout were stocked in August.

(b) How many trout were stocked in August?

Use a ruler or straightedge to line up the August dot with the numbers along the left edge of the graph. (See the red dashed line on the graph.)

The August dot is halfway between the 2 and 3. Notice that the label on the left side says *in ten-thousands*. So the August dot is halfway between (2 • 10,000) and (3 • 10,000). It is halfway between 20,000 and 30,000. That means 25,000 trout were stocked in August.

CAUTION
Use a ruler or straightedge to line up each dot with the number on the left side of the graph.

◀ *Work Problem* **3** *at the Side.*

OBJECTIVE 4 Read and understand a comparison line graph.
Two sets of data can also be compared by drawing two line graphs together as a **comparison line graph.** For example, the line graph below compares the number of minivans sold and the number of Sport Utility Vehicles (SUVs) sold during each of five years.

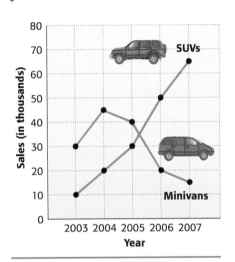

SALES OF MINIVANS AND SUVS

EXAMPLE 4 **Interpreting a Comparison Line Graph**

Use the comparison line graph above to find the following.

(a) The number of minivans sold in 2004
Find the dot on the blue line above 2004. Use a ruler or straightedge to line up the dot with the numbers along the left edge. The dot is halfway between 40 and 50, which is 45. Then, 45 times 1000 is 45,000 minivans sold in 2004.

(b) The number of SUVs sold in 2007
The red line on the graph shows that 65,000 SUVs were sold in 2007.

(c) The amount of decrease and the percent of decrease in minivan sales from 2004 to 2005. Round to the nearest whole percent.

Use subtraction to find the *amount* of decrease.

minivan sales in 2004	−	minivan sales in 2005	=	amount of decrease
45,000	−	40,000	=	5000

Now use the percent equation to find the *percent* of decrease.

percent of original sales = amount of decrease

$$p \cdot 45{,}000 = 5000$$

$$\frac{p \cdot \overset{1}{\cancel{45{,}000}}}{\cancel{45{,}000}_{1}} = \frac{5000}{45{,}000} \quad \text{Divide both sides by 45,000}$$

$$p = 0.11\overline{1} \leftarrow \text{Solution in } decimal \text{ form}$$

Multiply by 100% to change the decimal to a percent.

$$p = 0.11\overline{1} = 11.\overline{1}\% \approx 11\% \text{ to nearest whole percent}$$

The *amount* of decrease is 5000 minivans.
The **percent** of decrease is 11% (rounded).

Work Problem **4** *at the Side.* ▶

4 Use the comparison line graph at the left to find the following.

(a) The number of minivans sold in 2003, 2005, 2006, and 2007

(b) The number of SUVs sold in 2003, 2004, 2005, and 2006

(c) The first full year in which the number of SUVs sold was greater than the number of minivans sold

(d) The amount of increase and percent of increase in SUV sales from 2005 to 2006; round to the nearest whole percent

ANSWERS
4. **(a)** 30,000; 40,000; 20,000; 15,000 minivans
   (b) 10,000; 20,000; 30,000; 50,000 SUVs
   (c) 2006
   (d) increase of 20,000 SUVs; 67% increase (rounded)

Math in the Media

SURFING THE NET

1. Look at the "Source" information at the bottom of the graph. How were the numbers in the graph obtained?

2. (a) How many people in the poll said they cut back on television viewing to find time to use the Internet?

(b) Find the number of people in the poll who cut back on each of the other activities listed in the graph.

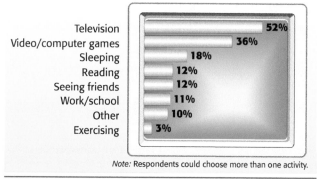

CAUGHT IN THE NET

Web users have cut back on the following activities to get more online time:

- Television — 52%
- Video/computer games — 36%
- Sleeping — 18%
- Reading — 12%
- Seeing friends — 12%
- Work/school — 11%
- Other — 10%
- Exercising — 3%

Note: Respondents could choose more than one activity.

Source: NUKE InterNETWORK poll of 500 regular users.

3. Add up all the responses to the poll from Problem 2. Why is the total more than the 500 people that were in the poll?

4. Suppose you took a poll on Internet use among 500 students at your school. Would you expect the results to be similar to those shown in the graph? Why or why not?

5. Conduct a survey of your class members. First find out if they regularly use the Internet, then ask which of the activities they cut back on to have more surfing time. Each person polled can select more than one activity.

(a) How many students are in your class poll? _____

(b) Complete the table using the responses from those who regularly use the Internet.

Activity	Number Who Cut Back on the Activity	Percent Who Cut Back on the Activity
Television		
Video/computer games		
Sleeping		
Reading		
Seeing friends		
Work/school		
Other		
Exercising		

(c) Make a bar graph showing your survey data. How is your data similar to the graph shown above? How is it different?

9.3 ▷▷▷ Exercises

FOR
EXTRA
HELP

MyMathLab

Math XL
PRACTICE

WATCH

DOWNLOAD

READ

REVIEW

This bar graph shows the top seven reasons people say they shop on-line. Use the graph to answer Exercises 1–6. See Example 1.

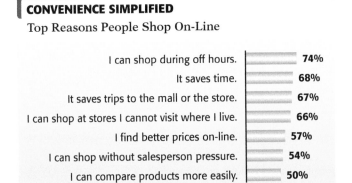

CONVENIENCE SIMPLIFIED

Top Reasons People Shop On-Line

I can shop during off hours.	**74%**
It saves time.	**68%**
It saves trips to the mall or the store.	**67%**
I can shop at stores I cannot visit where I live.	**66%**
I find better prices on-line.	**57%**
I can shop without salesperson pressure.	**54%**
I can compare products more easily.	**50%**

Source: EMARKETER.

5. Which reason(s) were given by $\frac{1}{2}$ of the people? Which reason(s) were given by nearly $\frac{3}{4}$ of the people?

1. What is the top reason people shop on-line? What percent gave this reason?

2. What is the second most popular reason for shopping on-line? What percent gave this reason?

3. What percent of the people say they find better prices on-line? If 600 people were surveyed, how many gave this answer?

4. What percent say it saves trips to the mall or store? If 600 people were surveyed, how many gave this answer?

6. Which reason(s) were given by about $\frac{2}{3}$ of the people?

This double-bar graph shows the number of workers who were unemployed in a city during the first six months of 2007 and 2008. Use this graph to answer Exercises 7–12. Round percents to the nearest whole number. See Example 2.

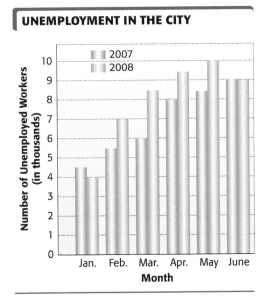

UNEMPLOYMENT IN THE CITY

7. In the first half of 2008, which month had the greatest number of unemployed workers? What was the total number unemployed in that month?

8. How many workers were unemployed in January of 2007?

9. How many more workers were unemployed in February of 2008 than in February of 2007?

10. How many fewer workers were unemployed in March of 2007 than in March of 2008?

11. Find the amount of increase and the percent of increase in the number of unemployed workers from February 2007 to April 2007.

12. Find the amount of increase and the percent of increase in the number of unemployed workers from January 2008 to June 2008.

This double-bar graph shows sales of super unleaded and supreme unleaded gasoline at a service station for each of five years. Use this graph to answer Exercises 13–18. See Example 2.

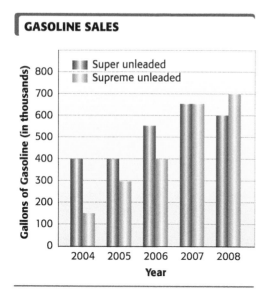

13. How many gallons of supreme unleaded gasoline were sold in 2004?

14. How many gallons of super unleaded gasoline were sold in 2007?

15. In which year did the greatest difference in sales between super unleaded and supreme unleaded gasoline occur? Find the difference.

16. In which year did the sales of supreme unleaded gasoline surpass the sales of super unleaded gasoline?

17. Find the amount of increase and percent of increase in supreme unleaded gasoline sales from 2004 to 2008. Round to the nearest whole percent.

18. Find the amount of increase and percent of increase in super unleaded gasoline sales from 2004 to 2008.

This line graph shows how sales of personal computers (PCs) have increased since they first became widely available in 1985. Use the line graph to answer Exercises 19–24. Round percents to the nearest whole percent. See Example 3.

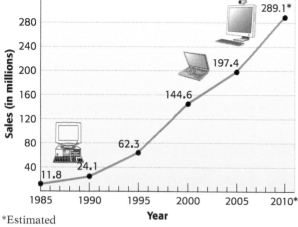

**A QUARTER CENTURY OF COMPUTING
WORLDWIDE PC SALES FROM 1985 TO 2010**

*Estimated

Source: Gartner Dataquest and ARS Technica.

19. How many PCs were shipped in 1990?

20. The number of PCs shipped in 2010 is an estimate. What is the estimated number?

21. How many more PCs were shipped in 2005 than in 1985?

22. Place a ruler or straightedge on the graph to find the year in which PC shipments reached (a) 40 million; (b) 120 million.

23. Find the amount of increase in shipments from 1995 to 2000. What was the percent of increase, to the nearest whole percent?

24. What was the amount of increase and the percent of increase in PC shipments from 1985 to 1990?

This comparison line graph shows the number of DVDs sold by two different chain stores during each of five years. Use this graph to find the annual number of DVDs sold in each year listed in Exercises 25–28. See Example 4.

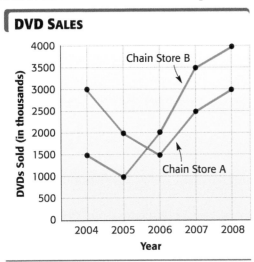

DVD SALES

25. (a) Chain Store A in 2004
    (b) Chain Store B in 2004

26. (a) Chain Store A in 2005
    (b) Chain Store B in 2005

27. (a) Chain Store A in 2007
    (b) Chain Store A in 2008

28. (a) Chain Store B in 2006
    (b) Chain Store B in 2007

29. Describe the pattern(s) or trend(s) you see in the graph.

30. Store B used to have lower sales than Store A. What might have happened to cause this change? Give four possible explanations.

This comparison line graph shows the sales and profits of Tacos-To-Go for each of four years. Use the graph to answer Exercises 31–36.

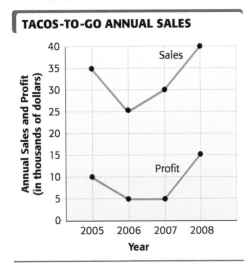

TACOS-TO-GO ANNUAL SALES

31. Find the year of lowest sales and the amount of sales.

32. Find the year of greatest profit and the amount of profit.

33. For each of the four years, the profit is what percent of sales? Round to the nearest whole percent.

34. Find the total sales for all four years and the total profit for all four years. Total profit is what percent of total sales? Round to the nearest whole percent.

35. Give two possible explanations for the decrease in sales from 2005 to 2006 and two possible explanations for the increase in sales from 2006 to 2008.

36. *Based on the graph,* what conclusion can you make about the relationship between sales and profits for Tacos-To-Go?

Relating Concepts (Exercises 37–44) For Individual or Group Work

Find the line graph on Worldwide Shipments of PCs and the double-line graph on DVD Sales earlier in this exercise set. Use the graphs as you **work Exercises 37–44 in order.** *Round percent answers to the nearest whole percent.*

37. What overall trend do you see in the line graph on worldwide shipments of Personal Computers (PCs)?

38. Give at least two possible explanations for the increase in PC shipments.

39. Look back at your earlier answers or find the percent of increase in PC shipments from

 (a) 1985 to 1990 (see Exercise 24)

 (b) 1990 to 1995

 (c) 1995 to 2000 (see Exercise 23)

 (d) 2000 to 2005

 (e) 2005 to 2010.

40. Look at the percents of increase in Exercise 39. What trend do you see?

41. What future conditions could result in a decrease in PC shipments? Give at least two possibilities.

42. Look back at the double-line graph of DVD sales. For each store, compare the sales of DVDs in 2008 to sales in 2004. Find the percent of increase or the percent of decrease for:

 (a) Chain Store A

 (b) Chain Store B.

43. *Based on the graph,* what amount of DVD sales would you predict for

 (a) Store A in 2009?

 (b) Store B in 2009?

 (c) Explain how you arrived at your predictions.

44. (a) *Based on the graph,* which store would you like to own? Explain why.

 (b) Name at least three other things you would want to know before deciding which store to buy.

9.4 ▶▶▶ **Problem Solving with Statistics:
Mean, Median, and Mode**

The word *statistics* originally came from words that mean *state numbers.* State numbers refer to numerical information, or *data,* gathered by the government such as the number of births, deaths, or marriages in a population. Today the word *statistics* has a much broader meaning; data from the fields of economics, social science, science, and business can all be organized and studied under the branch of mathematics called *statistics.*

OBJECTIVE **1** **Find the mean of a list of numbers.**   Making sense of a long list of numbers can be difficult. So when you analyze data, one of the first things to look for is a *measure of central tendency*—a single number that you can use to represent the entire list of numbers. One such measure is the *average* or **mean.** The mean can be found with the following formula.

> **OBJECTIVES**
>
> **1** Find the mean of a list of numbers.
>
> **2** Find a weighted mean.
>
> **3** Find the median.
>
> **4** Find the mode.

Finding the Mean (Average)

$$\text{mean} = \frac{\text{sum of all values}}{\text{number of values}}$$

---

1 Tanya had test scores of 95, 91, 81, 78, 81, and 90. Find her mean (average) score.

EXAMPLE 1 **Finding the Mean (Average)**

David had test scores of 84, 90, 95, 98, and 88. Find his mean (average) score.
   Use the formula for finding the mean. Add up all the test scores and then divide the sum by the number of tests.

$$\text{mean} = \frac{84 + 90 + 95 + 98 + 88}{5} \quad \text{← Add all the test scores.}$$

$$\text{mean} = \frac{455}{5} \quad \text{← Divide by the number of tests.}$$

$$\text{mean} = 91$$

David has a mean (average) score of 91.

———————— *Work Problem* **1** *at the Side.* ▶

2 Find the mean for each list of numbers.

   (a) Jorge's monthly cell phone bills last year were $25.12, $42.58, $76.19, $32, $81.11, $26.41, $49.76, $59.32, $71.18, $30.09, $60.50, and $79.84. Find his average monthly bill to the nearest cent.

EXAMPLE 2 **Applying the Mean (Average)**

The sales of photo albums at Sarah's Card Shop for each day last week were $86, $103, $118, $117, $126, $158, and $149. Find the mean daily sales of photo albums.
   To find the mean, add all the daily sales amounts and then divide the sum by the number of days (7).

$$\text{mean} = \frac{\$86 + \$103 + \$118 + \$117 + \$126 + \$158 + \$149}{7} \quad \begin{array}{l} \leftarrow \text{Sum of sales} \\ \leftarrow \text{Number of days} \end{array}$$

$$\text{mean} = \frac{\$857}{7}$$

$$\text{mean} \approx \$122.43 \qquad \text{Rounded to nearest cent}$$

———————— *Work Problem* **2** *at the Side.* ▶

   (b) The sales for one year at eight different office supply stores: $749,820; $765,480; $643,744; $824,222; $485,886; $668,178; $702,294; $525,800

ANSWERS

1. $\dfrac{516}{6} = 86$ average score

2. **(a)** $\dfrac{\$634.10}{12} \approx \$52.84$

   (b) $\dfrac{\$5,365,424}{8} = \$670,678$

3 Alison Nakano works downtown. Some days she can park in cheaper lots that charge $6, $7, or $8. Other days, she has to park in lots that charge $9 or $10. Last month she kept track of the amount she spent each day for parking and the number of days she spent that amount. Find her average daily parking cost.

Parking Fee	Frequency
$ 6	2
$ 7	6
$ 8	3
$ 9	4
$10	6

OBJECTIVE **2** **Find a weighted mean.** Some items in a list of data might appear more than once. In this case, we find a **weighted mean,** in which each value is "weighted" by multiplying it by the number of times it occurs.

EXAMPLE 3 **Finding a Weighted Mean**

The table below shows the amount of contribution and the number of times the amount was given (frequency) to a food pantry. Find the weighted mean.

Contribution Value	Frequency
$ 3	4
$ 5	2
$ 7	1
$ 8	5
$ 9	3
$10	2
$12	1
$13	2

4 people each contributed $3.

The same amount was given by more than one person: for example, $3 was given by four people, and $8 was given by five people. Other amounts, such as $12, were given by only one person.

To find the mean, multiply each contribution value by its frequency. Then add the products. Next, add the numbers in the *frequency* column to find the total number of values, that is, the total number of people who contributed money.

Value	Frequency	Product
$ 3	4	($3 • 4) = $12
$ 5	2	($5 • 2) = $10
$ 7	1	($7 • 1) = $ 7
$ 8	5	($8 • 5) = $40
$ 9	3	($9 • 3) = $27
$10	2	($10 • 2) = $20
$12	1	($12 • 1) = $12
$13	2	($13 • 2) = $26
Totals	20	$154

Finally, divide the totals.

$$\text{mean} = \frac{\$154}{20} = \$7.70$$

The mean contribution to the food pantry was $7.70.

◄ *Work Problem* **3** *at the Side.*

ANSWER

3. $\frac{\$174}{21} \approx \$8.29$ (to nearest cent)

A common use of the weighted mean is to find a student's *grade point average (GPA),* as shown in the next example.

EXAMPLE 4   **Applying the Weighted Mean**

Find the GPA (grade point average) for a student who earned the following grades last semester. Assume A = 4, B = 3, C = 2, D = 1, and F = 0. The number of credits determines how many times the grade is counted (the frequency).

Course	Credits	Grade	Credits • Grade
Mathematics	4	A (= 4)	4 • 4 = 16
Speech	3	C (= 2)	3 • 2 = 6
English	3	B (= 3)	3 • 3 = 9
Computer science	2	A (= 4)	2 • 4 = 8
Theater	2	D (= 1)	2 • 1 = 2
Totals	14		41

It is common to round grade point averages to the nearest hundredth. So the grade point average for this student is rounded to 2.93.

$$\text{GPA} = \frac{41}{14} \approx 2.93$$ This GPA is close to a B.

Work Problem **4** *at the Side.* ▶

OBJECTIVE 3 Find the median. Because it can be affected by extremely high or low numbers, the mean is often a poor indicator of central tendency for a list of numbers. In cases like this, another measure of central tendency, called the *median,* can be used. The **median** divides a group of numbers in half; half the numbers lie above the median, and half lie below the median.

Find the median by listing the numbers *in order* from *least* to *greatest.* If the list contains an *odd* number of items, the median is the *middle number.*

EXAMPLE 5   **Finding the Median (Odd Number of Items)**

Find the median for this list of prices.

$7, $23, $15, $6, $18, $12, $24

First, arrange the numbers in numerical order from least to greatest.

Least → 6, 7, 12, 15, 18, 23, 24 ← Greatest

Next, find the *middle* number in the list.

6, 7, 12, 15, 18, 23, 24   List the numbers from least to greatest **before** finding the middle.

Three are below. ↓ Three are above.
Middle number

The median price is $15.

Work Problem **5** *at the Side.* ▶

If a list contains an *even* number of items, there is no single middle number. In this case, the median is defined as the mean (average) of the *middle two* numbers.

4 Find the GPA (grade point average) for a student who earned the following grades. Round to the nearest hundredth.

Course	Credits	Grade
Mathematics	5	A (= 4)
English	3	C (= 2)
Biology	4	B (= 3)
History	3	B (= 3)

5 Find the median for the numbers of customers helped each hour at the order desk.

35, 33, 27, 30, 39, 50, 59, 25, 30

ANSWERS

4. GPA = $\frac{47}{15} \approx 3.13$

5. 33 customers (the middle number when the numbers are arranged from least to greatest)

6 Find the median for this list of measurements.

178 ft, 261 ft, 126 ft, 189 ft, 121 ft, 195 ft, 121 ft, 200 ft

EXAMPLE 6 Finding the Median (Even Number of Items)

Find the median for this list of ages, in years.

$$74, 7, 15, 13, 25, 28, 47, 59, 33, 68$$

First, arrange the numbers in numerical order from least to greatest. Then, because the list has an even number of ages, find the middle *two* numbers.

Least ⟶ 7, 13, 15, 25, 28, 33, 47, 59, 68, 74 ⟵ Greatest

Middle two numbers

The median age is the mean (average) of the two middle numbers.

$$\text{median} = \frac{28 + 33}{2} = \frac{61}{2} = 30.5 \text{ years}$$

◀ *Work Problem* **6** *at the Side.*

7 Find the mode for each list of numbers.

(a) Ages of part-time employees (in years): 28, 21, 16, 22, 28, 34, 22, 28, 19, 18

OBJECTIVE **4** **Find the mode.** Another statistical measure is the **mode,** which is the number that occurs *most often* in a list of numbers. For example, the test scores for ten students are shown below.

↓   ↓   ↓
74, 81, 39, 74, 82, 80, 100, 92, 74, 85

The mode is 74. Three students earned a score of 74, so 74 appears more times on the list than any other score. It is *not* necessary to place the numbers in numerical order when looking for the mode, although that may help you find it more easily.

A list can have two modes; such a list is sometimes called *bimodal.* If no number occurs more frequently than any other number in a list, the list has *no mode.*

(b) Total points on a screening exam: 312, 219, 782, 312, 219, 426, 507, 600

EXAMPLE 7 Finding the Mode

Find the mode for each list of numbers.

(a) 51, 32, 49, 51, 49, 90, 49, 60, 17, 60
   The number 49 occurs three times, which is more often than any other number. Therefore, **49** is the mode.

(b) 482, 485, 483, 485, 487, 487, 489, 486
   Because both **485** and **487** occur twice, each is a mode. This list is *bimodal.*

(c) Monthly commissions of salespeople: $1706, $1289, $1653, $1892, $1301, $1782, $1450, $1566

(c) $10,708; $11,519; $10,972; $12,546; $13,905; $12,182
   No price occurs more than once. This list has *no mode.*

Measures of Central Tendency

The **mean** is the sum of all the values divided by the number of values. It is the mathematical *average*.

The **median** is the *middle number* (or the average of the two middle numbers) in a group of values that are listed from least to greatest. It divides a group of numbers in half.

The **mode** is the value that occurs *most often* in a group of values.

ANSWERS

6. $\frac{178 + 189}{2} = 183.5$ ft

7. **(a)** 28 years
   (b) bimodal, 219 points and 312 points (this list has two modes)
   (c) no mode (no number occurs more than once)

◀ *Work Problem* **7** *at the Side.*

9.4 ▶▶▶ **Exercises**

FOR EXTRA HELP   *MyMathLab*   Math XL PRACTICE   WATCH   DOWNLOAD   READ   REVIEW

Find the mean for each list of numbers. Round answers to the nearest tenth when necessary. See Examples 1 and 2.

1. Final exam scores: 92, 51, 59, 86, 68, 73, 49, 80

2. Quiz scores: 18, 25, 21, 8, 16, 13, 23, 19

3. Annual salaries: $31,900; $32,850; $34,930; $39,712; $38,340, $60,000

4. Numbers of people attending baseball games: 27,500; 18,250; 17,357; 14,298; 33,110

5. The Athletic Shoe Store sold shoes at the following prices: $75.52, $36.15, $58.24, $21.86, $47.68, $106.57, $82.72, $52.14, $28.60, $72.92.

6. In one evening, a server collected the following checks from her dinner customers: $30.10, $42.80, $91.60, $51.20, $88.30, $21.90, $43.70, $51.20.

Find the weighted mean. Round answers to the nearest tenth when necessary. See Example 3.

7.

Quiz Score	Frequency
3 .	4
5	2
6	5
8	5
9	2

8.

Credits per Student	Frequency
9	3
12	5
13	2
15	6
18	1

Find the GPA (grade point average) for students earning the following grades. Assume A = 4, B = 3, C = 2, D = 1, and F = 0. Round answers to the nearest hundredth. See Example 4.

9.

Course	Credits	Grade
Biology	4	B
Biology lab	2	A
Mathematics	5	C
Health	1	F
Psychology	3	B

10.

Course	Credits	Grade
Chemistry	3	A
English	3	B
Mathematics	4	B
Theater	2	C
Astronomy	3	C

11. Look again at the grades in Exercise 9. Find the student's GPA in each of these situations.

   (a) The student earned a B instead of an F in the 1-credit class.

   (b) The student earned a B instead of a C in the 5-credit class.

   (c) Both (a) and (b) happened.

12. List the credits for the courses you're taking at this time. List the lowest grades you think you will earn in each class and find your GPA. Then list the highest grades you think you will earn and find your GPA.

Find the median for each list of numbers. See Examples 5 and 6.

13. Number of e-mail messages received:
9, 15, 23, 12, 14, 24, 28

14. Patients seen each day at a clinic:
99, 108, 123, 109, 126, 146, 129, 168, 170

15. Students enrolled in algebra each semester:
328, 549, 420, 592, 715, 483

16. Number of cars in the parking lot each day:
520, 523, 513, 1283, 338, 509, 290, 420

17. Pounds of shrimp sold each day: 51, 48, 96, 40, 47, 40, 95, 56, 34, 49

18. Number of gallons of paint sold per week:
1072, 1068, 1093, 1042, 1056, 205, 1009, 1081

The table lists the cruising speed and distance flown without refueling for several types of larger airplanes used to carry passengers. Use the table to answer Exercises 19–22.

Type of Airplane	Cruising Speed (miles per hour)	Distance without Refueling (miles)
747-400	565	7650
747-200	558	6450
DC-9	505	1100
DC-10	550	5225
727	530	1550
757	530	2875

Source: Northwest Airlines *World Traveler.*

19. What is the average distance flown without refueling, to the nearest mile?

20. Find the average cruising speed to the nearest mile per hour.

21. Find the median distance flown.

22. Find the median cruising speed.

Find the mode or modes for each list of numbers. See Example 7.

23. Number of samples taken each hour:
3, 8, 5, 1, 7, 6, 8, 4, 5, 8

24. Monthly water bills:
$21, $32, $46, $32, $49, $32, $49, $25, $32

25. Ages of senior residents (in years):
74, 68, 68, 68, 75, 75, 74, 74, 70, 77

26. Patients admitted to the hospital each week:
30, 19, 25, 78, 36, 20, 45, 85, 38

27. The number of boxes of candy sold by each child:
5, 9, 17, 3, 2, 8, 19, 1, 4, 20, 10, 6

28. The weights of soccer players (in pounds):
158, 161, 165, 162, 165, 157, 163, 162

The table lists monthly normal temperatures from November through April for two of the coldest U.S. cities. Use the table to answer Exercises 29–30. Round answers to the nearest whole degree.

City	Nov.	Dec.	Jan.	Feb.	Mar.	Apr.
Barrow, Alaska	−2	−11	−13	−18	−15	−2
Fairbanks, Alaska	3	−7	−10	−4	11	31

Normal Monthly Temperatures (in Degrees Fahrenheit)

Source: National Climatic Data Center.

29. Find Barrow's mean temperature and Fairbanks' mean temperature for the six-month period. How much warmer is Fairbanks' mean than Barrow's?

30. Find Barrow's median temperature and Fairbanks' median temperature for the six-month period. How much cooler is Barrow's median than Fairbanks'?

9.5 ▶▶▶ The Rectangular Coordinate System

OBJECTIVE 1 Plot a point, given the coordinates, and find the coordinates, given a point. A bar graph or line graph shows the relationship between two things. The line graph below is from Example 3 in **Section 9.3.** It shows the relationship between the month of the year and the number of trout stocked in the Feather River.

TROUT STOCKED IN FEATHER RIVER

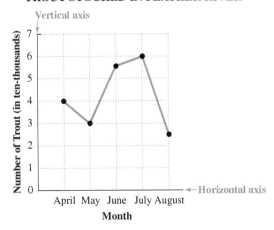

Each black dot on the graph represents a particular month paired with a particular number of trout. This is an example of **paired data.** We write each pair inside parentheses, with a comma separating the two items. To be consistent, we will always list the item on the *horizontal axis* first. In this case, the months are shown on the **horizontal axis** (the line that goes "left and right"), and the number of trout is shown along the **vertical axis** (the line that goes "up and down").

Paired Data from Line Graph on Trout Stocked in Feather River

(Apr, 40,000) (May, 30,000) (June, 55,000) (July, 60,000) (Aug, 25,000)

Each data pair gives you the location of a particular spot on the graph, and that spot is marked with a dot. This idea of paired data can be used to locate particular places on any flat surface.

Think of a small town laid out in a grid of square blocks, as shown below. To tell a taxi driver where to go, you could say, "the corner of 4th Avenue and 2nd Street" or just "4th and 2nd." As an *ordered pair*, it would be (4, 2). Of course, both you and the taxi driver need to know that the avenue is mentioned first (the number on the horizontal axis) and that the street is mentioned second (the number on the vertical axis). If the driver goes to (2, 4) instead, you'll be at the wrong corner.

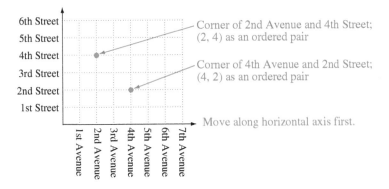

1 Plot each point on the grid. Write the ordered pair next to each point.

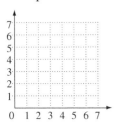

(a) $(1, 4)$

(b) $(5, 2)$

(c) $(4, 1)$

(d) $(3, 3)$

ANSWERS

1.

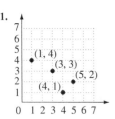

 EXAMPLE 1 **Plotting Points on a Grid**

Use the grid at the right to plot each point.

(a) $(3, 5)$

Start at 0. Move *to the right* along the horizontal axis until you reach 3. Then move *up* 5 units so that you are aligned with 5 on the vertical axis. Make a dot. This is the plot, or graph, of the point $(3, 5)$.

(b) $(5, 3)$

Start at 0. Move *to the right* along the horizontal axis until you reach 5. Then move *up* 3 units so that you are aligned with 3 on the vertical axis. Make a dot. This is the plot, or graph, of the point $(5, 3)$.

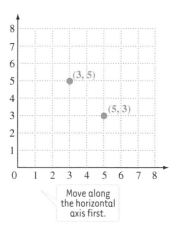

Move along the horizontal axis first.

CAUTION

In Example 1, notice that the points $(3, 5)$ and $(5, 3)$ are ***not*** the same. The "address" of a point is called an **ordered pair** because the *order* within the pair is important. Always move along the horizontal axis first.

◀ *Work Problem* **1** *at the Side.*

You have been using both positive and negative numbers throughout this book. We can extend our grid system to include negative numbers, as shown below. The horizontal axis is now a number line with 0 at the center, positive numbers extending to the right and negative numbers to the left. This horizontal number line is called the ***x*-axis.**

The vertical axis is also a number line, with positive numbers extending upward from 0 and negative numbers extending downward from 0. The vertical axis is called the ***y*-axis.** Together, the *x*-axis and the *y*-axis form a rectangular **coordinate system.** The point $(0, 0)$ is where the *x*-axis crosses the *y*-axis; it is called the **origin.**

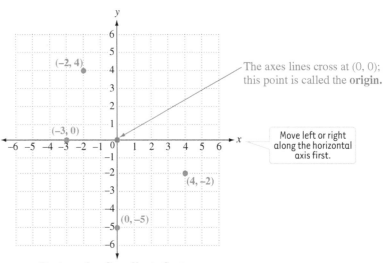

The axes lines cross at $(0, 0)$; this point is called the **origin.**

Move left or right along the horizontal axis first.

Rectangular Coordinate System

EXAMPLE 2 **Plotting Points on a Rectangular Coordinate System**

Plot each point on the rectangular coordinate system shown at the bottom of the previous page.

(a) $(4, -2)$

Start at 0. Then move left or right along the horizontal x-axis first.
Because 4 is *positive,* move *to the right* until you reach 4. Now, because the 2 is *negative,* move *down* 2 units so that you are aligned with -2 on the y-axis. Make a dot and label it $(4, -2)$.

(b) $(-2, 4)$

Starting at 0, move left or right along the horizontal x-axis first. In this case, move *to the left* until you reach -2. Then move *up* 4 units. Make a dot and label it $(-2, 4)$. Notice that $(-2, 4)$ is ***not*** the same as $(4, -2)$.

(c) $(0, -5)$

Start at 0. Move left or right along the horizontal x-axis first. However, because the first number is 0, do not move left or right. Then move *down* 5 units. Make a dot and label it $(0, -5)$.

(d) $(-3, 0)$

Starting at 0, move *to the left* along the horizontal x-axis to -3. Then, because the second number is 0, stay on -3. Do *not* move up or down. Make a dot and label it $(-3, 0)$.

> **Note**
>
> When the *first* number in an ordered pair is 0, the point is on the y-axis, as in Example 2(c) above. When the *second* number in an ordered pair is 0, the point is on the x-axis, as in Example 2(d) above.

Work Problem **2** *at the Side.* ▶

We can use a coordinate system and an ordered pair to show the location of any point. The numbers in the ordered pair are called the **coordinates** of the point.

EXAMPLE 3 **Finding the Coordinates of Points**

Find the coordinates of points A, B, C, and D.

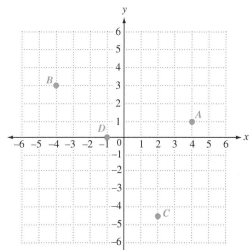

To reach point A from the origin, move 4 units *to the right;* then move *up* 1 unit. The coordinates are $(4, 1)$.

Continued on Next Page

---

2 Plot each point on the coordinate system below. Write the ordered pair next to each point.

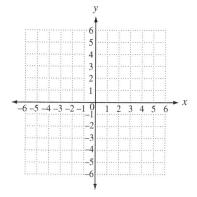

(a) $(5, -3)$

(b) $(-5, 3)$

(c) $(0, 3)$

(d) $(-4, -4)$

(e) $(-2, 0)$

ANSWERS

2.

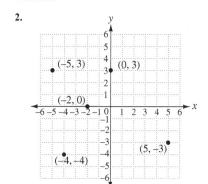

3 Find the coordinates of points *A*, *B*, *C*, *D*, and *E*.

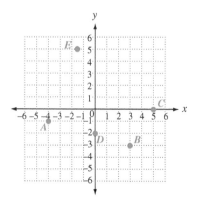

4 **(a)** All points in the fourth quadrant are similar in what way? Give two examples of points in the fourth quadrant.

To reach point *B* from the origin, move 4 units *to the left;* then move *up* 3 units. The coordinates are $(-4, 3)$.

To reach point *C* from the origin, move 2 units *to the right;* then move *down* approximately $4\frac{1}{2}$ units. The approximate coordinates are $(2, -4\frac{1}{2})$.

To reach point *D* from the origin, move 1 unit *to the left;* then do *not* move either up or down. The coordinates are $(-1, 0)$.

> **Note**
>
> If a point is between the lines on the coordinate system, you can use fractions to give the approximate coordinates. For example, the approximate coordinates of point *C* above are $(2, -4\frac{1}{2})$.

◀ *Work Problem* **3** *at the Side.*

OBJECTIVE 2 Identify the four quadrants and determine which points lie within each one. The *x*-axis and *y*-axis divide the coordinate system into four regions, called **quadrants.** These quadrants are numbered with Roman numerals, as shown below. Points on the axes lines are not in any quadrant.

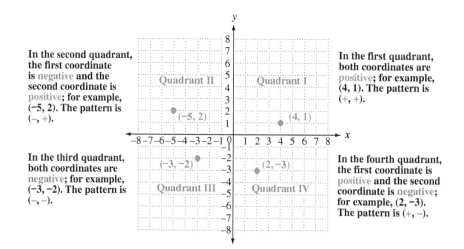

In the second quadrant, the first coordinate is negative and the second coordinate is positive; for example, $(-5, 2)$. The pattern is $(-, +)$.

In the first quadrant, both coordinates are positive; for example, $(4, 1)$. The pattern is $(+, +)$.

In the third quadrant, both coordinates are negative; for example, $(-3, -2)$. The pattern is $(-, -)$.

In the fourth quadrant, the first coordinate is positive and the second coordinate is negative; for example, $(2, -3)$. The pattern is $(+, -)$.

(b) In which quadrant is each point located: $(-2, -6)$; $(0, 5)$; $(-3, 1)$; $(4, -1)$?

> **EXAMPLE 4 Working with Quadrants**
>
> **(a)** All points in the third quadrant are similar in what way? Give two examples of points in the third quadrant.
>
> For all points in quadrant III, both coordinates are negative. The pattern is $(-, -)$. There are many possible examples, such as $(-2, -5)$ and $(-4, -4)$. Just be sure that both numbers are negative.
>
> **(b)** In which quadrant is each point located: $(3, 5)$; $(1, -6)$; $(-4, 0)$?
>
> For $(3, 5)$ the pattern is $(+, +)$, so the point is in **quadrant I.**
>
> For $(1, -6)$ the pattern is $(+, -)$, so the point is in **quadrant IV.**
>
> The point corresponding to $(-4, 0)$ is on the *x*-axis, so it isn't in any quadrant.

> When one of the numbers is 0, the point is on an axis line.

◀ *Work Problem* **4** *at the Side.*

ANSWERS

3. *A* is $(-4, -1)$; *B* is $(3, -3)$; *C* is $(5, 0)$;

   D is $(0, -2)$; *E* is approximately $\left(-1\frac{1}{2}, 5\right)$.

4. (a) The pattern for all points in quadrant IV is $(+, -)$. Examples will vary; just be sure that they fit the $(+, -)$ pattern.

   (b) III; no quadrant; II; IV

*Plot each point on the rectangular coordinate system. Label each point with its
coordinates. See Examples 1 and 2.*

1. $(3, 7)$ $(-2, 2)$ $(-3, -7)$ $(2, -2)$ $(0, 6)$
$(6, 0)$ $(0, -4)$ $(-4, 0)$

2. $(5, 2)$ $(-3, -3)$ $(4, -1)$ $(-4, 1)$ $(-1, 0)$
$(0, 3)$ $(2, 0)$ $(0, -5)$

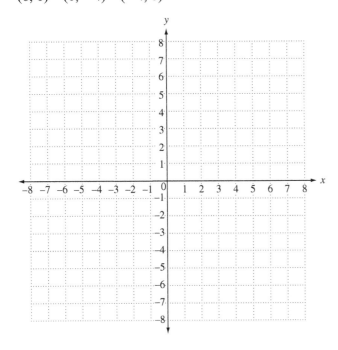

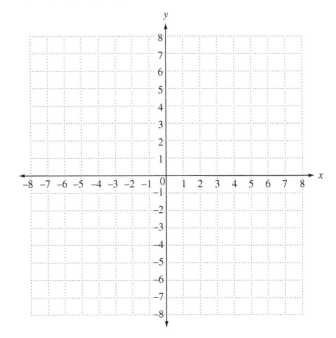

3. $(-5, 3)$ $(4, 4)$ $(-2\frac{1}{2}, 0)$ $(3, -5)$ $(0, 0)$
$(2, \frac{1}{2})$ $(-7, -5)$ $(-1, -6)$

4. $(1, 7)$ $(0, 3\frac{1}{2})$ $(-5, -1)$ $(6, -2)$ $(-2, 6)$
$(0, 0)$ $(-3, 3)$ $(-\frac{1}{2}, -2)$

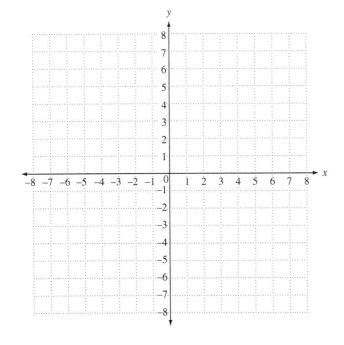

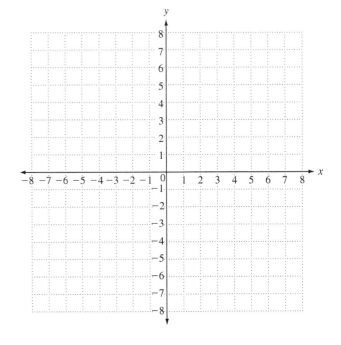

Give the coordinates of each point. See Example 3.

5.

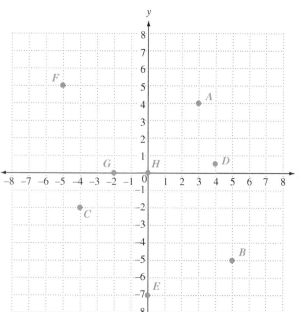

6.

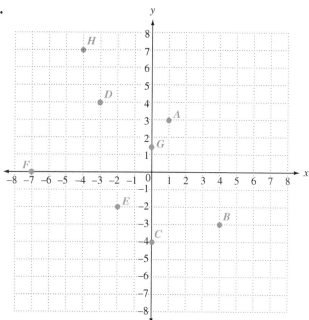

Identify the quadrant in which each point is located. See Example 4.

7. In which quadrant is each point located?
$(-3, -7)$ $(0, 4)$ $(10, -16)$ $(-9, 5)$

8. In which quadrant is each point located?
$(1, 12)$ $(20, -8)$ $(-5, 0)$ $(-14, 14)$

Complete each ordered pair with a number that will make the point fall in the specified quadrant.

9. (a) Quadrant II $(-4, \underline{\hspace{1cm}})$

(b) Quadrant IV $(7, \underline{\hspace{1cm}})$

(c) No quadrant $(\underline{\hspace{1cm}}, -2)$

(d) Quadrant III $(\underline{\hspace{1cm}}, -1\frac{1}{2})$

(e) Quadrant I $(3\frac{1}{4}, \underline{\hspace{1cm}})$

10. (a) Quadrant III $(-5, \underline{\hspace{1cm}})$

(b) Quadrant I $(\underline{\hspace{1cm}}, 3)$

(c) Quadrant IV $(\underline{\hspace{1cm}}, -\frac{1}{2})$

(d) No quadrant $(6, \underline{\hspace{1cm}})$

(e) Quadrant II $(\underline{\hspace{1cm}}, 1\frac{3}{4})$

11. Explain how to graph the ordered pair (a, b), where a and b are positive or negative integers.

12. Explain how to graph the ordered pair (a, b) where a is 0 and b is an integer. Explain how to graph (a, b) where a is an integer and b is 0.

9.6 ▶▶▶ Introduction to Graphing Linear Equations

In **Chapters 4–7** you solved equations that had only one variable, such as $2n - 3 = 7$ or $\frac{1}{3}x = 10$. Each of these equations had exactly one solution; n is 5 in the first equation, and x is 30 in the second equation. In other words, there was only *one* number that could replace the variable and make the equation balance. Later in this book, you will work with equations that have two variables and many different numbers that will make the equation balance. This section will get you started.

OBJECTIVES

1 Graph linear equations in two variables.

2 Identify the slope of a line as positive or negative.

OBJECTIVE 1 Graph linear equations in two variables.   Suppose that you have 6 hours of study time available during a weekend. You plan to study math and psychology. For example, you could spend 4 hours on math and then 2 hours on psychology, for a total of 6 hours. Or you could spend $1\frac{1}{2}$ hours on math and then $4\frac{1}{2}$ hours on psychology, for a total of 6 hours. Here is a list of *some* of the possible combinations.

Hours on Math	+	Hours on Psychology	=	Total Hours Studying
0	+	6	=	6
1	+	5	=	6
$1\frac{1}{2}$	+	$4\frac{1}{2}$	=	6
3	+	3	=	6
4	+	2	=	6
$5\frac{1}{2}$	+	$\frac{1}{2}$	=	6
6	+	0	=	6

We can write an equation to represent this situation.

$$\begin{array}{ccccc} \text{hours studying} & + & \text{hours studying} & = & \text{total of} \\ \text{math} & & \text{psychology} & & \text{6 hours} \\ m & + & p & = & 6 \end{array}$$

This equation, $m + p = 6$, has *two* variables. The hours spent on math (m) can vary, and the hours spent on psychology (p) can vary.

As you can see, there is more than one solution for this equation. We can list possible solutions as *ordered pairs*. The first number in the pair is the value of m (math), and the second number in the pair is the corresponding value of p (psychology).

$$\begin{array}{ccccccc} (m, p) & (m, p) & (m, p) & (m, p) & (m, p) & (m, p) & (m, p) \\ \downarrow\downarrow & \downarrow\downarrow & \downarrow\downarrow & \downarrow\downarrow & \downarrow\downarrow & \downarrow\downarrow & \downarrow\downarrow \\ (0, 6) & (1, 5) & \left(1\frac{1}{2}, 4\frac{1}{2}\right) & (3, 3) & (4, 2) & \left(5\frac{1}{2}, \frac{1}{2}\right) & (6, 0) \end{array}$$

Another way to show the solutions is to plot the ordered pairs, as you learned to do in **Section 9.5.** This method will give us a "picture" of the solutions that we listed on the previous page.

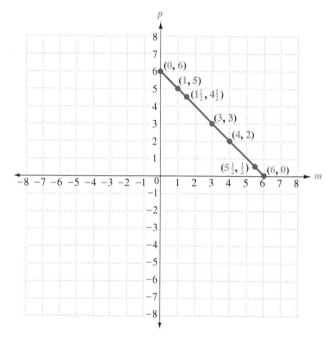

$m + p = 6$

The variables m and p represent hours, and hours can be 0 or positive numbers, but *not* negative numbers.

Notice that all the solutions (all the ordered pairs) lie on a straight line. When you draw a line connecting the ordered pairs, you have graphed the solutions. **Every point on the line is a solution.** You can use the line to find additional solutions besides the ones that we listed. For example, the point (5, 1) is on the line. This point tells you that another solution is 5 hours on math and 1 hour on psychology. The fact that the line is a *straight* line tells you that $m + p = 6$ is a *linear equation*. (The word *line* is part of the word *line*ar.) Later on in algebra you will work with equations whose solutions form a curve rather than a straight line when you graph them.

To draw the line for $m + p = 6$, we really needed only two solutions (two ordered pairs). But it's a good idea to use a third ordered pair as a check. If the three ordered pairs are *not* in a straight line, there is an error in your work.

> **Graphing a Linear Equation**
>
> To **graph a linear equation,** find at least three ordered pairs that satisfy the equation. Then plot the ordered pairs on a coordinate system and connect them with a straight line. *Every* point on the line is a solution of the equation.

EXAMPLE 1   **Graphing a Linear Equation**

Graph $x + y = 3$ by finding three solutions and plotting the ordered pairs. Then use the graph to find a fourth solution of the equation.

There are many possible solutions. Start by picking three different values for x. You can choose any numbers you like, but 0 and small numbers usually are easy to use. Then find the value of y that will make the sum equal to 3. Set up a table to organize the information.

Continued on Next Page

	x	y	Check that x + y = **3**	Ordered Pair (x, y)
Start by picking easy numbers for x.	0	3	0 + 3 = 3	(0, 3)
	1	2	1 + 2 = 3	(1, 2)
	2	1	2 + 1 = 3	(2, 1)

Plot the ordered pairs and draw a line through the points, extending it in both directions as shown below.

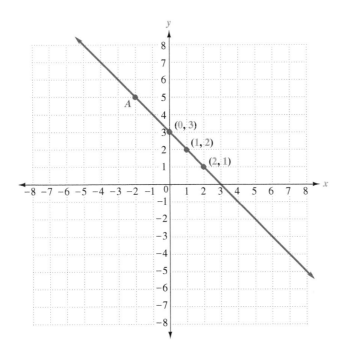

1 Graph $x + y = 5$ by finding three solutions and plotting the ordered pairs. Then use the graph to find *two* other solutions of the equation.

x	y	Check that x + y = 5	Ordered Pair (x, y)
0			
1			
2			

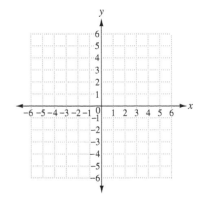

Two other solutions are (__, __) and (__, __).

Now you can use the graph to find more solutions of $x + y = 3$. *Every* point on the line is a solution. Suppose that you pick **point** A. The coordinates are $(-2, 5)$.

To check that $(-2, 5)$ is a solution, substitute -2 for x and 5 for y in the original equation.

$$x + y = 3 \quad \text{Original equation}$$
$$-2 + 5 = 3$$
$$3 = 3 \quad \text{Balances}$$

$(-2, 5)$ is a solution, **not** 3.

The equation balances, so $(-2, 5)$ is another solution of $x + y = 3$.

Note

The line in Example 1 above was extended in both directions because *every* point on the line is a solution of $x + y = 3$. However, when we graphed the line for the hours spent studying, $m + p = 6$, we did *not* extend the line. That is because the variables m and p represented hours, and hours can only be 0 or positive numbers; all the solutions had to be in the first quadrant.

ANSWERS

1. Plot (0, 5), (1, 4), and (2, 3).

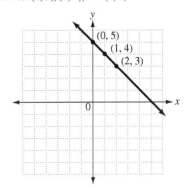

There are many other solutions. Some possibilities are $(-1, 6)$; $(3, 2)$; $(4, 1)$; $(5, 0)$; $(6, -1)$.

Work Problem **1** *at the Side.* ▶

2 Graph $y = 2x$ by finding three solutions and plotting the ordered pairs. Then use the graph to find *two* other solutions of the equation.

x	$y = 2 \cdot x$	Ordered Pair (x, y)
0		
1		
2		

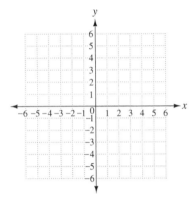

Two other solutions are (__, __) and (__, __).

EXAMPLE 2 Graphing a Linear Equation

Graph $y = -3x$ by finding three solutions and plotting the ordered pairs. Then use the graph to find a fourth solution of the equation.

You can choose any three values for x, but small numbers such as 0, 1, and 2 are easy to use. Then $y = -3x$ tells you that y is -3 times the value of x.

$$y = -3x$$

y is -3 times x

First set up a table.

	x	$y = -3 \cdot x$	Ordered Pair (x, y)
Start by picking easy numbers for x.	0	$-3 \cdot 0$ is 0	$(0, 0)$
	1	$-3 \cdot 1$ is -3	$(1, -3)$
	2	$-3 \cdot 2$ is -6	$(2, -6)$

Plot the ordered pairs and draw a line through the points. Be sure to draw arrows on both ends of the line to show that it continues in both directions.

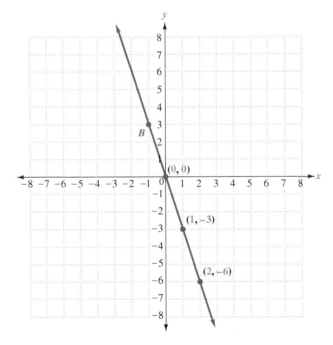

Now use the graph to find more solutions. *Every* point on the line is a solution.
Suppose that you pick **point B**. The coordinates are $(-1, 3)$. To check that $(-1, 3)$ is a solution, substitute -1 for x and 3 for y in the original equation.

$$y = -3x \quad \text{Original equation}$$

$$3 = -3(-1)$$

$$3 = 3 \quad \text{Balances}$$

The equation balances, so $(-1, 3)$ is another solution of $y = -3x$.

◀ *Work Problem* 2 *at the Side.*

ANSWERS

2. Plot (0, 0), (1, 2), and (2, 4).

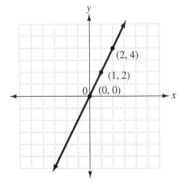

There are many other solutions. Some possibilities are (3, 6); (−1, −2); (−2, −4); (−3, −6).

EXAMPLE 3 **Graphing a Linear Equation**

Graph $y = \dfrac{1}{2}x$ by finding three solutions and plotting the ordered pairs.

Then use the graph to find a fourth solution of the equation.

Complete the table. The coefficient of x is $\frac{1}{2}$, so choose even numbers like 2, 4, and 6 as values for x because they are easy to divide in half. The equation $y = \frac{1}{2}x$ tells you that y is $\frac{1}{2}$ *times* the value of x.

Pick even numbers for x; they are easy to multiply by $\frac{1}{2}$

x	$y = \frac{1}{2} \cdot x$	Ordered Pair (x, y)
2	$\frac{1}{2} \cdot 2$ is 1	$(2, 1)$
4	$\frac{1}{2} \cdot 4$ is 2	$(4, 2)$
6	$\frac{1}{2} \cdot 6$ is 3	$(6, 3)$

Plot the ordered pairs and draw a line through the points.

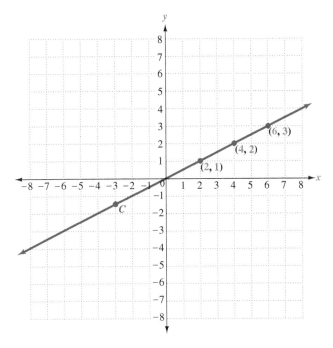

Now use the graph to find more solutions. *Every* point on the line is a solution.

Suppose that you pick **point C**. The coordinates are $(-3, -1\frac{1}{2})$. Check that $(-3, -1\frac{1}{2})$ is a solution by substituting -3 for x and $-1\frac{1}{2}$ for y.

$$y = \frac{1}{2}x \qquad \text{Original equation}$$

$$-1\frac{1}{2} = \frac{1}{2}(-3)$$

$-1\frac{1}{2}$ is equivalent to $-\frac{3}{2}$

$$-1\frac{1}{2} = -\frac{3}{2} \qquad \text{Balances}$$

The equation balances, so $(-3, -1\frac{1}{2})$ is another solution of $y = \frac{1}{2}x$.

Work Problem 3 *at the Side.* ▶

3 Graph $y = -\frac{1}{2}x$ by finding three solutions and plotting the ordered pairs. Then use the graph to find *two* more solutions.

x	$y = -\frac{1}{2} \cdot x$	Ordered Pair (x, y)
2		
4		
6		

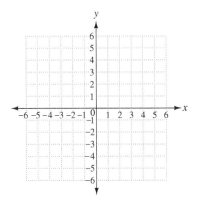

Two other solutions are (__, __) and (__, __).

ANSWERS

3. Plot $(2, -1)$, $(4, -2)$, and $(6, -3)$.

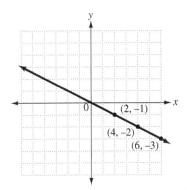

There are many other solutions. Some possibilities are $(0, 0)$; $(-2, 1)$; $(-4, 2)$; $(-6, 3)$; $\left(1, -\frac{1}{2}\right)$; $\left(3, -1\frac{1}{2}\right)$; $\left(5, -2\frac{1}{2}\right)$.

4 Graph the equation $y = x - 5$ by finding three solutions and plotting the ordered pairs. Then use the graph to find *two* more solutions.

x	y = x − 5	Ordered Pair (x, y)
1		
2		
3		

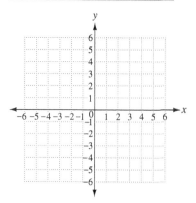

Two other solutions are (___, ___) and (___, ___).

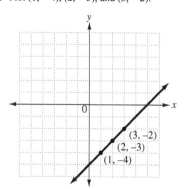
EXAMPLE 4 **Graphing a Linear Equation**

Graph the equation $y = x + 4$ by finding three solutions and plotting the ordered pairs. Then use the graph to find two more solutions of the equation.

First set up a table. The equation $y = x + 4$ tells you that y must be 4 more than the value of x.

x	y = x + 4	Ordered Pair (x, y)
0	0 + 4 is 4	(0, 4)
1	1 + 4 is 5	(1, 5)
2	2 + 4 is 6	(2, 6)

Plot the ordered pairs and draw a line through the points.

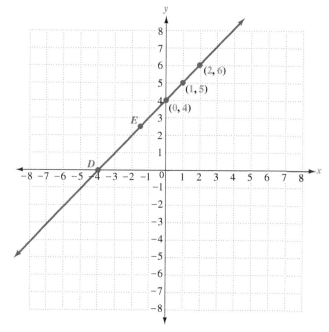

Now use the graph to find two more solutions. *Every* point on the line is a solution. Suppose that you pick **point D** at $(-4, 0)$ and **point E** at $(-1\frac{1}{2}, 2\frac{1}{2})$. Check that both ordered pairs are solutions.

Check $(-4, 0)$

$$y = x + 4$$
$$0 = -4 + 4$$
$$0 = 0 \quad \text{Balances}$$

$(-4, 0)$ is a solution, **not** 0.

Check $\left(-1\frac{1}{2}, 2\frac{1}{2}\right)$

$$y = x + 4$$
$$2\frac{1}{2} = -1\frac{1}{2} + 4$$
$$\frac{5}{2} = -\frac{3}{2} + \frac{8}{2}$$
$$\frac{5}{2} = \frac{5}{2} \quad \text{Balances}$$

$2\frac{1}{2}$ can be written as $\frac{5}{2}$ and $-1\frac{1}{2}$ can be written as $-\frac{3}{2}$

Both equations balance, so $(-4, 0)$ and $(-1\frac{1}{2}, 2\frac{1}{2})$ are also solutions of $y = x + 4$.

◀ *Work Problem* **4** *at the Side.*

OBJECTIVE 2 **Identify the slope of a line as positive or negative.** Let's look again at some of the lines that we graphed for various equations. All are straight lines, but some are almost flat and some tilt steeply upward or downward.

Graph from Example 1: $x + y = 3$

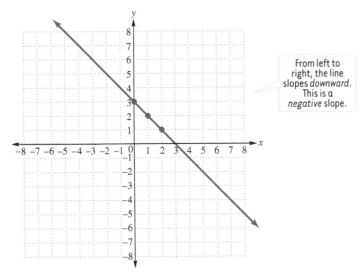

From left to right, the line slopes *downward*. This is a *negative* slope.

As you move from *left to right,* the line slopes downward, as if you were walking down a hill. When a line tilts downward, we say that it has a *negative slope.*

Now look at the table of solutions we used to draw the line.

The value of
x is *increasing*
from 0 to 1 to 2

x	y
0	3
1	2
2	1

The value of
y is *decreasing*
from 3 to 2 to 1

As the value of x *increases,* the value of y does the *opposite*—it *decreases.* Whenever one variable increases while the other variable decreases, the line will have a negative slope.

Graph from Example 3: $y = \dfrac{1}{2}x$

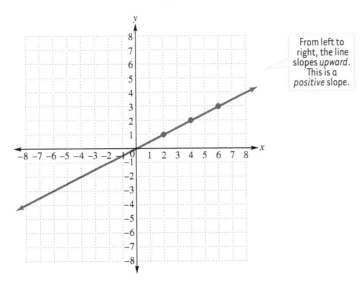

From left to right, the line slopes *upward.* This is a *positive* slope.

As you move from *left to right,* this line slopes upward, as if you were walking up a hill. When a line tilts upward, we say that it has a *positive slope.*

5 Look back at the graphs in Margin Problems 2 and 3. Then complete these sentences.

(a) The graph of $y = 2x$ has a _____ slope. As the value of x increases, the value of y _____.

(b) The graph of $y = -\frac{1}{2}x$ has a _____ slope. As the value of x increases, the value of y _____.

Now look at the table of solutions we used to draw the line.

The value of x is *increasing* from 2 to 4 to 6

x	y
2	1
4	2
6	3

The value of y is *increasing* from 1 to 2 to 3

As the value of x *increases,* the value of y does the *same* thing—it also *increases.* Whenever both variables do the same thing (both increase or both decrease), the line will have a positive slope.

Positive and Negative Slopes

As you move from left to right, a line with a *positive* slope tilts *upward* or rises. As the value of one variable increases, the value of the other variable also increases (does the same).

As you move from left to right, a line with a *negative* slope tilts *downward* or falls. As the value of one variable increases, the value of the other variable decreases (does the opposite).

EXAMPLE 5 **Identifying Positive or Negative Slope in a Line**

Look back at the graph of $y = -3x$ in Example 2. Then complete these sentences.

The graph of $y = -3x$ has a _____ slope.

As the value of x increases, the value of y _____.

The graph of $y = -3x$ has a $\underline{negative}$ slope (because it tilts downward).
As the value of x increases, the value of y $\underline{decreases}$ (does the opposite).

◀ *Work Problem* **5** *at the Side.*

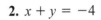

Graph each equation by completing the table to find three solutions and plotting the ordered pairs. Then use the graph to find two *other solutions. See Example 1.*

1. $x + y = 4$

x	y	Ordered Pair (x, y)
0		
1		
2		

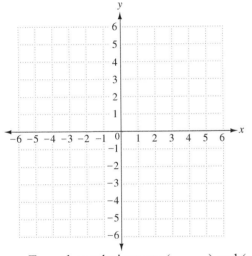

Two other solutions are (__, __) and (__, __).

2. $x + y = -4$

x	y	Ordered Pair (x, y)
0		
1		
2		

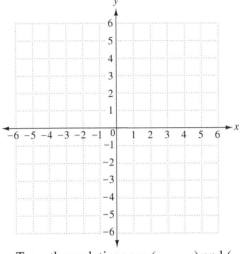

Two other solutions are (__, __) and (__, __).

3. $x + y = -1$

x	y	Ordered Pair (x, y)
0		
1		
2		

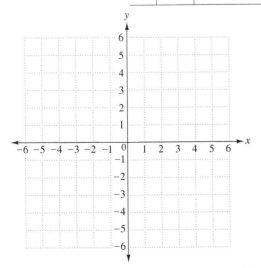

Two other solutions are (__, __) and (__, __).

4. $x + y = 1$

x	y	Ordered Pair (x, y)
0		
1		
2		

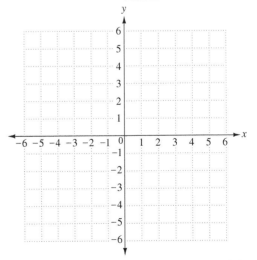

Two other solutions are (__, __) and (__, __).

5. The line in Exercise 1 crosses the *y*-axis at what point? _____ The line in Exercise 3 crosses the *y*-axis at what point? _____
Based on these examples, where would the graph of $x + y = -6$ cross the *y*-axis? _____
Where would the graph of $x + y = 99$ cross the *y*-axis? _____

6. Look at where the line crosses the *x*-axis and where it crosses the *y*-axis in Exercises 2 and 4. What pattern do you see?

Graph each equation. Make your own table using the listed values of x. See Examples 2 and 4.

7. $y = x - 2$

Use 1, 2, and 3 as the values of *x*.

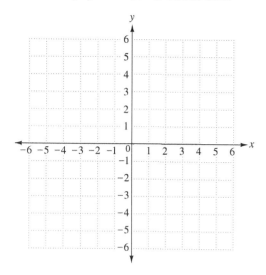

8. $y = x + 1$

Use 1, 2, and 3 as the values of *x*.

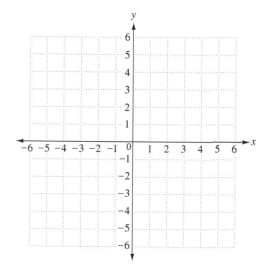

9. $y = x + 2$

Use 0, −1, and −2 as the values of *x*.

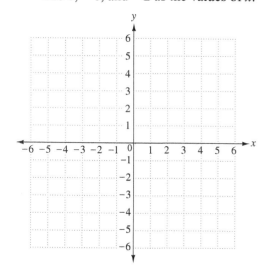

10. $y = x - 1$

Use 0, −1, and −2 as the values of *x*.

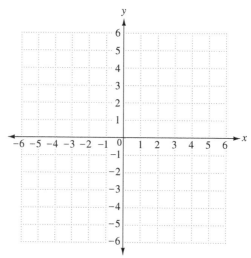

11. $y = -3x$

Use 0, 1, and 2 as the values of x.

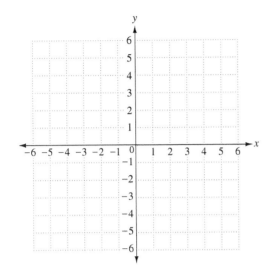

12. $y = -2x$

Use 0, 1, and 2 as the values of x.

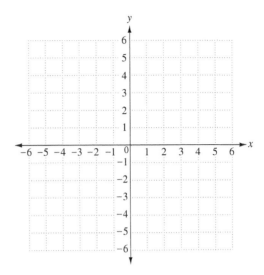

13. Look back at the graphs in Exercises 1, 3, 7, 9, and 11. Which lines have a positive slope? Which lines have a negative slope?

14. Look back at the graphs in Exercises 2, 4, 8, 10, and 12. Which lines have a positive slope? Which lines have a negative slope?

Graph each equation. Make your own table using the listed values of x. See Examples 1–4.

15. $y = \dfrac{1}{3}x$

Use 0, 3, and 6 as the values of x.

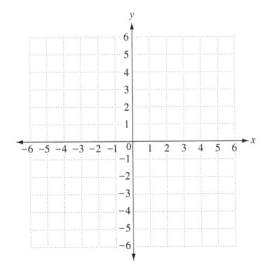

16. $y = \dfrac{1}{2}x$

Use 0, 2, and 4 as the values of x.

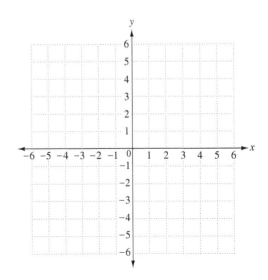

17. $y = x$

Use -1, -2, and -3 as the values of x.

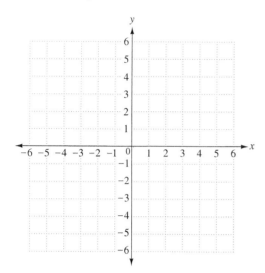

18. $x + y = 0$

Use 1, 2, and 3 as the values of x.

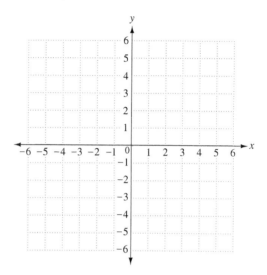

19. $y = -2x + 3$

Use 0, 1, and 2 as the values of x.

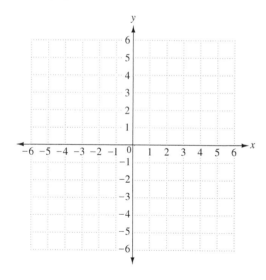

20. $y = 3x - 4$

Use 0, 1, and 2 as the values of x.

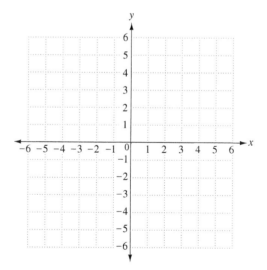

Graph each equation. Choose three values for x. Make a table showing your x values and the corresponding y values. After graphing the equation, state whether the line has a positive or negative slope. See Examples 1–5.

21. $x + y = -3$

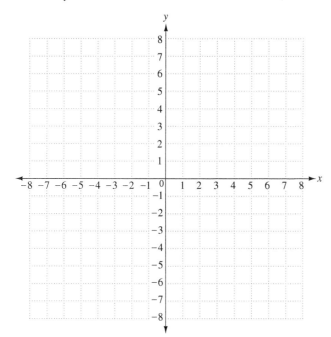

22. $x + y = 2$

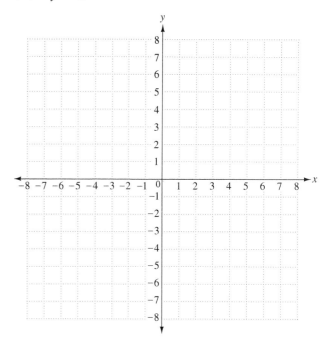

23. $y = \dfrac{1}{4}x$ (*Hint:* Try using 0 and multiples of 4 as the values of *x*.)

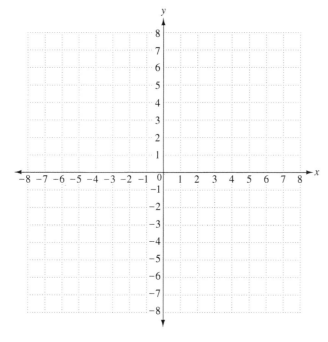

24. $y = -\dfrac{1}{3}x$ (*Hint:* Try using 0 and multiples of 3 as the values of *x*.)

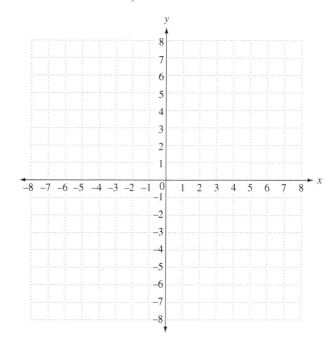

25. $y = x - 5$

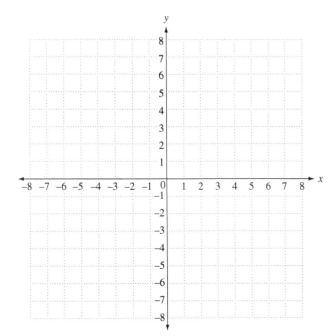

26. $y = x + 4$

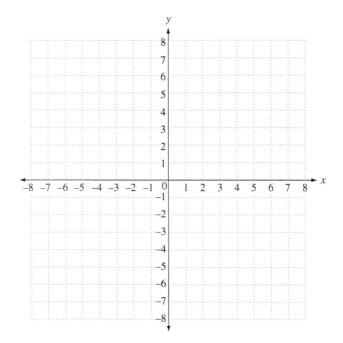

27. $y = -3x + 1$

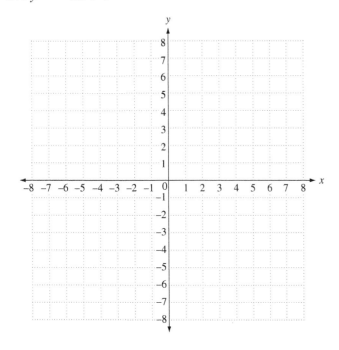

28. $y = 2x - 2$

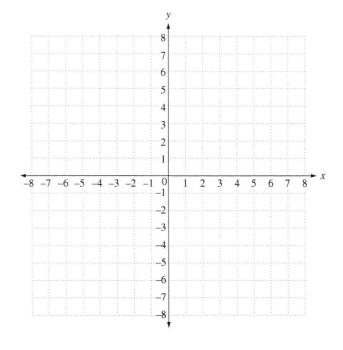

10

Solving Equations/Variation

10.1 ▶▶▶ Real Numbers and Expressions

OBJECTIVES

1 Identify rational numbers, irrational numbers, and real numbers.

2 Use the symbols $\neq$, $<$, $\leq$, $>$, and $\geq$ to compare real numbers.

3 Reverse the direction of inequality statements.

4 Use the order of operations to simplify expressions with brackets.

5 Remove parentheses and simplify expressions using the distributive property.

Throughout Chapters 3–9, you have been developing basic concepts and skills to help you understand and use algebra. In this chapter we will introduce some more advanced terminology and techniques.

OBJECTIVE 1 Identify rational numbers, irrational numbers, and real numbers. You have worked with different kinds of numbers: integers in Chapter 3, fractions in Chapter 5, decimals in Chapter 6, and so on. Now let's be more specific about these different groups, or *sets*, of numbers.

The first numbers a young child learns are the ones used for counting, called the set of **natural numbers.** The numbers in the set are written between braces.

$$\{1, 2, 3, 4, 5, \ldots\}$$

> Three dots indicate that the list of natural numbers goes on forever.

Once zero is included with the natural numbers, we have the set of **whole numbers.**

$$\{0, 1, 2, 3, 4, 5, \ldots\}$$

> The list of whole numbers goes on forever.

So far we have only zero and positive numbers. The next set of numbers, the **integers,** includes the natural numbers, their *opposites,* and zero. You worked with integers in Chapter 3.

$$\{\ldots -5, -4, -3, -2, -1, 0, 1, 2, 3, 4, 5, \ldots\}$$

> The list of integers goes on forever in both directions.

Recall how we used a number line to show the position of each integer.

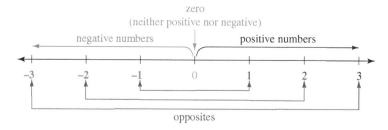

In Chapters 5 and 6 you used positive and negative fractions and decimals which are also located on the number line. All integers and fractions and some of the decimal numbers are examples of *rational numbers.*

> **Rational Numbers**
>
> **Rational numbers** are numbers that can be written as quotients of integers, with the denominator not equal to zero. In other words, rational numbers can be written in the form $\frac{a}{b}$ where a and b are integers and $b \neq 0$.

The name "*ratio*nal numbers" comes from the word *ratio*, which indicates a quotient. Some examples of rational numbers are shown here, including how to write them as a quotient of integers.

5   can be written as $\dfrac{5}{1}$

-18   can be written as $\dfrac{-18}{1}$

All integers are rational numbers.

$3\dfrac{1}{2}$ can be written as $\dfrac{7}{2}$

$-\dfrac{5}{8}$ can be written as $\dfrac{-5}{8}$ or $\dfrac{5}{-8}$

$\left. \phantom{\dfrac{5}{8}} \right\}$ *All fractions* are rational numbers.

0.19 can be written as $\dfrac{19}{100}$

2.7 can be written as $2\dfrac{7}{10} = \dfrac{27}{10}$

$0.333\ldots$ can be written as $\dfrac{1}{3}$

$0.\overline{72}$ can be written as $\dfrac{8}{11}$

$\left. \phantom{\dfrac{5}{8}} \right\}$ These decimals are rational numbers, but *not all decimals* are rational numbers.

1 Graph these rational numbers on the number line.
$$-3, -2.75, -\dfrac{3}{4}, 1\dfrac{1}{2}, \dfrac{17}{8}$$

Any integer can be written as the quotient of itself and 1, so all integers are rational numbers. A decimal number that comes to an end (terminates), such as 0.19 or 2.7, is a rational number. Decimal numbers that repeat in a *fixed block* of digits, such as 0.333... and $0.\overline{72}$, are also rational numbers. (Recall that the bar above the digits 7 and 2 means that they repeat indefinitely, so 0.727272... can be written as $0.\overline{72}$.)

Recall that to *graph* a number, we place a dot on the number line at the point corresponding to the number.

EXAMPLE 1   **Graphing Rational Numbers**

Graph these rational numbers on the number line.
$$-\dfrac{3}{2}, \quad -\dfrac{2}{3}, \quad \dfrac{1}{2}, \quad 1\dfrac{1}{3}, \quad \dfrac{23}{8}, \quad 3\dfrac{1}{4}$$

To locate the improper fractions on the number line, write them in the form of mixed numbers or decimals.

Work Problem **1** *at the Side.* ▶

There are also numbers that are *not* rational. For example, you worked with π. Recall that we found π by dividing the circumference of a circle by its diameter. In other words, π is a quotient, but it never ends and the digits never repeat in a fixed block, no matter how far you carry out the division.

$$\dfrac{\text{circumference of circle}}{\text{diameter of circle}} = 3.14159265\ldots$$

Powerful computers have calculated π out to millions of decimal places, but the pattern of digits never repeats and never ends. So π is an example of an *irrational number.*

Irrational Numbers

Irrational numbers are nonrational numbers represented by points on the number line. The decimal form of an irrational number does not terminate and does not repeat in a fixed block of digits.

ANSWER

1.

2 Identify each number as rational or irrational, and explain why.

(a) $\sqrt{36}$

(b) $0.6666\ldots$

(c) $\sqrt{13}$

(d) $0.454545\ldots$

(e) $0.131131113\ldots$

(f) 9.4375

(g) $0.\overline{27}$

The decimal form of an irrational number never terminates (never ends) and never repeats in a fixed block of digits. An example is the number $0.10110111011110\ldots$ Another example is $\sqrt{7}$. In **Section 6.7** we said that the *approximate* value for $\sqrt{7}$ is 2.646. It's approximate because $(2.646)^2$ is 7.001316, not 7. The actual value of $\sqrt{7}$ in decimal form never terminates and never repeats, so it is an irrational number. These numbers lie between rational numbers on the number line. You will work with irrational numbers in Chapter 16.

> **CAUTION**
>
> Some square roots are irrational. Examples are $\sqrt{2}$, $\sqrt{3}$, and $\sqrt{7}$. However, *not all* square roots are irrational. For example, $\sqrt{9}$ is *rational,* because $\sqrt{9} = 3$.

EXAMPLE 2 **Identifying Rational and Irrational Numbers**

Identify each number as *rational* or *irrational,* and explain why. Use your calculator to find square roots.

(a) $0.181818\ldots$ **(b)** 3.125 **(c)** $0.20220222022220\ldots$

(d) $\sqrt{11}$ **(e)** $\sqrt{16}$ **(f)** $0.\overline{36}$

(a) Rational, because the digits repeat in a fixed block.

(b) Rational, because the decimal terminates (comes to an end).

(c) Irrational, because the digits do *not* repeat in a fixed block.

(d) Irrational, because the decimal value of $\sqrt{11}$ never terminates or repeats.

(e) Rational, because $\sqrt{16} = 4$.

(f) Rational, because the digits repeat in a fixed block.

◀ *Work Problem* **2** *at the Side.*

Finally, *all* numbers that can be represented by points on the number line are called *real numbers.*

> **Real Numbers**
>
> The set of **real numbers** includes all the rational numbers *and* all the irrational numbers. All the real numbers can be represented by points on the number line.

All the numbers mentioned so far in this section are *real numbers.* The relationships between the various types of numbers are shown in the drawing on the next page. Notice that every real number is either a rational number or an irrational number.

ANSWERS

2. **(a)** rational because $\sqrt{36} = 6$
   (b) rational because the digit 6 repeats
   (c) irrational because decimal value of $\sqrt{13}$ never ends or repeats in a fixed block
   (d) rational because digits repeat in a fixed block
   (e) irrational because digits do not repeat in a fixed block
   (f) rational because the decimal terminates
   (g) rational because digits repeat in a fixed block

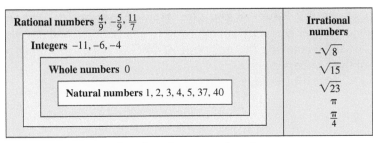

All numbers shown are real numbers.

OBJECTIVE 2 Use the symbols ≠, <, ≤, >, and ≥ to compare real numbers. The symbols you used in earlier chapters when comparing numbers are shown below.

=	<	>
is equal to	is less than	is greater than
$3(7) = 7(3)$	$-2 < 0$	$0.65 > 0.6$

Keep the meanings of $<$ and $>$ clear by remembering that the symbol always points to the lesser number. (See **Section 3.1** for more review.) Here are three other useful symbols.

≠	≤	≥
is not equal to	is less than or equal to	is greater than or equal to
$3 - 7 \neq 7 - 3$	$0 \leq 4$	$1.25 \geq 1.2$
$\frac{1}{2} \neq 0.3$	$\frac{3}{4} \leq \frac{3}{4}$	$-8 \geq -8$

Use $\neq$ when two numbers or quantities are *not* equal.

We read the inequality $0 \leq 4$ as "zero is less than or equal to 4." If either the $<$ part *or* the $=$ part is true, then the inequality is true. So $0 \leq 4$ is true because $0 < 4$. Then $\frac{3}{4} \leq \frac{3}{4}$ is true because $\frac{3}{4} = \frac{3}{4}$.

In a similar manner, $1.25 \geq 1.2$ is true because $1.25 > 1.2$. Also, $-8 \geq -8$ is true because $-8 = -8$.

EXAMPLE 3 Using the Symbols ≠, ≤, ≥

Label each statement as true or false and explain why.

(a) $-4 \leq -3$ **(b)** $\frac{1}{10} \geq \frac{1}{2}$ **(c)** $-6.2 \geq -6.2$ **(d)** $2 \div 1 \neq 1 \div 2$

(a) True, because $-4 < -3$. Recall that -4 is to the left of -3 on the number line.

(b) False, because $\frac{1}{10} < \frac{1}{2}$ and $\frac{1}{10} \neq \frac{1}{2}$.

(c) True, because $-6.2 = -6.2$.

(d) True, because they are not equal. $2 \div 1$ is 2, but $1 \div 2$ is $\frac{1}{2}$ or 0.5.

Work Problem **3** *at the Side.* ▶

---

3 Label each statement as true or false and explain why.

(a) $0 \geq -\dfrac{3}{4}$

(b) $\sqrt{25} \leq \sqrt{25}$

(c) $3.06 \geq 3.6$

(d) $\dfrac{2}{3}(10) \neq \dfrac{3}{2}(10)$

(e) $-15 \leq -16$

(f) $\dfrac{1}{4} \neq \dfrac{12}{48}$

(g) $0.5 \geq \dfrac{1}{2}$

ANSWERS

3. **(a)** True because $0 > -\dfrac{3}{4}$
   (b) True because $\sqrt{25} = \sqrt{25}$
   (c) False because $3.06 < 3.6$ and $3.06 \neq 3.6$
   (d) True because $6\dfrac{2}{3} \neq 15$
   (e) False because $-15 > -16$ and $-15 \neq -16$
   (f) False because $\dfrac{12}{48}$ in lowest terms is $\dfrac{1}{4}$
   (g) True because $0.5 = \dfrac{1}{2}$

4 Rewrite each statement with the inequality symbol reversed.

(a) $0.3 \leq 0.33$

(b) $\dfrac{2}{3} > \dfrac{2}{9}$

(c) $-5 < -1$

(d) $\dfrac{9}{10} \geq 0.7$

OBJECTIVE **3** **Reverse the direction of inequality statements.** Any statement with $<$ can be converted to one with $>$, and any statement with $>$ can be converted to one with $<$. We do this by reversing both the order of the numbers and the direction of the symbol. For example, the statement $6 < 10$ can be written as $10 > 6$.

Exchange numbers.

$$6 < 10 \quad \text{becomes} \quad 10 > 6$$

Reverse the symbol

You can verify that both statements are true: 6 is less than 10, and 10 is greater than 6.

EXAMPLE 4 **Converting Between $<$ and $>$**

The list below shows each statement written in two equally correct ways.

(a) $9 < 16$ becomes $16 > 9$

(b) $0 > -2$ becomes $-2 < 0$

(c) $\dfrac{1}{2} \leq \dfrac{3}{4}$ becomes $\dfrac{3}{4} \geq \dfrac{1}{2}$ Reverse the direction of the symbol **and** reverse the order of the numbers.

(d) $-7 \geq -8$ becomes $-8 \leq -7$

◀ *Work Problem* **4** *at the Side.*

OBJECTIVE **4** **Use the order of operations to simplify expressions with brackets.** We have been using parentheses to show several different things.

Parentheses used to indicate multiplication:	Parentheses used to indicate a negative number:	Parentheses used to indicate order of operations:
$3\,(5)$	$6 - (-4)$	$6 + (3 + 4)$
means multiply 3 times 5.	means 6 minus negative 4.	means add $3 + 4$ first.

An expression with double parentheses, such as the expression $2\,(8 + 3\,(6 + 5))$, can be confusing. We can avoid confusion by using square brackets, [ ], in place of one pair of parentheses.

5 Simplify each expression.

(a) $4[7 + 3\,(6 + 1)]$

(b) $3[(-20 \div 5) - 7]$

EXAMPLE 5 **Using Brackets**

Simplify. $2[8 + 3\,(6 + 5)]$

Begin inside the parentheses. Then follow the order of operations as you complete the work inside the brackets.

$2[8 + 3\,(6 + 5)]$	Work inside parentheses: add $6 + 5$.
$2[8 + 3\,(11)]$	Multiply $3\,(11)$.
$2[8 + 33]$	Add $8 + 33$.
$2[41]$	Multiply 2 times 41.
82	

◀ *Work Problem* **5** *at the Side.*

ANSWERS

4. **(a)** $0.33 \geq 0.3$ **(b)** $\dfrac{2}{9} < \dfrac{2}{3}$

(c) $-1 > -5$ **(d)** $0.7 \leq \dfrac{9}{10}$

5. **(a)** 112 **(b)** -33

OBJECTIVE **5** **Remove parentheses and simplify expressions using the distributive property.** In **Section 4.2** you used the *distributive property* to simplify expressions. Here are two examples.

$$6(y + 4) \qquad\qquad 5(3x - 2)$$

$$6 \cdot y + 6 \cdot 4 \qquad\qquad 5 \cdot 3x - 5 \cdot 2$$

$$6y + 24 \qquad\qquad 15x - 10$$

We can also use the distributive property to remove parentheses when there is a *negative* number in front of them.

EXAMPLE 6   **Using the Distributive Property to Remove Parentheses**

Write without parentheses.

(a) $-2(2y + 3)$

$$-2(2y + 3) \quad\longleftarrow\; \text{Multiply \textbf{every} term inside the parentheses by } -2.$$

$$(-2 \cdot 2y) + (-2 \cdot 3)$$

$$-4y + -6 \qquad \text{Use the definition of subtraction “in reverse” as in Section 2.2; change adding to subtracting; change } -6 \text{ to its opposite, } +6.$$

$$-4y - 6$$

The simplified expression is $-4y - 6$.

(b) $-5(3a - 4)$

$$-5(3a - 4)$$

$$(-5 \cdot 3a) - (-5 \cdot 4) \qquad \text{Multiply every term inside the parentheses by } -5.$$

$$-15a - (-20) \qquad \text{Use the definition of subtraction: change subtracting to adding; change } -20 \text{ to its opposite, } +20.$$

$$-15a + 20$$

The simplified expression is $-15a + 20$.

> **CAUTION**
> Watch the signs carefully when there is a *negative* number in front of the parentheses, as in Example 6. Notice that every term in the simplified expression has the *opposite sign* from the original expression.

Work Problem **6** *at the Side.* ▶

Sometimes an expression may have just a negative sign in front of parentheses, such as $-(3x + 5)$. We can rewrite this as $-1(3x + 5)$ and then use the distributive property to multiply every term inside the parentheses by -1.

6 Write without parentheses.

(a) $-3(4b + 1)$

(b) $-7(2x - 3)$

(c) $-4(h - 5)$

(d) $-6(-2y + 4)$

7 Write without parentheses.

(a) $-(6k - 5)$

(b) $-(-2 - r)$

(c) $-(-5y + 8)$

(d) $-(z + 4)$

EXAMPLE 7 **Using the Distributive Property to Remove Parentheses**

Write without parentheses.

(a) $-(3x + 5)$ can be written $-1(3x + 5)$ — Multiply **every** term inside the parentheses by -1.

$$\underbrace{(-1 \cdot 3x)} + \underbrace{(-1 \cdot 5)}$$

$$\begin{array}{ccc} -3x & + & (-5) \\ \downarrow & & \downarrow \\ -3x & - & 5 \end{array}$$ Use the definition of subtraction "in reverse."

The simplified expression is $-3x - 5$.

(b) $-(-7r - 8)$ can be written as $-1(-7r - 8)$ Multiply every term inside the parentheses by -1.

$$\underbrace{(-1 \cdot -7r)} - \underbrace{(-1 \cdot 8)}$$

$$\begin{array}{ccc} 7r & - & (-8) \\ \downarrow & & \downarrow \\ 7r & + & 8 \end{array}$$ Use the definition of subtraction.

The simplified expression is $7r + 8$.

◀ Work Problem **7** at the Side.

---

8 Simplify.

(a) $10p + 3(5 + 2p)$

(b) $7x - 2 - (1 + x)$

(c) $-(3k^2 + 5k) + 7(k^2 - 4k)$

(d) $-2(4b - 3) - 5(2b^2 + 1)$

EXAMPLE 8 **Simplifying Expressions Involving Like Terms**

Simplify each expression.

(a) $14y + 2(6 + 3y)$

$$14y + 2(6 + 3y)$$ Multiply every term inside the parentheses by 2.

$$14y + 12 + 6y$$ Combine like terms.

$$20y + 12$$

(b) $-(2 - r) + 10r$ is written $-1(2 - r) + 10r$ Rewrite $-(2 - r)$ as $-1(2 - r)$. Then use the distributive property.

$$-2 + r + 10r$$

$$-2 + r + 10r$$ Combine like terms.

$$-2 + 11r$$

(c) $5(2a^2 - 6a) - 3(4a^2 - 9)$

Multiply every term inside these parentheses by 5. — $5(2a^2 - 6a) - 3(4a^2 - 9)$ — Multiply every term inside these parentheses by -3.

$$10a^2 - 30a - 12a^2 + 27$$ Combine like terms.

$$-2a^2 - 30a + 27$$

◀ Work Problem **8** at the Side.

ANSWERS

7. **(a)** $-6k + 5$ **(b)** $2 + r$ **(c)** $5y - 8$
(d) $-z - 4$
8. **(a)** $16p + 15$ **(b)** $6x - 3$ **(c)** $4k^2 - 33k$
(d) $-10b^2 - 8b + 1$

10.1 ▶▶▶ **Exercises**

*Identify each number as **rational** or **irrational** and explain why. See Example 2.*

1. -0.0625

2. $\sqrt{5}$

3. π

4. 0

5. $\dfrac{3}{4}$

6. $-5\dfrac{2}{3}$

7. $0.636363\ldots$

8. $0.3233233323333\ldots$

9. $\sqrt{2}$

10. $0.416666\ldots$

*List all numbers from each set that are **(a)** natural numbers, **(b)** whole numbers, **(c)** integers, **(d)** rational numbers, **(e)** irrational numbers, **(f)** real numbers.*

11. $\left\{-9, -\sqrt{7}, -1\dfrac{1}{4}, -\dfrac{3}{5}, 0, \sqrt{5}, 3, 5.9, 7\right\}$

12. $\left\{-5.3, -5, -\sqrt{3}, -1, -\dfrac{1}{9}, 0, 1.2, 4, \sqrt{12}\right\}$

Write each statement in words. Then label the statement as true or false, and explain why. See Example 3.

13. $0.75 \neq \dfrac{3}{4}$

14. $0 \geq -1$

15. $-4 \leq -5$

16. $\dfrac{1}{3} \neq 0.3$

17. $0 \geq 0$

18. $4 \leq 5$

Write each statement with the inequality symbol reversed. See Example 4.

19. $12 < 19$

20. $0.55 > 0.5$

21. $\dfrac{4}{5} \geq \dfrac{1}{2}$

22. $-40 \leq -30$

First simplify each statement wherever possible. Then label the statement as true or false. See Examples 3 and 5.

23. $-17 \leq 1 - 18$

24. $-12 \geq -10 - 2$

25. $-6(8) + 9(5) \geq 0$

26. $-4(-20) - 15(5) \geq 0$

27. $6[5 - 3(4 - 2)] \neq 6$

28. $-3[(0 - 5) + 2] \neq 9$

29. $3^2[(-10 \div 5) + 7] \le 40$ **30.** $-(5^2)[-3 + 2(-6 \div 2)] \le -225$ **31.** $[6 - 4(4)] \div (-10) \ge 1$

32. $-1 \ne 4 \div [8(2) - 20]$ **33.** $0 \ne 12 \div [3(2) - 6]$ **34.** $[12 - 2(36 \div 6)] \div 9 \le 0$

Relating Concepts (Exercises 35–38) For Individual or Group Work

Use the table on movie gross receipts (all the income, before paying expenses) to work Exercises 35–38 in order.

ALL-TIME TOP AMERICAN MOVIES THROUGH OCTOBER 2008

Rank	Title (Year)	Gross Receipts (millions)
1	*Titanic (1997)*	$600.8
2	*The Dark Knight (2008)*	527.4
3	*Star Wars (1977)*	461.0
4	*Shrek 2 (2004)*	436.5
5	*E.T.: The Extra-Terrestrial (1982)*	435.1
6	*The Phantom Menace (1999)*	431.1

Source: www.boxofficereport.com

35. (a) Which films had gross receipts greater than 461 million dollars?

(b) Which films had gross receipts greater than or equal to 461 million dollars?

36. (a) Which films had gross receipts less than 435.1 million dollars?

(b) Which films had gross receipts less than or equal to 435.1 million dollars?

37. Write a statement using the $\le$ symbol that describes the gross receipts for the films ranked 4, 5, and 6.

38. Write a statement using the $\ge$ symbol that describes the gross receipts for the top four films.

Use the distributive property to simplify each expression. See Example 7.

39. $-(4t + 5m)$ **40.** $-(9x + 12y)$ **41.** $-(-5c - 4d)$ **42.** $-(-13x - 15y)$

43. $-(6h - n)$ **44.** $-(a - 7b)$ **45.** $-(-3q + 5r - 8s)$ **46.** $-(-4z + 5w - 9y)$

Simplify each expression. See Examples 6–8.

47. $13p + 4(4 - 8p)$ **48.** $5x + 3(7 - 2x)$ **49.** $-4(y - 7) - 6$

50. $-5(t - 13) - 4$ **51.** $-(6 - y) + y^2 - 6$ **52.** $-(w + 5) - w^2 + 5$

53. $2(3b^2 - b) - 4(b - 2)$ **54.** $7(x^2 - 3) - 5(x + 6)$ **55.** $-3(-a + 1) - (2a - 4)$

56. $-8(-5 + c^2) - (10 - 7c^2)$ **57.** $-10(-3k - 2) + 6(-4 - k)$ **58.** $-7(-4 + 3x^2) + 5(x^2 - 6)$

10.2 ▸▸▸ Linear Equations in One Variable

OBJECTIVES

1 Decide whether a number is a solution of a linear equation.

2 Solve linear equations using the addition and multiplication properties of equality.

3 Solve linear equations using the distributive property.

4 Solve linear equations with fractions or decimals.

5 Identify conditional equations, contradictions, and identities.

In **Chapter 3,** we reviewed *algebraic expressions.* Examples include

$$8x + 9, \quad y - 4, \quad \text{and} \quad \frac{x^3 y^8}{z}. \quad \text{Algebraic expressions}$$

Equations and inequalities compare algebraic expressions, just as a balance scale compares the weights of two quantities. Recall that an *equation* is a statement that two algebraic expressions are equal. *An equation always contains an equals sign, while an expression does not.*

$$\underbrace{3x - 7}_{\text{Left side}} = \underbrace{2}_{\text{Right side}} \qquad \underset{\uparrow}{3x - 7}$$

Equation   Expression
(to solve)   (to simplify or evaluate)

Work Problem **1** *at the Side.* ▶

A *linear equation in one variable* involves only real numbers and one variable raised to the first power. Examples include

$$x + 1 = -2, \quad x - 3 = 5, \quad \text{and} \quad 2k + 5 = 10. \quad \text{Linear equations}$$

> **Linear Equation in One Variable**
>
> A **linear equation in one variable** can be written in the form
>
> $$Ax + B = C,$$
>
> where A, B, and C are real numbers, with $A \neq 0$.

A linear equation is a **first-degree equation** since the greatest power on the variable is one. Some examples of equations that are not linear (that is, *nonlinear*) are

$$x^2 + 3y = 5, \quad \frac{8}{x} = -22, \quad \text{and} \quad \sqrt{x} = 6. \quad \text{Nonlinear equations}$$

OBJECTIVE 1 Decide whether a number is a solution of a linear equation. If the variable in an equation can be replaced by a real number that makes the statement true, then that number is a **solution** of the equation. For example, 8 is a solution of the equation $x - 3 = 5$, since replacing x with 8 gives a true statement, $8 - 3 = 5$. An equation is *solved* by finding its **solution set,** the set of all solutions. The solution set of the equation $x - 3 = 5$ is $\{8\}$.

Work Problem **2** *at the Side.* ▶

Equivalent equations are equations that have the same solution set. To solve an equation, we usually start with the given equation and replace it with a series of simpler equivalent equations. For example,

$$5x + 2 = 17, \quad 5x = 15, \quad \text{and} \quad x = 3 \quad \text{Equivalent equations}$$

are all equivalent since each has the solution set $\{3\}$.

1 Decide whether each of the following is an *equation* or an *expression.*

(a) $9x = 10$

(b) $9x + 10$

(c) $3 + 5x - 8x + 9$

(d) $3 + 5x = -8x + 9$

2 Are the given numbers solutions of the given equations?

(a) $3k = 15; 5$

(b) $r + 5 = 4; 1$

(c) $-8m = 12; \dfrac{3}{2}$

ANSWERS
1. (a) equation   (b) expression
   (c) expression   (d) equation
2. (a) yes   (b) no   (c) no

3 Solve and check.

(a) $3p + 2p + 1 = -24$

(b) $3p = 2p + 4p + 5$

(c) $4x + 8x = 17x - 9 - 1$

(d) $-7 + 3t - 9t = 12t - 5$

OBJECTIVE **2** **Solve linear equations using the addition and multiplication properties of equality.** We use two important properties to produce equivalent equations.

> **Addition and Multiplication Properties of Equality**
>
> **Addition Property of Equality**
> For all real numbers A, B, and C, the equations
> $$A = B \quad \text{and} \quad A + C = B + C \quad \text{are equivalent.}$$
> In words, *the same number may be added to each side of an equation without changing the solution set.*
>
> **Multiplication Property of Equality**
> For all real numbers A and B, and for $C \neq 0$, the equations
> $$A = B \quad \text{and} \quad AC = BC \quad \text{are equivalent.}$$
> In words, *each side of an equation may be multiplied by the same nonzero number without changing the solution set.*

Because subtraction and division are defined in terms of addition and multiplication, respectively, these properties can be extended:

> *The same number may be subtracted from each side of an equation, and each side of an equation may be divided by the same nonzero number, without changing the solution set.*

Example 1 **Solving a Linear Equation**

Solve $4x - 2x - 5 = 4 + 6x + 3$.

The goal is to get x alone on one side of the equation.

$$2x - 5 = 7 + 6x \qquad \text{Combine like terms.}$$

Next, use the addition property to get the terms with x on the same side of the equation and the remaining terms (the numbers) on the other side. One way to do this is to first subtract $6x$ from each side.

$$2x - 5 - 6x = 7 + 6x - 6x \qquad \text{Subtract } 6x.$$
$$-4x - 5 = 7 \qquad \text{Combine like terms.}$$
$$-4x - 5 + 5 = 7 + 5 \qquad \text{Add 5.}$$
$$-4x = 12 \qquad \text{Combine like terms.}$$
$$\frac{-4x}{-4} = \frac{12}{-4} \qquad \text{Divide by } -4.$$
$$x = -3 \qquad \text{Proposed solution}$$

Check by substituting -3 for x in the *original* equation.

Check $\qquad 4x - 2x - 5 = 4 + 6x + 3 \qquad$ Original equation
$$4(-3) - 2(-3) - 5 \stackrel{?}{=} 4 + 6(-3) + 3 \qquad \text{Let } x = -3.$$
$$-12 + 6 - 5 \stackrel{?}{=} 4 - 18 + 3 \qquad \text{Multiply.}$$
$$-11 = -11 \qquad \text{True}$$

Use parentheses around substituted values to avoid errors.

This is *not* the solution.

The true statement indicates that $\{-3\}$ is the solution set.

◀ *Work Problem* **3** *at the Side.*

The steps to solve a linear equation in one variable are as follows.

> **Solving a Linear Equation in One Variable**
>
> **Step 1**   **Clear fractions.** Eliminate any fractions by multiplying each side by the least common denominator.
>
> **Step 2**   **Simplify each side separately.** Use the distributive property to clear parentheses and combine like terms as needed.
>
> **Step 3**   **Isolate the variable terms on one side.** Use the addition property to get all terms with variables on one side of the equation and all numbers on the other.
>
> **Step 4**   **Isolate the variable.** Use the multiplication property to get an equation with just the variable (with coefficient 1) on one side.
>
> **Step 5**   **Check.** Substitute the proposed solution into the original equation.

OBJECTIVE 3 Solve linear equations using the distributive property.   In Example 1 we did not use Step 1 or the distributive property in Step 2 as given in the box. Many equations require one or both of these steps.

Example 2   Solving a Linear Equation

Solve $2(k - 5) + 3k = k + 6$.

Step 1   Since there are no fractions in this equation, Step 1 does not apply.

Step 2   Use the distributive property to simplify and combine like terms on the left side of the equation.

$$2(k - 5) + 3k = k + 6$$
$$2k - 10 + 3k = k + 6 \qquad 2(k - 5) = 2(k) - 2(5) = 2k - 10$$

Be sure to distribute over *all* terms within parentheses.

$$5k - 10 = k + 6 \qquad \text{Combine like terms.}$$

Step 3   Next, use the addition property of equality.

$$5k - 10 - k = k + 6 - k \qquad \text{Subtract } k.$$
$$4k - 10 = 6 \qquad \text{Combine like terms.}$$
$$4k - 10 + 10 = 6 + 10 \qquad \text{Add 10.}$$
$$4k = 16 \qquad \text{Combine like terms.}$$

Step 4   Use the multiplication property of equality to get just k on the left.

$$\frac{4k}{4} = \frac{16}{4} \qquad \text{Divide by 4.}$$
$$k = 4$$

Step 5   Check by substituting 4 for k in the original equation.

Check $2(k - 5) + 3k = k + 6$ Original equation
$$2(4 - 5) + 3(4) \overset{?}{=} 4 + 6 \qquad \text{Let } k = 4.$$

Always check your work.

$$2(-1) + 12 \overset{?}{=} 10$$
$$10 = 10 \qquad \text{True}$$

The solution checks, so the solution set is $\{4\}$.

Work Problem **4** *at the Side.* ▶

4 Solve and check.

(a) $5p + 4(3 - 2p)$
   $= 2 + p - 10$

(b) $3(z - 2) + 5z = 2$

(c) $-2 + 3(x + 4) = 8x$

(d) $6 - (4 + m)$
   $= 8m - 2(3m + 5)$

ANSWERS

4. (a) $\{5\}$ **(b)** $\{1\}$ **(c)** $\{2\}$ **(d)** $\{4\}$

5 Solve and check.

(a) $\dfrac{2p}{7} - \dfrac{p}{2} = -3$

(b) $\dfrac{k+1}{2} + \dfrac{k+3}{4} = \dfrac{1}{2}$

> **CAUTION**
> Notice in Examples 1 and 2 that the equals signs are aligned in columns. *Do not use more than one equals sign in a horizontal line of work when solving an equation.*

OBJECTIVE 4 Solve linear equations with fractions or decimals.
When fractions or decimals appear as coefficients in equations, our work can be made easier if we multiply each side of the equation by the least common denominator (LCD) of all the fractions. This is an application of the multiplication property of equality, and it produces an equivalent equation with integer coefficients.

Example 3 Solving a Linear Equation with Fractions

Solve $\dfrac{x+7}{6} + \dfrac{2x-8}{2} = -4$.

Step 1 Start by eliminating the fractions. Multiply each side by the LCD.

$$6\left(\dfrac{x+7}{6} + \dfrac{2x-8}{2}\right) = 6(-4) \qquad \text{The LCD is 6.}$$

Step 2
$$6\left(\dfrac{x+7}{6}\right) + 6\left(\dfrac{2x-8}{2}\right) = 6(-4) \qquad \text{Distributive property}$$
$$(x+7) + 3(2x-8) = -24 \qquad \text{Multiply.}$$
$$x + 7 + 3(2x) - 3(8) = -24 \qquad \text{Distributive property}$$
$$x + 7 + 6x - 24 = -24 \qquad \text{Multiply.}$$
$$7x - 17 = -24 \qquad \text{Combine like terms.}$$

Step 3
$$7x - 17 + 17 = -24 + 17 \qquad \text{Add 17.}$$
$$7x = -7 \qquad \text{Combine like terms.}$$

Step 4
$$\dfrac{7x}{7} = \dfrac{-7}{7} \qquad \text{Divide by 7.}$$
$$x = -1$$

Step 5 Check by substituting -1 for x in the original equation.

Check
$$\dfrac{x+7}{6} + \dfrac{2x-8}{2} = -4 \qquad \text{Original equation}$$
$$\dfrac{-1+7}{6} + \dfrac{2(-1)-8}{2} \stackrel{?}{=} -4 \qquad \text{Let } x = -1.$$
$$\dfrac{6}{6} + \dfrac{-10}{2} \stackrel{?}{=} -4$$
$$1 - 5 \stackrel{?}{=} -4$$
$$-4 = -4 \qquad \text{True}$$

The solution checks, so the solution set is $\{-1\}$.

◀ *Work Problem* **5** *at the Side.*

In **Sections 10.3** and **10.4** we solve problems involving interest rates and concentrations of solutions. These problems involve percents that are converted to decimals. The equations that are used to solve such problems involve decimal coefficients. We can clear these decimals by multiplying by a power of 10, such as

$$10^1 = 10, \quad 10^2 = 100, \quad \text{and so on,}$$

that will allow us to obtain integer coefficients.

6 Solve and check using the method of Example 4.

$$0.04x + 0.06(20 - x)$$
$$= 0.05(50)$$

Example 4 **Solving a Linear Equation with Decimals**

Solve $0.06x + 0.09(15 - x) = 0.07(15)$.

Because each decimal number is given in hundredths, multiply each side of the equation by 100. A number can be multiplied by 100 by moving the decimal point two places to the right.

$$0.06x + 0.09(15 - x) = 0.07(15)$$

$$0.06x + 0.09(15 - x) = 0.07(15) \qquad \text{Multiply by 100.}$$

Move decimal points 2 places to the right.

$$6x + 9(15 - x) = 7(15)$$

$$6x + 9(15) - 9(x) = 7(15) \qquad \text{Distributive property}$$

$$6x + 135 - 9x = 105 \qquad \text{Multiply.}$$

$$-3x + 135 = 105 \qquad \text{Combine like terms.}$$

$$-3x + 135 - 135 = 105 - 135 \qquad \text{Subtract 135.}$$

$$-3x = -30 \qquad \text{Combine like terms.}$$

$$\frac{-3x}{-3} = \frac{-30}{-3} \qquad \text{Divide by } -3.$$

$$x = 10$$

Check by substituting 10 for x in the original equation.

Check $\quad 0.06x + 0.09(15 - x) = 0.07(15) \qquad$ Original equation

$$0.06(10) + 0.09(15 - 10) \stackrel{?}{=} 0.07(15) \qquad \text{Let } x = 10.$$

$$0.06(10) + 0.09(5) \stackrel{?}{=} 0.07(15)$$

$$0.6 + 0.45 \stackrel{?}{=} 1.05$$

$$1.05 = 1.05 \qquad \text{True}$$

The solution set is $\{10\}$.

Work Problem **6** *at the Side.* ▶

Examples 3 and 4 illustrate related methods for solving equations with fractions or decimals as coefficients. In both cases, the first step is to eliminate (or "clear") the equation of fractions by multiplying both sides of the equation by the LCD or of decimals by multiplying both sides by a power of 10. Many students prefer these methods because they allow all of the remaining work to be done with integer coefficients.

Some students, however, prefer to solve an equation with decimal coefficients by working with the decimals, which requires fewer steps. The next example shows how to solve the equation from Example 4 without clearing decimals.

Answer

6. $\{-65\}$

7 Solve and check using the method of Example 5.

$$0.10(x - 6) + 0.05x$$
$$= 0.06(50)$$

> **Example 5** **Solving a Linear Equation without Clearing Decimals**
>
> Solve $0.06x + 0.09(15 - x) = 0.07(15)$.
>
> $0.06x + 0.09(15 - x) = 0.07(15)$
>
> $0.06x + 1.35 - 0.09x = 1.05$ Distributive property
>
> *Be careful with decimal points.* $\quad -0.03x + 1.35 = 1.05$ Combine like terms.
>
> $-0.03x + 1.35 - 1.35 = 1.05 - 1.35$ Subtract 1.35.
>
> $-0.03x = -0.3$ Combine like terms.
>
> $\dfrac{-0.03x}{-0.03} = \dfrac{-0.3}{-0.03}$ Divide by -0.03.
>
> $x = 10$
>
> As in Example 4, we see that the solution set is $\{10\}$.

◀ *Work Problem* **7** *at the Side.*

Either of the methods illustrated in Examples 4 and 5 can be used to solve any equation with decimal coefficients.

> **Note**
>
> Because of space limitations, we will not always show the check when solving an equation. ***To be sure that your solution is correct, you should always check your work.***

OBJECTIVE 5 Identify conditional equations, contradictions, and identities. All of the preceding equations had solution sets containing one element; for example, $2(k - 5) + 3k = k + 6$ has solution set $\{4\}$. This is an example of a *conditional equation,* one which is true only for certain values of the variables. Some linear equations, called *contradictions,* have no solution, while others, called *identities,* have an infinite number of solutions. The table below summarizes these types of equations.

Type of Linear Equation	Number of Solutions	Indication When Solving
Conditional	One	Final line is $x =$ a number. (See Example 6(a).)
Identity	Infinite; solution set {all real numbers}	Final line is true, such as $0 = 0$. (See Example 6(b).)
Contradiction	None; solution set $\emptyset$	Final line is false, such as $-15 = -20$. (See Example 6(c).)

> **Note**
>
> Recall that we use the symbol $\emptyset$ to represent the empty set (or null set), which is the set containing no elements. If an equation has no solution, there are no elements in its solution set, so the solution set is the empty set.

Example 6 **Recognizing Conditional Equations, Identities, and Contradictions**

Solve each equation. Decide whether it is a *conditional equation,* an *identity,* or a *contradiction.*

(a) $5(2x + 6) - 2 = 7(x + 4)$

$10x + 30 - 2 = 7x + 28$	Distributive property
$10x + 28 = 7x + 28$	Combine like terms.
$10x + 28 - 7x - 28 = 7x + 28 - 7x - 28$	Subtract $7x$; subtract 28.
$3x = 0$	Combine like terms.
$\dfrac{3x}{3} = \dfrac{0}{3}$	Divide by 3.
$x = 0$	

The solution set, $\{0\}$, has only one element, so $5(2x + 6) - 2 = 7(x + 4)$ is a conditional equation.

(b) $5x - 15 = 5(x - 3)$

$5x - 15 = 5x - 15$	Distributive property
$5x - 15 - 5x + 15 = 5x - 15 - 5x + 15$	Subtract $5x$; add 15.
$0 = 0$	True

The final line, the *true* statement $0 = 0$, indicates that the solution set is {all real numbers}, and the equation $5x - 15 = 5(x - 3)$ is an identity. (Notice that the first step yielded $5x - 15 = 5x - 15$, which is true for all values of x. We could have identified the equation as an identity at that point.)

(c) $5x - 15 = 5(x - 4)$

$5x - 15 = 5x - 20$	Distributive property
$5x - 15 - 5x = 5x - 20 - 5x$	Subtract $5x$.
$-15 = -20$	False

Since the result, $-15 = -20$, is *false,* the equation has no solution. The solution set is $\emptyset$, so the equation $5x - 15 = 5(x - 4)$ is a contradiction.

Work Problem **8** *at the Side.* ▶

CAUTION
A common error in solving an equation like that in Example 6(a) is to think that the equation has no solution and write the solution set as $\emptyset$. This equation has one solution, the number 0, so it is a conditional equation with solution set $\{0\}$.

---

8 Solve each equation. Decide whether it is a *conditional equation,* an *identity,* or a *contradiction.*

(a) $5(x + 2) - 2(x + 1)$
$= 3x + 1$

(b) $\dfrac{x + 1}{3} + \dfrac{2x}{3} = x + \dfrac{1}{3}$

(c) $5(3x + 1) = x + 5$

10.2 ▶▶▶ **Exercises**

FOR EXTRA HELP

MyMathLab

 Math XL PRACTICE

 WATCH

 DOWNLOAD

READ

 REVIEW

1. Which equations are linear equations in x?

  A. $3x + x - 2 = 0$ **B.** $12 = x^2$

  C. $9x - 4 = 9$ **D.** $\dfrac{1}{8}x - \dfrac{1}{x} = 0$

2. Which of the equations in Exercise 1 are nonlinear equations in x? Explain why.

3. Decide whether 6 is a solution of $3(x + 4) = 5x$ by substituting 6 for x. If it is not a solution, explain why.

4. Use substitution to decide whether -2 is a solution of $5(x + 4) - 3(x + 6) = 9(x + 1)$. If it is not a solution, explain why.

5. The equation $4[x + (2 - 3x)] = 2(4 - 4x)$ is an identity. Let x represent the number of letters in your last name. Is this number a solution of this equation? Check your answer.

6. In Example 1, a student looked at the check and thought that $\{-11\}$ should be given as the solution set. Explain why this is not correct.

7. Identify each as an *expression* or an *equation*.

  (a) $5x = 10$

  (b) $5x + 10$

  (c) $5x + 6(x - 3) = 12x + 6$

  (d) $5x + 6(x - 3) - (12x + 6)$

8. Explain why $7x + 10 = 7x + 9$ cannot have a solution. (No work is necessary.)

9. The following work contains a common student error.

$$8x - 2(2x - 3) = 3x + 7$$

$$8x - 4x - 6 = 3x + 7 \quad \text{Distributive property}$$

$$4x - 6 = 3x + 7 \quad \text{Combine like terms.}$$

$$x = 13 \quad \text{Subtract } 3x; \text{ add } 6.$$

WHAT WENT WRONG? Give the correct solution.

10. When clearing parentheses in the expression

$$-5m - (2m - 4) + 5$$

on the right side of the equation in Exercise 35 to follow, the $-$ sign before the parenthesis acts like a factor representing what number? Clear parentheses and simplify this expression.

Solve and check each equation. See Examples 1 and 2.

11. $9x + 10 = 1$

12. $7x - 4 = 31$

13. $5x + 2 = 3x - 6$

14. $9p + 1 = 7p - 9$

🌐 **15.** $7x - 5x + 15 = x + 8$

16. $2x + 4 - x = 4x - 5$

17. $12w + 15w - 9 + 5 = -3w + 5 - 9$

18. $-4t + 5t - 8 + 4 = 6t - 4$

19. $3(2t - 4) = 20 - 2t$
🌐

20. $2(3 - 2x) = x - 4$

21. $-5(x + 1) + 3x + 2 = 6x + 4$

22. $5(x + 3) + 4x - 5 = 4 - 2x$

23. $2(x + 3) = -4(x + 1)$

24. $4(t - 9) = 8(t + 3)$

25. $3(2w + 1) - 2(w - 2) = 5$

26. $4(x - 2) + 2(x + 3) = 6$

27. $2x + 3(x - 4) = 2(x - 3)$

28. $6x - 3(5x + 2) = 4(1 - x)$

29. $6p - 4(3 - 2p) = 5(p - 4) - 10$

30. $-2k - 3(4 - 2k) = 2(k - 3) + 2$

31. $2[w - (2w + 4) + 3] = 2(w + 1)$

32. $4[2t - (3 - t) + 5] = -(2 + 7t)$

33. $-[2z - (5z + 2)] = 2 + (2z + 7)$

34. $-[6x - (4x + 8)] = 9 + (6x + 3)$

35. $-3m + 6 - 5(m - 1) = -5m - (2m - 4) + 5$

36. $4(k + 2) - 8k - 5 = -3k + 9 - 2(k + 6)$

37. $-3(x + 2) + 4(3x - 8) = 2(4x + 7) + 2(3x - 6)$

38. $-7(2x + 1) + 5(3x + 2) = 6(2x - 4) - (12x + 3)$

39. In order to solve the linear equation
$$\frac{3}{4}x - \frac{1}{3}x = \frac{5}{6}x - 5,$$
we are allowed to multiply each side by the least common denominator of all the fractions in the equation. What is this least common denominator?

40. Suppose that in solving the equation
$$\frac{1}{3}x + \frac{1}{2}x = \frac{1}{6}x,$$
you begin by multiplying each side by 12, rather than the *least* common denominator, 6. Would you get the correct solution anyway? Explain.

41. To solve a linear equation with decimals, we multiply by a power of 10 so that all coefficients are integers. What is the smallest power of 10 that will accomplish this goal in each equation?

(a) $0.05x + 0.12(x + 5000) = 940$ (Exercise 55)

(b) $0.006(x + 2) = 0.007x + 0.009$ (Exercise 61)

42. The expression $0.06(10 - x)(100)$ is equivalent to which of the following?

A. $0.06 - 0.06x$ **B.** $60 - 6x$

C. $6 - 6x$ **D.** $6 - 0.06x$

Solve and check each equation. See Examples 3–5.

43. $\frac{m}{2} + \frac{m}{3} = 10$

44. $\frac{x}{5} - \frac{x}{4} = 2$

45. $\frac{3}{4}x + \frac{5}{2}x = 13$

46. $\frac{8}{3}x - \frac{1}{2}x = -13$

47. $\frac{1}{5}x - 2 = \frac{2}{3}x - \frac{2}{5}x$

48. $\frac{3}{4}x - \frac{1}{3}x = \frac{5}{6}x - 5$

49. $\frac{x - 8}{5} + \frac{8}{5} = -\frac{x}{3}$

50. $\frac{2r - 3}{7} + \frac{3}{7} = -\frac{r}{3}$

51. $\frac{3x - 1}{4} + \frac{x + 3}{6} = 3$

52. $\frac{3x + 2}{7} - \frac{x + 4}{5} = 2$

53. $\frac{4t + 1}{3} = \frac{t + 5}{6} + \frac{t - 3}{6}$

54. $\frac{2x + 5}{5} = \frac{3x + 1}{2} + \frac{-x + 7}{2}$

55. $0.05x + 0.12(x + 5000) = 940$

56. $0.09k + 0.13(k + 300) = 61$

57. $0.02(50) + 0.08r = 0.04(50 + r)$

58. $0.20(14{,}000) + 0.14t = 0.18(14{,}000 + t)$

59. $0.05x + 0.10(200 - x) = 0.45x$

60. $0.08x + 0.12(260 - x) = 0.48x$

61. $0.006(x + 2) = 0.007x + 0.009$

62. $0.004x + 0.006(50 - x) = 0.004(68)$

63. Explain the distinction between a conditional equation, an identity, and a contradiction.

64. A student tried to solve the equation $8x = 7x$ by dividing each side by x, obtaining $8 = 7$. He gave the solution set as $\emptyset$. *WHAT WENT WRONG?*

65. Suppose you solve a linear equation and obtain, as your final result, an equation in Column I. Match each result with the solution set in Column II for the original equation.

I	II
(a) $7 = 7$	**A.** $\{0\}$
(b) $x = 0$	**B.** {all real numbers}
(c) $7 = 0$	**C.** $\emptyset$

66. Which one of the following linear equations does *not* have {all real numbers} as its solution set?

A. $4x = 5x - x$ **B.** $3(x + 4) = 3x + 12$

C. $4x = 3x$ **D.** $\frac{3}{4}x = 0.75x$

Decide whether each equation is a conditional equation, *an* identity, *or a* contradiction. *Give the solution set. See Example 6.*

67. $-x + 4x - 9 = 3(x - 4) - 5$

68. $-12x + 2x - 11 = -2(5x - 3) + 4$

69. $-11x + 4(x - 3) + 6x = 4x - 12$

70. $3x - 5(x + 4) + 9 = -11 + 15x$

71. $-2(t + 3) - t - 4 = -3(t + 4) + 2$

72. $4(2d + 7) = 2d + 25 + 3(2d + 1)$

73. $7[2 - (3 + 4x)] - 2x = -9 + 2(1 - 15x)$

74. $4[6 - (1 + 2x)] + 10x = 2(10 - 3x) + 8x$

Study Skills

HOMEWORK: HOW, WHY, AND WHEN

OBJECTIVES

1 Select an appropriate strategy for homework.

2 Use textbook features effectively.

Preview before Class; Read Carefully after Class

Read Carefully before Class

Why Are These Techniques Brain Friendly?

The steps here encourage you to be actively working with the material in your text. You learn best when you are actively doing something.

These methods require you to try several different techniques, not just the same thing over and over.

Also, the techniques allow you to take small breaks in your learning. Those rest periods are crucial for good learning.

It is best for your brain if you keep up with the reading and homework in your math class. The more times you work with the information, the more you learn. So, give yourself every opportunity to read, work problems, and review your mathematics.

Here are two options for reading your math textbook. Read the short descriptions below and decide which will be best for you.

Abby learns best by listening to her teacher explain things. She "gets it" when she sees the instructor work problems on the board. She likes to ask questions in class and put the information in her notes. She has learned that it helps if she has *previewed* the section before the lecture, so she knows generally what to expect in class. *But after the class instruction*, when Abby gets home, she finds that she can better understand the math textbook. She remembers what her teacher said, and she can double-check her notes if she gets confused. So, **Abby carefully reads the section in her text *after* she hears the classroom lecture on the topic.**

De'Lore, on the other hand, feels he learns well by reading on his own. He prefers to read the section and try working the example problems before coming to class. That way, he already knows what the teacher is going to talk about. Then, he can follow the teacher's examples more easily. It is also easier for him to take notes in class. De'Lore likes to have his questions answered right away, which he can do if he has already read the chapter section. So, **De'Lore carefully reads the section in his text *before* he hears the classroom lecture on the topic.**

Notice that there is no one right way to work with your textbook. You must always figure out what works best for you. Note also that both Abby and De'Lore work with one section at a time. ***The key is that you read the textbook regularly.*** The rest of this activity will give you some ideas of how to make the most of your reading.

Try the following steps as you read your math textbook.

▶ **Read slowly.** Read only one section—or even part of a section—at a time.

▶ **Do the sample problems in the margins as you go.** Check them right away. The answers are at the bottom of the page.

▶ If your mind wanders, **work problems on separate paper and write explanations in your own words.**

▶ **Make study cards as you read each section.** Pay special attention to the colored boxes in the book. Make cards for new vocabulary, rules, procedures, formulas, and sample problems.

▶ **NOW,** you are ready to do your homework assignment.

> **Which two or three steps will be most helpful for you?**
>
> 1. _____ 2. _____ 3. _____

Teachers assign homework so you can learn the material and then remember the material through practice. In learning, you get good at what you practice. So, completing homework every day will build your confidence, strengthen your skills, and prepare you for exams.

If you have read each section in your textbook according to the steps above, you will probably encounter few difficulties with the exercises in the homework. Here are some additional suggestions that will help you succeed with the homework.

▶ **If you have trouble with a problem,** find a similar worked example problem in the section. Pay attention to *every line* of the worked example to see how to get from step to step. Work it yourself too, on separate paper; don't just look at it.

▶ **If it is hard to remember the steps** to follow for certain procedures, write the steps on a separate card. Then write a short explanation of each step. Keep the card nearby while you do the exercises, but try *not* to look at it.

▶ **If you aren't sure you are working the assigned exercises correctly,** choose two or three odd-numbered problems that are a similar type and work them. Then check the answers in the answer section of your book and see if you are doing them correctly. If you aren't, go back to the section in the text and review the examples and find out how to correct your errors. Finally, when you are sure you understand, try the assigned problems again.

▶ **If the problem or a similar problem has a blue screen around the problem number,** such as **11.** , there is a worked-out solution in the selected solutions section at the back of the book. Study this solution.

▶ **Make sure you do some homework every day,** even if your math class does not meet each day.

> **What are your biggest homework concerns?**
> List your two main concerns below. Then write a **solution** for each one.
>
> 1. **Concern:** _____ **Solution:** _____
>
> 2. **Concern:** _____ **Solution:** _____

Homework

10.3 ▶▶▶ Formulas and Percent

OBJECTIVES

1 Solve a formula for a specified variable.

2 Solve applied problems using formulas.

3 Solve percent problems.

4 Solve problems involving percent increase or decrease.

A **mathematical model** is an equation or inequality that describes a real situation. Models for many applied problems already exist; they are called *formulas*. A **formula** is an equation in which variables are used to describe a relationship. Some formulas that we will be using are

$$d = rt, \quad I = prt, \quad \text{and} \quad P = 2L + 2W. \quad \text{Formulas}$$

A list of some common formulas used in algebra is given inside the covers of this book.

OBJECTIVE 1 Solve a formula for a specified variable. In some applications, the appropriate formula may be solved for a different variable than the one to be found. For example, the formula $I = prt$ says that interest on a loan or investment equals principal (amount borrowed or invested) times rate (percent) times time at interest (in years). To determine how long it will take for an investment at a stated interest rate to earn a predetermined amount of interest, it would help to first solve the formula for t. This process is called **solving for a specified variable** or **solving a literal equation.**

1 Solve $I = prt$ for each given variable.

(a) p

The steps used in the following examples are very similar to those used in solving linear equations from **Section 10.2.** *When you are solving for a specified variable, the key is to treat that variable as if it were the only one; treat all other variables like numbers (constants).*

(b) r

Example 1 Solving for a Specified Variable

Solve the formula $I = prt$ for t.

We solve this formula for t by treating I, p, and r as constants (having fixed values) and treating t as the only variable. We first write the formula so that the variable for which we are solving, t, is on the left side. Then we use the properties of the previous section as follows.

$$prt = I \qquad \text{Our goal is to isolate } t.$$
$$(pr)t = I \qquad \text{Associative property}$$
$$\frac{(pr)t}{pr} = \frac{I}{pr} \qquad \text{Divide by } pr.$$
$$t = \frac{I}{pr}$$

The result is a formula for t, time in years.

◀ *Work Problem* **1** *at the Side.*

To solve an equation for a specified variable, follow these steps.

Solving for a Specified Variable

Step 1 If the equation contains fractions, multiply both sides by the LCD to clear the fractions.

Step 2 Transform so that all terms containing the specified variable are on one side of the equation and all terms without that variable are on the other side.

Step 3 Divide each side by the factor that is the coefficient of the specified variable.

Example 2 **Solving for a Specified Variable**

Solve the formula $P = 2L + 2W$ for W.

This formula gives the relationship between perimeter of a rectangle, P, length of the rectangle, L, and width of the rectangle, W. See Figure 1.

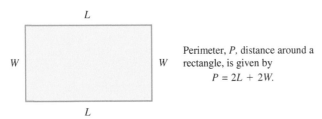

Perimeter, P, distance around a rectangle, is given by
$$P = 2L + 2W.$$

Figure 1

We solve the formula for W by isolating W on one side of the equals sign.

$$P = 2L + 2W$$

Step 1 is not needed here.

Step 2
$$P - 2L = 2L + 2W - 2L \qquad \text{Subtract } 2L.$$
$$P - 2L = 2W$$

Step 3
$$\frac{P - 2L}{2} = \frac{2W}{2} \qquad \text{Divide by 2.}$$

$$\frac{P - 2L}{2} = W, \quad \text{or} \quad W = \frac{P - 2L}{2}$$

Work Problem **2** *at the Side.* ▶

CAUTION

In Step 3 of Example 2, we cannot simplify the fraction by dividing 2 into the term $2L$. Based on the order of operations **(Section 3.2)**, the fraction bar serves as a grouping symbol. Thus, the subtraction in the numerator must be done before the division.

$$\frac{P - 2L}{2} \neq P - L$$

---

2 **(a)** Solve the formula
$$P = a + b + c$$
for a.

(b) Solve the formula
$$V = \frac{1}{3}\pi r^2 h$$
for h.

3 Solve the formula

$$M = \frac{1}{3}(a + b + c)$$

for b.

Example 3 **Solving a Formula with Parentheses**

The formula for the perimeter of a rectangle is sometimes written in the equivalent form $P = 2(L + W)$. Solve this form for W.

One way to begin is to use the distributive property on the right side of the equation to get $P = 2L + 2W$, which we would then solve as in Example 2. Another way to begin is to divide by the coefficient 2.

$$P = 2(L + W)$$

$$\frac{P}{2} = L + W \qquad \text{Divide by 2.}$$

$$\frac{P}{2} - L = W, \quad \text{or} \quad W = \frac{P}{2} - L \quad \text{Subtract } L.$$

We can show that this result is equivalent to our result in Example 2 by rewriting L as $\frac{2}{2}L$.

$$\frac{P}{2} - L = W$$

$$\frac{P}{2} - \frac{2}{2}(L) = W \qquad \frac{2}{2} = 1, \text{ so } L = \frac{2}{2}(L).$$

$$\frac{P}{2} - \frac{2L}{2} = W$$

$$\frac{P - 2L}{2} = W \qquad \text{Subtract fractions.}$$

The final line agrees with the result in Example 2.

◀ *Work Problem* **3** *at the Side.*

---

4 Solve each equation for y.

(a) $2x + 7y = 5$

In Examples 1–3, we solved formulas for specified variables. In Example 4, we solve an equation with two variables for one of these variables. This process will be useful when we work with equations like this one, called *linear equations in two variables,* in **Chapter 5.**

Example 4 **Solving an Equation for One of the Variables**

Solve the equation $3x - 4y = 12$ for y.

Our goal is to isolate y on one side of the equation.

$$3x - 4y = 12$$

$$3x - 4y - 3x = 12 - 3x \qquad \text{Subtract } 3x.$$

$$-4y = 12 - 3x$$

$$\frac{-4y}{-4} = \frac{12 - 3x}{-4} \qquad \text{Divide by } -4.$$

$$y = \frac{12 - 3x}{-4}$$

(b) $5x - 6y = 12$

There are other equivalent forms of the final answer that are also correct. For example, since $\frac{a}{-b} = \frac{-a}{b}$ (**Section 3.1**),

> Multiply *both* terms of the numerator by -1.

3. $b = 3M - a - c$

4. (a) $y = \dfrac{5 - 2x}{7}$

(b) $y = \dfrac{12 - 5x}{-6}$, or $y = \dfrac{5x - 12}{6}$

$$y = \frac{12 - 3x}{-4} \quad \text{can be written as} \quad y = \frac{-(12 - 3x)}{4}, \quad \text{or} \quad y = \frac{3x - 12}{4}.$$

◀ *Work Problem* **4** *at the Side.*

OBJECTIVE **2** **Solve applied problems using formulas.** The distance formula, $d = rt$, relates d, the distance traveled, r, the rate or speed, and t, the travel time.

Example 5 **Finding Average Speed**

Janet Branson found that on average it took her $\frac{3}{4}$ hr each day to drive a distance of 15 mi to work. What was her average speed?

Find the formula for speed (rate) r by solving $d = rt$ for r.

$$d = rt$$

$$\frac{d}{t} = \frac{rt}{t} \qquad \text{Divide by } t.$$

$$\frac{d}{t} = r, \quad \text{or} \quad r = \frac{d}{t}$$

Notice that only Step 3 was needed to solve for r in this example. Now find the speed by substituting the given values of d and t into this formula.

$$r = \frac{15}{\frac{3}{4}} \qquad \text{Let } d = 15, t = \frac{3}{4}.$$

$$r = 15 \cdot \frac{4}{3} \qquad \text{Multiply by the reciprocal of } \frac{3}{4}.$$

$$r = 20$$

Her average speed was 20 mph. (That is, at times she may have traveled a little faster or slower than 20 mph, but overall her speed was 20 mph.)

Work Problem **5** *at the Side.* ▶

OBJECTIVE **3** **Solve percent problems.** An important everyday use of mathematics involves the concept of percent. Percent is written with the symbol %. The word **percent** means "per one hundred." One percent means "one per one hundred" or "one one-hundredth."

$$1\% = 0.01 \quad \text{or} \quad 1\% = \frac{1}{100}$$

Solving a Percent Problem

Let a represent a partial amount of b, the base, or whole amount. Then the following equation can be used to solve a percent problem.

$$\frac{\text{amount } a}{\text{base } b} = \text{percent (represented as a decimal)}$$

For example, if a class consists of 50 students and 32 are males, then the percent of males in the class is

$$\frac{\text{amount } a}{\text{base } b} = \frac{32}{50} \qquad \text{Let } a = 32, b = 50.$$

$$= 0.64$$

$$= 64\%.$$

5 Solve each problem.

(a) A triangle has an area of 36 in.^{2} (square inches) and a base of 12 in. Find its height.

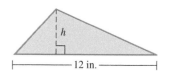

(b) The distance is 500 mi and the time is 20 hr. Find the rate.

(c) In 2006, Sam Hornish, Jr. won the Indianapolis 500 (mile) race with a speed of 157.085 mph. (*Source:* www.indy500.com) Find his time to the nearest thousandth.

ANSWERS

5. **(a)** 6 in. **(b)** 25 mph **(c)** 3.183 hr

6 Solve each problem.

(a) A mixture of gasoline and oil contains 20 oz, of which 1 oz is oil. What percent of the mixture is oil?

Example 6 **Solving Percent Problems**

(a) A 50-L mixture of acid and water contains 10 L of acid. What is the percent of acid in the mixture?

The given amount of the mixture is 50 L, and the part that is acid is 10 L. Let x represent the percent of acid in the mixture. Then,

$$x = \frac{10 \leftarrow \text{partial amount}}{50 \leftarrow \text{whole amount}}$$

$$x = 0.20, \quad \text{or} \quad 20\%.$$

(b) If a savings account balance of $4780 earns 5% interest in one year, how much interest is earned?

Let x represent the amount of interest earned (that is, the part of the whole amount invested). Since $5\% = 0.05$, the equation is

$$\frac{x}{4780} = 0.05 \qquad \frac{\text{amount } a}{\text{base } b} = \text{percent}$$

$$x = 0.05\,(4780) \qquad \text{Multiply by 4780.}$$

$$x = 239.$$

The interest earned is $239.

(b) An automobile salesman earns a 6% commission on every car he sells. How much does he earn on a car that sells for $22,000?

◀ *Work Problem* **6** *at the Side.*

Example 7 **Interpreting Percents from a Graph**

In 2007, Americans spent about $41.2 billion on their pets. Use the graph in Figure 2 to determine how much of this amount was spent on pet food.

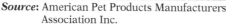

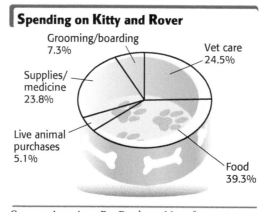

Spending on Kitty and Rover

Grooming/boarding 7.3%

Vet care 24.5%

Supplies/medicine 23.8%

Live animal purchases 5.1%

Food 39.3%

Dotty

7 Refer to Figure 2. How much was spent on pet supplies/medicine? Round your answer to the nearest tenth.

Source: American Pet Products Manufacturers Association Inc.

Figure 2

According to the graph, 39.3% was spent on food. Let x represent this amount in billions of dollars.

$$\frac{x}{41.2} = 0.393 \qquad 39.3\% = 0.393$$

$$x = 41.2\,(0.393) \qquad \text{Multiply by 41.2.}$$

$$x \approx 16.2 \qquad \text{Nearest tenth}$$

Therefore, about $16.2 billion was spent on pet food.

ANSWERS

6. (a) 5% **(b)** $1320
7. $9.8 billion

◀ *Work Problem* **7** *at the Side.*

OBJECTIVE 4 Solve problems involving percent increase or decrease. Percent is often used to express a change in some quantity. Buying an item that has been marked up, getting a raise at your job, and the inflation rate are all common applications of **percent increase.** Buying an item on sale, being offered a special discount on tickets to an event, and declining population are common applications of *percent decrease.* To solve problems of this type, we use the percent equation from page 811 in the following form:

$$\text{percent change} = \frac{\text{amount of change}}{\text{base}}.$$

[Subtract to find this.]

Example 8 **Solving Problems About Percent Increase or Decrease**

(a) An electronics store marked up a laptop computer from their cost of $1200 to a selling price of $1464. What was the percent markup?
"Markup" is a name for an increase. Let $x =$ the percent increase (as a decimal).

$$\text{percent increase} = \frac{\text{amount of increase}}{\text{base}}$$

[Subtract to find the *amount* of increase.]
$$x = \frac{1464 - 1200}{1200}$$ Substitute the given values.

[Use the original cost.]
$$x = \frac{264}{1200}$$

$$x = 0.22$$ Use a calculator.

The computer was marked up 22%.

(b) The enrollment in a community college declined from 12,750 during one school year to 11,350 the following year. Find the percent decrease to the nearest tenth.
Let $x =$ the percent decrease (as a decimal).

$$\text{percent decrease} = \frac{\text{amount of decrease}}{\text{base}}$$

[Subtract to find the amount of decrease.]
$$x = \frac{12,750 - 11,350}{12,750}$$ Substitute the given values.

[Use the original number.]
$$x = \frac{1400}{12,750}$$

$$x \approx 0.11$$ Use a calculator.

The college enrollment decreased by about 11%.

CAUTION
When calculating a percent increase or decrease, be sure that you use the original number (*before* the increase or decrease) as the base. A common error is to use the final number (*after* the increase or decrease) in the denominator of the fraction.

8 Solve each problem.

(a) Cara bought a jacket on sale for $56. The regular price of the jacket was $80. What was the percent markdown?

(b) When it was time for Liam to renew the lease on his apartment, the landlord raised his rent from $650 to $689 a month. What was the percent increase?

Work Problem **8** *at the Side.* ▶

ANSWERS

8. (a) 30% **(b)** 6%

Relating Concepts (Exercises 1–6) For Individual or Group Work

Consider the following equations:

First Equation	*Second Equation*
$\dfrac{7x + 8}{3} = 12$	$\dfrac{ax + k}{c} = t \quad (c \neq 0).$

Solving the second equation for x requires the same logic as solving the first equation for x. When solving for x, we treat all other variables as though they were constants. **Work Exercises 1–6 in order,** *to see the "parallel logic" of solving for x in the two equations.*

1. **(a)** Clear the first equation of fractions by multiplying each side by 3.

   (b) Clear the second equation of fractions by multiplying each side by c.

2. **(a)** Transform so that the term involving x is the left side of the first equation and the constants are on the right by subtracting 8 from each side.

   (b) Transform so that the term involving x is on the left side of the second equation by subtracting k from each side.

3. **(a)** Simplify the terms in the first equation.

   (b) Simplify the terms in the second equation.

4. **(a)** Divide each side of the first equation by the coefficient of x.

   (b) Divide each side of the second equation by the coefficient of x.

5. Look at your answer for the second equation. What restriction must be placed on the variables? Why is this necessary?

6. Write a short paragraph summarizing what you have learned in this group of exercises.

Solve each formula for the specified variable. See Examples 1–3.

7. $A = LW$ for W (area of a rectangle)

8. $d = rt$ for t (distance)

9. $P = 2L + 2W$ for L (perimeter of a rectangle)

10. $A = bh$ for b (area of a parallelogram)

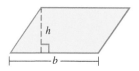

11. $V = LWH$ (volume of a rectangular solid)
     (a) for W **(b)** for H

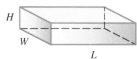

12. $P = a + b + c$ (perimeter of a triangle)
     (a) for b **(b)** for c

13. $C = 2\pi r$ for r (circumference of a circle)

14. $A = \dfrac{1}{2}bh$ for h (area of a triangle)

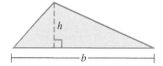

15. $A = \dfrac{1}{2}h(b + B)$ (area of a trapezoid)
     (a) for h **(b)** for B

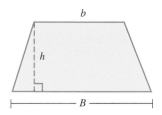

16. $V = \pi r^2 h$ for h
     (volume of a right circular cylinder)

17. $F = \dfrac{9}{5}C + 32$ for C (Celsius to Fahrenheit)

18. $C = \dfrac{5}{9}(F - 32)$ for F (Fahrenheit to Celsius)

Solve each equation for y. See Example 4.

19. $4x + 9y = 11$

20. $-7x + 8y = 11$

21. $-3x + 2y = 5$

22. $5x - 3y = 12$

23. $6x - 5y = 7$

Relating Concepts (Exercises 24–26) For Individual or Group Work

The **surface area** *of any solid three-dimensional figure is the total area of its surface. For a rectangular solid like that shown in the figure, the surface area A is*

$$A = 2HW + 2LW + 2LH.$$

We can solve this formula for L as follows:

$$A = 2HW + 2LW + 2LH$$

$$A - 2HW = 2LW + 2LH \qquad \text{Subtract } 2HW.$$

$$A - 2HW = L(2W + 2H) \qquad \text{Distributive property}$$

$$\frac{A - 2HW}{2W + 2H} = L, \quad \text{or} \quad L = \frac{A - 2HW}{2W + 2H}. \qquad \text{Divide by } 2W + 2H.$$

In the third line, we used the distributive property in reverse to write $2LW + 2LH$ *as* $L(2W + 2H)$.
This is called **factoring***, a topic of* **Chapter 7.**

     Use the distributive property to solve each formula for the specified variable.

24. $k = dF - DF$ for F

25. $Mv = mv - Vm$ for m

26. $A = 2HW + 2LW + 2LH$ for W

Solve each problem. See Example 5.

27. In 2008, Ryan Newman won the Daytona 500 (mile) race with a speed of 152.672 mph. Find his time to the nearest thousandth. (*Source:* www.daytona500.com)

28. In 2007, rain shortened the Indianapolis 500 race to 415 mi. It was won by Dario Franchitti, who averaged 151.774 mph. What was his time to the nearest thousandth? (*Source:* www.indy500.com)

29. As of 2006, the highest temperature ever recorded in Tennessee was 45°C. Find the corresponding Fahrenheit temperature. (*Source:* National Climatic Data Center.)

30. As of 2006, the lowest temperature ever recorded in South Dakota was −58°F. Find the corresponding Celsius temperature. (*Source:* National Climatic Data Center.)

31. The base of the Great Pyramid of Cheops is a square whose perimeter is 920 m. What is the length of each side of this square? (*Source: Atlas of Ancient Archaeology*, 1994.)

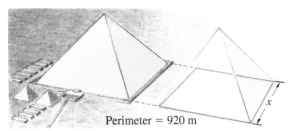

Perimeter = 920 m

32. Marina City in Chicago is a complex of two residential towers that resemble corncobs. Each tower has a concrete cylindrical core with a 35-ft diameter and is 588 ft tall. Find the volume of the core of one of the towers to the nearest whole number. (*Hint:* Use the π key on your calculator.) (*Source:* www.architechgallery.com; www.aviewoncities.com)

33. The circumference of a circle is 370π in. What is its radius? What is its diameter?

34. The radius of a circle is 2.5 in. What is its diameter? What is its circumference?

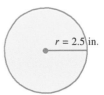

$r = 2.5$ in.

35. A sheet of standard-size copy paper measures 8.5 in. by 11 in. If a ream (500 sheets) of this paper has a volume of 187 in.^{3}, how thick is the ream?

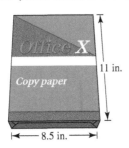

11 in.

Copy paper

8.5 in.

36. Copy paper (Exercise 35) also comes in legal size, which has the same width, but is longer than standard size. If a ream of legal-size copy paper has the same thickness as the standard-size paper and a volume of 238 in.^{3}, what is the length of a sheet of legal paper?

Solve each problem. See Example 6.

37. A mixture of alcohol and water contains a total of 36 oz of liquid. There are 9 oz of pure alcohol in the mixture. What percent of the mixture is water? What percent is alcohol?

38. A mixture of acid and water is 35% acid. If the mixture contains a total of 40 L, how many liters of pure acid are in the mixture? How many liters of pure water are in the mixture?

39. A real estate agent earned $6900 commission on a property sale of $230,000. What is her rate of commission?

40. A certificate of deposit for one year pays $288 simple interest on a principal of $6400. What is the annual interest rate being paid on this deposit?

When a consumer loan is paid off ahead of schedule, the finance charge is smaller than if the loan were paid off over its scheduled life. By one method, called the **rule of 78,** the amount of unearned interest (finance charge that need not be paid) is given by

$$u = f \cdot \frac{k(k+1)}{n(n+1)},$$

where u is the amount of unearned interest (money saved) when a loan scheduled to run n payments is paid off k payments ahead of schedule. The total scheduled finance charge is f. Use this formula to solve Exercises 41–44.

41. Rhonda Alessi bought a new Ford and agreed to pay it off in 36 monthly payments. The total finance charge is $700. Find the unearned interest if she pays the loan off 4 payments ahead of schedule.

42. Finley Westmoreland bought a car and agreed to pay it off in 36 monthly payments. The total finance charge on the loan was $600. With 12 payments remaining, Finley decided to pay the loan in full. Find the amount of unearned interest.

43. The finance charge on a loan taken out by Vic Denicola is $380.50. If there were 24 equal monthly installments needed to repay the loan, and the loan is paid in full with 8 months remaining, find the amount of unearned interest.

44. Joe Maggiore is scheduled to repay a loan in 24 equal monthly installments. The total finance charge on the loan is $450. With 9 payments remaining, he decides to repay the loan in full. Find the amount of unearned interest.

Exercises 45 and 46 deal with winning percentage in the team standings for Major League Baseball. Winning percentage (Pct.) is commonly expressed as a decimal rounded to the nearest thousandth. To find the winning percentage of a team, divide the number of wins (W) by the total number of games played (W + L).

45. The final 2007 standings of the Central Division of the American League are shown in the table. Find the winning percentage of each team.

(a) Detroit   **(b)** Minnesota
(c) Chicago   **(d)** Kansas City

	W	L	Pct.
Cleveland	96	66	.593
Detroit	88	74	
Minnesota	79	83	
Chicago	72	90	
Kansas City	69	93	

46. Repeat Exercise 45 for the following standings for the Central Division of the National League.

(a) Chicago   **(b)** St. Louis
(c) Houston   **(d)** Pittsburgh

	W	L	Pct.
Chicago	85	77	
Milwaukee	83	79	.512
St. Louis	78	84	
Houston	73	89	
Cincinnati	72	90	.444
Pittsburgh	68	94	

As mentioned in the chapter introduction, 111.4 million U.S. households owned at least one TV set in 2006. (Source: Nielsen Media Research.) Use this information to solve Exercises 47 and 48. Round answers to the nearest percent.

47. About 57.9 million U.S. households owned 3 or more TV sets in 2006. What percent of those owning at least one TV set was this?

48. About 93.6 million households that owned at least one TV set in 2006 had a DVD player. What percent of those owning at least one TV set had a DVD player?

📺 *An average middle-income family will spend $242,070 to raise a child born in 2004 from birth to age 17. The graph shows the percents spent for various categories. Use the graph to answer Exercises 49–52. See Example 7.*

49. To the nearest dollar, how much will be spent to 🌐 provide housing for the child?

50. To the nearest dollar, how much will be spent for health care?

The Cost of Parenthood

Housing 34%

Miscellaneous 11%

Child care/ education 11%

Health care 7%

Clothing 6%

Transportation 14%

Food 17%

Source: U.S. Department of Agriculture.

51. About $41,000 will be spent for food. To the nearest percent, what percent of the cost of raising a child from birth to age 17 is this? Does your answer agree with the percent shown in the graph?

52. About $34,000 will be spent for transportation. To the nearest percent, what percent of the cost of raising a child to age 17 is this? Does your answer agree with the percent shown in the graph?

📺 *Solve each problem about percent increase or percent decrease. See Example 8.*

53. After 1 yr on the job, Mollie got a raise from $10.50 per hour to $11.34 per hour. What was the percent increase in her hourly wage?

54. Sean bought a ticket to a rock concert at a discount. The regular price of the ticket was $70.00, but he only paid $59.50. What was the percent discount?

55. Between July 1, 2000, and July 1, 2007, the estimated population of Pittsfield, Massachusetts declined from 134,953 to 129,798. What was the percent decrease to the nearest tenth? (*Source:* U.S. Census Bureau.)

56. Between July 1, 2000, and July 1, 2007, the estimated population of Anchorage, Alaska grew from 320,391 to 362,340. What was the percent increase to the nearest tenth? (*Source:* U.S. Census Bureau.)

57. In April 2008, the audio CD of the Original 2003 Broadway Cast Recording of the musical *Wicked* was available on amazon.com for $9.97. The list price (full price) of this CD was $18.98. To the nearest tenth, what was the percent discount? (*Source:* www.amazon.com)

58. In April 2008, the DVD of the movie *Alvin and the Chipmunks* was released. This DVD had a list price of $29.99 and was for sale on amazon.com at $15.99. To the nearest tenth, what was the percent discount? (*Source:* www.amazon.com)

10.4 ▶▶▶ Applications of Linear Equations

OBJECTIVES

1 Translate from words to mathematical expressions.

2 Write equations from given information.

3 Distinguish between expressions and equations.

4 Use the six steps in solving an applied problem.

5 Solve percent problems.

6 Solve investment problems.

7 Solve mixture problems.

OBJECTIVE 1 Translate from words to mathematical expressions. Producing a mathematical model of a real situation often involves translating verbal statements into mathematical statements. Although the problems we will be working with are simple ones, the methods we use will also apply to more difficult problems later.

> **Problem-Solving Hint**
>
> Usually there are key words and phrases in a verbal problem that translate into mathematical expressions involving addition, subtraction, multiplication, and division. Translations of some commonly used expressions follow.

TRANSLATING FROM WORDS TO MATHEMATICAL EXPRESSIONS

Verbal Expression	Mathematical Expression (where x and y are numbers)
Addition	
The **sum** of a number and 7	$x + 7$
6 **more than** a number	$x + 6$
3 **plus** a number	$3 + x$
24 **added to** a number	$x + 24$
A number **increased by** 5	$x + 5$
The **sum** of two numbers	$x + y$
Subtraction	
2 **less than** a number	$x - 2$
2 **less** a number	$2 - x$
12 **minus** a number	$12 - x$
A number **decreased by** 12	$x - 12$
A number **subtracted from** 10	$10 - x$
The **difference between** two numbers	$x - y$
Multiplication	
16 **times** a number	$16x$
A number **multiplied by** 6	$6x$
$\frac{2}{3}$ **of** a number (used with fractions and percent)	$\frac{2}{3}x$
$\frac{3}{4}$ **as much as** a number	$\frac{3}{4}x$
Twice (2 times) a number	$2x$
The **product** of two numbers	xy
Division	
The **quotient** of 8 and a number	$\frac{8}{x}$ $(x \neq 0)$
A number **divided by** 13	$\frac{x}{13}$
The **ratio** of two numbers or the **quotient** of two numbers	$\frac{x}{y}$ $(y \neq 0)$

1 Translate each verbal expression as a mathematical expression. Use x as the variable.

(a) 9 added to a number

(b) The difference between 7 and a number

(c) Four times a number

(d) The quotient of 7 and a nonzero number

ANSWERS

1. **(a)** $9 + x$, or $x + 9$ **(b)** $7 - x$
   (c) $4x$ **(d)** $\frac{7}{x}$ $(x \neq 0)$

◀ *Work Problem* **1** *at the Side.*

CAUTION

Because subtraction and division are not commutative operations, be careful to correctly translate expressions involving them. For example, "2 less than a number" is translated as $x - 2$, *not* $2 - x$. "A number subtracted from 10" is expressed as $10 - x$, *not* $x - 10$.

For division, the number *by which* we are dividing is the denominator, and the number *into which* we are dividing is the numerator. For example, "a number divided by 13" and "13 divided into x" both translate as $\frac{x}{13}$. Similarly, "the quotient of x and y" is translated as $\frac{x}{y}$.

OBJECTIVE 2 Write equations from given information. The symbol for equality, $=$, is often indicated by the word *is*. In fact, any words that indicate the idea of "sameness" translate to $=$.

Example 1 Translating Words into Equations

Translate each verbal sentence into an equation.

Verbal Sentence	Equation
Twice a number, decreased by 3, is 42.	$2x - 3 = 42$
If the product of a number and 12 is decreased by 7, the result is 105.	$12x - 7 = 105$
The quotient of a number and the number plus 4 is 28.	$\dfrac{x}{x+4} = 28$
The quotient of a number and 4, plus the number, is 10.	$\dfrac{x}{4} + x = 10$

Work Problem **2** *at the Side.* ▶

OBJECTIVE 3 Distinguish between expressions and equations. An expression translates as a phrase. An equation includes the $=$ symbol and translates as a sentence.

Example 2 Distinguishing between Expressions and Equations

Decide whether each is an *expression* or an *equation*.

(a) $2(3 + x) - 4x + 7$
There is no equals sign, so this is an expression.

(b) $2(3 + x) - 4x + 7 = -1$
Because of the equals sign, this is an equation.

Note that the expression in part (a) simplifies to the expression $-2x + 13$, and the equation in part (b) has solution 7.

Work Problem **3** *at the Side.* ▶

OBJECTIVE 4 Use the six steps in solving an applied problem. While there is no one method that will allow us to solve all types of applied problems, the following six steps are helpful.*

*****Appendix A** *Strategies for Problem Solving* introduces additional methods and tips for solving applied problems.

2 Translate each verbal sentence into an equation. Use x as the variable.

(a) The sum of a number and 6 is 28.

(b) If twice a number is decreased by 3, the result is 17.

(c) The product of a number and 7 is twice the number plus 12.

(d) The quotient of a number and 6, added to twice the number, is 7.

3 Decide whether each is an *expression* or an *equation*.

(a) $5x - 3(x + 2) = 7$

(b) $5x - 3(x + 2)$

ANSWERS

2. (a) $x + 6 = 28$ **(b)** $2x - 3 = 17$

(c) $7x = 2x + 12$ **(d)** $\dfrac{x}{6} + 2x = 7$

3. (a) equation **(b)** expression

4 Solve the problem.

The length of a rectangle is 5 cm more than its width. The perimeter is five times the width. What are the dimensions of the rectangle?

Solving an Applied Problem

Step 1   **Read** the problem, several times if necessary, until you *understand* what is given and what is to be found.

Step 2   **Assign a variable** to represent the unknown value, using diagrams or tables as needed. Write down what the variable represents. Express any other unknown values in terms of the variable.

Step 3   **Write an equation** using the variable expression(s).

Step 4   **Solve** the equation.

Step 5   **State the answer** to the problem. Does it seem reasonable?

Step 6   **Check** the answer in the words of the original problem.

Example 3   **Solving a Geometry Problem**

The length of a rectangle is 1 cm more than twice the width. The perimeter of the rectangle is 110 cm. Find the length and the width of the rectangle.

Step 1   **Read** the problem. We must find the length and width of the rectangle. We are given that the length is 1 cm more than twice the width, and the perimeter is 110 cm.

Step 2   **Assign a variable.** Let W = the width; then $1 + 2W$ = the length. Make a sketch, as in Figure 3.

$1 + 2W$

Figure 3

Step 3   **Write an equation.** The perimeter of a rectangle is given by the formula $P = 2L + 2W$.

$$P = 2L + 2W$$
$$110 = 2(1 + 2W) + 2W \qquad \text{Let } L = 1 + 2W \text{ and } P = 110.$$

Step 4   **Solve** the equation obtained in Step 3.

$$110 = 2 + 4W + 2W \qquad \text{Distributive property}$$
$$110 = 2 + 6W \qquad \text{Combine like terms.}$$
$$110 - 2 = 2 + 6W - 2 \qquad \text{Subtract 2.}$$
$$108 = 6W$$
$$\frac{108}{6} = \frac{6W}{6} \qquad \text{Divide by 6.}$$
$$18 = W \qquad \boxed{\text{We also need to find the length.}}$$

Step 5   **State the answer.** The width of the rectangle is 18 cm and the length is $1 + 2W = 1 + 2(18) = 37$ cm.

Step 6   **Check.** The length, 37 cm, is 1 more than twice the width, $2(18)$ cm. The perimeter is $2(37) + 2(18) = 110$ cm, as required.

◀ *Work Problem* **4** *at the Side.*

ANSWER

4. width: 10 cm; length: 15 cm

Example 4 Finding Unknown Numerical Quantities

Two outstanding major league pitchers in recent years are Johan Santana and Aaron Harang. In 2006, they combined for a total of 461 strikeouts. Santana had 29 more strikeouts than Harang. How many strikeouts did each pitcher have? (*Source: World Almanac and Book of Facts.*)

5 Solve the problem.

For the 2007 baseball season, the Major League Baseball leaders for RBIs (runs batted in) were Matt Holliday of the Colorado Rockies and Alex Rodriguez of the New York Yankees. These two players had a total of 293 RBIs, and Holliday had 19 fewer RBIs than Rodriguez. How many RBIs did each player have? (*Source: World Almanac and Book of Facts.*)

Step 1 **Read** the problem. We are asked to find the number of strikeouts each pitcher had.

Step 2 **Assign a variable** to represent the number of strikeouts for one of the men.

Let s = the number of strikeouts for Aaron Harang.

We must also find the number of strikeouts for Johan Santana. Since he had 29 more strikeouts than Harang,

$s + 29$ = the number of strikeouts for Santana.

Step 3 **Write an equation.** The sum of the numbers of strikeouts is 461, so

Harang's strikeouts	+	Santana's strikeouts	=	Total
↓		↓		↓
s	+	$(s + 29)$	=	461.

Step 4 **Solve** the equation.

$$s + (s + 29) = 461$$
$$2s + 29 = 461 \qquad \text{Combine like terms.}$$
$$2s + 29 - 29 = 461 - 29 \qquad \text{Subtract 29.}$$
$$2s = 432$$
$$\frac{2s}{2} = \frac{432}{2} \qquad \text{Divide by 2.}$$
$$s = 216$$

Don't stop here.

Step 5 **State the answer.** We let s represent the number of strikeouts for Harang, so Harang had 216. Then Santana had

$$s + 29 = 216 + 29 = 245 \text{ strikeouts}.$$

Step 6 **Check.** 245 is 29 more than 216, and the sum of 216 and 245 is 461. The conditions of the problem are satisfied, and our answer checks.

CAUTION

A common error in solving applied problems is forgetting to answer all the questions asked in the problem. In Example 4, we were asked for the number of strikeouts *each* player had, so there was an extra step at the end in order to find the number Santana had.

Work Problem **5** *at the Side.* ▶

Answer

5. Holliday: 137; Rodriguez: 156

6 Solve each problem.

(a) Mark Schorr bought an LCD high-definition TV that had been marked up 25% over cost. If he paid $2375 for the TV, what was the store's cost?

OBJECTIVE 5 Solve percent problems.   Recall from **Section 10.3** that percent means "per one hundred," so 5% means 0.05, 14% means 0.14, and so on.

Example 5   **Solving a Percent Problem**

In 2006, total annual health expenditures in the United States were about $2000 billion (or $2 trillion). This was an increase of 180% over the total for 1990. What were the approximate total health expenditures in billions of dollars in the United States in 1990? (*Source:* U.S. Centers for Medicare & Medicaid Services.)

Step 1   **Read** the problem. We are given that the total health expenditures increased by 180% from 1990 to 2006, and $2000 million was spent in 2006. We must find the expenditures in 1990.

Step 2   **Assign a variable.** Let x represent the total health expenditures for 1990.

$$180\% = 180\,(0.01) = 1.8,$$

so $1.8x$ represents the additional expenditures since 1990.

Step 3   **Write an equation** from the given information.

the expenditures in 1990 + the increase = 2000

$$x \quad + \quad 1.8x \quad = 2000$$

Note the x in $1.8x$.

(b) Michelle Raymond was paid $162 for a week's work at her part-time job after 10% deductions for taxes. How much did she earn before the deductions were made?

Step 4   **Solve** the equation.

$$1x + 1.8x = 2000 \qquad \text{Identity property}$$
$$2.8x = 2000 \qquad \text{Combine like terms.}$$
$$x \approx 714 \qquad \text{Divide by 2.8.}$$

Step 5   **State the answer.** Total health expenditures in the United States for 1990 were about $714 billion.

Step 6   **Check** that the increase, $2000 - 714 = 1286$, is about 180% of 714.

CAUTION

Avoid two common errors that occur in solving problems like the one in Example 5.

1. Do not try to find 180% of 2000 and subtract that amount from 2000. The 180% should be applied to *the amount in 1990, not the amount in 2006.*

2. Do not write the equation as

$$x + 1.8 = 2000. \qquad \text{Incorrect}$$

The percent must be multiplied by some number; in this case, the number is the amount spent in 1990, giving $1.8x$.

◀ *Work Problem* **6** *at the Side.*

OBJECTIVE **6** **Solve investment problems.** The investment problems in this chapter deal with *simple interest*. In most real-world applications, *compound interest* (covered in a later chapter) is used.

Example 6 **Solving an Investment Problem**

Mark LeBeau has $40,000 to invest. He will put part of the money in an account paying 4% interest and the remainder into stocks paying 6% interest. His accountant tells him that the total annual income from these investments should be $2040. How much should he invest at each rate?

Step 1 **Read** the problem again. We must find the two amounts.

Step 2 **Assign a variable.**

Let x = the amount to invest at 4%;

$40,000 - x$ = the amount to invest at 6%.

The formula for interest is $I = prt$. Here the time, t, is 1 year. Make a table to organize the given information.

Principal	Rate (as a decimal)	Interest	
x	0.04	$0.04x$	Multiply principal, rate, and time (here, 1 yr) to find the interest.
$40,000 - x$	0.06	$0.06(40,000 - x)$	
40,000		2040	← Total

Step 3 **Write an equation.** The last column of the table gives the equation.

interest at 4%   +   interest at 6%   =   total interest

$$0.04x \quad + \quad 0.06(40,000 - x) = \quad 2040$$

Step 4 **Solve** the equation. We do so without clearing decimals.

$$0.04x + 0.06(40,000) - 0.06x = 2040 \qquad \text{Distributive property}$$
$$0.04x + 2400 - 0.06x = 2040 \qquad \text{Multiply.}$$
$$-0.02x + 2400 = 2040 \qquad \text{Combine like terms.}$$
$$-0.02x = -360 \qquad \text{Subtract 2400.}$$
$$x = 18,000 \qquad \text{Divide by } -0.02.$$

Step 5 **State the answer.** Mark should invest $18,000 at 4%. At 6%, he should invest $40,000 - $18,000 = $22,000.

Step 6 **Check.** Find the annual interest at each rate and the total.

$$0.04(\$18,000) = \$720 \quad \text{and} \quad 0.06(\$22,000) = \$1320$$
$$\$720 + \$1320 = \$2040, \quad \text{as required.}$$

Work Problem **7** *at the Side.* ▶

Problem-Solving Hint

In Example 6, we chose to let the variable represent the amount invested at 4%. Students often ask, "Can I let the variable represent the other unknown?" The answer is yes. The equation will be different, but in the end the two answers will be the same.

7 Solve each problem.

(a) A woman invests $72,000 in two ways—some at 5% and some at 3%. Her total annual interest income is $3160. Find the amount she invests at each rate.

(b) A man has $34,000 to invest. He invests some at 5% and the balance at 4%. His total annual interest income is $1545. Find the amount he invests at each rate.

8 Solve each problem.

(a) How many liters of a 10% solution should be mixed with 60 L of a 25% solution to get a 15% solution?

OBJECTIVE 7 Solve mixture problems. Mixture problems involving rates of concentration can be solved with linear equations.

Example 7 **Solving a Mixture Problem**

A chemist must mix 8 L of a 40% acid solution with some 70% solution to get a 50% solution. How much of the 70% solution should be used?

Step 1 **Read** the problem. The problem asks for the amount of 70% solution to be used.

Step 2 **Assign a variable.** Let x = the number of liters of 70% solution to be used. The information in the problem is illustrated in Figure 4.

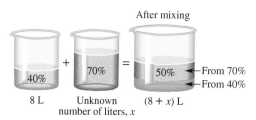

After mixing

8 L   Unknown number of liters, x $(8 + x)$ L

Figure 4

Use the given information to complete the following table.

Number of Liters	Percent (as a decimal)	Liters of Pure Acid
8	0.40	$0.40(8) = 3.2$
x	0.70	$0.70x$
$8 + x$	0.50	$0.50(8 + x)$

Sum must equal

The numbers in the right column were found by multiplying the strengths and the numbers of liters. The number of liters of pure acid in the 40% solution plus the number of liters of pure acid in the 70% solution must equal the number of liters of pure acid in the 50% solution.

Step 3 **Write an equation.**

$$3.2 + 0.70x = 0.50(8 + x)$$

Step 4 **Solve.**

$$3.2 + 0.70x = 4 + 0.50x \quad \text{Distributive property}$$
$$0.20x = 0.8 \quad \text{Subtract 3.2 and } 0.50x.$$
$$x = 4 \quad \text{Divide by 0.20.}$$

Step 5 **State the answer.** The chemist should use 4 L of the 70% solution.

Step 6 **Check.** 8 L of 40% solution plus 4 L of 70% solution is

$$8(0.40) + 4(0.70) = 6 \text{ L}$$

of acid. Similarly, $8 + 4$ or 12 L of 50% solution has

$$12(0.50) = 6 \text{ L}$$

of acid in the mixture. The total amount of pure acid is 6 L both before and after mixing, so the answer checks.

(b) How many pounds of candy worth $8 per lb should be mixed with 100 lb of candy worth $4 per lb to get a mixture that can be sold for $7 per lb?

◀ *Work Problem* **8** *at the Side.*

Problem-Solving Hint

When pure water is added to a solution, remember that water is 0% of the chemical (acid, alcohol, etc.). Similarly, pure chemical is 100% chemical.

Example 8   **Solving a Mixture Problem When One Ingredient Is Pure**

The octane rating of gasoline is a measure of its antiknock qualities. For a standard fuel, the octane rating is the percent of isooctane. How many liters of pure isooctane should be mixed with 200 L of 94% isooctane, referred to as 94 octane, to get a mixture that is 98% isooctane?

Step 1 **Read** the problem. The problem asks for the amount of pure isooctane.

Step 2 **Assign a variable.** Let x = the number of liters of pure (100%) isooctane. Complete a table with the given information. Recall that $100\% = 100\,(0.01) = 1$.

Number of Liters	Percent (as a decimal)	Liters of Pure Isooctane
x	1	x
200	0.94	$0.94\,(200)$
$x + 200$	0.98	$0.98\,(x + 200)$

Step 3 **Write an equation.** The equation comes from the last column of the table, as in Example 7.

$$x + 0.94\,(200) = 0.98\,(x + 200)$$

Step 4 **Solve.**

$$
\begin{aligned}
x + 0.94\,(200) &= 0.98x + 0.98\,(200) && \text{Distributive property}\\
x + 188 &= 0.98x + 196 && \text{Multiply.}\\
0.02x &= 8 && \text{Subtract } 0.98x \text{ and } 188.\\
x &= 400 && \text{Divide by } 0.02.
\end{aligned}
$$

Step 5 **State the answer.** 400 L of isooctane are needed.

Step 6 **Check** by showing that

$$400 + 0.94\,(200) = 0.98\,(400 + 200)$$

is true.

Work Problem 9 *at the Side.* ▶

9 Solve each problem.

(a) How much pure acid should be added to 6 L of 30% acid to increase the concentration to 50% acid?

(b) How much water must be added to 20 L of 50% antifreeze solution to reduce it to 40% antifreeze?

*In each of the following, (**a**) translate as an expression and (**b**) translate as an equation or inequality. Use x to represent the number.*

1. (a) 12 more than a number _____

   (b) 12 is more than a number. _____

2. (a) 3 less than a number _____

   (b) 3 is less than a number. _____

3. (a) 4 less than a number _____

   (b) 4 is less than a number. _____

4. (a) 6 greater than a number _____

   (b) 6 is greater than a number. _____

5. Which one of the following is *not* a valid translation of "20% of a number"?

   A. $0.20x$ **B.** $0.2x$ **C.** $\dfrac{x}{5}$ **D.** $20x$

6. Explain why $24 - x$ is *not* a correct translation of "24 less than a number."

Translate each verbal phrase into a mathematical expression. Use x to represent the unknown number. See Example 1.

7. Twice a number, increased by 18

8. The product of 8 and a number, increased by 14

9. 15 decreased by four times a number

10. 12 less than one-third of a number

11. The product of 10 and 6 less than a number

12. The product of 8 less than a number and 7 more than the number

13. The quotient of five times a number and 9

14. The quotient of 12 and seven times a nonzero number

Use the variable x for the unknown, and write an equation representing the verbal sentence. Then solve the problem. See Example 1.

15. The sum of a number and 6 is -31. Find the number.

16. The sum of a number and -4 is 12. Find the number.

17. If the product of a number and -4 is subtracted from the number, the result is 9 more than the number. Find the number.

18. If the quotient of a number and 6 is added to twice the number, the result is 8 less than the number. Find the number.

19. When $\frac{2}{3}$ of a number is subtracted from 12, the result is 10. Find the number.

20. When 75% of a number is added to 6, the result is 3 more than the number. Find the number.

Decide whether each is an expression *or an* equation. *See Example 2.*

21. $5(x + 3) - 8(2x - 6)$

22. $-7(y + 4) + 13(y - 6)$

23. $5(x + 3) - 8(2x - 6) = 12$

24. $-7(y + 4) + 13(y - 6) = 18$

25. $\dfrac{t}{2} - \dfrac{t + 5}{6} - 8$

26. $\dfrac{t}{2} - \dfrac{t + 5}{6} = 8$

In Exercises 27 and 28, complete the six suggested problem-solving steps to solve each problem.

27. Two of the leading U.S. research universities are Massachusetts Institute of Technology (MIT) and Stanford University. In a recent year, these two universities secured 230 patents on various inventions. Stanford secured 38 fewer patents than MIT. How many patents did each university secure? (*Source:* Association of University Technology Managers.)

Step 1   **Read** the problem carefully. What are you asked to find?

_____

_____

Step 2   **Assign a variable.** Let x = the number of patents MIT secured.

Then $x - 38 = $ _____

_____.

Step 3   **Write an equation.**

_____ + _____ = 230

Step 4   **Solve** the equation.

$x = $ _____

Step 5   **State the answer.** MIT secured _____ patents, and Stanford secured _____ patents.

Step 6   **Check.** The number of Stanford patents was _____ fewer than the number of _____,

and the total number of patents was

$134 + $ _____ = _____ .

28. In a recent sample of book buyers, 70 more shopped at large chain bookstores than at small chain/independent bookstores. A total sample of 442 book buyers shopped at these two types of stores. How many buyers shopped at each type of bookstore? (*Source:* Book Industry Study Group.)

Step 1   **Read** the problem carefully. What are you asked to find?

_____

_____

Step 2   **Assign a variable.** Let x = the number of book buyers at large chain bookstores.

Then $x - 70 = $ _____

_____.

Step 3   **Write an equation.**

_____ + _____ = 442

Step 4   **Solve** the equation.

$x = $ _____

Step 5   **State the answer.** There were _____ large chain bookstore shoppers and _____ small chain/independent shoppers.

Step 6   **Check.** The number of _____

_____ was

_____ more than the number of

_____,

and the total number of these shoppers was

$256 + $ _____ = _____ .

Solve each problem. See Examples 3 and 4.

29. The John Hancock Center in Chicago has a rectangular base. The length of the base measures 65 ft less than twice the width. The perimeter of this base is 860 ft. What are the dimensions of the base?

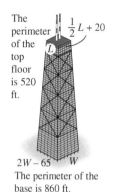

The perimeter of the top floor is 520 ft.

$\frac{1}{2}L + 20$

L

$2W - 65$ W

The perimeter of the base is 860 ft.

30. The Vietnam Veterans Memorial in Washington, D.C., is in the shape of two sides of an isosceles triangle. If the two walls of equal length were joined by a straight line of 438 ft, the perimeter of the resulting triangle would be 931.5 ft. Find the lengths of the two walls. (*Source:* Pamphlet obtained at Vietnam Veterans Memorial.)

438 ft

31. The Bermuda Triangle supposedly causes trouble for aircraft pilots. It has a perimeter of 3075 mi. The shortest side measures 75 mi less than the middle side, and the longest side measures 375 mi more than the middle side. Find the lengths of the three sides.

32. The John Hancock Center (Exercise 29) tapers as it rises. The top floor is rectangular and has perimeter 520 ft. The width of the top floor measures 20 ft more than one-half its length. What are the dimensions of the top floor?

33. Galileo Galilei conducted experiments involving Italy's famous Leaning Tower of Pisa to investigate the relationship between an object's speed of fall and its weight. The Leaning Tower is 804 ft shorter than the Eiffel Tower in Paris, France. The two towers have a total height of 1164 ft. How tall is each tower? (*Source: Microsoft Encarta Encyclopedia.*)

34. Two of the longest-running Broadway shows were *Cats*, which played from 1982 through 2000, and *Les Misérables,* which played from 1987 through 2005. Together, there were 14,165 performances of these two shows during their Broadway runs. There were 805 fewer performances of *Les Misérables* than of *Cats*. How many performances were there of each show? (*Source:* The League of American Theatres and Producers.)

35. In 2008, the New York Yankees and the Detroit Tigers had the highest payrolls in Major League Baseball. The Tigers' payroll was $70.4 million less than the Yankees' payroll, and the two payrolls totaled $347.8 million. What was the payroll for each team? (*Source:* The Associated Press.)

36. Ted Williams and Rogers Hornsby were two great hitters. Together they got 5584 hits in their careers. Hornsby got 276 more hits than Williams. How many base hits did each get? (*Source:* Neft, D. S. and Cohen, R. M., *The Sports Encyclopedia: Baseball,* St. Martins Griffin; New York, 2006.)

Solve each percent problem. See Example 5.

37. In 2005, the average cost of a traditional Thanksgiving dinner for 10, featuring turkey, stuffing, cranberries, pumpkin pie, and trimmings, was $36.78, an increase of 3.1% over the cost in 2004. What was the cost, to the nearest cent, in 2004? (*Source:* American Farm Bureau.)

38. Refer to Exercise 37. The first year that information on the cost of a traditional Thanksgiving dinner was collected was 1987. The 2005 cost of $36.78 was an increase of 37.5% over the cost in 1987. What was the cost, to the nearest cent, in 1987? (*Source:* American Farm Bureau.)

39. In 2000, the population of Cedar Rapids, Iowa, was 237,230. The 2007 population was estimated at 106.6% of the 2000 population. What was the 2007 population? (*Source:* U.S. Census Bureau.)

40. The consumer price index (CPI) in November 2007 was 210.2. This represented a 4.3% increase from a year earlier. To the nearest tenth, what was the CPI in November 2006? (*Source:* U.S. Bureau of Labor Statistics.)

41. At the end of a day, Erich Bergen found that the total cash register receipts at the motel where he works amounted to $2725. This included the 9% sales tax charged. Find the amount of the tax.

42. Phlash Phelps sold his house for $159,000. He got this amount knowing that he would have to pay a 6% commission to his agent. What amount did he have after the agent was paid?

Solve each investment problem. See Example 6.

43. Jay Jenkins earned $12,000 last year by giving tennis lessons. He invested part at 3% simple interest and the rest at 4%. He earned a total of $440 in interest. How much did he invest at each rate?

Principal	Rate (as a decimal)	Interest
x	0.03	
	0.04	
12,000	✕✕✕✕✕	440

44. Stuart Sudak won $60,000 on a slot machine in Las Vegas. He invested part at 2% simple interest and the rest at 3%. He earned a total of $1600 in annual interest. How much was invested at each rate?

Principal	Rate (as a decimal)	Interest
x	0.02	
✕✕✕✕✕		1600

45. Michelle Renda invested some money at 4.5% simple interest and $1000 less than twice this amount at 3%. Her total annual income from the interest was $1020. How much was invested at each rate?

46. Toshira Hashimoto invested some money at 3.5% simple interest, and $5000 more than 3 times this amount at 4%. He earned $1440 in annual interest. How much did he invest at each rate?

47. Vincente and Ricarda Pérez have invested $27,000 in bonds paying 7%. How much additional money should they invest in a certificate of deposit paying 4% simple interest so that the total annual return on the two investments will be 6%?

48. Carol Hurst received a year-end bonus of $17,000 from her company and invested the money in an account paying 6.5%. How much additional money should she deposit in an account paying 5% so that the annual return on the two investments will be 6%?

Solve each problem involving rates of concentration and mixtures. See Examples 7 and 8.

49. Ten liters of a 4% acid solution must be mixed with a 10% solution to get a 6% solution. How many liters of the 10% solution are needed?

Liters of Solution	Percent (as a decimal)	Liters of Pure Acid
10	0.04	
x	0.10	
	0.06	

50. How many liters of a 14% alcohol solution must be mixed with 20 L of a 50% solution to get a 30% solution?

Liters of Solution	Percent (as a decimal)	Liters of Pure Alcohol
x	0.14	
	0.50	

51. In a chemistry class, 12 L of a 12% alcohol solution must be mixed with a 20% solution to get a 14% solution. How many liters of the 20% solution are needed?

52. How many liters of a 10% alcohol solution must be mixed with 40 L of a 50% solution to get a 40% solution?

53. How much pure dye must be added to 4 gal of a 25% dye solution to increase the solution to 40%? (*Hint:* Pure dye is 100% dye.)

54. How much water must be added to 6 gal of a 4% insecticide solution to reduce the concentration to 3%? (*Hint:* Water is 0% insecticide.)

55. Randall Albritton wants to mix 50 lb of nuts worth $2 per lb with some nuts worth $6 per lb to make a mixture worth $5 per lb. How many pounds of $6 nuts must he use?

56. Lee Ann Spahr wants to mix tea worth 2¢ per oz with 100 oz of tea worth 5¢ per oz to make a mixture worth 3¢ per oz. How much 2¢ tea should be used?

57. Why is it impossible to add two mixtures of candy worth $4 per lb and $5 per lb to obtain a final mixture worth $6 per lb?

58. Write an equation based on the following problem, solve the equation, and explain why the problem has no solution.

How much 30% acid should be mixed with 15 L of 50% acid to obtain a mixture that is 60% acid?

Relating Concepts (Exercises 59–63) For Individual or Group Work

Consider each problem.

Problem A
Jack has $800 invested in two accounts. One pays 5% interest per year and the other pays 10% interest per year. The amount of yearly interest is the same as he would get if the entire $800 was invested at 8.75%. How much does he have invested at each rate?

Problem B
Jill has 800 L of acid solution. She obtained it by mixing some 5% acid with some 10% acid. Her final mixture of 800 L is 8.75% acid. How much of each of the 5% and 10% solutions did she use to get her final mixture?

In Problem A, let x represent the amount invested at 5% interest, and in Problem B, let y represent the amount of 5% acid used. **Work Exercises 59–63 in order.**

59. (a) Write an expression in x that represents the amount of money Jack invested at 10% in Problem A.

  (b) Write an expression in y that represents the amount of 10% acid solution Jill used in Problem B.

60. (a) Write expressions that represent the amount of interest Jack earns per year at 5% and at 10%.

  (b) Write expressions that represent the amount of pure acid in Jill's 5% and 10% acid solutions.

61. (a) The sum of the two expressions in part (a) of Exercise 60 must equal the total amount of interest earned in one year. Write an equation representing this fact.

  (b) The sum of the two expressions in part (b) of Exercise 60 must equal the amount of pure acid in the final mixture. Write an equation representing this fact.

62. (a) Solve Problem A.

  (b) Solve Problem B.

63. Explain the similarities between the processes used in solving Problems A and B.

Study Skills

TAKING LECTURE NOTES

OBJECTIVE

1 **Identify and apply note taking strategies.**

Study the set of sample math notes below, and read the comments about them. Then try to incorporate the techniques into your own math note taking in class.

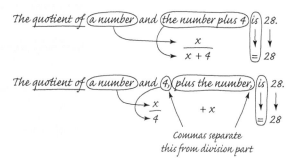

Translating Words to Expressions and Equations   Sept. 1

Problem solving: key words or phrases translate to algebraic expressions.

| Caution | *Subtraction is not commutative; the order does matter.* |

	Correct	Wrong
Examples: 10 less than a number	$x - 10$	$10 - x$
a number subtracted from 10	$10 - x$	$x - 10$
10 minus a number	$10 - x$	$x - 10$

A phrase (part of a sentence) → *algebraic expression*

A sentence → *equation with = sign*

| Note difference | *No equal sign in an expression. $3x + 2$* |
| | *Equation has an equal sign. $3x + 2 = 14$* |

☆ *Pay close attention to exact wording of the sentence; watch for commas.*

The quotient of a number and the number plus 4 is 28.
$$\frac{x}{x+4} = 28$$

The quotient of a number and 4, plus the number, is 28.
$$\frac{x}{4} + x = 28$$
Commas separate this from division part

◀ **Always include the date and title** of the day's lecture topic at the top of every page. **Always begin a new day with a new page.**

◀ **Skipping lines** makes the notes easier to read.

◀ **A Caution box alerts you to a common error or point of confusion.**

◀ **The examples show the correct answers as well as typical mistakes** students make.

◀ The notes connect familiar concepts (sentences) to new concepts (algebra).

◀ **A star marks an important reminder.** This is a warning to avoid future mistakes. **Note the underlining,** too, which highlights important information.

◀ Notice the use of columns, which allows for examples and explanations or related concepts to be close together. Whenever you know you'll be given concepts to compare or contrast, a series of steps to follow, or examples with explanations, **try the column method.**

◀ **Note the arrows,** which clearly show connections in the material.

The notes are easy to look at, and you are more likely to respond positively to things that are visually pleasing. Other techniques that are visually memorable are the use of spacing (the two columns), stars, underlining, and circling. All of these methods allow you to take note of important concepts and steps.

The notes are also systematic, which means that they use certain techniques regularly. This way, you can easily recognize the topic of the day, the signals that show an important point, and the steps to follow for procedures. When you develop a system that you always use in your notes, they are easy to understand later when you are reviewing for a test.

Why Are These Notes Brain Friendly?

◀◀◀ **Now Try This**

Find one or two people in your math class to work with. Compare each other's lecture notes over a period of a week or so. Ask yourself the following questions as you examine the notes.

1. **What are you doing to show the main points** or larger concepts in your notes (such as underlining, boxing, using stars or capital letters, etc.)?

2. **In what ways do you set off the explanations** for worked problems, examples, and subpoints or smaller concepts (such as indenting, using arrows, circling or boxing, etc.)?

3. **What does your instructor do** to show that he or she is moving from one idea to the next (such as saying "Next," "Any questions," "Now," or erasing the board, etc.)?

4. **How do you mark a change in ideas** or topics in your notes (such as skipping lines, using dashes or numbers, etc.)?

5. **What explanations (in words) do you give yourself** in your notes, so that when those new concepts from lecture are fading, you can read your notes and still remember them when doing your homework?

6. **What new ideas did you learn** by examining your classmates' notes?

7. **What new techniques will you try in your own note taking?** List two or three of these techniques that you will use next time you take notes in math class.

10.5 ▶▶▶ Further Applications of Linear Equations

OBJECTIVES

1 Solve problems about different denominations of money.

2 Solve problems about uniform motion.

3 Solve problems about angles.

There are three common applications of linear equations that we did not discuss in **Section 10.4**—money problems, uniform motion problems, and problems involving the angles of a triangle.

OBJECTIVE 1 Solve problems about different denominations of money. These problems are very similar to the simple interest problems in **Section 10.4**.

Problem-Solving Hint

In problems involving money, use the fact that

$$\text{number of monetary units of the same kind} \times \text{denomination} = \text{total monetary value}.$$

For example, 30 dimes have a monetary value of $\$0.10\,(30) = \$3$. Fifteen five-dollar bills have a value of $\$5\,(15) = \$75$.

---

1 Solve the problem.

At the end of a day, a cashier had 26 coins consisting of dimes and half-dollars. The total value of these coins was $8.60. How many of each type did he have?

Example 1   Solving a Money Denomination Problem

For a bill totaling $5.65, a cashier received 25 coins consisting of nickels and quarters. How many of each type of coin did the cashier receive?

Step 1   **Read** the problem. The problem asks that we find the number of nickels and the number of quarters the cashier received.

Step 2   **Assign a variable.**

Let $x =$ the number of nickels;

then $25 - x =$ the number of quarters.

We can organize the information in a table.

	Number of Coins	Denomination	Value
Nickels	x	$0.05	$0.05x$
Quarters	$25 - x$	$0.25	$0.25\,(25 - x)$
			5.65 ← Total

Step 3   **Write an equation.** From the last column of the table,

$$0.05x + 0.25\,(25 - x) = 5.65.$$

Step 4   **Solve.**

Move decimal points 2 places to the right.

$$5x + 25\,(25 - x) = 565 \qquad \text{Multiply by 100.}$$
$$5x + 625 - 25x = 565 \qquad \text{Distributive property}$$
$$-20x = -60 \qquad \text{Subtract 625; combine like terms.}$$
$$x = 3 \qquad \text{Divide by } -20.$$

Step 5   **State the answer.** There are 3 nickels and $25 - 3 = 22$ quarters.

Step 6   **Check.** The cashier has $3 + 22 = 25$ coins, and the value of the coins is $\$0.05\,(3) + \$0.25\,(22) = \$5.65$, as required.

◀ *Work Problem* **1** *at the Side.*

ANSWER

1. 11 dimes, 15 half-dollars

> **CAUTION**
> ***Be sure that your answer is reasonable*** when working problems like Example 1. Because you are dealing with a number of coins, the correct answer can neither be negative nor a fraction.

OBJECTIVE **2** **Solve problems about uniform motion.**

> **Problem-Solving Hint**
> Uniform motion problems use the distance formula, $d = rt$. ***When rate (or speed) is given in miles per hour, time must be given in hours.*** To solve such problems, ***draw a sketch*** to illustrate what is happening, and ***make a table*** to summarize the given information.

Example 2 **Solving a Motion Problem (Opposite Directions)**

Two cars leave the same place at the same time, one going east and the other west. The eastbound car averages 40 mph, while the westbound car averages 50 mph. In how many hours will they be 300 mi apart?

Step 1 **Read** the problem. We must find the time it takes for the two cars to be 300 mi apart.

Step 2 **Assign a variable.** A sketch shows what is happening in the problem: The cars are going in *opposite* directions. See Figure 5.

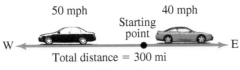

50 mph   40 mph
Starting point
W ←——————————●——————————→ E
Total distance = 300 mi

Figure 5

Let x represent the time traveled by each car. Organize the information in a table. ***Fill in each distance by multiplying rate by time*** using the formula $d = rt$. The sum of the two distances is 300.

	Rate	Time	Distance
Eastbound Car	40	x	$40x$
Westbound Car	50	x	$50x$
			300 ← Total

Step 3 **Write an equation.** $40x + 50x = 300$

Step 4 **Solve.** $90x = 300$ Combine like terms.

$$x = \frac{300}{90} = \frac{10}{3}$$ Divide by 90; lowest terms

Step 5 **State the answer.** The cars travel $\frac{10}{3} = 3\frac{1}{3}$ hr, or 3 hr and 20 min.

Step 6 **Check.** The eastbound car traveled $40\left(\frac{10}{3}\right) = \frac{400}{3}$ mi, and the westbound car traveled $50\left(\frac{10}{3}\right) = \frac{500}{3}$ mi, for a total of $\frac{400}{3} + \frac{500}{3} = \frac{900}{3} = 300$ mi, as required.

2 Solve the problem.

Two cars leave the same location at the same time. One travels north at 60 mph and the other south at 45 mph. In how many hours will they be 420 mi apart?

> **CAUTION**
> It is a common error to write 300 as the distance for *each* car in Example 2. Three hundred miles is the *total* distance traveled.

As in Example 2, in general, the equation for a problem involving motion in *opposite* directions is of the form

partial distance + partial distance = total distance.

◄ *Work Problem* **2** *at the Side.*

Example 3 **Solving a Motion Problem (Same Direction)**

Geoff can bike to work in $\frac{3}{4}$ hr. By bus, the trip takes $\frac{1}{4}$ hr. If the bus travels 20 mph faster than Geoff rides his bike, how far is it to his workplace?

Step 1 **Read** the problem. We must find the distance between Geoff's home and his workplace.

Step 2 **Assign a variable.** Although the problem asks for a distance, it is easier here to let x be Geoff's speed when he rides his bike to work. Then the speed of the bus is $x + 20$. For the trip by bike,

$$d = rt = x \cdot \frac{3}{4} = \frac{3}{4}x,$$

and by bus,

$$d = rt = (x + 20) \cdot \frac{1}{4} = \frac{1}{4}(x + 20).$$

Summarize this information in a table.

	Rate	Time	Distance
Bike	x	$\frac{3}{4}$	$\frac{3}{4}x$
Bus	$x + 20$	$\frac{1}{4}$	$\frac{1}{4}(x + 20)$

Same

Step 3 **Write an equation.** The key to setting up the correct equation is to realize that the distance in each case is the same. See Figure 6.

Home   Workplace

Figure 6

$$\frac{3}{4}x = \frac{1}{4}(x + 20) \qquad \text{The distance is the same.}$$

Step 4 **Solve.** $4\left(\frac{3}{4}x\right) = 4\left(\frac{1}{4}\right)(x + 20)$ Multiply by 4.

$3x = x + 20$ Multiply; identity property

$2x = 20$ Subtract x.

$x = 10$ Divide by 2.

ANSWER

2. 4 hr

Step 5 **State the answer.** The required distance is given by

$$d = \frac{3}{4}x = \frac{3}{4}(10) = \frac{30}{4} = 7.5 \text{ mi.}$$

Step 6 **Check** by finding the distance using

$$d = \frac{1}{4}(x + 20) = \frac{1}{4}(10 + 20) = \frac{30}{4} = 7.5 \text{ mi.}$$

The same result

As in Example 3, the equation for a problem involving motion in the same direction is often of the form

one distance = other distance.

> **Problem-Solving Hint**
>
> In Example 3 it was easier to let the variable represent a quantity other than the one that we were asked to find. This is the case in some problems. It takes practice to learn when this approach is best, and practice means working lots of problems.

Work Problem **3** *at the Side.* ▶

OBJECTIVE 3 Solve problems about angles. An important result of Euclidean geometry (the geometry of the Greek mathematician Euclid) is that *the sum of the angle measures of any triangle is 180°*. This property is used in the next example.

Example 4   Finding Angle Measures

Find the value of x, and determine the measure of each angle in Figure 7.

Step 1 **Read** the problem. We are asked to find the measure of each angle.

Step 2 **Assign a variable.** Let x represent the measure of one angle.

Step 3 **Write an equation.** The sum of the three measures shown in the figure must be 180°.

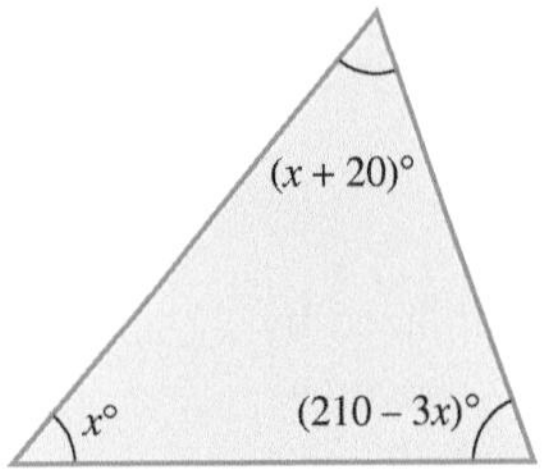

Figure 7

$$x + (x + 20) + (210 - 3x) = 180$$

Step 4 **Solve.** $-x + 230 = 180$ Combine like terms.

$$-x = -50 \quad \text{Subtract 230.}$$

$$x = 50 \quad \text{Divide by } -1.$$

Step 5 **State the answer.** One angle measures 50°, another measures $x + 20 = 50 + 20 = 70°$, and the third measures $210 - 3x = 210 - 3(50) = 60°$.

Step 6 **Check.** Since $50° + 70° + 60° = 180°$, the answer is correct.

Work Problem **4** *at the Side.* ▶

3 Solve the problem.
Elayn begins jogging at 5:00 A.M., averaging 3 mph. Clay leaves at 5:30 A.M., following her, averaging 5 mph. How long will it take him to catch up to her? (*Hint:* 30 min $= \frac{1}{2}$ hr.)

4 Solve the problem.
One angle in a triangle is 15° larger than a second angle. The third angle is 25° larger than twice the second angle. Find the measure of each angle.

ANSWERS

3. $\frac{3}{4}$ hr, or 45 min

4. 35°, 50°, and 95°

10.5 ▶▶▶ **Exercises**

Solve each problem.

1. What amount of money is found in a piggy bank containing 38 nickels and 26 dimes?

2. The distance between Cape Town, South Africa, and Miami is 7700 mi. If a jet averages 480 mph between the two cities, what is its travel time in hours?

3. Tri Phong traveled from Denver to Pittsburgh, a distance of 1320 mi, in 24 hr. What was his rate in miles per hour?

4. A square has perimeter 40 in. What would be the perimeter of an equilateral triangle whose sides each measure the same length as the side of the square?

Solve each problem. See Example 1.

5. Otis Taylor has a box of coins that he uses when playing poker with his friends. The box currently contains 44 coins, consisting of pennies, dimes, and quarters. The number of pennies is equal to the number of dimes, and the total value is $4.37. How many of each denomination of coin does he have in the box?

Number of Coins	Denomination	Value
x	0.01	$0.01x$
x		
	0.25	
✗✗✗✗✗✗✗		4.37 ← Total

6. Nana Nantambu found some coins while looking under her sofa pillows. There were equal numbers of nickels and quarters, and twice as many half-dollars as quarters. If she found $2.60 in all, how many of each denomination of coin did she find?

Number of Coins	Denomination	Value
x	0.05	$0.05x$
x		
$2x$	0.50	
✗✗✗✗✗✗✗		2.60 ← Total

7. In Canada, $1 and $2 bills have been replaced by coins. The $1 coins are called "loonies" because they have a picture of a loon (a well-known Canadian bird) on the reverse, and the $2 coins are called "toonies." When Marissa returned home to San Francisco from a trip to Vancouver, she found that she had acquired 37 of these coins, with a total value of 51 Canadian dollars. How many coins of each denomination did she have?

8. Luke Corey works at an ice cream shop. At the end of his shift, he counted the bills in his cash drawer and found 119 bills with a total value of $347. If all of the bills are $5 bills and $1 bills, how many of each denomination were in his cash drawer?

9. Dave Bowers collects U.S. gold coins. He has a collection of 53 coins. Some are $10 coins, and the rest are $20 coins. If the face value of the coins is $780, how many of each denomination does he have?

10. In the 19th century, the United States minted two-cent and three-cent pieces. Frances Steib has three times as many three-cent pieces as two-cent pieces, and the face value of these coins is $2.42. How many of each denomination does she have?

11. In 2008, general admission to the Field Museum in Chicago cost $14 for adults and $11 for children and seniors. If $24,726 was collected from the sale of 2010 general admission tickets, how many adult tickets were sold? (*Source:* www.fieldmuseum.org)

12. For a high school production of *West Side Story,* student tickets cost $5 each while nonstudent tickets cost $8. If 480 tickets were sold for the Saturday night show and a total of $2895 was collected, how many tickets of each type were sold?

🔳 *In Exercises 13–16, find the rate based on the information provided. Round your answers to the nearest hundredth. All events were at the 2004 Summer Olympics in Athens, Greece. (Source: World Almanac and Book of Facts.)*

	Event	Participant	Distance	Time
13.	100-m hurdles, women	Joanna Hayes, USA	100 m	12.37 sec
14.	400-m hurdles, women	Fani Halkia, Greece	400 m	52.82 sec
15.	400-m hurdles, men	Felix Sánchez, DO	400 m	47.63 sec
16.	400-m run, men	Jeremy Wariner, USA	400 m	44.00 sec

Solve each problem. See Examples 2 and 3.

17. Two steamers leave a port on a river at the same time, traveling in opposite directions. Each is traveling 22 mph. How long will it take for them to be 110 mi apart?

	Rate	Time	Distance
First Steamer		t	
Second Steamer	22		
			110

18. A train leaves Dayton, Ohio, and travels north at 85 km per hr. Another train leaves at the same time and travels south at 95 km per hr. How long will it take before they are 315 km apart?

	Rate	Time	Distance
First Train	85	t	
Second Train			
			315

19. Agents Mulder and Scully are driving to Georgia to investigate "Big Blue," a giant aquatic reptile reported to inhabit one of the local lakes. Mulder leaves Washington at 8:30 A.M. and averages 65 mph. His partner, Scully, leaves at 9:00 A.M., following the same path and averaging 68 mph. At what time will Scully catch up with Mulder?

20. Lois and Clark are covering separate stories and have to travel in opposite directions. Lois leaves the *Daily Planet* at 8:00 A.M. and travels at 35 mph. Clark leaves at 8:15 A.M. and travels at 40 mph. At what time will they be 140 mi apart?

🌐 **21.** It took Charmaine 3.6 hr to drive to her mother's house on Saturday morning for a weekend visit. On her return trip on Sunday night, traffic was heavier, so the trip took her 4 hr. Her average speed on Sunday was 5 mph slower than on Saturday. What was her average speed on Sunday?

22. Sarah Kueffer commutes to her office in Redwood City, California, by train. When she walks to the train station, it takes her 40 min. When she rides her bike, it takes her 12 min. Her average walking speed is 7 mph less than her average biking speed. Find the distance from Sarah's house to the train station.

23. Johnny leaves Memphis to visit his cousin, Anne Hoffman, in the town of Hornsby, Tennessee, 80 mi away. He travels at an average speed of 50 mph. One-half hour later, Anne leaves to visit Johnny, traveling at an average speed of 60 mph. How long after Anne leaves will it be before they meet?

24. On an automobile trip, Heather Dowdell maintained a steady speed for the first two hours. Rush-hour traffic slowed her speed by 25 mph for the last part of the trip. The entire trip, a distance of 125 mi, took $2\frac{1}{2}$ hr. What was her speed during the first part of the trip?

Find the measure of each angle in the triangles shown. See Example 4.

25.

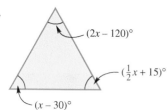

$(2x - 120)°$

$(\frac{1}{2}x + 15)°$

$(x - 30)°$

26.

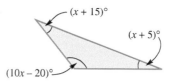

$(x + 15)°$

$(x + 5)°$

$(10x - 20)°$

🌐 **27.**

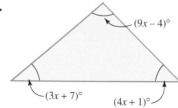

$(9x - 4)°$

$(3x + 7)°$

$(4x + 1)°$

28.

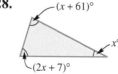

$(x + 61)°$

$x°$

$(2x + 7)°$

Relating Concepts (Exercises 29–32) For Individual or Group Work

Consider the following two figures. **Work Exercises 29–32 in order.**

29. Solve for the measures of the unknown angles in Figure A.

30. Solve for the measure of the unknown angle marked $y°$ in Figure B.

31. Add the measures of the two angles you found in Exercise 29. How does the sum compare to the measure of the angle you found in Exercise 30?

$2x°$

$x°$

$60°$

Figure A

$60°$

$y°$

Figure B

32. From Exercises 29–31, make a conjecture (an educated guess) about the relationship among the angles marked ①, ②, and ③ in the figure shown here.

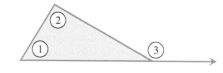

*In Exercises 33 and 34, the angles marked with variable expressions are called **vertical angles.** It is shown in geometry that vertical angles have equal measures. Find the measure of each angle.*

33.

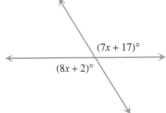

$(7x + 17)°$

$(8x + 2)°$

34.

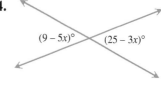

$(9 - 5x)°$ $(25 - 3x)°$

35. Two angles whose sum is equal to 90° are called **complementary angles.** Find the measures of the complementary angles shown in the figure.

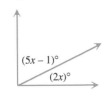

$(5x - 1)°$

$(2x)°$

36. Two angles whose sum is equal to 180° are called **supplementary angles.** Find the measures of the supplementary angles shown in the figure.

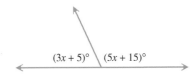

$(3x + 5)°$ $(5x + 15)°$

Another type of application often studied in algebra courses involves *consecutive integers*. **Consecutive integers** are integers that follow each other in counting order, such as 8, 9, and 10. Suppose we wish to solve the following problem:

Find three consecutive integers such that the sum of the first and third, increased by 3, is 50 more than the second.

Let x represent the first of the unknown integers. Then $x + 1 =$ the second, and $x + 2 =$ the third. The equation to solve would be

Sum of the first and third	increased by 3	is	50 more than the second.
↓	↓	↓	↓
$x + (x + 2)$	$+ 3$	$=$	$(x + 1) + 50.$

$$2x + 5 = x + 51$$
$$x = 46$$

The solution of this equation is 46, meaning that the first integer is $x = 46$, the second is $46 + 1 = 47$, and the third is $46 + 2 = 48$. The three integers are 46, 47, and 48. Check by substituting these numbers back into the words of the original problem.

Solve each problem involving consecutive integers.

37. Find three consecutive integers such that the sum of the first and twice the second is 22 more than twice the third.

38. Find four consecutive integers such that the sum of the first three is 62 more than the fourth.

39. If I add my current age to the age I will be next year on this date, the sum is 95 yr. How old will I be 10 years from today?

40. Two pages facing each other in this book have 365 as the sum of their page numbers. What are the two page numbers?

10.6 ▶▶▶ Variation

OBJECTIVES

1 Write an equation expressing direct variation.

2 Find the constant of variation, and solve direct variation problems.

3 Solve inverse variation problems.

4 Solve joint variation problems.

5 Solve combined variation problems.

Certain types of functions are very common, especially in business and the physical sciences. These are functions where y depends on a multiple of x, or y depends on a number divided by x. In such situations, y is said to *vary directly as x* (in the first case) or *vary inversely as x* (in the second case). For example, by the distance formula, the distance traveled varies directly as the rate (or speed) and the time. The simple interest formula and the formulas for area and volume are other familiar examples of *direct variation*.

By contrast, the force required to keep a car from skidding on a curve varies inversely as the radius of the curve. Another example of *inverse variation* is how travel time is inversely proportional to rate or speed.

OBJECTIVE **1** **Write an equation expressing direct variation.** The circumference of a circle is given by the formula $C = 2\pi r$, where r is the radius of the circle. See the figure. Circumference is always a constant multiple of the radius. (C is always found by multiplying r by the constant 2π.) Thus,

$C = 2\pi r$

> As the *radius increases*, the *circumference increases*.

The reverse is also true.

> As the *radius decreases*, the *circumference decreases*.

Because of this, the circumference is said to *vary directly* as the radius.

Direct Variation

y **varies directly as** *x* if there exists a real number k such that

$$y = kx.$$

Also, y is said to be **proportional to** x. The number k is called the **constant of variation.** In direct variation, for $k > 0$, as the value of x increases, the value of y also increases. Similarly, as x decreases, y decreases.

OBJECTIVE **2** **Find the constant of variation, and solve direct variation problems.** *The direct variation equation $y = kx$ defines a linear function, where the constant of variation k is the slope of the line.* For example, we wrote the equation

$$y = 4.50\,x$$

to describe the cost y to buy x gallons of gas in Example 6 of **Section 5.3.** The cost varies directly as, or is proportional to, the number of gallons of gas purchased. That is,

> As the *number* of gallons of gas *increases, cost increases.*

The reverse is also true.

> As the *number* of gallons of gas *decreases, cost decreases.*

The constant of variation k is 4.50, the cost of 1 gallon of gas.

EXAMPLE 1 **Finding the Constant of Variation and the Variation Equation**

Stella Frolick is paid an hourly wage. One week she worked 43 hr and was paid $795.50. How much does she earn per hour?

Let h represent the number of hours she works and P represent her corresponding pay. Then, P *varies directly as* h, so

$$P = kh.$$

Here k represents Stella's hourly wage. Since $P = 795.50$ when $h = 43$,

$$795.50 = 43k$$

> This is the constant of variation.

$$k = 18.50. \quad \text{Use a calculator.}$$

Her hourly wage is $18.50, and P and h are related by

$$P = 18.50h.$$

Work Problem **1** *at the Side.* ▶

EXAMPLE 2 **Solving a Direct Variation Problem**

Hooke's law for an elastic spring states that the distance a spring stretches is proportional to the force applied. If a force of 150 newtons* stretches a certain spring 8 cm, how much will a force of 400 newtons stretch the spring?

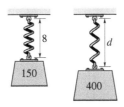

Figure 5

See Figure 5. If d is the distance the spring stretches and f is the force applied, then $d = kf$ for some constant k. Since a force of 150 newtons stretches the spring 8 cm, we can use these values to find k.

$$d = kf \quad \text{Variation equation}$$

$$8 = k \cdot 150 \quad \text{Let } d = 8 \text{ and } f = 150.$$

$$k = \frac{8}{150} \quad \text{Solve for } k.$$

$$k = \frac{4}{75} \quad \text{Lowest terms}$$

Substitute $\frac{4}{75}$ for k in the variation equation $d = kf$ to get

$$d = \frac{4}{75}f.$$

For a force of 400 newtons,

$$d = \frac{4}{75}(400) = \frac{64}{3}. \quad \text{Let } f = 400.$$

The spring will stretch $\frac{64}{3}$ cm, or $21\frac{1}{3}$ cm, if a force of 400 newtons is applied.

Work Problem **2** *at the Side.* ▶

---

*A newton is a unit of measure of force used in physics.

1 Find the constant of variation, and write a direct variation equation.

 (a) Ginny Michaud is paid a daily wage. One month she worked 17 days and earned $1334.50.

 (b) Distance varies directly as time (at a constant speed). A car travels 100 mi at a constant speed in 2 hr.

2 The charge (in dollars) to customers for electricity (in kilowatt-hours) varies directly as the number of kilowatt-hours used. It costs $52 to use 800 kilowatt-hours. Find the cost to use 1000 kilowatt-hours.

ANSWERS

1. **(a)** $k = 78.50$; Let E represent her earnings for d days. Then $E = 78.50d$.
   (b) $k = 50$; Let d represent the distance traveled in h hours. Then $d = 50h$.

In summary, use the following steps to solve a variation problem.

3 The area of a circle varies directly as the square of its radius. A circle with radius 3 in. has area 28.278 in.^{2}.

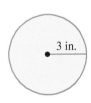

3 in.

(a) Write a variation equation and give the value of k.

Solving a Variation Problem

Step 1   Write the variation equation.

Step 2   Substitute the initial values and solve for k.

Step 3   Rewrite the variation equation with the value of k from Step 2.

Step 4   Substitute the remaining values, solve for the unknown, and find the required answer.

The direct variation equation $y = kx$ is a linear equation. However, other kinds of variation involve other types of equations. For example, one variable can be proportional to a power of another variable.

Direct Variation as a Power

y **varies directly as the** *n***th power of** *x* if there exists a real number k such that

$$y = kx^n.$$

An example of direct variation as a power is the formula for the area of a circle, $A = \pi r^2$. Here, π is the constant of variation, and the area varies directly as the square of the radius.

EXAMPLE 3   **Solving a Direct Variation Problem**

The distance a body falls from rest varies directly as the square of the time it falls (disregarding air resistance). If a skydiver falls 64 ft in 2 sec, how far will she fall in 8 sec?

Step 1   If d represents the distance the skydiver falls and t the time it takes to fall, then d is a function of t, and

$$d = kt^2$$

for some constant k.

(b) What is the area of a circle with radius 4.1 in.?

Step 2   To find the value of k, use the fact that the skydiver falls 64 ft in 2 sec.

$$d = kt^2 \qquad \text{Variation equation}$$
$$64 = k(2)^2 \qquad \text{Let } d = 64 \text{ and } t = 2.$$
$$k = 16 \qquad \text{Find } k.$$

Step 3   Using 16 for k, the variation equation becomes

$$d = 16t^2.$$

Step 4   Let $t = 8$ to find the number of feet the skydiver will fall in 8 sec.

$$d = 16(8)^2 = 1024 \qquad \text{Let } t = 8.$$

The skydiver will fall 1024 ft in 8 sec.

◀ *Work Problem* **3** *at the Side.*

OBJECTIVE 3 Solve inverse variation problems.   In direct variation, where $k > 0$, as x increases, y increases. Similarly, as x decreases, y decreases. Another type of variation is *inverse variation*. ***With inverse variation, where $k > 0$, as one variable increases, the other variable decreases.***

For example, in a closed space, volume decreases as pressure increases, as illustrated by a trash compactor. See Figure 6. As the compactor presses down, the pressure on the trash increases; in turn, the trash occupies a smaller space.

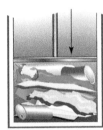

As pressure on trash increases, volume of trash decreases.

Figure 6

> **Inverse Variation**
>
> ***y varies inversely as x*** if there exists a real number k such that
> $$y = \frac{k}{x}.$$
> Also, ***y varies inversely as the nth power of x*** if there exists a real number k such that
> $$y = \frac{k}{x^n}.$$

The inverse variation equation also defines a function. Since x is in the denominator, these functions are rational functions, as seen in **Section 8.1.** Another example of inverse variation comes from the distance formula. In its usual form, the formula is

$$d = rt.$$

Dividing each side by r gives

$$t = \frac{d}{r}.$$

Here, t (time) varies inversely as r (rate or speed), with d (distance) serving as the constant of variation. For example, if the distance between Chicago and Des Moines is 300 mi, then

$$t = \frac{300}{r},$$

and the values of r and t might be any of the following.

$\left. \begin{array}{l} r = 50, t = 6 \\ r = 60, t = 5 \\ r = 75, t = 4 \end{array} \right\}$ As r increases, t decreases. $\left. \begin{array}{l} r = 30, t = 10 \\ r = 25, t = 12 \\ r = 20, t = 15 \end{array} \right\}$ As r decreases, t increases.

If we *increase* the rate (speed) we drive, time *decreases*. If we *decrease* the rate (speed) we drive, time *increases*.

4 If the temperature is constant, the volume of a gas varies inversely as the pressure. For a certain gas, the volume is 10 cm³ when the pressure is 6 kg per cm².

(a) Find the variation equation.

(b) Find the volume when the pressure is 12 kg per cm².

EXAMPLE 4 **Solving an Inverse Variation Problem**

The weight of an object above Earth varies inversely as the square of its distance from the center of Earth. A space shuttle in an elliptical orbit has a maximum distance from the center of Earth **(apogee)** of 6700 mi. Its minimum distance from the center of Earth **(perigee)** is 4090 mi. See Figure 7. If an astronaut in the shuttle weighs 57 lb at its apogee, what does the astronaut weigh at its perigee?

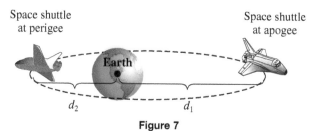

Space shuttle at perigee   Space shuttle at apogee

d_2 d_1

Figure 7

If w is the weight and d is the distance from the center of Earth, then

$$w = \frac{k}{d^2}$$

for some constant k. At the apogee the astronaut weighs 57 lb, and the distance from the center of Earth is 6700 mi. Use these values to find k.

$$57 = \frac{k}{(6700)^2} \qquad \text{Let } w = 57 \text{ and } d = 6700.$$

$$k = 57(6700)^2 \qquad \text{Solve for } k.$$

Then the weight at the perigee with $d = 4090$ mi is

$$w = \frac{57(6700)^2}{(4090)^2} \approx 153 \text{ lb.} \qquad \text{Use a calculator.}$$

◀ *Work Problem* **4** *at the Side.*

OBJECTIVE **4** **Solve joint variation problems.** It is possible for one variable to depend on several others. If one variable varies directly as the *product* of several other variables (perhaps raised to powers), the first variable is said to *vary jointly* as the others.

Joint Variation

y varies jointly as x and z if there exists a real number k such that

$$y = kxz.$$

CAUTION

Note that *and* in the expression "y varies jointly as x *and* z" translates as the product

$$y = kxz.$$

The word *and* does not indicate addition here.

EXAMPLE 5   **Solving a Joint Variation Problem**

The interest on a loan or an investment is given by the formula $I = prt$. Here, for a given principal p, the interest earned I varies jointly as the interest rate r and the time t that the principal is left at interest. If an investment earns $100 interest at 5% for 2 yr, how much interest will the same principal earn at 4.5% for 3 yr?

We use the formula $I = prt$, where p is the constant of variation because it is the same for both investments. For the first investment,

$$I = prt$$

$$100 = p(0.05)(2) \qquad \text{Let } I = 100, r = 0.05, \text{ and } t = 2.}$$

$$100 = 0.1p$$

$$p = 1000. \qquad \text{Divide by 0.1.}$$

Now we find I when $p = 1000$, $r = 0.045$, and $t = 3$.

$$I = 1000(0.045)(3) = 135 \qquad \text{Let } p = 1000, r = 0.045, \text{ and } t = 3.}$$

The interest will be $135.

Work Problem **5** *at the Side.* ▶

OBJECTIVE 5   Solve combined variation problems.   There are many combinations of direct and inverse variation, called **combined variation.**

EXAMPLE 6   **Solving a Combined Variation Problem**

Body mass index, or BMI, is used by physicians to assess a person's level of fatness. A BMI from 19 through 25 is considered desirable. BMI varies directly as an individual's weight in pounds and inversely as the square of the individual's height in inches. A man who weighs 118 lb and is 64 in. tall has a BMI of 20. (The BMI is rounded to the nearest whole number.) Find the BMI of a man who weighs 165 lb with a height of 70 in.

Let B represent the BMI, w the weight, and h the height. Then

$$B = \frac{kw}{h^2}. \begin{array}{l} \longleftarrow \text{ BMI varies directly as the weight.} \\ \longleftarrow \text{ BMI varies inversely as the square of the height.} \end{array}$$

To find k, let $B = 20$, $w = 118$, and $h = 64$.

$$20 = \frac{k(118)}{64^2}$$

$$k = \frac{20(64^2)}{118} \qquad \begin{array}{l}\text{Multiply by } 64^2; \\ \text{divide by } 118.\end{array}$$

$$k \approx 694 \qquad \text{Use a calculator.}$$

Now find B when $k = 694$, $w = 165$, and $h = 70$.

$$B = \frac{694(165)}{70^2} \approx 23 \qquad \begin{array}{l}\text{Nearest whole} \\ \text{number}\end{array}$$

The man's BMI is 23.

Work Problem **6** *at the Side.* ▶

5 The volume of a rectangular box of a given height is proportional to its width and length. A box with width 2 ft and length 4 ft has volume 12 ft^3. Find the volume of a box with the same height that is 3 ft wide and 5 ft long.

6 The maximum load that a cylindrical column with a circular cross section can hold varies directly as the fourth power of the diameter of the cross section and inversely as the square of the height. A 9-m column 1 m in diameter will support 8 metric tons. How many metric tons can be supported by a column 12 m high and $\frac{2}{3}$ m in diameter?

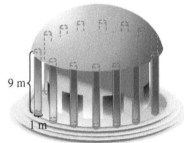

Load = 8 metric tons

10.6 ▶▶▶ **Exercises**

FOR
EXTRA
HELP

 Math XL
PRACTICE

 WATCH

DOWNLOAD

READ

 REVIEW

Determine whether each equation represents direct, inverse, joint, *or* combined *variation.*

1. $y = \dfrac{3}{x}$

2. $y = \dfrac{8}{x}$

3. $y = 10x^2$

4. $y = 2x^3$

5. $y = 3xz^4$

6. $y = 6x^3z^2$

7. $y = \dfrac{4x}{wz}$

8. $y = \dfrac{6x}{st}$

Solve each problem. See Examples 2–5.

9. If x varies directly as y, and $x = 9$ when $y = 3$, find x when $y = 12$.

10. If x varies directly as y, and $x = 10$ when $y = 7$, find y when $x = 50$.

11. If z varies inversely as w, and $z = 10$ when $w = 0.5$, find z when $w = 8$.

12. If t varies inversely as s, and $t = 3$ when $s = 5$, find s when $t = 5$.

13. p varies jointly as q and r^2, and $p = 200$ when $q = 2$ and $r = 3$. Find p when $q = 5$ and $r = 2$.

14. f varies jointly as g^2 and h, and $f = 50$ when $g = 4$ and $h = 2$. Find f when $g = 3$ and $h = 6$.

15. For $k > 0$, if y varies directly as x, when x increases, y _____, and when x decreases, y _____.

16. For $k > 0$, if y varies inversely as x, when x increases, y _____, and when x decreases, y _____.

17. Explain the difference between inverse variation and direct variation.

18. What is meant by the constant of variation in a direct variation problem? If you were to graph the linear equation $y = kx$ for some constant k, what role would the value of k play in the graph?

Solve each problem involving variation. See Examples 1–6.

19. Matt bought 8 gal of gasoline and paid $36.79. To the nearest tenth of a cent, what is the price of gasoline per gallon?

20. Nora gives horseback rides at Shadow Mountain Ranch. A 2.5-hr ride costs $50.00. What is the price per hour?

21. The volume of a can of tomatoes is proportional to the height of the can. If the volume of the can is 300 cm^3 when its height is 10.62 cm, find the volume of a can with height 15.92 cm.

10.62 cm

22. The weight of an object on Earth is directly proportional to the weight of that same object on the moon. A 200-lb astronaut would weigh 32 lb on the moon. How much would a 50-lb dog weigh on the moon?

23. For a body falling freely from rest (disregarding air resistance), the distance the body falls varies directly as the square of the time. If an object is dropped from the top of a tower 576 ft high and hits the ground in 6 sec, how far did it fall in the first 4 sec?

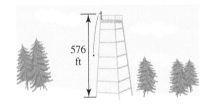

576 ft

24. The amount of water emptied by a pipe varies directly as the square of the diameter of the pipe. For a certain constant water flow, a pipe emptying into a canal will allow 200 gal of water to escape in an hour. The diameter of the pipe is 6 in. How much water would a 12-in. pipe empty into the canal in an hour, assuming the same water flow?

25. The current in a simple electrical circuit is inversely proportional to the resistance. If the current is 20 amperes (an **ampere** is a unit for measuring current) when the resistance is 5 ohms, find the current when the resistance is 7.5 ohms.

26. The frequency (number of vibrations per second) of a vibrating guitar string varies inversely as its length. That is, a longer string vibrates fewer times in a second than a shorter string. Suppose a guitar string 0.65 m long vibrates 4.3 times per sec. What frequency would a string 0.5 m long have?

27. The amount of light (measured in foot-candles) produced by a light source varies inversely as the square of the distance from the source. If the illumination produced 1 m from a light source is 768 foot-candles, find the illumination produced 6 m from the same source.

1 meter

28. The force with which Earth attracts an object above Earth's surface varies inversely with the square of the distance of the object from the center of Earth. If an object 4000 mi from the center of Earth is attracted with a force of 160 lb, find the force of attraction if the object were 6000 mi from the center of Earth.

29. For a given interest rate, simple interest varies jointly as principal and time. If $2000 left in an account for 4 yr earned interest of $280, how much interest would be earned in 6 yr?

30. The collision impact of an automobile varies jointly as its weight and the square of its speed. Suppose a 2000-lb car traveling at 55 mph has a collision impact of 6.1. What is the collision impact of the same car at 65 mph?

31. The force needed to keep a car from skidding on a curve varies inversely as the radius of the curve and jointly as the weight of the car and the square of the speed. If 242 lb of force keep a 2000-lb car from skidding on a curve of radius 500 ft at 30 mph, what force (to the nearest tenth) would keep the same car from skidding on a curve of radius 750 ft at 50 mph?

32. Almost 70% of the new single-family homes sold in the United States in 2006 used natural gas as the primary heating fuel. (*Source:* U.S. Census Bureau.) The volume of gas varies inversely as the pressure and directly as the temperature. (Temperature must be measured in *Kelvin* (K), a unit of measurement used in physics.) If a certain gas occupies a volume of 1.3 L at 300 K and a pressure of 18 newtons per cm^2, find the volume at 340 K and a pressure of 24 newtons per cm^2.

33. The number of long-distance phone calls between two cities in a certain time period varies jointly as the populations of the cities, p_1 and p_2, and inversely as the distance between them. If 80,000 calls are made between two cities 400 mi apart, with populations of 70,000 and 100,000, how many calls are made between cities with populations of 50,000 and 75,000 that are 250 mi apart?

34. A body mass index from 27 through 29 carries a slight risk of weight-related health problems, while one of 30 or more indicates a great increase in risk. Use your own height and weight and the information in Example 6 to determine whether you are at risk.

Exercises 35 and 36 describe weight-estimation formulas that fishermen have used over the years. Girth *is the distance around the body of the fish. Give answers to the nearest tenth.* (*Source: Sacramento Bee,* November 9, 2000.)

35. The weight of a bass varies jointly as its girth and the square of its length. A prize-winning bass weighed in at 22.7 lb and measured 36 in. long with 21 in. girth. How much would a bass 28 in. long with 18 in. girth weigh?

36. The weight of a trout varies jointly as its length and the square of its girth. One angler caught a trout that weighed 10.5 lb and measured 26 in. long with 18 in. girth. Find the weight of a trout that is 22 in. long with 15 in. girth.

Relating Concepts (Exercises 37–42) For Individual or Group Work

A routine activity such as pumping gasoline can be related to many of the concepts studied in this chapter. Suppose that premium unleaded costs $4.45 per gal. **Work Exercises 37–42 in order.**

37. 0 gal of gasoline cost $0.00, while 1 gal costs $4.45. Represent these two pieces of information as ordered pairs of the form (gallons, price).

38. Use the information from Exercise 37 to find the slope of the line on which the two points lie.

39. Write the slope-intercept form of the equation of the line on which the two points lie.

40. Using function notation, if $f(x) = ax + b$ represents the line from Exercise 39, what are the values of a and b?

41. How does the value of a from Exercise 40 relate to gasoline in this situation? With relationship to the line, what do we call this number?

42. Why does the equation from Exercise 40 satisfy the conditions for direct variation? In the context of variation, what do we call the value of a?

11

Linear Graphing

11.1 ▶▶▶ Reading Graphs; Linear Equations in Two Variables

OBJECTIVES

1. **Interpret graphs.**
2. **Write a solution as an ordered pair.**
3. **Decide whether a given ordered pair is a solution of a given equation.**
4. **Complete ordered pairs for a given equation.**
5. **Complete a table of values.**
6. **Plot ordered pairs.**

As we saw in **Chapter 9,** circle graphs (pie charts) provide a convenient way to organize and communicate information. Along with *bar graphs* and *line graphs,* they can be used to analyze data, make predictions, or simply to entertain us.

OBJECTIVE 1 Interpret graphs. A **bar graph** is used to show comparisons. It consists of a series of bars (or simulations of bars) arranged either vertically or horizontally. In a bar graph, values from two categories are paired with each other.

EXAMPLE 1 Interpreting a Bar Graph

The bar graph in Figure 1 shows U.S. sales of motor scooters, which have gained popularity due to their fuel efficiency. The graph compares sales in thousands.

Source: Motorcycle Industry Council.

Figure 1

1 Refer to the bar graph in Figure 1.

(a) Which years had sales less than 50 thousand?

(b) Estimate sales of motor scooters in 1999 and 2001.

(c) Describe the change in sales of motor scooters from 1999 to 2001.

(a) In what years were sales greater than 50 thousand?

Locate 50 on the vertical scale and follow the line across to the right. Three years—2002, 2003, and 2004—have bars that extend above the line for 50, so sales were greater than 50 thousand in those years.

(b) Estimate sales in 2000 and 2004.

Locate the top of the bar for 2000, and move horizontally across to the vertical scale to see that it is about 40. Sales in 2000 were about 40 thousand. Follow the top of the bar for 2004 across to the vertical scale to see that it lies about halfway between 80 and 90 thousand, so sales in 2004 were about 85,000.

(c) Describe the change in sales as the years progressed.

As the years progressed, sales increased steadily, from about 15 thousand in 1998 to about 85 thousand in 2004.

◀ *Work Problem* **1** *at the Side.*

A **line graph** is used to show changes or trends in data over time. To form a line graph, we connect a series of points representing data with line segments.

2 Refer to the line graph in Figure 2.

(a) Which year has the greatest amount of Medicare funds?

EXAMPLE 2 **Interpreting a Line Graph**

Current projections indicate that funding for Medicare will not cover its costs unless the program changes. The line graph in Figure 2 shows Medicare funds in billions of dollars for the years 2004 through 2013.

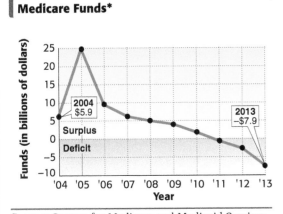

Medicare Funds*

Source: Centers for Medicare and Medicaid Services.
*Projected

Figure 2

(b) Estimate projected Medicare funds for 2010. Is there a surplus or a deficit in 2010?

(a) Which is the only period in which Medicare funds increased?
Because the graph *rises* from 2004 to 2005 and falls in every other case, funds increased between these two years.

(b) What is the projected trend from 2005 to 2013?
Funds will decrease, since the graph *falls* during this period.

(c) In which year is it projected that funds will first show a deficit?
From 2004 to 2010, the graph is always above 0, but in 2011, it falls slightly below 0 for the first time, indicating a deficit.

(c) About how much is it projected that funds will decrease from 2006 to 2011?

(d) Based on the figures shown in the graph, what is the difference in Medicare funds from 2004 to 2013?

$$\underbrace{-\$7.9 \text{ billion}}_{\text{2013 amount}} - \underbrace{\$5.9 \text{ billion}}_{\text{2004 amount}} = \underbrace{-\$13.8 \text{ billion}}_{\text{Difference}}$$

The fund amount will have *decreased* $13.8 billion (as indicated by the negative sign in −$13.8).

Work Problem **2** *at the Side.* ▶

The line graph in Figure 2 relates years to Medicare funds. We can also represent these two related quantities using a table of data, as shown at the side. Notice that in table form, we can see specific data rather than estimating it. Trends in the data are easier to see from the graph, however, which gives us a "picture" of the data.

We can extend these ideas to the subject of this chapter, *linear equations in two variables*. A linear equation in two variables, one for each of the quantities being related, can be used to represent the data in the table or graph. We introduced this concept in **Section 9.5** and extend the topic in this chapter.

Year	Medicare Funds (in billions of dollars)*
2004	5.9
2005	25.0
2006	9.5
2007	6.0
2008	5.0
2009	4.0
2010	2.0
2011	−0.5
2012	−2.5
2013	−7.9

*Projected

2. (a) 2005
  (b) $2 billion; surplus
  (c) $10 billion

The graph of a linear equation in two variables is a line.

3 Write each solution as an ordered pair.

(a) $x = 5$ and $y = 7$

> **Linear Equation in Two Variables**
>
> A **linear equation in two variables** is an equation that can be written in the form
>
> $$Ax + By = C,$$
>
> where A, B, and C are real numbers and A and B are not both 0.

Some examples of linear equations in two variables in this form, called *standard form,* are

(b) $y = 6$ and $x = -1$

$$3x + 4y = 9, \quad x - y = 0, \quad \text{and} \quad x + 2y = -8. \qquad \text{Linear equations in two variables}$$

> **Note**
>
> Other linear equations in two variables, such as
>
> $$y = 4x + 5 \quad \text{and} \quad 3x = 7 - 2y,$$
>
> are not written in standard form but could be. We discuss the forms of linear equations in more detail in **Section 11.4.**

(c) $y = 4$ and $x = -3$

OBJECTIVE **2** **Write a solution as an ordered pair.** Recall from Section 2.3 that a *solution* of an equation is a number that makes the equation true when it replaces the variable. For example, the linear equation in one variable $x - 2 = 5$ has solution 7, since replacing x with 7 gives a true statement.

(d) $x = \dfrac{2}{3}$ and $y = -12$

A solution of a linear equation in two variables requires two numbers, one for each variable. For example, a true statement results when we replace x with 2 and y with 13 in the equation $y = 4x + 5$ since

$$13 = 4(2) + 5. \qquad \text{Let } x = 2, y = 13.$$

The pair of numbers $x = 2$ and $y = 13$ gives one solution of the equation $y = 4x + 5$. The phrase "$x = 2$ and $y = 13$" is abbreviated

$$x\text{-value} \searrow \quad \swarrow y\text{-value}$$
$$(2, 13)$$
$$\text{Ordered pair}$$

(e) $y = 1.5$ and $x = -2.4$

with the x-value, 2, and the y-value, 13, given as a pair of numbers written inside parentheses. *The x-value is always given first.* A pair of numbers such as (2, 13) is called an **ordered pair.** As the name indicates, the order in which the numbers are written is important. The ordered pairs (2, 13) and (13, 2) are *not* the same. The second pair indicates that $x = 13$ and $y = 2$. *For two ordered pairs to be equal, their x-values must be equal and their y-values must be equal.*

(f) $x = 0$ and $y = 0$

◀ *Work Problem* **3** *at the Side.*

ANSWERS

3. (a) $(5, 7)$ **(b)** $(-1, 6)$ **(c)** $(-3, 4)$

(d) $\left(\dfrac{2}{3}, -12\right)$ **(e)** $(-2.4, 1.5)$ **(f)** $(0, 0)$

OBJECTIVE **3** **Decide whether a given ordered pair is a solution of a given equation.** We substitute the x- and y-values of an ordered pair into a linear equation in two variables to see whether the ordered pair is a solution.

EXAMPLE 3   **Deciding Whether Ordered Pairs Are Solutions of an Equation**

Decide whether each ordered pair is a solution of the equation $2x + 3y = 12$.

(a) $(3, 2)$

To see whether $(3, 2)$ is a solution of the given equation $2x + 3y = 12$, substitute 3 for x and 2 for y in the equation.

$$2x + 3y = 12$$
$$2(3) + 3(2) \overset{?}{=} 12 \qquad \text{Let } x = 3; \text{ let } y = 2.$$
$$6 + 6 \overset{?}{=} 12 \qquad \text{Multiply.}$$
$$12 = 12 \qquad \text{True}$$

This result is true, so $(3, 2)$ is a solution of $2x + 3y = 12$.

(b) $(-2, -7)$

$$2x + 3y = 12$$
$$2(-2) + 3(-7) \overset{?}{=} 12 \qquad \text{Let } x = -2; \text{ let } y = -7.$$

> Use parentheses to avoid errors.

$$-4 + (-21) \overset{?}{=} 12 \qquad \text{Multiply.}$$
$$-25 = 12 \qquad \text{False}$$

This result is false, so $(-2, -7)$ is *not* a solution of $2x + 3y = 12$.

Work Problem 4 *at the Side.* ▶

OBJECTIVE 4 **Complete ordered pairs for a given equation.**
Choosing a number for one variable in a linear equation makes it possible to find the value of the other variable.

EXAMPLE 4   **Completing Ordered Pairs**

Complete each ordered pair for the equation $y = 4x + 5$.

(a) $(7, \underline{\quad})$ [The x-value always comes first.]

In this ordered pair, $x = 7$. To find the corresponding value of y, replace x with 7 in the equation.

$$y = 4x + 5$$
$$y = 4(7) + 5 \qquad \text{Let } x = 7.$$
$$y = 28 + 5 \qquad \text{Multiply.}$$
$$y = 33 \qquad \text{Add.}$$

The ordered pair is $(7, 33)$.

(b) $(\underline{\quad}, -3)$

In this ordered pair, $y = -3$. Find the value of x by replacing y with -3 in the equation; then solve for x.

$$y = 4x + 5$$
$$-3 = 4x + 5 \qquad \text{Let } y = -3.$$
$$-8 = 4x \qquad \text{Subtract 5 from each side.}$$
$$-2 = x \qquad \text{Divide each side by 4.}$$

The ordered pair is $(-2, -3)$.

Work Problem 5 *at the Side.* ▶

---

4 Decide whether each ordered pair is a solution of the equation $5x + 2y = 20$.

(a) $(0, 10)$

$$5x + 2y = 20$$
$$5(\underline{\quad}) + 2(\underline{\quad}) \overset{?}{=} 20$$
$$\underline{\quad} + 20 \overset{?}{=} 20$$
$$\underline{\quad} = 20$$

Is $(0, 10)$ a solution?

(b) $(2, -5)$

(c) $(3, 2)$

(d) $(-4, 20)$

5 Complete each ordered pair for the equation $y = 2x - 9$.

(a) $(5, \underline{\quad})$

$$y = 2(\underline{\quad}) - 9$$
$$y = \underline{\quad} - 9$$
$$y = \underline{\quad}$$

The ordered pair is $\underline{\quad}$.

(b) $(2, \underline{\quad})$

(c) $(\underline{\quad}, 7)$

(d) $(\underline{\quad}, -13)$

ANSWERS
4. **(a)** 0; 10; 0; 20; yes   **(b)** no   **(c)** no
   (d) yes
5. **(a)** 5; 10; 1; (5, 1)   **(b)** (2, −5)   **(c)** (8, 7)
   (d) (−2, −13)

6 Complete the table of values for each equation.

(a) $2x - 3y = 12$

x	y
0	
	0
3	
	−3

(b) $x = -1$

x	y
	−4
	0
	2

(c) $y = 4$

x	y
−3	
2	
5	

ANSWERS

6. (a)

x	y
0	−4
6	0
3	−2
$\frac{3}{2}$	−3

(b)

x	y
−1	−4
−1	0
−1	2

(c)

x	y
−3	4
2	4
5	4

OBJECTIVE **5** **Complete a table of values.** Ordered pairs are often displayed in a **table of values.** The table may be written either vertically or horizontally.

EXAMPLE 5 **Completing Tables of Values**

Complete the table of values for each equation. Then write the results as ordered pairs.

(a) $x - 2y = 8$

x	y
2	
10	
	0
	−2

To complete the first two ordered pairs of the table, let $x = 2$ and $x = 10$, respectively.

If $x = 2$,	If $x = 10$,
then $x - 2y = 8$	then $x - 2y = 8$
becomes $2 - 2y = 8$	becomes $10 - 2y = 8$
$-2y = 6$	$-2y = -2$
$y = -3$.	$y = 1$.

Now complete the last two ordered pairs by letting $y = 0$ and $y = -2$, respectively.

If $y = 0$,	If $y = -2$,
then $x - 2y = 8$	then $x - 2y = 8$
becomes $x - 2(0) = 8$	becomes $x - 2(-2) = 8$
$x - 0 = 8$	$x + 4 = 8$
$x = 8$.	$x = 4$.

The completed table of values follows.

x	y	
2	−3	Write y-values here.
10	1	
8	0	
4	−2	

Write x-values here.

The corresponding ordered pairs are $(2, -3)$, $(10, 1)$, $(8, 0)$, and $(4, -2)$. Each ordered pair is a solution of the given equation $x - 2y = 8$.

(b) $x = 5$

x	y
	−2
	6
	3

The given equation is $x = 5$. No matter which value of y is chosen, the value of x is *always* 5.

x	y
5	−2
5	6
5	3

The corresponding ordered pairs are $(5, -2)$, $(5, 6)$, and $(5, 3)$.

◀ *Work Problem* **6** *at the Side.*

Note

We can think of $x = 5$ in Example 5(b) as an equation in two variables by rewriting $x = 5$ as $x + 0y = 5$. This form of the equation shows that for any value of y, the value of x is 5. Similarly, $y = 4$ in Problem 6(c) in the margin on the preceding page is the same as $0x + y = 4$.

OBJECTIVE 6 Plot ordered pairs. We saw that linear equations in *one* variable had either one, zero, or an infinite number of real number solutions. These solutions could be graphed on *one* number line.

For example, the linear equation in one variable $x - 2 = 5$ has solution 7, which is graphed on the number line in Figure 3.

Figure 3

Every linear equation in *two* variables has an infinite number of ordered pairs as solutions. Each choice of a number for one variable leads to a particular real number for the other variable.

To graph these solutions, represented as the ordered pairs (x, y), we need *two* number lines, one for each variable, as drawn in Figure 4. The horizontal number line is called the **x-axis,** and the vertical line is called the **y-axis.** Together, the x-axis and y-axis form a **rectangular coordinate system,** also called the **Cartesian coordinate system,** in honor of René Descartes, the French mathematician who is credited with its invention.

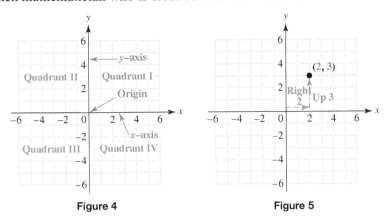

Figure 4   **Figure 5**

The coordinate system is divided into four regions, called **quadrants.** These quadrants are numbered counterclockwise, as shown in Figure 4. *Points on the axes themselves are not in any quadrant.* The point at which the x-axis and y-axis cross is called the **origin.** The origin, which is labeled 0 in Figure 4, is the point corresponding to $(0, 0)$.

Work Problem 7 at the Side. ▶

The x-axis and y-axis determine a **plane**—a flat surface illustrated by a sheet of paper. By referring to the two axes, every point in the plane can be associated with an ordered pair. The numbers in the ordered pair are called the **coordinates** of the point.

For example, we locate the point associated with the ordered pair $(2, 3)$ by starting at the origin. Since the x-coordinate is 2, we go 2 units to the right along the x-axis. Then, since the y-coordinate is 3, we turn and go up 3 units on a line parallel to the y-axis. The point $(2, 3)$ is **plotted** in Figure 5. From now on, we will refer to the point with x-coordinate 2 and y-coordinate 3 as the point $(2, 3)$.

7 Name the quadrant in which each point in the figure is located.

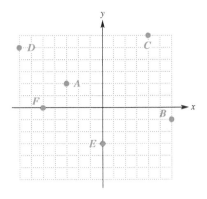

René Descartes
(1596–1650)

ANSWER

7. A: II; B: IV; C: I; D: II; E: no quadrant; F: no quadrant

8 Plot each ordered pair on a coordinate system.

(a) (3, 5) (b) (−2, 6)

(b) (−4.5, 0) (d) (−5, −2)

(e) (6, −2) (f) (0, −6)

(g) (0, 0) (h) $\left(-3, \frac{5}{2}\right)$

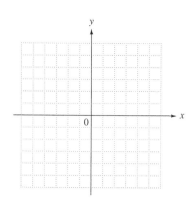

Note

When we graph on a number line (as in Figure 3), one number corresponds to each point. On a plane, however, *both* numbers in an ordered pair are needed to locate a point (as in Figure 5). The ordered pair is a name for the point.

We mentioned that René Descartes is credited with inventing the Cartesian coordinate system. Legend has it that Descartes, who was lying in bed ill, was watching a fly crawl about on the ceiling near a corner of the room. It occurred to him that the location of the fly could be described by determining its distances from the two adjacent walls. See the figure.

Locating a fly on a ceiling

EXAMPLE 6 **Plotting Ordered Pairs**

Plot each ordered pair on a coordinate system.

(a) (1, 5) (b) (−2, 3) (c) (−1, −4) (d) (3, −2)

(e) $\left(\frac{3}{2}, 2\right)$ (f) (5, 0) (g) (0, −3) (h) (4, −3.75)

See Figure 6. In each case, begin at the origin. Move right or left the number of units that corresponds to the *x*-coordinate in the ordered pair—*right if the x-coordinate is positive or left if it is negative.* Then turn and move up or down the number of units that corresponds to the *y*-coordinate—*up if the y-coordinate is positive or down if it is negative.* So in part (c), locate the point (−1, −4) by first going 1 unit to the *left* along the *x*-axis. Then turn and go 4 units *down,* parallel to the *y*-axis.

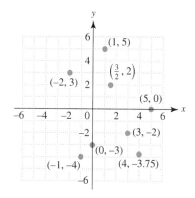

Figure 6

Notice the difference in the locations of the points (−2, 3) and (3, −2) in parts (b) and (d). The point (−2, 3) is in quadrant II, whereas the point (3, −2) is in quadrant IV. *The order of the coordinates is important. Remember that the x-coordinate is always given first in an ordered pair.*

To plot the point $\left(\frac{3}{2}, 2\right)$ in part (e), think of the improper fraction $\frac{3}{2}$ as the mixed number $1\frac{1}{2}$ and move $\frac{3}{2}$ (or $1\frac{1}{2}$) units to the right along the *x*-axis. Then turn and go 2 units up, parallel to the *y*-axis. The point (4, −3.75) in part (h) is plotted similarly, by approximating the location of the decimal *y*-coordinate.

In part (f), the point (5, 0) lies on the *x*-axis since the *y*-coordinate is 0. In part (g), the point (0, −3) lies on the *y*-axis since the *x*-coordinate is 0.

ANSWERS

8.

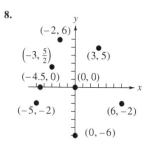

◀ *Work Problem* **8** *at the Side.*

Sometimes we can use a linear equation in two variables to mathematically describe, or *model*, a real-life situation, as shown in the next example.

EXAMPLE 7   **Completing Ordered Pairs to Estimate the Number of Twin Births**

The number of twin births in the United States has increased steadily in recent years. The annual number of twin births from 2000 through 2005 can be closely approximated by the linear equation

Number of twin births ———┐   ┌— Year

$$y = 3.074x - 6029.7,$$

which relates x, the year, and y, the number of twin births in thousands. (*Source: National Vital Statistics Reports,* Vol. 56, No. 6, December 5, 2007.)

(a) Complete the table of values for the given linear equation.

x (Year)	y (Number of Twin Births, in thousands)
2000	
2002	
2005	

To find y when $x = 2000$, substitute into the equation.

$$y = 3.074x - 6029.7$$

$\approx$ means "is approximately equal to." $y = 3.074(2000) - 6029.7$ Let $x = 2000$.

$y \approx 118$ Use a calculator.

This means that in 2000, there were about 118 thousand (or 118,000) twin births in the United States.

Work Problem **9** *at the Side.* ▶

Including the results from Problem 9 at the side gives the completed table that follows.

x (Year)	y (Number of Twin Births, in thousands)
2000	118
2002	124
2005	134

We can write the results from the table of values as ordered pairs (x, y). Each year x is paired with its number of twin births y (in thousands):

$(2000, 118)$, $(2002, 124)$,   and $(2005, 134)$.

Continued on Next Page

9 Refer to the linear equation in Example 7.

(a) Find the y-value for $x = 2002$. Round to the nearest whole number.

(b) Find the y-value for $x = 2005$. Interpret your result.

(b) Graph the ordered pairs found in part (a).

The ordered pairs (2000, 118), (2002, 124), and (2005, 134) are graphed in Figure 7. This graph of ordered pairs of data is called a **scatter diagram.** Notice how the axes are labeled: x represents the year, and y represents the number of twin births in thousands. Different scales are used on the two axes. Here, each square represents one unit in the horizontal direction and 5 units in the vertical direction. Because the numbers in the first ordered pair are large, we show a break in the axes near the origin.

x (Year)	y (Number of Twin Births, in thousands)
2000	118
2002	124
2005	134

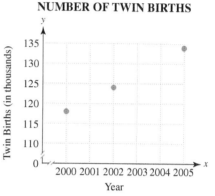

NUMBER OF TWIN BIRTHS

Figure 7

A scatter diagram enables us to tell whether two quantities are related to each other. In Figure 7, the plotted points could be connected to closely approximate a straight *line,* so the variables x (year) and y (number of twin births) have a *line*ar relationship. The increase in the number of twin births is also reflected.

CAUTION
The equation in Example 7 is valid only for the years 2000 through 2005 because it was based on data for those years. *Do not assume that this equation would provide reliable data for other years since the data for those years may not follow the same pattern.*

11.1 ▶▶▶ Exercises

The bar graph shows total U.S. milk production in billions of pounds for the years 2001 through 2007. Use the bar graph to work Exercises 1–4. See Example 1.

1. In what years was U.S. milk production greater than 175 billion pounds?

2. In what years was U.S. milk production about the same?

3. Estimate U.S. milk production in 2001 and 2007.

4. Describe the change in U.S. milk production from 2001 to 2007.

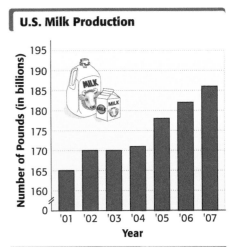

U.S. Milk Production

Source: U.S. Department of Agriculture.

The line graph shows the average price, adjusted for inflation, that Americans have paid for a gallon of gasoline for selected years since 1970. Use the line graph to work Exercises 5–8. See Example 2.

5. Over which period of years did the greatest increase in the price of a gallon of gas occur? About how much was this increase?

6. Estimate the price of a gallon of gas during 1985, 1990, 1995, and 2000.

7. Describe the trend in gas prices from 1980 to 1995.

8. During which year(s) did a gallon of gas cost approximately $1.50?

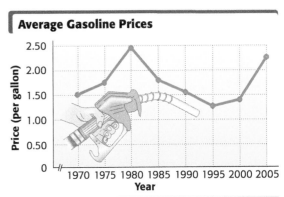

Average Gasoline Prices

Source: Energy Information Administration.

Use the concepts of this section to fill in each blank with the correct response.

9. The symbol (x, y) _____ represent an ordered pair, while the
                                    (does/does not)

symbols $[x, y]$ and $\{x, y\}$ _____ represent ordered pairs.
                                    (do/do not)

10. The point whose graph has coordinates $(-4, 2)$ is in quadrant _____.

11. The point whose graph has coordinates $(0, 5)$ lies on the _____-axis.

12. The ordered pair $(4, \underline{\hspace{1cm}})$ is a solution of the equation $y = 3$.

13. The ordered pair $(\underline{\hspace{1cm}}, -2)$ is a solution of the equation $x = 6$.

14. The ordered pair $(3, 2)$ is a solution of the equation $2x - 5y = \underline{\hspace{0.5cm}}$.

Decide whether each ordered pair is a solution of the given equation. See Example 3.

15. $x + y = 9$; $(0, 9)$

16. $x + y = 8$; $(0, 8)$

17. $2x - y = 6$; $(4, 2)$

18. $2x + y = 5$; $(3, -1)$

19. $4x - 3y = 6$; $(2, 1)$

20. $5x - 3y = 15$; $(5, 2)$

21. $y = \dfrac{2}{3}x$; $(-6, -4)$

22. $y = -\dfrac{1}{4}x$; $(-8, 2)$

23. $x = -6$; $(5, -6)$

24. $y = 2$; $(2, 4)$

25. Do $(4, -1)$ and $(-1, 4)$ represent the same ordered pair? Explain.

26. Explain why it would be easier to find the corresponding y-value for $x = \frac{1}{3}$ in the equation $y = 6x + 2$ than it would be for $x = \frac{1}{7}$.

Complete each ordered pair for the equation $y = 2x + 7$. See Example 4.

27. $(2, \underline{\hspace{0.5cm}})$

28. $(0, \underline{\hspace{0.5cm}})$

29. $(\underline{\hspace{0.5cm}}, 0)$

30. $(\underline{\hspace{0.5cm}}, -3)$

Complete each ordered pair for the equation $y = -4x - 4$. See Example 4.

31. $(0, \underline{\hspace{0.5cm}})$

32. $(\underline{\hspace{0.5cm}}, 0)$

33. $(\underline{\hspace{0.5cm}}, 16)$

34. $(\underline{\hspace{0.5cm}}, 24)$

Complete each table of values. In Exercises 35–38, write the results as ordered pairs. See Example 5.

35. $2x + 3y = 12$

x	y
0	
	0
	8

36. $4x + 3y = 24$

x	y
0	
	0
	4

37. $3x - 5y = -15$

x	y
0	
	0
	-6

38. $4x - 9y = -36$

x	y
	0
0	
	8

39. $x = -9$

x	y
	6
	2
	-3

40. $x = 12$

x	y
	3
	8
	0

41. $y = -6$

x	y
8	
4	
-2	

42. $y = -10$

x	y
4	
0	
-4	

43. $x - 8 = 0$

x	y
	8
	3
	0

44. $y + 2 = 0$

x	y
	9
	2
	0

Give the ordered pairs for the points labeled A–F in the figure. Tell the quadrant in which each point is located.

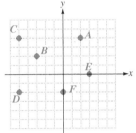

45. A   **46.** B   **47.** C

48. D   **49.** E   **50.** F

Fill in each blank with the word positive *or the word* negative.

The point with coordinates (x, y) is in

51. quadrant III if x is _____ and y is _____.

52. quadrant II if x is _____ and y is _____.

53. quadrant IV if x is _____ and y is _____.

54. quadrant I if x is _____ and y is _____.

55. A point (x, y) has the property that $xy < 0$. In which quadrant(s) must the point lie? Explain.

56. A point (x, y) has the property that $xy > 0$. In which quadrant(s) must the point lie? Explain.

Plot each ordered pair on the rectangular coordinate system provided. See Example 6.

 57. $(6, 2)$ **58.** $(5, 3)$ **59.** $(-4, 2)$ **60.** $(-3, 5)$

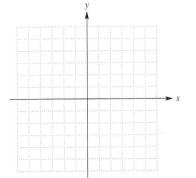

 61. $\left(-\dfrac{4}{5}, -1\right)$ **62.** $\left(-\dfrac{3}{2}, -4\right)$ **63.** $(3, -1.75)$ **64.** $(5, -4.25)$

65. $(0, 4)$ **66.** $(0, -3)$ **67.** $(4, 0)$ **68.** $(-3, 0)$

Complete each table of values, and then plot the ordered pairs. See Examples 5 and 6.

69. $x - 2y = 6$

x	y
0	
	0
2	
	−1

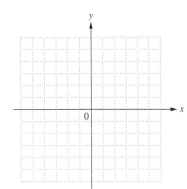

70. $2x - y = 4$

x	y
0	
	0
1	
	−6

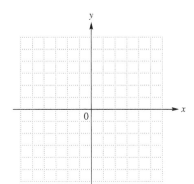

71. $3x - 4y = 12$

x	y
0	
	0
−4	
	−4

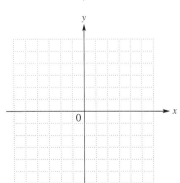

72. $2x - 5y = 10$

x	y
0	
	0
−5	
	−3

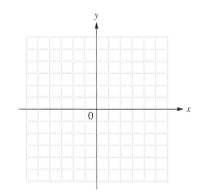

73. $y + 4 = 0$

x	y
0	
5	
−2	
−3	

74. $x - 5 = 0$

x	y
	1
	0
	6
	−4

75. Look at the graphs of the ordered pairs in Exercises 69–74. Describe the pattern indicated by the plotted points.

Work each problem. See Example 7.

76. Suppose that it costs $5000 to start up a business selling snow cones. Furthermore, it costs $0.50 per cone in labor, ice, syrup, and overhead. Then the cost to make *x* snow cones is given by *y* dollars, where

$$y = 0.50x + 5000.$$

Express each of the following as an ordered pair.

  (a) When 100 snow cones are made, the cost is $5050. (*Hint:* What does *x* represent? What does *y* represent?)

  (b) When the cost is $6000, the number of snow cones made is 2000.

77. It costs a flat fee of $20 plus $5 per day to rent a pressure washer. Therefore, the cost to rent the pressure washer for *x* days is given by

$$y = 5x + 20,$$

where *y* is in dollars. Express each of the following as an ordered pair.

  (a) When the washer is rented for 5 days, the cost is $45. (*Hint:* What does *x* represent? What does *y* represent?)

  (b) I paid $50 when I returned the washer, so I must have rented it for 6 days.

78. The table shows the number of U.S. students studying abroad (in thousands) for several academic years.

Academic Year	Number of Students (in thousands)
2000	154
2001	161
2002	175
2003	191
2004	206
2005	224

Source: Institute of International Education.

(a) Write the data from the table as ordered pairs (x, y), where x represents the year and y represents the number of U.S. students studying abroad.

(b) What does the ordered pair (2004, 206) mean in the context of this problem?

(c) Make a scatter diagram of the data using the ordered pairs from part (a).

U.S. STUDENTS STUDYING ABROAD

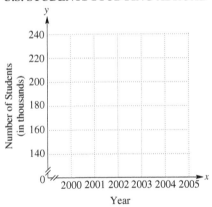

(d) Describe the pattern indicated by the points on the scatter diagram. What is the trend in the number of U.S. students studying abroad?

79. The table shows the rate (in percent) at which 2-year college students (public) complete a degree within 3 years.

Year	Percent
2000	32.4
2001	31.6
2002	31.6
2003	30.1
2004	29.0
2005	27.5

Source: ACT.

(a) Write the data from the table as ordered pairs (x, y), where x represents the year and y represents the percent.

(b) What would the ordered pair (2007, 27.1) mean in the context of this problem?

(c) Make a scatter diagram of the data using the ordered pairs from part (a).

2-YEAR COLLEGE STUDENTS COMPLETING A DEGREE WITHIN 3 YEARS

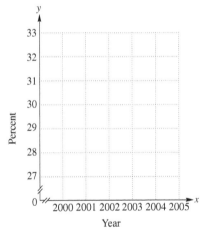

(d) Describe the pattern indicated by the points on the scatter diagram. What is happening to the rates at which 2-year college students complete a degree within 3 years?

80. The maximum benefit for the heart from exercising occurs if the heart rate is in the target heart rate zone. The lower limit of this target zone can be approximated by the linear equation

$$y = -0.5x + 108,$$

where x represents age and y represents heartbeats per minute. (*Source:* www.fitresource.com)

(a) Complete the table of values for this linear equation.

Age	Heartbeats (per minute)
20	
40	
60	
80	

(b) Write the data from the table of values as ordered pairs.

(c) Make a scatter diagram of the data. Do the points lie in a linear pattern?

TARGET HEART RATE ZONE
(Lower Limit)

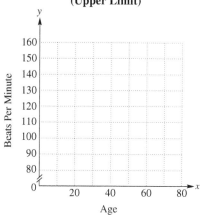

81. (See Exercise 80.) The upper limit of the target heart rate zone can be approximated by the linear equation

$$y = -0.8x + 173,$$

where x represents age and y represents heartbeats per minute. (*Source:* www.fitresource.com)

(a) Complete the table of values for this linear equation.

Age	Heartbeats (per minute)
20	
40	
60	
80	

(b) Write the data from the table of values as ordered pairs.

(c) Make a scatter diagram of the data. Describe the pattern indicated by the data.

TARGET HEART RATE ZONE
(Upper Limit)

82. Refer to Exercises 80 and 81. What is the target heart rate zone for age 20? age 40?

11.2 ▶▶▶ Graphing Linear Equations in Two Variables

OBJECTIVE **1** **Graph linear equations by plotting ordered pairs.** There are infinitely many ordered pairs that satisfy an equation in two variables. We find these ordered-pair solutions by choosing as many values of x (or y) as we wish and then completing each ordered pair.

For example, consider the equation $x + 2y = 7$. If we choose $x = 1$, then $y = 3$, so the ordered pair $(1, 3)$ is a solution of the equation $x + 2y = 7$.

$$1 + 2(3) = 7$$

Work Problem **1** *at the Side.* ▶

Figure 8 shows a graph of all the ordered-pair solutions found above and in Problem 1 at the side for $x + 2y = 7$.

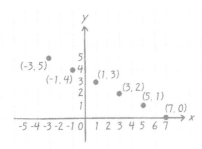

Figure 8

Notice that the points plotted in Figure 8 all appear to lie on a straight line, as shown in Figure 9. In fact, the following is true.

> *Every point on the line represents a solution of the equation $x + 2y = 7$, and every solution of the equation corresponds to a point on the line.*

The line gives a "picture" of all the solutions of the equation $x + 2y = 7$. Only a portion of the line is shown here, but it extends indefinitely in both directions, as suggested by the arrowhead on each end.

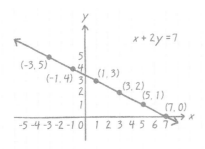

Figure 9

The line in Figure 9 is called the **graph** of the equation $x + 2y = 7$, and the process of plotting the ordered pairs and drawing the line through the corresponding points is called **graphing.**

OBJECTIVES

1 **Graph linear equations by plotting ordered pairs.**

2 **Find intercepts.**

3 **Graph linear equations of the form $Ax + By = 0$.**

4 **Graph linear equations of the form $y = k$ or $x = k$.**

5 **Use a linear equation to model data.**

---

1 Complete each ordered pair for the equation $x + 2y = 7$.

(a) $(-3, \underline{\quad})$

(b) $(-1, \underline{\quad})$

(c) $(3, \underline{\quad})$

(d) $(5, \underline{\quad})$

(e) $(7, \underline{\quad})$

ANSWERS

1. **(a)** $(-3, 5)$ **(b)** $(-1, 4)$ **(c)** $(3, 2)$
   (d) $(5, 1)$ **(e)** $(7, 0)$

The preceding discussion can be generalized.

2 Complete the table of values, and graph the linear equation.

$x + y = 6$

x	y
0	
	0
2	

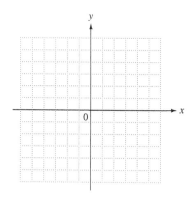

> **Graph of a Linear Equation**
>
> The graph of any linear equation in two variables is a straight line.

(Notice that the word **line** appears in the term "**line**ar equation.")

Because two distinct points determine a line, a straight line can be graphed by finding any two different points on the line. However, it is a good idea to plot a third point as a check.

EXAMPLE 1 Graphing a Linear Equation

Graph the linear equation $4x - 5y = 20$.

At least two different points are needed to draw the graph. First let $x = 0$ and then let $y = 0$ to complete two ordered pairs.

$4x - 5y = 20$	$4x - 5y = 20$
$4(0) - 5y = 20$ Let $x = 0$.	$4x - 5(0) = 20$ Let $y = 0$.
$0 - 5y = 20$	$4x - 0 = 20$
$-5y = 20$	$4x = 20$
$y = -4$	$x = 5$

Write each x-value first.

The ordered pairs are $(0, -4)$ and $(5, 0)$. Find a third ordered pair (as a check) by choosing a number other than 0 for x or y. We choose $y = 2$.

$$4x - 5y = 20$$
$$4x - 5(2) = 20 \qquad \text{Let } y = 2.$$
$$4x - 10 = 20$$
$$4x = 30 \qquad \text{Add 10.}$$
$$x = \frac{30}{4}, \quad \text{or} \quad \frac{15}{2} \qquad \text{Divide by 4; lowest terms}$$

This gives the ordered pair $(\frac{15}{2}, 2)$, or $(7\frac{1}{2}, 2)$. Plot the three ordered pairs $(0, -4)$, $(5, 0)$, and $(7\frac{1}{2}, 2)$, and draw a line through them. This line, shown in Figure 10, is the graph of $4x - 5y = 20$.

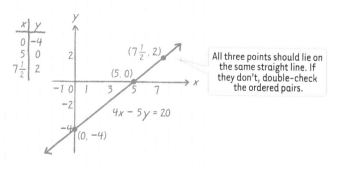

All three points should lie on the same straight line. If they don't, double-check the ordered pairs.

Figure 10

◀ *Work Problem* **2** *at the Side.*

ANSWER

2.

x	y
0	6
6	0
2	4

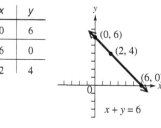

EXAMPLE 2 Graphing a Linear Equation

Graph the linear equation $y = -\frac{3}{2}x + 3$.

Although this equation is not in the form $Ax + By = C$, it *could* be written in that form, so it is a linear equation. Two different points on the graph can be found by first letting $x = 0$ and then letting $y = 0$.

If $x = 0$, then

$$y = -\frac{3}{2}x + 3$$

$$y = -\frac{3}{2}(0) + 3 \qquad \text{Let } x = 0.$$

$$y = 0 + 3 \qquad \text{Multiply.}$$

$$y = 3. \qquad \text{Add.}$$

If $y = 0$, then

$$y = -\frac{3}{2}x + 3$$

$$0 = -\frac{3}{2}x + 3 \qquad \text{Let } y = 0.$$

$$\frac{3}{2}x = 3 \qquad \text{Add } \frac{3}{2}x.$$

$$x = 2. \qquad \text{Multiply by } \frac{2}{3}.$$

This gives the ordered pairs $(0, 3)$ and $(2, 0)$. We find a third point (as a check) by letting x or y equal some other number. For example, let $x = -2$.

$$y = -\frac{3}{2}x + 3$$

> Choosing a multiple of 2 makes multiplying by $-\frac{3}{2}$ easier.

$$y = -\frac{3}{2}(-2) + 3 \qquad \text{Let } x = -2.$$

$$y = 3 + 3 \qquad \text{Multiply.}$$

$$y = 6 \qquad \text{Add.}$$

This gives the ordered pair $(-2, 6)$. These three ordered pairs are shown in the table with Figure 11. Plot the corresponding points, and then draw a line through them. This line, shown in Figure 11, is the graph of $y = -\frac{3}{2}x + 3$.

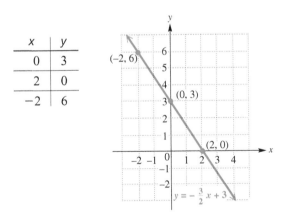

x	y
0	3
2	0
−2	6

Figure 11

Work Problem **3** *at the Side.* ▶

3 Make a table of values, and graph the linear equation.

$$y = \frac{2}{3}x - 2$$

x	y

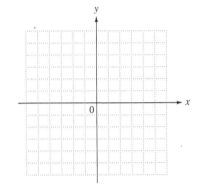

ANSWER

3.

$y = \frac{2}{3}x - 2$

4 Find the intercepts for the graph of $5x + 2y = 10$. Then draw the graph. (Be sure to get a third point as a check.)

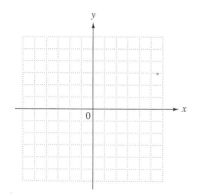

OBJECTIVE **2** **Find intercepts.** In Figure 11, the graph crosses, or intersects, the y-axis at $(0, 3)$ and the x-axis at $(2, 0)$. For this reason, $(0, 3)$ is called the **y-intercept,** and $(2, 0)$ is called the **x-intercept** of the graph.

The intercepts are particularly useful for graphing linear equations. The intercepts are found by replacing, in turn, each variable with 0 in the equation and solving for the value of the other variable.

Finding Intercepts

To find the x-intercept, let $y = 0$ in the given equation and solve for x. Then $(x, 0)$ is the x-intercept.

To find the y-intercept, let $x = 0$ in the given equation and solve for y. Then $(0, y)$ is the y-intercept.

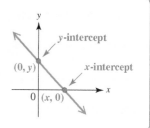

EXAMPLE 3 **Finding Intercepts**

Find the intercepts for the graph of $2x + y = 4$. Then draw the graph.

To find the y-intercept, let $x = 0$; to find the x-intercept, let $y = 0$.

$2x + y = 4$	$2x + y = 4$
$2(0) + y = 4$ Let $x = 0$.	$2x + 0 = 4$ Let $y = 0$.
$0 + y = 4$	$2x = 4$
$y = 4$	$x = 2$

The y-intercept is $(0, 4)$. The x-intercept is $(2, 0)$. Find a third point as a check. For example, choosing $x = 1$ gives $y = 2$. Plot $(0, 4)$, $(2, 0)$, and $(1, 2)$ and draw the line through them. This line, shown in Figure 12, is the graph.

x	y
0	4
2	0
1	2

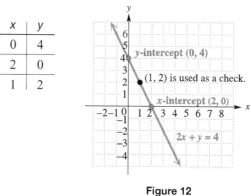

Figure 12

◄ *Work Problem* **4** *at the Side.*

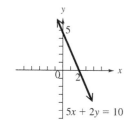
OBJECTIVE **3** **Graph linear equations of the form Ax + By = 0.**
In the preceding examples, the x- and y-intercepts were used to help draw the graphs. This is not always possible. Example 4 shows what to do when the x- and y-intercepts are the same point (that is, coincide).

EXAMPLE 4 **Graphing an Equation of the Form Ax + By = 0**

Graph the linear equation $x - 3y = 0$.

If we let $x = 0$, then $y = 0$, giving the ordered pair $(0, 0)$. Letting $y = 0$ also gives $(0, 0)$. This is the same ordered pair, so we choose two *other* values for x or y. Choosing 2 for y gives $x - 3 \cdot 2 = 0$, leading to $x = 6$, so another ordered pair is $(6, 2)$. Choosing -2 for y gives $x - 3(-2) = 0$, leading to $x = -6$, so a third ordered pair is $(-6, -2)$. We use the ordered pairs $(-6, -2)$, $(0, 0)$, and $(6, 2)$ to sketch the graph in Figure 13.

x	y
0	0
6	2
-6	-2

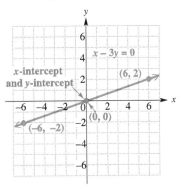

Figure 13

Work Problem **5** *at the Side.* ▶

Line through the Origin

If A and B are nonzero real numbers, the graph of a linear equation of the form

$$Ax + By = 0$$

passes through the origin $(0, 0)$.

OBJECTIVE **4** **Graph linear equations of the form y = k or x = k.** The equation $y = -4$ is a linear equation in which the coefficient of x is 0. (To see this, write $y = -4$ as $0x + y = -4$.) Also, $x = 3$ is a linear equation in which the coefficient of y is 0. These equations lead to horizontal or vertical straight lines, as the next examples show.

EXAMPLE 5 **Graphing an Equation of the Form y = k**

Graph $y = -4$.

As the equation states, for any value of x, y is always equal to -4. Three ordered pairs that satisfy the equation are shown. The graph is the horizontal line in Figure 14. The y-intercept is $(0, -4)$; there is no x-intercept.

x	y
-2	-4
0	-4
3	-4

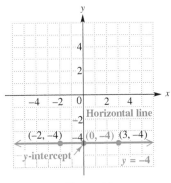

Figure 14

Work Problem **6** *at the Side.* ▶

5 Graph $2x - y = 0$.

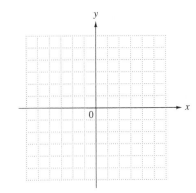

6 Graph $y = -5$.

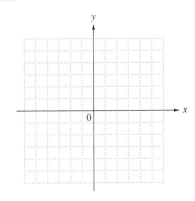

ANSWERS

5.

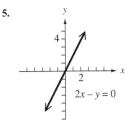

6.

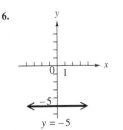

7 Graph $x + 4 = 6$.

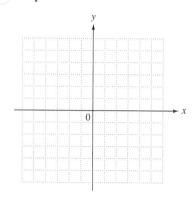

EXAMPLE 6 **Graphing an Equation of the Form $x = k$**

Graph $x - 3 = 0$.

First add 3 to each side of $x - 3 = 0$ to get $x = 3$. All the ordered pairs that satisfy this equation have x-coordinate 3. Any number can be used for y. See Figure 15 for the graph of this vertical line, along with a table of values. The x-intercept is $(3, 0)$; there is no y-intercept.

x	y
3	3
3	0
3	-2

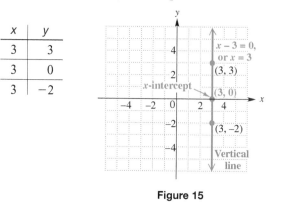

Figure 15

◀ *Work Problem* **7** *at the Side.*

From the results in Examples 5 and 6, we make the following observations.

Horizontal and Vertical Lines

The graph of the linear equation $y = k$, where k is a real number, is the horizontal line with y-intercept $(0, k)$ and no x-intercept.

The graph of the linear equation $x = k$, where k is a real number, is the vertical line with x-intercept $(k, 0)$ and no y-intercept.

In particular, notice that the horizontal line $y = 0$ is the x-axis and the vertical line $x = 0$ is the y-axis. The different forms of linear equations from this section and the methods of graphing them are summarized below.

Graphing a Linear Equation

Equation	Graphing Method	Example
$y = k$	Draw a horizontal line through $(0, k)$.	
$x = k$	Draw a vertical line through $(k, 0)$.	

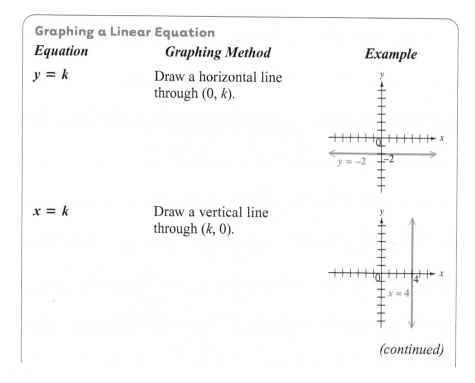

(continued)

ANSWER

7.

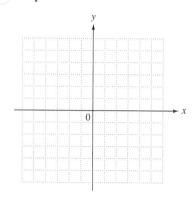

Equation	Graphing Method	Example
$Ax + By = 0$	Graph passes through $(0, 0)$. To get additional points that lie on the graph, choose any values for x or y, except 0.	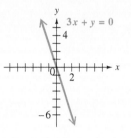
$Ax + By = C$ (but not of the types above)	Find any two points on the line. A good choice is to find the intercepts. Let $x = 0$, and find the corresponding value of y; then let $y = 0$, and find x. As a check, get a third point by choosing a value of x or y that has not yet been used.	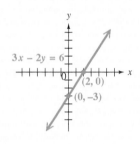

8 Match the information about the graphs in parts (a)–(d) with the linear equations in A–D.

A. $x = 5$
B. $2x - 5y = 8$
C. $y - 2 = 3$
D. $x + 4y = 0$

(a) The graph of the equation is a horizontal line.

(b) The graph of the equation passes through the origin.

(c) The graph of the equation is a vertical line.

(d) The graph of the equation passes through $(9, 2)$.

Work Problem **8** *at the Side.* ▶

> **Note**
> Another method of graphing linear equations, using the concepts of slope and y-intercept, will be covered in Objective 2 of **Section 11.4.**

OBJECTIVE 5 Use a linear equation to model data.

EXAMPLE 7 Using a Linear Equation to Model Credit Card Debt

Credit card debt in the United States has increased steadily during recent years. The amount of debt y in billions of dollars can be modeled by the linear equation

$$y = 38.7x + 450,$$

where $x = 0$ represents the year 1995, $x = 1$ represents 1996, and so on. (*Source:* Board of Governors of the Federal Reserve System.)

(a) Use the equation to approximate credit card debt in the years 1995, 2000, and 2003.

Substitute the appropriate value for each year x to find credit card debt in that year.

For 1995: $y = 38.7(0) + 450$ Replace x with 0.
            $y = 450$ billion dollars

For 2000: $y = 38.7(5) + 450$ $2000 - 1995 = 5$;
            $y = 643.5$ billion dollars   Replace x with 5.

For 2003: $y = 38.7(8) + 450$ $2003 - 1995 = 8$;
            $y = 759.6$ billion dollars   Replace x with 8.

Continued on Next Page

ANSWERS
8. **(a)** C **(b)** D **(c)** A **(d)** B

9 Use the graph and then the equation in Example 7 to approximate credit card debt in 1997.

(b) Write the information from part (a) as three ordered pairs, and use them to graph the given linear equation.

Since x represents the year and y represents the debt, the ordered pairs are (0, 450), (5, 643.5), and (8, 759.6). See Figure 16. (Arrowheads are not included with the graphed line, since the data are for the years 1995 to 2003 only—that is, from $x = 0$ to $x = 8$.)

U.S. CREDIT CARD DEBT

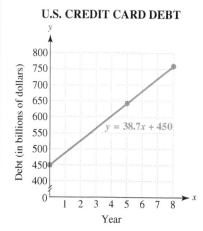

Figure 16

(c) Use the graph and then the equation to approximate credit card debt in 2002.

For 2002, $x = 7$. On the graph, find 7 on the horizontal axis, move up to the graphed line and then across to the vertical axis. It appears that credit card debt in 2002 was about 725 billion dollars. To use the equation, substitute 7 for x.

$$y = 38.7x + 450$$
$$y = 38.7(7) + 450 \qquad \text{Let } x = 7.$$
$$y = 720.9 \text{ billion dollars}$$

This result for 2002 is close to our estimate of 725 billion dollars from the graph.

◀ Work Problem 9 at the Side.

11.2 ▶▶▶ **Exercises**

Complete the given ordered pairs for each equation. Then graph each equation by plotting the points and drawing the line through them. See Examples 1 and 2.

1. $x + y = 5$

$(0, \underline{}), (\underline{}, 0), (2, \underline{})$

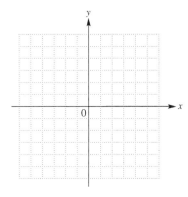

2. $x - y = 2$

$(0, \underline{}), (\underline{}, 0), (5, \underline{})$

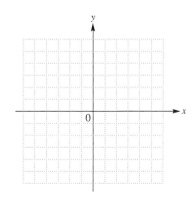

3. $y = \dfrac{2}{3}x + 1$

$(0, \underline{}), (3, \underline{}), (-3, \underline{})$

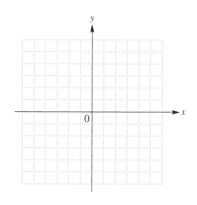

4. $y = -\dfrac{3}{4}x + 2$

$(0, \underline{}), (4, \underline{}), (-4, \underline{})$

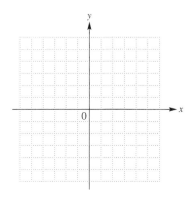

5. $3x = -y - 6$

$(0, \underline{}), (\underline{}, 0), \left(-\dfrac{1}{3}, \underline{}\right)$

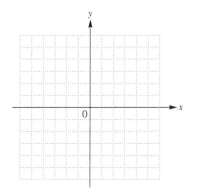

6. $x = 2y + 3$

$(\underline{}, 0), (0, \underline{}), \left(\underline{}, \dfrac{1}{2}\right)$

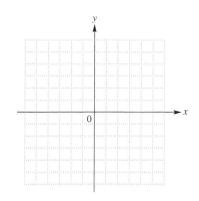

7. Match the information about each graph in Column I with the correct linear equation in Column II.

I

(a) The graph of the equation has y-intercept $(0, -4)$.

(b) The graph of the equation has $(0, 0)$ as x-intercept and y-intercept.

(c) The graph of the equation does not have an x-intercept.

(d) The graph of the equation has x-intercept $(4, 0)$.

II

A. $3x + y = -4$

B. $x - 4 = 0$

C. $y = 4x$

D. $y = 4$

8. Write a few sentences summarizing how to graph a linear equation in two variables.

Find the intercepts for the graph of each equation. See Example 3.

9. $2x - 3y = 24$

x-intercept:

y-intercept:

10. $-3x + 8y = 48$

x-intercept:

y-intercept:

11. $x + 6y = 0$

x-intercept:

y-intercept:

12. $3x - y = 0$

x-intercept:

y-intercept:

Graph each linear equation. See Examples 1–6.

13. $y = x - 2$

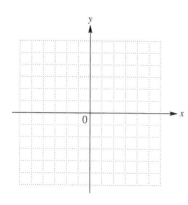

14. $y = -x + 6$

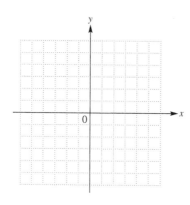

15. $x - y = 4$

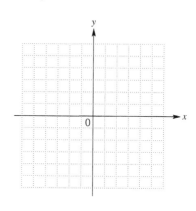

16. $x - y = 5$

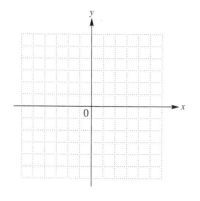

17. $2x + y = 6$

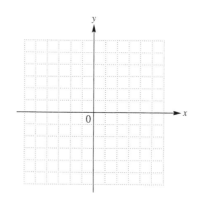

18. $-3x + y = -6$

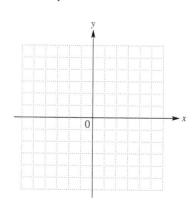

19. $3x + 7y = 14$

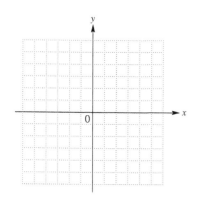

20. $6x - 5y = 18$

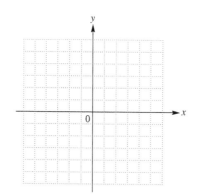

21. $y - 2x = 0$

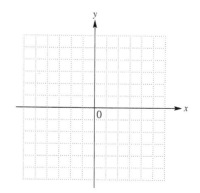

22. $y + 3x = 0$

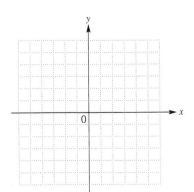

23. $y = -6x$

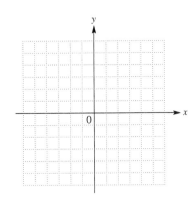

24. $y = 4x$

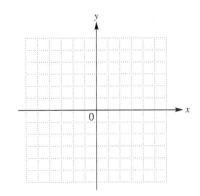

🌐 **25.** $x = -2$

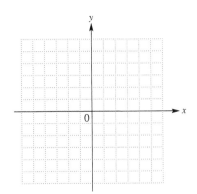

26. $x = 4$

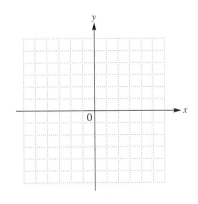

27. $y - 3 = 0$

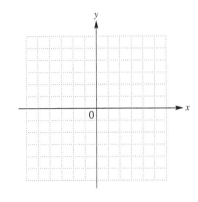

28. $y + 1 = 0$

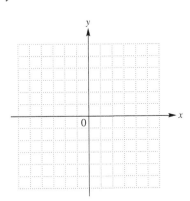

29. $-3y = 15$

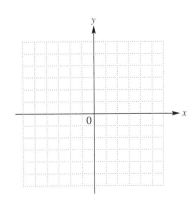

30. $-2y = 12$

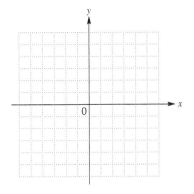

In Exercises 31–34, describe what the graph of each linear equation will look like on the coordinate plane. (Hint: Rewrite the equation if necessary so that it is in a more recognizable form.)

31. $3x = y - 9$

32. $x - 10 = 1$

33. $3y = -6$

34. $2x = 4y$

35. A student attempted to graph $4x + 5y = 0$ by finding intercepts. She first let $x = 0$ and found y; then she let $y = 0$ and found x. In both cases, the resulting point was $(0, 0)$. She knew that she needed at least two points to graph the line, but was unsure what to do next because finding intercepts gave her only one point. How would you explain to her what to do next?

36. What is the equation of the x-axis? What is the equation of the y-axis?

Solve each problem. See Example 7.

37. The height y (in centimeters) of a woman is related to the length of her radius bone x (from the wrist to the elbow) and is approximated by the linear equation

$$y = 3.9x + 73.5.$$

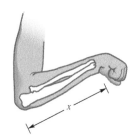

(a) Use the equation to find the approximate heights of women with radius bones of lengths 20 cm, 22 cm, and 26 cm.

(b) Write the information from part (a) as three ordered pairs.

(c) Graph the equation using the data from part (b).

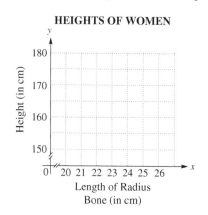

HEIGHTS OF WOMEN

(d) Use the graph to estimate the length of the radius bone in a woman who is 167 cm tall. Then use the equation to find the length of this radius bone to the nearest centimeter. (*Hint:* Substitute for y in the equation.)

38. The weight y (in pounds) of a man taller than 60 in. can be roughly approximated by the linear equation

$$y = 5.5x - 220,$$

where x is the height of the man in inches.

(a) Use the equation to approximate the weights of men whose heights are 62 in., 66 in., and 72 in.

(b) Write the information from part (a) as three ordered pairs.

(c) Graph the equation using the data from part (b).

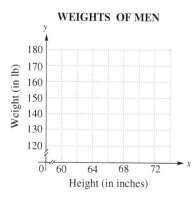

WEIGHTS OF MEN

(d) Use the graph to estimate the height of a man who weighs 155 lb. Then use the equation to find the height of this man to the nearest inch. (*Hint:* Substitute for y in the equation.)

39. As a fundraiser, a school club is selling posters. The printer charges a $25 set-up fee, plus $0.75 for each poster. Then the cost y in dollars to print x posters is given by the linear equation

$$y = 0.75x + 25.$$

(a) What is the cost y in dollars to print 50 posters? to print 100 posters?

(b) Find the number of posters x if the printer billed the club for costs of $175.

(c) Write the information from parts (a) and (b) as three ordered pairs.

(d) Use the data from part (c) to graph the equation.

POSTER COSTS

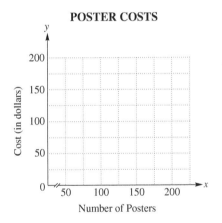

40. A gas station is selling gasoline for $4.50 per gallon and charges $7 for a car wash. Then the cost y in dollars for x gallons of gasoline and a car wash is given by the linear equation

$$y = 4.50x + 7.$$

(a) What is the cost y in dollars for 9 gallons of gasoline and a car wash? for 4 gallons of gasoline and a car wash?

(b) Find the number of gallons of gasoline x if the cost for the gasoline and a car wash is $43.00.

(c) Write the information from parts (a) and (b) as three ordered pairs.

(d) Use the data from part (c) to graph the equation.

GASOLINE AND CAR WASH COSTS

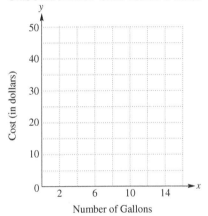

41. The graph shows the value of a certain sport-utility vehicle over the first five years of ownership. Use the graph to do the following.

(a) Determine the initial value of the SUV.

(b) Find the **depreciation** (loss in value) from the original value after the first three years.

(c) What is the annual or yearly depreciation in each of the first five years?

SUV VALUE

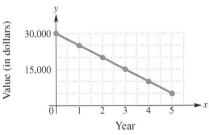

(d) What does the ordered pair (5, 5000) mean in the context of this problem?

42. Demand for an item is often closely related to its price. As price increases, demand decreases, and as price decreases, demand increases. Suppose demand for a video game is 2000 units when the price is $40, and demand is 2500 units when the price is $30.

(a) Let x be the price and y be the demand for the game. Graph the two given pairs of prices and demands.

VIDEO GAME PRICE/DEMAND

(b) Assume the relationship is linear. Draw a line through the two points from part (a). From your graph, estimate the demand if the price drops to $20.

(c) Use the graph to estimate the price if the demand is 3500 units.

(d) Write the prices and demands from parts (b) and (c) as ordered pairs.

43. U.S. per capita consumption of cheese increased for the years 1980 through 2005 as shown in the graph. If $x = 0$ represents 1980, $x = 5$ represents 1985, and so on, per capita consumption y in pounds can be modeled by the linear equation

$$y = 0.5383x + 18.74.$$

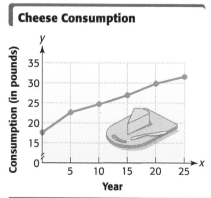

Cheese Consumption

Source: U.S. Department of Agriculture.

(a) Use the equation to approximate consumption in 1990, 2000, and 2005 to the nearest tenth.

(b) Use the graph to estimate consumption for the same years.

(c) How do the approximations using the equation compare to the estimates from the graph?

44. In the United States, sporting goods sales y (in billions of dollars) from 2000 through 2006 are shown in the graph and modeled by the linear equation

$$y = 3.018x + 72.52,$$

where $x = 0$ corresponds to 2000, $x = 1$ corresponds to 2001, and so on.

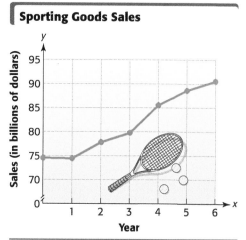

Sporting Goods Sales

Source: National Sporting Goods Association.

(a) Use the equation to approximate sporting goods sales in 2000, 2004, and 2006. Round your answers to the nearest billion dollars.

(b) Use the graph to estimate sales for the same years.

(c) How do the approximations using the equation compare to the estimates using the graph?

An important characteristic of the lines we graphed in the previous section is their slant or "steepness", as viewed from *left to right*. See Figure 17.

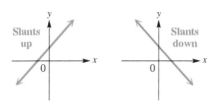

Figure 17

OBJECTIVES

1 Find the slope of a line given two points.

2 Find the slope from the equation of a line.

3 Use slope to determine whether two lines are parallel, perpendicular, or neither.

One way to measure the steepness of a line is to compare the vertical change in the line to the horizontal change while moving along the line from one fixed point to another. This measure of steepness is called the *slope* of the line.

OBJECTIVE 1 Find the slope of a line given two points.   To find the steepness, or slope, of the line in Figure 18, we begin at point Q and move to point P. The vertical change, or **rise,** is the change in the y-values, which is the difference $6 - 1 = 5$ units. The horizontal change, or **run,** from Q to P is the change in the x-values, which is the difference $5 - 2 = 3$ units.

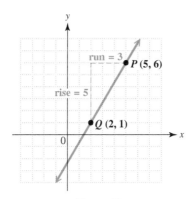

Figure 18

Remember from **Section 6.1** that one way to compare two numbers is by using a ratio. The **slope** is the ratio of the vertical change in y to the horizontal change in x. The line in Figure 18 has

$$\text{slope} = \frac{\text{vertical change in } y \text{ (rise)}}{\text{horizontal change in } x \text{ (run)}} = \frac{5}{3}.$$

To confirm this ratio, we can count grid squares. We start at point Q in Figure 18 and count *up* 5 grid squares to find the vertical change (rise). To find the horizontal change (run) and arrive at point P, we count to the *right* 3 grid squares. The slope is $\frac{5}{3}$, as found above. ***Slope is a single number that allows us to determine the direction in which a line is slanting from left to right, as well as how much slant there is to the line.***

1 Find the slope ratio of each line.

(a)

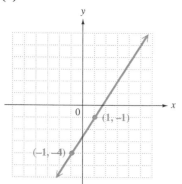

(b)

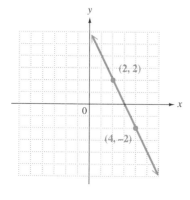

EXAMPLE 1 **Finding the Slope of a Line**

Find the slope of the line in Figure 19.

We use the two points shown on the line. The vertical change is the difference in the y-values, or $-1 - 3 = -4$, and the horizontal change is the difference in the x-values, or $6 - 2 = 4$. Thus, the line has

$$\text{slope} = \frac{\text{change in } y \text{ (rise)}}{\text{change in } x \text{ (run)}} = \frac{-4}{4}, \quad \text{or} \quad -1.$$

Counting grid squares, we begin at point P and count *down* 4 grid squares. Because we counted down, we write the vertical change as a negative number, -4 here. Then we count to the *right* 4 grid squares to reach point Q. The slope is $\frac{-4}{4}$, or -1.

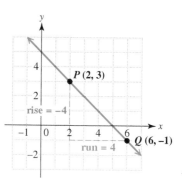

Figure 19

◄ Work Problem **1** at the Side.

Note

The slope of a line is the same for any two points on the line. To see this, refer to Figure 19. Find the points $(3, 2)$ and $(5, 0)$, which also lie on the line. If we start at $(3, 2)$ and count *down* 2 units and then to the *right* 2 units, we arrive at $(5, 0)$. The slope is $\frac{-2}{2}$, or -1, the same slope we found in Example 1.

The concept of slope is used in many everyday situations. See Figure 20. For example, a highway with a 10%, or $\frac{1}{10}$, grade (or slope) rises 1 m for every 10 m horizontally. Architects specify the pitch of a roof by using slope; a $\frac{5}{12}$ roof means that the roof rises 5 ft for every 12 ft that it runs in the horizontal direction. The slope of a stairwell also indicates the ratio of the vertical rise to the horizontal run. In the figure, the slope of the stairwell is $\frac{8}{12}$, or $\frac{2}{3}$.

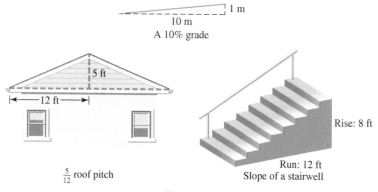

Figure 20

We can generalize the preceding discussion and find the slope of a line through two nonspecific points (x_1, y_1) and (x_2, y_2). (This notation is called **subscript notation.** Read x_1 as "***x*-sub-one**" and x_2 as "***x*-sub-two**.") See Figure 21.

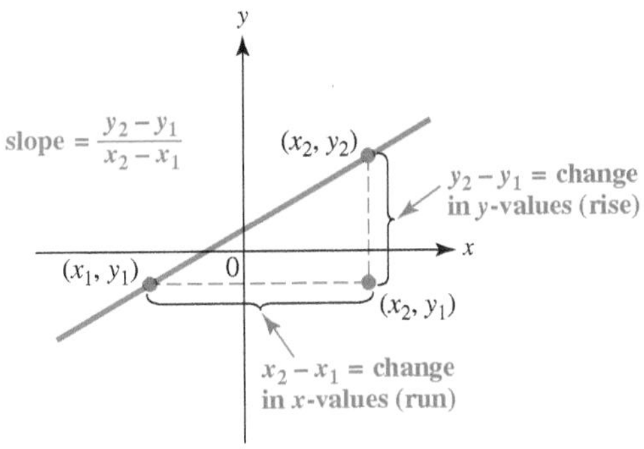

slope $= \dfrac{y_2 - y_1}{x_2 - x_1}$

(x_2, y_2)

$y_2 - y_1$ = change in y-values (rise)

(x_1, y_1)

(x_2, y_1)

$x_2 - x_1$ = change in x-values (run)

Figure 21

Moving along the line from the point (x_1, y_1) to the point (x_2, y_2), we see that y changes by $y_2 - y_1$ units. This is the vertical change (rise). Similarly, x changes by $x_2 - x_1$ units, which is the horizontal change (run). The slope of the line is the ratio of $y_2 - y_1$ to $x_2 - x_1$.

> **Note**
> Subscript notation is used to identify a point. It does *not* indicate any operation. Note the difference between x_2, a nonspecific value, and x^2, which means $x \cdot x$. Read x_2 as "x-sub-two," *not* "x squared."

Traditionally, the letter *m* represents slope. The slope *m* of a line is defined as follows.

> **Slope Formula**
> The **slope** of the line through the points (x_1, y_1) and (x_2, y_2) is
> $$m = \frac{\textbf{change in } y}{\textbf{change in } x} = \frac{y_2 - y_1}{x_2 - x_1} \quad (x_1 \neq x_2).$$

The slope gives the change in y for each unit of change in x.

Work Problem **2** at the Side. ▶

EXAMPLE 2 **Finding Slopes of Lines**

Find the slope of each line.

(a) The line through $(-4, 7)$ and $(1, -2)$

Use the slope formula. Let $(-4, 7) = (x_1, y_1)$ and $(1, -2) = (x_2, y_2)$.

$$\text{slope } m = \frac{\text{change in } y}{\text{change in } x} = \frac{y_2 - y_1}{x_2 - x_1} = \frac{-2 - 7}{1 - (-4)} = \frac{-9}{5} = -\frac{9}{5}$$

Substitute carefully here.

Continued on Next Page

---

2 Find $\dfrac{y_2 - y_1}{x_2 - x_1}$ for the following values.

(a) $y_2 = 4, y_1 = -1,$
$x_2 = 3, x_1 = 4$

(b) $x_1 = 3, x_2 = -5,$
$y_1 = 7, y_2 = -9$

(c) $x_1 = 2, x_2 = 7,$
$y_1 = 4, y_2 = 9$

3 Find the slope of each line.

(a) The line through $(6, -2)$ and $(5, 4)$

Count grid squares in Figure 22 to confirm that the slope is $-\frac{9}{5}$.

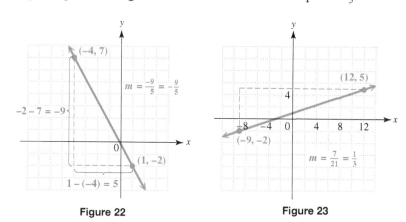

Figure 22   **Figure 23**

(b) The line through $(-9, -2)$ and $(12, 5)$

$$\text{slope } m = \frac{\overset{\text{y-value}}{\downarrow}}{\underset{\uparrow}{12 - (-9)}} = \frac{7}{21} = \frac{1}{3}$$

x-value from the *same* ordered pair

See Figure 23. Note that the same slope is obtained by subtracting in reverse order.

(b) The line through $(-3, 5)$ and $(-4, -7)$

$$\text{slope } m = \frac{\overset{\text{y-value}}{\downarrow}}{\underset{\uparrow}{-9 - 12}} = \frac{-7}{-21} = \frac{1}{3}$$

x-value from the *same* ordered pair

(c) The line through $(6, -8)$ and $(-2, 4)$

(Find this slope in two different ways as in Example 2(b).)

> **CAUTION**
> *It makes no difference which point is (x_1, y_1) or (x_2, y_2); however, be consistent.* Start with the *x*- and *y*-values of one point (either one), and subtract the corresponding values of the other point.

◀ *Work Problem* **3** *at the Side.*

The slopes we found for the lines in Figures 22 and 23 suggest the following generalization.

> **Positive and Negative Slopes**
> A line with positive slope rises (slants up) from left to right.
> A line with negative slope falls (slants down) from left to right.

EXAMPLE 3 **Showing that the Slope of a Horizontal Line Is Zero**

Find the slope of the line through $(-8, 4)$ and $(2, 4)$.

$$m = \frac{y_2 - y_1}{x_2 - x_1} = \frac{4 - 4}{-8 - 2} = \frac{0}{-10} = 0 \quad \text{Zero slope}$$

As shown in Figure 24, the line through the given points is horizontal, with equation $y = 4$. *All horizontal lines have slope* **0** since the difference in their y-values is always 0.

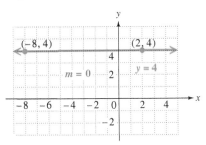

Figure 24

EXAMPLE 4 **Showing that a Vertical Line Has Undefined Slope**

Find the slope of the line through $(6, 2)$ and $(6, -4)$.

$$m = \frac{y_2 - y_1}{x_2 - x_1} = \frac{2 - (-4)}{6 - 6} = \frac{6}{0} \quad \text{Undefined slope}$$

Because division by 0 is undefined, this line has undefined slope. (This is why the slope formula at the beginning of this section had the restriction $x_1 \neq x_2$.) The graph in Figure 25 shows that this line is vertical, with equation $x = 6$. All points on a vertical line have the same x-value, so *all vertical lines have undefined slope.*

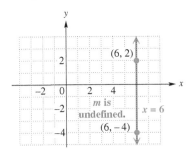

Figure 25

Slopes of Horizontal and Vertical Lines

Horizontal lines, which have equations of the form $y = k$, have **slope 0.**

Vertical lines, which have equations of the form $x = k$, have **undefined slope.**

Work Problem **4** *at the Side.* ▶

4 Find the slope of each line.

(a) The line through $(2, 5)$ and $(-1, 5)$

(b) The line through $(3, 1)$ and $(3, -4)$

(c) The line with equation $y = -1$

(d) The line with equation $x - 4 = 0$

Figure 26 summarizes the four cases for slopes of lines.

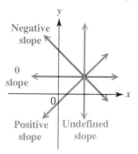

Slopes of lines

Figure 26

OBJECTIVE 2 Find the slope from the equation of a line.
Consider the equation

$$y = -3x + 5.$$

We can find its slope using any two points on the line. We get these two points by first choosing two different values of x and then finding the corresponding values of y. For example, choose $x = -2$ and $x = 4$.

$y = -3x + 5$	$y = -3x + 5$
$y = -3(-2) + 5$ Let $x = -2$.	$y = -3(4) + 5$ Let $x = 4$.
$y = 6 + 5$	$y = -12 + 5$
$y = 11$	$y = -7$

The ordered pairs are $(-2, 11)$ and $(4, -7)$. Now use the slope formula.

$$m = \frac{11 - (-7)}{-2 - 4} = \frac{18}{-6} = -3$$

The slope, $m = -3$, is the same number as the coefficient of x in the equation $y = -3x + 5$. It can be shown that this always happens, *as long as the equation is solved for y.* This fact is used to find the slope of a line from its equation.

Finding the Slope of a Line from Its Equation

Step 1 Solve the equation for y.

Step 2 The slope is given by the coefficient of x.

Note

We will see in **Section 11.4** that the equation $y = -3x + 5$ is written using a special form of the equation of a line, called *slope-intercept form,*

$$y = mx + b.$$

EXAMPLE 5   **Finding Slopes from Equations**

Find the slope of each line.

(a) $2x - 5y = 4$

  Step 1   Solve the equation for y.

$$2x - 5y = 4 \quad \text{Isolate } y \text{ on one side.}$$

$$-5y = -2x + 4 \quad \text{Subtract } 2x.$$

$$y = \frac{2}{5}x - \frac{4}{5} \quad \text{Divide by } -5.$$

  Step 2   The slope is given by the coefficient of x, so the slope is $\frac{2}{5}$.

(b)
$$8x + 4y = 1$$

Solve for y.
$$4y = -8x + 1 \quad \text{Subtract } 8x.$$

$$y = -2x + \frac{1}{4} \quad \text{Divide by } 4.$$

The slope of this line is given by the coefficient of x, which is -2.

Work Problem **5** *at the Side.* ▶

OBJECTIVE **3** **Use slope to determine whether two lines are parallel, perpendicular, or neither.** Two lines in a plane that never intersect are **parallel.** We use slopes to tell whether two lines are parallel. For example, Figure 27 shows the graphs of $x + 2y = 4$ and $x + 2y = -6$. These lines appear to be parallel. Solving $x + 2y = 4$ for y gives $y = -\frac{1}{2}x + 2$. Solving $x + 2y = -6$ for y gives $y = -\frac{1}{2}x - 3$. Both lines have slope $-\frac{1}{2}$. ***Nonvertical parallel lines always have equal slopes.***

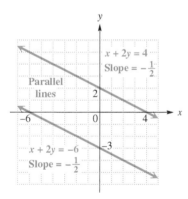

Figure 27

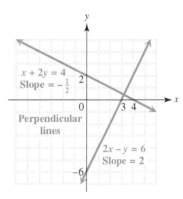

Figure 28

Figure 28 shows the graphs of $x + 2y = 4$ and $2x - y = 6$. These lines appear to be **perpendicular** (that is, they intersect at a 90° angle). Solving $x + 2y = 4$ for y gives $y = -\frac{1}{2}x + 2$, with slope $-\frac{1}{2}$. Solving $2x - y = 6$ for y gives $y = 2x - 6$, with slope 2. The product of $-\frac{1}{2}$ and 2 is

$$-\frac{1}{2}(2) = -1.$$

This condition is true in general. ***The product of the slopes of two perpendicular lines, neither of which is vertical, is always −1.*** This means that the slopes of perpendicular lines are negative (or opposite) reciprocals—if one slope is the nonzero number a, then the other is $-\frac{1}{a}$. The table in the margin shows several examples.

5 Find the slope of each line.

(a) $y = -\dfrac{7}{2}x + 1$

(b) $3x + 2y = 9$

(c) $y + 4 = 0$

(d) $x + 3 = 7$

Number	Negative Reciprocal
$\frac{3}{4}$	$-\frac{4}{3}$
$\frac{1}{2}$	$-\frac{2}{1}$, or -2
-6, or $-\frac{6}{1}$	$\frac{1}{6}$
-0.4, or $-\frac{4}{10}$	$\frac{10}{4}$, or 2.5

The product of each number and its negative reciprocal is −1.

6 Decide whether each pair of lines is *parallel, perpendicular,* or *neither*.

(a) $x + y = 6$
$x + y = 1$

(b) $3x - y = 4$
$x + 3y = 9$

(c) $2x - y = 5$
$2x + y = 3$

(d) $3x - 7y = 35$
$7x - 3y = -6$

> **Slopes of Parallel and Perpendicular Lines**
>
> Two lines with the same slope are parallel.
>
> Two lines whose slopes have a product of -1 are perpendicular.

EXAMPLE 6 **Deciding Whether Lines Are Parallel, Perpendicular, or Neither**

Decide whether each pair of lines is *parallel, perpendicular,* or *neither*.

(a) $x + 2y = 7$
$-2x + y = 3$

Find the slope of each line by first solving each equation for y.

$x + 2y = 7$
$\quad 2y = -x + 7$ Subtract x.
$\quad\quad y = -\dfrac{1}{2}x + \dfrac{7}{2}$ Divide by 2.

Slope is $-\dfrac{1}{2}$.

$-2x + y = 3$
$\quad\quad y = 2x + 3$ Add $2x$.

Slope is 2.

Because the slopes are not equal, the lines are not parallel. Check the product of the slopes: $-\dfrac{1}{2}(2) = -1$. The two lines are perpendicular because the product of their slopes is -1. See Figure 29.

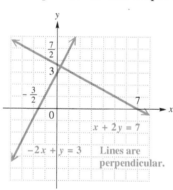

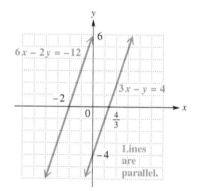

Figure 29

Figure 30

(b) $3x - y = 4$ Solve for y. $y = 3x - 4$
$6x - 2y = -12$ $y = 3x + 6$

Both lines have slope 3, so the lines are parallel. See Figure 30.

(c) $4x + 3y = 6$ $y = -\dfrac{4}{3}x + 2$
$\quad\quad\quad\quad\quad\quad$ Solve for y.
$2x - y = 5$ $y = 2x - 5$

Here the slopes are $-\dfrac{4}{3}$ and 2. Because $-\dfrac{4}{3} \neq 2$ and $-\dfrac{4}{3}(2) \neq -1$, these lines are neither parallel nor perpendicular.

(d) $5x - y = 1$ $y = 5x - 1$
$\quad\quad\quad\quad\quad\quad$ Solve for y.
$x - 5y = -10$ $y = \dfrac{1}{5}x + 2$

The slopes are 5 and $\dfrac{1}{5}$. The lines are not parallel, nor are they perpendicular. (*Be careful!* $5\left(\dfrac{1}{5}\right) = 1$, *not* -1.)

ANSWERS

6. (a) parallel (b) perpendicular
(c) neither (d) neither

11.3 ▶▶▶ **Exercises**

FOR
EXTRA
HELP

Use the coordinates of the indicated points to find the slope of each line. See Example 1.

1.

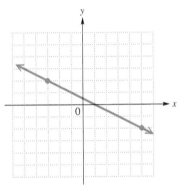

2.

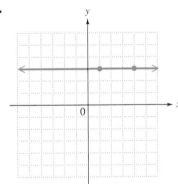

3.

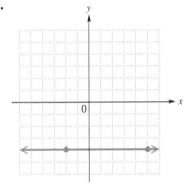

4.

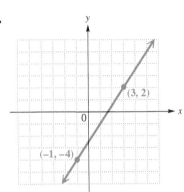

5.

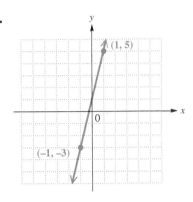

6.

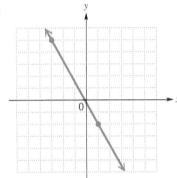

7. In the context of the graph of a straight line, what is meant by "rise"? What is meant by "run"?

8. Look at the graph in Exercise 1, and answer the following.

 (a) Start at the point $(-1, -4)$ and count vertically up to the horizontal line that goes through the other plotted point. What is this vertical change? (Remember: "up" means positive, "down" means negative.) _____

 (b) From this new position, count horizontally to the other plotted point. What is this horizontal change? (Remember: "right" means positive, "left" means negative.) _____

 (c) What is the quotient of the numbers found in parts (a) and (b)? _____
 What do we call this number? _____

 (d) If we were to *start* at the point $(3, 2)$ and *end* at the point $(-1, -4)$, would the answer to part (c) be the same? Explain why or why not.

On the given coordinate system, sketch the graph of a straight line with the indicated slope.

9. Negative

10. Positive

11. Undefined

12. Zero

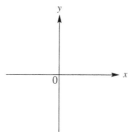

13. Decide whether the line with the given slope rises from left to right, falls from left to right, is horizontal, or is vertical.

    (a) $m = -4$ **(b)** $m = 0$ **(c)** m is undefined.   **(d)** $m = \dfrac{3}{7}$

14. Explain in your own words what is meant by the *slope* of a line.

15. A student found the slope of the line through the points $(2, 5)$ and $(-1, 3)$ and got $-\frac{2}{3}$ as his answer. He showed his work as

$$\frac{3 - 5}{2 - (-1)} = \frac{-2}{3} = -\frac{2}{3}.$$

    WHAT WENT WRONG? Give the correct slope.

Find the slope of the line through each pair of points. See Examples 2–4.

16. $(4, -1)$ and $(-2, -8)$ **17.** $(1, -2)$ and $(-3, -7)$ **18.** $(-8, 0)$ and $(0, -5)$

19. $(0, 3)$ and $(-2, 0)$ **20.** $(-4, -5)$ and $(-5, -8)$ **21.** $(-2, 4)$ and $(-3, 7)$

22. $(6, -5)$ and $(-12, -5)$ **23.** $(4, 3)$ and $(-6, 3)$ **24.** $(-8, 6)$ and $(-8, -1)$

25. $(-12, 3)$ and $(-12, -7)$ **26.** $(3.1, 2.6)$ and $(1.6, 2.1)$ **27.** $\left(-\dfrac{7}{5}, \dfrac{3}{10}\right)$ and $\left(\dfrac{1}{5}, -\dfrac{1}{2}\right)$

Find the slope of each line. See Example 5.

28. $y = 2x - 3$ **29.** $y = 5x + 12$ **30.** $2y = -x + 4$ **31.** $4y = x + 1$

32. $-6x + 4y = 4$ **33.** $3x - 2y = 3$ **34.** $y = 4$ **35.** $y = 6$

36. $x = 5$ **37.** $x = -2$ **38.** $x + y = 0$ **39.** $x - y = 0$

The figure at the right shows a line that has a positive slope (because it rises from left to right) and a positive y-value for the y-intercept (because it intersects the y-axis above the origin).

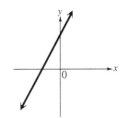

*For each figure in Exercises 40–45, decide whether **(a)** the slope is* positive, negative, *or 0 and whether **(b)** the y-value of the y-intercept is* positive, negative, *or 0.*

40. (a) _____   **41. (a)** _____   **42. (a)** _____

  (b) _____   **(b)** _____   **(b)** _____

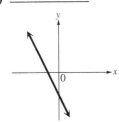   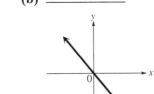   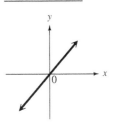

43. (a) _____   **44. (a)** _____   **45. (a)** _____

  (b) _____   **(b)** _____   **(b)** _____

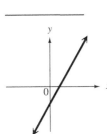   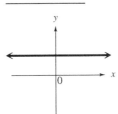   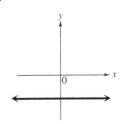

In each pair of equations, give the slope of each line, and then determine whether the two lines are parallel, perpendicular, *or* neither parallel nor perpendicular. *See Example 6.*

46. $2x + 5y = 4$ **47.** $-4x + 3y = 4$ **48.** $8x - 9y = 6$
  $4x + 10y = 1$ $-8x + 6y = 0$ $8x + 6y = -5$

49. $5x - 3y = -2$ **50.** $3x - 2y = 6$ **51.** $3x - 5y = -1$
  $3x - 5y = -8$ $2x + 3y = 3$ $5x + 3y = 2$

52. What is the slope (or pitch) of this roof?

53. What is the slope (or grade) of this hill?

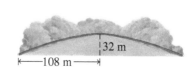

54. What is the slope (or grade) of this ski slope?

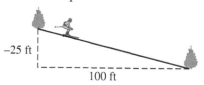

Relating Concepts (Exercises 55–60) For Individual or Group Work

Figure A gives public school enrollment (in thousands) in grades 9–12 in the United States. Figure B gives the (average) number of public school students per computer.

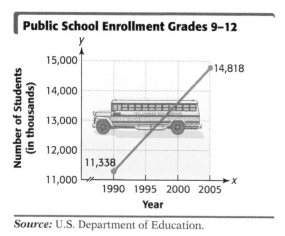

Public School Enrollment Grades 9–12

Number of Students (in thousands)

14,818

11,338

1990 1995 2000 2005

Year

Source: U.S. Department of Education.

Figure A

Students Per Computer

Number of Students Per Computer

20

3.8

'90 '93 '96 '99 '02 '05 '07

Year

Source: Quality Education Data, Inc.

Figure B

Work Exercises 55–60 in order.

55. Use the ordered pairs (1990, 11,338) and (2005, 14,818) to find the slope of the line in Figure A.

56. The slope of the line in Figure A is _____. This means that during
(positive/negative)
the period represented, enrollment _____.
(increased/decreased)

57. The slope of a line represents its *rate of change*. Based on Figure A, what was the increase in students *per year* during the period shown?

58. Use the given information to find the slope, to the nearest hundredth, of the line in Figure B.

59. The slope of the line in Figure B is _____. This means that during
(positive/negative)
the period represented, the number of students per computer _____.
(increased/decreased)

60. Based on Figure B, what was the decrease in students per computer *per year* during the period shown?

11.4 ▶▶▶ Equations of Lines

In **Section 11.3,** we found the slope (steepness) of a line from the equation of the line by solving the equation for y. In that form, the slope is the coefficient of x. For example, the slope of the line with equation $y = 2x + 3$ is 2, the coefficient of x. What does the number 3 represent? If $x = 0$, the equation becomes

$$y = 2(0) + 3$$
$$y = 3.$$

Since $y = 3$ corresponds to $x = 0$, $(0, 3)$ is the y-intercept of the graph of $y = 2x + 3$. An equation like $y = 2x + 3$ that is solved for y is said to be in **slope-intercept form** because both the slope and the y-intercept of the line can be read directly from the equation.

Slope-Intercept Form

The slope-intercept form of the equation of a line with slope m and y-intercept $(0, b)$ is

$$y = mx + b.$$

Slope —↑   ↑— $(0, b)$ is the y-intercept.

REMEMBER: The intercept in slope-intercept form is the y-intercept.

Note

The slope-intercept form is the most useful form for a linear equation because of the information we can determine from it. It is also the form used by graphing calculators and the one that describes a *linear function,* an important concept in mathematics.

OBJECTIVE 1 Write an equation of a line given its slope and y-intercept. Given the slope and y-intercept of a line, we can use the slope-intercept form to write an equation of the line.

EXAMPLE 1 Writing an Equation of a Line

Write an equation of the line with slope $\frac{2}{3}$ and y-intercept $(0, -1)$.
Here $m = \frac{2}{3}$ and $b = -1$, so an equation is

Slope ———↓ ↓——— y-intercept $(0, b)$
$$y = mx + b$$
$$y = \frac{2}{3}x + (-1), \quad \text{or} \quad y = \frac{2}{3}x - 1.$$

Work Problem **1** *at the Side.* ▶

OBJECTIVES

1 Write an equation of a line given its slope and y-intercept.

2 Graph a line given its slope and a point on the line.

3 Write an equation of a line given its slope and any point on the line.

4 Write an equation of a line given two points on the line.

5 Find an equation of a line that fits a data set.

1 Write an equation of the line with the given slope and y-intercept.

(a) slope $\frac{1}{2}$; y-intercept $(0, -4)$

(b) slope -1; y-intercept $(0, 8)$

(c) slope 3; y-intercept $(0, 0)$

(d) slope 0; y-intercept $(0, 2)$

(e) slope 1; y-intercept $(0, 0.75)$

ANSWERS

1. (a) $y = \frac{1}{2}x - 4$ (b) $y = -x + 8$
(c) $y = 3x$ (d) $y = 2$
(e) $y = x + 0.75$

2 Graph $3x - 4y = 8$ by using the slope and y-intercept.

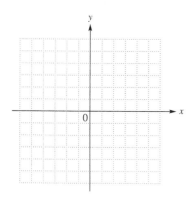

OBJECTIVE 2 **Graph a line given its slope and a point on the line.** We can use the slope and y-intercept to graph a line.

> **Graphing a Line by Using the Slope and y-Intercept**
>
> **Step 1**   Write the equation in slope-intercept form, if necessary, by solving for y.
>
> **Step 2**   Identify the y-intercept. Graph the point $(0, b)$.
>
> **Step 3**   Identify slope m of the line. Use the geometric interpretation of slope ("rise over run") to find another point on the graph by counting from the y-intercept.
>
> **Step 4**   Join the two points with a line to obtain the graph.

EXAMPLE 2   **Graphing a Line by Using the Slope and y-Intercept**

Graph $2x - 3y = 3$ by using the slope and y-intercept.

Step 1   Solve for y to write the equation in slope-intercept form.

$$2x - 3y = 3 \qquad \text{Given equation}$$

Isolate y on one side. →
$$-3y = -2x + 3 \qquad \text{Subtract } 2x.$$

$$y = \frac{2}{3}x - 1 \qquad \text{Divide by } -3.$$

Slope m ⟶   ⟶ y-intercept $(0, b)$

Step 2   The y-intercept is $(0, -1)$. Graph this point. See Figure 31.

Step 3   The slope is $\frac{2}{3}$. By the definition of slope,

$$m = \frac{\text{change in } y}{\text{change in } x} = \frac{2}{3}.$$

Counting from the y-intercept 2 units up and 3 units to the right, we obtain another point on the graph, $(3, 1)$.

Step 4   Draw the line through the points $(0, -1)$ and $(3, 1)$ to obtain the graph of the given equation $2x - 3y = 3$. See Figure 31.

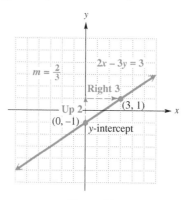

Figure 31

◀ *Work Problem* **2** *at the Side.*

ANSWER

2.

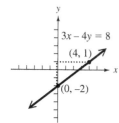

The method of Example 2 can be extended to graph a line given its slope and *any* point on the line.

EXAMPLE 3 **Graphing a Line by Using the Slope and a Point**

Graph the line passing through the point $(-2, 3)$, with slope -4.

First, locate the point $(-2, 3)$. See Figure 32. Then write the slope -4 as

$$\text{slope } m = \frac{\text{change in } y}{\text{change in } x} = -4 = \frac{-4}{1}.$$

Locate another point on the line by counting 4 units *down* (because of the negative sign) from $(-2, 3)$ and then 1 unit to the right. Finally, draw the line through this new point P and the given point $(-2, 3)$. See Figure 32.

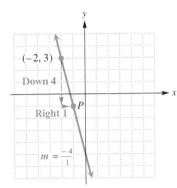

Figure 32

Note

In Example 3, we could have written the slope as $\frac{4}{-1}$ instead. In this case, we would move 4 units up from $(-2, 3)$ and then 1 unit to the *left* (because of the negative sign). Verify that this produces the same line.

Work Problem **3** *at the Side.* ▶

OBJECTIVE **3** **Write an equation of a line given its slope and any point on the line.** We can use the slope-intercept form to write the equation of a line if we know the slope and any point on the line.

EXAMPLE 4 **Using the Slope-Intercept Form to Write an Equation of a Line**

Write an equation, in slope-intercept form, of the line having slope 4 passing through the point $(2, 5)$.

Since the line passes through the point $(2, 5)$, we can substitute $x = 2, y = 5$, and the given slope $m = 4$ into $y = mx + b$ and solve for b.

$$y = mx + b \quad \text{Slope-intercept form}$$
$$5 = 4(2) + b \quad \text{Let } x = 2, y = 5, \text{ and } m = 4.$$

> Remember: $(0, b)$ is the y-intercept. Don't stop here.

$$5 = 8 + b \quad \text{Multiply.}$$
$$-3 = b \quad \text{Subtract 8.}$$

The y-intercept is $(0, -3)$. Using the given slope, 4, an equation of the line is

$$y = 4x - 3. \quad \text{Slope-intercept form}$$

Work Problem **4** *at the Side.* ▶

3 Graph the line passing through the point $(2, -3)$, with slope $-\frac{1}{3}$.

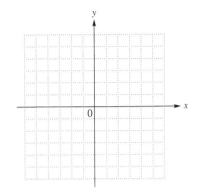

4 Write an equation, in slope-intercept form, of the line having slope -2 and passing through the point $(-1, 4)$.

ANSWERS

3.

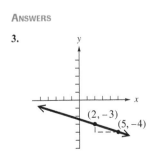

4. $y = -2x + 2$

5 Write an equation of each line. Give the final answer in slope-intercept form.

(a) The line through $(-1, 3)$, with slope -2

$$y - y_1 = m(x - x_1)$$

$$y - \underline{\quad} = \underline{\quad} [x - (\underline{\quad})]$$

$$y - 3 = -2(x + \underline{\quad})$$

$$y - 3 = -2x - \underline{\quad}$$

$$y = \underline{\quad\quad}$$

There is another form that can be used to write the equation of a line. To develop this form, let m represent the slope of a line and let (x_1, y_1) represent a given point on the line. Let (x, y) represent any other point on the line. See Figure 33. Then,

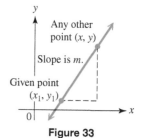

Figure 33

$$m = \frac{y - y_1}{x - x_1} \qquad \text{Definition of slope}$$

$$m(x - x_1) = y - y_1 \qquad \text{Multiply each side by } x - x_1.$$

$$y - y_1 = m(x - x_1). \qquad \text{Rewrite.}$$

This result is the **point-slope form** of the equation of a line.

Point-Slope Form

The point-slope form of the equation of a line with slope m passing through the point (x_1, y_1) is

$$\overset{\text{Slope}}{\underset{\underset{\text{point}}{\text{Given}}}{y - y_1 = m(x - x_1).}}$$

EXAMPLE 5 **Using the Point-Slope Form to Write Equations**

Write an equation of each line. Give the final answer in slope-intercept form.

(a) The line through $(-2, 4)$, with slope -3

The given point is $(-2, 4)$ so $x_1 = -2$ and $y_1 = 4$. Also, $m = -3$. Substitute these values into the point-slope form.

$$y - y_1 = m(x - x_1) \qquad \text{Point-slope form}$$

$$y - 4 = -3[x - (-2)] \qquad \text{Let } x_1 = -2, y_1 = 4, m = -3.$$

$$y - 4 = -3(x + 2) \qquad \fbox{Be careful substituting.}$$

$$y - 4 = -3x - 6 \qquad \text{Distributive property}$$

$$y = -3x - 2 \qquad \text{Add 4.}$$

(b) The line through $(5, 2)$, with slope $-\frac{1}{3}$

(b) The line through $(4, 2)$, with slope $\frac{3}{5}$

$$y - y_1 = m(x - x_1) \qquad \text{Point-slope form}$$

$$y - 2 = \frac{3}{5}(x - 4) \qquad \text{Let } x_1 = 4, y_1 = 2, m = \frac{3}{5}.$$

$$y - 2 = \frac{3}{5}x - \frac{12}{5} \qquad \text{Distributive property}$$

$$y = \frac{3}{5}x - \frac{12}{5} + \frac{10}{5} \qquad \text{Add 2} = \frac{10}{5}.$$

$$y = \frac{3}{5}x - \frac{2}{5} \qquad \text{Combine like terms.}$$

We did not clear fractions after the substitution step because we want the equation in slope-intercept form—that is, solved for y.

◀ *Work Problem* **5** *at the Side.*

ANSWERS

5. (a) $3; -2; -1; 1; 2; -2x + 1$

(b) $y = -\frac{1}{3}x + \frac{11}{3}$

OBJECTIVE **4** **Write an equation of a line given two points on the line.** We can also use the point-slope form to find an equation of a line when two points on the line are known.

EXAMPLE 6 **Writing an Equation of a Line Given Two Points**

Write an equation of the line through the points $(-2, 5)$ and $(3, 4)$. Give the final answer in slope-intercept form.

First, find the slope of the line, using the slope formula.

$$\text{slope } m = \frac{y_2 - y_1}{x_2 - x_1} = \frac{5 - 4}{-2 - 3} = \frac{1}{-5} = -\frac{1}{5}$$

Now use either $(-2, 5)$ or $(3, 4)$ and the point-slope form. Using $(3, 4)$ gives

$$y - y_1 = m(x - x_1) \qquad \text{Point-slope form}$$

$$y - 4 = -\frac{1}{5}(x - 3) \qquad \text{Let } x_1 = 3, y_1 = 4, m = -\frac{1}{5}.$$

$$y - 4 = -\frac{1}{5}x + \frac{3}{5} \qquad \text{Distributive property}$$

$$y = -\frac{1}{5}x + \frac{3}{5} + \frac{20}{5} \qquad \text{Add } 4 = \frac{20}{5}.$$

$$y = -\frac{1}{5}x + \frac{23}{5}. \qquad \text{Combine like terms.}$$

The same result would be found using $(-2, 5)$ for (x_1, y_1).

Work Problem **6** *at the Side.* ▶

> **Note**
>
> In Example 6, the same result would also be found by substituting the slope and either given point in slope-intercept form $y = mx + b$ and then solving for b, as in Example 4. Try this.

Many of the linear equations in **Sections 11.1–11.3** were given in the form

$$Ax + By = C,$$

called **standard form,** where A, B, and C are real numbers and A and B are not both 0. In most cases, A, B, and C are rational numbers. For consistency in this book, we give answers so that A, B, and C are integers with greatest common factor 1 and $A \geq 0$.

> **Note**
>
> The definition of standard form is not the same in all texts. A linear equation can be written in many different, equally correct, ways. For example,
>
> $$3x + 4y = 12, \quad 6x + 8y = 24, \quad \text{and} \quad -9x - 12y = -36$$
>
> all represent the same set of ordered pairs. When giving answers, let us agree that $3x + 4y = 12$ is preferable to the other forms because the greatest common factor of 3, 4, and 12 is 1 and $A \geq 0$.

6 Write an equation in slope-intercept form of the line through each pair of points.

(a) $(-3, 1)$ and $(2, 4)$

(b) $(2, 5)$ and $(-1, 6)$

A summary of the forms of linear equations follows.

Forms of Linear Equations

Equation	Description	Example
$x = k$	**Vertical line** Slope is undefined; x-intercept is $(k, 0)$.	$x = 3$
$y = k$	**Horizontal line** Slope is 0; y-intercept is $(0, k)$.	$y = 3$
$y = mx + b$	**Slope-intercept form** Slope is m; y-intercept is $(0, b)$.	$y = \dfrac{3}{2}x - 6$
$y - y_1 = m(x - x_1)$	**Point-slope form** Slope is m; line passes through (x_1, y_1).	$y + 3 = \dfrac{3}{2}(x - 2)$
$Ax + By = C$	**Standard form** Slope is $-\frac{A}{B}$; x-intercept is $\left(\frac{C}{A}, 0\right)$; y-intercept is $\left(0, \frac{C}{B}\right)$.	$3x - 2y = 12$

OBJECTIVE 5 Find an equation of a line that fits a data set.
Earlier in this chapter, we gave linear equations that modeled real data, such as number of twin births and amounts of credit card debt, and then used these equations to estimate or predict values. We now develop a procedure to find such an equation if the given set of data fits a linear pattern—that is, its graph consists of points lying close to a straight line.

EXAMPLE 7 **Finding an Equation of a Line That Describes Data**

The table lists the average annual cost (in dollars) of tuition and fees for in-state students at public 4-year colleges and universities for selected years. Year 1 represents 2001, year 3 represents 2003, and so on.

Year	Cost (in dollars)
1	3766
3	4645
5	5491
7	6185

Source: The College Board.

Plot the data and find an equation that approximates it.

Letting y represent the cost in year x, we plot the data as shown in Figure 34 on the next page.

Continued on Next Page

**AVERAGE ANNUAL COSTS AT
PUBLIC 4-YEAR COLLEGES**

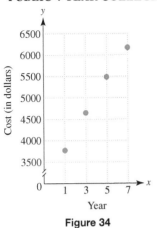

Figure 34

7 Use the points (3, 4645) and (7, 6185) to find an equation in slope-intercept form that approximates the data of Example 7. How well does this equation approximate the cost in 2005?

The points appear to lie approximately in a straight line. We can use two of the data pairs and the slope-intercept form of the equation of a line to get an equation that describes the relationship between the year and the cost. We choose the ordered pairs (5, 5491) and (7, 6185) from the table and find the slope of the line through these points.

$$m = \frac{y_2 - y_1}{x_2 - x_1} = \frac{6185 - 5491}{7 - 5} = 347 \qquad \text{Let } (7, 6185) = (x_2, y_2)$$
$$\text{and } (5, 5491) = (x_1, y_1).$$

As we might expect, the slope, 347, is positive, indicating that tuition and fees *increased* \$347 each year. Now use this slope and the point (5, 5491) in the slope-intercept form to find an equation of the line.

$$y = mx + b \qquad \text{Slope-intercept form}$$

Solve for *b*, the *y*-value of the *y*-intercept.

$$5491 = 347\,(5) + b \qquad \text{Substitute for } x, y, \text{ and } m.$$
$$5491 = 1735 + b \qquad \text{Multiply.}$$
$$3756 = b \qquad \text{Subtract 1735.}$$

Thus, $m = 347$ and $b = 3756$, so an equation of the line is

$$y = 347x + 3756.$$

To see how well this equation approximates the ordered pairs in the data table, let $x = 3$ (for 2003) and find y.

$$y = 347x + 3756 \qquad \text{Equation of the line}$$
$$y = 347\,(3) + 3756 \qquad \text{Substitute 3 for } x.$$
$$y = 4797 \qquad \text{Multiply; add.}$$

The corresponding value in the table for $x = 3$ is 4645, so the equation approximates the data reasonably well. With caution, the equation could be used to predict values for years that are not included in the table.

Note

In Example 7, if we had chosen two different data points, we would have gotten a slightly different equation.

Work Problem **7** *at the Side.* ▶

Answer

7. $y = 385x + 3490$;
   The equation gives $y = 5415$ when $x = 5$, which is a very good approximation.

Math in the Media

The graph shown here is typical of many graphs that appear in magazines and newspapers. This one shows that between 1996 and 2006, the number of McDonald's restaurants worldwide rose from 20,000 to 31,000. This is depicted by the line segment joining the two points labeled A and B.

Use the graph to answer each of the following.

1. To represent point A, write an ordered pair in the form

   (year, number of restaurants in thousands).

   Do this for point B also.

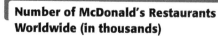

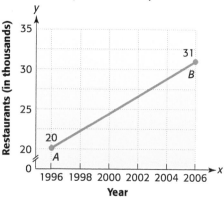

Number of McDonald's Restaurants Worldwide (in thousands)

Source: McDonald's Corp.; Hoovers.

2. The points A and B as well as the points on line AB between them make up line segment AB. We can find the coordinates of a point M on line segment AB that is exactly halfway between A and B. (This point is called the **midpoint** of the segment.)

   (a) To find the x-coordinate of M, we find the average of the x-coordinates of A and B by adding them and dividing by 2. What is the x-coordinate of M?

   (b) To find the y-coordinate of M, we find the average of the y-coordinates of A and B. What is the y-coordinate of M?

3. Fill in the blanks with the appropriate responses: The ordered pair that represents M, the midpoint of segment AB, is (_____, _____). This suggests that in the year _____, there were _____ thousand McDonald's restaurants worldwide.

4. Use the points (1996, 20) and (2006, 31) to find the $y = mx + b$ form of the equation of the line containing A and B.

5. Use the result of Exercise 4 to find the value of y when $x = 2001$. Does this correspond to the result you found in Exercise 2(b)?

6. The actual number of McDonald's restaurants worldwide was 30 thousand in 2001. How does this compare to your answers in Exercises 3 and 5? Explain how a line graph such as this one can be misleading. Use the concept of *slope* in your explanation.

1. Match the correct equation in Column II with the description given in Column I.

I	**II**
(a) Slope -2, the line through the point $(4, 1)$	**A.** $y = 4x$
(b) Slope -2, y-intercept $(0, 1)$	**B.** $y = \dfrac{1}{4}x$
(c) The line through the points $(0, 0)$ and $(4, 1)$	**C.** $y = -2x + 1$
(d) The line through the points $(0, 0)$ and $(1, 4)$	**D.** $y - 1 = -2(x - 4)$

2. In the summary box on page 266, we give the equations $y = \frac{3}{2}x - 6$ and $y + 3 = \frac{3}{2}(x - 2)$ as examples of equations in slope-intercept form and point-slope form, respectively. Write each of these equations in standard form. What do you notice?

Use the geometric interpretation of slope (rise divided by run, from **Section 11.3**) *to find the slope of each line. Then, by identifying the y-intercept from the graph, write the slope-intercept form of the equation of the line.*

3.

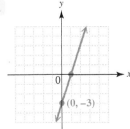

4.

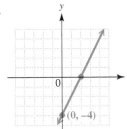

5.

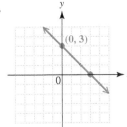

6.

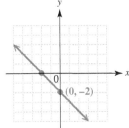

7.

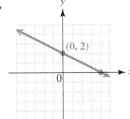

8.

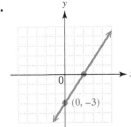

Write the equation of the line with the given slope and y-intercept. See Example 1.

9. slope 4;
 y-intercept $(0, -3)$

10. slope -5;
 y-intercept $(0, 6)$

11. slope 0;
 y-intercept $(0, 3)$

12. slope 3;
 y-intercept $(0, 0)$

13. Match each equation with the graph that would most closely resemble its graph.

(a) $y = x + 3$

(b) $y = -x + 3$

(c) $y = x - 3$

(d) $y = -x - 3$

A.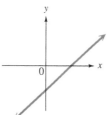

B.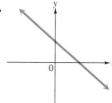

C.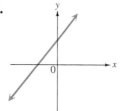

D.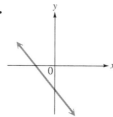

14. Explain why the equation of a vertical line cannot be written in the form $y = mx + b$.

Graph each equation by finding the slope and y-intercept, and using their definitions to find two points on the line. See Example 2.

15. $y = 3x + 2$

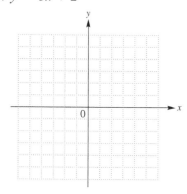

16. $y = 4x - 4$

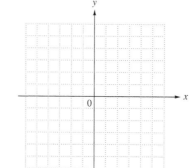

17. $2x + y = -5$

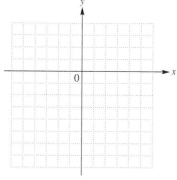

18. $3x + y = -2$

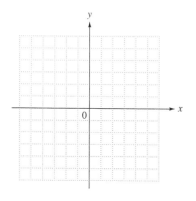

19. $x + 2y = 4$

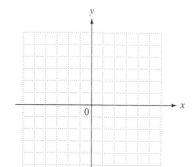

20. $x + 3y = 12$

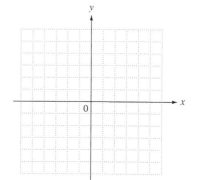

Graph each line passing through the given point and having the given slope. (In Exercises 25–28, recall the types of lines having slope 0 and undefined slope.) Give the slope-intercept form of the equation of the line if possible. See Example 3.

21. $(-2, 3)$, $m = \dfrac{1}{2}$

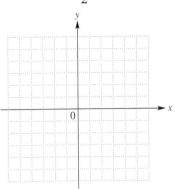

22. $(-4, -1)$, $m = \dfrac{3}{4}$

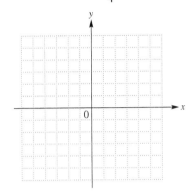

🌐 **23.** $(1, -5)$, $m = -\dfrac{2}{5}$

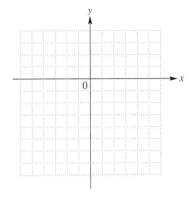

24. $(2, -1)$, $m = -\dfrac{1}{3}$

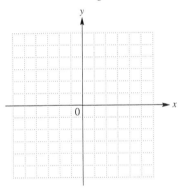

25. $(3, 2)$, $m = 0$

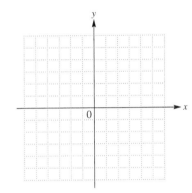

26. $(-2, 3)$, $m = 0$

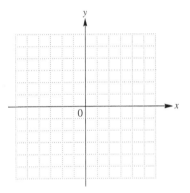

27. $(3, -2)$, undefined slope

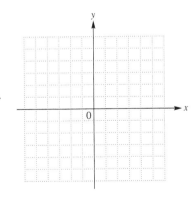

28. $(2, 4)$, undefined slope

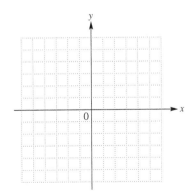

29. $(0, 0)$, $m = \dfrac{2}{3}$

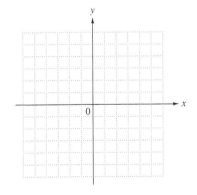

30. (a) What is the common name given to the vertical line whose x-intercept is the origin?

(b) What is the common name given to the line with slope 0 whose y-intercept is the origin?

Write an equation of the line passing through the given point and having the given slope. Give the final answer in slope-intercept form. See Examples 4 and 5.

31. $(4, 1)$, $m = 2$

32. $(2, 7)$, $m = 3$

33. $(3, -10)$, $m = -2$

34. $(2, -5)$, $m = -4$

35. $(-2, 5)$, $m = \dfrac{2}{3}$

36. $(-4, 1)$, $m = \dfrac{3}{4}$

Write an equation of the line passing through each pair of points. Give the final answer in slope-intercept form, if possible. See Example 6.

37. $(8, 5)$ and $(9, 6)$

38. $(4, 10)$ and $(6, 12)$

39. $(-1, -7)$ and $(-8, -2)$

40. $(-2, -1)$ and $(3, -4)$

41. $(0, -2)$ and $(-3, 0)$

42. $(-4, 0)$ and $(0, 2)$

43. $(3, 5)$ and $(3, -2)$

44. $(3, -5)$ and $(-1, -5)$

45. $\left(\dfrac{1}{2}, \dfrac{3}{2}\right)$ and $\left(-\dfrac{1}{4}, \dfrac{5}{4}\right)$

46. $\left(-\dfrac{2}{3}, \dfrac{8}{3}\right)$ and $\left(\dfrac{1}{3}, \dfrac{7}{3}\right)$

Write an equation of the line satisfying the given conditions. Give the final answer in slope-intercept form.

47. The line through $(2, -3)$, parallel to $3x = 4y + 5$

48. The line through $(-1, 4)$, perpendicular to $2x + 3y = 8$

49. The line perpendicular to $x - 2y = 7$, y-intercept $(0, -3)$

50. The line parallel to $5x = 2y + 10$, y-intercept $(0, 4)$

Relating Concepts (Exercises 51–58) For Individual or Group Work

If we think of ordered pairs of the form (C, F), then the two most common methods of measuring temperature, Celsius and Fahrenheit, can be related as follows: When C = 0, F = 32, and when C = 100, F = 212. **Work Exercises 51–58 in order.**

51. Write two ordered pairs relating these two temperature scales.

52. Find the slope of the line through the two points.

53. Use the point-slope form to find an equation of the line. (Your variables should be C and F rather than x and y.)

54. Write an equation for F in terms of C.

55. Use the equation from Exercise 54 to write an equation for C in terms of F.

56. Use the equation from Exercise 54 to find the Fahrenheit temperature when $C = 30$.

57. Use the equation from Exercise 55 to find the Celsius temperature when $F = 50$.

58. For what temperature is $F = C$?

*The cost to produce x items is, in some cases, expressed as y = mx + b. The number b gives the **fixed cost** (the cost that is the same no matter how many items are produced), and the number m is the **variable cost** (the cost to produce an additional item). Use this information to work Exercises 59 and 60.*

59. It costs $400 to start up a business selling campaign buttons. Each button costs $0.25 to produce.

(a) What is the fixed cost?

(b) What is the variable cost?

(c) Write the cost equation.

(d) What will be the cost to produce 100 campaign buttons, based on the cost equation?

(e) How many campaign buttons will be produced if total cost is $775?

60. It costs $2000 to purchase a copier, and each copy costs $0.02 to make.

(a) What is the fixed cost?

(b) What is the variable cost?

(c) Write the cost equation.

(d) What will be the cost to produce 10,000 copies, based on the cost equation?

(e) How many copies will be produced if total cost is $2600?

▦ *Solve each problem. See Example 7.*

61. The table lists the average annual cost (in dollars) of tuition and fees at 2-year colleges for selected years, where year 1 represents 2003, year 2 represents 2004, and so on.

Year	Cost (in dollars)
1	1909
2	2079
3	2182
4	2272
5	2361

Source: The College Board.

(a) Write five ordered pairs for the data.

(b) Plot the ordered pairs. Do the points lie approximately in a straight line?

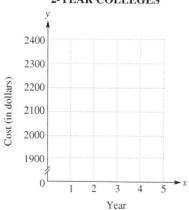

AVERAGE ANNUAL COSTS AT
2-YEAR COLLEGES

(c) Use the ordered pairs (2, 2079) and (5, 2361) to find the equation of a line that approximates the data. Write the final equation in slope-intercept form.

(d) Use the equation from part (c) to estimate the average annual cost at 2-year colleges in 2008 to the nearest dollar. (*Hint:* What is the value of x for 2008?)

62. The table gives heavy-metal nuclear waste (in thousands of metric tons) from spent reactor fuel now stored temporarily at reactor sites, awaiting permanent storage. (*Source:* "Burial of Radioactive Nuclear Waste Under the Seabed," *Scientific American*, January 1998.)

Year x	Waste y
1995	32
2000	42
2010*	61
2020*	76

*Estimates by the U.S. Department of Energy.

Let $x = 0$ represent 1995, $x = 5$ represent 2000 (since $2000 - 1995 = 5$), and so on.

(a) For 1995, the ordered pair is (0, 32). Write ordered pairs for the data for the other years given in the table.

(b) Plot the ordered pairs (x, y). Do the points lie approximately in a straight line?

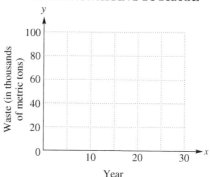

HEAVY-METAL NUCLEAR
WASTE AWAITING STORAGE

(c) Use the ordered pairs (0, 32) and (25, 76) to find the equation of a line that approximates the data. Write the equation in slope-intercept form.

(d) Use the equation from part (c) to estimate the amount of nuclear waste in 2015. (*Hint:* What is the value of x for 2015?)

12

Exponents/Polynomials

12.1 ▶▶▶ Adding and Subtracting Polynomials

OBJECTIVES

1. Review combining like terms.
2. Know the vocabulary for polynomials.
3. Evaluate polynomials.
4. Add polynomials.
5. Subtract polynomials.
6. Add and subtract polynomials with more than one variable.

Recall from **Section 4.2** that in an expression such as

$$4x^3 + 6x^2 + 5x + 8,$$

the quantities that are added, $4x^3$, $6x^2$, $5x$, and 8, are called **terms.** In the term $4x^3$, the number 4 is called the **numerical coefficient,** or simply the **coefficient,** of x^3. In the same way, 6 is the coefficient of x^2 in the term $6x^2$, 5 is the coefficient of x in the term $5x$, and 8 is the **constant** term. Other examples are given in the table at the side.

OBJECTIVE 1 Review combining like terms. Recall from **Section 4.2** that **like terms** have exactly the same combination of variables, with the same exponents on the variables. *Only the coefficients may differ.*

$$\left.\begin{array}{ll} 19m^5 \quad \text{and} \quad 14m^5 \\ -37y^9 \quad \text{and} \quad y^9 \\ 3pq \quad \text{and} \quad -2pq \\ 2xy^2 \quad \text{and} \quad -xy^2 \end{array}\right\} \begin{array}{c}\text{Examples}\\\text{of}\\\text{like terms}\end{array} \qquad \left.\begin{array}{ll} 7x \quad \text{and} \quad 7y \\ z^4 \quad \text{and} \quad z \\ 2pq \quad \text{and} \quad 2p \\ -4xy^2 \quad \text{and} \quad 5x^2y \end{array}\right\} \begin{array}{c}\text{Examples}\\\text{of}\\\text{unlike terms}\end{array}$$

Using the distributive property, we combine, or add, like terms by adding their coefficients.

Term	Numerical Coefficient
$-7y$	-7
$34r^3$	34
$-26x^5yz^4$	-26
$-k = -1k$	-1
$r = 1r$	1
$\frac{3x}{8} = \frac{3}{8}x$	$\frac{3}{8}$
$\frac{x}{3} = \frac{1x}{3} = \frac{1}{3}x$	$\frac{1}{3}$

EXAMPLE 1 Adding Like Terms

Simplify each expression by adding like terms.

(a) $-4x^3 + 6x^3$

$= (-4 + 6)x^3$ Distributive property

$= 2x^3$

(b) $9x^6 - 14x^6 + x^6$

$= (9 - 14 + 1)x^6$ $x^6 = 1x^6$

$= -4x^6$

(c) $12m^2 + 5m + 4m^2$

$= (12 + 4)m^2 + 5m$

$= 16m^2 + 5m$

(d) $3x^2y + 4x^2y - x^2y$

$= (3 + 4 - 1)x^2y$

$= 6x^2y$

1 Add like terms.

(a) $5x^4 + 7x^4$

(b) $9pq + 3pq - 2pq$

(c) $r^2 + 3r + 5r^2$

(d) $x + \dfrac{1}{2}x$

(e) $8t + 6w$

(f) $3x^4 - 3x^2$

In Example 1(c), we cannot combine $16m^2$ and $5m$. These two terms are unlike because the exponents on the variables are different. *Unlike terms have different variables or different exponents on the same variables.*

◀ Work Problem **1** at the Side.

OBJECTIVE 2 Know the vocabulary for polynomials. A **polynomial in x** is a term or the sum of a finite number of terms of the form ax^n, for any real number a and any whole number n. For example,

$$16x^8 - 7x^6 + 5x^4 - 3x^2 + 4 \qquad \text{Polynomial}$$

is a polynomial in x. This polynomial is written in **descending powers,** because the exponents on x decrease from left to right.

ANSWERS

1. **(a)** $12x^4$ **(b)** $10pq$ **(c)** $6r^2 + 3r$ **(d)** $\dfrac{3}{2}x$

   (e) These are unlike terms. They cannot be added.

   (f) These are unlike terms. They cannot be added.

On the other hand, $2x^3 - x^2 + \frac{4}{x}$ is not a polynomial, since a variable appears in a denominator. We can define a *polynomial* using any variable, not just x, as in Example 1(c). Polynomials may have terms with more than one variable, as in Example 1(d).

Work Problem **2** *at the Side.* ▶

The **degree of a term** is the sum of the exponents on the variables. A constant term has degree 0. For example, $3x^4$ has degree 4, while $6x^{17}$ has degree 17. The term $5x$ (or $5x^1$) has degree 1, -7 has degree 0, and $2x^2y$ has degree $2 + 1 = 3$ (y has an exponent of 1).

The **degree of a polynomial** is the greatest degree of any nonzero term of the polynomial. For example, $3x^4 - 5x^2 + 6$ is of degree 4, the polynomial $5x + 7$ is of degree 1, 3 is of degree 0, and $x^2y + xy - 5xy^2$ is of degree 3.

Three types of polynomials are very common and are given special names. A polynomial with only one term is called a **monomial.** (*Mono-* means "one," as in *mono*rail.) Examples are

$$9m, \quad -6y^5, \quad a^2, \quad \text{and} \quad 6. \quad \text{Monomials}$$

A polynomial with exactly two terms is called a **binomial.** (*Bi-* means "two," as in *bi*cycle.) Examples are

$$-9x^4 + 9x^3, \quad 8m^2 + 6m, \quad \text{and} \quad 3m^5 - 9m^2. \quad \text{Binomials}$$

A polynomial with exactly three terms is called a **trinomial.** (*Tri-* means "three," as in *tri*angle.) Examples are

$$9m^3 - 4m^2 + 6, \quad \frac{19}{3}y^2 + \frac{8}{3}y + 5, \quad \text{and} \quad -3m^5 - 9m^2 + 2. \quad \text{Trinomials}$$

EXAMPLE 2 **Classifying Polynomials**

Simplify each polynomial if possible. Then give the degree and tell whether the polynomial is a *monomial,* a *binomial,* a *trinomial,* or *none of these.*

(a) $2x^3 + 5$ We cannot simplify further. This is a binomial of degree 3.

(b) $4x - 5x + 2x$
    Add like terms to simplify: $4x - 5x + 2x = x$. The degree is 1 (since $x = x^1$). The simplified polynomial is a monomial.

Work Problem **3** *at the Side.* ▶

OBJECTIVE **3** **Evaluate polynomials.**   A polynomial usually represents different numbers for different values of the variable.

EXAMPLE 3 **Evaluating a Polynomial**

Find the value of $3x^4 + 5x^3 - 4x - 4$ when $x = -2$ and when $x = 3$.
    First, substitute -2 for x.

$$3x^4 + 5x^3 - 4x - 4$$

| Use parentheses to avoid errors. | $= 3(-2)^4 + 5(-2)^3 - 4(-2) - 4$ | Let $x = -2$. |

$$= 3(16) + 5(-8) - 4(-2) - 4 \quad \text{Apply the exponents.}$$

$$= 48 - 40 + 8 - 4 \quad \text{Multiply.}$$

$$= 12 \quad \text{Add and subtract.}$$

Continued on Next Page

---

2 Choose all descriptions that apply for each of the expressions in parts (a)–(d).

    A. Polynomial
    B. Polynomial written in descending powers
    C. Not a polynomial

(a) $3m^5 + 5m^2 - 2m + 1$

(b) $2p^4 + p^6$

(c) $\frac{1}{x} + 2x^2 + 3$

(d) $x - 3$

3 Simplify each polynomial if possible. Then give the degree and tell whether the polynomial is a *monomial, binomial, trinomial,* or *none of these.*

(a) $3x^2 + 2x - 4$

(b) $x^3 + 4x^3$

(c) $x^8 - x^7 + 2x^8$

ANSWERS

2. (a) A and B   **(b)** A   **(c)** C   **(d)** A and B
3. (a) degree 2; trinomial
    (b) degree 3; monomial (simplify to $5x^3$)
    (c) degree 8; binomial (simplify to $3x^8 - x^7$)

4 Find the value of
$2x^3 + 8x - 6$ in each case.

(a) When $x = -1$

(b) When $x = 4$

Next, replace x with 3.

$3x^4 + 5x^3 - 4x - 4$

$= 3(3)^4 + 5(3)^3 - 4(3) - 4$ Let $x = 3$.

$= 3(81) + 5(27) - 4(3) - 4$ Apply the exponents.

$= 243 + 135 - 12 - 4$ Multiply.

$= 362$ Add and subtract.

> **CAUTION**
> Use parentheses around the numbers that are substituted for the variable in Example 3, particularly when substituting a negative number for a variable that is raised to a power. Otherwise, a sign error may result.

◀ *Work Problem* **4** *at the Side.*

OBJECTIVE **4** **Add polynomials.** Polynomials may be added, subtracted, multiplied, and divided.

> **Adding Polynomials**
> To add two polynomials, add like terms.

5 Add each pair of polynomials.

(a) $4x^3 - 3x^2 + 2x$ and
$6x^3 + 2x^2 - 3x$

(b) $x^2 - 2x + 5$ and
$4x^2 - 2$

EXAMPLE 4 **Adding Polynomials Vertically**

(a) Add $6x^3 - 4x^2 + 3$ and $-2x^3 + 7x^2 - 5$.
Write like terms in columns.

$$6x^3 - 4x^2 + 3$$
$$\underline{-2x^3 + 7x^2 - 5}$$

Now add, column by column.

$$\begin{array}{ccc} 6x^3 & -4x^2 & 3 \\ \underline{-2x^3} & \underline{7x^2} & \underline{-5} \\ 4x^3 & 3x^2 & -2 \end{array}$$

Add the three sums together.

$$4x^3 + 3x^2 + (-2) = 4x^3 + 3x^2 - 2$$

(b) Add $2x^2 - 4x + 3$ and $x^3 + 5x$.
Write like terms in columns and add column by column.

$$2x^2 - 4x + 3$$
$$\underline{x^3 \qquad\quad + 5x}$$
$$x^3 + 2x^2 + \quad x + 3$$

> Leave spaces for missing terms.

◀ *Work Problem* **5** *at the Side.*

The polynomials in Example 4 also could be added horizontally.

ANSWERS

4. (a) -16 (b) 154
5. (a) $10x^3 - x^2 - x$ (b) $5x^2 - 2x + 3$

EXAMPLE 5 **Adding Polynomials Horizontally**

(a) Add $6x^3 - 4x^2 + 3$ and $-2x^3 + 7x^2 - 5$.
Combine like terms.

$(6x^3 - 4x^2 + 3) + (-2x^3 + 7x^2 - 5) = 4x^3 + 3x^2 - 2$ Same answer found in Example 4(a)

(b) Add $2x^2 - 4x + 3$ and $x^3 + 5x$.

$$(2x^2 - 4x + 3) + (x^3 + 5x)$$
$$= x^3 + 2x^2 - 4x + 5x + 3 \qquad \text{Commutative property}$$
$$= x^3 + 2x^2 + x + 3 \qquad \text{Combine like terms.}$$

Work Problem **6** *at the Side.* ▶

6 Find each sum.

(a) $(2x^4 - 6x^2 + 7)$
$\qquad + (-3x^4 + 5x^2 + 2)$

(b) $(3x^2 + 4x + 2)$
$\qquad + (6x^3 - 5x - 7)$

OBJECTIVE **5** **Subtract polynomials.** In **Section 3.3**, the difference $x - y$ was defined as $x + (-y)$. (We find the difference $x - y$ by adding x and the opposite of y.) For example,

$$7 - 2 = 7 + (-2) = 5 \quad \text{and} \quad -8 - (-2) = -8 + 2 = -6.$$

A similar method is used to subtract polynomials.

Subtracting Polynomials

To subtract two polynomials, change all the signs of the second polynomial and add the result to the first polynomial.

7 Subtract, and check your answers by addition.

(a) $(14y^3 - 6y^2 + 2y - 5)$
$\qquad - (2y^3 - 7y^2 - 4y + 6)$

EXAMPLE 6 **Subtracting Polynomials**

(a) Perform the subtraction $(5x - 2) - (3x - 8)$.
Change the signs in the second polynomial and add.

$$(5x - 2) - (3x - 8)$$
$$= (5x - 2) + (-3x + 8)$$
$$= 2x + 6$$

(b) Subtract $6x^3 - 4x^2 + 2$ from $11x^3 + 2x^2 - 8$.

$$(11x^3 + 2x^2 - 8) - (6x^3 - 4x^2 + 2) \quad \text{— Write the problem in the correct order.}$$
$$= (11x^3 + 2x^2 - 8) + (-6x^3 + 4x^2 - 2)$$
$$= 5x^3 + 6x^2 - 10$$

To check a subtraction problem, use the following fact:

$$\text{If} \quad a - b = c, \quad \text{then} \quad a = b + c.$$

For example, $6 - 2 = 4$, so we check by writing $6 = 2 + 4$, which is correct. We check the polynomial subtraction above as follows:

$$(6x^3 - 4x^2 + 2) + (5x^3 + 6x^2 - 10)$$
$$= 11x^3 + 2x^2 - 8.$$

Since the sum is $11x^3 + 2x^2 - 8$, the subtraction was performed correctly.

Work Problem **7** *at the Side.* ▶

(b) Subtract

$$\left(-\frac{3}{2}y^2 + \frac{4}{3}y + 6 \right)$$

from $\left(\frac{7}{2}y^2 - \frac{11}{3}y + 8 \right)$.

ANSWERS

6. (a) $-x^4 - x^2 + 9$
    (b) $6x^3 + 3x^2 - x - 5$
7. (a) $12y^3 + y^2 + 6y - 11$
    (b) $5y^2 - 5y + 2$

8 Subtract by columns.

$(4y^3 - 16y^2 + 2y)$
$\quad - (12y^3 - 9y^2 + 16)$

Subtraction also can be done in columns. We use vertical subtraction in **Section 12.7** when we study polynomial division.

EXAMPLE 7   Subtracting Polynomials Vertically

Subtract by columns: $(14y^3 - 6y^2 + 2y - 5) - (2y^3 - 7y^2 - 4y + 6)$.

$$\begin{array}{l} 14y^3 - 6y^2 + 2y - 5 \\ \underline{2y^3 - 7y^2 - 4y + 6} \end{array} \quad \text{Arrange like terms in columns.}$$

Change all signs in the second row, and then add.

$$\begin{array}{l} 14y^3 - 6y^2 + 2y - 5 \\ \underline{-2y^3 + 7y^2 + 4y - 6} \quad \text{Change signs.} \\ 12y^3 + y^2 + 6y - 11 \quad \text{Add.} \end{array}$$

◀ *Work Problem* **8** *at the Side.*

9 Perform the indicated operations.

$(6p^4 - 8p^3 + 2p - 1)$
$\quad - (-7p^4 + 6p^2 - 12)$
$\quad + (p^4 - 3p + 8)$

EXAMPLE 8   Adding and Subtracting More Than Two Polynomials

Perform the indicated operations to simplify the expression

$$(4 - x + 3x^2) - (2 - 3x + 5x^2) + (8 + 2x - 4x^2).$$

Rewrite, changing the subtraction to adding the opposite.

$(4 - x + 3x^2) - (2 - 3x + 5x^2) + (8 + 2x - 4x^2)$
$= (4 - x + 3x^2) + (-2 + 3x - 5x^2) + (8 + 2x - 4x^2)$
$= (2 + 2x - 2x^2) + (8 + 2x - 4x^2)$ Combine like terms.
$= 10 + 4x - 6x^2$ Combine like terms.

◀ *Work Problem* **9** *at the Side.*

10 Add or subtract.

(a) $(3mn + 2m - 4n)$
$\quad + (-mn + 4m + n)$

OBJECTIVE **6** **Add and subtract polynomials with more than one variable.**   Polynomials in more than one variable are added and subtracted by combining like terms, just as with single-variable polynomials.

EXAMPLE 9   Adding and Subtracting Multivariable Polynomials

Add or subtract as indicated.

(a) $(4a + 2ab - b) + (3a - ab + b)$
$\quad = 4a + 2ab - b + 3a - ab + b$
$\quad = 7a + ab$ Combine like terms.

(b) $(5p^2q^2 - 4p^2 + 2q)$
$\quad - (2p^2q^2 - p^2 - 3q)$

(b) $(2x^2y + 3xy + y^2) - (3x^2y - xy - 2y^2)$
$\quad = 2x^2y + 3xy + y^2 - 3x^2y + xy + 2y^2$
$\quad = -x^2y + 4xy + 3y^2$ Be careful with signs.

◀ *Work Problem* **10** *at the Side.*

ANSWERS
8. $-8y^3 - 7y^2 + 2y - 16$
9. $14p^4 - 8p^3 - 6p^2 - p + 19$
10. (a) $2mn + 6m - 3n$
   (b) $3p^2q^2 - 3p^2 + 5q$

12.1 ▶▶▶ **Exercises**

FOR
EXTRA
HELP   **MyMathLab**   Math XL
PRACTICE   WATCH   DOWNLOAD   READ   REVIEW

Fill in each blank with the correct response.

1. In the term $7x^5$, the coefficient is _____ and the exponent is _____.

2. The expression $5x^3 - 4x^2$ has _____ term(s).
                                    (how many?)

3. The degree of the term $-4x^8$ is _____.

4. The polynomial $4x^2 - y^2$ _____ an example of a trinomial.
                                  (is/is not)

5. When $x^2 + 10$ is evaluated for $x = 4$, the result is _____.

6. _____ is an example of a monomial with coefficient 5, in the variable x, having degree 9.

For each polynomial, determine the number of terms, and name the coefficient of each term.

7. $6x^4$ **8.** $-9y^5$ **9.** t^4 **10.** s^7 **11.** $\dfrac{x}{5}$ **12.** $\dfrac{z}{8}$

13. $-19r^2 - r$ **14.** $2y^3 - y$ **15.** $x - 8x^2 + \dfrac{2}{3}x^3$ **16.** $v - 2v^3 + \dfrac{3}{4}v^2$

In each polynomial, combine like terms whenever possible. Write the result with descending powers. See Example 1.

17. $-3m^5 + 5m^5$ **18.** $-4y^3 + 3y^3$ **19.** $2r^5 + (-3r^5)$ **20.** $-19y^2 + 9y^2$

21. $\dfrac{1}{2}x^4 + \dfrac{1}{6}x^4$ **22.** $\dfrac{3}{10}x^6 + \dfrac{1}{5}x^6$ **23.** $0.2m^5 - 0.5m^2$ **24.** $-0.9y + 0.9y^2$

25. $-3x^5 + 2x^5 - 4x^5$ **26.** $6x^3 - 8x^3 + 9x^3$ **27.** $-4p^7 + 8p^7 + 5p^9$

28. $-3a^8 + 4a^8 - 3a^2$ **29.** $-4y^2 + 3y^2 - 2y^2 + y^2$ **30.** $3r^5 - 8r^5 + r^5 + 2r^5$

For each polynomial, first simplify, if possible, and write it with descending powers. Then give the degree of the resulting polynomial, and tell whether it is a monomial, a binomial, a trinomial, or none of these. See Example 2.

31. $6x^4 - 9x$ **32.** $7t^3 - 3t$ **33.** $5m^4 - 3m^2 + 6m^5 - 7m^3$

34. $6p^5 + 4p^3 - 8p^4 + 10p^2$

35. $\dfrac{5}{3}x^4 - \dfrac{2}{3}x^4 + \dfrac{1}{3}x^2 - 4$

36. $\dfrac{4}{5}r^6 + \dfrac{1}{5}r^6 - r^4 + \dfrac{2}{5}r$

37. $0.8x^4 - 0.3x^4 - 0.5x^4 + 7$

38. $1.2t^3 - 0.9t^3 - 0.3t^3 + 9$

39. $2.5x^2 + 0.5x + x^2 - x - 2x^2$

*Find the value of each polynomial **(a)** when $x = 2$ and **(b)** when $x = -1$. See Example 3.*

40. $5x - 4$

41. $-2x + 3$

42. $-3x^2 + 14x - 2$

43. $2x^2 + 5x + 1$

44. $x^4 - 6x^3 + x^2 + 1$

45. $2x^5 - 4x^4 + 5x^3 - x^2$ **46.** $2x^6 - 4x$

47. $-4x^5 + x^2$

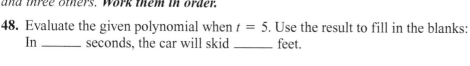

Relating Concepts (Exercises 48–52) For Individual or Group Work

A polynomial can model the distance in feet that a car going approximately 68 mph will skid in t seconds. If we let D represent this distance, then

$$D = 100t - 13t^2.$$

*Each time we evaluate this polynomial for a value of t, we get one and only one output value D. This idea is basic to the concept of a **function,** an important concept in mathematics. Exercises 48–52 illustrate this idea with this polynomial and three others. **Work them in order.***

48. Evaluate the given polynomial when $t = 5$. Use the result to fill in the blanks: In _____ seconds, the car will skid _____ feet.

49. Use the polynomial equation $D = 100t - 13t^2$ to find the distance the car will skid in 1 sec. Write an ordered pair of the form (t, D).

50. If gasoline costs \$4.00 per gal, then the monomial $4.00x$ gives the cost, in dollars, of x gallons. How much would 4 gal cost?

51. If it costs \$15 plus \$2 per day to rent a chain saw, the binomial $2x + 15$ gives the cost in dollars to rent the chain saw for x days. How much would it cost to rent the saw for 6 days?

52. If an object is projected upward under certain conditions, its height in feet is given by the trinomial $-16t^2 + 60t + 80$, where t is in seconds. Evaluate this trinomial for $t = 2.5$, and then use the result to fill in the blanks: If _____ seconds have elapsed, the height of the object is _____ feet.

Add or subtract as indicated. See Examples 4 and 7.

53. Add.
$$3m^2 + 5m$$
$$\underline{2m^2 - 2m}$$

54. Add.
$$4a^3 - 4a^2$$
$$\underline{6a^3 + 5a^2}$$

55. Subtract.
$$12x^4 - x^2$$
$$\underline{8x^4 + 3x^2}$$

56. Subtract.
$$13y^5 - y^3$$
$$\underline{7y^5 + 5y^3}$$

57. Add.
$$\frac{2}{3}x^2 + \frac{1}{5}x + \frac{1}{6}$$
$$\underline{\frac{1}{2}x^2 - \frac{1}{3}x + \frac{2}{3}}$$

58. Add.
$$\frac{4}{7}y^2 - \frac{1}{5}y + \frac{7}{9}$$
$$\underline{\frac{1}{3}y^2 - \frac{1}{3}y + \frac{2}{5}}$$

59. Subtract.
$$12m^3 - 8m^2 + 6m + 7$$
$$\underline{\qquad 5m^2 \qquad - 4}$$

60. Subtract.
$$5a^4 - 3a^3 + 2a^2 - a + 6$$
$$\underline{-6a^4 \qquad - a^2 + a - 1}$$

61. Subtract.
$$4.3x^3 - 6.1x^2 - 3.0x - 5$$
$$\underline{1.4x^3 - 2.6x^2 - 1.5x + 4}$$

Perform the indicated operations. See Examples 5, 6, and 8.

62. $(3r^2 + 5r - 6) + (2r - 5r^2)$

63. $(2r^2 + 3r - 12) + (6r^2 + 2r)$

64. $(x^2 + x) - (3x^2 + 2x - 1)$

65. $(8m^2 - 7m) - (3m^2 + 7m - 6)$

66. $(-2b^6 + 3b^4 - b^2) + (b^6 + 2b^4 + 2b^2)$

67. $(16x^3 - x^2 + 3x) + (-12x^3 + 3x^2 + 2x)$

68. $(8t^5 + 3t^3 + 5t) - (19t^4 - 6t^2 + t)$

69. $(7y^4 + 3y^2 + 2y) - (18y^5 - 5y^3 + y)$

70. $[(9b^3 - 4b^2 + 3b + 2) - (-2b^3 + b)] - (8b^3 + 6b + 4)$

71. $[(8m^2 + 4m - 7) - (2m^3 - 5m + 2)] - (m^2 + m)$

72. Subtract $-5w^3 + 5w^2 - 7$ from $6w^3 + 8w + 5$.

73. Subtract $9x^2 - 3x + 7$ from $-2x^2 - 6x + 4$.

74. Find the difference when $9x^4 + 3x^2 + 5$ is subtracted from $8x^4 - 2x^3 + x - 1$.

Find a polynomial that represents the perimeter of each square, rectangle, or triangle.

75.
$\frac{1}{2}x^2 + 2x$

76.
$\frac{3}{4}x^2 + x$

77.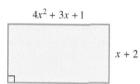
$4x^2 + 3x + 1$

$x + 2$

78.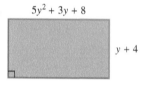
$5y^2 + 3y + 8$

$y + 4$

79.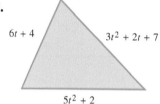
$6t + 4$ $3t^2 + 2t + 7$

$5t^2 + 2$

80.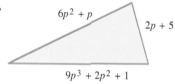
$6p^2 + p$ $2p + 5$

$9p^3 + 2p^2 + 1$

Add or subtract as indicated. See Example 9.

81. $(9a^2b - 3a^2 + 2b) + (4a^2b - 4a^2 - 3b)$

82. $(4xy^3 - 3x + y) + (5xy^3 + 13x - 4y)$

83. $(2c^4d + 3c^2d^2 - 4d^2) - (c^4d + 8c^2d^2 - 5d^2)$

84. $(3k^2h^3 + 5kh + 6k^3h^2) - (2k^2h^3 - 9kh + k^3h^2)$

85. Subtract.
$$9m^3n - 5m^2n^2 + 4mn^2$$
$$\underline{-3m^3n + 6m^2n^2 + 8mn^2}$$

86. Subtract.
$$12r^5t + 11r^4t^2 - 7r^3t^3$$
$$\underline{-8r^5t + 10r^4t^2 + 3r^3t^3}$$

*Find **(a)** a polynomial that represents the perimeter of each triangle and **(b)** the measures of the angles of the triangle. (Hint: In part (b), the sum of the measures of the angles of any triangle is 180°.)*

87.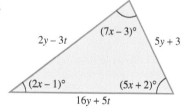
$2y - 3t$ $(7x - 3)°$ $5y + 3t$

$(2x - 1)°$ $(5x + 2)°$

$16y + 5t$

88.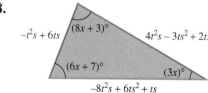
$-t^2s + 6ts$ $(8x + 3)°$ $4t^2s - 3ts^2 + 2ts$

$(6x + 7)°$

$(3x)°$

$-8t^2s + 6ts^2 + ts$

12.2 ▷▷▷ The Product Rule and Power Rules for Exponents

OBJECTIVE **1** **Use exponents.** In **Section 3.7,** we used exponents to write repeated products. Recall that in the expression 5^2, the number 5 is called the **base** and 2 is called the **exponent,** or **power.** The expression 5^2 is called an **exponential expression.** Although we do not usually write a quantity with an exponent of 1, in general, for any quantity a, $a = a^1$.

EXAMPLE 1 **Using Exponents**

Write $3 \cdot 3 \cdot 3 \cdot 3 \cdot 3$ in exponential form and evaluate.
   Since 3 occurs as a factor five times, the base is **3** and the exponent is **5.** The exponential expression is 3^5, read "3 to the fifth power," or simply "3 to the fifth."

$$\underbrace{3 \cdot 3 \cdot 3 \cdot 3 \cdot 3}_{\text{5 factors of 3}} \quad \text{means} \quad 3^5, \quad \text{or} \quad 243.$$

Work Problem **1** *at the Side.* ▶

EXAMPLE 2 **Evaluating Exponential Expressions**

Evaluate. Name the base and the exponent.

	Base	Exponent
(a) $5^4 = 5 \cdot 5 \cdot 5 \cdot 5 = 625$	5	4
(b) $-5^4 = -1 \cdot 5^4 = -1 \cdot (5 \cdot 5 \cdot 5 \cdot 5) = -625$	5	4
(c) $(-5)^4 = (-5)(-5)(-5)(-5) = 625$	-5	4

> **CAUTION**
> Look at Examples 2(b) and (c). In -5^4, the absence of parentheses shows that the exponent 4 applies only to the base 5, and not -5. In $(-5)^4$, the parentheses show that the exponent 4 applies to the base -5. In summary, $-a^n$ and $(-a)^n$ are not necessarily the same.
>
> | Expression | Base | Exponent | Example |
> |---|---|---|---|
> | $-a^n$ | a | n | $-3^2 = -(3 \cdot 3) = -9$ |
> | $(-a)^n$ | $-a$ | n | $(-3)^2 = (-3)(-3) = 9$ |

Work Problem **2** *at the Side.* ▶

OBJECTIVE **2** **Use the product rule for exponents.** To develop the product rule, we use the definition of an exponent.

$$2^4 \cdot 2^3 = \overbrace{(2 \cdot 2 \cdot 2 \cdot 2)}^{\text{4 factors}}\overbrace{(2 \cdot 2 \cdot 2)}^{\text{3 factors}}$$

$$= \underbrace{2 \cdot 2 \cdot 2 \cdot 2 \cdot 2 \cdot 2 \cdot 2}_{4 + 3 = 7 \text{ factors}}$$

$$= 2^7$$

OBJECTIVES

1 Use exponents.

2 Use the product rule for exponents.

3 Use the rule $(a^m)^n = a^{mn}$.

4 Use the rule $(ab)^m = a^m b^m$.

5 Use the rule $\left(\dfrac{a}{b}\right)^m = \dfrac{a^m}{b^m}$.

6 Use combinations of the rules for exponents.

7 Use the rules for exponents in a geometry application.

1 Write $2 \cdot 2 \cdot 2 \cdot 2$ in exponential form and evaluate.

2 Evaluate. Name the base and the exponent.

(a) $(-2)^5$ **(b)** -2^5

(c) -4^2 **(d)** $(-4)^2$

ANSWERS

1. 2^4, or 16
2. (a) -32; -2; 5   **(b)** -32; 2; 5
   (c) -16; 4; 2   **(d)** 16; -4; 2

3 Simplify by using the product rule, if possible.

(a) $8^2 \cdot 8^5$

(b) $(-7)^5 (-7)^3$

(c) $y^3 \cdot y$

(d) $z^2 z^5 z^6$

(e) $4^2 \cdot 3^5$

(f) $6^4 + 6^2$

Also,
$$6^2 \cdot 6^3 = (6 \cdot 6)(6 \cdot 6 \cdot 6)$$
$$= 6 \cdot 6 \cdot 6 \cdot 6 \cdot 6$$
$$= 6^5.$$

Generalizing from these examples,
$$2^4 \cdot 2^3 = 2^{4+3} = 2^7 \quad \text{and} \quad 6^2 \cdot 6^3 = 6^{2+3} = 6^5.$$

In each case, adding the exponents gives the exponent of the product, suggesting the **product rule for exponents.**

Product Rule for Exponents

For any positive integers m and n, $a^m \cdot a^n = a^{m+n}.$
(Keep the same base and add the exponents.)

Example: $6^2 \cdot 6^5 = 6^{2+5} = 6^7$

CAUTION
Do not multiply the bases when using the product rule. ***Keep the same base and add the exponents.*** For example,
$$6^2 \cdot 6^5 = 6^7, \quad \textit{\textbf{not}} \quad 36^7.$$

EXAMPLE 3   **Using the Product Rule**

Use the product rule for exponents to simplify, if possible.

(a) $6^3 \cdot 6^5 = 6^{3+5} = 6^8$ **(b)** $(-4)^7 (-4)^2 = (-4)^{7+2} = (-4)^9$

   Keep the same base.

(c) $x^2 \cdot x = x^2 \cdot x^1 = x^{2+1} = x^3$ **(d)** $m^4 m^3 m^5 = m^{4+3+5} = m^{12}$

(e) $2^3 \cdot 3^2$
   The product rule does not apply to the product $2^3 \cdot 3^2$ because the bases are different.
$$2^3 \cdot 3^2 = 8 \cdot 9 = 72 \quad \text{Evaluate } 2^3 \text{ and } 3^2; \text{ then multiply.}$$
   Think: 2^3 means $2 \cdot 2 \cdot 2$.   Think: 3^2 means $3 \cdot 3$.

(f) $2^3 + 2^4$
   The product rule does not apply to $2^3 + 2^4$ because it is a *sum,* not a *product.*
$$2^3 + 2^4 = 8 + 16 = 24 \quad \text{Evaluate } 2^3 \text{ and } 2^4; \text{ then add.}$$

CAUTION
The bases of the factors must be the same before we can apply the product rule for exponents.

ANSWERS
3. **(a)** 8^7 **(b)** $(-7)^8$ **(c)** y^4
   (d) z^{13} **(e)** The product rule does not apply.
   (product: 3888)   **(f)** The product rule does not apply. (sum: 1332)

◀ *Work Problem* **3** *at the Side.*

EXAMPLE 4 **Using the Product Rule**

Multiply $2x^3$ and $3x^7$.

$2x^3 \cdot 3x^7$ $\boxed{2x^3 = 2 \cdot x^3;\ 3x^7 = 3 \cdot x^7}$

$= (2 \cdot 3) \cdot (x^3 \cdot x^7)$ Commutative and associative properties

$= 6x^{3+7}$ Multiply; product rule

$= 6x^{10}$ Add the exponents.

CAUTION
Be sure you understand the difference between *adding* and *multiplying* exponential expressions. For example,

$$8x^3 + 5x^3 \quad \text{means} \quad (8 + 5)\,x^3, \quad \text{or} \quad 13x^3,$$

but $\quad (8x^3)(5x^3) \quad$ means $\quad (8 \cdot 5)\,x^{3+3}, \quad$ or $\quad 40x^6.$

Work Problem 4 *at the Side.* ▶

OBJECTIVE 3 Use the rule $(a^m)^n = a^{mn}$. We can simplify an expression such as $(8^3)^2$ with the product rule for exponents, as follows.

$$(8^3)^2 = (8^3)(8^3) = 8^{3+3} = 8^6$$

The product of the exponents in $(8^3)^2$, $3 \cdot 2$, gives the exponent in 8^6. Also,

$(5^2)^4 = 5^2 \cdot 5^2 \cdot 5^2 \cdot 5^2$ Definition of exponent

$= 5^{2+2+2+2}$ Product rule

$= 5^8,$ Add the exponents.

and $2 \cdot 4 = 8$. These examples suggest **power rule (a) for exponents.**

Power Rule (a) for Exponents
For any positive integers m and n, $(a^m)^n = a^{mn}$.
(Raise a power to a power by multiplying exponents.)

Example: $(3^2)^4 = 3^{2 \cdot 4} = 3^8$

EXAMPLE 5 **Using Power Rule (a)**

Use power rule (a) for exponents to simplify.

(a) $(2^5)^3 = 2^{5 \cdot 3} = 2^{15}$ **(b)** $(5^7)^2 = 5^{7 \cdot 2} = 5^{14}$ **(c)** $(x^2)^5 = x^{2 \cdot 5} = x^{10}$

Work Problem 5 *at the Side.* ▶

OBJECTIVE 4 Use the rule $(ab)^m = a^m b^m$. We can rewrite the expression $(4x)^3$ as shown below.

$(4x)^3 = (4x)(4x)(4x)$ Definition of exponent

$= 4 \cdot 4 \cdot 4 \cdot x \cdot x \cdot x$ Commutative and associative properties

$= 4^3 x^3$ Definition of exponent

This example suggests **power rule (b) for exponents.**

---

4 Multiply.

(a) $5m^2 \cdot 2m^6$

(b) $3p^5 \cdot 9p^4$

(c) $-7p^5 \cdot (3p^8)$

5 Simplify.

(a) $(5^3)^4$

(b) $(6^2)^5$

(c) $(3^2)^4$

(d) $(a^6)^5$

ANSWERS
4. (a) $10m^8$ **(b)** $27p^9$ **(c)** $-21p^{13}$
5. (a) 5^{12} **(b)** 6^{10} **(c)** 3^8 **(d)** a^{30}

6 Simplify.

(a) $(2ab)^4$

Power Rule (b) for Exponents

For any positive integer m, $(ab)^m = a^m b^m$.

(Raise a product to a power by raising each factor to the power.)

Example: $(2p)^5 = 2^5 p^5$

EXAMPLE 6 **Using Power Rule (b)**

Use power rule (b) for exponents to simplify.

(a) $(3xy)^2$

$= 3^2 x^2 y^2$ Power rule (b)

$= 9x^2 y^2$ $3^2 = 3 \cdot 3 = 9$

(b) $9(pq)^2$

$= 9(p^2 q^2)$ Power rule (b)

$= 9p^2 q^2$ Multiply.

(b) $5(mn)^3$

(c) $5(2m^2 p^3)^4$

$= 5[2^4 (m^2)^4 (p^3)^4]$ Power rule (b)

$= 5(2^4 m^8 p^{12})$ Power rule (a)

$= 5 \cdot 2^4 m^8 p^{12}$

$= 80 m^8 p^{12}$ $5 \cdot 2^4 = 5 \cdot 16 = 80$

(d) $\qquad (-5^6)^3$

$= (-1 \cdot 5^6)^3$ $-a = -1 \cdot a$

$= (-1)^3 (5^6)^3$ Power rule (b)

Raise -1 to the designated power.

$= -1 \cdot 5^{18}$ Power rule (a)

(c) $(3a^2 b^4)^5$

$= -5^{18}$

CAUTION

Power rule (b) does not apply to a sum:

$$(4x)^2 = 4^2 x^2, \quad \text{but} \quad (4+x)^2 \neq 4^2 + x^2.$$

◀ *Work Problem* **6** *at the Side.*

(d) $(-5m^2)^3$

OBJECTIVE **5** **Use the rule** $\left(\frac{a}{b}\right)^m = \frac{a^m}{b^m}$**.** Since the quotient $\frac{a}{b}$ can be written as $a \cdot \frac{1}{b}$, we can use power rule (b), together with some of the properties of real numbers, to get **power rule (c) for exponents.**

Power Rule (c) for Exponents

For any positive integer m, $\left(\dfrac{a}{b}\right)^m = \dfrac{a^m}{b^m}$ $(b \neq 0)$.

(Raise a quotient to a power by raising both the numerator and the denominator to the power.)

Example: $\left(\dfrac{5}{3}\right)^2 = \dfrac{5^2}{3^2}$

ANSWERS

6. (a) $16a^4 b^4$ (b) $5m^3 n^3$ (c) $243a^{10} b^{20}$

(d) $-125m^6$

EXAMPLE 7 Using Power Rule (c)

Use power rule (c) for exponents to simplify.

(a) $\left(\dfrac{2}{3}\right)^5 = \dfrac{2^5}{3^5} = \dfrac{32}{243}$

(b) $\left(\dfrac{m}{n}\right)^4 = \dfrac{m^4}{n^4}, \quad n \neq 0$

(c) $\left(\dfrac{1}{5}\right)^4 = \dfrac{1^4}{5^4} = \dfrac{1}{5^4} = \dfrac{1}{625}$ $\quad 1^4 = 1 \cdot 1 \cdot 1 \cdot 1 = 1$

Note
In Example 7(c), we used the fact that $1^4 = 1$.

In general, $\quad 1^n = 1, \quad$ *for any integer n.*

Work Problem **7** at the Side. ▶

The rules for exponents discussed in this section are basic to the study of algebra and should be *memorized*.

Rules for Exponents

For positive integers m and n: $\qquad$ *Examples*

Product rule $\quad a^m \cdot a^n = a^{m+n}$ $\qquad 6^2 \cdot 6^5 = 6^{2+5} = 6^7$

Power rules (a) $(a^m)^n = a^{mn}$ $\qquad (3^2)^4 = 3^{2 \cdot 4} = 3^8$

(b) $(ab)^m = a^m b^m$ $\qquad (2p)^5 = 2^5 p^5$

(c) $\left(\dfrac{a}{b}\right)^m = \dfrac{a^m}{b^m} \quad (b \neq 0).$ $\qquad \left(\dfrac{5}{3}\right)^2 = \dfrac{5^2}{3^2}$

OBJECTIVE 6 Use combinations of the rules for exponents.
More than one rule may be needed to simplify an exponential expression.

EXAMPLE 8 Using Combinations of Rules

Simplify each expression.

(a) $\left(\dfrac{2}{3}\right)^2 \cdot 2^3$

$= \dfrac{2^2}{3^2} \cdot \dfrac{2^3}{1}$ $\quad$ Power rule (c)

$= \dfrac{2^2 \cdot 2^3}{3^2 \cdot 1}$ $\quad$ Multiply fractions.

$= \dfrac{2^{2+3}}{3^2}$ $\quad$ Product rule

$= \dfrac{2^5}{3^2}$

$= \dfrac{32}{9}$

(b) $(5x)^3 (5x)^4$

$= (5x)^7 \quad$ Product rule

$= 5^7 x^7 \quad$ Power rule (b)

Continued on Next Page

7 Simplify. Assume that all variables represent nonzero real numbers.

(a) $\left(\dfrac{5}{2}\right)^4$

(b) $\left(\dfrac{p}{q}\right)^2$

(c) $\left(\dfrac{r}{t}\right)^3$

(d) $\left(\dfrac{1}{3}\right)^5$

(e) $\left(\dfrac{1}{x}\right)^{10}$

ANSWERS

7. (a) $\dfrac{625}{16}$ (b) $\dfrac{p^2}{q^2}$ (c) $\dfrac{r^3}{t^3}$ (d) $\dfrac{1}{243}$ (e) $\dfrac{1}{x^{10}}$

8 Simplify.

(a) $(2m)^3 (2m)^4$

(b) $\left(\dfrac{5k^3}{3}\right)^2$

(c) $\left(\dfrac{1}{5}\right)^4 (2x)^2$

(d) $(-3xy^2)^3 (x^2y)^4$

(c) $(2x^2y^3)^4 (3xy^2)^3$

$= 2^4 (x^2)^4 (y^3)^4 \cdot 3^3 x^3 (y^2)^3$ Power rule (b)

$= 2^4 x^8 y^{12} \cdot 3^3 x^3 y^6$ Power rule (a)

$= 2^4 \cdot 3^3 x^8 x^3 y^{12} y^6$ Commutative and associative properties

$= 16 \cdot 27 x^{11} y^{18}$ Product rule

$= 432 x^{11} y^{18}$ Multiply.

Notice that $(2x^2y^3)^4$ means $2^4 x^{2\cdot4} y^{3\cdot4}$, **not** $(2\cdot4) x^{2\cdot4} y^{3\cdot4}$.

> Do *not* multiply the coefficient 2 and the exponent 4.

(d) $(-x^3y)^2 (-x^5y^4)^3$

> Think of the negative sign in each factor as -1.

$= (-1x^3y)^2 (-1x^5y^4)^3$ $-a = -1 \cdot a$

$= (-1)^2 (x^3)^2 (y^2) \cdot (-1)^3 (x^5)^3 (y^4)^3$ Power rule (b)

$= (-1)^2 (x^6)(y^2) \cdot (-1)^3 (x^{15})(y^{12})$ Power rule (a)

$= (-1)^5 (x^{6+15})(y^{2+12})$ Product rule

$= -1x^{21}y^{14}$

$= -x^{21}y^{14}$

◀ *Work Problem* **8** *at the Side.*

OBJECTIVE 7 Use the rules for exponents in a geometry application.

EXAMPLE 9 Using Area Formulas

Find a polynomial that represents the area of each geometric figure.

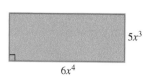

Figure 1   **Figure 2**

For Figure 1, use the formula for the area of a rectangle, $A = lw$.

$A = (6x^4)(5x^3)$ Area formula

$A = 6 \cdot 5 \cdot x^{4+3}$ Product rule

$A = 30x^7$

Figure 2 is a triangle with base $6m^4$ and height $3m^3$. Substitute into the formula for the area of a triangle and simplify.

$A = \dfrac{1}{2} bh$ Area formula

$A = \dfrac{1}{2} (6m^4)(3m^3)$ Substitute.

$A = \dfrac{1}{2} (18m^7)$, or $9m^7$ Product rule; multiply.

◀ *Work Problem* **9** *at the Side.*

9 Find a polynomial that represents the area of the figure.

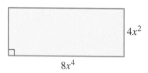

ANSWERS

8. (a) 2^7m^7, or $128m^7$ **(b)** $\dfrac{5^2k^6}{3^2}$, or $\dfrac{25k^6}{9}$

    (c) $\dfrac{2^2x^2}{5^4}$, or $\dfrac{4x^2}{625}$

    (d) $-3^3x^{11}y^{10}$, or $-27x^{11}y^{10}$

9. $32x^6$

1. What exponent is understood on the base x in the expression xy^2?

2. How are the expressions 3^2, 5^3, and 7^4 read?

Decide whether each statement is true *or* false.

3. $3^3 = 9$

4. $(-2)^4 = 2^4$

5. $(a^2)^3 = a^5$

6. $\left(\dfrac{1}{4}\right)^2 = \dfrac{1}{4^2}$

Write each expression using exponents. See Example 1.

7. $t \cdot t \cdot t \cdot t \cdot t \cdot t \cdot t \cdot t$

8. $w \cdot w \cdot w \cdot w \cdot w \cdot w$

9. $\left(\dfrac{1}{2}\right)\left(\dfrac{1}{2}\right)\left(\dfrac{1}{2}\right)\left(\dfrac{1}{2}\right)\left(\dfrac{1}{2}\right)$

10. $\left(-\dfrac{1}{4}\right)\left(-\dfrac{1}{4}\right)\left(-\dfrac{1}{4}\right)\left(-\dfrac{1}{4}\right)$

11. $(-8p)(-8p)$

12. $(-7x)(-7x)(-7x)$

13. Explain how the expressions $(-3)^4$ and -3^4 are different.

14. Explain how the expressions $(5x)^3$ and $5x^3$ are different.

Identify the base and the exponent for each exponential expression. In Exercises 15–18, also evaluate the expression. See Example 2.

15. 3^5

16. 2^7

17. $(-3)^5$

18. $(-2)^7$

19. $(-6x)^4$

20. $(-8x)^4$

21. $-6x^4$

22. $-8x^4$

23. Explain why the product rule does not apply to the expression $5^2 + 5^3$. Then evaluate the expression.

24. Explain why the product rule does not apply to the expression $3^2 \cdot 4^3$. Then evaluate the expression.

Use the product rule for exponents to simplify each expression, if possible. Write each answer in exponential form. See Examples 3 and 4.

25. $5^2 \cdot 5^6$

26. $3^6 \cdot 3^7$

27. $4^2 \cdot 4^7 \cdot 4^3$

28. $5^3 \cdot 5^8 \cdot 5^2$

29. $(-7)^3(-7)^6$

30. $(-9)^8(-9)^5$

31. $t^3 t^8 t^{13}$

32. $n^5 n^6 n^9$

33. $(-8r^4)(7r^3)$

34. $(10a^7)(-4a^3)$

35. $(-6p^5)(-7p^5)$

36. $(-5w^8)(-9w^8)$

37. $3^8 + 3^9$

38. $4^{12} + 4^5$

39. $5^8 \cdot 3^8$

40. $6^3 \cdot 8^3$

Use the power rules for exponents to simplify each expression. See Examples 5–7.

41. $(4^3)^2$

42. $(8^3)^6$

43. $(t^4)^5$

44. $(y^6)^5$

45. $(7r)^3$

46. $(11x)^4$

47. $(-5^2)^6$

48. $(-9^4)^8$

49. $(-8^3)^5$

50. $(-7^5)^7$

51. $(5xy)^5$

52. $(9pq)^6$

53. $8(qr)^3$

54. $4(vw)^5$

55. $\left(\dfrac{1}{2}\right)^3$

56. $\left(\dfrac{1}{3}\right)^5$

57. $\left(\dfrac{a}{b}\right)^3, \quad b \neq 0$

58. $\left(\dfrac{r}{t}\right)^4, \quad t \neq 0$

59. $\left(\dfrac{9}{5}\right)^8$

60. $\left(\dfrac{12}{7}\right)^6$

61. $(-2x^2y)^3$

62. $(-5m^4p^2)^3$

63. $(3a^3b^2)^2$

64. $(4x^3y^5)^4$

Simplify each expression. See Example 8.

65. $\left(\dfrac{5}{2}\right)^3 \cdot \left(\dfrac{5}{2}\right)^2$

66. $\left(\dfrac{3}{4}\right)^5 \cdot \left(\dfrac{3}{4}\right)^6$

67. $\left(\dfrac{9}{8}\right)^3 \cdot 9^2$

68. $\left(\dfrac{8}{5}\right)^4 \cdot 8^3$

69. $(2x)^9 (2x)^3$

70. $(6y)^5 (6y)^8$

71. $(-6p)^4 (-6p)$

72. $(-13q)^3 (-13q)$

73. $(6x^2y^3)^5$

74. $(5r^5t^6)^7$

75. $(x^2)^3 (x^3)^5$

76. $(y^4)^5 (y^3)^5$

77. $(2w^2x^3y)^2 (x^4y)^5$

78. $(3x^4y^2z)^3 (yz^4)^5$

79. $(-r^4s)^2 (-r^2s^3)^5$

80. $(-ts^6)^4 (-t^3s^5)^3$

81. $\left(\dfrac{5a^2b^5}{c^6}\right)^3, \quad c \neq 0$

82. $\left(\dfrac{6x^3y^9}{z^5}\right)^4, \quad z \neq 0$

83. $(-5m^3p^4q)^2 (p^2q)^3$

84. $(-a^4b^5)(-6a^3b^3)^2$

85. $(2x^2y^3z)^4 (xy^2z^3)^2$

Find a polynomial that represents the area of each figure. See Example 9.

86.

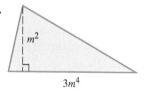

87.

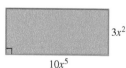

88.

12.3 ▷▷▷ Multiplying Polynomials

OBJECTIVE 1 Multiply a monomial and a polynomial. As shown in **Section 12.2,** we find the product of two monomials by using the rules for exponents and the commutative and associative properties. For example,

$$(-8m^6)(-9n^6)$$

$$= (-8)(-9)(m^6)(n^6)$$

$$= 72m^6n^6.$$

> **CAUTION**
> *Do not confuse addition of terms with multiplication of terms.*
> $$7q^5 + 2q^5 = 9q^5, \quad \text{but} \quad (7q^5)(2q^5) = 7 \cdot 2q^{5+5} = 14q^{10}.$$

To find the product of a monomial and a polynomial with more than one term, we use the distributive property and multiplication of monomials.

EXAMPLE 1 Multiplying Monomials and Polynomials

Find each product.

(a) $4x^2(3x + 5)$

$$4x^2(3x + 5) = 4x^2(3x) + 4x^2(5) \quad \text{Distributive property}$$

$$= 12x^3 + 20x^2 \quad \text{Multiply monomials.}$$

(b) $-8m^3(4m^3 + 3m^2 + 2m - 1)$

$$= -8m^3(4m^3) + (-8m^3)(3m^2)$$

$$+ (-8m^3)(2m) + (-8m^3)(-1) \quad \text{Distributive property}$$

$$= -32m^6 - 24m^5 - 16m^4 + 8m^3 \quad \text{Multiply monomials.}$$

Work Problem **1** *at the Side.* ▶

OBJECTIVE 2 Multiply two polynomials. We can use the distributive property repeatedly to find the product of any two polynomials. For example, to find the product of the polynomials $x^2 + 3x + 5$ and $x - 4$, think of $x - 4$ as a single quantity and use the distributive property as follows.

$$(x^2 + 3x + 5)(x - 4)$$

$$= x^2(x - 4) + 3x(x - 4) + 5(x - 4) \quad \text{Distributive property}$$

$$= x^2(x) + x^2(-4) + 3x(x) + 3x(-4) + 5(x) + 5(-4)$$

$$\text{Distributive property again}$$

$$= x^3 - 4x^2 + 3x^2 - 12x + 5x - 20 \quad \text{Multiply monomials.}$$

$$= x^3 - x^2 - 7x - 20 \quad \text{Combine like terms.}$$

This example suggests the following rule.

> **Multiplying Polynomials**
> To multiply two polynomials, multiply each term of the second polynomial by each term of the first polynomial and add the products.

OBJECTIVES

1 Multiply a monomial and a polynomial.

2 Multiply two polynomials.

3 Multiply binomials by the FOIL method.

1 Find each product.

(a) $5m^3(2m + 7)$

(b) $2x^4(3x^2 + 2x - 5)$

(c) $-4y^2(3y^3 + 2y^2 - 4y + 8)$

2 Multiply.

(a) $(m + 3)(m^2 - 2m + 1)$

EXAMPLE 2 **Multiplying Two Polynomials**

Multiply $(m^2 + 5)(4m^3 - 2m^2 + 4m)$.

   Multiply each term of the second polynomial by each term of the first.

$(m^2 + 5)(4m^3 - 2m^2 + 4m)$

$\quad = m^2(4m^3) + m^2(-2m^2) + m^2(4m) + 5(4m^3) + 5(-2m^2) + 5(4m)$

$\quad = 4m^5 - 2m^4 + 4m^3 + 20m^3 - 10m^2 + 20m$

$\quad = 4m^5 - 2m^4 + 24m^3 - 10m^2 + 20m$ Combine like terms.

◀ *Work Problem* **2** *at the Side.*

(b) $(6p^2 + 2p - 4)(3p^2 - 5)$

EXAMPLE 3 **Multiplying Polynomials Vertically**

Multiply $(x^3 + 2x^2 + 4x + 1)(3x + 5)$ vertically.

   Write the polynomials as follows.

$$x^3 + 2x^2 + 4x + 1$$
$$\underline{3x + 5}$$

Begin by multiplying each of the terms in the top row by 5.

$$x^3 + 2x^2 + 4x + 1$$
$$\underline{3x + 5}$$
$$5x^3 + 10x^2 + 20x + 5 \quad 5(x^3 + 2x^2 + 4x + 1)$$

Notice how this process is similar to multiplication of whole numbers. Now multiply each term in the top row by $3x$. Then add like terms.

3 Find the product.

$$3x^2 + 4x - 5$$
$$\underline{x + 4}$$

$$x^3 + 2x^2 + 4x + 1$$

Place *like* terms in columns so they can be added.

$$\underline{3x + 5}$$
$$5x^3 + 10x^2 + 20x + 5$$
$$\underline{3x^4 + 6x^3 + 12x^2 + 3x} \qquad 3x(x^3 + 2x^2 + 4x + 1)$$
$$3x^4 + 11x^3 + 22x^2 + 23x + 5 \qquad \text{Add.}$$

The product is $3x^4 + 11x^3 + 22x^2 + 23x + 5$.

◀ *Work Problem* **3** *at the Side.*

4 Use the rectangle method to find each product.

(a) $(4x + 3)(x + 2)$

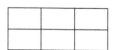

We can use a rectangle to model polynomial multiplication. For example, to find the product

$$(2x + 1)(3x + 2),$$

label a rectangle with each term as shown below on the left. Then put the product of each pair of monomials in the appropriate box as shown on the right.

	$3x$	2
$2x$		
1		

	$3x$	2
$2x$	$6x^2$	$4x$
1	$3x$	2

(b) $(x + 5)(x^2 + 3x + 1)$

The product of the binomials is the sum of these four monomial products.

$$(2x + 1)(3x + 2)$$
$$= 6x^2 + 4x + 3x + 2$$
$$= 6x^2 + 7x + 2$$

◀ *Work Problem* **4** *at the Side.*

OBJECTIVE 3 Multiply binomials by the FOIL method. In algebra, many of the polynomials to be multiplied are both binomials (with just two terms). For these products, the **FOIL method** reduces the rectangle method to a systematic approach without the rectangle. To develop the FOIL method, we use the distributive property to find $(x + 3)(x + 5)$.

$$(x + 3)(x + 5)$$
$$= (x + 3)x + (x + 3)5 \qquad \text{Distributive property}$$
$$= x(x) + 3(x) + x(5) + 3(5) \qquad \text{Distributive property again}$$
$$= x^2 + 3x + 5x + 15 \qquad \text{Multiply.}$$
$$= x^2 + 8x + 15 \qquad \text{Combine like terms.}$$

Here is where the letters of the word FOIL originate.

$(x + 3)(x + 5)$ Multiply the **First terms**: $x(x)$.   **F**

$(x + 3)(x + 5)$ Multiply the **Outer terms**: $x(5)$.   **O**
                   This is the **outer product.**

$(x + 3)(x + 5)$ Multiply the **Inner terms**: $3(x)$.   **I**
                   This is the **inner product.**

$(x + 3)(x + 5)$ Multiply the **Last terms**: $3(5)$.   **L**

The outer product, $5x$, and the inner product, $3x$, should be added mentally so that the three terms of the answer can be written without extra steps.

$$(x + 3)(x + 5)$$
$$= x^2 + 8x + 15$$

A summary of the steps in the FOIL method follows.

Multiplying Binomials by the FOIL Method

Step 1 Multiply the two **First** terms of the binomials to get the first term of the answer.

Step 2 Find the **Outer** product and the **Inner** product and add them (when possible) to get the middle term of the answer.

Step 3 Multiply the two **Last** terms of the binomials to get the last term of the answer.

$$\mathbf{F} = x^2 \qquad \mathbf{L} = 15$$
$$(x + 3)(x + 5)$$
$$\mathbf{I} = 3x$$
$$\underline{\mathbf{O} = 5x}$$
$$8x \qquad \text{Add.}$$

Work Problem **5** *at the Side.* ▶

5 For the product
$$(2p - 5)(3p + 7),$$
find the following.

(a) Product of first terms

(b) Outer product

(c) Inner product

(d) Product of last terms

(e) Complete product in simplified form

ANSWERS

5. (a) $2p(3p) = 6p^2$ **(b)** $2p(7) = 14p$
(c) $-5(3p) = -15p$ **(d)** $-5(7) = -35$
(e) $6p^2 - p - 35$

6 Use the FOIL method to find each product.

(a) $(m + 4)(m - 3)$

(b) $(y + 7)(y + 2)$

(c) $(r - 8)(r - 5)$

EXAMPLE 4 **Using the FOIL Method**

Use the FOIL method to find the product $(x + 8)(x - 6)$.

Step 1 F Multiply the **first** terms: $x(x) = x^2$.

Step 2 O Find the **outer** product: $x(-6) = -6x$.

   I Find the **inner** product: $8(x) = 8x$.

   Add the outer and inner products mentally: $-6x + 8x = 2x$.

Step 3 L Multiply the **last** terms: $8(-6) = -48$.

The product $(x + 8)(x - 6)$ is $x^2 + 2x - 48$, the sum of the terms found in Steps 1–3. As a shortcut, this product can be found as follows.

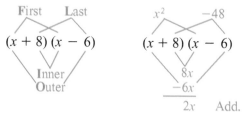

◀ *Work Problem* **6** *at the Side.*

EXAMPLE 5 **Using the FOIL Method**

Multiply $(9x - 2)(3y + 1)$.

First	$(9x - 2)(3y + 1)$	$27xy$
Outer	$(9x - 2)(3y + 1)$	$9x$
Inner	$(9x - 2)(3y + 1)$	$-6y$
Last	$(9x - 2)(3y + 1)$	-2

These unlike terms cannot be added.

F   O   I   L

The product $(9x - 2)(3y + 1)$ is $27xy + 9x - 6y - 2$.

◀ *Work Problem* **7** *at the Side.*

7 Find the product.

$(4x - 3)(2y + 5)$

---

8 Find each product.

(a) $(6m + 5)(m - 4)$

(b) $(3r + 2t)(3r + 4t)$

(c) $y^2(8y + 3)(2y + 1)$

EXAMPLE 6 **Using the FOIL Method**

Find each product.

(a) $(2k + 5y)(k + 3y)$

 F O I L

$= 2k(k) + 2k(3y) + 5y(k) + 5y(3y)$

$= 2k^2 + 6ky + 5ky + 15y^2$

$= 2k^2 + 11ky + 15y^2$

(b) $(7p + 2q)(3p - q)$

$= 21p^2 - 7pq + 6pq - 2q^2$

$= 21p^2 - pq - 2q^2$

(c) $2x^2(x - 3)(3x + 4)$

$= 2x^2(3x^2 - 5x - 12)$

$= 6x^4 - 10x^3 - 24x^2$

◀ *Work Problem* **8** *at the Side.*

Note

In Example 6(c), we could have multiplied $2x^2$ and $x - 3$ first.

$2x^2(x - 3)(3x + 4)$

$= (2x^3 - 6x^2)(3x + 4)$

$= 6x^4 - 10x^3 - 24x^2$ Same answer

12.3 ▶▶▶ Exercises

Find each product using the rectangle method shown in the text.

1. $(x + 3)(x + 4)$

2. $(x + 5)(x + 2)$

3. $(2x + 1)(x^2 + 3x + 2)$

4. $(x + 4)(3x^2 + 2x + 1)$

5. In multiplying a monomial by a polynomial, such as in $4x(3x^2 + 7x^3) = 4x(3x^2) + 4x(7x^3)$, the first property that is used is the _____ property.

6. Match each product in parts (a)–(d) with the correct polynomial in choices A–D.

(a) $(x - 5)(x + 3)$ **(b)** $(x + 5)(x + 3)$ **(c)** $(x - 5)(x - 3)$ **(d)** $(x + 5)(x - 3)$

A. $x^2 + 8x + 15$ **B.** $x^2 - 8x + 15$ **C.** $x^2 - 2x - 15$ **D.** $x^2 + 2x - 15$

Find each product. See Example 1.

7. $-2m(3m + 2)$

8. $-5p(6 + 3p)$

9. $\frac{3}{4}p(8 - 6p + 12p^3)$

10. $\frac{4}{3}x(3 + 2x + 5x^3)$

11. $2y^5(3 + 2y + 5y^4)$

12. $2m^4(3m^2 + 5m + 6)$

Find each product. See Examples 2 and 3.

13. $(6x + 1)(2x^2 + 4x + 1)$

14. $(9y - 2)(8y^2 - 6y + 1)$

15. $(2r - 1)(3r^2 + 4r - 4)$

16. $(9a + 2)(9a^2 + a + 1)$

17. $(4m + 3)(5m^3 - 4m^2 + m - 5)$

18. $(y + 4)(3y^3 - 2y^2 + y + 3)$

19. $(5x^2 + 2x + 1)(x^2 - 3x + 5)$

20. $(2m^2 + m - 3)(m^2 - 4m + 5)$

Find each product. See Examples 4–6.

21. $(m + 7)(m + 5)$

22. $(x + 4)(x + 7)$

23. $(n - 2)(n + 3)$

24. $(r - 6)(r + 8)$

25. $(4r + 1)(2r - 3)$

26. $(5x + 2)(2x - 7)$

27. $(3x + 2)(3x - 2)$

28. $(7x + 3)(7x - 3)$

29. $(3q + 1)(3q + 1)$ **30.** $(4w + 7)(4w + 7)$ **31.** $(5x + 7)(3y - 8)$

32. $(4x + 3)(2y - 1)$ **33.** $(3t + 4s)(2t + 5s)$ **34.** $(8v + 5w)(2v + 3w)$

35. $(-0.3t + 0.4)(t + 0.6)$ **36.** $(-0.5x + 0.9)(x - 0.2)$ **37.** $\left(x - \dfrac{2}{3} \right)\left(x + \dfrac{1}{4} \right)$

38. $\left(-\dfrac{8}{3} + 3k \right)\left(-\dfrac{2}{3} - k \right)$ **39.** $\left(-\dfrac{5}{4} + 2r \right)\left(-\dfrac{3}{4} - r \right)$ **40.** $2m^3(4m - 1)(2m + 3)$

41. $x(2x - 5)(x + 3)$ **42.** $5t^4(t + 3)(3t - 1)$ **43.** $3y^3(2y + 3)(y - 5)$

Relating Concepts (Exercises 44–48)   For Individual or Group Work

Work Exercises 44–48 in order. *(All units are in yards.)*

44. Find a polynomial that represents the area of the rectangle.

$3x + 6$

10

45. Suppose you know that the area of the rectangle is 600 yd². Use this information and the polynomial from Exercise 44 to write an equation in x, and solve it.

46. (a) What are the dimensions of the rectangle?

     (b) Use the result of part (a) to find the perimeter of the lawn.

47. Suppose the rectangle represents a lawn and it costs \$3.50 per square yard to lay sod on the lawn. How much will it cost to sod the entire lawn?

48. Again, suppose the rectangle represents a lawn and it costs \$9.00 per yard to fence the lawn. How much will it cost to fence the lawn?

---

49. Perform the following multiplications: $(x + 4)(x - 4)$; $(y + 2)(y - 2)$; $(r + 7)(r - 7)$. Observe your answers, and explain the pattern that can be found in the answers.

50. Repeat Exercise 49 for the following: $(x + 4)(x + 4)$; $(y - 2)(y - 2)$; $(r + 7)(r + 7)$.

12.4 ▶▶▶ Special Products

In this section, we develop shortcuts to find certain binomial products.

OBJECTIVE 1 Square binomials. The square of a binomial can be found quickly by using the method shown in Example 1.

EXAMPLE 1 Squaring a Binomial

Find $(m + 3)^2$.

> $(m + 3)^2$ means $(m + 3)(m + 3)$.

$$(m + 3)(m + 3)$$
$$= m^2 + 3m + 3m + 9 \quad \text{FOIL}$$
$$= m^2 + 6m + 9 \quad \text{Combine like terms.}$$

This result has the squares of the first and the last terms of the binomial:

$$m^2 = m^2 \quad \text{and} \quad 3^2 = 9.$$

The middle term, 6m, is twice the product of the two terms of the binomial, since the outer and inner products are $m(3)$ and $3(m)$, and

$$m(3) + 3(m) = 2(m)(3) = 6m.$$

Work Problem **1** *at the Side.* ▶

Example 1 suggests the following rules.

Square of a Binomial

The square of a binomial is a trinomial consisting of the square of the first term, plus twice the product of the two terms, plus the square of the last term of the binomial. For a and b,

$$(a + b)^2 = a^2 + 2ab + b^2.$$

Also,

$$(a - b)^2 = a^2 - 2ab + b^2.$$

EXAMPLE 2 Squaring Binomials

Square each binomial.

$$(a - b)^2 = a^2 - 2 \cdot a \cdot b + b^2$$

(a) $(5z - 1)^2 = (5z)^2 - 2(5z)(1) + (1)^2$
$$= 25z^2 - 10z + 1 \qquad (5z)^2 = 5^2 z^2 = 25z^2$$

(b) $(3b + 5r)^2$
$$= (3b)^2 + 2(3b)(5r) + (5r)^2$$
$$= 9b^2 + 30br + 25r^2$$

(c) $(2a - 9x)^2$
$$= (2a)^2 - 2(2a)(9x) + (9x)^2$$
$$= 4a^2 - 36ax + 81x^2$$

Continued on Next Page

OBJECTIVES

1 Square binomials.

2 Find the product of the sum and difference of two terms.

3 Find greater powers of binomials.

1 Consider the binomial $x + 4$.

(a) What is the first term of the binomial? Square it.

(b) What is the last term of the binomial? Square it.

(c) Find twice the product of the two terms of the binomial.

(d) Find $(x + 4)^2$.

ANSWERS

1. (a) $x; x^2$ **(b)** $4; 16$ **(c)** $8x$
(d) $x^2 + 8x + 16$

2 Square each binomial.

(a) $(t - 6)^2$

(b) $(2m - p)^2$

(c) $(4p + 3q)^2$

(d) $(5r - 6s)^2$

(e) $\left(3k - \dfrac{1}{2}\right)^2$

(f) $x(2x + 7)^2$

(d) $\left(4m + \dfrac{1}{2}\right)^2$

$\qquad = (4m)^2 + 2\,(4m)\left(\dfrac{1}{2}\right) + \left(\dfrac{1}{2}\right)^2 \quad (a + b)^2 = a^2 + 2ab + b^2$

$\qquad = 16m^2 + 4m + \dfrac{1}{4}$

(e) $x(4x - 3)^2$ $\qquad$ Remember the middle term.

$\qquad = x(16x^2 - 24x + 9) \qquad$ Square the binomial.

$\qquad = 16x^3 - 24x^2 + 9x \qquad$ Distributive property

Notice that in the square of a sum, all of the terms are positive, as in Examples 2(b) and (d). *In the square of a difference, the middle term is negative,* as in Examples 2(a) and (c).

> **CAUTION**
> A common error when squaring a binomial is to forget the middle term of the product. In general,
> $$(a + b)^2 = a^2 + 2ab + b^2, \quad \textbf{\textit{not}} \quad a^2 + b^2,$$
> and $\qquad (a - b)^2 = a^2 - 2ab + b^2, \quad \textbf{\textit{not}} \quad a^2 - b^2.$

◀ *Work Problem* **2** *at the Side.*

OBJECTIVE **2** **Find the product of the sum and difference of two terms.** In binomial products of the form $(a + b)(a - b)$, one binomial is the sum of two terms, and the other is the difference of the *same* two terms. For example, the product of $x + 2$ and $x - 2$ is

$$(x + 2)(x - 2)$$
$$= x^2 - 2x + 2x - 4 \qquad \text{FOIL}$$
$$= x^2 - 4. \qquad \text{Combine like terms.}$$

As the above example suggests, the product of $a + b$ and $a - b$ is the difference of two squares.

> **Product of the Sum and Difference of Two Terms**
> $$(a + b)(a - b) = a^2 - b^2$$

> **Note**
> The expressions $a + b$ and $a - b$, the sum and difference of the *same* two terms, are called **conjugates.** In the example above, $x + 2$ and $x - 2$ are conjugates.

ANSWERS

2. **(a)** $t^2 - 12t + 36$
  (b) $4m^2 - 4mp + p^2$
  (c) $16p^2 + 24pq + 9q^2$
  (d) $25r^2 - 60rs + 36s^2$
  (e) $9k^2 - 3k + \dfrac{1}{4}$
  (f) $4x^3 + 28x^2 + 49x$

EXAMPLE 3 **Finding the Product of the Sum and Difference of Two Terms**

Find each product.

(a) $(x + 4)(x - 4)$

Use the rule for the product of the sum and difference of two terms.

$$(x + 4)(x - 4)$$
$$= x^2 - 4^2$$
$$= x^2 - 16$$

(b) $\left(\dfrac{2}{3} - w\right)\left(\dfrac{2}{3} + w\right)$

$$= \left(\dfrac{2}{3} + w\right)\left(\dfrac{2}{3} - w\right) \qquad \text{Commutative property}$$

$$= \left(\dfrac{2}{3}\right)^2 - w^2 \qquad \text{Multiply.}$$

$$= \dfrac{4}{9} - w^2 \qquad \text{Square } \tfrac{2}{3}.$$

(c) $x(x + 2)(x - 2)$

$$= x(x^2 - 4) \qquad \text{Find the product of the sum and difference of two terms.}$$

$$= x^3 - 4x \qquad \text{Distributive property}$$

EXAMPLE 4 **Finding the Product of the Sum and Difference of Two Terms**

Find each product.

$$\begin{array}{cccc} (a & + \ b) & (a & - \ b) \\ \downarrow & \downarrow & \downarrow & \downarrow \end{array}$$

(a) $(5m + 3)(5m - 3)$

Use the rule for the product of the sum and difference of two terms.

$$(5m + 3)(5m - 3)$$
$$= (5m)^2 - 3^2 \qquad (a + b)(a - b) = a^2 - b^2$$
$$= 25m^2 - 9 \qquad \text{Apply the exponents.}$$

(b) $(4x + y)(4x - y)$

$$= (4x)^2 - y^2$$
$$= 16x^2 - y^2$$

(c) $\left(z - \dfrac{1}{4}\right)\left(z + \dfrac{1}{4}\right)$

$$= z^2 - \left(\dfrac{1}{4}\right)^2$$

$$= z^2 - \dfrac{1}{16}$$

(d) $2p(p^2 + 3)(p^2 - 3)$

$$= 2p(p^4 - 9) \qquad \text{Multiply the conjugates.}$$

$$= 2p^5 - 18p \qquad \text{Distributive property}$$

Work Problem **3** *at the Side.* ▶

3 Find each product.

(a) $(y + 3)(y - 3)$

(b) $(10m + 7)(10m - 7)$

(c) $(7p + 2q)(7p - 2q)$

(d) $\left(3r - \dfrac{1}{2}\right)\left(3r + \dfrac{1}{2}\right)$

(e) $3x(x^3 - 4)(x^3 + 4)$

ANSWERS

3. (a) $y^2 - 9$ **(b)** $100m^2 - 49$
(c) $49p^2 - 4q^2$ **(d)** $9r^2 - \dfrac{1}{4}$
(e) $3x^7 - 48x$

4 Find each product.

(a) $(m + 1)^3$

OBJECTIVE **3** **Find greater powers of binomials.** The methods used in the previous section and this section can be combined to find greater powers of binomials.

EXAMPLE 5 **Finding Greater Powers of Binomials**

Find each product.

(a) $(x + 5)^3$

$$= (x + 5)^2(x + 5) \qquad a^3 = a^2 \cdot a$$

$$= (x^2 + 10x + 25)(x + 5) \qquad \text{Square the binomial.}$$

$$= x^3 + 10x^2 + 25x + 5x^2 + 50x + 125 \qquad \text{Multiply polynomials.}$$

$$= x^3 + 15x^2 + 75x + 125 \qquad \text{Combine like terms.}$$

(b) $(3k - 2)^4$

(b) $(2y - 3)^4$

$$= (2y - 3)^2(2y - 3)^2 \qquad a^4 = a^2 \cdot a^2$$

$$= (4y^2 - 12y + 9)(4y^2 - 12y + 9) \qquad \text{Square each binomial.}$$

$$= 16y^4 - 48y^3 + 36y^2 - 48y^3 + 144y^2 \qquad \text{Multiply polynomials.}$$

$$- 108y + 36y^2 - 108y + 81$$

$$= 16y^4 - 96y^3 + 216y^2 - 216y + 81 \qquad \text{Combine like terms.}$$

(c) $-2r(r + 2)^3$

$$= -2r(r + 2)(r + 2)^2$$

$$= -2r(r + 2)(r^2 + 4r + 4)$$

$$= -2r(r^3 + 4r^2 + 4r + 2r^2 + 8r + 8)$$

$$= -2r(r^3 + 6r^2 + 12r + 8)$$

$$= -2r^4 - 12r^3 - 24r^2 - 16r$$

(c) $-3x(x - 4)^3$

◀ *Work Problem* **4** *at the Side.*

FOR EXTRA HELP  | PRACTICE | WATCH | DOWNLOAD | READ | REVIEW

1. Consider the square $(2x + 3)^2$.

   (a) What is the square of the first term, $(2x)^2$?

   (b) What is twice the product of the two terms, $2(2x)(3)$?

   (c) What is the square of the last term, 3^2?

   (d) Write the final product, which is a trinomial, using your results from parts (a)–(c).

2. Repeat Exercise 1 for the square $(3x - 2)^2$.

Find each square. See Examples 1 and 2.

3. $(p + 2)^2$ **4.** $(r + 5)^2$ **5.** $(z - 5)^2$ **6.** $(x - 3)^2$

7. $(4x - 3)^2$ **8.** $(5y + 2)^2$ **9.** $(2p + 5q)^2$ **10.** $(8a - 3b)^2$

11. $(0.8t + 0.7s)^2$ **12.** $(0.7z - 0.3w)^2$ **13.** $\left(5x + \dfrac{2}{5}y\right)^2$ **14.** $\left(6m - \dfrac{4}{5}n\right)^2$

15. $t(3t - 1)^2$ **16.** $x(2x + 5)^2$ **17.** $-(4r - 2)^2$ **18.** $-(3y - 8)^2$

19. Consider the product $(7x + 3y)(7x - 3y)$.

   (a) What is the product of the first terms, $7x(7x)$?

   (b) Multiply the outer terms, $7x(-3y)$. Then multiply the inner terms, $3y(7x)$. Add the results. What is this sum?

   (c) What is the product of the last terms, $3y(-3y)$?

   (d) Write the complete product using your answers in parts (a) and (c). Why is the sum found in part (b) omitted here?

20. Repeat Exercise 19 for the product $(5x + 7y)(5x - 7y)$.

Find each product. See Examples 3 and 4.

21. $(q + 2)(q - 2)$ **22.** $(x + 8)(x - 8)$ **23.** $(2w + 5)(2w - 5)$ **24.** $(3z + 8)(3z - 8)$

25. $(10x + 3y)(10x - 3y)$ **26.** $(13r + 2z)(13r - 2z)$ **27.** $(2x^2 - 5)(2x^2 + 5)$ **28.** $(9y^2 - 2)(9y^2 + 2)$

29. $\left(7x + \dfrac{3}{7}\right)\left(7x - \dfrac{3}{7}\right)$ **30.** $\left(9y + \dfrac{2}{3}\right)\left(9y - \dfrac{2}{3}\right)$ **31.** $p(3p + 7)(3p - 7)$ **32.** $q(5q - 1)(5q + 1)$

Relating Concepts (Exercises 33–42) For Individual or Group Work

Special products can be illustrated by using areas of rectangles. Use the figure and **work Exercises 33–38 in order,** *to justify the special product* $(a + b)^2 = a^2 + 2ab + b^2$.

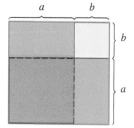

33. Express the area of the entire square figure as the square of a binomial.

34. Give the monomial that represents the area of the red square.

35. Give the monomial that represents the sum of the areas of the blue rectangles.

36. Give the monomial that represents the area of the yellow square.

37. What is the sum of the monomials you obtained in Exercises 34–36?

38. Explain why the binomial square you found in Exercise 33 must equal the polynomial you found in Exercise 37.

To understand how the special product $(a + b)^2 = a^2 + 2ab + b^2$ *can be applied to a purely numerical problem,* **work Exercises 39–42 in order.**

39. Evaluate 35^2 using either traditional paper-and-pencil methods or a calculator.

40. The number 35 can be written as $30 + 5$. Therefore, $35^2 = (30 + 5)^2$. Use the special product for squaring a binomial with $a = 30$ and $b = 5$ to write an expression for $(30 + 5)^2$. Do not simplify at this time.

41. Use the order of operations to simplify the expression you found in Exercise 40.

42. How do the answers in Exercises 39 and 41 compare?

Find each product. See Example 5.

43. $(m - 5)^3$

44. $(p + 3)^3$

45. $(y + 2)^3$

46. $(x - 7)^3$

47. $(2a + 1)^3$

48. $(3m - 1)^3$

49. $(3r - 2t)^4$

50. $(2z + 5y)^4$

51. $3x^2(x - 3)^3$

52. $4p^3(p + 4)^3$

53. $-8x^2y(x + y)^4$

In Exercises 54 and 55, refer to the figure shown here.

54. Find a polynomial that represents the volume of the cube.

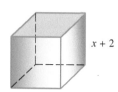

$x + 2$

55. If the value of x is 6, what is the volume of the cube?

12.5 ▷▷▷ Integer Exponents and the Quotient Rule

In all our earlier work, exponents were positive integers. Now we want to develop meaning for exponents that are *not* positive integers.

Consider the following list.

$$2^4 = 16$$
$$2^3 = 8$$
$$2^2 = 4$$

Do you see the pattern in the values? Each time we reduce the exponent by 1, the value is divided by 2 (the base). Using this pattern, we can continue the list to smaller and smaller integer exponents.

$$2^1 = 2$$
$$2^0 = 1$$
$$2^{-1} = \frac{1}{2}$$

Work Problem **1** *at the Side.* ▶

From the preceding list and the answers to Problem 1 at the side, it appears that we should define 2^0 as 1 and negative exponents as reciprocals.

OBJECTIVE **1** **Use 0 as an exponent.** We want the definitions of 0 and negative exponents to satisfy the rules for exponents from **Section 12.2.** For example, if $6^0 = 1$,

$$6^0 \cdot 6^2 = 1 \cdot 6^2 = 6^2 \quad \text{and} \quad 6^0 \cdot 6^2 = 6^{0+2} = 6^2,$$

so the product rule is satisfied. Check that the power rules are also valid for a 0 exponent. Thus, we define a 0 exponent as follows.

Zero Exponent

For any nonzero real number a, $\quad a^0 = 1.$

Example: $17^0 = 1$

EXAMPLE 1 **Using Zero Exponents**

Evaluate.

(a) $60^0 = 1$ (b) $(-60)^0 = 1$

(c) $-60^0 = -(1) = -1$ (d) $y^0 = 1, \quad y \neq 0$

(e) $6y^0 = 6(1) = 6, \quad y \neq 0$ (f) $(6y)^0 = 1, \quad y \neq 0$

CAUTION

Look again at Examples 1(b) and (c). In $(-60)^0$, the base is -60 and the exponent is 0. Any nonzero base raised to the exponent 0 is 1. In -60^0, the base is 60. Then $60^0 = 1$, and $-60^0 = -1$.

Work Problem **2** *at the Side.* ▶

OBJECTIVES

1 Use 0 as an exponent.

2 Use negative numbers as exponents.

3 Use the quotient rule for exponents.

4 Use combinations of rules.

1 Continue the list of exponentials using $-2, -3$, and -4 as exponents.

$$2^{-2} = \underline{\hspace{1cm}}$$
$$2^{-3} = \underline{\hspace{1cm}}$$
$$2^{-4} = \underline{\hspace{1cm}}$$

2 Evaluate.

(a) 28^0

(b) $(-16)^0$

(c) -7^0

(d) $m^0, \quad m \neq 0$

(e) $-p^0, \quad p \neq 0$

ANSWERS

1. $2^{-2} = \frac{1}{4}; 2^{-3} = \frac{1}{8}; 2^{-4} = \frac{1}{16}$

2. **(a)** 1   **(b)** 1   **(c)** -1 **(d)** 1   **(e)** -1

OBJECTIVE 2 **Use negative numbers as exponents.** From the lists at the beginning of this section and margin Problem 1, since $2^{-2} = \frac{1}{4}$ and $2^{-3} = \frac{1}{8}$, we can deduce that 2^{-n} should equal $\frac{1}{2^n}$. Is the product rule valid in such cases? For example, if we multiply 6^{-2} by 6^2, we get

$$6^{-2} \cdot 6^2 = 6^{-2+2} = 6^0 = 1.$$

The expression 6^{-2} behaves as if it were the reciprocal of 6^2, because their product is 1. The reciprocal of 6^2 may be written $\frac{1}{6^2}$, leading us to define 6^{-2} as $\frac{1}{6^2}$. This is a particular case of the definition of negative exponents.

Negative Exponents

For any nonzero real number a and any integer n, $a^{-n} = \dfrac{1}{a^n}$.

Example: $3^{-2} = \dfrac{1}{3^2}$

By definition, a^{-n} and a^n are reciprocals, since

$$a^n \cdot a^{-n} = a^n \cdot \frac{1}{a^n} = 1.$$

Since $1^n = 1$, the definition of a^{-n} can also be written

$$a^{-n} = \frac{1}{a^n} = \frac{1^n}{a^n} = \left(\frac{1}{a}\right)^n.$$

For example, $6^{-3} = \left(\dfrac{1}{6}\right)^3$ and $\left(\dfrac{1}{3}\right)^{-2} = 3^2.$

EXAMPLE 2 **Using Negative Exponents**

Simplify by writing with positive exponents. Assume that all variables represent nonzero real numbers.

(a) $3^{-2} = \dfrac{1}{3^2} = \dfrac{1}{9}$ $a^{-n} = \frac{1}{a^n}$ **(b)** $5^{-3} = \dfrac{1}{5^3} = \dfrac{1}{125}$

(c) $\left(\dfrac{1}{2}\right)^{-3} = 2^3 = 8$ $\frac{1}{2}$ and 2 are reciprocals.

Notice that we can change the base to its reciprocal if we also change the sign of the exponent.

(d) $\left(\dfrac{2}{5}\right)^{-4} = \left(\dfrac{5}{2}\right)^4 = \dfrac{5^4}{2^4} = \dfrac{625}{16}$ **(e)** $\left(\dfrac{4}{3}\right)^{-5} = \left(\dfrac{3}{4}\right)^5 = \dfrac{3^5}{4^5} = \dfrac{243}{1024}$

$\frac{2}{5}$ and $\frac{5}{2}$ are reciprocals.

(f) $4^{-1} - 2^{-1}$

$= \dfrac{1}{4} - \dfrac{1}{2} = \dfrac{1}{4} - \dfrac{2}{4} = -\dfrac{1}{4}$ Apply the exponents first; then subtract.

Continued on Next Page

(g) $p^{-2} = \dfrac{1}{p^2}$

(h) $\dfrac{1}{x^{-4}} = \dfrac{1^{-4}}{x^{-4}}$ $1^n = 1$, for any integer n

$= \left(\dfrac{1}{x}\right)^{-4}$ Power rule (c)

$= x^4$ $\frac{1}{x}$ and x are reciprocals.

Notice that, in general, $\dfrac{1}{a^{-n}} = a^n.$

(i) $x^3 y^{-4} = \dfrac{x^3}{1} \cdot \dfrac{1}{y^4} = \dfrac{x^3}{y^4}$

CAUTION

A negative exponent does not indicate a negative number. Negative exponents lead to reciprocals.

Expression	Example	
a^{-n}	$3^{-2} = \dfrac{1}{3^2} = \dfrac{1}{9}$	Not negative
$-a^{-n}$	$-3^{-2} = -\dfrac{1}{3^2} = -\dfrac{1}{9}$	Negative

Work Problem **3** *at the Side.* ▶

Consider the following:

$$\dfrac{2^{-3}}{3^{-4}} = \dfrac{\frac{1}{2^3}}{\frac{1}{3^4}} = \dfrac{1}{2^3} \div \dfrac{1}{3^4} = \dfrac{1}{2^3} \cdot \dfrac{3^4}{1} = \dfrac{3^4}{2^3}.$$

To divide by a fraction, multiply by its reciprocal.

Therefore,

$$\dfrac{2^{-3}}{3^{-4}} = \dfrac{3^4}{2^3}.$$

Changing from Negative to Positive Exponents

For any nonzero numbers a and b, and any integers m and n,

$$\dfrac{a^{-m}}{b^{-n}} = \dfrac{b^n}{a^m} \quad \text{and} \quad \left(\dfrac{a}{b}\right)^{-m} = \left(\dfrac{b}{a}\right)^m.$$

Examples: $\dfrac{3^{-5}}{2^{-4}} = \dfrac{2^4}{3^5}$ and $\left(\dfrac{4}{5}\right)^{-3} = \left(\dfrac{5}{4}\right)^3$

3 Simplify by writing with positive exponents. Assume that all variables represent nonzero real numbers.

(a) 4^{-3}

(b) 6^{-2}

(c) $\left(\dfrac{1}{4}\right)^{-2}$

(d) $\left(\dfrac{2}{3}\right)^{-2}$

(e) $2^{-1} + 5^{-1}$

(f) m^{-5}

(g) $\dfrac{1}{z^{-4}}$

(h) $p^2 q^{-5}$

ANSWERS

3. **(a)** $\dfrac{1}{4^3} = \dfrac{1}{64}$ **(b)** $\dfrac{1}{6^2} = \dfrac{1}{36}$ **(c)** $4^2 = 16$
(d) $\left(\dfrac{3}{2}\right)^2 = \dfrac{9}{4}$ **(e)** $\dfrac{1}{2} + \dfrac{1}{5} = \dfrac{7}{10}$
(f) $\dfrac{1}{m^5}$ **(g)** z^4 **(h)** $\dfrac{p^2}{q^5}$

④ Simplify. Assume that all variables represent nonzero real numbers.

(a) $\dfrac{7^{-1}}{5^{-4}}$

(b) $\dfrac{x^{-3}}{y^{-2}}$

(c) $\dfrac{4h^{-5}}{m^{-2}k}$

(d) $\left(\dfrac{3m}{p}\right)^{-2}$

EXAMPLE 3   **Changing from Negative to Positive Exponents**

Simplify. Assume that all variables represent nonzero real numbers.

(a) $\dfrac{4^{-2}}{5^{-3}} = \dfrac{5^3}{4^2} = \dfrac{125}{16}$

(b) $\dfrac{m^{-5}}{p^{-1}} = \dfrac{p^1}{m^5} = \dfrac{p}{m^5}$

(c) $\dfrac{a^{-2}b}{3d^{-3}} = \dfrac{bd^3}{3a^2}$ Notice that b in the numerator and the coefficient 3 in the denominator are not affected.

(d) $\left(\dfrac{x}{2y}\right)^{-4}$

$= \left(\dfrac{2y}{x}\right)^4$ Negative-to-positive rule

$= \dfrac{2^4 y^4}{x^4}$ Power rule (c)

$= \dfrac{16y^4}{x^4}$

◀ Work Problem ④ at the Side.

CAUTION

Be careful. We cannot use the rule $\dfrac{a^{-m}}{b^{-n}} = \dfrac{b^n}{a^m}$ to change negative exponents to positive exponents if the exponents occur in a *sum* or *difference* of terms. For example,

$\dfrac{5^{-2} + 3^{-1}}{7 - 2^{-3}}$ would be written with positive exponents as $\dfrac{\dfrac{1}{5^2} + \dfrac{1}{3}}{7 - \dfrac{1}{2^3}}$.

OBJECTIVE 3 Use the quotient rule for exponents.   Consider a quotient of two exponential expressions with the same base.

$$\dfrac{6^5}{6^3} = \dfrac{6 \cdot 6 \cdot 6 \cdot 6 \cdot 6}{6 \cdot 6 \cdot 6} = 6^2$$

Notice that the difference between the exponents, $5 - 3 = 2$, is the exponent in the quotient. Also,

$$\dfrac{6^2}{6^4} = \dfrac{6 \cdot 6}{6 \cdot 6 \cdot 6 \cdot 6} = \dfrac{1}{6^2} = 6^{-2}.$$

Here, $2 - 4 = -2$. These examples suggest the **quotient rule for exponents.**

Quotient Rule for Exponents

For any nonzero real number a and any integers m and n,

$$\dfrac{a^m}{a^n} = a^{m-n}.$$

(Keep the same base and subtract the exponents.)

Example: $\dfrac{5^8}{5^4} = 5^{8-4} = 5^4$

ANSWERS

4. **(a)** $\dfrac{625}{7}$ **(b)** $\dfrac{y^2}{x^3}$ **(c)** $\dfrac{4m^2}{h^5k}$

(d) $\dfrac{p^2}{9m^2}$

CAUTION
A common **error** is to write $\dfrac{5^8}{5^4} = 1^{8-4} = 1^4$. ***This is incorrect.*** By the quotient rule, the quotient must have the *same base*, 5, so

$$\frac{5^8}{5^4} = 5^{8-4} = 5^4.$$

We can confirm this by using the definition of exponents to write out the factors:

$$\frac{5^8}{5^4} = \frac{5\cdot5\cdot5\cdot5\cdot5\cdot5\cdot5\cdot5}{5\cdot5\cdot5\cdot5} = 5^4.$$

5 Simplify. Assume that all variables represent nonzero real numbers.

(a) $\dfrac{5^{11}}{5^8}$

EXAMPLE 4   Using the Quotient Rule

Simplify. Assume that all variables represent nonzero real numbers.

(b) $\dfrac{4^7}{4^{10}}$

(a) $\dfrac{5^8}{5^6} = 5^{8-6} = 5^2 = 25$ (b) $\dfrac{4^2}{4^9} = 4^{2-9} = 4^{-7} = \dfrac{1}{4^7}$

<small>Keep the same base.</small>

(c) $\dfrac{5^{-3}}{5^{-7}} = 5^{-3-(-7)} = 5^4 = 625$ (d) $\dfrac{q^5}{q^{-3}} = q^{5-(-3)} = q^8$

<small>Be careful with signs.</small>

(e) $\dfrac{3^2 x^5}{3^4 x^3}$ (f) $\dfrac{(m+n)^{-2}}{(m+n)^{-4}}$ (c) $\dfrac{6^{-5}}{6^{-2}}$

$\quad = \dfrac{3^2}{3^4}\cdot\dfrac{x^5}{x^3}$ $\quad = (m+n)^{-2-(-4)}$

$\quad = 3^{2-4}\cdot x^{5-3}$ $\quad = (m+n)^{-2+4}$

$\quad = 3^{-2}x^2$ $\quad = (m+n)^2,\quad m \neq -n$

$\quad = \dfrac{x^2}{3^2}$ <small>The restriction $m \neq -n$ is necessary to prevent a denominator of 0 in the original expression. Division by 0 is undefined.</small>

$\quad = \dfrac{x^2}{9}$ (d) $\dfrac{8^4 m^9}{8^5 m^{10}}$

(g) $\dfrac{7x^{-3}y^2}{2^{-1}x^2 y^{-5}}$

$\quad = \dfrac{7\cdot2^1 y^2 y^5}{x^2 x^3}$ <small>Definition of negative exponent</small>

$\quad = \dfrac{14y^7}{x^5}$ <small>Multiply; product rule</small>   (e) $\dfrac{3^{-1}(x+y)^{-3}}{2^{-2}(x+y)^{-4}},\quad x \neq -y$

Work Problem **5** *at the Side.* ▶

The definitions and rules for exponents given in this section and **Section 13.2** are summarized on the next page.

Definitions and Rules for Exponents

For any integers m and n:

Examples

Product rule	$a^m \cdot a^n = a^{m+n}$	$7^4 \cdot 7^5 = 7^{4+5} = 7^9$
Zero exponent	$a^0 = 1 \quad (a \neq 0)$	$(-3)^0 = 1$
Negative exponent	$a^{-n} = \dfrac{1}{a^n} \quad (a \neq 0)$	$5^{-3} = \dfrac{1}{5^3}$
Quotient rule	$\dfrac{a^m}{a^n} = a^{m-n} \quad (a \neq 0)$	$\dfrac{2^2}{2^5} = 2^{2-5} = 2^{-3} = \dfrac{1}{2^3}$
Power rule (a)	$(a^m)^n = a^{mn}$	$(4^2)^3 = 4^{2\cdot3} = 4^6$
Power rule (b)	$(ab)^m = a^m b^m$	$(3k)^4 = 3^4 k^4$
Power rule (c)	$\left(\dfrac{a}{b}\right)^m = \dfrac{a^m}{b^m} \quad (b \neq 0)$	$\left(\dfrac{2}{3}\right)^2 = \dfrac{2^2}{3^2}$
Negative-to-positive rules	$\dfrac{a^{-m}}{b^{-n}} = \dfrac{b^n}{a^m} \quad (a, b \neq 0)$	$\dfrac{2^{-4}}{5^{-3}} = \dfrac{5^3}{2^4}$
	$\left(\dfrac{a}{b}\right)^{-m} = \left(\dfrac{b}{a}\right)^m.$	$\left(\dfrac{4}{7}\right)^{-2} = \left(\dfrac{7}{4}\right)^2$

OBJECTIVE 4 Use combinations of rules. We sometimes need to use more than one rule to simplify an expression.

EXAMPLE 5 **Using a Combination of Rules**

Simplify each expression. Assume that all variables represent nonzero real numbers.

(a) $\dfrac{(4^2)^3}{4^5}$

$= \dfrac{4^6}{4^5}$ Power rule (a)

$= 4^{6-5}$ Quotient rule

$= 4^1$

$= 4$

(b) $(2x)^3 (2x)^2$

$= (2x)^5$ Product rule

$= 2^5 x^5$ Power rule (b)

$= 32x^5$

(c) $\left(\dfrac{2x^3}{5}\right)^{-4}$

$= \left(\dfrac{5}{2x^3}\right)^4$ Negative-to-positive rule

$= \dfrac{5^4}{2^4 x^{12}}$ Power rules (a)–(c)

$= \dfrac{625}{16x^{12}}$

(d) $\left(\dfrac{3x^{-2}}{4^{-1}y^3}\right)^{-3}$

$= \dfrac{3^{-3}x^6}{4^3 y^{-9}}$ Power rules (a)–(c)

$= \dfrac{x^6 y^9}{4^3 \cdot 3^3}$ Negative-to-positive rule

$= \dfrac{x^6 y^9}{1728}$ $4^3 \cdot 3^3 = 64 \cdot 27 = 1728$

Continued on Next Page

(e) $\dfrac{(4m)^{-3}}{(3m)^{-4}}$

$= \dfrac{4^{-3}m^{-3}}{3^{-4}m^{-4}}$ Power rule (b)

$= \dfrac{3^4 m^4}{4^3 m^3}$ Negative-to-positive rule

$= \dfrac{3^4 m^{4-3}}{4^3}$ Quotient rule

$= \dfrac{3^4 m}{4^3}$

$= \dfrac{81m}{64}$

Note

Since the steps can be done in several different orders, there are many equally correct ways to simplify expressions like those in Examples 5(c) through 5(e).

Work Problem 6 *at the Side.* ▶

6 Simplify each expression. Assume that all variables represent nonzero real numbers.

(a) $\dfrac{(3^4)^2}{3^3}$

(b) $(4x)^2 (4x)^4$

(c) $\dfrac{(6x)^{-1}}{(3x^2)^{-2}}$

(d) $\dfrac{3^9 \cdot (x^2 y)^{-2}}{3^3 \cdot x^{-4} y}$

ANSWERS

6. (a) 243   (b) $4^6 x^6$, or $4096x^6$ (c) $\dfrac{3x^3}{2}$

(d) $\dfrac{729}{y^3}$

Math in the Media

MORE POWER TO YOU, CAPTAIN KIRK

The original *Star Trek* series first aired during the 1966 to 1967 television season and started the phenomenon that continues today. There have been five different television series and 10 feature movies with the *Star Trek* theme.

Captain James T. Kirk, portrayed by William Shatner, led the Starship Enterprise during its first three seasons. During the first season, the February 2, 1967, episode "Court Martial" told the story of Kirk being put on trial. He was accused of negligence in the death of a crewmember, because the computer records of the ship contradicted Kirk's logs. As the trial begins, Kirk explains how the sounds on the ship can be recorded and magnified:

Kirk: *Gentlemen, this computer has an auditory sensor. It can, in effect, hear sounds. By installing a booster we can increase that capability on an order of one to the fourth power. The computer should be able to bring us every sound occurring on the ship.*

1. Read Captain Kirk's statement carefully. What error did he make?

2. What is the result if we raise the number 1 to any whole number power?

3. It is possible that Kirk meant "10 to the fourth power." Express 10^4 in expanded form.

4. The word **googol** was invented to express a very large power of 10. The search engine Google was named in honor of it. Look up the meaning of googol, and write it in exponential form.

5. Investigate the meaning of the word **googolplex.**

12.5 ▶▶▶ **Exercises**

FOR
EXTRA
HELP    WATCH DOWNLOAD READ REVIEW

Decide whether each expression is positive, negative, or 0.

1. $(-2)^{-3}$ **2.** $(-3)^{-2}$ **3.** -2^4 **4.** -3^6

5. $\left(\dfrac{1}{4}\right)^{-2}$ **6.** $\left(\dfrac{1}{5}\right)^{-2}$ **7.** $1 - 5^0$ **8.** $1 - 7^0$

Decide whether each expression is equal to either 0, 1, *or* -1. *See Example 1.*

9. 9^0 **10.** 5^0 **11.** $(-4)^0$ **12.** $(-10)^0$ **13.** -9^0

14. -5^0 **15.** $(-2)^0 - 2^0$ **16.** $(-8)^0 - 8^0$ **17.** $\dfrac{0^{10}}{10^0}$ **18.** $\dfrac{0^5}{5^0}$

Evaluate each expression. See Examples 1 and 2.

19. $7^0 + 9^0$ **20.** $8^0 + 6^0$ 🌐 **21.** 4^{-3} **22.** 5^{-4} **23.** $\left(\dfrac{1}{2}\right)^{-4}$

24. $\left(\dfrac{1}{3}\right)^{-3}$ 🌐 **25.** $\left(\dfrac{6}{7}\right)^{-2}$ **26.** $\left(\dfrac{2}{3}\right)^{-3}$ **27.** $(-3)^{-4}$ **28.** $(-4)^{-3}$

29. $5^{-1} + 3^{-1}$ **30.** $6^{-1} + 2^{-1}$ **31.** $-2^{-1} + 3^{-2}$ **32.** $(-3)^{-2} + (-4)^{-1}$

Relating Concepts (Exercises 33–36) For Individual or Group Work

In Objective 1, we used the product rule to motivate the definition of a 0 *exponent. We can also use the quotient rule. To see this,* **work Exercises 33–36 in order.**

33. Consider the expression $\dfrac{25}{25}$. What is its simplest form?

34. Write the quotient in Exercise 33 using the fact that $25 = 5^2$.

35. Apply the quotient rule for exponents to your answer for Exercise 34. Give the answer as a power of 5.

36. Because your answers for Exercises 33 and 35 both represent $\dfrac{25}{25}$, they must be equal. Write this equality. What definition does it support?

Simplify by writing each expression with positive exponents. Assume that all variables represent nonzero real numbers. See Examples 2–4.

37. $\dfrac{9^4}{9^5}$ **38.** $\dfrac{7^3}{7^4}$ **39.** $\dfrac{6^{-3}}{6^2}$ **40.** $\dfrac{4^{-2}}{4^3}$ **41.** $\dfrac{1}{6^{-3}}$

42. $\dfrac{1}{5^{-2}}$ **43.** $\dfrac{2}{r^{-4}}$ **44.** $\dfrac{3}{s^{-8}}$ **45.** $\dfrac{4^{-3}}{5^{-2}}$ **46.** $\dfrac{6^{-2}}{5^{-4}}$

47. $p^5 q^{-8}$ **48.** $x^{-8} y^4$ **49.** $\dfrac{r^5}{r^{-4}}$ **50.** $\dfrac{a^6}{a^{-4}}$ **51.** $\dfrac{6^4 x^8}{6^5 x^3}$

52. $\dfrac{3^8 y^5}{3^{10} y^2}$ **53.** $\dfrac{6 y^3}{2y}$ **54.** $\dfrac{5 m^2}{m}$ **55.** $\dfrac{3 x^5}{3 x^2}$ **56.** $\dfrac{10 p^8}{2 p^4}$

57. $\dfrac{x^{-3} y}{4 z^{-2}}$ **58.** $\dfrac{p^{-5} q^{-4}}{9 r^{-3}}$ **59.** $\dfrac{(a+b)^{-3}}{(a+b)^{-4}}$ **60.** $\dfrac{(x+y)^{-8}}{(x+y)^{-9}}$

Simplify by writing each expression with positive exponents. Assume that all variables represent nonzero real numbers. See Example 5.

61. $\dfrac{(7^4)^3}{7^9}$ **62.** $\dfrac{(5^3)^2}{5^2}$ **63.** $x^{-3} \cdot x^5 \cdot x^{-4}$ **64.** $y^{-8} \cdot y^5 \cdot y^{-2}$

65. $\dfrac{(3x)^{-2}}{(4x)^{-3}}$ **66.** $\dfrac{(2y)^{-3}}{(5y)^{-4}}$ **67.** $\left(\dfrac{x^{-1} y}{z^2}\right)^{-2}$ **68.** $\left(\dfrac{p^{-4} q}{r^{-3}}\right)^{-3}$

69. $(6x)^4 (6x)^{-3}$ **70.** $(10y)^9 (10y)^{-8}$ **71.** $\dfrac{(m^7 n)^{-2}}{m^{-4} n^3}$ **72.** $\dfrac{(m^8 n^{-4})^2}{m^{-2} n^5}$

73. $\dfrac{5 x^{-3}}{(4x)^2}$ **74.** $\dfrac{-3 k^5}{(2k)^2}$ **75.** $\left(\dfrac{2 p^{-1} q}{3^{-1} m^2}\right)^2$ **76.** $\left(\dfrac{4 x y^2}{x^{-1} y}\right)^{-2}$

Summary Exercises on the Rules for Exponents

Simplify each expression. Assume that all variables represent nonzero real numbers.

1. $\left(\dfrac{6x^2}{5}\right)^{12}$

2. $\left(\dfrac{rs^2t^3}{3t^4}\right)^6$

3. $(10x^2y^4)^2(10xy^2)^3$

4. $(-2ab^3c)^4(-2a^2b)^3$

5. $\left(\dfrac{9wx^3}{y^4}\right)^3$

6. $(4x^{-2}y^{-3})^{-2}$

7. $\dfrac{c^{11}(c^2)^4}{(c^3)^3(c^2)^{-6}}$

8. $\left(\dfrac{k^4t^2}{k^2t^{-4}}\right)^{-2}$

9. $5^{-1}+6^{-1}$

10. $\dfrac{(3y^{-1}z^3)^{-1}(3y^2)}{(y^3z^2)^{-3}}$

11. $\dfrac{(2xy^{-1})^3}{2^3x^{-3}y^2}$

12. $-8^0+(-8)^0$

13. $(z^4)^{-3}(z^{-2})^{-5}$

14. $\left(\dfrac{r^2st^5}{3r}\right)^{-2}$

15. $\dfrac{(3^{-1}x^{-3}y)^{-1}(2x^2y^{-3})^2}{(5x^{-2}y^2)^{-2}}$

16. $\left(\dfrac{5x^2}{3x^{-4}}\right)^{-1}$

17. $\left(\dfrac{-2x^{-2}}{2x^2}\right)^{-2}$

18. $\dfrac{(x^{-4}y^2)^3(x^2y)^{-1}}{(xy^2)^{-3}}$

19. $\dfrac{(a^{-2}b^3)^{-4}}{(a^{-3}b^2)^{-2}(ab)^{-4}}$

20. $(2a^{-30}b^{-29})(3a^{31}b^{30})$

21. $5^{-2}+6^{-2}$

22. $\left(\dfrac{(x^{47}y^{23})^2}{x^{-26}y^{-42}}\right)^0$

23. $\left(\dfrac{7a^2b^3}{2}\right)^3$

24. $-(-12^0)$

25. $-(-12)^0$

26. $\dfrac{0^{12}}{12^0}$

27. $\dfrac{(2xy^{-3})^{-2}}{(3x^{-2}y^4)^{-3}}$

28. $\left(\dfrac{a^2b^3c^4}{a^{-2}b^{-3}c^{-4}}\right)^{-2}$

29. $(6x^{-5}z^3)^{-3}$

30. $(2p^{-2}qr^{-3})(2p)^{-4}$

31. $\dfrac{(xy)^{-3}(xy)^5}{(xy)^{-4}}$

32. $42^0 - (-12)^0$

33. $\dfrac{(7^{-1}x^{-3})^{-2}(x^4)^{-6}}{7^{-1}x^{-3}}$

34. $\left(\dfrac{3^{-4}x^{-3}}{3^{-3}x^{-6}}\right)^{-2}$

35. $(5p^{-2}q)^{-3}(5pq^3)^4$

36. $8^{-1} + 6^{-1}$

37. $\left(\dfrac{4r^{-6}s^{-2}t}{2r^8s^{-4}t^2}\right)^{-1}$

38. $(13x^{-6}y)(13x^{-6}y)^{-1}$

39. $\dfrac{(8pq^{-2})^4}{(8p^{-2}q^{-3})^3}$

40. $\left(\dfrac{mn^{-2}p}{m^2np^4}\right)^{-2}\left(\dfrac{mn^{-2}p}{m^2np^4}\right)^3$

41. $-(-3^0)^0$

42. $5^{-1} - 8^{-1}$

43. A student simplified $(10^2)^3$ as 1000^6. **WHAT WENT WRONG?** Give the correct answer.

44. A student simplified -5^4 as shown:
$$-5^4 = (-5)^4 = 625.$$
WHAT WENT WRONG? Give the correct answer.

12.6 ▶▶▶ Dividing a Polynomial by a Monomial

OBJECTIVE 1 Divide a polynomial by a monomial. We add two fractions with a common denominator as follows.

$$\frac{a}{c} + \frac{b}{c} = \frac{a+b}{c}$$

In reverse, this statement gives a rule for dividing a polynomial by a monomial.

OBJECTIVE

1 Divide a polynomial by a monomial.

Dividing a Polynomial by a Monomial

To divide a polynomial by a monomial, divide each term of the polynomial by the monomial:

$$\frac{a+b}{c} = \frac{a}{c} + \frac{b}{c} \quad (c \neq 0).$$

Examples: $\frac{2+5}{3} = \frac{2}{3} + \frac{5}{3}$ and $\frac{x+3z}{2y} = \frac{x}{2y} + \frac{3z}{2y}$ $(y \neq 0)$

1 Divide.

(a) $\dfrac{6p^4 + 18p^7}{3p^2}$

The parts of a division problem are named here.

Dividend → $\dfrac{12x^2 + 6x}{6x}$ = 2x + 1 ← Quotient
Divisor →

EXAMPLE 1 Dividing a Polynomial by a Monomial

Divide $5m^5 - 10m^3$ by $5m^2$.

$$\frac{5m^5 - 10m^3}{5m^2}$$

$$= \frac{5m^5}{5m^2} - \frac{10m^3}{5m^2} \quad \text{Use the preceding rule, with + replaced by −.}$$

$$= m^3 - 2m \quad \text{Quotient rule}$$

(b) $\dfrac{12m^6 + 18m^5 + 30m^4}{6m^2}$

Check   Multiply: $5m^2 \cdot (m^3 - 2m) = 5m^5 - 10m^3.$

Divisor Quotient   Original polynomial (Dividend)

Because division by 0 is undefined, the quotient $\frac{5m^5 - 10m^3}{5m^2}$ is undefined if $m = 0$. From now on, we assume that no denominators are 0.

Work Problem 1 at the Side. ▶

(c) $(18r^7 - 9r^2) \div (3r)$

EXAMPLE 2 Dividing a Polynomial by a Monomial

Divide $\dfrac{16a^5 - 12a^4 + 8a^2}{4a^3}.$

$$\frac{16a^5 - 12a^4 + 8a^2}{4a^3}$$

$$= \frac{16a^5}{4a^3} - \frac{12a^4}{4a^3} + \frac{8a^2}{4a^3} \quad \text{Divide each term by } 4a^3.$$

$$= 4a^2 - 3a + \frac{2}{a} \quad \text{Quotient rule}$$

ANSWERS
1. (a) $2p^2 + 6p^5$ (b) $2m^4 + 3m^3 + 5m^2$
   (c) $6r^6 - 3r$

Continued on Next Page

2 Divide.

(a) $\dfrac{20x^4 - 25x^3 + 5x}{5x^2}$

(b) $\dfrac{50m^4 - 30m^3 + 20m}{10m^3}$

The quotient $4a^2 - 3a + \frac{2}{a}$ is not a polynomial because of the expression $\frac{2}{a}$, which has a variable in the denominator. While the sum, difference, and product of two polynomials are always polynomials, the quotient of two polynomials may not be.

Check $\qquad 4a^3\left(4a^2 - 3a + \dfrac{2}{a}\right) \qquad$ Divisor $\times$ Quotient should equal Dividend.

$\qquad\qquad = 4a^3(4a^2) + 4a^3(-3a) + 4a^3\left(\dfrac{2}{a}\right) \qquad$ Distributive property

$\qquad\qquad = 16a^5 - 12a^4 + 8a^2 \qquad$ Dividend

◀ *Work Problem* 2 *at the Side.*

EXAMPLE 3 **Dividing a Polynomial by a Monomial with a Negative Coefficient**

Divide $-7x^3 + 12x^4 - 4x$ by $-4x$.

Write the polynomial in descending powers as $12x^4 - 7x^3 - 4x$ before dividing.

Write in descending powers. $\qquad \dfrac{12x^4 - 7x^3 - 4x}{-4x}$

$\qquad = \dfrac{12x^4}{-4x} - \dfrac{7x^3}{-4x} - \dfrac{4x}{-4x} \qquad$ Divide each term by $-4x$.

$\qquad = -3x^3 - \dfrac{7x^2}{-4} - (-1) \qquad$ Quotient rule

$\qquad = -3x^3 + \dfrac{7}{4}x^2 + 1 \qquad$ Be sure to include the 1 in the answer.

Check by multiplying.

◀ *Work Problem* 3 *at the Side.*

3 Divide.

(a) $\dfrac{-9y^6 + 8y^7 - 11y - 4}{y^2}$

(b) $\dfrac{-8p^4 - 6p^3 - 12p^5}{-3p^3}$

EXAMPLE 4 **Dividing a Polynomial by a Monomial**

Divide $180x^4y^{10} - 150x^3y^8 + 120x^2y^6 - 90xy^4 + 100y$ by $-30xy^2$.

$\qquad \dfrac{180x^4y^{10} - 150x^3y^8 + 120x^2y^6 - 90xy^4 + 100y}{-30xy^2}$

$\qquad = \dfrac{180x^4y^{10}}{-30xy^2} - \dfrac{150x^3y^8}{-30xy^2} + \dfrac{120x^2y^6}{-30xy^2} - \dfrac{90xy^4}{-30xy^2} + \dfrac{100y}{-30xy^2}$

$\qquad = -6x^3y^8 + 5x^2y^6 - 4xy^4 + 3y^2 - \dfrac{10}{3xy}$

◀ *Work Problem* 4 *at the Side.*

4 Divide.

$\dfrac{45x^4y^3 + 30x^3y^2 - 60x^2y}{-15x^2y}$

ANSWERS

2. (a) $4x^2 - 5x + \dfrac{1}{x}$ (b) $5m - 3 + \dfrac{2}{m^2}$

3. (a) $8y^5 - 9y^4 - \dfrac{11}{y} - \dfrac{4}{y^2}$

(b) $4p^2 + \dfrac{8p}{3} + 2$

4. $-3x^2y^2 - 2xy + 4$

Fill in each blank with the correct response.

1. In the statement $\dfrac{6x^2 + 8}{2} = 3x^2 + 4$, _____ is the dividend, _____ is the divisor, and _____ is the quotient.

2. The expression $\dfrac{3x + 12}{x}$ is undefined if $x =$ _____.

3. To check the division shown in Exercise 1, multiply _____ by _____ and show that the product is _____.

4. The expression $5x^2 - 3x + 6 + \frac{2}{x}$ _____ a polynomial.
   (is/is not)

5. Explain why the division problem $\dfrac{16m^3 - 12m^2}{4m}$ can be performed using the method of this section, while the division problem $\dfrac{4m}{16m^3 - 12m^2}$ cannot.

6. Evaluate $\dfrac{5y + 6}{2}$ when $y = 2$. Evaluate $5y + 3$ when $y = 2$. Does $\dfrac{5y + 6}{2}$ equal $5y + 3$?

Perform each division. See Examples 1–4.

7. $\dfrac{60x^4 - 20x^2 + 10x}{2x}$

8. $\dfrac{120x^6 - 60x^3 + 80x^2}{2x}$

9. $\dfrac{20m^5 - 10m^4 + 5m^2}{-5m^2}$

10. $\dfrac{12t^5 - 6t^3 + 6t^2}{-6t^2}$

11. $\dfrac{8t^5 - 4t^3 + 4t^2}{2t}$

12. $\dfrac{8r^4 - 4r^3 + 6r^2}{2r}$

13. $\dfrac{4a^5 - 4a^2 + 8}{4a}$

14. $\dfrac{5t^8 + 5t^7 + 15}{5t}$

15. $\dfrac{12x^5 - 4x^4 + 6x^3}{-6x^2}$

16. $\dfrac{24x^6 - 12x^5 + 30x^4}{-6x^2}$

17. $\dfrac{4x^2 + 20x^3 - 36x^4}{4x^2}$

18. $\dfrac{5x^2 - 30x^4 + 30x^5}{5x^2}$

19. $\dfrac{-3x^3 - 4x^4 + 2x}{-3x^2}$

20. $\dfrac{-8x + 6x^3 - 5x^4}{-3x^2}$

21. $\dfrac{27r^4 - 36r^3 - 6r^2 + 3r - 2}{3r}$

22. $\dfrac{8k^4 - 12k^3 - 2k^2 - 2k - 3}{2k}$

23. $\dfrac{2m^5 - 6m^4 + 8m^2}{-2m^3}$

24. $\dfrac{6r^5 - 8r^4 + 10r^2}{-2r^4}$

25. $(120x^{11} - 60x^{10} + 140x^9 - 100x^8) \div (10x^{12})$

26. $(120x^{12} - 84x^9 + 60x^8 - 36x^7) \div (12x^9)$

27. $(20a^4b^3 - 15a^5b^2 + 25a^3b) \div (-5a^4b)$

28. $(16y^5z - 8y^2z^2 + 12yz^3) \div (-4y^2z^2)$

29. What polynomial represents the length of the rectangle?

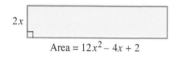

$2x$

Area $= 12x^2 - 4x + 2$

30. What polynomial represents the length of the base of the triangle?

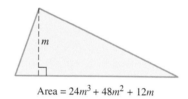

m

Area $= 24m^3 + 48m^2 + 12m$

31. What polynomial, when divided by $5x^3$, yields $3x^2 - 7x + 7$ as a quotient?

32. The quotient of a certain polynomial and $-12y^3$ is $6y^3 - 5y^2 + 2y - 3 + \dfrac{7}{y}$. Find the polynomial.

Relating Concepts (Exercises 33—36) For Individual or Group Work

Our system of numeration is called a decimal system. It is based on powers of ten. In a whole number such as 2846, each digit is understood to represent the number of powers of ten for its place value. The 2 represents two thousands (2×10^3), the 8 represents eight hundreds (8×10^2), the 4 represents four tens (4×10^1), and the 6 represents six ones (or units) (6×10^0). In expanded form we write

$$2846 = (2 \times 10^3) + (8 \times 10^2) + (4 \times 10^1) + (6 \times 10^0).$$

Keeping this information in mind, **work Exercises 33–36 in order.**

33. Divide 2846 by 2, using paper-and-pencil methods: $2\overline{)2846}$.

34. Write your answer in Exercise 33 in expanded form.

35. Use the methods of this section to divide the polynomial $2x^3 + 8x^2 + 4x + 6$ by 2.

36. Compare your answers in Exercises 34 and 35. How are they similar? How are they different? For what value of x does the answer in Exercise 35 equal the answer in Exercise 34?

12.7 ▷▷▷ Dividing a Polynomial by a Polynomial

OBJECTIVE 1 Divide a polynomial by a polynomial.   We use a method of "long division" to divide a polynomial by a polynomial (other than a monomial). ***Both polynomials must be written in descending powers.***

OBJECTIVES

1 Divide a polynomial by a polynomial.

2 Apply division to a geometry problem.

Dividing Whole Numbers	Dividing Polynomials
Step 1	
Divide 6696 by 27.	Divide $8x^3 - 4x^2 - 14x + 15$ by $2x + 3$.
$27\overline{)6696}$	$2x + 3\overline{)8x^3 - 4x^2 - 14x + 15}$

Step 2

66 divided by 27 = 2;
$2 \cdot 27 = 54$.

$$27\overline{)6696} \quad \begin{array}{r} 2 \\ \hline \end{array}$$
$$54$$

$8x^3$ divided by $2x = 4x^2$;
$4x^2(2x + 3) = 8x^3 + 12x^2$.

$$2x + 3\overline{)8x^3 - 4x^2 - 14x + 15} \quad \begin{array}{r} 4x^2 \\ \hline \end{array}$$
$$8x^3 + 12x^2$$

Step 3

Subtract; then bring down the next digit.

$$\begin{array}{r} 2 \\ 27\overline{)6696} \\ 54\downarrow \\ \hline 129 \end{array}$$

Subtract; then bring down the next term.

$$\begin{array}{r} 4x^2 \\ 2x + 3\overline{)8x^3 - 4x^2 - 14x + 15} \\ 8x^3 + 12x^2 \downarrow \\ \hline -16x^2 - 14x \end{array}$$

(To subtract two polynomials, change the signs of the second and then add.)

Step 4

129 divided by 27 = 4;
$4 \cdot 27 = 108$.

$$\begin{array}{r} 24 \\ 27\overline{)6696} \\ 54 \\ \hline 129 \\ 108 \end{array}$$

$-16x^2$ divided by $2x = -8x$;
$-8x(2x + 3) = -16x^2 - 24x$.

$$\begin{array}{r} 4x^2 - 8x \\ 2x + 3\overline{)8x^3 - 4x^2 - 14x + 15} \\ 8x^3 + 12x^2 \\ \hline -16x^2 - 14x \\ -16x^2 - 24x \end{array}$$

Step 5

Subtract; then bring down the next digit.

$$\begin{array}{r} 24 \\ 27\overline{)6696} \\ 54 \\ \hline 129 \\ 108 \\ \hline 216 \end{array}$$

Subtract; then bring down the next term.

$$\begin{array}{r} 4x^2 - 8x \\ 2x + 3\overline{)8x^3 - 4x^2 - 14x + 15} \\ 8x^3 + 12x^2 \\ \hline -16x^2 - 14x \\ -16x^2 - 24x \\ \hline 10x + 15 \end{array}$$

(continued)

Step 6

216 divided by 27 = **8**;
8 · 27 = **216**.

$$
\begin{array}{r}
248 \\
27\overline{)6696} \\
54 \\
\hline
129 \\
108 \\
\hline
216 \\
216 \\
\hline
\end{array}
$$
Remainder → 0

6696 divided by 27 is 248.

10x divided by 2x = **5**;
5(2x + 3) = **10x + 15.**

$$
\begin{array}{r}
4x^2 - 8x + 5 \\
2x + 3\overline{)8x^3 - 4x^2 - 14x + 15} \\
8x^3 + 12x^2 \\
\hline
-16x^2 - 14x \\
-16x^2 - 24x \\
\hline
10x + 15 \\
10x + 15 \\
\hline
\end{array}
$$
Remainder → 0

$8x^3 - 4x^2 - 14x + 15$ divided by $2x + 3$ is $4x^2 - 8x + 5$.

Step 7 Multiply to check.

Check 27 · 248 = 6696

Check $(2x + 3)(4x^2 - 8x + 5)$
$= 8x^3 - 4x^2 - 14x + 15$

EXAMPLE 1 **Dividing a Polynomial by a Polynomial**

Divide $5x + 4x^3 - 8 - 4x^2$ by $2x - 1$.

The first polynomial must be written with the exponents in descending powers as $4x^3 - 4x^2 + 5x - 8$. Then divide by $2x - 1$.

$$
\begin{array}{r}
2x^2 - x + 2 \\
2x - 1\overline{)4x^3 - 4x^2 + 5x - 8} \\
4x^3 - 2x^2 \\
\hline
-2x^2 + 5x \\
-2x^2 + x \\
\hline
4x - 8 \\
4x - 2 \\
\hline
-6 \leftarrow \text{Remainder}
\end{array}
$$

To subtract, add the opposite.

Write in descending powers.

Step 1 $4x^3$ divided by $2x = \mathbf{2x^2}$; $2x^2(2x - 1) = 4x^3 - 2x^2$.

Step 2 Subtract; bring down the next term.

Step 3 $-2x^2$ divided by $2x = \mathbf{-x}$; $-x(2x - 1) = -2x^2 + x$.

Step 4 Subtract; bring down the next term.

Step 5 $4x$ divided by $2x = \mathbf{2}$; $2(2x - 1) = 4x - 2$.

Step 6 Subtract. The remainder is -6. Write the remainder as the numerator of a fraction that has $2x - 1$ as its denominator. The answer is not a polynomial because of the nonzero remainder.

Dividend →
Divisor →
$$\frac{4x^3 - 4x^2 + 5x - 8}{2x - 1} = \underbrace{2x^2 - x + 2}_{\substack{\text{Quotient} \\ \text{polynomial}}} + \frac{-6}{2x - 1}$$

Continued on Next Page

Step 7   Multiply to check.

Check $(2x - 1)\left(2x^2 - x + 2 + \dfrac{-6}{2x - 1}\right)$

$= (2x - 1)(2x^2) + (2x - 1)(-x) + (2x - 1)(2)$

$\quad + (2x - 1)\left(\dfrac{-6}{2x - 1}\right)$

$= 4x^3 - 2x^2 - 2x^2 + x + 4x - 2 - 6$

$= 4x^3 - 4x^2 + 5x - 8$

Work Problem **1** *at the Side.* ▶

EXAMPLE 2   **Dividing into a Polynomial with Missing Terms**

Divide $x^3 - 1$ by $x - 1$.

Here the polynomial $x^3 - 1$ is missing the x^2-term and the x-term. When terms are missing, use 0 as the coefficient for each missing term. (Zero acts as a placeholder here, just as it does in our numeration system.) Thus, $x^3 - 1 = x^3 + 0x^2 + 0x - 1$. Now divide.

$$
\begin{array}{r}
x^2 + \ x + 1 \\
x - 1\overline{)x^3 + 0x^2 + 0x - 1} \\
\underline{x^3 - \ x^2} \\
x^2 + 0x \\
\underline{x^2 - \ x} \\
x - 1 \\
\underline{x - 1} \\
0
\end{array}
$$

Insert placeholders for the missing terms.

The remainder is 0. The quotient is $x^2 + x + 1$.

Check $(x - 1)(x^2 + x + 1)$

$= x^3 + x^2 + x - x^2 - x - 1$

$= x^3 - 1$

Work Problem **2** *at the Side.* ▶

EXAMPLE 3   **Dividing by a Polynomial with Missing Terms**

Divide $x^4 + 2x^3 + 2x^2 - x - 1$ by $x^2 + 1$.

Since $x^2 + 1$ has a missing x-term, write it as $x^2 + 0x + 1$.

$$
\begin{array}{r}
x^2 + 2x + 1 \\
x^2 + 0x + 1\overline{)x^4 + 2x^3 + 2x^2 - \ x - 1} \\
\underline{x^4 + 0x^3 + \ x^2} \\
2x^3 + \ x^2 - \ x \\
\underline{2x^3 + 0x^2 + 2x} \\
x^2 - 3x - 1 \\
\underline{x^2 + 0x + 1} \\
-3x - 2 \leftarrow \text{Remainder}
\end{array}
$$

Insert a placeholder for the missing term.

Continued on Next Page

---

1 Divide.

(a) $(x^3 + x^2 + 4x - 6)$
$\div (x - 1)$

(b) $\dfrac{p^3 - 2p^2 - 5p + 9}{p + 2}$

2 Divide.

(a) $\dfrac{r^2 - 5}{r + 4}$

(b) $(x^3 - 8) \div (x - 2)$

ANSWERS

1. (a) $x^2 + 2x + 6$

   (b) $p^2 - 4p + 3 + \dfrac{3}{p + 2}$

2. (a) $r - 4 + \dfrac{11}{r + 4}$

   (b) $x^2 + 2x + 4$

3 Divide.

(a)

$(2x^4 + 3x^3 - x^2 + 6x + 5)$
$\div (x^2 - 1)$

When the result of subtracting $(-3x - 2$, in this case) is a constant or a polynomial of degree less than the divisor $(x^2 + 0x + 1)$, that constant or polynomial is the remainder. We write the answer as

$$x^2 + 2x + 1 + \frac{-3x - 2}{x^2 + 1}.$$

Remember to include " $+ \frac{remainder}{divisor}$ "

Multiply to check that this is the correct quotient.

◀ Work Problem **3** at the Side.

EXAMPLE 4 **Dividing a Polynomial when the Quotient Has Fractional Coefficients**

Divide $4x^3 + 2x^2 + 3x + 2$ by $4x - 4$.

(b)

$$\frac{2m^5 + m^4 + 6m^3 - 3m^2 - 18}{m^2 + 3}$$

$$\frac{6x^2}{4x} = \frac{3}{2}x$$

$$x^2 + \frac{3}{2}x + \frac{9}{4} \longleftarrow \frac{9x}{4x} = \frac{9}{4}$$

$$4x - 4 \overline{)4x^3 + 2x^2 + 3x + 2}$$
$$\underline{4x^3 - 4x^2}$$
$$6x^2 + 3x$$
$$\underline{6x^2 - 6x}$$
$$9x + 2$$
$$\underline{9x - 9}$$
$$11$$

The answer is $x^2 + \dfrac{3}{2}x + \dfrac{9}{4} + \dfrac{11}{4x - 4}$.

4 Divide $3x^3 + 7x^2 + 7x + 10$ by $3x + 6$.

◀ Work Problem **4** at the Side.

OBJECTIVE 2 Apply division to a geometry problem.

EXAMPLE 5 **Using an Area Formula**

The area of the rectangle in Figure 3 is $x^3 + 4x^2 + 8x + 8$ square units and the width is $x + 2$ units. What is its length?

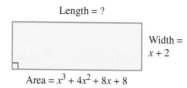

Length = ?

Width = $x + 2$

Area $= x^3 + 4x^2 + 8x + 8$

Figure 3

5 Divide $x^3 + 4x^2 + 8x + 8$ by $x + 2$.

Since $A = lw$, solving for l gives $l = \frac{A}{w}$. Divide $x^3 + 4x^2 + 8x + 8$ by the width, $x + 2$.

◀ Work Problem **5** at the Side.

The quotient from Problem 5 at the side, $x^2 + 2x + 4$, represents the length of the rectangle in units.

ANSWERS

3. (a) $2x^2 + 3x + 1 + \dfrac{9x + 6}{x^2 - 1}$

(b) $2m^3 + m^2 - 6$

4. $x^2 + \dfrac{1}{3}x + \dfrac{5}{3}$

5. $x^2 + 2x + 4$

12.7 ▷▷▷ Exercises

1. In the division problem $(4x^4 + 2x^3 - 14x^2 + 19x + 10) \div (2x + 5) = 2x^3 - 4x^2 + 3x + 2$, which polynomial is the divisor? Which is the quotient?

2. When dividing one polynomial by another, how do you know when to stop dividing?

3. In dividing $12m^2 - 20m + 3$ by $2m - 3$, what is the first step?

4. In the division in Exercise 3, what is the second step?

Perform each division. See Example 1.

5. $\dfrac{x^2 - x - 6}{x - 3}$

6. $\dfrac{m^2 - 2m - 24}{m - 6}$

7. $\dfrac{2y^2 + 9y - 35}{y + 7}$

8. $\dfrac{2y^2 + 9y + 7}{y + 1}$

9. $\dfrac{p^2 + 2p + 20}{p + 6}$

10. $\dfrac{x^2 + 11x + 16}{x + 8}$

11. $(r^2 - 8r + 15) \div (r - 3)$

12. $(t^2 + 2t - 35) \div (t - 5)$

13. $\dfrac{4a^2 - 22a + 32}{2a + 3}$

14. $\dfrac{9w^2 + 6w + 10}{3w - 2}$

15. $\dfrac{8x^3 - 10x^2 - x + 3}{2x + 1}$

16. $\dfrac{12t^3 - 11t^2 + 9t + 18}{4t + 3}$

Perform each division. See Examples 2–4.

 17. $\dfrac{3y^3 + y^2 + 2}{y + 1}$

18. $\dfrac{2r^3 - 6r - 36}{r - 3}$

19. $\dfrac{2x^3 + x + 2}{x + 1}$

20. $\dfrac{3x^3 + x + 5}{x + 1}$

21. $\dfrac{3k^3 - 4k^2 - 6k + 10}{k^2 - 2}$

22. $\dfrac{5z^3 - z^2 + 10z + 2}{z^2 + 2}$

23. $(x^4 - x^2 - 2) \div (x^2 - 2)$

24. $(r^4 + 2r^2 - 3) \div (r^2 - 1)$

25. $\dfrac{x^4 - 1}{x^2 - 1}$

26. $\dfrac{y^3 + 1}{y + 1}$

27. $\dfrac{6p^4 - 15p^3 + 14p^2 - 5p + 10}{3p^2 + 1}$

28. $\dfrac{6r^4 - 10r^3 - r^2 + 15r - 8}{2r^2 - 3}$

29. $\dfrac{2x^5 + x^4 + 11x^3 - 8x^2 - 13x + 7}{2x^2 + x - 1}$

30. $\dfrac{4t^5 - 11t^4 - 6t^3 + 5t^2 - t + 3}{4t^2 + t - 3}$

31. $(10x^3 + 13x^2 + 4x + 1) \div (5x + 5)$

32. $(6x^3 - 19x^2 - 19x - 4) \div (2x - 8)$

Work each problem. See Example 5.

33. What is the length of the rectangle if the area is $5x^3 + 7x^2 - 13x - 6$ square units?

$5x + 2$

34. Find the measure of the base of the parallelogram if the area is $2x^3 + 2x^2 - 3x + 1$ square units.

$x - 1$

Relating Concepts (Exercises 35–38) For Individual or Group Work

We can find the value of a polynomial in x for a given value of x by substituting that number for x. Surprisingly, we can accomplish the same thing by division. For example, to find the value of $2x^2 - 4x + 3$ for $x = -3$, we would divide $2x^2 - 4x + 3$ by $x - (-3)$. The remainder will give the value of the polynomial for $x = -3$. **Work Exercises 35–38 in order.**

35. Find the value of $2x^2 - 4x + 3$ for $x = -3$ by substitution.

36. Divide $2x^2 - 4x + 3$ by $x + 3$. Give the remainder.

37. Compare your answers to Exercises 35 and 36. What do you notice?

38. Choose another polynomial and evaluate it both ways for some value of the variable. Do the answers agree?

12.8 ▶▶▶ An Application of Exponents: Scientific Notation

OBJECTIVE 1 Express numbers in scientific notation. Numbers occurring in science are often extremely large (such as the distance from Earth to the sun, 93,000,000 mi) or extremely small (the wavelength of yellow-green light, approximately 0.0000006 m). Because of the difficulty of working with many zeros, scientists often express such numbers with exponents, using a form called *scientific notation*.

OBJECTIVES

1 Express numbers in scientific notation.

2 Convert numbers in scientific notation to numbers without exponents.

3 Use scientific notation in calculations.

> **Scientific Notation**
>
> A number is written in **scientific notation** when it is expressed in the form
>
> $$a \times 10^n,$$
>
> where $1 \le |a| < 10$ and n is an integer.

In **scientific notation,** there is always one nonzero digit before the decimal point. This is shown in the following examples.

$3.19 \times 10^1 = 3.19 \times 10 = 31.9$ Decimal point moves 1 place to the right.

$3.19 \times 10^2 = 3.19 \times 100 = 319.$ Decimal point moves 2 places to the right.

$3.19 \times 10^3 = 3.19 \times 1000 = 3190.$ Decimal point moves 3 places to the right.

$3.19 \times 10^{-1} = 3.19 \times 0.1 = 0.319$ Decimal point moves 1 place to the left.

$3.19 \times 10^{-2} = 3.19 \times 0.01 = 0.0319$ Decimal point moves 2 places to the left.

$3.19 \times 10^{-3} = 3.19 \times 0.001 = 0.00319$ Decimal point moves 3 places to the left.

> **Note**
>
> In scientific notation, the times symbol, $\times$, is commonly used.

A number in scientific notation is always written with the decimal point after the first nonzero digit and then multiplied by the appropriate power of 10. For example, 56,200 is written 5.62×10^4, since

$$56,200 = 5.62 \times 10,000 = 5.62 \times 10^4.$$

Other examples include

42,000,000	written	4.2×10^7,
0.000586	written	5.86×10^{-4},
and 2,000,000,000	written	2×10^9.

It is not necessary to write 2.0.

To write a number in scientific notation, follow the steps given on the next page. (For a negative number, follow these steps using the *absolute value* of the number; then make the result negative.)

1 Write each number in scientific notation.

(a) 63,000

Writing a Number in Scientific Notation

Step 1 Move the decimal point to the right of the first nonzero digit.

Step 2 Count the number of places you moved the decimal point.

Step 3 The number of places in Step 2 is the absolute value of the exponent on 10.

Step 4 The exponent on 10 is positive if the original number is greater than the number in Step 1; the exponent is negative if the original number is less than the number in Step 1. If the decimal point is not moved, the exponent is 0.

(b) 5,870,000

EXAMPLE 1 Using Scientific Notation

Write each number in scientific notation.

(a) 93,000,000

Move the decimal point to follow the first nonzero digit (the 9). Count the number of places the decimal point was moved.

$$93,000,000. \leftarrow \text{Decimal point}$$
7 places

(c) 7.0065

The number will be written in scientific notation as 9.3×10^n. To find the value of n, first compare the original number, 93,000,000, with 9.3. Since 93,000,000 is *greater* than 9.3, we must multiply by a *positive* power of 10 so that the product 9.3×10^n will equal the larger number.

Since the decimal point was moved 7 places, and since n is positive,

$$93,000,000 = 9.3 \times 10^7.$$

(b) $63,200,000,000 = 6.3200000000 = 6.32 \times 10^{10}$
10 places

(c) $3.021 = 3.021 \times 10^0$

(d) 0.0571

(d) 0.00462

Move the decimal point to the right of the first nonzero digit and count the number of places the decimal point was moved.

$$0.00462 \qquad 3 \text{ places}$$

Since 0.00462 is *less* than 4.62, the exponent must be *negative*.

$$0.00462 = 4.62 \times 10^{-3}$$

(e) $-0.0000762 = -7.62 \times 10^{-5}$
5 places

Remember the negative sign.

(e) −0.00062

◄ *Work Problem* 1 *at the Side.*

Note

To choose the exponent when you write a number in scientific notation, think: If the original number is "large," like 93,000,000, use a *positive* exponent on 10, since positive is greater than negative. However, if the original number is "small," like 0.00462, use a *negative* exponent on 10, since negative is less than positive.

OBJECTIVE **2** **Convert numbers in scientific notation to numbers without exponents.** To convert a number written in scientific notation to a number without exponents, work in reverse. *Multiplying a number by a positive power of 10 will make the number greater; multiplying by a negative power of 10 will make the number less.*

2 Write without exponents.

(a) 4.2×10^3

EXAMPLE 2 **Writing Numbers without Exponents**

Write each number without exponents.

(a) 6.2×10^3

Since the exponent is positive, make 6.2 greater by moving the decimal point 3 places to the right. It is necessary to attach two 0s.

$$6.2 \times 10^3 = 6.200 = 6200$$

(b) 8.7×10^5

(b) $4.283 \times 10^5 = 4.28300 = 428{,}300$ Move 5 places to the right; attach 0s as necessary.

(c) $-9.73 \times 10^{-2} = -09.73 = -0.0973$ Move 2 places to the left.

(c) 6.42×10^{-3}

The exponent tells the number of places and the direction that the decimal point is moved.

Work Problem **2** *at the Side.* ▶

OBJECTIVE **3** **Use scientific notation in calculations.** The next example uses scientific notation with products and quotients.

3 Perform each calculation. Write answers in scientific notation and also without exponents.

(a) $(2.6 \times 10^4)(2 \times 10^{-6})$

EXAMPLE 3 **Multiplying and Dividing with Scientific Notation**

Perform each calculation. Write answers in scientific notation and also without exponents.

(a)
$$(7 \times 10^3)(5 \times 10^4)$$
$$= (7 \times 5)(10^3 \times 10^4) \quad \text{Commutative and associative properties}$$

> Don't stop! This number is *not* in scientific notation, since 35 is not between 1 and 10.

$$= 35 \times 10^7 \quad \text{Multiply; product rule}$$
$$= (3.5 \times 10^1) \times 10^7 \quad \text{Write 35 in scientific notation.}$$
$$= 3.5 \times (10^1 \times 10^7) \quad \text{Associative property}$$
$$= 3.5 \times 10^8 \quad \text{Product rule}$$
$$= 350{,}000{,}000 \quad \text{Write without exponents.}$$

(b) $(3 \times 10^5)(5 \times 10^{-2})$

(b) $\dfrac{4 \times 10^{-5}}{2 \times 10^3} = \dfrac{4}{2} \times \dfrac{10^{-5}}{10^3} = 2 \times 10^{-8} = 0.00000002$

Work Problem **3** *at the Side.* ▶

(c) $\dfrac{4.8 \times 10^2}{2.4 \times 10^{-3}}$

Note

Multiplying or dividing numbers written in scientific notation may produce an answer in the form $a \times 10^0$. Since $10^0 = 1$, $a \times 10^0 = a$. For example,

$$(8 \times 10^{-4})(5 \times 10^4) = 40 \times 10^0 = 40. \quad 10^0 = 1$$

Also, if $a = 1$, then $a \times 10^n = 10^n$. For example, we could write $1{,}000{,}000$ as 10^6 instead of 1×10^6.

ANSWERS
2. (a) 4200 (b) 870,000 (c) 0.00642
3. (a) 5.2×10^{-2}; 0.052
   (b) 1.5×10^4; 15,000
   (c) 2×10^5; 200,000

4 The speed of light is approximately 3.0×10^5 km per sec. How far does light travel in 6.0×10^1 sec? (*Source: World Almanac and Book of Facts.*)

▦ **Calculator Tip**   Calculators usually have a key labeled EE or EXP for scientific notation. See your owner's manual for more information.

EXAMPLE 4   **Using Scientific Notation to Solve an Application**

A *nanometer* is a very small unit of measure that is equivalent to about 0.00000003937 in. About how much would 700,000 nanometers measure in inches? (*Source: World Almanac and Book of Facts.*)
   Write each number in scientific notation, and then multiply.

$$700,000\,(0.00000003937)$$

$$= (7 \times 10^5)(3.937 \times 10^{-8}) \qquad \text{Write in scientific notation.}$$

$$= (7 \times 3.937)(10^5 \times 10^{-8}) \qquad \text{Properties of real numbers}$$

Don't stop here. $= 27.559 \times 10^{-3} \qquad \text{Multiply; product rule}$

$$= (2.7559 \times 10^1) \times 10^{-3} \qquad \text{Write 27.559 in scientific notation.}$$

$$= 2.7559 \times 10^{-2} \qquad \text{Product rule}$$

$$= 0.027559 \qquad \text{Write without exponents.}$$

Thus, 700,000 nanometers would measure

$$2.7559 \times 10^{-2}\ \text{in.,} \quad \text{or} \quad 0.027559\ \text{in.}$$

◀ *Work Problem* 4 *at the Side.*

5 If the speed of light is approximately 3.0×10^5 km per sec, how many seconds does it take light to travel approximately 1.5×10^8 km from the sun to Earth? (*Source: World Almanac and Book of Facts.*)

EXAMPLE 5   **Using Scientific Notation to Solve an Application**

In 2003, the national debt was $\$3.9136 \times 10^{12}$ (which is more than \$3 trillion). The population of the United States was approximately 290 million that year. About how much would each person have had to contribute in order to pay off the national debt? (*Source:* U.S. Office of Management and Budget; U.S. Census Bureau.)
   Write the population in scientific notation. Then divide to obtain the per person contribution.

$$\frac{3.9136 \times 10^{12}}{290,000,000}$$

$$= \frac{3.9136 \times 10^{12}}{2.9 \times 10^8} \qquad \text{Write 290 million in scientific notation.}$$

$$= \frac{3.9136}{2.9} \times 10^4 \qquad \text{Quotient rule}$$

$$\approx 1.3495 \times 10^4 \qquad \text{Divide; round to 4 decimal places.}$$

$$\approx 13,495 \qquad \text{Write without exponents.}$$

Each person would have to pay about \$13,495.

◀ *Work Problem* 5 *at the Side.*

12.8 ▶▶▶   **Exercises**

  FOR EXTRA HELP    MyMathLab   Math XL PRACTICE   WATCH   DOWNLOAD   READ   REVIEW

Write the numbers (other than dates) mentioned in the following statements in scientific notation.

1. NASA has budgeted $6,130,900,000 for 2003 and $5,868,900,000 for 2004 for the international space station. (*Source:* U.S. National Aeronautics and Space Administration.)

2. The mass of Pluto is 0.0021 times that of Earth; the mass of Jupiter is 317.83 times that of Earth. (*Source: World Almanac and Book of Facts.*)

Determine whether or not the given number is written in scientific notation as defined in Objective 1. If it is not, write it as such.

3. 4.56×10^3

4. 7.34×10^5

5. 5,600,000

6. 34,000

7. 0.004

8. 0.0007

9. 0.8×10^2

10. 0.9×10^3

11. Explain in your own words what it means for a number to be written in scientific notation.

12. Explain how to multiply a number by a positive power of ten. Then explain how to multiply a number by a negative power of ten.

Write each number in scientific notation. See Example 1.

13. 5,876,000,000

14. 9,994,000,000

15. 82,350

16. 78,330

17. 0.000007

18. 0.0000004

19. −0.00203

20. −0.0000578

Write each number without exponents. See Example 2.

21. 7.5×10^5

22. 8.8×10^6

23. 5.677×10^{12}

24. 8.766×10^9

25. 1×10^{12}

26. 1×10^7

27. -6.21×10^0

28. -8.56×10^0

29. 7.8×10^{-4}

30. 8.9×10^{-5}

31. 5.134×10^{-9}

32. 7.123×10^{-10}

Perform the indicated operations. Write the answers in scientific notation and then without exponents. See Example 3.

33. $(2 \times 10^8)(3 \times 10^3)$

34. $(3 \times 10^7)(3 \times 10^3)$

🌐 **35.** $(5 \times 10^4)(3 \times 10^2)$

36. $(8 \times 10^5)(2 \times 10^3)$

37. $(4 \times 10^{-6})(2 \times 10^3)$

38. $(3 \times 10^{-7})(2 \times 10^2)$

39. $(6 \times 10^3)(4 \times 10^{-2})$

40. $(7 \times 10^5)(3 \times 10^{-4})$

41. $(9 \times 10^4)(7 \times 10^{-7})$

42. $(6 \times 10^4)(8 \times 10^{-8})$

🔲 **43.** $(3.15 \times 10^{-4})(2.04 \times 10^8)$

🔲 **44.** $(4.92 \times 10^{-3})(2.25 \times 10^7)$

45. $\dfrac{9 \times 10^{-5}}{3 \times 10^{-1}}$

46. $\dfrac{12 \times 10^{-4}}{4 \times 10^{-3}}$

47. $\dfrac{8 \times 10^3}{2 \times 10^2}$

48. $\dfrac{15 \times 10^4}{3 \times 10^3}$

49. $\dfrac{2.6 \times 10^{-3}}{2 \times 10^2}$

50. $\dfrac{9.5 \times 10^{-1}}{5 \times 10^3}$

51. $\dfrac{4 \times 10^5}{8 \times 10^2}$

52. $\dfrac{3 \times 10^9}{6 \times 10^5}$

53. $\dfrac{2.6 \times 10^{-3} \times 7.0 \times 10^{-1}}{2 \times 10^2 \times 3.5 \times 10^{-3}}$

54. $\dfrac{9.5 \times 10^{-1} \times 2.4 \times 10^4}{5 \times 10^3 \times 1.2 \times 10^{-2}}$

🔲 **55.** $\dfrac{(1.65 \times 10^8)(5.24 \times 10^{-2})}{(6 \times 10^4)(2 \times 10^7)}$

🔲 *Work each problem. In Exercises 58–60, give answers without exponents. See Examples 4 and 5.*

56. Pollux, one of the brightest stars in the night sky, is 33.7 light-years from Earth. If one light-year is about 6,000,000,000,000 mi (that is, 6 trillion mi), about how many miles is Pollux from Earth? (*Source: World Almanac and Book of Facts.*)

57. In March 2006, astronomers using the Spitzer Space Telescope discovered a twisted double-helix nebula, a conglomeration of dust and gas stretching across the center of the Milky Way galaxy. This nebula is 25,000 light-years from Earth. If one light-year is about 6,000,000,000,000 mi, about how many miles is the twisted double-helix nebula from Earth? (*Source:* http://articles.news.aol.com)

58. In 2003, the U.S. government collected about $6730 per person in taxes. If the population at that time was 290,000,000, how much did the government collect in taxes for 2003? (*Source:* U.S. Internal Revenue Service.)

59. In 2000, the population of the United States was about 281.4 million. To the nearest dollar, calculate how much each person in the United States would have had to contribute in order to make one lucky person a trillionaire (that is, to give that person $1,000,000,000,000). (*Source:* U.S. Census Bureau.)

60. In 2006, Congress raised the government's debt limit to 9×10^{12}. When this national debt limit is reached, about how much is it for every man, woman, and child in the country? Use 300 million as the population of the United States. (*Source: The Gazette*, Cedar Rapids, Iowa, March 17, 2006.)

13

Solving Inequalities/Absolute Values/Intro to Functions

13.1 ▶▶▶ Basic Concepts

OBJECTIVES

1 Write sets using set notation.

2 Use number lines.

3 Know the common sets of numbers.

4 Find additive inverses.

5 Use absolute value.

6 Use inequality symbols.

1 Consider the set

$$\left\{ 0, 10, \frac{3}{10}, 52, 98.6 \right\}.$$

(a) Which elements of the set are natural numbers?

(b) Which elements of the set are whole numbers?

2 List the elements in each set.

(a) $\{x \mid x$ is a whole number less than 5$\}$

(b) $\{y \mid y$ is a whole number greater than 12$\}$

OBJECTIVE **1** **Write sets using set notation.** A **set** is a collection of objects called the **elements,** or **members,** of the set. In algebra, the elements of a set are usually numbers. Set braces, { }, are used to enclose the elements. For example, 2 is an element of the set $\{1, 2, 3\}$. Since we can count the number of elements in the set $\{1, 2, 3\}$ and the counting process comes to an end, it is a **finite set.**

In algebra, we refer to certain sets of numbers by name. The set

$$N = \{1, 2, 3, 4, 5, 6, \ldots\} \quad \text{Natural (counting) numbers}$$

is called the **natural numbers,** or the **counting numbers.** The three dots (called *ellipsis points*) show that the list continues in the same pattern indefinitely. We cannot list all of the elements of the set of natural numbers, so it is an **infinite set.**

When 0 is included with the set of natural numbers, we have the set of **whole numbers,** written

$$W = \{0, 1, 2, 3, 4, 5, 6, \ldots\}. \quad \text{Whole numbers}$$

A set containing no elements, such as the set of whole numbers less than 0, is called the **empty set,** or **null set,** usually written $\emptyset$.

> **CAUTION**
> Do *not* write $\{\emptyset\}$ for the empty set; $\{\emptyset\}$ is a set with one element, $\emptyset$. Use only the notation $\emptyset$ for the empty set.

◀ *Work Problem* **1** *at the Side.*

In algebra, letters called **variables** are often used to represent numbers or to define sets of numbers. For example,

$$\{x \mid x \text{ is a natural number between 3 and 15}\}$$

(read "the set of all elements x such that x is a natural number between 3 and 15") defines the set

$$\{4, 5, 6, 7, \ldots, 14\}.$$

The notation $\{x \mid x$ is a natural number between 3 and 15$\}$ is an example of **set-builder notation.**

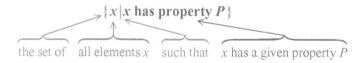

the set of   all elements x such that x has a given property P

Example 1 **Listing the Elements in Sets**

List the elements in each set.

(a) $\{x \mid x$ is a natural number less than 4$\}$
The natural numbers less than 4 are 1, 2, and 3. This set is $\{1, 2, 3\}$.

(b) $\{y \mid y$ is one of the first five even natural numbers$\}$ is $\{2, 4, 6, 8, 10\}$.

(c) $\{z \mid z$ is a natural number greater than or equal to 7$\}$
The set of natural numbers greater than or equal to 7 is an infinite set, written with ellipsis points as $\{7, 8, 9, 10, \ldots\}$.

◀ *Work Problem* **2** *at the Side.*

ANSWERS
1. **(a)** 10 and 52   **(b)** 0, 10, and 52
2. **(a)** $\{0, 1, 2, 3, 4\}$ **(b)** $\{13, 14, 15, \ldots\}$

> **Example 2** **Using Set-Builder Notation to Describe Sets**
>
> Use set-builder notation to describe each set.
>
> **(a)** $\{1, 3, 5, 7, 9\}$
>
> There are often several ways to describe a set with set-builder notation. One way is $\{y \mid y \text{ is one of the first five odd natural numbers}\}$.
>
> **(b)** $\{5, 10, 15, \ldots\}$
>
> This set can be described as $\{x \mid x \text{ is a multiple of 5 greater than } 0\}$.

Work Problem **3** *at the Side.* ▶

OBJECTIVE **2** **Use number lines.** A good way to get a picture of a set of numbers is by using a **number line.** To construct a number line, choose any point on a horizontal line and label it 0. Next, choose a point to the right of 0 and label it 1. The distance from 0 to 1 establishes a scale that can be used to locate more points, with positive numbers to the right of 0 and negative numbers to the left of 0. The number 0 is neither positive nor negative. A number line is shown in Figure 1.

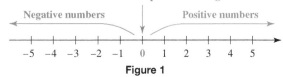

Figure 1

The set of numbers identified on the number line in Figure 1, including positive and negative numbers and 0, is part of the set of **integers,** written

$$I = \{\ldots, -3, -2, -1, 0, 1, 2, 3, \ldots\}. \quad \text{Integers}$$

Each number on a number line is called the **coordinate** of the point that it labels, while the point is the **graph** of the number. Figure 2 shows a number line with several selected points graphed on it.

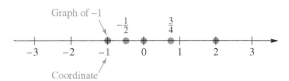

Figure 2

Work Problem **4** *at the Side.* ▶

The fractions $-\frac{1}{2}$ and $\frac{3}{4}$, graphed on the number line in Figure 2, are examples of *rational numbers.* A **rational number** can be expressed as the quotient of two integers, with denominator not 0. The set of all rational numbers is written

$$\left\{ \frac{p}{q} \; \middle| \; p \text{ and } q \text{ are integers}, q \neq 0 \right\}. \quad \text{Rational numbers}$$

The set of rational numbers includes the natural numbers, whole numbers, and integers, since these numbers can be written as fractions. For example, $14 = \frac{14}{1}$, $-3 = \frac{-3}{1}$, and $0 = \frac{0}{1}$. A rational number written as a fraction, such as $\frac{1}{8}$ or $\frac{2}{3}$, can also be expressed as a decimal by dividing the numerator by the denominator, as shown on the next page.

---

3 Use set-builder notation to describe each set.

(a) $\{0, 1, 2, 3, 4, 5\}$

(b) $\{7, 14, 21, 28, \ldots\}$

4 Graph the elements of each set.

(a) $\{-4, -2, 0, 2, 4, 6\}$

(b) $\left\{-1, 0, \dfrac{2}{3}, 2.5\right\}$

(c) $\left\{5, \dfrac{16}{3}, 6, \dfrac{13}{2}, 7, \dfrac{29}{4}\right\}$

ANSWERS

3. **(a)** One answer is $\{x \mid x \text{ is a whole number less than 6}\}$. **(b)** One answer is $\{x \mid x \text{ is a multiple of 7 greater than 0}\}$.

4. **(a)**
-4 -2 0 2 4 6

(b)
-2 -1 0 1 2 3

(c)
4 5 6 7 8

$$
\begin{array}{r}
0.125 \leftarrow \text{Terminating decimal} \\
8\overline{)1.000} \\
\underline{8} \\
20 \\
\underline{16} \\
40 \\
\underline{40} \\
0 \leftarrow \text{Remainder is 0.}
\end{array}
$$

$$
\frac{1}{8} = 0.125
$$

$$
\begin{array}{r}
0.666\ldots \leftarrow \text{Repeating decimal} \\
3\overline{)2.000\ldots} \\
\underline{18} \\
20 \\
\underline{18} \\
20 \\
\underline{18} \\
2 \leftarrow \text{Remainder is never 0.}
\end{array}
$$

$$
\frac{2}{3} = 0.\overline{6} \leftarrow \text{A bar is written over the repeating digit(s).}
$$

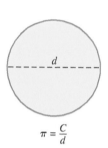

$$\pi = \frac{C}{d}$$

Figure 3

Thus, terminating decimals, such as $0.125 = \frac{1}{8}$, $0.8 = \frac{4}{5}$, and $2.75 = \frac{11}{4}$, and repeating decimals, such as $0.\overline{6} = \frac{2}{3}$ and $0.\overline{27} = \frac{3}{11}$, are rational numbers.

Decimal numbers that neither terminate nor repeat are *not* rational, and thus are called **irrational numbers.** Many square roots are irrational numbers; for example, $\sqrt{2} = 1.4142135\ldots$ and $-\sqrt{7} = -2.6457513\ldots$ repeat indefinitely without pattern. (Some square roots *are* rational: $\sqrt{16} = 4$, $\sqrt{100} = 10$, and so on.) Another irrational number is π (pronounced "pie"), the ratio of the distance around, or circumference, C of a circle to its diameter d. See Figure 3.

Some of the rational and irrational numbers discussed above are graphed on the number line in Figure 4. The rational numbers together with the irrational numbers make up the set of **real numbers.** *Every point on a number line corresponds to a real number, and every real number corresponds to a point on the number line.*

Real numbers

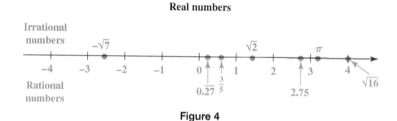

Figure 4

OBJECTIVE 3 Know the common sets of numbers. The sets of numbers listed below will be used throughout the rest of this text.

Sets of Numbers

Natural numbers	$\{1, 2, 3, 4, 5, 6, \ldots\}$
Whole numbers	$\{0, 1, 2, 3, 4, 5, 6, \ldots\}$
Integers	$\{\ldots, -3, -2, -1, 0, 1, 2, 3, \ldots\}$
Rational numbers	$\left\{\frac{p}{q} \middle\| p \text{ and } q \text{ are integers, } q \neq 0\right\}$ *Examples:* $\frac{4}{1}$, 1.3, $-\frac{9}{2}$, $\frac{16}{8}$ or 2, $\sqrt{9}$ or 3, $0.\overline{6}$
Irrational numbers	$\{x \| x \text{ is a real number that is not rational}\}$ *Examples:* $\sqrt{3}$, $-\sqrt{2}$, π
Real numbers	$\{x \| x \text{ is a rational number or an irrational number}\}$*

*An example of a number that is not real is $\sqrt{-1}$. This number is part of the *complex number system.*

Figure 5 shows that the set of real numbers includes both the rational and irrational numbers. ***Every real number is either rational or irrational.*** Also, notice that the integers are elements of the set of rational numbers, and that the whole numbers and natural numbers are elements of the set of integers.

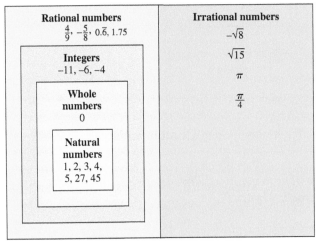

Real numbers

Figure 5 The Real Numbers

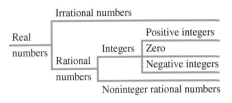

Example 3 **Identifying Examples of Number Sets**

Which numbers in

$$\left\{ -8, -\sqrt{2}, -\frac{9}{64}, 0, 0.5, \frac{2}{3}, 1.\overline{12}, \sqrt{3}, 2 \right\}$$

are elements of each set?

(a) Integers
$-8, 0$, and 2 are integers.

(b) Rational numbers
$-8, -\frac{9}{64}, 0, 0.5, \frac{2}{3}, 1.\overline{12}$, and 2 are rational numbers.

(c) Irrational numbers
$-\sqrt{2}$ and $\sqrt{3}$ are irrational numbers.

(d) Real numbers
All the numbers in the given set are real numbers.

Work Problem **5** *at the Side.* ▶

Example 4 **Determining Relationships between Sets of Numbers**

Decide whether each statement is *true* or *false.*

(a) All irrational numbers are real numbers.
This is true. As shown in Figure 5, the set of real numbers includes all irrational numbers.

(b) Every rational number is an integer.
This statement is false. Although some rational numbers are integers, other rational numbers, such as $\frac{2}{3}$ and $-\frac{1}{4}$, are not.

Work Problem **6** *at the Side.* ▶

---

5 Select all the sets from the following list that apply to each number.
Whole number
Rational number
Irrational number
Real number

(a) -6 **(b)** 12

(c) $0.\overline{3}$ **(d)** $-\sqrt{15}$

(e) π **(f)** $\frac{22}{7}$

(g) 3.14

6 Decide whether the statement is *true* or *false.* If *false,* tell why.

(a) All whole numbers are integers.

(b) Some integers are whole numbers.

(c) Every real number is irrational.

ANSWERS

5. (a) rational, real   **(b)** whole, rational, real
(c) rational, real   **(d)** irrational, real
(e) irrational, real   **(f)** rational, real
(g) rational, real
6. (a) true   **(b)** true
(b) false; Some real numbers are irrational, but others are rational numbers.

7 Give the additive inverse of each number.

(a) 9

(b) −12

(c) $-\dfrac{6}{5}$

(d) 0

(e) 1.5

OBJECTIVE 4 Find additive inverses. Look at the number line in Figure 6. For each positive number, there is a negative number on the opposite side of 0 that lies the same distance from 0. These pairs of numbers are called *additive inverses, negatives,* or *opposites* of each other. For example, 3 is the additive inverse of −3, and −3 is the additive inverse of 3.

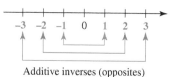

Additive inverses (opposites)

Figure 6

> **Additive Inverse**
>
> For any real number a, the number $-a$ is the **additive inverse** of a.

Change the sign of a number to get its additive inverse. The sum of a number and its additive inverse is always 0.

> **Uses of the Symbol −**
>
> The symbol "−" can be used to indicate any of the following:
> **1.** a negative number, such as −9 or −15;
> **2.** the additive inverse of a number, as in "−4 is the additive inverse of 4";
> **3.** subtraction, as in 12 − 3.

In the expression −(−5), the symbol "−" is being used in two ways: the first − indicates the additive inverse (or opposite) of −5, and the second indicates a negative number, −5. Since the additive inverse of −5 is 5, then

$$-(-5) = 5.$$

This example suggests the following property.

> **−(−a)**
>
> For any real number a, $\quad -(-a) = a.$

Numbers written with positive or negative signs, such as +4, +8, −9, and −5, are called **signed numbers.** A positive number can be called a signed number even though the positive sign is usually left off. The following table shows the additive inverses of several signed numbers. The number 0 is its own additive inverse.

Number	Additive Inverse
6	−6
−4	4
$\frac{2}{3}$	$-\frac{2}{3}$
−8.7	8.7
0	0

◀ Work Problem **7** at the Side.

OBJECTIVE **5** **Use absolute value.** Geometrically, the **absolute value** of a number a, written $|a|$, is the distance on the number line from 0 to a. For example, the absolute value of 5 is the same as the absolute value of -5 because each number lies five units from 0. See Figure 7. That is,

$$|5| = 5 \quad \text{and} \quad |-5| = 5.$$

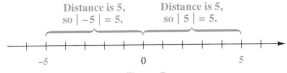

Distance is 5,
so $|-5| = 5$.   Distance is 5,
so $|5| = 5$.

Figure 7

CAUTION
Because absolute value represents distance, and distance is never negative, the absolute value of a number is always positive or 0.

The formal definition of absolute value follows.

Absolute Value

$$|a| = \begin{cases} a & \text{if } a \text{ is positive or } 0 \\ -a & \text{if } a \text{ is negative} \end{cases}$$

The second part of this definition, $|a| = -a$ if a is negative, requires careful thought. If a is a *negative* number, then $-a$, the additive inverse or opposite of a, is a positive number. Thus, $|a|$ is positive. For example, if $a = -3$, then

$$|a| = |-3| = -(-3) = 3. \quad |a| = -a \text{ if } a \text{ is negative.}$$

Example 5 **Finding Absolute Value**

Simplify by finding each absolute value.

(a) $|13| = 13$

(b) $|-2| = -(-2) = 2$

(c) $|0| = 0$

(d) $|-0.75| = 0.75$

(e) $-|8|$
Evaluate the absolute value first. Then find the additive inverse.
$$-|8| = -(8) = -8$$

(f) $-|-8|$
Work as in part (e): $|-8| = 8$, so
$$-|-8| = -(8) = -8.$$

(g) $|-2| + |5|$
Evaluate each absolute value first, and then add.
$$|-2| + |5| = 2 + 5 = 7$$

(h) $-|5 - 2| = -|3| = -3$

Work Problem **8** *at the Side.* ▶

8 Find the value of each expression.

(a) $|6|$

(b) $|-3|$

(c) $-\left|\dfrac{1}{4}\right|$

(d) $-|-2|$

(e) $-|-7.25|$

(f) $|-6| + |-3|$

(g) $|-9| - |-4|$

(h) $-|9 - 4|$

ANSWERS
8. **(a)** 6 **(b)** 3 **(c)** $-\dfrac{1}{4}$ **(d)** -2
(e) -7.25 **(f)** 9 **(g)** 5 **(h)** -5

Absolute value is useful when comparing size without regard to sign.

9 Refer to the table in Example 6. Of the software publishers and fabric mills industries, which will show the greater change (without regard to sign)?

Example 6 **Comparing Rates of Change in Industries**

The projected annual rates of change in employment (in percent) in some of the fastest-growing and in some of the most rapidly declining industries from 2002 through 2012 are shown in the table.

Industry (2002–2012)	Annual Rate of Change (in percent)
Software publishers	5.3
Care services for the elderly	4.5
Child day-care services	3.6
Cut-and-sew apparel manufacturing	−12.2
Fabric mills	−5.9
Metal ore mining	−4.8

Source: U.S. Bureau of Labor Statistics.

What industry in the list is expected to see the greatest change? the least change?

We want the greatest *change,* without regard to whether the change is an increase or a decrease. Look for the number in the list with the largest absolute value. That number is found in cut-and-sew apparel manufacturing, since

$$|-12.2| = 12.2.$$

Similarly, the least change is in the child day-care services industry:

$$|3.6| = 3.6.$$

◀ *Work Problem* **9** *at the Side.*

OBJECTIVE **6** **Use inequality symbols.**   The statement

$$4 + 2 = 6$$

is an **equation**—a statement that two quantities are equal. The statement

$$4 \neq 6$$

(read "4 is not equal to 6") is an **inequality**—a statement that two quantities are *not* equal. When two numbers are not equal, one must be less than the other. The symbol $<$ means "is less than." For example,

$$8 < 9, \quad -6 < 15, \quad -6 < -1, \quad 0.5 < 0.9, \quad \text{and} \quad 0 < \frac{4}{3}.$$

The symbol $>$ means "is greater than." For example,

$$12 > 5, \quad 9 > -2, \quad -4 > -6, \quad 1.25 > 1.2, \quad \text{and} \quad \frac{6}{5} > 0.$$

In each case, the symbol "points" toward the lesser number.

ANSWER

9. Fabric mills

The number line in Figure 8 shows the graphs of the numbers 4 and 9. We know that $4 < 9$. On the graph, 4 is to the left of 9. ***The lesser of two numbers is always to the left of the other on a number line.***

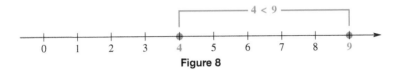

Figure 8

Inequalities on a Number Line

On a number line,

$\quad a < b$ if a is to the left of b; $\qquad a > b$ if a is to the right of b.

We can use a number line to determine order. As shown on the number line in Figure 9, -6 is located to the left of 1. For this reason, $-6 < 1$. Also, $1 > -6$. From the same number line, $-5 < -2$, or $-2 > -5$.

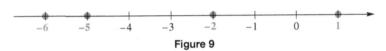

Figure 9

CAUTION

Be careful when ordering negative numbers. Since -5 is to the left of -2 on the number line in Figure 9, $-5 < -2$, or $-2 > -5$. In each case, the symbol points to -5, the lesser number.

Work Problem **10** *at the Side.* ▶

The following table summarizes results about positive and negative numbers in both words and symbols.

Words	Symbols
Every negative number is less than 0.	If a is negative, then $a < 0$.
Every positive number is greater than 0.	If a is positive, then $a > 0$.
0 is neither positive nor negative.	

In addition to the symbols $\neq$, $<$, and $>$, the symbols $\leq$ and $\geq$ are often used.

INEQUALITY SYMBOLS

Symbol	Meaning	Example
$\neq$	is not equal to	$3 \neq 7$
$<$	is less than	$-4 < -1$
$>$	is greater than	$3 > -2$
$\leq$	is less than or equal to	$6 \leq 6$
$\geq$	is greater than or equal to	$-8 \geq -10$

10 Insert $<$ or $>$ in each blank to make a true statement.

(a) 3 _____ 7

(b) 9 _____ 2

(c) -4 _____ -8

(d) -2 _____ -1

(e) 0 _____ -3.5

(f) $\dfrac{5}{8}$ _____ $\dfrac{3}{4}$

(g) -0.3 _____ -0.5

The following table shows several inequalities and why each is true.

11 Answer *true* or *false*.

(a) $-2 \leq -3$

Inequality	Why It Is True
$6 \leq 8$	$6 < 8$
$-2 \leq -2$	$-2 = -2$
$-9 \geq -12$	$-9 > -12$
$-3 \geq -3$	$-3 = -3$
$6 \cdot 4 \leq 5\,(5)$	$24 < 25$

Notice the reason why $-2 \leq -2$ is true. ***With the symbol $\leq$, if either the < part or the = part is true, then the inequality is true. This is also the case with the $\geq$ symbol.***

(b) $0.5 \leq 0.5$

In the last row of the table, recall that the dot in $6 \cdot 4$ indicates the product 6×4, or 24, and $5\,(5)$ means 5×5, or 25. Thus, the inequality $6 \cdot 4 \leq 5\,(5)$ becomes $24 \leq 25$, which is true.

◀ *Work Problem* **11** *at the Side.*

(c) $-9 \geq -1$

(d) $5 \cdot 8 \leq 7 \cdot 7$

(e) $3\,(4) > 2\,(6)$

ANSWERS

11. (a) false **(b)** true **(c)** false
(d) true **(e)** false

Write each set by listing its elements. See Example 1.

1. $\{x \mid x$ is a natural number less than $6\}$

2. $\{m \mid m$ is a natural number less than $9\}$

3. $\{z \mid z$ is an integer greater than $4\}$

4. $\{y \mid y$ is an integer greater than $8\}$

5. $\{a \mid a$ is an even integer greater than $8\}$

6. $\{k \mid k$ is an odd integer less than $1\}$

7. $\{x \mid x$ is an irrational number that is also rational$\}$

8. $\{r \mid r$ is a number that is both positive and negative$\}$

9. $\{p \mid p$ is a number whose absolute value is $4\}$

10. $\{w \mid w$ is a number whose absolute value is $7\}$

Write each set using set-builder notation. See Example 2. (More than one description is possible.)

11. $\{2, 4, 6, 8\}$

12. $\{11, 12, 13, 14\}$

13. $\{4, 8, 12, 16, \dots\}$

14. $\{\dots, -6, -3, 0, 3, 6, \dots\}$

Graph the elements of each set on a number line.

15. $\{-3, -1, 0, 4, 6\}$

16. $\{-4, -2, 0, 3, 5\}$

17. $\left\{-\dfrac{2}{3}, 0, \dfrac{4}{5}, \dfrac{12}{5}, \dfrac{9}{2}, 4.8\right\}$

18. $\left\{-\dfrac{6}{5}, -\dfrac{1}{4}, 0, \dfrac{5}{6}, \dfrac{13}{4}, 5.2, \dfrac{11}{2}\right\}$

*Which elements of each set are (**a**) natural numbers, (**b**) whole numbers, (**c**) integers, (**d**) rational numbers, (**e**) irrational numbers, (**f**) real numbers? See Example 3.*

19. $\left\{-8, -\sqrt{5}, -0.6, 0, \dfrac{3}{4}, \sqrt{3}, \pi, 5, \dfrac{13}{2}, 17, \dfrac{40}{2}\right\}$

20. $\left\{-9, -\sqrt{6}, -0.7, 0, \dfrac{6}{7}, \sqrt{7}, 4.\overline{6}, 8, \dfrac{21}{2}, 13, \dfrac{75}{5}\right\}$

Decide whether each statement is true *or* false. *If* false, *tell why. See Example 4.*

21. Every rational number is an integer.

22. Every natural number is an integer.

23. Every irrational number is an integer.

24. Every integer is a rational number.

25. Every natural number is a whole number.

26. Some rational numbers are irrational.

27. Some rational numbers are whole numbers.

28. Some real numbers are integers.

29. The absolute value of any number is the same as the absolute value of its additive inverse.

30. The absolute value of any nonzero number is positive.

*Give **(a)** the additive inverse and **(b)** the absolute value of each number. See the discussion of additive inverses and Example 5.*

31. 6

32. 8

33. -12

34. -15

35. $\dfrac{6}{5}$

36. 0.13

Find the value of each expression. See Example 5.

37. $|-8|$

38. $|-11|$

39. $\left|\dfrac{3}{2}\right|$

40. $\left|\dfrac{7}{4}\right|$

41. $-|5|$

42. $-|17|$

43. $-|-2|$

44. $-|-8|$

45. $-|4.5|$

46. $-|12.6|$

47. $|-2| + |3|$

48. $|-16| + |12|$

49. $|-9| - |-3|$

50. $|-10| - |-5|$

51. $|-1| + |-2| - |-3|$

52. $|-6| + |-4| - |-10|$

Solve each problem. See Example 6.

53. The table shows the percent change in population from 2000 through 2006 for selected states.

State	Percent Change
Alabama	3.4
Iowa	1.9
Louisiana	−4.1
Michigan	1.6
North Dakota	−1.0
West Virginia	0.6

Source: U.S. Census Bureau.

(a) Which state had the greatest change in population? What was this change? Was it an increase or a decrease?

(b) Which state had the least change in population? What was this change? Was it an increase or a decrease?

54. The table gives the net trade balance, in millions of dollars, for selected U.S. trade partners for January 2006.

Country	Trade Balance (in millions of dollars)
India	−1257
China	−17,911
Netherlands	756
France	−85
Turkey	−78

Source: U.S. Census Bureau.

A negative balance means that imports to the United States exceeded exports from the United States, while a positive balance means that exports exceeded imports.

(a) Which country had the greatest discrepancy between exports and imports? Explain.

(b) Which country had the least discrepancy between exports and imports? Explain.

Sea level refers to the surface of the ocean. The depth of a body of water such as an ocean or sea can be expressed as a negative number, representing average depth in feet below sea level. On the other hand, the altitude of a mountain can be expressed as a positive number, indicating its height in feet above sea level. The table gives selected depths and heights.

Body of Water	Average Depth in Feet (as a negative number)	Mountain	Altitude in Feet (as a positive number)
Pacific Ocean	−12,925	McKinley	20,320
South China Sea	−4,802	Point Success	14,158
Gulf of California	−2,375	Matlalcueyetl	14,636
Caribbean Sea	−8,448	Rainier	14,410
Indian Ocean	−12,598	Steele	16,644

Source: World Almanac and Book of Facts.

55. List the bodies of water in order, starting with the deepest and ending with the shallowest.

56. List the mountains in order, starting with the shortest and ending with the tallest.

57. *True* or *false:* The absolute value of the depth of the Pacific Ocean is greater than the absolute value of the depth of the Indian Ocean.

58. *True* or *false:* The absolute value of the depth of the Gulf of California is greater than the absolute value of the depth of the Caribbean Sea.

Use order on a number line to answer true *or* false *to each statement.*

59. $-6 < -2$

60. $-4 < -3$

61. $-4 > -3$

62. $-2 > -1$

63. $3 > -2$

64. $5 > -3$

65. $-3 \geq -3$

66. $-4 \leq -4$

Use an inequality symbol to write each statement.

67. 7 is greater than y.

68. -4 is less than 12.

69. 5 is greater than or equal to 5.

70. -3 is less than or equal to -3.

71. $3t - 4$ is less than or equal to 10.

72. $5x + 4$ is greater than or equal to 19.

73. $5x + 3$ is not equal to 0.

74. $6x + 7$ is not equal to -3.

First simplify each side of the inequality. Then tell whether the resulting statement is true *or* false.

75. $-6 < 7 + 3$

76. $-7 < 4 + 2$

77. $2 \cdot 5 \geq 4 + 6$

78. $8 + 7 \leq 3 \cdot 5$

79. $-|-3| \geq -3$

80. $-|-5| \leq -5$

81. $-8 > -|-6|$

82. $-9 > -|-4|$

The graph shows egg production in millions of eggs in selected states for 2005 and 2006.
Use this graph to work Exercises 83–87.

83. In 2005, was egg production in Iowa (IA) less than or greater than egg production in California (CA)?

84. In 2006, which states had production greater than 6000 million eggs?

85. In which states was 2006 egg production less than 2005 production?

86. If x represents 2006 egg production for Texas (TX) and y represents 2006 egg production for California (CA), which is true: $x < y$ or $x > y$?

87. If x represents 2005 egg production for Ohio (OH) and y represents 2006 egg production for Ohio (OH), which is true: $x < y$ or $x > y$?

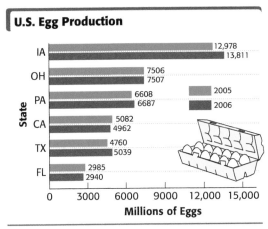

U.S. Egg Production

Source: U.S. Department of Agriculture.

13.2 ▶▶▶ Linear Inequalities in One Variable

OBJECTIVES

1 Graph intervals on a number line.

2 Solve linear inequalities using the addition property.

3 Solve linear inequalities using the multiplication property.

4 Solve linear inequalities with three parts.

5 Solve applied problems using linear inequalities.

Solving inequalities is closely related to solving equations. In this section we introduce properties for solving inequalities.

Inequalities are algebraic expressions related by

$<$ "is less than," $\leq$ "is less than or equal to,"

$>$ "is greater than," $\geq$ "is greater than or equal to."

We solve an inequality by finding all real number solutions for it. For example, the solution set of $x \leq 2$ includes *all* real numbers that are less than or equal to 2, not just the integers less than or equal to 2. For example, $-2.5, -1.7, -1, \frac{1}{2}, \sqrt{2}, \frac{7}{4}$, and 2 are real numbers less than or equal to 2 and are therefore solutions of $x \leq 2$.

OBJECTIVE 1 Graph intervals on a number line. A good way to show the solution set of an inequality is by graphing. We graph all the real numbers satisfying $x \leq 2$ by placing a square bracket at 2 on a number line and drawing an arrow extending from the bracket to the left (to represent the fact that all numbers less than 2 are also part of the graph). The graph is shown in Figure 1.

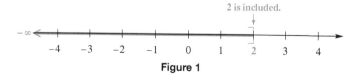

Figure 1

The set of numbers less than or equal to 2 is an example of an **interval** on the number line. To write intervals, we use **interval notation.** For example, the interval of all numbers less than or equal to 2 is written $(-\infty, 2]$. The negative infinity symbol $-\infty$ does not indicate a number. It is used to show that the interval includes all real numbers less than 2. As on the number line, the square bracket indicates that 2 is included in the solution set. *A parenthesis is always used next to the infinity symbol. The set of real numbers is written in interval notation as $(-\infty, \infty)$.*

Example 1 **Graphing Intervals Written in Interval Notation on Number Lines**

Write each inequality in interval notation and graph it.

(a) $x > -5$

The statement $x > -5$ says that x can represent any number greater than -5, but x cannot equal -5. This interval is written $(-5, \infty)$. We show this solution set on a number line by placing a parenthesis at -5 and drawing an arrow to the right, as in Figure 2. The parenthesis at -5 shows that -5 is *not* part of the graph.

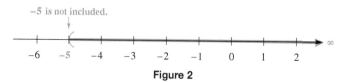

Figure 2

Continued on Next Page

(b) $-1 \leq x < 3$

This statement is read "-1 is less than or equal to x *and* x is less than 3." Thus, we want the set of numbers that are *between* -1 and 3, with -1 included and 3 excluded. In interval notation, we write the solution set as $[-1, 3)$, using a square bracket at -1 because it is part of the graph and a parenthesis at 3 because it is not part of the graph. See Figure 3.

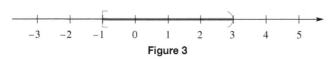

Figure 3

Work Problem **1** *at the Side.* ▶

We now summarize the various types of intervals.

Type of Interval	Set-Builder Notation	Interval Notation	Graph
Open interval	$\{x \mid a < x < b\}$	(a, b)	
Closed interval	$\{x \mid a \leq x \leq b\}$	$[a, b]$	
Half-open (or half-closed) interval	$\{x \mid a \leq x < b\}$	$[a, b)$	
	$\{x \mid a < x \leq b\}$	$(a, b]$	
Disjoint interval*	$\{x \mid x < a \text{ or } x > b\}$	$(-\infty, a) \cup (b, \infty)$	
Infinite interval	$\{x \mid x > a\}$	(a, ∞)	
	$\{x \mid x \geq a\}$	$[a, \infty)$	
	$\{x \mid x < a\}$	$(-\infty, a)$	
	$\{x \mid x \leq a\}$	$(-\infty, a]$	
	$\{x \mid x \text{ is a real number}\}$	$(-\infty, \infty)$	

An **inequality** is a statement with algebraic expressions related by $<$, $\leq$, $>$, or $\geq$.

Linear Inequality

A **linear inequality in one variable** can be written in the form

$$Ax + B < C,$$

where A, B, and C are real numbers, with $A \neq 0$.

(While we give definitions and rules only for $<$, they are also valid for $>$, $\leq$, and $\geq$.)

---

*We will work with disjoint intervals in **Section 13.3** when we study *set operations* and *compound inequalities*.

1 Write each inequality in interval notation and graph it.

(a) $x < -1$

(b) $x \geq -3$

(c) $-4 \leq x < 2$

(d) $0 < x < 3.5$

ANSWERS

1. (a) $(-\infty, -1)$

(b) $[-3, \infty)$

(c) $[-4, 2)$

(d) $(0, 3.5)$

2 Solve each inequality, check your solutions, and graph the solution set.

(a) $x - 3 < -9$

Examples of linear inequalities include

$$x + 5 < 2, \quad t - 3 \geq 5, \quad \text{and} \quad 2k + 5 \leq 10. \quad \text{Linear inequalities}$$

OBJECTIVE 2 Solve linear inequalities using the addition property. We solve an inequality by finding all numbers that make the inequality true. Usually, an inequality has an infinite number of solutions. These solutions, like solutions of equations, are found by producing a series of simpler equivalent inequalities. **Equivalent inequalities** are inequalities with the same solution set. We use the *addition property of inequality* to produce equivalent inequalities.

Addition Property of Inequality

For all real numbers A, B, and C, the inequalities

$$A < B \quad \text{and} \quad A + C < B + C$$

are equivalent.

In words, adding the same number to each side of an inequality does not change the solution set.

(b) $p + 6 < 8$

Example 2   Using the Addition Property of Inequality

Solve $x - 7 < -12$, and graph the solution set.

$$x - 7 < -12$$
$$x - 7 + 7 < -12 + 7 \qquad \text{Add 7.}$$
$$x < -5$$

Check   Substitute -5 for x in the *equation* $x - 7 = -12$.

$$x - 7 = -12$$
$$-5 - 7 \overset{?}{=} -12 \qquad \text{Let } x = -5.$$
$$-12 = -12 \qquad \text{True}$$

The result, a true statement, shows that -5 is the boundary point. Now we test a number on each side of -5 to verify that numbers *less than* -5 make the *inequality* true. We choose -4 and -6.

$$x - 7 < -12$$

$-4 - 7 \overset{?}{<} -12 \quad \text{Let } x = -4.$	$-6 - 7 \overset{?}{<} -12 \quad \text{Let } x = -6.$
$-11 < -12 \quad \text{False}$	$-13 < -12 \quad \text{True}$
-4 is *not* in the solution set.	-6 is in the solution set.

Thus, $(-\infty, -5)$, the infinite interval graphed in Figure 4, is the solution set.

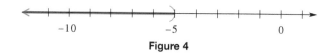

Figure 4

2. (a) $(-\infty, -6)$

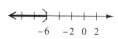

(b) $(-\infty, 2)$

As with equations, the addition property of inequality can be used to *subtract* the same number from each side of an inequality. For example, to solve the inequality $x + 4 > 10$, we subtract 4 from each side to get $x > 6$.

◀ *Work Problem* **2** *at the Side.*

Example 3   **Using the Addition Property of Inequality**

Solve $14 + 2m \leq 3m$, and graph the solution set.

$$14 + 2m \leq 3m$$

$$14 + 2m - 2m \leq 3m - 2m \qquad \text{Subtract } 2m.$$

Pay careful attention here.

$$14 \leq m \qquad \text{Combine like terms.}$$

$$m \geq 14 \qquad \text{Rewrite.}$$

The inequality $14 \leq m$ (14 is less than or equal to m) can also be written $m \geq 14$ (m is greater than or equal to 14). *Notice that in each case, the inequality symbol points to the lesser number,* **14.**

Check

$$14 + 2m = 3m$$

$$14 + 2(14) \overset{?}{=} 3(14) \qquad \text{Let } m = 14.$$

$$42 = 42 \qquad \text{True}$$

So 14 satisfies the equality part of $\leq$. Choose 10 and 15 as test points.

$$14 + 2m < 3m$$

$$14 + 2(10) \overset{?}{<} 3(10) \qquad \text{Let } m = 10. \qquad \Big| \qquad 14 + 2(15) \overset{?}{<} 3(15) \qquad \text{Let } m = 15.$$

$$34 < 30 \qquad \text{False} \qquad \Big| \qquad 44 < 45 \qquad \text{True}$$

10 is not in the solution set. | 15 is in the solution set.

The check confirms that $[14, \infty)$ is the solution set. See Figure 5.

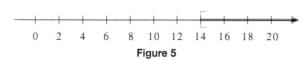

Figure 5

Work Problem 3 *at the Side.* ▶

> **CAUTION**
> To avoid errors, rewrite an inequality such as $14 \leq m$ as $m \geq 14$ so that the variable is on the left, as in Example 3.

OBJECTIVE 3 **Solve linear inequalities using the multiplication property.**   Solving an inequality such as $3x \leq 15$ requires dividing each side by 3 using the *multiplication property of inequality*. Consider

$$-2 < 5,$$

a true statement. Multiply each side by 8.

$$-2(8) < 5(8) \qquad \text{Multiply by 8.}$$

$$-16 < 40 \qquad \text{True}$$

The result is true. Start again with $-2 < 5$, and multiply each side by -8.

$$-2(-8) < 5(-8) \qquad \text{Multiply by } -8.$$

$$16 < -40 \qquad \text{False}$$

The result, $16 < -40$, is false. To make it true, we must change the direction of the inequality symbol to get

$$16 > -40. \qquad \text{True}$$

Work Problem 4 *at the Side.* ▶

---

3 Solve $2k - 5 \geq 1 + k$, check, and graph the solution set.

4 Multiply both sides of each inequality by -5. Then insert the correct symbol, either $<$ or $>$, in the first blank, and fill in the other blanks in part (b).

(a) $7 < 8$

$$-35 \rule{1.5cm}{0.4pt} -40$$

(b) $-1 > -4$

$$5 \rule{1cm}{0.4pt} \rule{1cm}{0.4pt}$$

ANSWERS

3. $[6, \infty)$

$$\text{─┼─┼─┼─┼─[━━▶}$$
$$\text{-2 0 2 4 6}$$

4. (a) $>$ **(b)** $<$; 20

5 Solve, check, and graph the solution set of each inequality.

(a) $2x < -10$

(b) $-7k \geq 8$

(c) $-9m < -81$

As these examples suggest, multiplying each side of an inequality by a *negative* number reverses the direction of the inequality symbol. The same is true for dividing by a negative number since division is defined in terms of multiplication.

> **Multiplication Property of Inequality**
>
> For all real numbers A, B, and C, with $C \neq 0$,
> **(a)** the inequalities
>
> $$A < B \quad \text{and} \quad AC < BC \quad \text{are equivalent if } C > 0;$$
>
> **(b)** the inequalities
>
> $$A < B \quad \text{and} \quad AC > BC \quad \text{are equivalent if } C < 0.$$
>
> In words, each side of an inequality may be multiplied (or divided) by a *positive* number without changing the direction of the inequality symbol. *Multiplying (or dividing) by a negative number requires that we reverse the direction of the inequality symbol.*

Example 4   **Using the Multiplication Property of Inequality**

Solve each inequality, and graph the solution set.

(a) $5m \leq -30$

Use the multiplication property to divide each side by 5. *Since 5 is positive, do not reverse the direction of inequality symbol.*

$$5m \leq -30$$

$$\frac{5m}{5} \leq \frac{-30}{5} \qquad \text{Divide by 5.}$$

$$m \leq -6$$

Check that the solution set is the interval $(-\infty, -6]$, graphed in Figure 6.

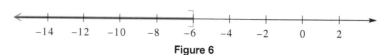

Figure 6

(b) $-4k \leq 32$

Divide each side by -4. *Since -4 is negative, reverse the direction of inequality symbol.*

$$-4k \leq 32$$

$$\frac{-4k}{-4} \geq \frac{32}{-4} \qquad \text{Divide by } -4; \text{ reverse the direction of the symbol.}$$

Reverse the inequality symbol when dividing by a negative number.

$$k \geq -8$$

Check the solution set. Figure 7 shows the graph of the solution set, $[-8, \infty)$.

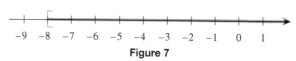

Figure 7

◀ *Work Problem* **5** *at the Side.*

ANSWERS

5. (a) $(-\infty, -5)$

(b) $\left(-\infty, -\dfrac{8}{7}\right]$

(c) $(9, \infty)$

Solving a Linear Inequality

Step 1 **Simplify each side separately.** Clear parentheses, fractions, and decimals using the distributive property as needed, and combine like terms.

Step 2 **Isolate the variable terms on one side.** Use the addition property of inequality to get all terms with variables on one side of the inequality and all numbers on the other side.

Step 3 **Isolate the variable.** Use the multiplication property of inequality to change the inequality to the form $x < k$ or $x > k$.

6 Solve, check, and graph the solution set of each inequality.

(a) $x + 4(2x - 1) \geq x + 2$

CAUTION
Reverse the direction of the inequality symbol only when multiplying or dividing each side of an inequality by a negative number.

Example 5 **Solving a Linear Inequality**

Solve $-3(x + 4) + 2 \geq 7 - x$, and graph the solution set.

Step 1 $-3(x + 4) + 2 \geq 7 - x$

$\qquad -3x - 12 + 2 \geq 7 - x$ Distributive property

$\qquad\qquad -3x - 10 \geq 7 - x$ Combine like terms.

Step 2 $-3x - 10 + x \geq 7 - x + x$ Add x.

$\qquad\qquad -2x - 10 \geq 7$ Combine like terms.

$\qquad -2x - 10 + 10 \geq 7 + 10$ Add 10.

$\qquad\qquad\qquad -2x \geq 17$ Combine like terms.

(b) $m - 2(m - 4) \leq 3m$

Step 3 $\qquad \dfrac{-2x}{-2} \leq \dfrac{17}{-2}$ Divide by -2; change $\geq$ to $\leq$.

> Be sure to reverse the inequality symbol.

$\qquad\qquad x \leq -\dfrac{17}{2}$

Figure 8 shows the graph of the solution set, $\left(-\infty, -\frac{17}{2}\right]$.

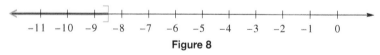

Figure 8

Work Problem **6** *at the Side.* ▶

Note
In Step 2 of Example 5, if we add $3x$ (instead of x) to both sides, we get

$\qquad -3x - 10 + 3x \geq 7 - x + 3x$ Add $3x$.

$\qquad\qquad\qquad -10 \geq 2x + 7$

$\qquad\qquad -10 - 7 \geq 2x + 7 - 7$ Subtract 7.

$\qquad\qquad\qquad -17 \geq 2x$

$\qquad -\dfrac{17}{2} \geq x, \quad \text{or} \quad x \leq -\dfrac{17}{2}.$ Divide by 2; rewrite.

The result "$-\frac{17}{2}$ is greater than or equal to x" means the same thing as "x is less than or equal to $-\frac{17}{2}$." Thus, the solution set is the same.

ANSWERS

6. (a) $\left[\dfrac{3}{4}, \infty\right)$

(b) $[2, \infty)$

7 Solve, check, and graph the solution set of each inequality.

(a) $5 - 3(m - 1)$
$\leq 2(m + 3) + 1$

(b) $\frac{1}{4}(m + 3) + 2 \leq \frac{3}{4}(m + 8)$

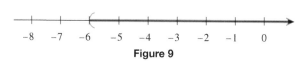

8 Rewrite each three-part inequality using the order in which the numbers appear on the number line.

(a) $1 > x > -1$

(b) $16 \geq p \geq 11$

(c) $-2 > t \geq -8$

ANSWERS

7. **(a)** $\left[\frac{1}{5}, \infty\right)$

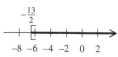

(b) $\left[-\frac{13}{2}, \infty\right)$

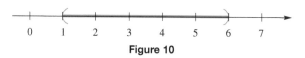

8. **(a)** $-1 < x < 1$
  (b) $11 \leq p \leq 16$
  (c) $-8 \leq t < -2$

Example 6 **Solving a Linear Inequality with Fractions**

Solve $-\frac{2}{3}(r - 3) - \frac{1}{2} < \frac{1}{2}(5 - r)$, and graph the solution set.

Step 1 To clear fractions, multiply by the least common denominator, 6.

$$-\frac{2}{3}(r - 3) - \frac{1}{2} < \frac{1}{2}(5 - r)$$

$$6\left[-\frac{2}{3}(r - 3) - \frac{1}{2}\right] < 6\left[\frac{1}{2}(5 - r)\right] \quad \text{Multiply by 6, the LCD.}$$

Be careful here.

$$6\left[-\frac{2}{3}(r - 3)\right] - 6\left(\frac{1}{2}\right) < 6\left[\frac{1}{2}(5 - r)\right] \quad \text{Distributive property}$$

$$-4(r - 3) - 3 < 3(5 - r) \quad \text{Multiply.}$$

$$-4r + 12 - 3 < 15 - 3r \quad \text{Distributive property}$$

$$-4r + 9 < 15 - 3r$$

Step 2 $$-4r + 9 + 3r < 15 - 3r + 3r \quad \text{Add } 3r.$$

$$-r + 9 < 15$$

$$-r + 9 - 9 < 15 - 9 \quad \text{Subtract 9.}$$

$$-r < 6$$

Step 3 $$-1(-r) > -1(6) \quad \text{Multiply by } -1; \text{ change } < \text{ to } >.$$

$$r > -6$$

Check that the solution set is $(-6, \infty)$. See Figure 9.

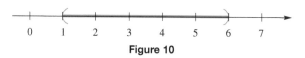

Figure 9

◀ *Work Problem* **7** *at the Side.*

OBJECTIVE **4** **Solve linear inequalities with three parts.** For some applications, it is necessary to work with a **three-part inequality** such as

$$3 < x + 2 < 8,$$

where $x + 2$ is *between* 3 and 8. We solve this inequality as follows.

$$3 - 2 < x + 2 - 2 < 8 - 2 \quad \text{Subtract 2 from } each \text{ part.}$$

$$1 < x < 6$$

Thus, x must be between 1 and 6 so that $x + 2$ will be between 3 and 8. The solution set, the open interval $(1, 6)$, is graphed in Figure 10.

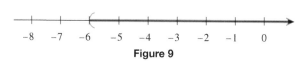

Figure 10

CAUTION

In three-part inequalities, the order of the parts is important. For example, do *not* write $8 < x + 2 < 3$, since this implies that $8 < 3$, a false statement. *We write three-part inequalities so that the symbols point in the same direction, and both point toward the lesser number.*

◀ *Work Problem* **8** *at the Side.*

| Example 7 | **Solving a Three-Part Inequality** |

Solve $-2 \le -3k - 1 \le 5$, and graph the solution set.

Begin by adding 1 to each of the three parts to isolate the variable term in the middle.

$$-2 + 1 \le -3k - 1 + 1 \le 5 + 1 \qquad \text{Add 1 to each part.}$$

$$-1 \le -3k \le 6$$

$$\frac{-1}{-3} \ge \frac{-3k}{-3} \ge \frac{6}{-3} \qquad \begin{array}{l}\text{Divide each part by } -3; \\ \text{reverse the direction of the} \\ \text{inequality symbols.}\end{array}$$

$$\frac{1}{3} \ge k \ge -2$$

$$-2 \le k \le \frac{1}{3} \qquad \begin{array}{l}\text{Rewrite in order based on the} \\ \text{number line.}\end{array}$$

Check that the solution set is the closed interval $[-2, \frac{1}{3}]$. See Figure 11.

Figure 11

Work Problem ⑨ *at the Side.* ▶

Examples of the types of solution sets to be expected from solving linear equations and linear inequalities are shown below.

SOLUTIONS OF LINEAR EQUATIONS AND INEQUALITIES

Equation or Inequality	Typical Solution Set	Graph of Solution Set
Linear equation $5x + 4 = 14$	$\{2\}$	
Linear inequality $5x + 4 < 14$	$(-\infty, 2)$	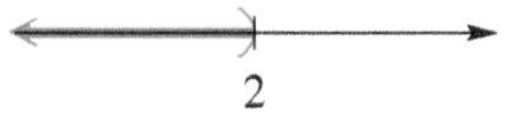
$5x + 4 > 14$	$(2, \infty)$	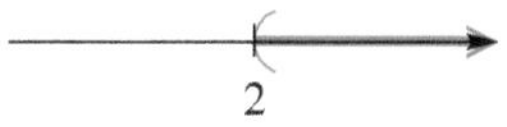
Three-part inequality $-1 \le 5x + 4 \le 14$	$[-1, 2]$	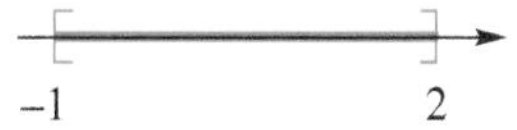

OBJECTIVE ⑤ Solve applied problems using linear inequalities.
Besides the familiar "is less than" and "is greater than," other expressions also indicate inequalities, as shown in the table below.

Word Expression	Interpretation
a exceeds b	$a > b$
a is at least b	$a \ge b$
a is no less than b	$a \ge b$
a is at most b	$a \le b$
a is no more than b	$a \le b$

⑨ Solve, check, and graph the solution set of each inequality.

(a) $-3 \le x - 1 \le 7$

(b) $5 < 3x - 4 < 9$

ANSWERS

9. (a) $[-2, 8]$

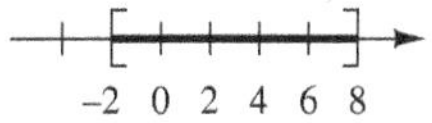

(b) $\left(3, \dfrac{13}{3}\right)$

10 Solve the problem.

A rental company charges $10 to rent a leaf blower, plus $7.50 per hr. Marge Ruhberg can spend no more than $40 to blow leaves from her driveway and pool deck. What is the *maximum* amount of time she can use the rented leaf blower?

In Examples 8 and 9, we use the six problem-solving steps from **Section 2.3,** changing Step 3 from "Write an equation" to "Write an inequality."

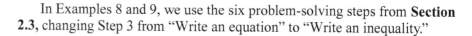

Example 8 **Using a Linear Inequality to Solve a Rental Problem**

A rental company charges $20 to rent a chain saw, plus $9 per hr. Tom Ruhberg can spend no more than $65 to clear some logs from his yard. What is the *maximum* amount of time he can use the rented saw?

Step 1 **Read** the problem again.

Step 2 **Assign a variable.** Let h = the number of hours he can rent the saw.

Step 3 **Write an inequality.** He must pay $20, plus $9h$, to rent the saw for h hours, and this amount must be *no more than* $65.

$$\underbrace{20 + 9h}_{\text{Cost of renting}} \quad \underbrace{\leq}_{\text{is no more than}} \quad \underbrace{65}_{\text{65 dollars.}}$$

Step 4 **Solve.**
$$9h \leq 45 \qquad \text{Subtract 20.}$$
$$h \leq 5 \qquad \text{Divide by 9.}$$

Step 5 **State the answer.** He can use the saw for a maximum of 5 hr. (He may use it for less time, as indicated by the inequality $h \leq 5$.)

Step 6 **Check.** If Tom uses the saw for **5** hr, he will spend
$$20 + 9(5) = 65 \text{ dollars,} \quad \text{the maximum amount.}$$

◀ *Work Problem* **10** *at the Side.*

11 Solve the problem.

Alex Lose has grades of 92, 90, and 84 on his first three history tests. What grade must he make on his fourth test in order to keep an average of at least 90?

Example 9 **Finding an Average Test Score**

Emma Saska has scores of 88, 86, and 90 on her first three algebra tests. An average score of at least 90 will earn an A in the class. What possible scores on her fourth test will earn her an A average?

Let x represent the score on the fourth test. Her average score must be at least 90. To find the average of four numbers, add them and then divide by 4.

$$\underbrace{\frac{88 + 86 + 90 + x}{4}}_{\text{Average}} \quad \underbrace{\geq}_{\substack{\text{is at}\\\text{least}}} \quad \underbrace{90}_{90.}$$

$$\frac{264 + x}{4} \geq 90 \qquad \text{Add the scores.}$$

$$264 + x \geq 360 \qquad \text{Multiply by 4.}$$

$$x \geq 96 \qquad \text{Subtract 264.}$$

She must score **96** or more on her fourth test.

Check $\quad \dfrac{88 + 86 + 90 + 96}{4} = \dfrac{360}{4} = 90,$ the minimum score.

A score of 96 or more will give an average of at least 90, as required.

◀ *Work Problem* **11** *at the Side.*

Match each inequality in Column I with the correct graph or interval in Column II.

I

1. $x \leq 3$

2. $x > 3$

3. $x < 3$

4. $x \geq 3$

5. $-3 \leq x \leq 3$

6. $-3 < x < 3$

II

A.

B.

C. $(3, \infty)$

D. $(-\infty, 3]$

E. $(-3, 3)$

F. $[-3, 3]$

7. Refer to the graph, and write an inequality or a three-part inequality for each description.

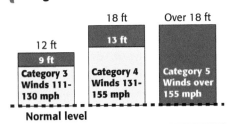

Storm Surges Depend on Hurricane Categories

- Category 3 Winds 111–130 mph — 9 ft, 12 ft
- Category 4 Winds 131–155 mph — 13 ft, 18 ft
- Category 5 Winds over 155 mph — Over 18 ft

Normal level

Source: National Oceanic and Atmospheric Administration.

(a) The wind speed s (in miles per hour) of a Category 4 hurricane

(b) The wind speed s (in miles per hour) of a Category 5 hurricane

(c) The storm surge x (in feet) from a Category 3 hurricane

(d) The storm surge x (in feet) from a Category 5 hurricane

9. A student solved the following inequality as shown.

$$4x \geq -64$$
$$\frac{4x}{4} \leq \frac{-64}{4}$$
$$x \leq -16$$

Solution set: $(-\infty, -16]$

WHAT WENT WRONG? Give the correct solution set.

8. Dr. Paul Donohue writes a syndicated column in which readers question him on a variety of health topics. Reader C. J. wrote, "Many people say they can weigh more because they have a large frame. How is frame size determined?" Here is Dr. Donohue's response:

> "For a man, a wrist circumference between 6.75 and 7.25 in. *[inclusive] indicates a medium frame. Anything above is a large frame and anything below, a small frame.*"

Using x to represent wrist circumference in inches, write an inequality or a three-part inequality that represents wrist circumference for a male with the indicated frame size.

(a) Small frame

(b) Medium frame

(c) Large frame

(*Source: The Gazette,* Cedar Rapids, Iowa, October 4, 2004.)

10. Explain how you will determine whether to use parentheses or brackets when graphing the solution set of an inequality.

Solve each inequality, giving solution sets in both interval and graph forms. Check your answers. See Examples 1–6.

11. $x - 4 \leq 3$

12. $t - 3 \leq 1$

13. $4x + 1 \geq 21$

14. $5t + 2 \geq 52$

15. $5x > -25$

16. $7x < -28$

17. $-4x < 16$

18. $-2m > 10$

19. $-\dfrac{3}{4}r \geq 30$

20. $-\dfrac{2}{3}x \leq 12$

21. $-1.3m \geq -5.2$

22. $-2.5x \leq -1.25$

23. $\dfrac{3k - 1}{4} > 5$

24. $\dfrac{5z - 6}{8} < 8$

25. $\dfrac{2k - 5}{-4} > 5$

26. $\dfrac{3z - 2}{-5} < 6$

27. $3k + 1 < -20$

28. $5z + 6 > -29$

29. $x + 4(2x - 1) \geq x$

30. $m - 2(m - 4) \leq 3m$

31. $-(4 + r) + 2 - 3r < -14$

32. $-(9 + k) - 5 + 4k \geq 4$

33. $-3(z - 6) > 2z - 2$

34. $-2(x + 4) \leq 6x + 16$

35. $\dfrac{2}{3}(3k - 1) \geq \dfrac{3}{2}(2k - 3)$

36. $\dfrac{7}{5}(10m - 1) < \dfrac{2}{3}(6m + 5)$

⊕ 37. $-\dfrac{1}{4}(p + 6) + \dfrac{3}{2}(2p - 5) < 10$

38. $\dfrac{3}{5}(k - 2) - \dfrac{1}{4}(2k - 7) \leq 3$

Relating Concepts (Exercises 39–43) For Individual or Group Work

Work Exercises 39–43 in order.

39. Solve the linear equation
$$5(x + 3) - 2(x - 4) = 2(x + 7),$$
and graph the solution set on a number line.

40. Solve the linear inequality
$$5(x + 3) - 2(x - 4) > 2(x + 7),$$
and graph the solution set on a number line.

41. Solve the linear inequality
$$5(x + 3) - 2(x - 4) < 2(x + 7),$$
and graph the solution set on a number line.

42. Graph all the solution sets of the equation and inequalities in Exercises 39–41 on the same number line. What set do you obtain?

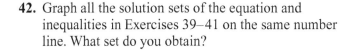

43. Based on the results of Exercises 39–41, complete the following using a conjecture (educated guess): The solution set of
$$-3(x + 2) = 3x + 12$$
is $\{-3\}$, and the solution set of
$$-3(x + 2) < 3x + 12$$
is $(-3, \infty)$. Therefore the solution set of
$$-3(x + 2) > 3x + 12$$
is _____ .

44. Which is the graph of $-2 < x$?

A. $\longleftrightarrow$
$\quad\quad -2\quad 0$

B. $\longleftrightarrow$
$\quad\quad\quad\quad -2\quad 0$

C. $\longleftrightarrow$
$\quad\quad\quad\quad -2\quad 0$

D. $\longleftrightarrow$
$\quad\quad\quad\quad -2\quad 0$

Solve each inequality, giving solution sets in both interval and graph forms. Check your answers. See Example 7.

45. $-4 < x - 5 < 6$

46. $-1 < x + 1 < 8$

47. $-9 \le k + 5 \le 15$

48. $-4 \le m + 3 \le 10$

49. $-6 \le 2(z + 2) \le 16$

50. $-15 < 3(p + 2) < 24$

51. $-16 < 3t + 2 < -10$

52. $-19 < 3x - 5 \le 1$

 **53.** $4 < -9x + 5 \le 8$

54. $4 < -2x + 3 \le 8$

55. $-1 \le \dfrac{2x - 5}{6} \le 5$

56. $-3 < \dfrac{3m + 1}{4} \le 3$

The weather forecast by time of day for the U.S. Olympic Track and Field Trials,
in Sacramento, California, is shown in the figure. Use this graph to work Exercises 57–60.

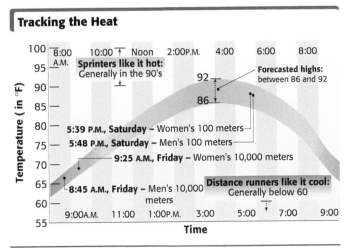

Tracking the Heat

Sprinters like it hot:
Generally in the 90's

Forecasted highs:
between 86 and 92

5:39 P.M., Saturday – Women's 100 meters
5:48 P.M., Saturday – Men's 100 meters
9:25 A.M., Friday – Women's 10,000 meters
8:45 A.M., Friday – Men's 10,000 meters

Distance runners like it cool:
Generally below 60

Temperature (in °F)

Time

Source: Accuweather, Bee research.

57. Sprinters prefer Fahrenheit temperatures in the 90's. Using the upper boundary of the forecast, in what time period is the temperature expected to be at least 90°F?

58. Distance runners prefer cool temperatures. During what time period are temperatures predicted to be no more than 70°F? Use the lower forecast boundary.

59. What range of temperatures is predicted for the Women's 100-m event?

60. What range of temperatures is forecast for the Men's 10,000-m event?

Solve each problem. See Examples 8 and 9.

61. Amber is signing up for cell phone service. She is trying to decide between Plan A, which costs $54.99 a month with a free phone included, and Plan B, which costs $49.99 a month, but would require her to buy a phone for $129. Under either plan, Amber does not expect to go over the included number of monthly minutes. After how many months would Plan B be a better deal?

62. Stuart and Tracy Sudak need to rent a truck to move their belongings to their new apartment. They can rent a truck of the size they need from U-Haul for $29.95 a day plus 28 cents per mile or from Budget Truck Rentals for $34.95 a day plus 25 cents per mile. After how many miles would the Budget rental be a better deal than the U-Haul one?

63. Bonnie Boehme earned scores of 90 and 82 on her first two tests in English Literature. What score must she make on her third test to keep an average of 84 or greater?

64. Scott Barnett scored 92 and 96 on his first two tests in Methods in Teaching Mathematics. What score must he make on his third test to keep an average of 90 or greater?

A product will produce a profit only when the revenue (R) from selling the product exceeds the cost (C) of producing it. Find the least whole number of units x that must be sold for each business to show a profit for the item described.

65. Peripheral Visions, Inc. finds that the cost to produce x studio-quality DVDs is

$$C = 20x + 100,$$

while the revenue produced from them is $R = 24x$ (C and R in dollars).

66. Speedy Delivery finds that the cost to make x deliveries is

$$C = 3x + 2300,$$

while the revenue produced from them is $R = 5.50x$ (C and R in dollars).

67. A BMI (body mass index) between 19 and 25 is considered healthy. Use the formula

$$\text{BMI} = \frac{704 \times (\text{weight in pounds})}{(\text{height in inches})^2}$$

to find the weight range w, to the nearest pound, that gives a healthy BMI for each height. (*Source: Washington Post.*)

(a) 72 in.   **(b)** Your height in inches

68. To achieve the maximum benefit from exercising, the heart rate in beats per minute should be in the target heart rate zone (*THR*). For a person aged A, the formula is

$$0.7(220 - A) \leq THR \leq 0.85(220 - A).$$

Find the *THR* to the nearest whole number for each age. (*Source:* Hockey, Robert V., *Physical Fitness: The Pathway to Healthful Living*, Times Mirror/Mosby College Publishing, 1989.)

(a) 35   **(b)** Your age

Find the unknown numbers in each description.

69. Six times a number is between -12 and 12.

70. Half a number is between -3 and 2.

71. When 1 is added to twice a number, the result is greater than or equal to 7.

72. If 8 is subtracted from a number, then the result is at least 5.

73. One third of a number is added to 6, giving a result of at least 3.

74. Three times a number, minus 5, is no more than 7.

Study Skills

▶▶▶ USING STUDY CARDS

You may have used "flash cards" in other classes. In math, "study cards" can be helpful. The main things to remember in math besides terms and definitions are *sets of steps to follow* to solve problems (and how to know which set of steps to follow) and *concepts about how math works* (principles). So, the cards may look different but will be just as useful.

In this two-part activity, you will find four types of study cards to use in math. Look carefully at what kinds of information to put on them and where to put it. Then use them the way you would any flash card:

▶ to quickly review when you have a few minutes,

▶ for daily reviews,

▶ to review before a quiz or test.

Remember, the most helpful thing about study cards is making them. After each card description you will find an assignment to try, marked **Now Try This**.

To make a new vocabulary card, put the word (spelled correctly) and the page number where it is found on the front of the card. On the back, write:

▶ the definition (in your own words if possible),

▶ an example, including any exceptions or other special information,

▶ any related words, and

▶ a sample problem (if appropriate).

New Vocabulary Cards

Interval notation　　　　　　　　　*p. 128*　　　Front of Card

Definition: Using symbols to describe an interval on a number line.

Symbols: ∞　$-\infty$　$(\ )$　$[\ ]$　$(\ ]$　$[\ )$

Use interval notation to tell what numbers are in the solution set for an inequality.

Examples: $(-5, \infty)$　*All numbers greater than -5, not including -5*

$[-5, 5)$　*All numbers between -5 and 5, including -5, excluding 5*

Back of Card

List 4 new vocabulary words/concepts you need to learn right now. Make a card for each one.

◀◀◀ **Now Try This**

_____　_____　_____　_____

Procedure ("Steps") Cards

To make a procedure (steps) card, write the name of the procedure at the top on the front of the card. Then write each step *in words*. If you need to learn abbreviations for some words, include them along with the whole words written out. On the back of the card, put an example of the procedure, showing each step you need to take. You can review by looking at the front and practicing a new worked example, or by looking at the back and remembering the procedure and its steps.

Front of Card

Solving a Linear Inequality

1. *Simplify each side separately. (Clear parentheses and combine like terms.)*

2. *Isolate variable terms on one side. (Add or subtract the same number from both sides.)*

3. *Isolate the variable. (Divide both sides by the same number; if dividing by a negative number, reverse direction of inequality.)*

Back of Card

Solve $-3(x + 4) + 2 \geq 7 - x$ *and graph the solution set.*

$-3(x + 4) + 2 \geq 7 - x$	*Clear parentheses.*
$-3x - 12 + 2 \geq 7 - x$	*Combine like terms.*
$-3x - 10 \geq 7 - x$	*Both sides are simplified.*
$-3x - 10 + x \geq 7 - x + x$	*Add x to both sides.*
$-2x - 10 \geq 7$	*Variable term still not isolated.*
$-2x - 10 + 10 \geq 7 + 10$	*Add 10 to both sides.*
$\dfrac{-2x}{-2} \geq \dfrac{17}{-2}$	*Divide both sides by -2; dividing by negative, reverse direction of inequality symbol.*
$x \leq -\dfrac{17}{2}$	$-\dfrac{17}{2} = -8\dfrac{1}{2}$

Now Try This ▶▶▶

What procedure are you learning right now? Write below the steps that you will put on your study card.

Procedure: _____

Step 1 _____

Step 2 _____

Step 3 _____

Step 4 _____

Step 5 _____

13.3 ▶▶▶ Set Operations and Compound Inequalities

The table shows symptoms of an overactive thyroid and an underactive thyroid.

Underactive Thyroid	Overactive Thyroid
Sleepiness, s	Insomnia, i
Dry hands, d	Moist hands, m
Intolerance of cold, c	Intolerance of heat, h
Goiter, g	Goiter, g

Source: The Merck Manual of Diagnosis and Therapy,
16th Edition, Merck Research Laboratories, 1992.

Let N be the set of symptoms for an underactive thyroid, and let O be the set of symptoms for an overactive thyroid. Suppose we are interested in the set of symptoms that are found in *both* sets N and O. In this section, we discuss the use of the words *and* and *or* as they relate to sets and inequalities.

OBJECTIVE 1 Find the intersection of two sets. The intersection of two sets is defined using the word *and*.

Intersection of Sets

For any two sets A and B, the **intersection** of A and B, symbolized $A \cap B$, is defined as follows:

$$A \cap B = \{x \mid x \text{ is an element of } A \text{ and } x \text{ is an element of } B\}.$$

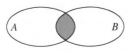

Example 1 **Finding the Intersection of Two Sets**

Let $A = \{1, 2, 3, 4\}$ and $B = \{2, 4, 6\}$. Find $A \cap B$.
   The set $A \cap B$ contains those elements that belong to both A *and* B.

$$A \cap B = \{1, 2, 3, 4\} \cap \{2, 4, 6\}$$
$$= \{2, 4\}$$

Work Problem **1** *at the Side.* ▶

A **compound inequality** consists of two inequalities linked by a connective word such as *and* or *or*. Examples of compound inequalities are

$$x + 1 \leq 9 \quad \text{and} \quad x - 2 \geq 3$$

and $$2x > 4 \quad \text{or} \quad 3x - 6 < 5.$$

Compound inequalities

OBJECTIVE 2 Solve compound inequalities with the word *and*.

Solving a Compound Inequality with *and*

Step 1 Solve each inequality individually.

Step 2 Since the inequalities are joined with *and*, the solution set of the compound inequality will include all numbers that satisfy both inequalities in Step 1 (the intersection of the solution sets).

OBJECTIVES

1 Find the intersection of two sets.

2 Solve compound inequalities with the word *and*.

3 Find the union of two sets.

4 Solve compound inequalities with the word *or*.

1 List the elements in each set.

(a) $A \cap B$, if $A = \{3, 4, 5, 6\}$ and $B = \{5, 6, 7\}$

(b) $N \cap O$ (Refer to the thyroid table.)

ANSWERS

1. (a) $\{5, 6\}$ (b) $\{g\}$

2 Solve each compound inequality, and graph the solution set.

(a) $x < 10$ and $x > 2$

_____→

(b) $x + 3 \leq 1$ and
$x - 4 \geq -12$

_____→

3 Solve
$2x \geq x - 1$ and $3x \geq 3 + 2x$,
and graph the solution set.

_____→

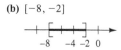

Example 2 **Solving a Compound Inequality with *and***

Solve the compound inequality $x + 1 \leq 9$ and $x - 2 \geq 3$.

Step 1 Solve each inequality individually.

$$x + 1 \leq 9 \qquad \text{and} \qquad x - 2 \geq 3$$
$$x + 1 - 1 \leq 9 - 1 \quad \text{and} \quad x - 2 + 2 \geq 3 + 2$$
$$x \leq 8 \qquad \text{and} \qquad x \geq 5$$

Step 2 Because the inequalities are joined with the word *and,* the solution set will include all numbers that satisfy *both* inequalities in Step 1 at the same time. Thus, the compound inequality is true whenever $x \leq 8$ and $x \geq 5$ are both true. The top graph in Figure 12 shows $x \leq 8$, and the bottom graph shows $x \geq 5$.

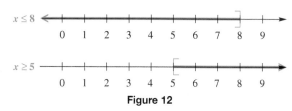

Figure 12

Find the intersection of the two graphs in Figure 12 to get the solution set of the compound inequality. The intersection of the two graphs in Figure 13 shows that the solution set is the closed interval $[5, 8]$.

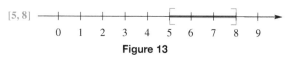

Figure 13

◀ *Work Problem* **2** *at the Side.*

Example 3 **Solving a Compound Inequality with *and***

Solve the compound inequality $-3x - 2 > 5$ and $5x - 1 \leq -21$.

Step 1 Solve each inequality individually.

$$-3x - 2 > 5 \qquad \text{and} \quad 5x - 1 \leq -21$$
$$-3x > 7 \qquad \text{and} \qquad 5x \leq -20$$

Remember to reverse the inequality symbol.

$$x < -\frac{7}{3} \qquad \text{and} \qquad x \leq -4$$

The graphs of $x < -\frac{7}{3}$ and $x \leq -4$ are shown in Figure 14.

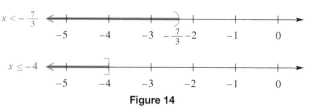

Figure 14

Step 2 Now find all values of x that satisfy both conditions; that is, the real numbers that are less than $-\frac{7}{3}$ and also less than or equal to -4. See Figure 15. The solution set is the infinite interval $(-\infty, -4]$.

Figure 15

◀ *Work Problem* **3** *at the Side.*

Example 4 | **Solving a Compound Inequality with *and***

Solve $x + 2 < 5$ and $x - 10 > 2$.

First solve each inequality individually.

$$x + 2 < 5 \quad \text{and} \quad x - 10 > 2$$
$$x < 3 \quad \text{and} \qquad x > 12$$

The graphs of $x < 3$ and $x > 12$ are shown in Figure 16.

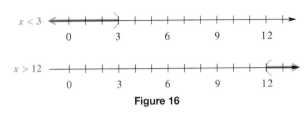

Figure 16

There is no number that is both less than 3 *and* greater than 12, so the given compound inequality has no solution. The solution set is $\emptyset$. See Figure 17.

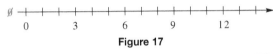

Figure 17

Work Problem **4** _at the Side._ ▶

OBJECTIVE **3** **Find the union of two sets.** The union of two sets is defined using the word *or*.

Union of Sets

For any two sets A and B, the **union** of A and B, symbolized $A \cup B$, is defined as follows:

$$A \cup B = \{x \mid x \text{ is an element of } A \text{ or } x \text{ is an element of } B\}.$$

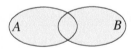

Example 5 | **Finding the Union of Two Sets**

Let $A = \{1, 2, 3, 4\}$ and $B = \{2, 4, 6\}$. Find $A \cup B$.

Begin by listing all the elements of set A: 1, 2, 3, 4. Then list any additional elements from set B. In this case the elements 2 and 4 are already listed, so the only additional element is 6. Therefore,

$$A \cup B = \{1, 2, 3, 4\} \cup \{2, 4, 6\}$$
$$= \{1, 2, 3, 4, 6\}.$$

The union consists of all elements in either A *or* B (or both).

Note

Although the elements 2 and 4 appeared in both sets A and B, they are written only once in $A \cup B$.

Work Problem **5** _at the Side._ ▶

---

4 Solve.

(a) $x < 5$ and $x > 5$

(b) $x + 2 > 3$ and
$\quad 2x + 1 < -3$

5 List the elements in each set.

(a) $A \cup B$, if $A = \{3, 4, 5, 6\}$
$\quad$ and $B = \{5, 6, 7\}$

(b) $N \cup O$ from the thyroid
$\quad$ table at the beginning of
$\quad$ this section

ANSWERS
4. **(a)** $\emptyset$ **(b)** $\emptyset$
5. **(a)** $\{3, 4, 5, 6, 7\}$ **(b)** $\{s, d, c, g, i, m, h\}$

6 Solve. Give each solution set in both interval and graph forms.

(a) $x + 2 > 3$ or
$2x + 1 < -3$

OBJECTIVE 4 Solve compound inequalities with the word *or*.
Use the following steps.

> **Solving a Compound Inequality with *or***
>
> **Step 1** Solve each inequality individually.
>
> **Step 2** Since the inequalities are joined with *or*, the solution set includes all numbers that satisfy either one of the two inequalities in Step 1 (the union of the solution sets).

Example 6 **Solving a Compound Inequality with *or***

Solve $6x - 4 < 2x$ or $-3x \leq -9$.

Step 1 Solve each inequality individually.

$$6x - 4 < 2x \quad \text{or} \quad -3x \leq -9$$
$$4x < 4$$

Remember to reverse the inequality symbol.

$$x < 1 \quad \text{or} \quad x \geq 3$$

The graphs of these two inequalities are shown in Figure 18.

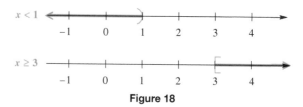

Figure 18

(b) $x - 1 > 2$ or
$3x + 5 < 2x + 6$

Step 2 Since the inequalities are joined with *or*, we find the union of the two solution sets, as shown in Figure 19. The solution set is the disjoint interval

$$(-\infty, 1) \cup [3, \infty).$$

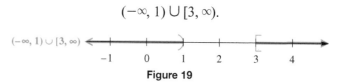

Figure 19

> **CAUTION**
>
> When inequalities are used to write the solution set in Example 6, it *must* be written as
>
> $$x < 1 \quad \text{or} \quad x \geq 3,$$
>
> which keeps the numbers 1 and 3 in their order on the number line. Writing $3 \leq x < 1$ would imply that $3 \leq 1$, which is **FALSE**. There is no other way to write the solution set of such a union.

ANSWERS

◀ *Work Problem* **6** *at the Side.*

6. (a) $(-\infty, -2) \cup (1, \infty)$

$-2\ -1\ 0\ 1\ 2$

(b) $(-\infty, 1) \cup (3, \infty)$

$0\ 1\ 2\ 3\ 4$

Example 7 **Solving a Compound Inequality with *or***

Solve $-4x + 1 \geq 9$ or $5x + 3 \leq -12$.
 First, solve each inequality individually.

$$-4x + 1 \geq 9 \quad \text{or} \quad 5x + 3 \leq -12$$
$$-4x \geq 8 \quad \text{or} \quad 5x \leq -15$$
$$x \leq -2 \quad \text{or} \quad x \leq -3$$

The graphs of these two inequalities are shown in Figure 20.

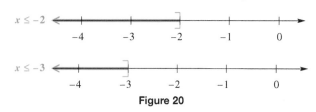

Figure 20

By taking the union, we obtain the interval $(-\infty, -2]$. See Figure 21.

Figure 21

Work Problem **7** *at the Side.* ▶

7 Solve. Give each solution set in both interval and graph forms.

(a) $2x + 1 \leq 9$ or $2x + 3 \leq 5$

(b) $3x - 4 > 2$ or
$-2x + 5 < 3$

Example 8 **Solving a Compound Inequality with *or***

Solve $-2x + 5 \geq 11$ or $4x - 7 \geq -27$.
 Solve each inequality individually.

$$-2x + 5 \geq 11 \quad \text{or} \quad 4x - 7 \geq -27$$
$$-2x \geq 6 \quad \text{or} \quad 4x \geq -20$$
$$x \leq -3 \quad \text{or} \quad x \geq -5$$

The graphs of these two inequalities are shown in Figure 22.

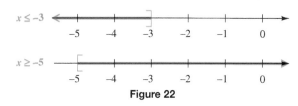

Figure 22

By taking the union, we obtain every real number as a solution, since every real number satisfies at least one of the two inequalities. The set of all real numbers is written in interval notation as $(-\infty, \infty)$ and graphed as in Figure 23.

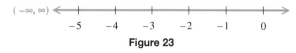

Figure 23

Work Problem **8** *at the Side.* ▶

8 Solve
$$3x - 2 \leq 13 \text{ or } x + 5 \geq 7.$$
Give the solution set in both interval and graph forms.

ANSWERS

7. (a) $(-\infty, 4]$

(b) $(1, \infty)$

8. $(-\infty, \infty)$

9 From Example 9, list the elements that satisfy each set.

(a) The set of films with admissions greater than 130,000,000 and gross income less than $800,000,000

> ### Example 9   Applying Intersection and Union
>
> The five highest-grossing domestic films (adjusted for inflation) as of July, 2005, are listed in the table.
>
> FIVE ALL-TIME HIGHEST GROSSING DOMESTIC FILMS
>
> | Film | Admissions | Gross Income |
> |---|---|---|
> | *Gone with the Wind* | 202,044,569 | $1,293,085,000 |
> | *Star Wars* | 178,119,595 | $1,139,965,000 |
> | *The Sound of Music* | 142,415,376 | $911,458,000 |
> | *E.T.* | 141,925,359 | $908,322,298 |
> | *The Ten Commandments* | 131,000,000 | $838,400,000 |
>
> *Source:* Exhibitor Relations Co., Inc.
>
> List the elements of the following sets.
>
> **(a)** The set of top-five films with admissions greater than 180,000,000 *and* gross income greater than $1,000,000,000
> The only film that satisfies both conditions is *Gone with the Wind,* so the set is
>
> $$\{Gone \ with \ the \ Wind\}.$$
>
> **(b)** The set of top-five films with admissions less than 170,000,000 *or* gross income greater than $1,000,000,000
> Here, a film that satisfies at least one of the conditions is in the set. This set includes all five films:
>
> $$\{Gone \ with \ the \ Wind, \ Star \ Wars, \ The \ Sound \ of \ Music, \ E.T.,$$
> $$The \ Ten \ Commandments\}.$$

◀ *Work Problem* **9** *at the Side.*

(b) The set of films with admissions greater than 130,000,000 or gross income less than $800,000,000

Decide whether each statement is true *or* false. *If it is* false, *explain why.*

1. The union of the solution sets of $2x + 1 = 3$, $2x + 1 > 3$, and $2x + 1 < 3$ is $(-\infty, \infty)$.

2. The intersection of the sets $\{x \mid x \geq 5\}$ and $\{x \mid x \leq 5\}$ is $\emptyset$.

3. The union of the sets $(-\infty, 6)$ and $(6, \infty)$ is $\{6\}$.

4. The intersection of the sets $[6, \infty)$ and $(-\infty, 6]$ is $\{6\}$.

Let $A = \{1, 2, 3, 4, 5, 6\}$, $B = \{1, 3, 5\}$, $C = \{1, 6\}$, and $D = \{4\}$. Specify each set. See Examples 1 and 5.

◉ 5. $A \cap D$

6. $B \cap C$

7. $B \cap \emptyset$

8. $A \cap \emptyset$

◉ 9. $A \cup B$

10. $B \cup D$

11. $B \cup C$

12. $C \cup B$

Two sets are specified by graphs. Graph the intersection of the two sets.

13.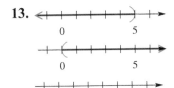

14.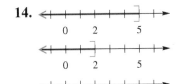

15.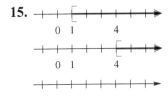

Two sets are specified by graphs. Graph the union of the two sets.

16.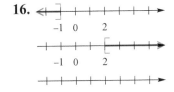

17.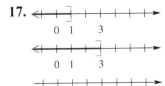

18.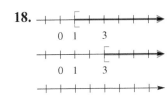

19. Give an example of intersection applied to a real-life situation.

20. A compound inequality uses one of the words *and* or *or*. Explain how you will determine whether to use *intersection* or *union* when graphing the solution set.

For each compound inequality, give the solution set in both interval and graph forms. See Examples 2–4.

21. $x < 2$ and $x > -3$

22. $x < 5$ and $x > 0$

23. $x \leq 2$ and $x \leq 5$

24. $x \geq 3$ and $x \geq 6$

◉ 25. $x \leq 3$ and $x \geq 6$

26. $x \leq -1$ and $x \geq 3$

27. $x - 3 \leq 6$ and $x + 2 \geq 7$

28. $x + 5 \leq 11$ and $x - 3 \geq -1$

29. $3x - 4 \leq 8$ and $4x - 1 \leq 15$

30. $7x + 6 \leq 48$ and $-4x \geq -24$

For each compound inequality, give the solution set in both interval and graph forms.
See Examples 6–8.

31. $x \leq 1$ or $x \leq 8$

32. $x \geq 1$ or $x \geq 8$

33. $x \geq -2$ or $x \geq 5$

34. $x \leq -2$ or $x \leq 6$

35. $x + 3 \geq 1$ or $x - 8 \leq -4$

36. $x + 6 \geq 11$ or $x - 4 \leq 3$

37. $x + 2 > 7$ or $1 - x > 6$

38. $x + 1 > 3$ or $x + 4 < 2$

39. $x + 1 > 3$ or $-4x + 1 \geq 5$

40. $3x < x + 12$ or $x + 1 > 10$

41. $4x - 8 > 0$ or $4x - 1 < 7$

42. $3x < x + 12$ or $3x - 8 > 10$

Express each set in the simplest interval form.

43. $(-\infty, -1] \cap [-4, \infty)$

44. $[-1, \infty) \cap (-\infty, 9]$

45. $(-\infty, -6] \cap [-9, \infty)$

46. $(5, 11] \cap [6, \infty)$

47. $(-\infty, 3) \cup (-\infty, -2)$

48. $[-9, 1] \cup (-\infty, -3)$

49. $[3, 6] \cup (4, 9)$

50. $[-1, 2] \cup (0, 5)$

For each compound inequality, state whether intersection or union should be used. Then give the solution set in both interval and graph forms. See Examples 2–4 and 6–8.

51. $x < -1$ and $x > -5$

52. $x > -1$ and $x < 7$

53. $x < 4$ or $x < -2$

54. $x < 5$ or $x < -3$

55. $x + 1 \geq 5$ and $x - 2 \leq 10$

56. $2x - 6 \leq -18$ and $2x \geq -18$

57. $-3x \leq -6$ or $-3x \geq 0$

58. $-8x \leq -24$ or $-5x \geq 15$

Relating Concepts (Exercises 59—64) For Individual or Group Work

The figures represent the backyards of neighbors Luigi, Mario, Than, and Joe. Find the area and the perimeter of each yard. Suppose that each resident has 150 ft of fencing and enough sod to cover 1400 ft² of lawn.

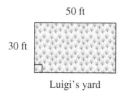
50 ft
30 ft
Luigi's yard

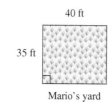
40 ft
35 ft
Mario's yard

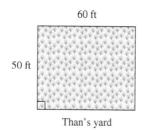
60 ft
50 ft
Than's yard

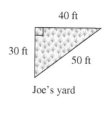
40 ft
30 ft   50 ft
Joe's yard

Give the name or names of the residents whose yards satisfy each description.

59. The yard can be fenced *and* the yard can be sodded.

60. The yard can be fenced *and* the yard cannot be sodded.

61. The yard cannot be fenced *and* the yard can be sodded.

62. The yard cannot be fenced *and* the yard cannot be sodded.

63. The yard can be fenced *or* the yard can be sodded.

64. The yard cannot be fenced *or* the yard can be sodded.

Average expenses for full-time college students at 2-year institutions during the 2005–2006 academic year are shown in the table.

COLLEGE EXPENSES (IN DOLLARS), 2-YEAR INSTITUTIONS

Type of Expense	Public Schools	Private Schools
Tuition and fees	1935	12,450
Board rates	2306	4726
Dormitory charges	2251	3994

Source: National Center for Education Statistics, U.S. Department of Education.

Use the table to list the elements of each set. See Example 9.

65. The set of expenses that are less than $2500 for public schools *and* are greater than $5000 for private schools

66. The set of expenses that are greater than $2300 for public schools *and* are less than $12,000 for private schools

67. The set of expenses that are less than $2300 for public schools *or* are greater than $10,000 for private schools

68. The set of expenses that are greater than $12,000 *or* are less than $2000

Study Skills

This is the second part of the Study Cards activity. As you get further into a chapter, you can choose particular problems that will serve as a good test review. Here are two more types of study cards that will help you.

Tough Problems Card

When you are doing your homework and find yourself saying, "This is really hard," or "I'm having trouble with this," make a tough problem study card. On the front, write out the procedure to work the type of problem *in words*. If there are special notes (like what *not* to do), include them. On the back, work at least one example. Make sure you label what you are doing.

Solving a Linear Inequality with Fractions
First step: Clear the inequality of fractions.
    — *Find a common denominator.*
    — *Multiply each term by the common*
      denominator.

Front of Card

Solve $\frac{3}{4}(m-3) + 2 \le \frac{1}{2}(m+8)$ and graph the solution set

$\frac{4}{1}\left[\frac{3}{4}(m-3)\right] + 4(2) \le \frac{4}{1}\left[\frac{1}{2}(m+8)\right]$ *Common denom. is 4.*
                                Multiply every term by 4.

$3(m-3) + 8 \le 2(m+8)$ *Simplify each side.*
$3m - 9 + 8 \le 2m + 16$
$3m - 1 \le 2m + 16$
$3m - 1 - 2m \le 2m + 16 - 2m$ *Subtract 2m.*
$m - 1 \le 16$
$m - 1 + 1 \le 16 + 1$
$m \le 17$

⟵————————————┤
                            17

Back of Card

Choose three types of difficult problems, and work them out on study cards. *Be sure to put the words for solving the problem on one side and the worked problem on the other side.*

◀◀◀ **Now Try This**

1011

Practice Quiz Cards

Quiz study cards cover each type of problem you learn. They are useful when you prepare for a test. To make a quiz card, put the problem with the direction words (like *solve, simplify, estimate*) on the front of a card, and work the problem on the back. If you like, include the page number from the text. When you review, work the problem on a separate paper and check it by looking at the back of your quiz card.

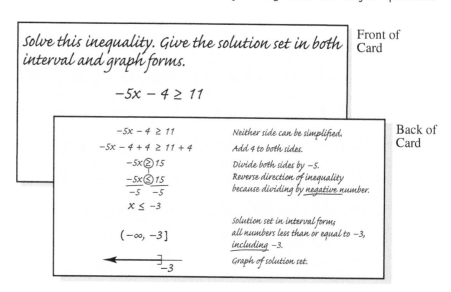

Front of Card

Back of Card

Now Try This ▶▶▶

Choose three problems from different sections of this chapter, and work them on study cards. Be sure you don't just choose the easiest problems.

Why Are Study Cards Brain Friendly?

First, **making the study cards is an active technique.** You have to make decisions about what is most important and how to put it on a card. This kind of thinking is more involved than just memorizing, and as a result, you will understand the concepts better and remember them longer.

Second, **the cards are visually appealing** (if you write neatly and try some color). You will remember a visual image longer and may even be able to "picture in your mind" how your cards look. This will help you during tests.

Third, because **study cards are small and portable,** you can review them easily whenever you have a few minutes. Even while you're waiting for a bus or have a few minutes between classes, you can take out your cards and read over them. After a while, the information will become automatic and easier to remember.

13.4 ▶▶▶ Absolute Value Equations and Inequalities

OBJECTIVES

1 Use the distance definition of absolute value.

2 Solve equations of the form $|ax + b| = k$, for $k > 0$.

3 Solve inequalities of the form $|ax + b| < k$ and of the form $|ax + b| > k$, for $k > 0$.

4 Solve absolute value equations that involve rewriting.

5 Solve equations of the form $|ax + b| = |cx + d|$.

6 Solve special cases of absolute value equations and inequalities.

In a production line, quality is controlled by randomly choosing items from the line and checking to see how selected measurements vary from the optimum measure. These differences are sometimes positive and sometimes negative, so they are expressed with absolute value. For example, a machine that fills quart milk cartons might be set to release 1 qt (32 oz) plus or minus 2 oz per carton. Then the number of ounces in each carton should satisfy the *absolute value inequality* $|x - 32| \le 2$, where x is the number of ounces.

OBJECTIVE 1 Use the distance definition of absolute value.
In **Section 1.1,** we saw that the absolute value of a number x, written $|x|$, represents the distance from x to 0 on the number line. For example, the solutions of $|x| = 4$ are 4 and -4, as shown in Figure 24.

4 units from 0   4 units from 0

$x = -4$ or $x = 4$

Figure 24

Because absolute value represents distance from 0, it is reasonable to interpret the solutions of $|x| > 4$ to be all numbers that are *more* than 4 units from 0. The set $(-\infty, -4) \cup (4, \infty)$ fits this description. Figure 25 shows the graph of the solution set of $|x| > 4$. Because the graph consists of two separate intervals, the solution set is described using *or* as $x < -4$ or $x > 4$.

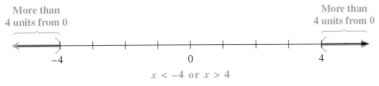

More than   More than
4 units from 0   4 units from 0

$x < -4$ or $x > 4$

Figure 25

The solution set of $|x| < 4$ consists of all numbers that are *less* than 4 units from 0 on the number line. Another way of thinking of this is to think of all numbers *between* -4 and 4. This set of numbers is given by $(-4, 4)$, as shown in Figure 26. Here, the graph shows that $-4 < x < 4$, which means $x > -4$ *and* $x < 4$.

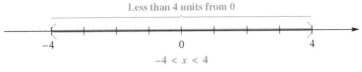

Less than 4 units from 0

$-4 < x < 4$

Figure 26

Work Problem **1** *at the Side.* ▶

The equation and inequalities just described are examples of **absolute value equations and inequalities.** They involve the absolute value of a variable expression and generally take the form

$$|ax + b| = k, \quad |ax + b| > k, \quad \text{or} \quad |ax + b| < k,$$

where k is a positive number. From Figures 24–26, we see that

$\quad |x| = 4$ has the same solution set as $x = -4$ or $x = 4$,

$\quad |x| > 4$ has the same solution set as $x < -4$ or $x > 4$,

$\quad |x| < 4$ has the same solution set as $x > -4$ *and* $x < 4$.

1 Graph the solution set of each equation or inequality.

(a) $|x| = 3$

_____→

(b) $|x| > 3$

_____→

(c) $|x| < 3$

_____→

ANSWERS

1. **(a)**
$\quad$ -3 -2 -1 0 1 2 3

(b)
$\quad$ -3 -2 -1 0 1 2 3

(c)
$\quad$ -3 -2 -1 0 1 2 3

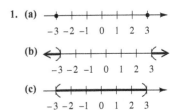

2 Solve, check, and graph the solution set of each equation.

(a) $|x + 2| = 3$

(b) $|3x - 4| = 11$

Thus, we can solve an absolute value equation or inequality by solving the appropriate compound equation or inequality.

Solving Absolute Value Equations and Inequalities

Let k be a positive real number, and p and q be real numbers.

Case 1 To solve $|ax + b| = k$, solve the compound equation

$$ax + b = k \quad \text{or} \quad ax + b = -k.$$

The solution set is usually of the form $\{p, q\}$, which includes two numbers.

Case 2 To solve $|ax + b| > k$, solve the compound inequality

$$ax + b > k \quad \text{or} \quad ax + b < -k.$$

The solution set is of the form $(-\infty, p) \cup (q, \infty)$, which is a disjoint interval.

Case 3 To solve $|ax + b| < k$, solve the three-part inequality

$$-k < ax + b < k.$$

The solution set is of the form (p, q), an open interval.

OBJECTIVE 2 Solve equations of the form $|ax + b| = k$, for $k > 0$. *Remember that because absolute value refers to distance from the origin, an absolute value equation will have two parts.*

Example 1 **Solving an Absolute Value Equation**

Solve $|2x + 1| = 7$.

For $|2x + 1|$ to equal 7, $2x + 1$ must be 7 units from 0 on the number line. This can happen only when $2x + 1 = 7$ or $2x + 1 = -7$. This is Case 1 in the preceding box. Solve this compound equation as follows.

$$2x + 1 = 7 \quad \text{or} \quad 2x + 1 = -7$$
$$2x = 6 \quad \text{or} \quad 2x = -8$$
$$x = 3 \quad \text{or} \quad x = -4$$

Check by substituting 3 and then -4 in the original absolute value equation to verify that the solution set is $\{-4, 3\}$. The graph is shown in Figure 27.

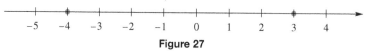

Figure 27

◀ *Work Problem* **2** *at the Side.*

Note

Some people prefer to write the compound statements in Cases 1 and 2 of the box on the previous page as the equivalent forms

$$ax + b = k \quad \text{or} \quad -(ax + b) = k$$

and

$$ax + b > k \quad \text{or} \quad -(ax + b) > k.$$

These forms produce the same results.

OBJECTIVE 3 Solve inequalities of the form $|ax + b| < k$ and of the form $|ax + b| > k$, for $k > 0$.

Example 2 Solving an Absolute Value Inequality with $>$

Solve $|2x + 1| > 7$.

By Case 2 in the box on the preceding page, this absolute value inequality is rewritten as

$$2x + 1 > 7 \quad \text{or} \quad 2x + 1 < -7,$$

because $2x + 1$ must represent a number that is *more* than 7 units from 0 on either side of the number line. Now, solve the compound inequality.

$$2x + 1 > 7 \quad \text{or} \quad 2x + 1 < -7$$
$$2x > 6 \quad \text{or} \quad 2x < -8$$
$$x > 3 \quad \text{or} \quad x < -4$$

Check these solutions. The solution set is $(-\infty, -4) \cup (3, \infty)$, a disjoint interval. See the graph in Figure 28.

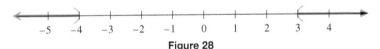

Figure 28

Work Problem **3** *at the Side.* ▶

Example 3 Solving an Absolute Value Inequality with $<$

Solve $|2x + 1| < 7$.

The expression $2x + 1$ must represent a number that is less than 7 units from 0 on either side of the number line. Another way of thinking of this is to realize that $2x + 1$ must be between -7 and 7. As Case 3 in the box on the preceding page shows, this is written as the three-part inequality

$$-7 < 2x + 1 < 7.$$
$$-8 < 2x < 6 \qquad \text{Subtract 1 from each part.}$$
$$-4 < x < 3 \qquad \text{Divide each part by 2.}$$

Check that the solution set is $(-4, 3)$, so the graph consists of the open interval shown in Figure 29.

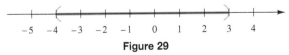

Figure 29

Work Problem **4** *at the Side.* ▶

---

3 Solve, check, and graph the solution set of each inequality.

(a) $|x + 2| > 3$

_____

(b) $|3x - 4| \geq 11$

_____

4 Solve, check, and graph the solution set of each inequality.

(a) $|x + 2| < 3$

_____

(b) $|3x - 4| \leq 11$

_____

ANSWERS

3. (a) $(-\infty, -5) \cup (1, \infty)$

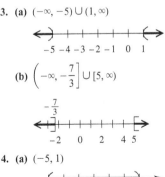

(b) $\left(-\infty, -\dfrac{7}{3}\right] \cup [5, \infty)$

4. (a) $(-5, 1)$

(b) $\left[-\dfrac{7}{3}, 5\right]$

5 Solve $|5x + 2| - 9 = -7$.
Check your solutions.

Look back at Figures 27, 28, and 29, with the graphs of $|2x + 1| = 7$, $|2x + 1| > 7$, and $|2x + 1| < 7$. If we find the union of the three sets, we get the set of all real numbers. This is because, for any value of x, $|2x + 1|$ will satisfy one and only one of the following: It is either equal to 7, greater than 7, or less than 7.

CAUTION

When solving absolute value equations and inequalities of the types in Examples 1, 2, and 3, remember the following.

1. The methods described apply when the constant is alone on one side of the equation or inequality and is *positive.*

2. Absolute value equations and absolute value inequalities of the form $|ax + b| > k$ translate into "or" compound statements.

3. Absolute value inequalities of the form $|ax + b| < k$ translate into "and" compound statements, which may be written as three-part inequalities.

4. An "or" statement *cannot* be written in three parts. It would be incorrect to use $-7 > 2x + 1 > 7$ in Example 2, because this would imply that $-7 > 7$, which is *false.*

OBJECTIVE 4 Solve absolute value equations that involve rewriting. Sometimes an absolute value equation or inequality requires some rewriting before it can be set up as a compound statement.

Example 4 **Solving an Absolute Value Equation That Requires Rewriting**

Solve $|x + 3| + 5 = 12$.

First, get the absolute value alone on one side of the equals sign.

$$|x + 3| + 5 = 12$$
$$|x + 3| + 5 - 5 = 12 - 5 \quad \text{Subtract 5.}$$
$$|x + 3| = 7$$

Now use the method shown in Example 1.

$$x + 3 = 7 \quad \text{or} \quad x + 3 = -7$$
$$x = 4 \quad \text{or} \quad x = -10$$

Check these solutions by substituting each one in the original equation.

Check $\qquad\qquad |x + 3| + 5 = 12$

$|4 + 3| + 5 \overset{?}{=} 12$ Let $x = 4$.	$|-10 + 3| + 5 \overset{?}{=} 12$ Let $x = -10$.
$|7| + 5 \overset{?}{=} 12$	$|-7| + 5 \overset{?}{=} 12$
$12 = 12$ True	$12 = 12$ True

The check confirms that the solution set is $\{-10, 4\}$.

◀ *Work Problem* **5** *at the Side.*

CAUTION

When solving an equation like the one in Example 4, do *not* simply drop the absolute value bars.

ANSWER

5. $\left\{ -\dfrac{4}{5}, 0 \right\}$

We use a method similar to that used in Example 4 to solve an absolute value *inequality* that requires rewriting:

$$|x + 3| + 5 \geq 12 \qquad\qquad |x + 3| + 5 \leq 12$$

$$|x + 3| \geq 7 \qquad\qquad\qquad |x + 3| \leq 7$$

$$x + 3 \geq 7 \quad \text{or} \quad x + 3 \leq -7 \qquad -7 \leq x + 3 \leq 7$$

$$x \geq 4 \quad \text{or} \qquad x \leq -10. \qquad -10 \leq x \leq 4.$$

Solution set: $(-\infty, -10] \cup [4, \infty)$ Solution set: $[-10, 4]$

Work Problem **6** *at the Side.* ▶

OBJECTIVE 5 Solve equations of the form $|ax + b| = |cx + d|$.

By definition, for two expressions to have the same absolute value, they must either be equal or be negatives of each other.

Solving $|ax + b| = |cx + d|$

To solve an absolute value equation of the form

$$|ax + b| = |cx + d|,$$

solve the compound equation

$$ax + b = cx + d \quad \text{or} \quad ax + b = -(cx + d).$$

Example 5 **Solving an Equation with Two Absolute Values**

Solve $|z + 6| = |2z - 3|$.

This equation is satisfied either if $z + 6$ and $2z - 3$ are equal to each other, or if $z + 6$ and $2z - 3$ are negatives of each other. Thus,

$$z + 6 = 2z - 3 \quad \text{or} \quad z + 6 = -(2z - 3)$$

$$z + 9 = 2z \qquad \text{or} \quad z + 6 = -2z + 3$$

$$9 = z \qquad\quad \text{or} \qquad 3z = -3$$

$$z = 9 \qquad\quad \text{or} \qquad z = -1.$$

Check that the solution set is $\{9, -1\}$.

Work Problem **7** *at the Side.* ▶

OBJECTIVE 6 Solve special cases of absolute value equations and inequalities.

When a typical absolute value equation or inequality involves a *negative* constant or 0 alone on one side, we use the properties of absolute value to solve. Keep the following in mind.

Special Cases of Absolute Value

Case 1 The absolute value of an expression can never be negative—that is, $|a| \geq 0$ for all real numbers a.

Case 2 The absolute value of an expression equals 0 only when the expression is equal to 0.

---

6 Solve each inequality, and graph the solution set.

(a) $|x + 2| - 3 > 2$

_____ ▶

(b) $|3x + 2| + 4 \leq 15$

_____ ▶

7 Solve each equation.

(a) $|k - 1| = |5k + 7|$

(b) $|4r - 1| = |3r + 5|$

ANSWERS

6. (a) $(-\infty, -7) \cup (3, \infty)$

   $-7 \quad -4\ -2 \quad 0 \quad 3$

(b) $\left[-\dfrac{13}{3}, 3\right]$

   $-\dfrac{13}{3} \quad -2 \quad 0 \quad 2\ 3$

7. (a) $\{-1, -2\}$ **(b)** $\left\{-\dfrac{4}{7}, 6\right\}$

8 Solve each equation.

(a) $|6x + 7| = -5$

(b) $\left|\dfrac{1}{4}x - 3\right| = 0$

9 Solve.

(a) $|x| > -1$

(b) $|x| < -5$

(c) $|x + 2| \leq 0$

(d) $|t - 10| - 2 \leq -3$

Example 6 **Solving Special Cases of Absolute Value Equations**

Solve each equation.

(a) $|5r - 3| = -4$

See Case 1 in the box on the preceding page. *The absolute value of an expression can never be negative,* so there are no solutions for this equation. The solution set is $\emptyset$.

(b) $|7x - 3| = 0$

See Case 2 in the box on the preceding page. The expression $7x - 3$ will equal 0 *only* if

$$7x - 3 = 0$$
$$7x = 3 \qquad \text{Add 3.}$$
$$x = \frac{3}{7}. \qquad \text{Divide by 7.}$$

Thus, the solution set of the original equation is $\left\{\frac{3}{7}\right\}$, with just one element. Check this solution by substituting it in the original equation.

◀ *Work Problem* **8** *at the Side.*

Example 7 **Solving Special Cases of Absolute Value Inequalities**

Solve each inequality.

(a) $|x| \geq -4$

The absolute value of a number is always greater than or equal to 0. Thus, $|x| \geq -4$ is true for *all* real numbers. The solution set is $(-\infty, \infty)$.

(b) $|x + 6| - 3 < -5$

$$|x + 6| < -2 \qquad \text{Add 3 to each side.}$$

There is no number whose absolute value is less than -2, so this inequality has no solution. The solution set is $\emptyset$.

(c) $|x - 7| + 4 \leq 4$

$$|x - 7| \leq 0 \qquad \text{Subtract 4 from each side.}$$

The value of $|x - 7|$ will never be less than 0. However, $|x - 7|$ will *equal* 0 when $x = 7$. Therefore, the solution set is $\{7\}$.

◀ *Work Problem* **9** *at the Side.*

ANSWERS

8. (a) $\emptyset$ (b) $\{12\}$
9. (a) $(-\infty, \infty)$ (b) $\emptyset$ (c) $\{-2\}$ (d) $\emptyset$

Match each absolute value equation or inequality in Column I with the graph of its solution set in Column II.

I	II	I	II
1. $\lvert x \rvert = 5$	**A.**	**2.** $\lvert x \rvert = 9$	**A.**
$\lvert x \rvert < 5$	**B.**	$\lvert x \rvert > 9$	**B.**
$\lvert x \rvert > 5$	**C.**	$\lvert x \rvert \geq 9$	**C.**
$\lvert x \rvert \leq 5$	**D.**	$\lvert x \rvert < 9$	**D.**
$\lvert x \rvert \geq 5$	**E.**	$\lvert x \rvert \leq 9$	**E.**

3. How many solutions will $\lvert ax + b \rvert = k$ have if
   (a) $k = 0$;   **(b)** $k > 0$;   **(c)** $k < 0$?

4. Explain when to use *and* and when to use *or* if you are solving an absolute value equation or inequality of the form $\lvert ax + b \rvert = k$, $\lvert ax + b \rvert < k$, or $\lvert ax + b \rvert > k$, where k is a positive number.

Solve each equation. See Example 1.

5. $\lvert x \rvert = 12$

6. $\lvert x \rvert = 14$

7. $\lvert 4x \rvert = 20$

8. $\lvert 5x \rvert = 30$

9. $\lvert x - 3 \rvert = 9$

10. $\lvert p - 5 \rvert = 13$

11. $\lvert 2x + 1 \rvert = 9$

12. $\lvert 2x + 3 \rvert = 19$

13. $\lvert 4r - 5 \rvert = 17$

14. $\lvert 5t - 1 \rvert = 21$

15. $\lvert 2x + 5 \rvert = 14$

16. $\lvert 2x - 9 \rvert = 18$

17. $\left\lvert \dfrac{1}{2}x + 3 \right\rvert = 2$

18. $\left\lvert \dfrac{2}{3}q - 1 \right\rvert = 5$

19. $\left\lvert 1 - \dfrac{3}{4}k \right\rvert = 7$

20. $\left\lvert 2 - \dfrac{5}{2}m \right\rvert = 14$

Solve each inequality, and graph the solution set. See Example 2.

21. $|x| > 3$

22. $|x| > 2$

23. $|k| \geq 4$

24. $|r| \geq 1$

25. $|t + 2| > 8$

26. $|r + 5| > 20$

27. $|3x - 1| \geq 8$

28. $|4x + 1| \geq 21$

29. $|3 - x| > 5$

30. $|5 - x| > 3$

31. The graph of the solution set of $|2x + 1| = 9$ is given here.

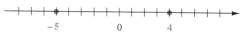

Without actually doing the algebraic work, graph the solution set of each inequality, referring to the graph above.

(a) $|2x + 1| < 9$

(b) $|2x + 1| > 9$

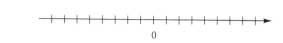

32. The graph of the solution set of $|3x - 4| < 5$ is given here.

Without actually doing the algebraic work, graph the solution set of the equation and the inequality, referring to the graph above.

(a) $|3x - 4| = 5$

(b) $|3x - 4| > 5$

Solve each inequality, and graph the solution set. See Example 3. (Hint: Compare
your answers to those in Exercises 21–30.)

33. $|x| \leq 3$

34. $|x| \leq 2$

35. $|k| < 4$

36. $|r| < 1$

37. $|t + 2| \leq 8$

38. $|r + 5| \leq 20$

39. $|3x - 1| < 8$

40. $|4x + 1| < 21$

41. $|3 - x| \leq 5$

42. $|5 - x| \leq 3$

Exercises 43–50 represent a sampling of the various types of absolute value equations
and inequalities. Decide which method of solution applies, find the solution set, and graph.
See Examples 1–3.

43. $|-4 + k| > 6$

44. $|-3 + t| > 5$

45. $|7 + 2z| = 5$

46. $|9 - 3p| = 3$

47. $|3r - 1| \leq 11$

48. $|2s - 6| \leq 6$

49. $|-3x - 8| \leq 4$

50. $|-2x - 6| \leq 5$

Solve each equation or inequality. Give the solution set using set notation for equations and interval notation for inequalities. See Example 4.

51. $|x| - 1 = 4$

52. $|x| + 3 = 10$

🌐 **53.** $|x + 4| + 1 = 2$

54. $|x + 5| - 2 = 12$

55. $|2x + 1| + 3 > 8$

56. $|6x - 1| - 2 > 6$

57. $|x + 5| - 6 \leq -1$

58. $|r - 2| - 3 \leq 4$

Solve each equation. See Example 5.

59. $|3x + 1| = |2x + 4|$
🌐

60. $|7x + 12| = |x - 8|$

61. $\left| m - \dfrac{1}{2} \right| = \left| \dfrac{1}{2}m - 2 \right|$

62. $\left| \dfrac{2}{3}r - 2 \right| = \left| \dfrac{1}{3}r + 3 \right|$

63. $|6x| = |9x + 1|$

64. $|13x| = |2x + 1|$

65. $|2p - 6| = |2p + 11|$

66. $|3x - 1| = |3x + 9|$

Solve each equation or inequality. See Examples 6 and 7.

67. $|x| \geq -10$

68. $|x| \geq -15$

69. $|12t - 3| = -8$

70. $|13w + 1| = -3$

71. $|4x + 1| = 0$

72. $|6r - 2| = 0$

73. $|2q - 1| < -6$

74. $|8n + 4| < -4$

75. $|x + 5| > -9$

76. $|x + 9| > -3$

77. $|7x + 3| \leq 0$

78. $|4x - 1| \leq 0$

79. $|5x - 2| \geq 0$

80. $|4 + 7x| \geq 0$

81. $|10z + 7| > 0$

82. $|4x + 1| > 0$

83. $|x - 2| + 3 \geq 2$

84. $|k - 4| + 5 \geq 4$

85. The 2007 recommended daily intake (RDI) of calcium for females aged 19–50 is 1000 mg/day. Actual vitamin needs vary from person to person. Write an absolute value inequality to express the RDI plus or minus 100 mg and solve it. (*Source:* Food and Nutrition Board, National Academy of Sciences Institute of Medicine.)

86. The average clotting time of blood is 7.45 sec with a variation of plus or minus 3.6 sec. Write this statement as an absolute value inequality and solve it.

Relating Concepts (Exercises 87–90) For Individual or Group Work

The 10 tallest buildings in Kansas City, Missouri, are listed along with their heights.

Building	Height (in feet)
One Kansas City Place	632
Town Pavilion	591
Hyatt Regency Crown Center	504
Kansas City Power and Light	481
Fidelity Bank and Trust Building	454
City Hall	443
1201 Walnut	427
Federal Office Building	413
Commerce Tower	407
City Center Square	404

Source: World Almanac and Book of Facts.

Use this information to **work Exercises 87–90 in order.**

87. To find the average of a group of numbers, we add the numbers and then divide by the number of items added. Use a calculator to find the average of the heights.

88. Let k represent the average height of these buildings. If a height x satisfies the inequality

$$|x - k| < t,$$

then the height is said to be within t feet of the average. Using your result from Exercise 87, list the buildings that are within 50 ft of the average.

89. Repeat Exercise 88, but find the buildings that are within 75 ft of the average.

90. (a) Write an absolute value inequality that describes the height of a building that is *not* within 75 ft of the average.

(b) Solve the inequality you wrote in part (a).

(c) Use the result of part (b) to find the buildings that are not within 75 ft of the average.

(d) Confirm that your answer to part (c) makes sense by comparing it with your answer to Exercise 89.

Summary Exercises on Solving Linear and Absolute Value Equations and Inequalities

This section of miscellaneous equations and inequalities provides practice in solving all the types introduced in **Chapters 2 and 3.** You might wish to refer to the boxes in these chapters that summarize the various methods of solution.

Solve each equation or inequality. Give the solution set using set notation for equations and interval notation for inequalities.

1. $4z + 1 = 49$

2. $|m - 1| = 6$

3. $6q - 9 = 12 + 3q$

4. $3p + 7 = 9 + 8p$

5. $|a + 3| = -4$

6. $2m + 1 \le m$

7. $8r + 2 \ge 5r$

8. $4(a - 11) + 3a = 20a - 31$

9. $2q - 1 = -7$

10. $|3q - 7| - 4 = 0$

11. $6z - 5 \le 3z + 10$

12. $|5z - 8| + 9 \ge 7$

13. $9x - 3(x + 1) = 8x - 7$

14. $|x| \ge 8$

15. $9x - 5 \ge 9x + 3$

16. $13p - 5 > 13p - 8$

17. $|q| < 5.5$

18. $4z - 1 = 12 + z$

19. $\dfrac{2}{3}x + 8 = \dfrac{1}{4}x$

20. $-\dfrac{5}{8}x \ge -20$

21. $\dfrac{1}{4}p < -6$

22. $7z - 3 + 2z = 9z - 8z$

23. $\dfrac{3}{5}q - \dfrac{1}{10} = 2$

24. $|r - 1| < 7$

25. $r + 9 + 7r = 4(3 + 2r) - 3$ **26.** $6 - 3(2 - p) < 2(1 + p) + 3$ **27.** $|2p - 3| > 11$

28. $\dfrac{x}{4} - \dfrac{2x}{3} = -10$ **29.** $|5a + 1| \leq 0$ **30.** $5z - (3 + z) \geq 2(3z + 1)$

31. $-2 \leq 3x - 1 \leq 8$ **32.** $-1 \leq 6 - x \leq 5$ **33.** $|7z - 1| = |5z + 3|$

34. $|p + 2| = |p + 4|$ **35.** $|1 - 3x| \geq 4$ **36.** $\dfrac{1}{2} \leq \dfrac{2}{3}r \leq \dfrac{5}{4}$

37. $-(m + 4) + 2 = 3m + 8$ **38.** $\dfrac{p}{6} - \dfrac{3p}{5} = p - 86$ **39.** $-6 \leq \dfrac{3}{2} - x \leq 6$

40. $|5 - x| < 4$ **41.** $|x - 1| \geq -6$ **42.** $|2r - 5| = |r + 4|$

43. $8q - (1 - q) = 3(1 + 3q) - 4$ **44.** $8x - (x + 3) = -(2x + 1) - 12$

45. $|r - 5| = |r + 9|$ **46.** $|r + 2| < -3$

47. $2x + 1 > 5$ or $3x + 4 < 1$ **48.** $1 - 2x \geq 5$ and $7 + 3x \geq -2$

13.5 ▷▷▷ Linear Inequalities in Two Variables

OBJECTIVE 1 Graph linear inequalities in two variables. In Section 3.1 we graphed linear inequalities in one variable on the number line. We now graph linear inequalities in two variables on a rectangular coordinate system.

Linear Inequality in Two Variables

An inequality that can be written as

$$Ax + By < C \quad \text{or} \quad Ax + By > C,$$

where A, B, and C are real numbers and A and B are not both 0, is a **linear inequality in two variables.**

The symbols $\leq$ and $\geq$ may replace $<$ and $>$ in the definition.

Consider the graph in Figure 30. The graph of the line $x + y = 5$ divides the points in the rectangular coordinate system into three sets:

1. Those points that lie on the line itself and satisfy the equation $x + y = 5$ [like $(0, 5)$, $(2, 3)$, and $(5, 0)$];

2. Those that lie in the half-plane above the line and satisfy the inequality $x + y > 5$ [like $(5, 3)$ and $(2, 4)$];

3. Those that lie in the half-plane below the line and satisfy the inequality $x + y < 5$ [like $(0, 0)$ and $(-3, -1)$].

The graph of the line $x + y = 5$ is called the **boundary line** for the inequalities $x + y > 5$ and $x + y < 5$. Graphs of linear inequalities in two variables are *regions* in the real number plane that may or may not include boundary lines.

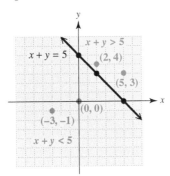

Figure 30

To graph a linear inequality in two variables, follow these steps.

Graphing a Linear Inequality

Step 1 **Draw the graph of the straight line that is the boundary.** Make the line solid if the inequality involves $\leq$ or $\geq$; make the line dashed if the inequality involves $<$ or $>$.

Step 2 **Choose a test point.** Choose any point not on the line, and substitute the coordinates of this point in the inequality.

Step 3 **Shade the appropriate region.** Shade the region that includes the test point if it satisfies the original inequality; otherwise, shade the region on the other side of the boundary line.

---

1 Graph each inequality.

(a) $x + y \leq 4$

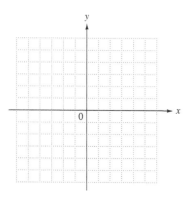

(b) $3x + y \geq 6$

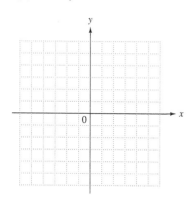

1. **(a)**

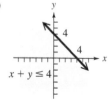

(b)

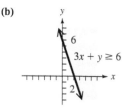

Example 1   **Graphing a Linear Inequality**

Graph $3x + 2y \geq 6$.

Step 1 First graph the line $3x + 2y = 6$. The graph of this line, the boundary of the graph of the inequality, is shown in Figure 31.

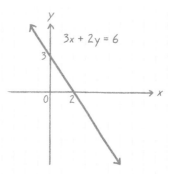

Figure 31

Step 2 The graph of the inequality $3x + 2y \geq 6$ includes the points of the boundary line $3x + 2y = 6$ and either the points *above* the line $3x + 2y = 6$ or the points *below* that line. To decide which, select any point not on the line $3x + 2y = 6$ as a test point. The origin, $(0, 0)$, is often a good choice. Substitute the values from the test point $(0, 0)$ for x and y in the inequality.

$$3x + 2y > 6$$
$$3(0) + 2(0) \stackrel{?}{>} 6 \quad \text{Let } x = 0 \text{ and } y = 0.$$
$$0 > 6 \quad \text{False}$$

Step 3 Because the result is false, $(0, 0)$ does *not* satisfy the inequality, and so the solution set includes all points on the other side of the line. This region is shaded in Figure 32.

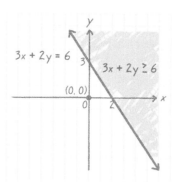

Figure 32

◄ *Work Problem* **1** *at the Side.*

If the inequality is written in the form $y > mx + b$ or $y < mx + b$, the inequality symbol indicates which half-plane to shade.

If $y > mx + b$, shade above the boundary line.

If $y < mx + b$, shade below the boundary line.

This method works only if the inequality is solved for y.

Example 2 **Graphing a Linear Inequality with Boundary Passing through the Origin**

Graph $3x - 4y > 0$.

First graph the boundary line. If $x = 0$, then $y = 0$. Thus, this line passes through the origin. Two other points on the line are $(4, 3)$ and $(-4, -3)$. The points of the boundary line do not belong to the inequality $3x - 4y > 0$ (because inequality symbol does not include equality). For this reason, the line is dashed. Now solve the inequality for y.

$$3x - 4y > 0$$
$$-4y > -3x \qquad \text{Subtract } 3x.$$
$$y < \frac{3}{4}x \qquad \text{Divide by } -4; \text{ change } > \text{ to } <.$$

Because of the *is less than* symbol, shade *below* the line. As a check, choose a test point not on the line. Because the origin is on the line, we must choose a different point, such as $(2, -1)$. Substitute for x and y in the original inequality.

$$3x - 4y > 0$$
$$3(2) - 4(-1) \overset{?}{>} 0 \qquad \text{Let } x = 2 \text{ and } y = -1.$$
$$6 + 4 \overset{?}{>} 0$$
$$10 > 0 \qquad \text{True}$$

This result agrees with the decision to shade below the line. The solution set, graphed in Figure 33, includes only those points in the shaded half-plane (not those on the line).

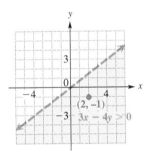

Figure 33

Work Problem **2** *at the Side.* ▶

2 Graph each inequality.

(a) $x + y > 0$

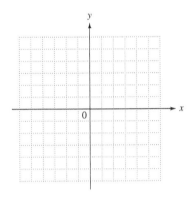

(b) $3x - 2y > 0$

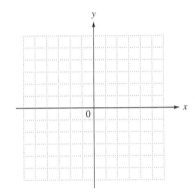

OBJECTIVE **2** **Graph the intersection of two linear inequalities.** In **Section 3.2** we discussed how the words *and* and *or* are used with compound inequalities. In that section, the inequalities had one variable. Those ideas can be extended to include inequalities in two variables.

A pair of inequalities joined with the word *and* is interpreted as the intersection of the solution sets of the inequalities. ***The graph of the intersection of two or more inequalities is the region of the plane where all points satisfy all of the inequalities at the same time.***

ANSWERS

2. **(a)**

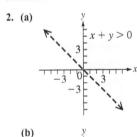

(b)

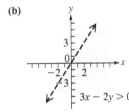

3 Graph $x - y \le 4$ and $x \ge -2$.

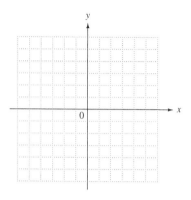

4 Graph $7x - 3y < 21$ or $x > 2$.

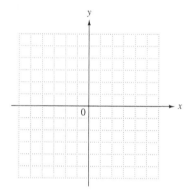

3.

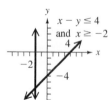

4.

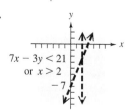

Εxample 3 **Graphing the Intersection of Two Inequalities**

Graph $2x + 4y \ge 5$ and $x \ge 1$.

To begin, we graph each of the two inequalities $2x + 4y \ge 5$ and $x \ge 1$ separately. The graph of $2x + 4y \ge 5$ is shown in Figure 34(a), and the graph of $x \ge 1$ is shown in Figure 34(b).

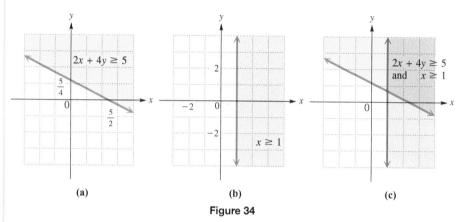

Figure 34

In practice, the two graphs in Figures 34(a) and 34(b) are graphed on the same axes. Then we use heavy shading to identify the intersection of the graphs, as shown in Figure 34(c). To check, we can use a test point from each of the four regions formed by the intersection of the boundary lines. Verify that only ordered pairs in the heavily shaded region satisfy both inequalities.

◀ *Work Problem* **3** *at the Side.*

OBJECTIVE 3 Graph the union of two linear inequalities. When two inequalities are joined by the word *or*, we must find the union of the graphs of the inequalities. ***The graph of the union of two inequalities includes all of the points that satisfy either inequality.***

Εxample 4 **Graphing the Union of Two Inequalities**

Graph $2x + 4y \ge 5$ or $x \ge 1$.

The graphs of the two inequalities are shown in Figures 34(a) and 34(b) in Example 3. The graph of the union is shown in Figure 35.

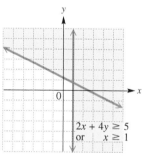

Figure 35

◀ *Work Problem* **4** *at the Side.*

FOR
EXTRA
HELP

MyMathLab  | MathXL PRACTICE | WATCH | DOWNLOAD | READ | REVIEW

In each statement, fill in the first blank with one of the words solid *or* dashed. *Fill in the second blank with one of the words* above *or* below.

1. The boundary of the graph of $y \leq -x + 2$ will be a

_____ line, and the shading will be _____

the line.

2. The boundary of the graph of $y < -x + 2$ will be a

_____ line, and the shading will be _____

the line.

3. The boundary of the graph of $y > -x + 2$ will be a

_____ line, and the shading will be _____

the line.

4. The boundary of the graph of $y \geq -x + 2$ will be a

_____ line, and the shading will be _____

the line.

5. How is the boundary line $Ax + By = C$ used in graphing either $Ax + By < C$ or $Ax + By > C$?

6. Describe the two methods discussed in the text for deciding which region is the solution set of a linear inequality in two variables.

Graph each linear inequality. See Examples 1 and 2.

🌐 **7.** $x + y \leq 2$

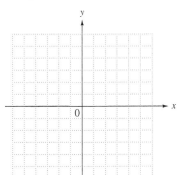

8. $x + y \leq -3$

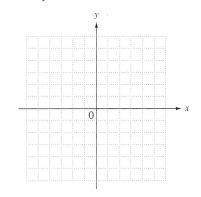

9. $4x - y < 4$

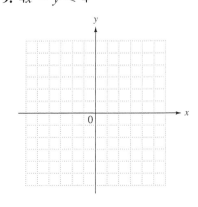

10. $3x - y < 3$

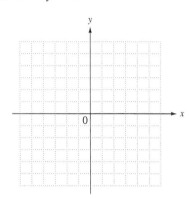

11. $x + 3y \geq -2$

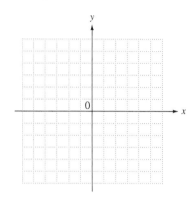

12. $x + 4y \geq -3$

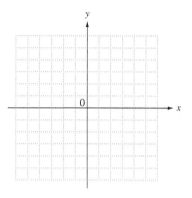

13. $x + y > 0$

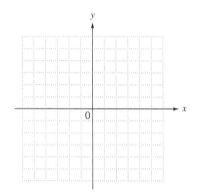

14. $x + 2y > 0$

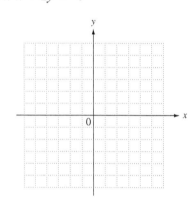

15. $x - 3y \leq 0$

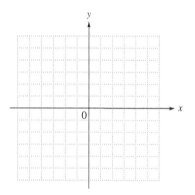

16. $x - 5y \leq 0$

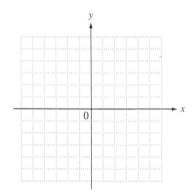

17. $y < x$

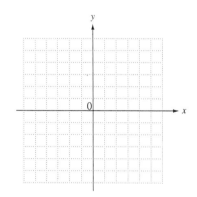

18. $y \leq 4x$

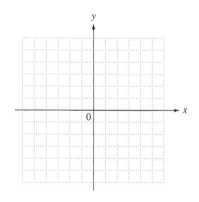

Graph the intersection of each pair of inequalities. See Example 3.

⊕ 19. $x + y \leq 1$ and $x \geq 1$

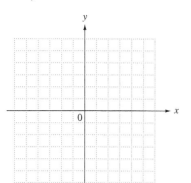

20. $x - y \geq 2$ and $x \geq 3$

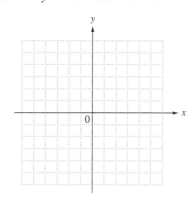

21. $2x - y \geq 2$ and $y < 4$

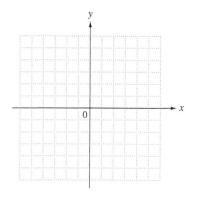

22. $3x - y \geq 3$ and $y < 3$

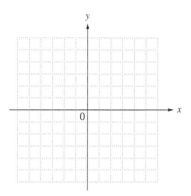

23. $x + y > -5$ and $y < -2$

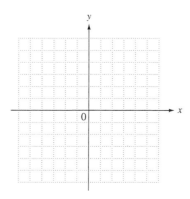

24. $6x - 4y < 10$ and $y > 2$

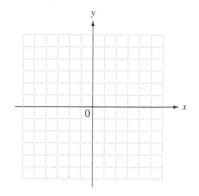

*Use the method described in **Section 3.3** to write each inequality as a compound inequality, and graph its solution set in the rectangular coordinate plane.*

25. $|x| \geq 3$

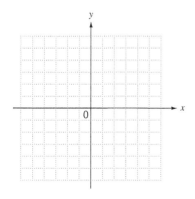

26. $|y| < 5$

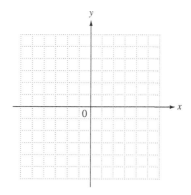

27. $|y + 1| < 2$

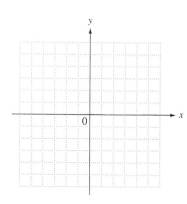

28. $|x - 2| \geq 1$

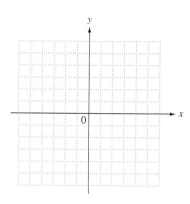

Graph the union of each pair of inequalities. See Example 4.

29. $x - y \geq 1$ or $y \geq 2$

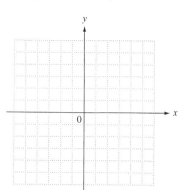

30. $x + y \leq 2$ or $y \geq 3$

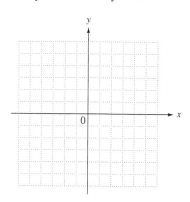

31. $x - 2 > y$ or $x < 1$

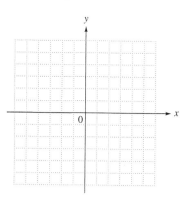

32. $x + 3 < y$ or $x > 3$

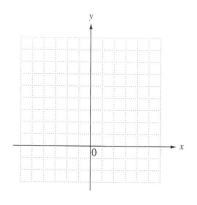

33. $3x + 2y < 6$ or $x - 2y > 2$

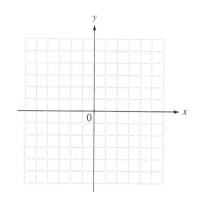

34. $x - y \geq 1$ or $x + y \leq 4$

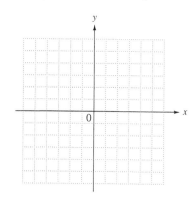

13.6 ▶▶▶ Introduction to Functions

We often describe one quantity in terms of another. Consider the following.

- The amount of your paycheck if you are paid hourly depends on the number of hours you worked.
- The cost at the gas station depends on the number of gallons of gas you pumped into your car.
- The distance traveled by a car moving at a constant speed depends on the time traveled.

We can use ordered pairs to represent these corresponding quantities. For example, we indicate the relationship between the amount of your paycheck and hours worked by writing ordered pairs in which the first number represents hours worked and the second number represents paycheck amount in dollars. Then the ordered pair (5, 40) indicates that when you work 5 hr, your paycheck is $40. Similarly, the ordered pairs (10, 80) and (20, 160) show that working 10 hr results in an $80 paycheck and working 20 hr results in a $160 paycheck.

Work Problem **1** *at the Side.* ▶

Since the amount of your paycheck *depends* on the number of hours worked, your paycheck amount is called the *dependent variable,* and the number of hours worked is called the *independent variable.* Generalizing, if the value of the variable y depends on the value of the variable x, then y is the **dependent variable** and x is the **independent variable.**

Independent variable ⌐ ⌐ Dependent variable
$$(x, y)$$

OBJECTIVE **1** **Define and identify relations and functions.**
Since we can write related quantities using ordered pairs, a set of ordered pairs such as

$$\{(5, 40), (10, 80), (20, 160), (40, 320)\}$$

is called a *relation*.

> **Relation**
> A **relation** is any set of ordered pairs.

A special kind of relation, called a *function,* is very important in mathematics and its applications.

> **Function**
> A **function** is a relation in which, for each value of the first component of the ordered pairs, there is *exactly one value* of the second component.

OBJECTIVES

1 Define and identify relations and functions.

2 Find domain and range.

3 Identify functions defined by graphs and equations.

4 Use function notation.

5 Graph linear and constant functions.

1 What would the ordered pair (40, 320) in the correspondence between number of hours worked and paycheck amount (in dollars) indicate?

2 Determine whether each relation defines a function.

(a) $\{(0, 3), (-1, 2), (-1, 3)\}$

Example 1 **Determining Whether Relations Are Functions**

Tell whether each relation defines a function.

$$F = \{(1, 2), (-2, 4), (3, -1)\}$$
$$G = \{(-2, -1), (-1, 0), (0, 1), (1, 2), (2, 2)\}$$
$$H = \{(-4, 1), (-2, 1), (-2, 0)\}$$

Relations F and G are functions, because for each different x-value there is exactly one y-value. Notice that in G, the last two ordered pairs have the same y-value (1 is paired with 2, and 2 is paired with 2). This does not violate the definition of function, since the first components (x-values) are different and each is paired with only one second component (y-value).

In relation H, however, the last two ordered pairs have the *same* x-value paired with *two different* y-values (-2 is paired with both 1 and 0), so H is a relation but not a function. ***In a function, no two ordered pairs can have the same first component and different second components.***

$$\begin{array}{c} \text{Different } y\text{-values} \\ \downarrow \qquad \downarrow \\ H = \{(-4, 1), (-2, 1), (-2, 0)\} \qquad \text{Not a function} \\ \uparrow \qquad \uparrow \\ \text{Same } x\text{-value} \end{array}$$

(b) $\{(2, -2), (4, -4), (6, -6)\}$

◀ *Work Problem* **2** *at the Side.*

In a function, there is **exactly one** ***value of the dependent variable, the second component, for each value of the independent variable, the first component. This is what makes functions so important in applications.***

Relations and functions can also be expressed as a correspondence or *mapping* from one set to another, as shown in Figure 36 for function F and relation H from Example 1. The arrow from 1 to 2 indicates that the ordered pair $(1, 2)$ belongs to F—each first component is paired with exactly one second component. In the mapping for set H, which is not a function, the first component -2 is paired with two different second components, 1 and 0.

(c) $\{(-1, 5), (0, 5)\}$

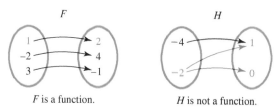

F is a function. H is not a function.

Figure 36

Since relations and functions are sets of ordered pairs, we can represent them using tables and graphs. A table and graph for function F is shown in Figure 37.

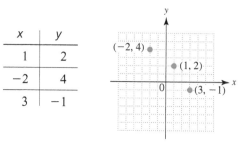

x	y
1	2
-2	4
3	-1

Graph of F

Figure 37

Finally, we can describe a relation or function using a rule that tells how to determine the dependent variable for a specific value of the independent variable. The rule may be given in words, such as "the dependent variable is twice the independent variable." Usually, however, the rule is given as an equation:

$$y = 2x.$$

Dependent variable ↑   Independent variable ↑

An equation is the most efficient way to define a relation or function.

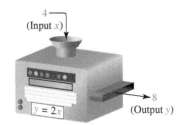

Function machine

Note
Another way to think of a function relationship is to think of the independent variable as an input and the dependent variable as an output. This is illustrated by the input-output (function) machine in the margin for the function defined by $y = 2x$.

OBJECTIVE 2 Find domain and range. For every relation, there are two important sets of elements called the *domain* and *range*.

Domain and Range
In a relation, the set of all values of the independent variable (x) is the **domain.** The set of all values of the dependent variable (y) is the **range.**

Example 2 Finding Domains and Ranges of Relations

Give the domain and range of each relation. Tell whether the relation defines a function.

(a) $\{(3, -1), (4, 2), (4, 5), (6, 8)\}$
The domain, the set of x-values, is $\{3, 4, 6\}$; the range, the set of y-values, is $\{-1, 2, 5, 8\}$. This relation is not a function because the same x-value 4 is paired with two different y-values, 2 and 5.

(b)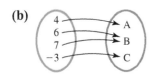

The domain of this relation is
$\{4, 6, 7, -3\}$.
The range is
$\{A, B, C\}$.
This mapping defines a function—each x-value corresponds to exactly one y-value.

(c)

x	y
-5	2
0	2
5	2

This is a table of ordered pairs, so the domain is the set of x-values, $\{-5, 0, 5\}$, and the range is the set of y-values, $\{2\}$. The table defines a function because each different x-value corresponds to exactly one y-value (even though it is the same y-value).

Work Problem **3** *at the Side.* ▶

3 Give the domain and range of each relation. Does the relation define a function?

(a) $\{(4, 0), (4, 1), (4, 2)\}$

(b)

(c)

Year	Cell Phone Subscribers (in thousands)
2002	140,766
2003	158,722
2004	182,140
2005	207,896
2006	233,041

Source: CTIA-The Wireless Association.

ANSWERS
3. **(a)** domain: $\{4\}$; range: $\{0, 1, 2\}$; No, the relation does not define a function.
(b) domain: $\{-1, 4, 7\}$; range: $\{0, -2, 3, 7\}$; No, the relation does not define a function.
(c) domain: $\{2002, 2003, 2004, 2005, 2006\}$; range: $\{140,766, 158,722, 182,140, 207,896, 233,041\}$; Yes, the relation defines a function.

4 Give the domain and range of each relation.

(a)

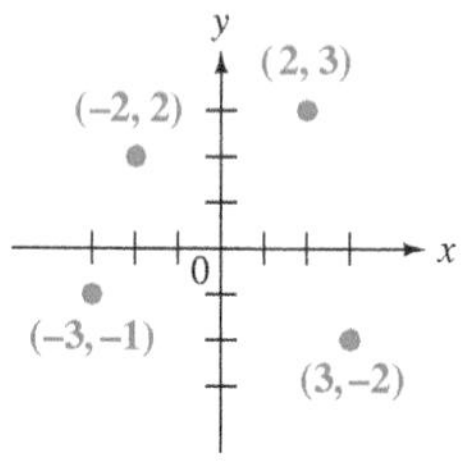

(b)

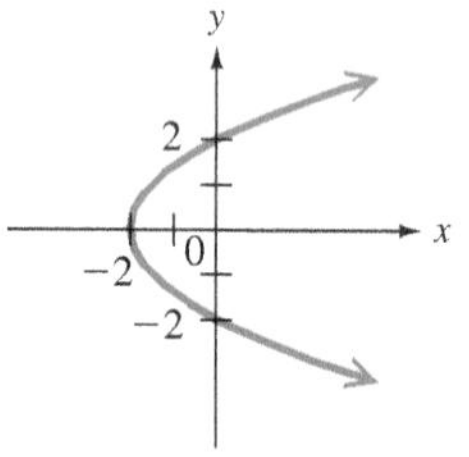

(c)

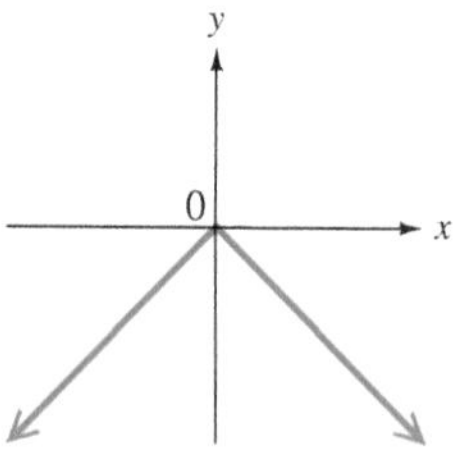

The graph of a relation gives a picture of the relation, which can be used to determine its domain and range.

Example 3 Finding Domains and Ranges from Graphs

Give the domain and range of each relation.

(a)

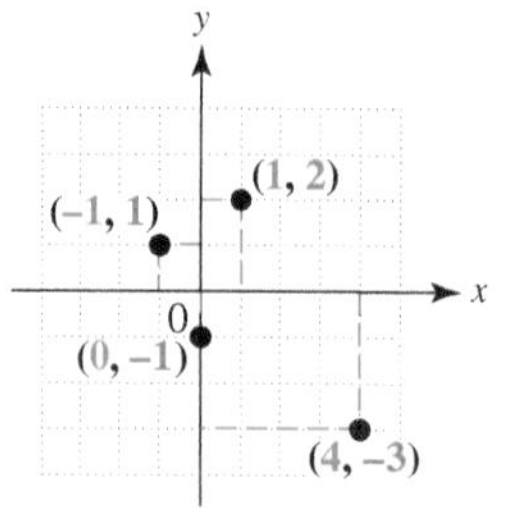

The domain is the set of x-values,

$$\{-1, 0, 1, 4\}.$$

The range is the set of y-values,

$$\{-3, -1, 1, 2\}.$$

(b)

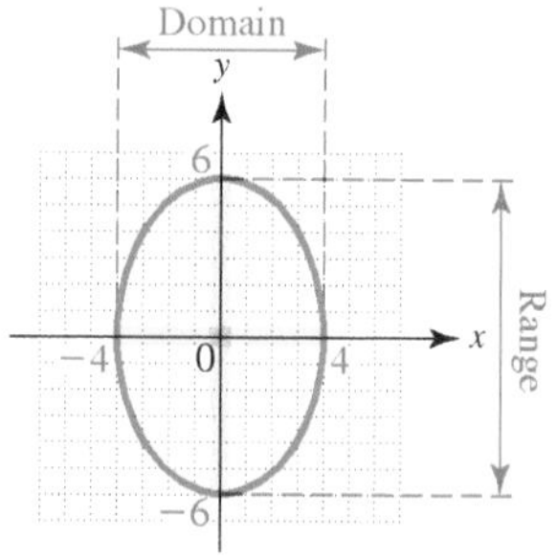

The x-values of the points on the graph include all numbers between -4 and 4, inclusive. The y-values include all numbers between -6 and 6, inclusive. Using interval notation,

the domain is $[-4, 4]$;

the range is $[-6, 6]$.

(c)

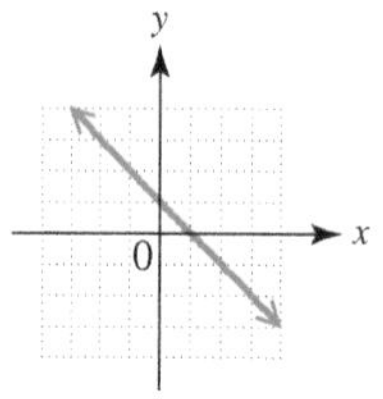

The arrowheads indicate that the line extends indefinitely left and right, as well as up and down. Therefore, both the domain and the range include all real numbers, written $(-\infty, \infty)$.

(d)

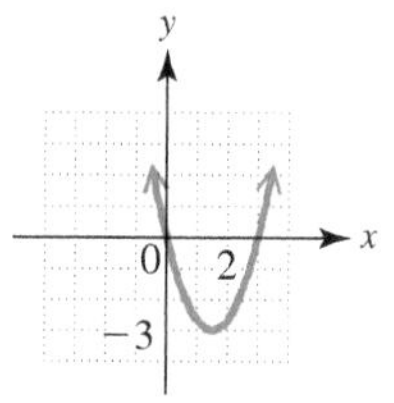

The arrowheads indicate that the graph extends indefinitely left and right, as well as upward. The domain is $(-\infty, \infty)$. Because there is a least y-value, -3, the range includes all numbers greater than or equal to -3, written $[-3, \infty)$.

◀ Work Problem 4 at the Side.

Since relations are often defined by equations, such as $y = 2x + 3$ and $y^2 = x$, we must sometimes determine the domain of a relation from its equation. We assume the following agreement on the domain of a relation.

Agreement on Domain

The domain of a relation is assumed to be all real numbers that produce real numbers when substituted for the independent variable.

To illustrate this agreement, since any real number can be used as a replacement for x in $y = 2x + 3$, the domain of this function is the set of all real numbers. The function defined by $y = \frac{1}{x}$ has all real numbers except 0 as domain, since y is undefined if $x = 0$. ***In general, the domain of a function defined by an algebraic expression is all real numbers, except those numbers that lead to division by 0 or an even root of a negative number.***

ANSWERS

4. (a) domain: $\{-3, -2, 2, 3\}$; range: $\{-2, -1, 2, 3\}$
(b) domain: $[-2, \infty)$; range: $(-\infty, \infty)$
(c) domain: $(-\infty, \infty)$; range: $(-\infty, 0]$

OBJECTIVE **3** **Identify functions defined by graphs and equations.** Since each value of x in a function corresponds to only one value of y, any vertical line drawn through the graph of a function must intersect the graph in at most one point. This is the *vertical line test* for a function.

Vertical Line Test

If every vertical line intersects the graph of a relation in no more than one point, then the relation represents a function.

For example, the graph shown in Figure 38(a) is not the graph of a function since a vertical line intersects the graph in more than one point. The graph in Figure 38(b) does represent a function.

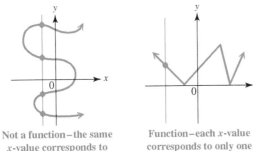

Not a function—the same x-value corresponds to four different y-values.

(a)

Function—each x-value corresponds to only one y-value.

(b)

Figure 38

Example 4 **Using the Vertical Line Test**

Use the vertical line test to determine whether each relation graphed in Example 3 is a function.

(a)

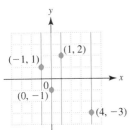

Function

(b)

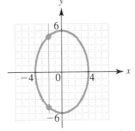

Not a function

(c)

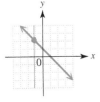

Function

(d)

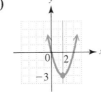

Function

The graphs in (a), (c), and (d) represent functions. The graph of the relation in (b) fails the vertical line test, since the same x-value corresponds to two different y-values; therefore, it is not the graph of a function.

Work Problem **5** *at the Side.* ▶

5 Use the vertical line test to decide which graphs represent functions.

A.

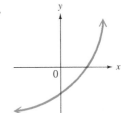

B.

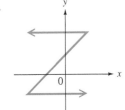

C.

ANSWER

5. A and C are graphs of functions.

6 Decide whether each relation defines a function, and give the domain.

(a) $y = 6x + 12$

(b) $y \leq 4x$

(c) $y = -\sqrt{3x - 2}$

(d) $y^2 = 25x$

Note

Graphs that do not represent functions are still relations. ***Remember that all equations and graphs represent relations and that all relations have a domain and range.***

It can be more difficult to decide whether a relation defined by an equation or an inequality is a function. The next example gives some hints that may help.

Example 5 **Identifying Functions from Their Equations**

Decide whether each relation defines a function and give the domain.

(a) $y = x + 4$

In the defining equation, $y = x + 4$, y is always found by adding 4 to x. Thus, each value of x corresponds to just one value of y and the relation defines a function; x can be any real number, so the domain is $(-\infty, \infty)$.

(b) $y = \sqrt{2x - 1}$

For any choice of x in the domain, there is exactly one corresponding value for y (the radical is a nonnegative number), so this equation defines a function. Since the equation involves a square root, the quantity under the radical sign cannot be negative. Thus,

$$2x - 1 \geq 0$$
$$2x \geq 1$$
$$x \geq \frac{1}{2},$$

and the domain of the function is $[\frac{1}{2}, \infty)$.

(c) $y^2 = x$

The ordered pairs $(16, 4)$ and $(16, -4)$ both satisfy this equation. Since one value of x, 16, corresponds to two values of y, 4 and -4, this equation does not define a function. Because x is equal to the square of y, the values of x must always be nonnegative. The domain of the relation is $[0, \infty)$.

(d) $y \leq x - 1$

By definition, y is a function of x if every value of x leads to exactly one value of y. Here a particular value of x, say 1, corresponds to many values of y. The ordered pairs $(1, 0)$, $(1, -1)$, $(1, -2)$, $(1, -3)$, and so on, all satisfy the inequality. Thus, this relation does not define a function. Any number can be used for x, so the domain is the set of real numbers, $(-\infty, \infty)$.

(e) $y = \dfrac{5}{x - 1}$

Given any value of x in the domain, we find y by subtracting 1, then dividing the result into 5. This process produces exactly one value of y for each value in the domain, so this equation defines a function. The domain includes all real numbers except those that make the denominator 0. We find these numbers by setting the denominator equal to 0 and solving for x.

$$x - 1 = 0$$
$$x = 1$$

The domain includes all real numbers *except* 1, written $(-\infty, 1) \cup (1, \infty)$.

◀ *Work Problem* **6** *at the Side.*

In summary, three variations of the definition of function are given here.

Variations of the Definition of Function

1. A **function** is a relation in which, for each value of the first component of the ordered pairs, there is exactly one value of the second component.

2. A **function** is a set of ordered pairs in which no first component is repeated.

3. A **function** is a rule or correspondence that assigns exactly one range value to each distinct domain value.

OBJECTIVE 4 Use function notation.   When a function f is defined with a rule or an equation using x and y for the independent and dependent variables, we say "y is a function of x" to emphasize that y *depends on x*. We use the notation

$$y = f(x),$$

called **function notation,** to express this and read $f(x)$ as "f of x." (In this special notation the parentheses do not indicate multiplication.) The letter f stands for *function*. For example, if $y = 9x - 5$, we can name this function f and write

$$f(x) = 9x - 5.$$

Note that *$f(x)$ is just another name for the dependent variable y.* For example, if $y = f(x) = 9x - 5$ and $x = 2$, then we find y, or $f(2)$, by replacing x with 2.

$$y = f(2)$$
$$= 9 \cdot 2 - 5$$
$$= 18 - 5$$
$$= 13.$$

For function f, the statement "if $x = 2$, then $y = 13$" is represented by the ordered pair $(2, 13)$ and is abbreviated with function notation as

$$f(2) = 13.$$

Read $f(2)$ as "f of 2" or "f at 2." Also,

$$f(0) = 9 \cdot 0 - 5 = -5 \qquad \text{and} \qquad f(-3) = 9(-3) - 5 = -32.$$

These ideas can be illustrated as follows.

CAUTION

The symbol $f(x)$ *does not* indicate "f times x," but represents the y-value for the indicated x-value. As just shown, $f(2)$ is the y-value that corresponds to the x-value 2.

7 Find $f(-3)$, $f(p)$, and $f(m + 1)$.

(a) $f(x) = 6x - 2$

(b) $f(x) = \dfrac{-3x + 5}{2}$

(c) $f(x) = \dfrac{1}{6}x - 1$

Example 6   **Using Function Notation**

Let $f(x) = -x^2 + 5x - 3$. Find the following.

(a) $f(2)$

Do not read this as "f times 2." Read it as "f of 2."

$$f(x) = -x^2 + 5x - 3 \qquad \text{The base in } -x^2 \text{ is } x, \text{ not } (-x).$$
$$f(2) = -2^2 + 5 \cdot 2 - 3 \qquad \text{Replace } x \text{ with 2.}$$
$$f(2) = -4 + 10 - 3 \qquad \text{Apply the exponent; multiply.}$$
$$f(2) = 3 \qquad \text{Add and subtract.}$$

Since $f(2) = 3$, the ordered pair $(2, 3)$ belongs to f.

(b) $f(q)$

$$f(x) = -x^2 + 5x - 3$$
$$f(q) = -q^2 + 5q - 3 \qquad \text{Replace } x \text{ with } q.$$

The replacement of one variable with another is important in later courses.

Sometimes letters other than f, such as g, h, or capital letters F, G, and H, are used to name functions.

Example 7   **Using Function Notation**

Let $g(x) = 2x + 3$. Find and simplify $g(a + 1)$.

$$g(x) = 2x + 3$$
$$g(a + 1) = 2(a + 1) + 3 \qquad \text{Replace } x \text{ with } a + 1.$$
$$g(a + 1) = 2a + 2 + 3$$
$$g(a + 1) = 2a + 5$$

◀ *Work Problem* **7** *at the Side.*

Functions can be evaluated in a variety of ways, as shown in Example 8.

Example 8   **Using Function Notation**

For each function, find $f(3)$.

(a) $f(x) = 3x - 7$
$$f(3) = 3(3) - 7$$
$$f(3) = 9 - 7$$
$$f(3) = 2$$

(b) $f = \{(-3, 5), (0, 3), (3, 1), (6, -1)\}$
We want $f(3)$, the y-value of the ordered pair where $x = 3$. As indicated by the ordered pair $(3, 1)$, when $x = 3$, $y = 1$, so $f(3) = 1$.

(c)

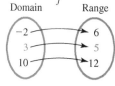

The domain element 3 is paired with 5 in the range, so $f(3) = 5$.

Continued on Next Page

(d)

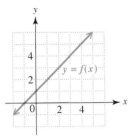

Figure 39

To evaluate $f(3)$, find 3 on the x-axis. See Figure 39. Then move up until the graph of f is reached. Moving horizontally to the y-axis gives 4 for the corresponding y-value. Thus, $f(3) = 4$.

Work Problem **8** *at the Side.* ▶

If a function f is defined by an equation with x and y instead of with function notation, use the following steps to find $f(x)$.

Writing an Equation Using Function Notation

Step 1 Solve the equation for y.

Step 2 Replace y with $f(x)$.

Example 9 **Writing Equations Using Function Notation**

Rewrite each equation using function notation $f(x)$. Then find $f(-2)$ and $f(a)$.

(a) $y = x^2 + 1$
This equation is already solved for y. Since $y = f(x)$,

$$f(x) = x^2 + 1.$$

To find $f(-2)$, let $x = -2$.

$$f(-2) = (-2)^2 + 1$$
$$f(-2) = 4 + 1$$
$$f(-2) = 5$$

Find $f(a)$ by letting $x = a$: $f(a) = a^2 + 1.$

(b) $x - 4y = 5$
First solve $x - 4y = 5$ for y. Then replace y with $f(x)$.

$$x - 4y = 5$$
$$x - 5 = 4y \qquad \text{Add } 4y; \text{ subtract 5.}$$
$$y = \frac{x - 5}{4}, \quad \text{so} \quad f(x) = \frac{1}{4}x - \frac{5}{4}.$$

Now find $f(-2)$ and $f(a)$.

$$f(-2) = \frac{1}{4}(-2) - \frac{5}{4} = -\frac{7}{4} \qquad \text{Let } x = -2.$$

$$f(a) = \frac{1}{4}a - \frac{5}{4} \qquad \text{Let } x = a.$$

Work Problem **9** *at the Side.* ▶

8 For each function, find $f(-2)$.

(a) $f(x) = -4x - 8$

(b) $f = \{(0, 5), (-1, 3), (-2, 1)\}$

(c)

x	$f(x)$
-4	16
-2	4
0	0
2	4
4	16

9 Rewrite each equation using function notation $f(x)$. Then find $f(-1)$.

(a) $y = \sqrt{x + 2}$

(b) $x^2 - 4y = 3$

ANSWERS

8. **(a)** 0   **(b)** 1   **(c)** 4

9. **(a)** $f(x) = \sqrt{x + 2}$; 1

(b) $f(x) = \dfrac{x^2 - 3}{4}$, or $f(x) = \dfrac{1}{4}x^2 - \dfrac{3}{4}$;

$-\dfrac{1}{2}$

10 Graph each linear function. Give the domain and range.

(a) $f(x) = \dfrac{3}{4}x - 2$

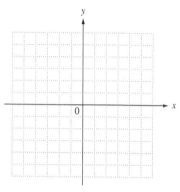

(b) $g(x) = 3$

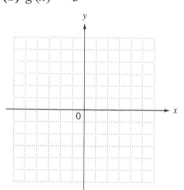

OBJECTIVE 5 Graph linear and constant functions. Our first two-dimensional graphing was of straight lines. Linear equations (except for vertical lines with equations $x = a$) define *linear functions*.

> **Linear Function**
>
> A function that can be defined by
>
> $$f(x) = ax + b,$$
>
> for real numbers a and b, is a **linear function.** The value of a is the slope m of the graph of the function.

A linear function defined by $f(x) = b$ (whose graph is a horizontal line) is sometimes called a **constant function.** The domain of any linear function is $(-\infty, \infty)$. The range of a nonconstant linear function is $(-\infty, \infty)$, while the range of the constant function defined by $f(x) = b$ is $\{b\}$.

Example 10   Graphing Linear and Constant Functions

Graph each function. Give the domain and range.

(a) $f(x) = \dfrac{1}{4}x - \dfrac{5}{4}$

Recall from **Section 4.3** that m is the slope of the line and $(0, b)$ is the y-intercept. In Example 9(b), we wrote the equation $x - 4y = 5$ as the linear function defined by

$$f(x) = \frac{1}{4}x - \frac{5}{4}.$$

Slope — y-intercept is $(0, -\frac{5}{4})$.

To graph this function, plot the y-intercept $(0, -\frac{5}{4})$ and use the definition of slope as $\frac{\text{rise}}{\text{run}}$ to find a second point on the line. Since the slope is $\frac{1}{4}$, move 1 unit up from $(0, -\frac{5}{4})$ and 4 units to the right to the point $(4, -\frac{1}{4})$. Draw the straight line through these points to obtain the graph shown in Figure 40. The domain and range are both $(-\infty, \infty)$.

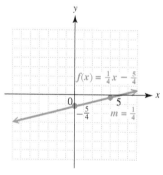

Figure 40

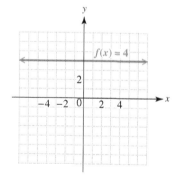

Figure 41

(b) $f(x) = 4$

This is a constant function. Its graph is the horizontal line containing all points with y-coordinate equal to 4. See Figure 41. The domain is $(-\infty, \infty)$ and the range is $\{4\}$.

◀ *Work Problem* **10** *at the Side.*

ANSWERS

10. (a)

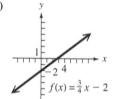

domain: $(-\infty, \infty)$; range: $(-\infty, \infty)$

(b)

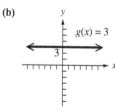

domain: $(-\infty, \infty)$; range: $\{3\}$

13.6 ▶▶▶ **Exercises**

FOR
EXTRA
HELP **MyMathLab** Math XL
PRACTICE WATCH DOWNLOAD READ REVIEW

1. In an ordered pair of a relation, is the first element the independent or the dependent variable?

2. Give an example of a relation that is not a function, having domain $\{-3, 2, 6\}$ and range $\{4, 6\}$. (There are many possible correct answers.)

3. Explain what is meant by each term.
   (a) Relation   **(b)** Domain of a relation
   (c) Range of a relation   **(d)** Function

4. Describe the use of the vertical line test.

Decide whether each relation is a function, and give the domain and the range. Use the vertical line test in Exercises 17–22. See Examples 1–4.

5. $\{(5, 1), (3, 2), (4, 9), (7, 3)\}$

6. $\{(8, 0), (5, 4), (9, 3), (3, 9)\}$

7. $\{(2, 4), (0, 2), (2, 6)\}$

8. $\{(9, -2), (-3, 5), (9, 1)\}$

9. $\{(-3, 1), (4, 1), (-2, 7)\}$

10. $\{(-12, 5), (-10, 3), (8, 3)\}$

⊕ 11. $\{(1, 1), (1, -1), (0, 0), (2, 4), (2, -4)\}$

12. $\{(2, 5), (3, 7), (4, 9), (5, 11)\}$

13.
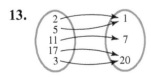

14.
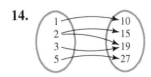

15.

x	y
1	5
1	2
1	−1
1	−4

16.

x	y
4	−3
2	−3
0	−3
−2	−3

17.

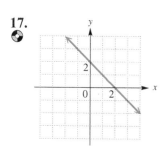

18.

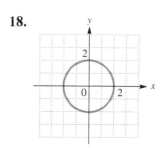

19.

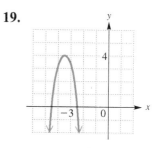

20.

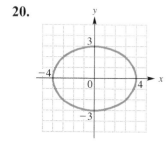

21.

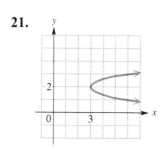

22.

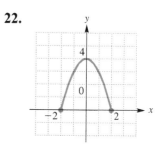

Decide whether each relation defines y as a function of x. Give the domain. See Example 5.

23. $y = x^2$

24. $y = x^3$

25. $x = y^6$

26. $x = y^4$

27. $y = 2x - 6$

28. $y = -6x + 8$

29. $x + y < 4$

30. $x - y < 3$

31. $y = \sqrt{x}$ **32.** $y = -\sqrt{x}$ **33.** $xy = 1$ **34.** $xy = -3$

35. $y = \sqrt{4x + 2}$ **36.** $y = \sqrt{9 - 2x}$ **37.** $y = \dfrac{2}{x - 9}$ **38.** $y = \dfrac{-7}{x - 16}$

39. Refer to the graph to answer the questions.

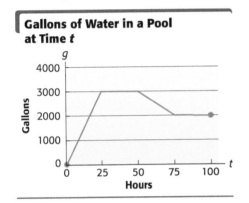

Gallons of Water in a Pool at Time t

(a) What numbers are possible values of the dependent variable?

(b) For how long is the water level increasing? decreasing?

(c) How many gallons are in the pool after 90 hr?

(d) Call this function g. What is $g(0)$? What does it mean in this example?

40. The graph shows the daily megawatts of electricity used on a record-breaking summer day in Sacramento, California.

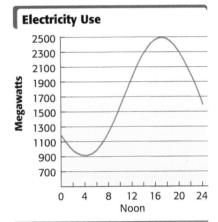

Electricity Use

Source: Sacramento Municipal Utility District.

(a) Is this the graph of a function?

(b) What is the domain?

(c) Estimate the number of megawatts used at 8 A.M.

(d) At what time was the most electricity used? the least electricity?

41. Give an example of a function from everyday life.

(*Hint:* Fill in the blanks: _____ depends on

_____ , so _____ is a function of _____.)

42. Choose the correct response: The notation $f(3)$ means

A. the variable f times 3 or $3f$

B. the value of the dependent variable when the independent variable is 3

C. the value of the independent variable when the dependent variable is 3

D. f equals 3.

Let $f(x) = -3x + 4$ and $g(x) = -x^2 + 4x + 1$. Find the following. See Examples 6 and 7.

43. $f(0)$ **44.** $f(-3)$ **45.** $g(-2)$ **46.** $g(10)$

47. $f(p)$ **48.** $g(k)$ **49.** $f(-x)$ **50.** $g(-x)$

51. $f(x + 2)$ **52.** $g\left(-\dfrac{1}{x}\right)$ **53.** $g\left(\dfrac{p}{3}\right)$ **54.** $f(3t - 2)$

*For each function, find **(a)** $f(2)$ and **(b)** $f(-1)$. See Example 8.*

55. $f = \{(-1, 3), (4, 7), (0, 6), (2, 2)\}$ **56.** $f = \{(2, 5), (3, 9), (-1, 11), (5, 3)\}$

57.

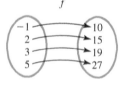

58.

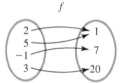

59.

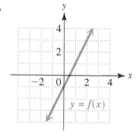

60.

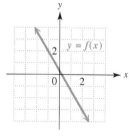

61. Fill in each blank with the correct response.

The equation $2x + y = 4$ has a straight _____ as its graph. One point that lies on the graph is $(3, \underline{\hspace{1cm}})$. If we solve the equation for y and use function notation, we have a _____ function defined by $f(x) = \underline{\hspace{1cm}}$. For this function, $f(3) = \underline{\hspace{1cm}}$, meaning that the point $(\underline{\hspace{1cm}}, \underline{\hspace{1cm}})$ lies on the graph of the function.

62. Which of the following defines a linear function?

A. $y = \dfrac{2}{5}x - 3$ **B.** $y = \dfrac{1}{x}$

C. $y = x^2$ **D.** $y = \sqrt{x}$

An equation that defines y as a function f of x is given. *(a) Solve for y in terms of x, and replace y with the function notation f(x). (b) Find f(3). See Example 9.*

🌐 **63.** $x + 3y = 12$

64. $x - 4y = 8$

65. $y + 2x^2 = 3$

66. $y - 3x^2 = 2$

67. $4x - 3y = 8$

68. $-2x + 5y = 9$

Graph each linear or constant function. Give the domain and range. See Example 10.

🌐 **69.** $f(x) = -2x + 5$

70. $g(x) = 4x - 1$

71. $h(x) = \dfrac{1}{2}x + 2$

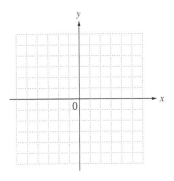

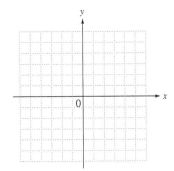

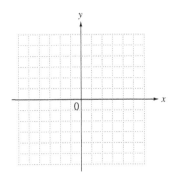

72. $F(x) = -\dfrac{1}{4}x + 1$

73. $g(x) = -4$

74. $f(x) = 5$

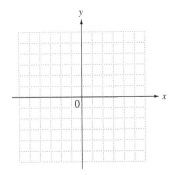

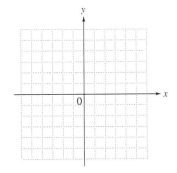

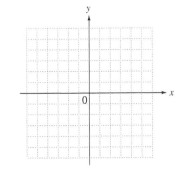

Solve each problem.

75. Suppose that a taxicab driver charges
$2.50 per mi.

(a) Fill in the table with the correct response for the price $f(x)$ he charges for a trip of x miles.

x	$f(x)$
0	
1	
2	
3	

(b) The linear function that gives a rule for the amount charged is

$f(x) =$ _____.

(c) Graph this function for the domain $\{0, 1, 2, 3\}$.

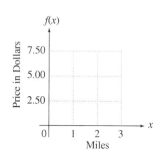

76. Suppose that a package weighing x pounds costs $f(x)$ dollars to ship to a given location, where $f(x) = 3.75x$.

(a) What is the value of $f(3)$?

(b) In your own words, describe what 3 and the value $f(3)$ mean in part (a), using the terms *independent variable* and *dependent variable*.

(c) How much would it cost to mail a 5-lb package? Write the answer using function notation.

Forensic scientists use the lengths of certain bones to calculate the height of a person. Two bones often used are the tibia (t), the bone from the ankle to the knee, and the femur (r), the bone from the knee to the hip socket. A person's height (h) is determined from the lengths of these bones using functions defined by the following formulas. All measurements are in centimeters.

Functions for men: $h(r) = 69.09 + 2.24r$ or $h(t) = 81.69 + 2.39t$

Functions for women: $h(r) = 61.41 + 2.32r$ or $h(t) = 72.57 + 2.53t$

Femur

Tibia

77. Find the height of a man with a femur measuring 56 cm.

78. Find the height of a man with a tibia measuring 40 cm.

79. Find the height of a woman with a femur measuring 50 cm.

80. Find the height of a woman with a tibia measuring 36 cm.

14

Systems of Equations

14.1 ▶▶▶ Solving Systems of Linear Equations by Graphing

OBJECTIVES

1 Decide whether a given ordered pair is a solution of a system.

2 Solve linear systems by graphing.

3 Solve special systems by graphing.

4 Identify special systems without graphing.

A **system of linear equations,** often called a **linear system,** consists of two or more linear equations with the same variables.

$$2x + 3y = 4 \qquad x + 3y = 1 \qquad x - y = 1 \qquad \text{Linear}$$
$$3x - y = -5 \qquad -y = 4 - 2x \qquad y = 3 \qquad \text{systems}$$

In the system on the right, think of $y = 3$ as an equation in two variables by writing it as $0x + y = 3$.

OBJECTIVE **1** **Decide whether a given ordered pair is a solution of a system.** A **solution of a system** of linear equations is an ordered pair that makes both equations true at the same time. A solution of an equation is said to *satisfy* the equation.

EXAMPLE 1 **Determining Whether an Ordered Pair Is a Solution**

Is $(4, -3)$ a solution of each system?

(a) $x + 4y = -8$
$3x + 2y = 6$
To decide whether $(4, -3)$ is a solution of the system, substitute 4 for x and -3 for y in each equation.

$$x + 4y = -8 \qquad\qquad 3x + 2y = 6$$
$$4 + 4(-3) \overset{?}{=} -8 \qquad\qquad 3(4) + 2(-3) \overset{?}{=} 6$$
$$4 + (-12) \overset{?}{=} -8 \quad \text{Multiply.} \qquad 12 + (-6) \overset{?}{=} 6 \quad \text{Multiply.}$$
$$-8 = -8 \quad \text{True} \qquad\qquad 6 = 6 \quad \text{True}$$

Because $(4, -3)$ satisfies both equations, it is a solution of the system.

(b) $2x + 5y = -7$
$3x + 4y = 2$
Again, substitute 4 for x and -3 for y in both equations.

$$2x + 5y = -7 \qquad\qquad 3x + 4y = 2$$
$$2(4) + 5(-3) \overset{?}{=} -7 \qquad\qquad 3(4) + 4(-3) \overset{?}{=} 2$$
$$8 + (-15) \overset{?}{=} -7 \quad \text{Multiply.} \qquad 12 + (-12) \overset{?}{=} 2 \quad \text{Multiply.}$$
$$-7 = -7 \quad \text{True} \qquad\qquad 0 = 2 \quad \text{False}$$

The ordered pair $(4, -3)$ is not a solution of this system because it does not satisfy the second equation.

◀ *Work Problem* **1** *at the Side.*

---

1 Fill in the blanks, and decide whether the given ordered pair is a solution of the system.

(a) $(2, 5)$

$$3x - 2y = -4$$
$$5x + y = 15$$

$$3x - 2y = -4$$
$$3(\underline{\quad}) - 2(\underline{\quad}) \overset{?}{=} -4$$

$$5x + y = 15$$
$$5(2) + \underline{\quad} \overset{?}{=} \underline{\quad}$$

$(2, 5)$ _____ a solution.
(is/is not)

(b) $(1, -2)$

$$x - 3y = 7$$
$$4x + y = 5$$

$(1, -2)$ _____ a solution.
(is/is not)

OBJECTIVE **2** **Solve linear systems by graphing.** The set of all ordered pairs that are solutions of a system is its **solution set.** One way to find the solution set of a system of two linear equations is to graph both equations on the same axes. The graph of each line shows points whose coordinates satisfy the equation of that line. Any intersection point would be on both lines and would therefore be a solution of *both* equations. ***Thus, the coordinates of any point where the lines intersect give a solution of the system.***

ANSWERS

1. **(a)** 2; 5; 5; 15; is **(b)** is not

The graph in Figure 1 shows that the solution of the system in Example 1(a) is the intersection point $(4, -3)$. Because *two different* straight lines can intersect at no more than one point, there can never be more than one solution for such a system.

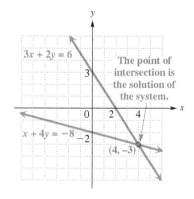

The point of intersection is the solution of the system.

Figure 1

2 Solve each system of equations by graphing both equations on the same axes. Check your solutions.

(a) $5x - 3y = 9$

$x + 2y = 7$

(One of the lines is already graphed.)

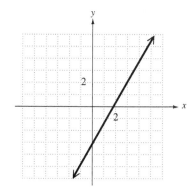

EXAMPLE 2 **Solving a System by Graphing**

Solve the system of equations by graphing both equations on the same axes.

$$2x + 3y = 4$$

$$3x - y = -5$$

We graph these two equations by plotting several points for each line. Recall from **Section 11.2** that the intercepts are often convenient choices.

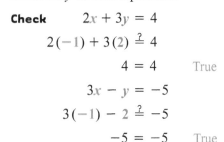

Find a third ordered pair as a check.

$2x + 3y = 4$

x	y
0	$\frac{4}{3}$
2	0
-2	$\frac{8}{3}$

$3x - y = -5$

x	y
0	5
$-\frac{5}{3}$	0
-2	-1

The lines in Figure 2 suggest that the graphs intersect at the point $(-1, 2)$. We check this by substituting -1 for x and 2 for y in both equations.

Check $2x + 3y = 4$

$2(-1) + 3(2) \stackrel{?}{=} 4$

$4 = 4$ True

$3x - y = -5$

$3(-1) - 2 \stackrel{?}{=} -5$

$-5 = -5$ True

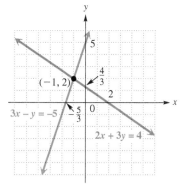

Figure 2

Because $(-1, 2)$ satisfies both equations, the *solution set* of this system is $\{(-1, 2)\}$. We write the ordered pair in the solution set between set braces.

(b) $x + y = 4$

$2x - y = -1$

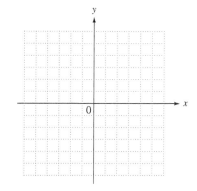

Work Problem **2** *at the Side.* ▶

Note

We can also graph a linear system by writing each equation in the system in slope-intercept form and using the slope and y-intercept to graph each line. For Example 2,

$2x + 3y = 4$ becomes $y = -\frac{2}{3}x + \frac{4}{3}$ y-intercept $(0, \frac{4}{3})$; slope $-\frac{2}{3}$

$3x - y = -5$ becomes $y = 3x + 5$. y-intercept $(0, 5)$; slope 3, or $\frac{3}{1}$

Confirm that graphing these equations results in the same lines and the same solution shown in Figure 2.

ANSWERS

2. (a) $\{(3, 2)\}$ (b) $\{(1, 3)\}$

To solve a linear system by graphing, follow these steps.

> **Solving a Linear System by Graphing**
>
> *Step 1* **Graph each equation** of the system on the same coordinate axes.
>
> *Step 2* **Find the coordinates of the point of intersection** of the graphs if possible. This is the solution of the system.
>
> *Step 3* **Check** the solution in *both* of the original equations. Then write the solution set.

> **CAUTION**
>
> A difficulty with the graphing method of solution is that it may not be possible to determine from the graph the exact coordinates of the point that represents the solution, particularly if these coordinates are not integers. For this reason, algebraic methods of solution are explained later in this chapter. The graphing method does, however, show geometrically how solutions are found and is useful when approximate answers will do.

OBJECTIVE 3 Solve special systems by graphing. Sometimes the graphs of the two equations in a system either do not intersect at all or are the same line, as in the systems in Example 3.

EXAMPLE 3 **Solving Special Systems**

Solve each system by graphing.

(a) $2x + y = 2$

$2x + y = 8$

The graphs of these lines are shown in Figure 3. The two lines are parallel and have no points in common. For such a system, **there is no solution.** Its solution set is the **empty set,** or **null set,** symbolized $\emptyset$.

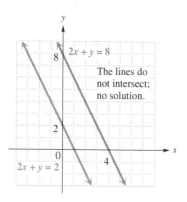

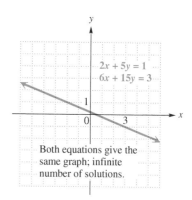

Figure 3   Figure 4

(b) $2x + 5y = 1$

$6x + 15y = 3$

The graphs of these two equations are the same line. See Figure 4. The second equation can be obtained by multiplying each side of the first equation by 3. In this case, every point on the line is a solution of the system, and *the solution set contains an infinite number of ordered pairs* that satisfy the equations.

Continued on Next Page

We write the solution set as

$$\{(x, y) \mid 2x + 5y = 1\},$$

This is the first equation in the system. See the Note below.

read "the set of ordered pairs (x, y) such that $2x + 5y = 1$." This notation is called **set-builder notation.** It is convenient to use this notation when it is not possible to list all the elements of a set

Note

When a system has an infinite number of solutions, as in Example 3(b), either equation of the system could be used to write the solution set. *We prefer to use the equation in standard form with coefficients that are integers having greatest common factor 1.* If neither of the given equations of the system is in this form, use an *equivalent* equation that is in standard form with coefficients that are integers having greatest common factor 1 to write the solution set with set-builder notation.

Work Problem **3** *at the Side.* ▶

The system in Example 2 has exactly one solution. A system with at least one solution is called a **consistent system.** A system of equations with no solution, such as the one in Example 3(a), is called an **inconsistent system.** The equations in Example 2 are **independent equations** with different graphs. The equations of the system in Example 3(b) have the same graph and are equivalent. Because they are different forms of the same equation, these equations are called **dependent equations.**

Examples 2 and 3 show the three cases that may occur when solving a system of two equations with two variables.

Three Cases for Solutions of Systems

1. The graphs intersect at exactly one point, which gives the (single) ordered-pair solution of the system. The **system is consistent** and the **equations are independent.** See Figure 5(a).
2. The graphs are parallel lines, so there is no solution and the solution set is ∅. The **system is inconsistent** and the **equations are independent.** See Figure 5(b).
3. The graphs are the same line. There is an infinite number of solutions, and the solution set is written in set-builder notation as $\{(x, y) \mid \underline{\qquad}\}$, where one of the equations is written after the | symbol. The **system is consistent** and the **equations are dependent.** See Figure 5(c).

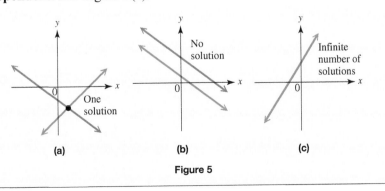

(a)   (b)   (c)

One solution   No solution   Infinite number of solutions

Figure 5

3 Solve each system of equations by graphing both equations on the same axes.

(a) $3x - y = 4$
$6x - 2y = 12$

(One of the lines is already graphed.)

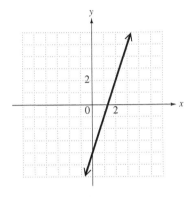

(b) $x - 3y = -2$
$2x - 6y = -4$

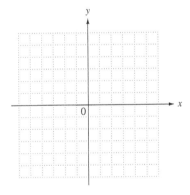

ANSWERS

3. **(a)** There is *no solution,* so write the solution set as ∅.
   (b) There is an *infinite number of solutions,* so use set-builder notation.
   $\{(x, y) \mid x - 3y = -2\}$

4 Describe each system without graphing. State the number of solutions.

(a) $2x - 3y = 5$
$3y = 2x - 7$

(b) $-x + 3y = 2$
$2x - 6y = -4$

(c) $6x + y = 3$
$2x - y = -11$

ANSWERS

4. (a) The equations represent parallel lines. The system has no solution.
   (b) The equations represent the same line. The system has an infinite number of solutions.
   (c) The equations represent lines that are neither parallel nor the same line. The system has exactly one solution.

OBJECTIVE 4 **Identify special systems without graphing.**
Example 3 showed that the graphs of an inconsistent system are parallel lines and the graphs of a system of dependent equations are the same line. We can recognize these special kinds of systems without graphing by using slopes.

EXAMPLE 4 **Identifying the Three Cases by Using Slopes**

Describe each system without graphing. State the number of solutions.

(a) $3x + 2y = 6$
$-2y = 3x - 5$
   Write each equation in slope-intercept form, $y = mx + b$, by solving for y.

$3x + 2y = 6$
$2y = -3x + 6$ Subtract 3x.
$y = -\frac{3}{2}x + 3$ Divide by 2.

$-2y = 3x - 5$
$y = -\frac{3}{2}x + \frac{5}{2}$ Divide by -2.

Both equations have slope $-\frac{3}{2}$ but they have different y-intercepts, 3 and $\frac{5}{2}$. In **Section 11.3,** we found that lines with the same slope are parallel, so these equations have graphs that are parallel lines. Thus, the system has no solution.

(b) $2x - y = 4$
$x = \frac{y}{2} + 2$

   Again, write the equations in slope-intercept form.

$2x - y = 4$
$-y = -2x + 4$
$y = 2x - 4$

$x = \frac{y}{2} + 2$
$\frac{y}{2} + 2 = x$
$\frac{y}{2} = x - 2$
$y = 2x - 4$

The equations are exactly the same—their graphs are the same line. Thus, the system has an infinite number of solutions.

(c) $x - 3y = 5$
$2x + y = 8$
   In slope-intercept form, the equations are as follows.

$x - 3y = 5$
$-3y = -x + 5$
$y = \frac{1}{3}x - \frac{5}{3}$

$2x + y = 8$
$y = -2x + 8$

The graphs of these equations are neither parallel nor the same line, since the slopes are different. This system has exactly one solution.

◀ *Work Problem* **4** *at the Side.*

1. Which ordered pair could be a solution of the system graphed? Why is it the only valid choice?

   A. $(2, 2)$

   B. $(-2, 2)$

   C. $(-2, -2)$

   D. $(2, -2)$

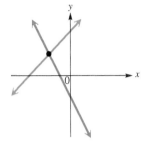

2. Which ordered pair could be a solution of the system graphed? Why is it the only valid choice?

   A. $(2, 0)$

   B. $(0, 2)$

   C. $(-2, 0)$

   D. $(0, -2)$

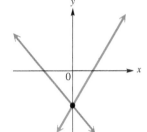

3. How can you tell without graphing that this system has no solution?

$$x + y = 2$$
$$x + y = 4$$

4. Explain why a system of two linear equations cannot have exactly two solutions.

Decide whether the given ordered pair is a solution of the given system. See Example 1.

5. $(2, -3)$
$$x + y = -1$$
$$2x + 5y = 19$$

6. $(4, 3)$
$$x + 2y = 10$$
$$3x + 5y = 3$$

7. $(-1, -3)$
$$3x + 5y = -18$$
$$4x + 2y = -10$$

8. $(-9, -2)$
$$2x - 5y = -8$$
$$3x + 6y = -39$$

9. $(7, -2)$
$$4x = 26 - y$$
$$3x = 29 + 4y$$

10. $(9, 1)$
$$2x = 23 - 5y$$
$$3x = 24 + 3y$$

11. $(6, -8)$
$$-2y = x + 10$$
$$3y = 2x + 30$$

12. $(-5, 2)$
$$5y = 3x + 20$$
$$3y = -2x - 4$$

Solve each system of equations by graphing. If the system is inconsistent or the equations are dependent, say so. See Examples 2 and 3.

13. $x - y = 2$
$x + y = 6$

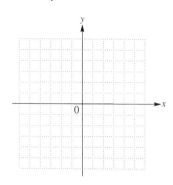

14. $x - y = 3$
$x + y = -1$

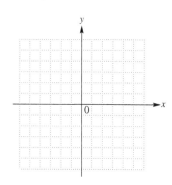

15. $x + y = 4$
$y - x = 4$

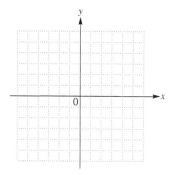

16. $x + y = -5$
$x - y = 5$

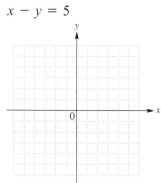

17. $x - 2y = 6$
$x + 2y = 2$

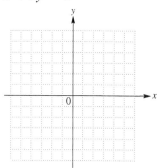

18. $2x - y = 4$
$4x + y = 2$

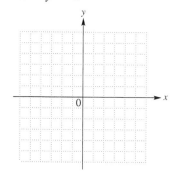

19. $3x - 2y = -3$
$-3x - y = -6$

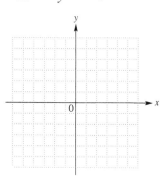

20. $2x - y = 4$
$2x + 3y = 12$

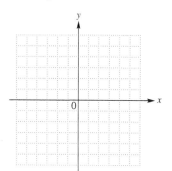

21. $2x - 3y = -6$
$y = -3x + 2$

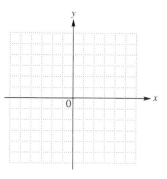

22. $-3x + y = -3$
$y = x - 3$

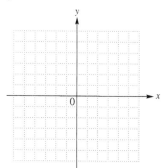

23. $x + 2y = 6$
$2x + 4y = 8$

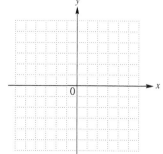

24. $2x - y = 6$
$6x - 3y = 12$

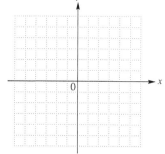
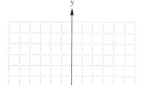

25. $4x - 2y = 8$
$2x = y + 4$

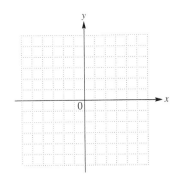

26. $3x = 5 - y$
$6x + 2y = 10$

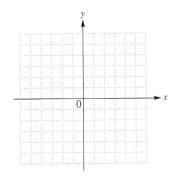

27. $3x - 4y = 24$
$y = -\dfrac{3}{2}x + 3$

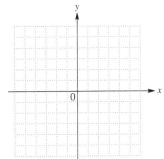

28. $3x - 2y = 12$
$y = -4x + 5$

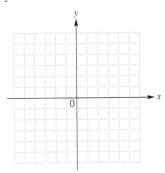

29. $3x = y + 5$
$6x - 5 = 2y$

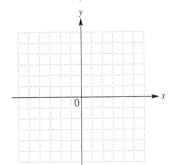

30. $2x = y - 4$
$4x - 2y = -4$

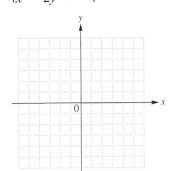

Without graphing, answer the following questions for each linear system. See Example 4.

(a) Is the system inconsistent, are the equations dependent, or neither?
(b) Is the graph a pair of intersecting lines, a pair of parallel lines, or one line?
(c) Does the system have one solution, no solution, or an infinite number of solutions?

31. $y - x = -5$
$x + y = 1$

32. $2x + y = 6$
$x - 3y = -4$

33. $x + 2y = 0$
$4y = -2x$

34. $y = 3x$
$y + 3 = 3x$

35. $5x + 4y = 7$
$10x + 8y = 4$

36. $4x - 6y = 10$
$-6x + 9y = -15$

The numbers of daily morning and evening newspapers in the United States in selected years are shown in the graph. Use the graph to work Exercises 37 and 38.

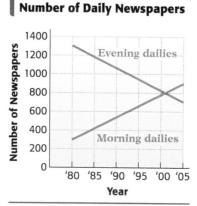

Number of Daily Newspapers

Source: Editor & Publisher International Year Book.

37. For which years were there more evening dailies than morning dailies?

38. Estimate the year in which the number of evening and morning dailies was closest to the same. About how many newspapers of each type were there in that year?

Work Exercises 39 and 40 using the graphs provided.

39. The graph shows how college students managed their money during the period 1997–2004.

    (a) During what period did ATM use dominate both credit card *and* debit card use?

    (b) In what year did debit card use overtake credit card use?

    (c) In what year did debit card use overtake ATM use?

    (d) Write an ordered pair for the debit card use data in the year 2004.

    (e) Describe the trend in debit card use over this period.

How College Students Manage Their Money

Source: Georgetown University Credit Research Center.

40. The graph shows how the average viewing hours for broadcast TV and cable/satellite TV in the United States has changed during the period 1998–2004.

    (a) In approximately what year did Americans spend almost the same number of hours watching broadcast and cable/satellite TV? How many hours per year was this?

    (b) Express the point of intersection of the two graphs as an ordered pair of the form (year, hours).

    (c) During what period was the time spent watching broadcast TV almost constant?

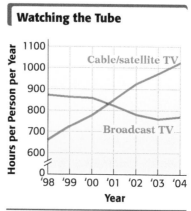

Watching the Tube

Source: Veronis Suhler Stevenson.

14.2 ►►► Solving Systems of Linear Equations by Substitution

OBJECTIVE 1 Solve linear systems by substitution.

Work Problem 1 at the Side. ▶

As we saw in Problem 1 at the side, graphing to solve a system of equations has a serious drawback: It is difficult to accurately find a solution such as $\left(\frac{11}{3}, -\frac{4}{9}\right)$ from a graph. One algebraic method for solving a system of equations is the **substitution method**.

EXAMPLE 1   Using the Substitution Method

Solve the system by the substitution method.

$$3x + 5y = 26$$
$$y = 2x$$

The second equation is already solved for y. This equation says that $y = 2x$. Substituting $2x$ for y in the first equation gives

$$3x + 5y = 26$$
$$3x + 5(2x) = 26 \qquad \text{Let } y = 2x.$$
$$3x + 10x = 26 \qquad \text{Multiply.}$$
$$13x = 26 \qquad \text{Combine like terms.}$$
$$x = 2. \qquad \text{Divide by 13.}$$

Because $x = 2$, we find y from the equation $y = 2x$ by substituting 2 for x.

$$y = 2(2) = 4 \qquad \text{Let } x = 2.$$

Check that the solution set of the given system is $\{(2, 4)\}$ by substituting 2 for x and 4 for y in *both* equations.

Work Problem 2 at the Side. ▶

EXAMPLE 2   Using the Substitution Method

Solve the system by the substitution method.

$$2x + 5y = 7$$
$$x = -1 - y$$

The second equation gives x in terms of y. Substitute $-1 - y$ for x in the first equation.

$$2x + 5y = 7$$
$$2(-1 - y) + 5y = 7 \qquad \text{Let } x = -1 - y.$$

Distribute 2 to *both* -1 and $-y$.

$$-2 - 2y + 5y = 7 \qquad \text{Distributive property}$$
$$-2 + 3y = 7 \qquad \text{Combine like terms.}$$
$$3y = 9 \qquad \text{Add 2.}$$
$$y = 3 \qquad \text{Divide by 3.}$$

To find x, substitute 3 for y in the equation $x = -1 - y$ to get

$$x = -1 - 3 = -4.$$

Write the x-coordinate first.

Check that the solution set of the given system is $\{(-4, 3)\}$.

Work Problem 3 at the Side. ▶

OBJECTIVES

1 Solve linear systems by substitution.

2 Solve special systems by substitution.

3 Solve linear systems with fractions and decimals by substitution.

1 Solve the system by graphing.

$$2x + 3y = 6$$
$$x - 3y = 5$$

Can you determine the answer? Why or why not?

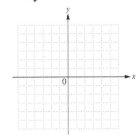

2 Fill in the blanks to solve by the substitution method. Check your solution.

$$3x + 5y = 69$$
$$y = 4x$$

$$3x + 5(\underline{}) = 69$$
$$\underline{} = 69$$
$$x = \underline{}$$
$$y = 4(\underline{}) = \underline{}$$

The solution set is ____.

3 Solve by the substitution method. Check your solution.

$$2x + 7y = -12$$
$$x = 3 - 2y$$

ANSWERS

1. The answer cannot be determined from the graph because it is too difficult to read the exact coordinates.
2. $4x$; $23x$; 3; 3; 12; $\{(3, 12)\}$
3. $\{(15, -6)\}$

CAUTION

Even though we found y first in Example 2, *the x-coordinate is always written first in the ordered-pair solution of a system.*

To solve a system by substitution, follow these steps.

4 Solve each system by substitution. Check each solution.

(a) Fill in the blanks to solve

$$x + 4y = -1$$
$$2x - 5y = 11.$$

Solve the first equation for x.

$$x = -1 - \underline{\quad}$$

Substitute into the second equation to find y.

$$2(\underline{\quad}) - 5y = 11$$
$$-2 - 8y - 5y = 11$$
$$-2 - \underline{\quad} y = 11$$
$$\underline{\quad} y = 13$$
$$y = \underline{\quad}$$

Find x.

$$x = -1 - \underline{\quad}$$
$$x = \underline{\quad}$$

The solution set is $\underline{\quad}$.

Solving a Linear System by Substitution

Step 1 **Solve one equation for either variable.** If one of the variables has coefficient 1 or -1, choose it, since it usually makes the substitution easier.

Step 2 **Substitute** for that variable in the other equation. The result should be an equation with just one variable.

Step 3 **Solve** the equation from Step 2.

Step 4 **Substitute** the result from Step 3 into the equation from Step 1 to find the value of the other variable.

Step 5 **Check** the solution in *both* of the original equations. Then write the solution set.

EXAMPLE 3　Using the Substitution Method

Use substitution to solve the system.

$$2x = 4 - y \qquad (1)$$
$$5x + 3y = 10 \qquad (2)$$

Step 1 For the substitution method, we must solve one of the equations for either x or y. Because the coefficient of y in equation (1) is -1, we choose equation (1) and solve for y.

$$2x = 4 - y \qquad (1)$$
$$y + 2x = 4 \qquad \text{Add } y.$$
$$y = -2x + 4 \qquad \text{Subtract } 2x.$$

Step 2 Now substitute $-2x + 4$ for y in equation (2).

$$5x + 3y = 10 \qquad (2)$$
$$5x + 3(-2x + 4) = 10 \qquad \text{Let } y = -2x + 4.$$

Step 3 Now solve the equation from Step 2.

Distribute 3 to both $-2x$ and 4.

$$5x - 6x + 12 = 10 \qquad \text{Distributive property}$$
$$-x + 12 = 10 \qquad \text{Combine like terms.}$$
$$-x = -2 \qquad \text{Subtract 12.}$$
$$x = 2 \qquad \text{Multiply by } -1.$$

Step 4 Since $y = -2x + 4$ and $x = 2$, $y = -2(2) + 4 = 0$.

Step 5 Check that $(2, 0)$ is the solution.

(b) $2x + 5y = 4$
$x + y = -1$

Check

$$2x = 4 - y \qquad (1)$$
$$2(2) \overset{?}{=} 4 - 0$$
$$4 = 4 \qquad \text{True}$$

$$5x + 3y = 10 \qquad (2)$$
$$5(2) + 3(0) \overset{?}{=} 10$$
$$10 = 10 \qquad \text{True}$$

Since both results are true, the solution set of the system is $\{(2, 0)\}$.

◀ Work Problem **4** at the Side.

ANSWERS

4. (a) $4y; -1 - 4y; 13; -13; -1; -4; 3;$
$\{(3, -1)\}$　**(b)** $\{(-3, 2)\}$

EXAMPLE 4 **Using the Substitution Method**

Use substitution to solve the system.

$$2x + 3y = 10 \quad (1)$$
$$-3x - 2y = 0 \quad (2)$$

Step 1 To use the substitution method, we must solve one of the equations for one of the variables. We choose equation (1) and solve for x.

$$2x + 3y = 10 \qquad (1)$$
$$2x = 10 - 3y \qquad \text{Subtract } 3y.$$
$$x = 5 - \frac{3}{2}y \qquad \text{Divide by 2.}$$

Step 2 Substitute this expression for x in equation (2).

$$-3x - 2y = 0 \qquad (2)$$
$$-3\left(5 - \frac{3}{2}y\right) - 2y = 0 \qquad \text{Let } x = 5 - \tfrac{3}{2}y.$$

Step 3
$$-15 + \frac{9}{2}y - 2y = 0 \qquad \text{Distributive property}$$

$$\boxed{\begin{array}{l} -3(-\tfrac{3}{2}) = (-\tfrac{3}{1})(-\tfrac{3}{2}) \\ \quad = \tfrac{9}{2} \end{array}}$$

$$-15 + \frac{5}{2}y = 0 \qquad \text{Combine like terms.}$$
$$\frac{5}{2}y = 15 \qquad \text{Add 15.}$$

$$\boxed{\begin{array}{l} \tfrac{2}{5}(\tfrac{5}{2}y) = (\tfrac{2}{5} \cdot \tfrac{5}{2})y \\ \quad = 1 \cdot y = y \end{array}}$$

$$y = \frac{30}{5} = 6 \qquad \text{Multiply by } \tfrac{2}{5}.$$

Step 4 Find x by substituting **6** for y in $x = 5 - \tfrac{3}{2}y$.

$$x = 5 - \frac{3}{2}(6) = -4$$

Step 5 Check that $(-4, 6)$ is the solution.

Check

$2x + 3y = 10 \quad (1)$	$-3x - 2y = 0 \quad (2)$
$2(-4) + 3(6) \overset{?}{=} 10$	$-3(-4) - 2(6) \overset{?}{=} 0$
$-8 + 18 \overset{?}{=} 10$	$12 - 12 \overset{?}{=} 0$
$10 = 10 \qquad$ True	$0 = 0 \qquad$ True

Both results are true, so the solution set of the system is $\{(-4, 6)\}$.

> **Note**
>
> In Example 4, we could have started the solution by solving the second equation for either x or y and then substituting the result into the first equation. The solution would be the same.

Work Problem **5** *at the Side.* ▶

5 Solve the system by substitution. Check your solution.

$$3x + 2y = 1$$
$$3x - 4y = -11$$

OBJECTIVE 2 **Solve special systems by substitution.** We can solve inconsistent systems with graphs that are parallel lines and systems of dependent equations with graphs that are the same line using the substitution method.

EXAMPLE 5 **Solving an Inconsistent System by Substitution**

Use substitution to solve the system.

$$x = 5 - 2y \quad \text{(1)}$$
$$2x + 4y = 6 \quad \text{(2)}$$

Substitute $5 - 2y$ for x in equation (2).

$$\begin{aligned}
2x + 4y &= 6 && \text{(2)} \\
2(5 - 2y) + 4y &= 6 && \text{Let } x = 5 - 2y. \\
10 - 4y + 4y &= 6 && \text{Distributive property} \\
10 &= 6 && \text{False}
\end{aligned}$$

This false result means that the equations in the system have graphs that are parallel lines. The system is inconsistent, and the solution set is $\emptyset$. See Figure 6.

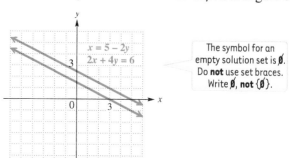

The symbol for an empty solution set is $\emptyset$. Do **not** use set braces. Write $\emptyset$, **not** $\{\emptyset\}$.

Figure 6

CAUTION
It is a common error to give "false" as the answer to an inconsistent system. The correct response is $\emptyset$.

EXAMPLE 6 **Solving a System with Dependent Equations by Substitution**

Solve the system by the substitution method.

$$3x - y = 4 \quad \text{(1)}$$
$$-9x + 3y = -12 \quad \text{(2)}$$

Begin by solving equation (1) for y to get $y = 3x - 4$. Substitute $3x - 4$ for y in equation (2) and solve the resulting equation.

$$\begin{aligned}
-9x + 3y &= -12 && \text{(2)} \\
-9x + 3(3x - 4) &= -12 && \text{Let } y = 3x - 4. \\
-9x + 9x - 12 &= -12 && \text{Distributive property} \\
0 &= 0 && \text{Add 12; combine like terms.}
\end{aligned}$$

Continued on Next Page

This true result means that every solution of one equation is also a solution of the other, so the system has an infinite number of solutions—all the ordered pairs corresponding to points that lie on the common graph. The solution set is $\{(x, y)\,|\,3x - y = 4\}$. A graph of the equations of this system is shown in Figure 7.

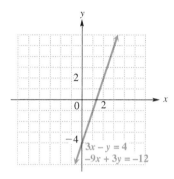

Figure 7

6 Solve each system by substitution.

(a) $8x - y = 4$
$y = 8x + 4$

CAUTION

It is a common error to give "true" as the solution of a system of dependent equations. Remember that we give the solution set in set-builder notation using an equation that is in standard form, with integer coefficients having greatest common factor 1.

Work Problem **6** *at the Side.* ▶

OBJECTIVE 3 Solve linear systems with fractions and decimals by substitution. When a system includes an equation with fractions as coefficients, eliminate the fractions by multiplying each side of the equation by a common denominator. Then solve the resulting system.

(b) $7x - 6y = 10$
$-14x + 20 = -12y$

EXAMPLE 7 **Using the Substitution Method with Fractions as Coefficients**

Solve the system by the substitution method.

$$3x + \frac{1}{4}y = 2 \qquad (1)$$

$$\frac{1}{2}x + \frac{3}{4}y = -\frac{5}{2} \qquad (2)$$

Clear equation (1) of fractions by multiplying each side by 4.

$$4\left(3x + \frac{1}{4}y\right) = 4\,(2) \qquad \text{Multiply by 4.}$$

$$4\,(3x) + 4\left(\frac{1}{4}y\right) = 4\,(2) \qquad \text{Distributive property}$$

$$12x + y = 8 \qquad (3)$$

Continued on Next Page

7 Solve the system by substitution. First clear all fractions.

$$\frac{2}{3}x + \frac{1}{2}y = 6$$

$$\frac{1}{2}x - \frac{3}{4}y = 0$$

Now clear equation (2) of fractions by multiplying each side by the common denominator 4.

$$\frac{1}{2}x + \frac{3}{4}y = -\frac{5}{2} \qquad (2)$$

$$4\left(\frac{1}{2}x + \frac{3}{4}y\right) = 4\left(-\frac{5}{2}\right) \qquad \text{Multiply by 4.}$$

$$4\left(\frac{1}{2}x\right) + 4\left(\frac{3}{4}y\right) = 4\left(-\frac{5}{2}\right) \qquad \text{Distributive property}$$

$$2x + 3y = -10 \qquad (4)$$

The given system of equations has been simplified to the equivalent system

$$12x + y = 8 \qquad (3)$$
$$2x + 3y = -10. \qquad (4)$$

To solve this system by substitution, equation (3) can be solved for y.

$$12x + y = 8 \qquad (3)$$
$$y = -12x + 8 \qquad \text{Subtract } 12x.$$

Now substitute this result for y in equation (4).

$$2x + 3y = -10 \qquad (4)$$
$$2x + 3(-12x + 8) = -10 \qquad \text{Let } y = -12x + 8.$$
$$2x - 36x + 24 = -10 \qquad \text{Distributive property}$$

> Distribute 3 to both $-12x$ and 8.

$$-34x = -34 \qquad \text{Combine like terms; subtract 24.}$$
$$x = 1 \qquad \text{Divide by } -34.$$

Substitute 1 for x in $y = -12x + 8$ to get

$$y = -12(1) + 8 = -4.$$

Check by substituting 1 for x and -4 for y in both of the original equations. The solution set is $\{(1, -4)\}$.

◀ *Work Problem* **7** *at the Side.*

8 Complete the process of solving the system given in Example 8 by substitution. (*Hint:* Solve equation (4) for x. Then substitute this result for x in equation (3) to find y.)

If any of the coefficients in the equations of a system are decimals, we can eliminate the decimals by multiplying by a power of 10, as we did when solving linear equations with decimal coefficients in **Section 10.2.**

EXAMPLE 8   **Using the Substitution Method with Decimals as Coefficients**

Solve the system by the substitution method.

$$0.5x + 2.4y = 4.2 \qquad (1)$$
$$-0.1x + 1.5y = 5.1 \qquad (2)$$

To eliminate (or "clear") decimals, multiply each equation by 10.

$$5x + 24y = 42 \qquad (3)$$
$$-x + 15y = 51 \qquad (4) \quad (-0.1x) \cdot 10 = -1x = -x$$

Now we can solve this equivalent system by substitution.

◀ *Work problem* **8** *at the Side.*

14.2 ▶▶▶ **Exercises**

1. A student solves the system

$$5x - y = 15$$
$$7x + y = 21$$

and finds that $x = 3$, which is the correct value for x. The student gives the solution set as $\{3\}$. ***WHAT WENT WRONG?***

2. When you use the substitution method, how can you tell that a system has

(a) no solution?　　　　　　　　　　**(b)** an infinite number of solutions?

Solve each system by the substitution method. Check each solution. See Examples 1–8.

3. $x + y = 12$
　　$y = 3x$

4. $x + 3y = -28$
　　$y = -5x$

5. $3x + 2y = 27$
　　$x = y + 4$

6. $4x + 3y = -5$
　　$x = y - 3$

7. $3x + 5y = 14$
　　$x - 2y = -10$

8. $5x + 2y = -1$
　　$2x - y = -13$

9. $3x + 4 = -y$
　　$2x + y = 0$

10. $2x - 5 = -y$
　　$x + 3y = 0$

11. $7x + 4y = 13$
　　$x + y = 1$

12. $3x - 2y = 19$
　　$x + y = 8$

13. $3x - y = 5$
　　$y = 3x - 5$

14. $4x - y = -3$
　　$y = 4x + 3$

15. $6x - 8y = 6$
　　$2y = -2 + 3x$

16. $3x + 2y = 6$
　　$6x = 8 + 4y$

17. $2x + 8y = 3$
　　$x = 8 - 4y$

18. $2x + 10y = 3$
  $x = 1 - 5y$

19. $12x - 16y = 8$
  $3x = 4y + 2$

20. $6x + 9y = 6$
  $2x = 2 - 3y$

21. $\frac{1}{5}x + \frac{2}{3}y = -\frac{8}{5}$
  $3x - y = 9$

22. $\frac{1}{3}x - \frac{1}{2}y = \frac{1}{6}$
  $3x - 2y = 9$

23. $\frac{x}{2} - \frac{y}{3} = 9$
  $\frac{x}{5} - \frac{y}{4} = 5$

24. $\frac{1}{6}x + \frac{1}{6}y = 2$
  $-\frac{1}{2}x - \frac{1}{3}y = -8$

25. $\frac{x}{5} + 2y = \frac{16}{5}$
  $\frac{3x}{5} + \frac{y}{2} = -\frac{7}{5}$

26. $\frac{x}{3} - \frac{3y}{4} = -\frac{1}{2}$
  $\frac{x}{6} + \frac{y}{8} = \frac{3}{4}$

27. $0.1x + 0.9y = -2$
  $0.5x - 0.2y = 4.1$

28. $0.2x - 1.3y = -3.2$
  $-0.1x + 2.7y = 9.8$

29. $0.08x - 0.01y = 1.3$
  $0.22x + 0.15y = 8.9$

Relating Concepts (Exercises 30–33) For Individual or Group Work

A system of linear equations can be used to model the cost and the revenue of a business. ***Work Exercises 30–33 in order.***

30. Suppose that you start a business manufacturing and selling bicycles, and it costs you $5000 to get started. You determine that each bicycle will cost $400 to manufacture. Explain why the linear equation $y_1 = 400x + 5000$ gives your *total* cost to manufacture x bicycles (y_1 in dollars).

31. You decide to sell each bike for $600. What expression in x represents the revenue you will take in if you sell x bikes? Write an equation using y_2 to express your revenue when you sell x bikes (y_2 in dollars).

32. Form a system from the two equations in Exercises 30 and 31, and then solve the system, assuming $y_1 = y_2$, that is, cost = revenue.

33. The value of x from Exercise 32 is the number of bikes it takes to *break even*. Fill in the blanks: When _____ bikes are sold, the break-even point is reached. At that point, you have spent _____ dollars and taken in _____ dollars.

14.3 ▶▶▶ Solving Systems of Linear Equations by Elimination

OBJECTIVE 1 Solve linear systems by elimination. An algebraic method that depends on the addition property of equality can be used to solve systems. As mentioned earlier, adding the same quantity to each side of an equation results in equal sums.

$$\text{If } A = B, \quad \text{then} \quad A + C = B + C.$$

This addition can be taken a step further. Adding *equal* quantities, rather than the *same* quantity, to both sides of an equation also results in equal sums.

$$\text{If } A = B \quad \text{and} \quad C = D, \quad \text{then} \quad A + C = B + D.$$

Using the addition property to solve systems is called the **elimination method.** When using this method, the idea is to *eliminate* one of the variables. ***To do this, one of the variables in the two equations must have coefficients that are opposites.***

EXAMPLE 1   Using the Elimination Method

Use the elimination method to solve the system.

$$x + y = 5$$
$$x - y = 3$$

Each equation in this system is a statement of equality, so the sum of the left sides equals the sum of the right sides. Adding in this way gives

$$(x + y) + (x - y) = 5 + 3.$$

Combine like terms and simplify to get

$$2x = 8$$
$$x = 4. \quad \text{Divide by 2.}$$

Notice that y has been eliminated. The result, $x = 4$, gives the x-value of the solution of the given system. To find the y-value of the solution, substitute 4 for x in either of the two equations of the system.

Work Problem ① *at the Side.* ▶

Check the solution set found at the side, $\{(4, 1)\}$, by substituting 4 for x and 1 for y in both equations of the given system.

Check

$x + y = 5$	$x - y = 3$
$4 + 1 \overset{?}{=} 5$	$4 - 1 \overset{?}{=} 3$
$5 = 5$ True	$3 = 3$ True

Since both results are true, the solution set of the system is $\{(4, 1)\}$.

CAUTION

A system is not completely solved until values for both x and y are found. Do not stop after finding the value of only one variable. Remember to write the solution set as a set containing an ordered pair.

OBJECTIVES

1. Solve linear systems by elimination.

2. Multiply when using the elimination method.

3. Use an alternative method to find the second value in a solution.

4. Use the elimination method to solve special systems.

① **(a)** Substitute 4 for x in the equation $x + y = 5$ to find the value of y.

(b) Give the solution set of the system.

◀ *Work Problem* ② *at the Side.*

2 Solve each system by the elimination method. Check each solution.

(a) Fill in the blanks to solve the following system.

$$x + y = 8$$
$$x - y = 2$$

Add.

$$(x + y) + (x - y) = 8 + \underline{\quad}$$
$$2\underline{\quad} = \underline{\quad}$$
$$x = \underline{\quad}$$

Find y.

$$x - y = 2$$
$$\underline{\quad} - y = 2$$
$$-y = \underline{\quad}$$
$$y = \underline{\quad}$$

The solution set is $\underline{\quad}$.

(b) $3x - y = 7$
$2x + y = 3$

In general, to solve a system by elimination, follow these steps.

Solving a Linear System by Elimination

Step 1 **Write both equations in standard form** $Ax + By = C$.

Step 2 **Transform so that the coefficients of one pair of variable terms are opposites.** Multiply one or both equations by appropriate numbers so that the sum of the coefficients of either the x- or y-terms is 0.

Step 3 **Add** the new equations to eliminate a variable. The sum should be an equation with just one variable.

Step 4 **Solve** the equation from Step 3 for the remaining variable.

Step 5 **Substitute** the result from Step 4 into *either* of the original equations and solve for the other variable.

Step 6 **Check** the solution in *both* of the original equations. Then write the solution set.

It does not matter which variable is eliminated first. Usually we choose the one that is more convenient to work with.

EXAMPLE 2 **Using the Elimination Method**

Solve the system.

$$y + 11 = 2x$$
$$5x = y + 26$$

Step 1 Rewrite both equations in the form $Ax + By = C$ to get the system

$$-2x + y = -11 \qquad \text{Subtract } 2x \text{ and } 11.$$
$$5x - y = 26. \qquad \text{Subtract } y.$$

Step 2 Because the coefficients of y are 1 and -1, adding will eliminate y. It is not necessary to multiply either equation by a number.

Step 3 Add the two equations. This time we use vertical addition.

$$-2x + y = -11$$
$$\underline{5x - y = 26}$$
$$3x = 15 \qquad \text{Add in columns.}$$

Step 4 Solve the equation.

$$3x = 15$$
$$x = 5 \qquad \text{Divide by 3.}$$

Don't stop here.

Step 5 Find the value of y by substituting 5 for x in either of the original equations. Choosing the first equation gives

$$y + 11 = 2x$$
$$y + 11 = 2(5) \qquad \text{Let } x = 5.$$
$$y + 11 = 10$$
$$y = -1. \qquad \text{Subtract 11.}$$

Continued on Next Page

Step 6 Check the solution by substituting $x = 5$ and $y = -1$ into both of the original equations.

Check

$$y + 11 = 2x$$
$$-1 + 11 \overset{?}{=} 2(5)$$
$$10 = 10 \qquad \text{True}$$

$$5x = y + 26$$
$$5(5) \overset{?}{=} -1 + 26$$
$$25 = 25 \qquad \text{True}$$

Since $(5, -1)$ is a solution of *both* equations, the solution set is $\{(5, -1)\}$.

Work Problem ▶ **3** *at the Side.* ▶

OBJECTIVE 2 Multiply when using the elimination method.
Sometimes we need to multiply each side of one or both equations in a system by some number before adding the equations will eliminate a variable.

EXAMPLE 3 **Multiplying Both Equations When Using the Elimination Method**

Solve the system.

$$2x + 3y = -15 \qquad (1)$$
$$5x + 2y = 1 \qquad (2)$$

Adding the two equations gives $7x + 5y = -14$, which does not eliminate either variable. However, we can multiply each equation by a suitable number so that the coefficients of one of the two variables are opposites. For example, to eliminate x, multiply each side of equation (1) by 5, and each side of equation (2) by -2.

$$
\begin{array}{ll}
10x + 15y = -75 & \text{Multiply equation (1) by 5.}\\
\underline{-10x - 4y = -2} & \text{Multiply equation (2) by } -2.\\
11y = -77 & \text{Add.}\\
y = -7 & \text{Divide by 11.}
\end{array}
$$

Substituting -7 for y in either equation (1) or (2) gives $x = 3$. Check that the solution set of the system is $\{(3, -7)\}$.

Work Problem **4** *at the Side.* ▶

OBJECTIVE 3 Use an alternative method to find the second value in a solution. Sometimes it is easier to find the value of the second variable in a solution by using the elimination method twice.

EXAMPLE 4 **Finding the Second Value Using an Alternative Method**

Solve the system.

$$4x = 9 - 3y \qquad (1)$$
$$5x - 2y = 8 \qquad (2)$$

Rearrange the terms in equation (1) so that like terms are aligned in columns. To do this, add $3y$ to each side to get the following system.

$$4x + 3y = 9 \qquad (3)$$
$$5x - 2y = 8 \qquad (2)$$

One way to proceed is to eliminate y by multiplying each side of equation (3) by 2 and each side of equation (2) by 3, and then adding.

Continued on Next Page

---

3 Solve each system by the elimination method. Check each solution.

(a) $2x - y = 2$
$\quad 4x + y = 10$

(b) $8x - 5y = 32$
$\quad 4x + 5y = 4$

4 (a) Solve the system in Example 3 by first eliminating the variable y. Check your solution.

(b) Solve

$$6x + 7y = 4$$
$$5x + 8y = -1,$$

and check your solution.

5 Solve each system of equations.

(a) $5x = 7 + 2y$
$5y = 5 - 3x$

(b) $3y = 8 + 4x$
$6x = 9 - 2y$

$$8x + 6y = 18 \quad \text{Multiply equation (3) by 2.}$$
$$\underline{15x - 6y = 24} \quad \text{Multiply equation (2) by 3.}$$
$$23x \qquad = 42 \quad \text{Add.}$$

$$x = \frac{42}{23} \quad \text{Divide by 23.}$$

Substituting $\frac{42}{23}$ for x in one of the given equations would give y, but the arithmetic involved would be messy. Instead, solve for y by starting again with the original equations and eliminating x. Multiply each side of equation (3) by 5 and each side of equation (2) by -4, and then add.

$$20x + 15y = \quad 45 \quad \text{Multiply equation (3) by 5.}$$
$$\underline{-20x + \quad 8y = -32} \quad \text{Multiply equation (2) by } -4.$$
$$23y = \quad 13 \quad \text{Add.}$$

$$y = \frac{13}{23} \quad \text{Divide by 23.}$$

Check that the solution set is $\{(\frac{42}{23}, \frac{13}{23})\}$.

◀ *Work Problem* **5** *at the Side.*

When the value of the first variable is a fraction, the method used in Example 4 helps avoid arithmetic errors. Of course, this method could be used to solve any system of equations.

OBJECTIVE 4 Use the elimination method to solve special systems.

6 Solve each system by the elimination method.

(a) $4x + 3y = 10$

$2x + \dfrac{3}{2}y = 12$

(b) $\quad 4x - 6y = 10$
$-10x + 15y = -25$

EXAMPLE 5   Using the Elimination Method for an Inconsistent System or Dependent Equations

Solve each system by the elimination method.

(a) $2x + 4y = 5$

$4x + 8y = -9$

Multiply each side of $2x + 4y = 5$ by -2; then add to $4x + 8y = -9$.

$$-4x - 8y = -10$$
$$\underline{4x + 8y = \quad -9}$$
$$0 = -19 \quad \text{False} \qquad \begin{array}{l}\text{Write } \emptyset, \\ \text{not } \{\emptyset\}.\end{array}$$

The false statement $0 = -19$ indicates that the solution set is $\emptyset$.

(b) $\quad 3x - y = 4$

$-9x + 3y = -12$

Multiply each side of the first equation by 3; then add the two equations.

$$9x - 3y = \quad 12$$
$$\underline{-9x + 3y = -12}$$
$$0 = \quad 0 \quad \text{True}$$

A true statement occurs when the equations are equivalent. As before, this indicates that every solution of one equation is also a solution of the other. The solution set is $\{(x, y) | 3x - y = 4\}$. (See **Section 14.2**, Example 6, where the same system was solved using substitution.)

◀ *Work Problem* **6** *at the Side.*

14.3 ▶▶▶ **Exercises**

In Exercises 1–4, answer true *or* false *for each statement. If* false, *tell why.*

1. The ordered pair $(0, 0)$ *must* be a solution of a system of the form

$$Ax + By = 0$$
$$Cx + Dy = 0.$$

2. To eliminate the y-terms in the system

$$2x + 12y = 7$$
$$3x + 4y = 1,$$

we should multiply the bottom equation by 3 and then add.

3. The system

$$x + y = 1$$
$$x + y = 2$$

has $\emptyset$ as its solution set.

4. The ordered pair $(4, -5)$ cannot be a solution of a system that contains the equation $5x - 4y = 0$.

Solve each system by the elimination method. Check each solution. See Examples 1 and 2.

◉ 5. $\quad x + y = 2$
$\quad 2x - y = -5$

6. $3x - y = -12$
$\quad x + y = 4$

7. $2x + y = -5$
$\quad x - y = 2$

8. $\quad 2x + y = -15$
$\quad -x - y = 10$

9. $\quad 3x + 2y = 0$
$\quad -3x - y = 3$

10. $\quad 5x - y = 5$
$\quad -5x + 2y = 0$

11. $6x - y = -1$
$\quad 5y = 17 + 6x$

12. $y = 9 - 6x$
$\quad -6x + 3y = 15$

Solve each system by the elimination method. Check each solution. See Examples 3–5.

13. $2x - y = 12$
$3x + 2y = -3$

14. $x + y = 3$
$-3x + 2y = -19$

15. $x + 3y = 19$
$2x - y = 10$

16. $4x - 3y = -19$
$2x + y = 13$

17. $x + 4y = 16$
$3x + 5y = 20$

18. $2x + y = 8$
$5x - 2y = -16$

19. $5x - 3y = -20$
$-3x + 6y = 12$

20. $4x + 3y = -28$
$5x - 6y = -35$

21. $2x - 8y = 0$
$4x + 5y = 0$

22. $3x - 15y = 0$
$6x + 10y = 0$

23. $x + y = 7$
$x + y = -3$

24. $x - y = 4$
$x - y = -3$

25. $-x + 3y = 4$
$-2x + 6y = 8$

26. $6x - 2y = 24$
$-3x + y = -12$

27. $4x - 3y = -19$
$3x + 2y = 24$

28. $5x + 4y = 12$
$3x + 5y = 15$

29. $3x - 7 = -5y$
$5x + 4y = -10$

30. $2x + 3y = 13$
$6 + 2y = -5x$

31. $2x + 3y = 0$
$4x + 12 = 9y$

32. $-4x + 3y = 2$
$5x + 3 = -2y$

33. $24x + 12y = -7$
$16x - 17 = 18y$

34. $9x + 4y = -3$
$6x + 7 = -6y$

35. $3x = 3 + 2y$
$-\dfrac{4}{3}x + y = \dfrac{1}{3}$

36. $3x = 27 + 2y$
$x - \dfrac{7}{2}y = -25$

37. $5x - 2y = 3$
$10x - 4y = 5$

38. $3x - 5y = 1$
$6x - 10y = 4$

39. $6x + 3y = 0$
$-18x - 9y = 0$

40. $3x - 5y = 0$
$9x - 15y = 0$

Relating Concepts (Exercises 41–46) For Individual or Group Work

Attending the movies is one of America's favorite forms of entertainment. The graph shows U.S. movie attendance from 1996 through 2004. In 1996, attendance was 1339 million, as represented by the point P(1996, 1339). In 2004, attendance was 1536 million, as represented by the point Q(2004, 1536). We can find an equation of line segment PQ by using a system of equations. Then we use the equation we found to approximate the attendance in any of the years between 1996 and 2004. **Work Exercises 41–46 in order.**

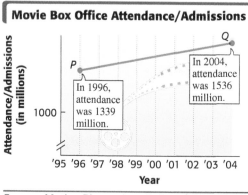

Movie Box Office Attendance/Admissions

In 1996, attendance was 1339 million.

In 2004, attendance was 1536 million.

Source: Motion Picture Association of America.

41. The line segment has an equation that can be written in the form $y = ax + b$. Using the coordinates of point P with $x = 1996$ and $y = 1339$, write an equation in the variables a and b.

42. Using the coordinates of point Q with $x = 2004$ and $y = 1536$, write a second equation in the variables a and b.

43. Write the system of equations formed from the two equations in Exercises 41 and 42, and solve the system using the elimination method.

44. What is the equation of the segment PQ?

45. Let $x = 2002$ in the equation of Exercise 44, and solve for y to the nearest tenth. How does the result compare with the actual figure of 1639 million?

46. The actual data points for the years 1996 through 2004 do not lie in a perfectly straight line. Explain the pitfalls of relying too heavily on using the equation in Exercise 44 to predict attendance.

Summary Exercises on Solving Systems of Linear Equations

The exercises in this summary include a variety of problems on solving systems of linear equations. Since we do not usually specify the method of solution, use the following guidelines to help you decide whether to use substitution or elimination.

Guidelines for Choosing a Method to Solve a System of Linear Equations

1. If one of the equations of the system is already solved for one of the variables, as in the systems

$$3x + 4y = 9 \qquad -5x + 3y = 9$$
$$\text{or}$$
$$y = 2x - 6 \qquad x = 3y - 7,$$

   the substitution method is the better choice.

2. If both equations are in standard $Ax + By = C$ form, as in

$$4x - 11y = 3$$
$$-2x + 3y = 4,$$

   and none of the variables has coefficient -1 or 1, the elimination method is the better choice.

3. If one or both of the equations are in standard form and the coefficient of one of the variables is -1 or 1, as in the systems

$$3x + y = -2 \qquad -x + 3y = -4$$
$$\text{or}$$
$$-5x + 2y = 4 \qquad 3x - 2y = 8,$$

   either method is appropriate.

Use the preceding guidelines to solve each problem.

1. Assuming you want to minimize the amount of work required, tell whether you would use the substitution or elimination method to solve each system. Explain your answers. *Do not actually solve.*

   (a) $3x + 2y = 18$
   $y = 3x$

   (b) $3x + y = -7$
   $x - y = -5$

   (c) $3x - 2y = 0$
   $9x + 8y = 7$

2. Which one of the following systems would be easier to solve using the substitution method? Why?

$$5x - 3y = 7 \qquad 7x + 2y = 4$$
$$2x + 8y = 3 \qquad y = -3x + 1$$

In Exercises 3 and 4, (a) solve the system by the elimination method, (b) solve the system by the substitution method, and (c) tell which method you prefer for that particular system and why.

3. $4x - 3y = -8$
$\quad\ x + 3y = 13$

4. $2x + 5y = 0$
$\quad\ x = -3y + 1$

Solve each system by the method of your choice. (For Exercises 5–7, see your answers for Exercise 1.)

5. $3x + 2y = 18$
$\quad\ y = 3x$

6. $3x + y = -7$
$\quad\ x - y = -5$

7. $3x - 2y = 0$
$\quad\ 9x + 8y = 7$

8. $x + y = 7$
$\quad x = -3 - y$

9. $\ 5x - 4y = 15$
$\quad -3x + 6y = -9$

10. $4x + 2y = 3$
$\quad\ y = -x$

11. $3x = 7 - y$
$\quad 2y = 14 - 6x$

12. $3x - 5y = 7$
$\quad 2x + 3y = 30$

13. $3y = 4x + 2$
$\quad 5x - 2y = -3$

14. $4x + 3y = 1$
$\quad\ 3x + 2y = 2$

15. $\ 2x - 3y = 7$
$\quad -4x + 6y = 14$

16. $\ 0.2x + 0.3y = 1.0$
$\quad -0.3x + 0.1y = 1.8$

17. $6x + 5y = 13$
$\quad\ 3x + 3y = 4$

18. $\ x - 3y = 7$
$\quad 4x + y = 5$

19. $\dfrac{1}{4}x - \dfrac{1}{5}y = 9$
$\quad y = 5x$

20. $\dfrac{1}{2}x + \dfrac{1}{3}y = -\dfrac{1}{3}$
$\quad \dfrac{1}{2}x + 2y = -7$

21. $-\dfrac{1}{2}x - \dfrac{1}{3}y = -5$
$\quad -\dfrac{1}{2}x - \dfrac{1}{3}y = -5$

22. $\dfrac{x}{5} + 2y = \dfrac{8}{5}$
$\quad \dfrac{3x}{5} + \dfrac{y}{2} = -\dfrac{7}{10}$

23. $\dfrac{x}{5} + y = \dfrac{6}{5}$
$\quad \dfrac{x}{10} + \dfrac{y}{3} = \dfrac{5}{6}$

24. $\dfrac{2}{5}x + \dfrac{4}{3}y = -8$
$\quad \dfrac{7}{10}x - \dfrac{2}{9}y = 9$

25. $0.5x + 0.2y = 0.2$
$\quad\ x - 0.6y = -0.5$

14.4 ▷▷▷ Systems of Linear Equations in Three Variables

A solution of an equation in three variables, such as

$$2x + 3y - z = 4, \quad \text{Linear equation in three variables}$$

is called an **ordered triple** and is written **(x, y, z)**. For example, the ordered triple $(0, 1, -1)$ is a solution of the equation, because

$$2(0) + 3(1) - (-1) = 4$$

is a true statement. Verify that another solution of this equation is $(10, -3, 7)$.
    We now extend the term *linear equation* to equations of the form

$$Ax + By + Cz + \ldots + Dw = K,$$

where not all the coefficients $A, B, C, \ldots, D$ equal 0. For example,

$$2x + 3y - 5z = 7 \quad \text{and} \quad x - 2y - z + 3u - 2w = 8$$

are linear equations, the first with three variables and the second with five.

OBJECTIVE 1 Understand the geometry of systems of three equations in three variables.   Consider the solution of a system such as

$$\begin{aligned} 4x + 8y + z &= 2 \\ x + 7y - 3z &= -14 \\ 2x - 3y + 2z &= 3. \end{aligned}$$

System of linear equations in three variables

Theoretically, a system of this type can be solved by graphing. However, the graph of a linear equation with three variables is a *plane,* not a line. Since the graph of each equation of the system is a plane, which requires three-dimensional graphing, the graphing method is not practical for solving such systems. However, it does illustrate the number of solutions possible for these systems, as shown in Figure 6.

OBJECTIVES

1 Understand the geometry of systems of three equations in three variables.

2 Solve linear systems (with three equations and three variables) by elimination.

3 Solve linear systems (with three equations and three variables) in which some of the equations have missing terms.

4 Solve special systems.

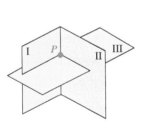

A single solution

(a)

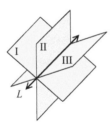

Points of a line in common

(b)

All points in common

(c)

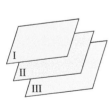

No points in common

(d)

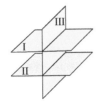

No points in common

(e)

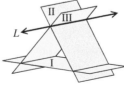

No points in common

(f)

No points in common

(g)

Figure 6

Figure 6 on the preceding page illustrates the following cases.

Graphs of Linear Systems in Three Variables

Case 1 **The three planes may meet at a single, common point** that forms the solution set of the system. See Figure 6(a).

Case 2 **The three planes may have the points of a line in common** so that the infinite set of points that satisfy the equation of the line forms the solution set of the system. See Figure 6(b).

Case 3 **The three planes may coincide** so that the solution set of the system is the set of all points on a plane. See Figure 6(c).

Case 4 **The planes may have no points common to all three** so that there is no solution of the system; the solution set is $\emptyset$. See Figures 6(d)–(g).

OBJECTIVE 2 Solve linear systems (with three equations and three variables) by elimination. Is it possible to solve a system of three equations in three variables such as the one that follows?

$$4x + 8y + z = 2$$
$$x + 7y - 3z = -14$$
$$2x - 3y + 2z = 3$$

As mentioned, graphing to find the solution set of such a system is impractical. We solve these systems with an extension of the elimination method from **Section 5.1,** summarized as follows.

Solving a Linear System in Three Variables*

Step 1 **Select a variable and an equation.** A good choice for the variable, which we call the *focus variable,* is one that has coefficient 1 or -1. Then select an equation, usually the one that contains the focus variable, as the *working equation.*

Step 2 **Eliminate the focus variable.** Use the working equation and one of the other two equations of the original system. The result is an equation in two variables.

Step 3 **Eliminate the focus variable again.** Use the working equation and the remaining equation of the original system. The result is another equation in two variables.

Step 4 **Write the equations in two variables that result from Steps 2 and 3 as a system, and solve it.** Doing this gives the values of two of the variables.

Step 5 **Find the value of the remaining variable.** Substitute the values of the two variables found in Step 4 into the working equation to obtain the value of the focus variable.

Step 6 **Check** the ordered-triple solution in *each* of the *original* equations of the system. Then write the solution set.

---

*The authors wish to thank Christine Heinecke Lehmann of Purdue University North Central for her suggestions here.

Example 1   **Solving a System in Three Variables**

Solve the system.

$$4x + 8y + z = 2 \qquad (1)$$
$$x + 7y - 3z = -14 \qquad (2)$$
$$2x - 3y + 2z = 3 \qquad (3)$$

Step 1 Since z in equation (1) has coefficient 1, we choose z as the focus variable and (1) as the working equation. (Another option would be to choose x as the focus variable, since it also has coefficient 1, and use (2) as the working equation.)

┌ Focus variable
↓
$$4x + 8y + z = 2 \qquad (1) \leftarrow \text{Working equation}$$

Step 2 Multiply working equation (1) by 3 and add the result to equation (2) to eliminate focus variable z.

$$12x + 24y + 3z = 6 \qquad \text{Multiply each side of (1) by 3.}$$
$$\underline{x + 7y - 3z = -14} \qquad (2)$$
$$13x + 31y = -8 \qquad \text{Add.} \quad (4)$$

Step 3 Multiply working equation (1) by -2 and add the result to remaining equation (3) to again eliminate focus variable z.

$$-8x - 16y - 2z = -4 \qquad \text{Multiply each side of (1) by } -2.$$
$$\underline{2x - 3y + 2z = 3} \qquad (3)$$
$$-6x - 19y = -1 \qquad \text{Add.} \quad (5)$$

Step 4 Write the equations in two variables that result in Steps 2 and 3 as a system.

Make sure these equations have the same variables.	

$$13x + 31y = -8 \qquad (4) \quad \text{The result from Step 2}$$
$$-6x - 19y = -1 \qquad (5) \quad \text{The result from Step 3}$$

Now solve this system. We choose to eliminate x.

$$78x + 186y = -48 \qquad \text{Multiply each side of (4) by 6.}$$
$$\underline{-78x - 247y = -13} \qquad \text{Multiply each side of (5) by 13.}$$
$$-61y = -61 \qquad \text{Add.}$$
$$y = 1 \qquad \text{Divide by } -61.$$

Substitute 1 for y in either equation (4) or (5) to find x.

$$-6x - 19y = -1 \qquad (5)$$
$$-6x - 19(1) = -1 \qquad \text{Let } y = 1.$$
$$-6x - 19 = -1 \qquad \text{Multiply.}$$
$$-6x = 18 \qquad \text{Add 19.}$$
$$x = -3 \qquad \text{Divide by } -6.$$

Step 5 Now substitute the two values we found in Step 4 in working equation (1) to find the value of the remaining variable, focus variable z.

$$4x + 8y + z = 2 \qquad (1)$$
$$4(-3) + 8(1) + z = 2 \qquad \text{Let } x = -3 \text{ and } y = 1.$$
$$-4 + z = 2 \qquad \text{Multiply; add.}$$
$$z = 6 \qquad \text{Add 4.}$$

Continued on Next Page

1 Check that the solution $(-3, 1, 6)$ satisfies equations (2) and (3) of Example 1.

(a) $x + 7y - 3z = -14$ (2)

Does the solution satisfy equation (2)?

(b) $2x - 3y + 2z = 3$ (3)

Does the solution satisfy equation (3)?

2 Solve each system.

(a)
$$x + y + z = 2$$
$$x - y + 2z = 2$$
$$-x + 2y - z = 1$$

(b)
$$2x + y + z = 9$$
$$-x - y + z = 1$$
$$3x - y + z = 9$$

Step 6 It appears that the ordered triple $(-3, 1, 6)$ is the only solution of the system. We must check that the solution satisfies all three original equations of the system. For equation (1),

Check
$$4x + 8y + z = 2 \quad (1)$$
$$4(-3) + 8(1) + 6 \stackrel{?}{=} 2$$
$$-12 + 8 + 6 \stackrel{?}{=} 2$$
$$2 = 2. \quad \text{True}$$

◀ *Work Problem* **1** *at the Side.*

Because $(-3, 1, 6)$ also satisfies equations (2) and (3), the solution set is $\{(-3, 1, 6)\}$.

◀ *Work Problem* **2** *at the Side.*

OBJECTIVE 3 Solve linear systems (with three equations and three variables) in which some of the equations have missing terms. If a linear system has an equation missing a term or terms, one elimination step can be omitted.

Example 2 **Solving a System of Equations with Missing Terms**

Solve the system.
$$6x - 12y = -5 \quad (1) \quad \text{Missing } z$$
$$8y + z = 0 \quad (2) \quad \text{Missing } x$$
$$9x - z = 12 \quad (3) \quad \text{Missing } y$$

Since equation (3) is missing the variable y, one way to begin is to eliminate y again using equations (1) and (2).

$$
\begin{aligned}
12x - 24y \phantom{{}+3z} &= -10 \quad \text{Multiply each side of (1) by 2.} \\
24y + 3z &= 0 \quad \text{Multiply each side of (2) by 3.} \\
\hline
12x \phantom{{}-24y} + 3z &= -10 \quad \text{Add.} \quad (4)
\end{aligned}
$$

Leave space for the missing terms.

Use the resulting equation (4) in x and z, together with equation (3), $9x - z = 12$, to eliminate z. Multiply equation (3) by 3.

$$
\begin{aligned}
27x - 3z &= 36 \quad \text{Multiply each side of (3) by 3.} \\
12x + 3z &= -10 \quad (4) \\
\hline
39x \phantom{{}+3z} &= 26 \quad \text{Add.}
\end{aligned}
$$

$$x = \frac{26}{39} = \frac{2}{3} \quad \text{Divide by 39; lowest terms}$$

We can find z by substituting this value for x into equation (3).

$$9x - z = 12 \quad (3)$$
$$9\left(\frac{2}{3}\right) - z = 12 \quad \text{Let } x = \tfrac{2}{3}.$$
$$6 - z = 12 \quad \text{Multiply.}$$
$$z = -6 \quad \text{Subtract 6; multiply by } -1.$$

Continued on Next Page

We can find y by substituting -6 for z in equation (2).

$$8y + z = 0 \qquad (2)$$
$$8y - 6 = 0 \qquad \text{Let } z = -6.$$
$$8y = 6 \qquad \text{Add 6.}$$
$$y = \frac{6}{8} = \frac{3}{4} \qquad \text{Divide by 8; lowest terms}$$

Thus, $x = \frac{2}{3}$, $y = \frac{3}{4}$, and $z = -6$. Check these values in each of the original equations of the system to verify that the solution set of the system is $\left\{\left(\frac{2}{3}, \frac{3}{4}, -6\right)\right\}$.

> **Note**
>
> Another way to solve the system in Example 2 is to begin by eliminating the variable z from equations (2) and (3). The resulting equation together with equation (1) forms a system of two equations in the variables x and y. Try working Example 2 this way to see that the same solution results.
>
> There are often multiple ways to solve a system of equations. Some ways may involve more work than others.

Work Problem ③ *at the Side.* ▶

OBJECTIVE ④ **Solve special systems.**   Linear systems with three variables may be inconsistent or may include dependent equations.

Example 3   **Solving an Inconsistent System with Three Variables**

Solve the system.

$$2x - 4y + 6z = 5 \qquad (1)$$
$$-x + 3y - 2z = -1 \qquad (2)$$
$$x - 2y + 3z = 1 \qquad (3)$$

> Use as the working equation, with focus variable x.

Eliminate x by adding equations (2) and (3) to get the equation

$$y + z = 0.$$

Eliminate x again, using equations (1) and (3).

$$\begin{array}{ll} -2x + 4y - 6z = -2 & \text{Multiply each side of (3) by } -2. \\ \underline{\;\;2x - 4y + 6z = \;\;\;5} & (1) \\ \qquad\qquad 0 = \;\;\;3 & \text{False} \end{array}$$

This false statement indicates that equations (1) and (3) have no common solution. Thus, the system is inconsistent and the solution set is $\emptyset$. The graph of this system would show these two planes parallel to one another.

> **Note**
>
> If a false statement results when adding as in Example 3, it is not necessary to go any further with the solution. Since two of the three planes are parallel, it is not possible for the three planes to have any common points.

Work Problem ④ *at the Side.* ▶

③ Solve each system.

(a) $\begin{aligned} x - y &= 6 \\ 2y + 5z &= 1 \\ 3x - 4z &= 8 \end{aligned}$

(b) $\begin{aligned} 5x - y &= 26 \\ 4y + 3z &= -4 \\ x + z &= 5 \end{aligned}$

④ Solve each system.

(a) $\begin{aligned} 3x - 5y + 2z &= 1 \\ 5x + 8y - z &= 4 \\ -6x + 10y - 4z &= 5 \end{aligned}$

(b) $\begin{aligned} 7x - 9y + 2z &= 0 \\ y + z &= 0 \\ 8x - z &= 0 \end{aligned}$

ANSWERS

3. (a) $\{(4, -2, 1)\}$ (b) $\{(5, -1, 0)\}$
4. (a) $\emptyset$ (b) $\{(0, 0, 0)\}$

5 Solve the system.

$$x - y + z = 4$$
$$-3x + 3y - 3z = -12$$
$$2x - 2y + 2z = 8$$

Example 4 **Solving a System of Dependent Equations with Three Variables**

Solve the system.

$$2x - 3y + 4z = 8 \qquad (1)$$
$$-x + \frac{3}{2}y - 2z = -4 \qquad (2)$$
$$6x - 9y + 12z = 24 \qquad (3)$$

Multiplying each side of equation (1) by 3 gives equation (3). Multiplying each side of equation (2) by -6 also gives equation (3). Because of this, the equations are dependent. All three equations have the same graph, as illustrated in Figure 6(c). The solution set is written

$$\{(x, y, z) \mid 2x - 3y + 4z = 8\}. \qquad \text{Set-builder notation}$$

Although any one of the three equations could be used to write the solution set, we use the equation with coefficients that are integers with greatest common factor 1, as we did in **Section 5.1.**

◀ *Work Problem* **5** *at the Side.*

6 Solve the system.

$$2x + 3y - z = 8$$
$$\frac{1}{2}x + \frac{3}{4}y - \frac{1}{4}z = 2$$
$$x + \frac{3}{2}y - \frac{1}{2}z = -6$$

Example 5 **Solving Another Special System**

Solve the system.

$$2x - y + 3z = 6 \qquad (1)$$
$$x - \frac{1}{2}y + \frac{3}{2}z = 3 \qquad (2)$$
$$4x - 2y + 6z = 1 \qquad (3)$$

Multiplying each side of equation (2) by 2 gives equation (1). Thus, these two equations are dependent.

Equations (1) and (3) are not equivalent, however. Multiplying equation (3) by $\frac{1}{2}$ gives

$$2x - y + 3z = \frac{1}{2}, \qquad \text{(3) multiplied by } \frac{1}{2}$$

which is *not* equivalent to equation (1). Instead, we obtain two equations with the same coefficients, but with different constant terms. The graphs of equations (1) and (3) have no points in common (that is, the planes are parallel). Thus, the system is inconsistent and the solution set is $\varnothing$, as illustrated in Figure 6(g).

◀ *Work Problem* **6** *at the Side.*

ANSWERS

5. $\{(x, y, z) \mid x - y + z = 4\}$

6. $\varnothing$

14.4 ▶▶▶ Exercises

1. Explain what the following statement means:
The solution set of the system

$$2x + y + z = 3$$
$$3x - y + z = -2$$
$$4x - y + 2z = 0$$

is $\{(-1, 2, 3)\}$.

2. The two equations

$$x + y + z = 6$$
$$2x - y + z = 3$$

have a common solution of $(1, 2, 3)$. Which equation would complete a system of three linear equations in three variables having solution set $\{(1, 2, 3)\}$?

A. $3x + 2y - z = 1$ **B.** $3x + 2y - z = 4$

C. $3x + 2y - z = 5$ **D.** $3x + 2y - z = 6$

Solve each system of equations. See Example 1.

3. $2x - 5y + 3z = -1$
$x + 4y - 2z = 9$
$x - 2y - 4z = -5$

4. $x + 3y - 6z = 7$
$2x - y + z = 1$
$x + 2y + 2z = -1$

5. $3x + 2y + z = 8$
$2x - 3y + 2z = -16$
$x + 4y - z = 20$

6. $-3x + y - z = -10$
$-4x + 2y + 3z = -1$
$2x + 3y - 2z = -5$

7. $x + 2y + z = 4$
$2x + y - z = -1$
$x - y - z = -2$

8. $x - 2y + 5z = -7$
$-2x - 3y + 4z = -14$
$-3x + 5y - z = -7$

9. $-x + 2y + 6z = 2$
$3x + 2y + 6z = 6$
$x + 4y - 3z = 1$

10. $2x + y + 2z = 1$
$x + 2y + z = 2$
$x - y - z = 0$

11. $2x + 5y + 2z = 0$
$4x - 7y - 3z = 1$
$3x - 8y - 2z = -6$

12. $5x - 2y + 3z = -9$
$4x + 3y + 5z = 4$
$2x + 4y - 2z = 14$

13. $x + 2y + 3z = 1$
$-x - y + 3z = 2$
$-6x + y + z = -2$

14. $x + y - z = -2$
$2x - y + z = -5$
$-x + 2y - 3z = -4$

Solve each system of equations. See Example 2.

15. $2x - 3y + 2z = -1$
$x + 2y + z = 17$
$2y - z = 7$

16. $2x - y + 3z = 6$
$x + 2y - z = 8$
$2y + z = 1$

17. $4x + 2y - 3z = 6$
$x - 4y + z = -4$
$-x + 2z = 2$

18. $2x + 3y - 4z = 4$
$x - 6y + z = -16$
$-x + 3z = 8$

19. $-5x + 2y + z = 5$
$-3x - 2y - z = 3$
$-x + 6y = 1$

20. $x + y - z = 0$
$2y - z = 1$
$2x + 3y - 4z = -4$

21. $2x + y = 6$
$3y - 2z = -4$
$3x - 5z = -7$

22. $4x - 8y = -7$
$4y + z = 7$
$-8x + z = -4$

23. Using your immediate surroundings, give an example of three planes that

    (a) intersect in a single point;

    (b) do not intersect;

    (c) intersect in infinitely many points.

24. Suppose that a system has infinitely many ordered triple solutions of the form (x, y, z) such that

$$x + y + 2z = 1.$$

Give three specific ordered triples that are solutions of the system.

Solve each system of equations. If the system is inconsistent or has dependent equations, say so. See Examples 1–5.

◑ 25.
$$\begin{aligned} 2x + 2y - 6z &= 5 \\ -3x + y - z &= -2 \\ -x - y + 3z &= 4 \end{aligned}$$

26.
$$\begin{aligned} -2x + 5y + z &= -3 \\ 5x + 14y - z &= -11 \\ 7x + 9y - 2z &= -5 \end{aligned}$$

27.
$$\begin{aligned} -5x + 5y - 20z &= -40 \\ x - y + 4z &= 8 \\ 3x - 3y + 12z &= 24 \end{aligned}$$

28.
$$\begin{aligned} x + 4y - z &= 3 \\ -2x - 8y + 2z &= -6 \\ 3x + 12y - 3z &= 9 \end{aligned}$$

◑ 29.
$$\begin{aligned} 2x + y - z &= 6 \\ 4x + 2y - 2z &= 12 \\ -x - \frac{1}{2}y + \frac{1}{2}z &= -3 \end{aligned}$$

30.
$$\begin{aligned} 2x - 8y + 2z &= -10 \\ -x + 4y - z &= 5 \\ \frac{1}{8}x - \frac{1}{2}y + \frac{1}{8}z &= -\frac{5}{8} \end{aligned}$$

31.
$$\begin{aligned} x + y - 2z &= 0 \\ 3x - y + z &= 0 \\ 4x + 2y - z &= 0 \end{aligned}$$

32.
$$\begin{aligned} 2x + 3y - z &= 0 \\ x - 4y + 2z &= 0 \\ 3x - 5y - z &= 0 \end{aligned}$$

◑ 33.
$$\begin{aligned} x - 2y + \frac{1}{3}z &= 4 \\ 3x - 6y + z &= 12 \\ -6x + 12y - 2z &= -3 \end{aligned}$$

34.
$$\begin{aligned} 4x + y - 2z &= 3 \\ x + \frac{1}{4}y - \frac{1}{2}z &= \frac{3}{4} \\ 2x + \frac{1}{2}y - z &= 1 \end{aligned}$$

35. $x + 5y - 2z = -1$
   $-2x + 8y + z = -4$
   $3x - y + 5z = 19$

36. $x + 3y + z = 2$
   $4x + y + 2z = -4$
   $5x + 2y + 3z = -2$

Relating Concepts (Exercises 37–44) For Individual or Group Work

Suppose that on a distant planet a function of the form

$$f(x) = ax^2 + bx + c \quad (a \neq 0)$$

describes the height in feet of a projectile x seconds after it has been projected upward.
Work Exercises 37–44 in order, *to see how this can be related to a system of three equations in three variables a, b, and c.*

37. After 1 sec, the height of a certain projectile is 128 ft. Thus, $f(1) = 128$. Use this information to write one equation in the variables a, b, and c. (*Hint:* Substitute 1 for x and 128 for $f(x)$.)

38. After 1.5 sec, the height is 140 ft. Write a second equation in a, b, and c.

39. After 3 sec, the height is 80 ft. Write a third equation in a, b, and c.

40. Write a system of three equations in a, b, and c, based on your answers in Exercises 37–39. Solve the system.

41. What is the function f for this particular projectile?

42. In the function f written in Exercise 41, the _____ of the projectile is a function of the _____ elapsed after it was projected.

43. What was the initial height of the projectile? (*Hint:* Find $f(0)$.)

44. The projectile reaches its maximum height in 1.625 sec. Find its maximum height.

14.5 ▸▸▸ Applications of Systems of Linear Equations

Many applied problems involve more than one unknown quantity. Although some problems with two unknowns can be solved using just one variable (as in **Chapter 2**), an alternative method of solution uses two variables. To solve a problem in this way using two unknowns, we must write two equations that relate the unknown quantities. The system formed by the pair of equations can then be solved using the methods of this chapter.

Problems that can be solved by writing a system of equations have been of interest historically. The following problem, which is given in the exercises for this section, first appeared in a Hindu work that dates back to about A.D. 850.

> *The mixed price of 9 citrons [a lemonlike fruit shown in the photo] and 7 fragrant wood apples is 107; again, the mixed price of 7 citrons and 9 fragrant wood apples is 101. O you arithmetician, tell me quickly the price of a citron and the price of a wood apple here, having distinctly separated those prices well.*

The following steps, based on the six-step problem-solving method first introduced in **Section 2.3,** give a strategy for solving applied problems using more than one variable.

OBJECTIVES

1 Solve geometry problems using two variables.

2 Solve money problems using two variables.

3 Solve mixture problems using two variables.

4 Solve distance-rate-time problems using two variables.

5 Solve problems with three variables using a system of three equations.

Solving an Applied Problem by Writing a System of Equations

Step 1 **Read** the problem, several times if necessary, until you understand what is given and what is to be found.

Step 2 **Assign variables** to represent the unknown values, using diagrams or tables as needed. *Write down* what each variable represents.

Step 3 **Write a system of equations** that relates the unknowns.

Step 4 **Solve** the system of equations.

Step 5 **State the answer** to the problem. Does it seem reasonable?

Step 6 **Check** the answer in the words of the original problem.

OBJECTIVE 1 Solve geometry problems using two variables.
Problems about the perimeter of a geometric figure often involve two unknowns and can be solved using systems of equations.

1 Solve the problem.

The length of the foundation of a rectangular house is to be 6 m more than its width. Find the length and width of the house if the perimeter must be 48 m.

Example 1   **Finding the Dimensions of a Soccer Field**

Unlike football, where the dimensions of a playing field cannot vary, a rectangular soccer field may have a width between 50 and 100 yd and a length between 100 and 130 yd. Suppose that one particular field has a perimeter of 320 yd. Its length measures 40 yd more than its width. What are the dimensions of this field? (*Source: Microsoft Encarta Encyclopedia.*)

Step 1   **Read** the problem again. We must find the dimensions of the field.

Step 2   **Assign variables.** Let L = the length and W = the width. Figure 7 shows a soccer field with these variables as labels.

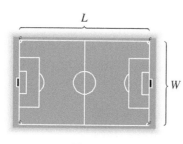

Figure 7

Step 3   **Write a system of equations.** Because the perimeter is 320 yd, we find one equation by using the perimeter formula:

$$2L + 2W = 320.$$

Because the length is 40 yd more than the width, we have

$$L = W + 40.$$

The system is, therefore,

$$2L + 2W = 320 \qquad (1)$$
$$L = W + 40. \qquad (2)$$

Step 4   **Solve** the system of equations. Since equation (2) is solved for L, we can use the substitution method. We substitute $W + 40$ for L in equation (1), and solve for W.

$$2L + 2W = 320 \qquad (1)$$

$2(W + 40) + 2W = 320$	Let $L = W + 40$.
$2W + 80 + 2W = 320$	Distributive property
$4W + 80 = 320$	Combine like terms.
$4W = 240$	Subtract 80.
$W = 60$	Divide by 4.

> Be sure to use parentheses around $W + 40$.

Let $W = 60$ in the equation $L = W + 40$ to find L.

$$L = 60 + 40 = 100$$

Step 5   **State the answer.** The length is **100** yd, and the width is **60** yd. Both dimensions are within the ranges given in the problem.

Step 6   **Check.** The perimeter is $2(100) + 2(60) = 320$ yd, and the length, 100 yd, is indeed 40 yd more than the width, since $100 - 40 = 60$. The answer is correct.

◀ *Work Problem* **1** *at the Side.*

Answer

1. length: 15 m; width: 9 m

OBJECTIVE **2** **Solve money problems using two variables.**

Example 2 **Solving a Problem about Ticket Prices**

For the 2005–2006 National Hockey League and National Basketball Association seasons, two hockey tickets and one basketball ticket purchased at their average prices would have cost $128.30. One hockey ticket and two basketball tickets would have cost $133.03. What were the average ticket prices for the two sports? (*Source:* Team Marketing Report, Chicago.)

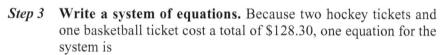

Step 1 **Read** the problem again. There are two unknowns.

Step 2 **Assign variables.**

Let h = the average price for a hockey ticket

and b = the average price for a basketball ticket.

Step 3 **Write a system of equations.** Because two hockey tickets and one basketball ticket cost a total of $128.30, one equation for the system is

$$2h + b = 128.30.$$

By similar reasoning, the second equation is

$$h + 2b = 133.03.$$

Therefore, the system is

$$2h + b = 128.30 \quad (1)$$
$$h + 2b = 133.03. \quad (2)$$

Step 4 **Solve** the system of equations. To eliminate h, multiply equation (2) by -2 and add.

$$
\begin{aligned}
2h + b &= 128.30 \quad &(1)\\
-2h - 4b &= -266.06 \quad &\text{Multiply each side of (2) by } -2.\\
\hline
-3b &= -137.76 \quad &\text{Add.}\\
b &= \textbf{45.92} \quad &\text{Divide by } -3.
\end{aligned}
$$

To find the value of h, let $b = 45.92$ in equation (2).

$$
\begin{aligned}
h + 2b &= 133.03 \quad &(2)\\
h + 2(\textbf{45.92}) &= 133.03 \quad &\text{Let } b = 45.92.\\
h + 91.84 &= 133.03 \quad &\text{Multiply.}\\
h &= \textbf{41.19} \quad &\text{Subtract 91.84.}
\end{aligned}
$$

Step 5 **State the answer.** The average price for one basketball ticket was $45.92. For one hockey ticket, the average price was $41.19.

Step 6 **Check** that these values satisfy the conditions stated in the problem.

Work Problem **2** *at the Side.* ▶

2 Solve the problem.

For recent Major League Baseball and National Football League seasons, based on average ticket prices, three baseball tickets and two football tickets would have cost $181.41, while two baseball tickets and one football ticket would have cost $101.29. What were the average ticket prices for the two sports? (*Source:* Team Marketing Report, Chicago.)

ANSWER

2. baseball: $21.17; football: $58.95

OBJECTIVE **3** **Solve mixture problems using two variables.** We solved mixture problems in **Section 2.3** using one variable. For many mixture problems we can use more than one variable and a system of equations.

Example 3 **Solving a Mixture Problem**

How many ounces each of 5% hydrochloric acid and 20% hydrochloric acid must be combined to get 10 oz of solution that is 12.5% hydrochloric acid?

Step 1 **Read** the problem. Two solutions of different strengths are being mixed together to get a specific amount of a solution with an "in-between" strength.

Step 2 **Assign variables.**

Let x = the number of ounces of 5% solution

and y = the number of ounces of 20% solution.

Use a table to summarize the information from the problem. We multiply the amount of each solution (given in the first column) by its concentration of acid (given in the second column) to get the amount of acid in that solution (given in the third column).

Ounces of Solution	Percent (as a decimal)	Ounces of Pure Acid
x	5% = 0.05	$0.05x$
y	20% = 0.20	$0.20y$
10	12.5% = 0.125	$(0.125)10$

Gives equation (1)   Gives equation (2)

Figure 8 also illustrates what is happening in the problem.

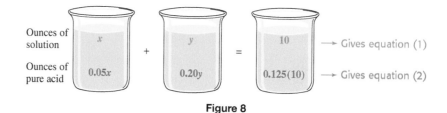

Figure 8

Step 3 **Write a system of equations.** When the x ounces of 5% solution and the y ounces of 20% solution are combined, the total number of ounces is 10, so

$$x + y = 10. \quad (1)$$

The ounces of acid in the 5% solution ($0.05x$) plus the ounces of acid in the 20% solution ($0.20y$) should equal the total ounces of acid in the mixture, which is $(0.125)10$, or 1.25. That is,

$$0.05x + 0.20y = 1.25. \quad (2)$$

Notice that these equations can be quickly determined by reading down in the table or across in Figure 8.

Continued on Next Page

Step 4 **Solve** the system of equations (1) and (2). Eliminate x by first multiplying equation (2) by 100 to clear it of decimals and then multiplying equation (1) by -5.

$$
\begin{array}{rl}
5x + 20y = & 125 \qquad \text{Multiply each side of (2) by 100.} \\
\underline{-5x - 5y = -50} & \qquad \text{Multiply each side of (1) by } -5. \\
15y = & 75 \qquad \text{Add.} \\
y = & 5 \qquad \text{Divide by 15.}
\end{array}
$$

Because $y = 5$ and $x + y = 10$, the value of x is also 5.

Step 5 **State the answer.** The desired mixture will require 5 oz of the 5% solution and 5 oz of the 20% solution.

Step 6 **Check.**

Total amount of solution: $x + y = 5 \text{ oz} + 5 \text{ oz}$
$$= 10 \text{ oz,} \quad \text{as required.}$$

Total amount of acid: 5% of 5 oz + 20% of 5 oz
$$= 0.05\,(5) + 0.20\,(5)$$
$$= 1.25 \text{ oz}$$

Percent of acid in solution:

$$\text{Total acid} \rightarrow \frac{1.25}{10} = 0.125, \quad \text{or} \quad 12.5\%, \quad \text{as required.}$$
$$\text{Total solution} \rightarrow$$

Work Problem **3** *at the Side.* ▶

3 Solve each problem.

(a) A grocer has some $4 per lb coffee and some $8 per lb coffee, which he will mix to make 50 lb of $5.60 per lb coffee. How many pounds of each should be used?

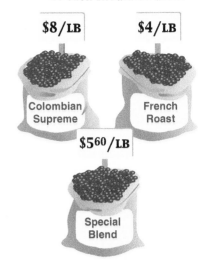

OBJECTIVE 4 Solve distance-rate-time problems using two variables. Motion problems require the distance formula, $d = rt$, where d is distance, r is rate (or speed), and t is time. These applications often lead to systems of equations.

Example 4 Solving a Motion Problem

A car travels 250 km in the same time that a truck travels 225 km. If the speed of the car is 8 km per hr faster than the speed of the truck, find both speeds.

Step 1 **Read** the problem again. Given the distances traveled, we need to find the speed of each vehicle.

Step 2 **Assign variables.**

Let $x =$ the speed of the car
and $y =$ the speed of the truck.

Fill in the given information for each vehicle (distances) and the assigned variables for the unknown speeds (rates) in a table.

	d	r	t
Car	250	x	$\frac{250}{x}$
Truck	225	y	$\frac{225}{y}$

The times must be equal.

(b) Some 40% ethyl alcohol solution is to be mixed with some 80% solution to get 200 L of a 50% solution. How many liters of each should be used?

To get the expressions for time, solve the distance formula, $d = rt$, for t. Since $\frac{d}{r} = t$, the two times can be written as $\frac{250}{x}$ and $\frac{225}{y}$.

Continued on Next Page

ANSWERS

3. (a) 30 lb of $4; 20 lb of $8
(b) 150 L of 40%; 50 L of 80%

4 Solve the problem.

A train travels 600 mi in the same time that a truck travels 520 mi. Find the speed of each vehicle if the train's average speed is 8 mph faster than the truck's.

Step 3 **Write a system of equations.** The problem states that the car travels 8 km per hr faster than the truck. Since the two speeds are x and y,

$$x = y + 8. \quad (1)$$

Both vehicles travel for the same time, so from the table,

$$\text{Time for car} \rightarrow \frac{250}{x} = \frac{225}{y}. \leftarrow \text{Time for truck}$$

This is not a linear equation. Multiplying each side by xy gives

$$xy \cdot \frac{250}{x} = \frac{225}{y} \cdot xy \quad \text{Multiply by the LCD, } xy.$$

$$\frac{250xy}{x} = \frac{225xy}{y}$$

$$250y = 225x, \quad (2)$$

which is linear. The system is

$$x = y + 8 \quad (1)$$
$$250y = 225x. \quad (2)$$

Step 4 **Solve** the system of equations by substitution. Replace x with $y + 8$ in equation (2).

$$250y = 225x \quad (2)$$

Be sure to use parentheses around $y + 8$.

$$250y = 225(y + 8) \quad \text{Let } x = y + 8.$$
$$250y = 225y + 1800 \quad \text{Distributive property}$$
$$25y = 1800 \quad \text{Subtract } 225y.$$
$$y = 72 \quad \text{Divide by 25.}$$

Because $x = y + 8$, the value of x is

$$72 + 8 = 80.$$

Step 5 **State the answer.** The car's speed is 80 km per hr, and the truck's speed is 72 km per hr.

Step 6 **Check.** This is especially important since one of the equations had variable denominators.

$$\text{Car:} \quad t = \frac{d}{r} = \frac{250}{80} = 3.125$$
$$\text{Truck:} \quad t = \frac{d}{r} = \frac{225}{72} = 3.125$$

Times are equal.

Since $80 - 72 = 8$, the conditions of the problem are satisfied.

◀ *Work Problem* **4** *at the Side.*

OBJECTIVE **5** **Solve problems with three variables using a system of three equations.**

Problem-Solving Hint

If an application requires finding *three* unknown quantities, we can use a system of *three* equations to solve it. We extend the method used for two unknowns.

Example 5 **Solving a Problem Involving Prices**

At Panera Bread, a loaf of honey wheat bread costs $2.95, a loaf of sunflower bread costs $2.99, and a loaf of French bread costs $5.79. On a recent day, three times as many loaves of honey wheat bread were sold as sunflower bread. The number of loaves of French bread sold was 5 less than the number of loaves of honey wheat bread sold. Total receipts for these breads were $87.89. How many loaves of each type of bread were sold? (*Source:* Panera Bread menu.)

Step 1 **Read** the problem again. There are three unknowns in this problem.

Step 2 **Assign variables** to represent the three unknowns.

Let x = the number of loaves of honey wheat bread,

y = the number of loaves of sunflower bread,

and z = the number of loaves of French bread.

Step 3 **Write a system of three equations.** Since three times as many loaves of honey wheat bread were sold as sunflower bread,

$$x = 3y, \quad \text{or} \quad x - 3y = 0. \quad \text{Subtract } 3y. \quad (1)$$

Also,

Number of loaves of French	equals	5 less than the number of loaves of honey wheat.
↓	↓	↓
z	$=$	$x - 5,$

$$-x + z = -5 \quad \text{Subtract } x.$$
$$x - z = 5. \quad \text{Multiply by } -1. \quad (2)$$

Multiplying the cost of a loaf of each kind of bread by the number of loaves of that kind sold and adding gives the total receipts.

$$2.95x + 2.99y + 5.79z = 87.89$$

Multiply each side of this equation by 100 to clear it of decimals.

$$295x + 299y + 579z = 8789 \quad (3)$$

Step 4 **Solve** the system of three equations,

$$x - 3y = 0 \quad (1)$$
$$x - z = 5 \quad (2)$$
$$295x + 299y + 579z = 8789, \quad (3)$$

using the method shown in **Section 5.2.**

Work Problem **5** *at the Side.* ▶

Thus, we find that $x = 12$, $y = 4$, and $z = 7$.

Step 5 **State the answer.** The solution set is $\{(12, 4, 7)\}$, meaning that 12 loaves of honey wheat bread, 4 loaves of sunflower bread, and 7 loaves of French bread were sold.

Step 6 **Check.** Since $12 = 3 \cdot 4$, the number of loaves of honey wheat bread is three times the number of loaves of sunflower bread. Also, $12 - 7 = 5$, so the number of loaves of French bread is 5 less than the number of loaves of honey wheat bread. Multiply the appropriate cost per loaf by the number of loaves sold and add the results to check that total receipts were $87.89.

Work Problem **6** *at the Side.* ▶

5 Solve the system of equations from Example 5.

$$x - 3y = 0 \quad (1)$$
$$x - z = 5 \quad (2)$$
$$295x + 299y + 579z = 8789 \quad (3)$$

6 Solve the problem.

A department store display features three kinds of perfume: Felice, Vivid, and Joy. There are 10 more bottles of Felice than Vivid, and 3 fewer bottles of Joy than Vivid. Each bottle of Felice costs $8, Vivid costs $15, and Joy costs $32. The total value of all the perfume is $589. How many bottles of each are there?

ANSWERS

5. $\{(12, 4, 7)\}$
6. 21 bottles of Felice; 11 of Vivid; 8 of Joy

7 Solve the problem.

A paper mill makes newsprint, bond, and copy machine paper. Each ton of newsprint requires 3 tons of recycled paper and 1 ton of wood pulp. Each ton of bond requires 2 tons of recycled paper, 4 tons of wood pulp, and 3 tons of rags. A ton of copy machine paper requires 2 tons of recycled paper, 3 tons of wood pulp, and 2 tons of rags. The mill has 4200 tons of recycled paper, 5800 tons of wood pulp, and 3900 tons of rags. How much of each kind of paper can be made from these supplies?

Example 6 **Solving a Business Production Problem**

A company produces three color television sets, models X, Y, and Z. Each model X set requires 2 hr of electronics work, 2 hr of assembly time, and 1 hr of finishing time. Each model Y requires 1, 3, and 1 hr of electronics, assembly, and finishing time, respectively. Each model Z requires 3, 2, and 2 hr of the same work, respectively. There are 100 hr available for electronics, 100 hr available for assembly, and 65 hr available for finishing per week. How many of each model should be produced each week if all available time must be used?

Step 1 **Read** the problem again. There are three unknowns.

Step 2 **Assign variables.**

Let x = the number of model X produced per week,

y = the number of model Y produced per week,

and z = the number of model Z produced per week.

We organize the information in a table.

	Each Model X	Each Model Y	Each Model Z	Totals	
Hours of Electronics Work	2	1	3	100	→ Gives equation (1)
Hours of Assembly Time	2	3	2	100	→ Gives equation (2)
Hours of Finishing Time	1	1	2	65	→ Gives equation (3)

Step 3 **Write a system of three equations.** The x model X sets require $2x$ hours of electronics, the y model Y sets require $1y$ (or y) hours of electronics, and the z model Z sets require $3z$ hours of electronics. Since 100 hr are available for electronics,

$$2x + y + 3z = 100. \quad (1)$$

Similarly, from the fact that 100 hr are available for assembly,

$$2x + 3y + 2z = 100, \quad (2)$$

and the fact that 65 hr are available for finishing leads to the equation

$$x + y + 2z = 65. \quad (3)$$

Notice that by reading *across* the table, we can quickly determine the coefficients and constants in the equations of the system.

Step 4 **Solve** the system of equations (1), (2), and (3), namely,

$$\begin{align} 2x + y + 3z &= 100 \quad (1) \\ 2x + 3y + 2z &= 100 \quad (2) \\ x + y + 2z &= 65 \quad (3) \end{align}$$

to find $x = 15$, $y = 10$, and $z = 20$.

Step 5 **State the answer.** The company should produce 15 model X, 10 model Y, and 20 model Z sets per week.

Step 6 **Check** that these values satisfy the conditions of the problem.

◀ *Work Problem* **7** *at the Side.*

ANSWER

7. 400 tons of newsprint; 900 tons of bond; 600 tons of copy machine paper

14.5 ▶▶▶ **Exercises**

FOR EXTRA HELP

MyMathLab

Math XL
PRACTICE

WATCH

DOWNLOAD

READ

REVIEW

Solve each problem. See Example 1.

1. During the 2007 Major League Baseball regular season, the Cleveland Indians played 162 games. They won 30 more games than they lost. What was their win-loss record that year?

2. Refer to Exercise 1. During the same 162-game season, the Chicago White Sox lost 18 more games than they won. What was the team's win-loss record?

2007 MLB Final Standings
American League Central

Team	W	L
Cleveland	—	—
Detroit	88	74
Minnesota	79	83
Chicago	—	—
Kansas City	69	93

Source: www.mlb.com

3. Venus and Serena measured a tennis court and found that it was 42 ft longer than it was wide and had a perimeter of 228 ft. What were the length and the width of the tennis court?

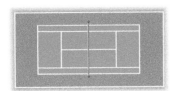

4. Wilt and Oscar found that the width of their basketball court was 44 ft less than the length. If the perimeter was 288 ft, what were the length and the width of their court?

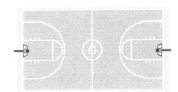

5. The two biggest Fortune 500 companies in 2005 were Wal-Mart and ExxonMobil. ExxonMobil's revenue was $24 billion more than that of Wal-Mart. Total revenue for the two companies was $656 billion. What was the revenue for each company? (*Source:* Fortune 500.)

6. In 2007, U.S. exports to Canada were $112 billion more than exports to Mexico. Together, exports to these two countries totaled $386 billion. How much were exports to each country? (*Source:* U.S. Census Bureau.)

In Exercises 7 and 8, find the measures of the angles marked x and y. Remember that (1) the sum of the measures of the angles of a triangle is 180°, (2) supplementary angles have a sum of 180°, and (3) vertical angles have equal measures.

7.

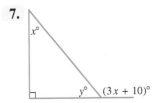

8.

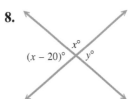

The Fan Cost Index (FCI) represents the cost of four average-price tickets, four small soft drinks, two small beers, four hot dogs, parking for one car, two game programs, and two souvenir caps to a sporting event. (Source: www.teammarketing.com)
Use the concept of FCI in Exercises 9 and 10. See Example 2.

9. For the 2005–2006 season, the FCI prices for the National Hockey League (NHL) and the National Basketball Association (NBA) totaled $514.69. The hockey FCI was $20.05 less than that of basketball. What were the FCIs for these sports?

10. In 2005, the FCI prices for Major League Baseball (MLB) and the National Football League (NFL) totaled $501.01. The football FCI was $158.63 more than that of baseball. What were the FCIs for these sports?

Solve each problem. See Example 2.

11. Andrew McGinnis works at Arby's. During one particular day he sold 15 Junior Roast Beef sandwiches and 10 Big Montana sandwiches, totaling $75.25. Another day he sold 30 Junior Roast Beef sandwiches and 5 Big Montana sandwiches, totaling $84.65. How much did each type of sandwich cost? (*Source:* Arby's menu.)

12. London and New York are among the most expensive cities worldwide for business travelers. On the basis of average costs per day for each city (which include the costs of business-class lodging and three meals), 2 days in London and 3 days in New York costs $2099, while 4 days in London and 2 days in New York costs $2586. What is the average cost per day for each city? (*Source:* Runzheimer International.)

The formulas $p = br$ (percentage $=$ base $\times$ rate) and $I = prt$ (simple interest $=$ principal $\times$ rate $\times$ time) are used in the applications in Exercises 17–24. To prepare to use these formulas, answer the questions in Exercises 13 and 14.

13. If a container of liquid contains 60 oz of solution, what is the number of ounces of pure acid if the given solution contains the following acid concentrations?

    (a) 10%   **(b)** 25%   **(c)** 40%   **(d)** 50%

14. If $5000 is invested in an account paying simple annual interest, how much interest will be earned during the first year at the following rates?

    (a) 2%   **(b)** 3%   **(c)** 4%   **(d)** 3.5%

15. If a pound of turkey costs $1.29, how much will x pounds cost?

16. If a ticket to the movie *The Final Season* costs $8.50 and y tickets are sold, how much is collected from the sale?

Solve each problem. See Example 3.

17. How many gallons each of 25% alcohol and 35% alcohol should be mixed to get 20 gal of 32% alcohol?

Gallons of Solution	Percent (as a Decimal)	Gallons of Pure Alcohol
x	25% = 0.25	
y	35% = 0.35	
20	32% =	

18. How many liters each of 15% acid and 33% acid should be mixed to get 120 L of 21% acid?

Liters of Solution	Percent (as a Decimal)	Liters of Pure Acid
x	15% = 0.15	
y	33% =	
120	21% =	

19. Pure acid is to be added to a 10% acid solution to obtain 54 L of a 20% acid solution. What amounts of each should be used? (*Hint:* Pure acid is 100% acid.)

20. A truck radiator holds 36 L of fluid. How much pure antifreeze must be added to a mixture that is 4% antifreeze to fill the radiator with a mixture that is 20% antifreeze?

21. A party mix is made by adding nuts that sell for $2.50 per kg to a cereal mixture that sells for $1 per kg. How much of each should be added to get 30 kg of a mix that will sell for $1.70 per kg?

	Number of Kilograms	Price per Kilogram	Value
Nuts	x	2.50	
Cereal	y	1.00	
Mixture		1.70	

22. A popular fruit drink is made by mixing fruit juices. Such a drink with 50% juice is to be mixed with another drink that is 30% juice to get 200 L of a drink that is 45% juice. How much of each should be used?

	Liters of Drink	Percent (as a Decimal)	Liters of Pure Juice
50% Juice	x	0.50	
30% Juice	y	0.30	
Mixture		0.45	

23. A total of $3000 is invested, part at 2% simple interest and part at 4%. If the total annual return from the two investments is $100, how much is invested at each rate?

Principal	Rate (as a Decimal)	Interest
x	0.02	$0.02x$
y	0.04	$0.04y$
3000		100

24. An investor must invest a total of $15,000 in two accounts, one paying 4% annual simple interest, and the other 3%. If he wants to earn $550 annual interest, how much should he invest at each rate?

Principal	Rate (as a Decimal)	Interest
x	0.04	
y	0.03	
15,000		

The formula d = rt (distance = rate × time) is used in the applications in Exercises 27–30. To prepare to use this formula, answer the questions in Exercises 25 and 26.

25. If the speed of a boat in still water is 10 mph, and the speed of the current of a river is x mph, what is the speed of the boat

(a) going upstream (that is, against the current, which slows the boat down);

(b) going downstream (that is, with the current, which speeds the boat up)?

26. If the speed of a killer whale is 25 mph and the whale swims for y hours, how many miles does the whale travel?

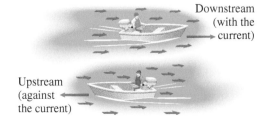

Solve each problem. See Example 4.

27. A motor scooter travels 20 mi in the same time that a bicycle covers 8 mi. If the speed of the scooter is 5 mph more than twice the speed of the bicycle, find both speeds.

28. A train travels 150 km in the same time that a plane covers 400 km. If the speed of the plane is 20 km per hr less than 3 times the speed of the train, find both speeds.

29. In his motorboat, Bill Ruhberg travels upstream at top speed to his favorite fishing spot, a distance of 36 mi, in 2 hr. Returning, he finds that the trip downstream, still at top speed, takes only 1.5 hr. Find the speed of Bill's boat and the speed of the current. Let x = the speed of the boat in still water and y = the speed of the current.

	r	t	d
Upstream	$x - y$	2	
Downstream	$x + y$		

30. Traveling for 3 hr into a steady headwind, a plane flies 1650 mi. The pilot determines that flying *with* the same wind for 2 hr, he could make a trip of 1300 mi. Find the speed of the plane and the speed of the wind.

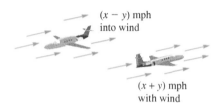

$(x - y)$ mph
into wind

$(x + y)$ mph
with wind

Solve each problem. See Examples 1–6.

31. (See the Chapter Introduction.) How many pounds of candy that sells for $0.75 per lb must be mixed with candy that sells for $1.25 per lb to obtain 9 lb of a mixture that should sell for $0.96 per lb?

32. The average cost of tuition and fees at a 4-yr public college or university during the 2007–2008 school year was $3824 more than at a 2-yr community college. Suppose a student plans to attend a local community college for 2 yr and then transfer to a public 4-yr university for 2 yr. The student expected to pay $17,092 tuition and fees for the 4 yr, assuming the 2007–2008 rates were locked in. What was the cost of tuition and fees during the 2007–2008 year at each type of school? (*Source:* The College Board.)

33. Tickets to a production of *Cats* at Shelton State Community College cost $5 for general admission or $4 with a student ID. If 184 people paid to see a performance and $812 was collected, how many of each type of ticket were sold?

34. At a business meeting at Panera Bread, the bill (without tax) for two cappuccinos and three house lattes was $14.55. At another table, the bill for one cappuccino and two house lattes was $8.77. How much did each type of beverage cost? (*Source:* Panera Bread menu.)

35. The mixed price of 9 citrons and 7 fragrant wood apples is 107; again, the mixed price of 7 citrons and 9 fragrant wood apples is 101. O you arithmetician, tell me quickly the price of a citron and the price of a wood apple here, having distinctly separated those prices well. (*Source:* Hindu work, A.D. 850.) (*Hint:* "Mixed price" refers to the price of a mixture of the two fruits.)

36. Braving blizzard conditions on the planet Hoth, Luke Skywalker sets out at top speed in his snow speeder for a rebel base 4800 mi away. He travels into a steady headwind and makes the trip in 3 hr. Returning, he finds that the trip back, still at top speed but now with a tailwind, takes only 2 hr. Find the top speed of Luke's snow speeder and the speed of the wind.

	r	t	d
Into Headwind			
With Tailwind			

Solve each problem involving three unknowns. See Examples 5 and 6. (In Exercises 37–40, remember that the sum of the measures of the angles of a triangle is 180°.)

37. In the figure, $z = x + 10$ and $x + y = 100$. Determine a third equation involving x, y, and z, and then find the measures of the three angles.

38. In the figure, x is 10 less than y and x is 20 less than z. Write a system of equations and find the measures of the three angles.

39. In a certain triangle, the measure of the second angle is 10° more than three times the first. The third angle measure is equal to the sum of the measures of the other two. Find the measures of the three angles.

40. The measure of the largest angle of a triangle is 12° less than the sum of the measures of the other two. The smallest angle measures 58° less than the largest. Find the measures of the angles.

41. The perimeter of a triangle is 70 cm. The longest side is 4 cm less than the sum of the other two sides. Twice the shortest side is 9 cm less than the longest side. Find the length of each side of the triangle.

42. The perimeter of a triangle is 56 in. The longest side measures 4 in. less than the sum of the other two sides. Three times the shortest side is 4 in. more than the longest side. Find the lengths of the three sides.

43. In a random sample of 100 Americans of voting age, 10 more Americans identify themselves as Independents than Republicans. Six fewer Americans identify themselves as Republicans than Democrats. Assuming that all of those sampled are Republican, Democrat, or Independent, how many of those in the sample identify themselves with each political affiliation? (*Source:* The Gallup Organization.)

44. In the 2004 Summer Olympics in Athens, Greece, the United States earned 6 more gold medals than bronze. The number of silver medals earned was 19 less than twice the number of bronze medals. The United Stated earned a total of 103 medals. How many of each kind of medal did the United States earn? (*Source: World Almanac and Book of Facts.*)

45. Tickets for one show on the Harlem Globetrotters' 2006 "Unstoppable" Tour cost $14, $20, or, for VIP seats, $50. Five times as many $14 tickets were sold as VIP tickets. The number of $14 tickets was 15 more than the sum of the number of $20 tickets and the number of VIP tickets. Sales of all three kinds of tickets totaled $11,700. How many of each kind of ticket were sold? (*Source*: www.ticketmaster.com)

46. Three kinds of tickets are available for a *Third Day* concert: "up close," "in the middle," and "far out." "Up close" tickets cost $10 more than "in the middle" tickets, while "in the middle" tickets cost $10 more than "far out" tickets. Twice the cost of an "up close" ticket is $20 more than 3 times the cost of a "far out" ticket. Find the price of each kind of ticket.

47. A wholesaler supplies college T-shirts to three college bookstores: A, B, and C. The wholesaler recently shipped a total of 800 T-shirts to the three bookstores. In order to meet student demand at the three colleges, twice as many T-shirts were shipped to bookstore B as to bookstore A, and the number shipped to bookstore C was 40 less than the sum of the numbers shipped to the other two bookstores. How many T-shirts were shipped to each bookstore?

48. An office supply store sells three models of computer desks: A, B, and C. In January, the store sold a total of 85 computer desks. The number of model B desks was five more than the number of model C desks, and the number of model A desks was four more than twice the number of model C desks. How many of each model did the store sell in January?

49. During the 2005–2006 National Hockey League regular season, the Calgary Flames played 82 games. Their wins and losses totaled 71. They tied 14 fewer games than they lost. How many wins, losses, and ties did they have?

50. (Refer to Exercise 49.) During the same 82-game season, the Minnesota Wild had a total of 44 losses and ties. They had two more wins than losses. How many wins, losses, and ties did they have?

2005-2006 NHL Final Standings

Team	W	L	T	Pts
Calgary	—	—	—	103
Colorado	43	30	9	95
Edmonton	41	28	13	95
Vancouver	42	32	8	92
Minnesota	—	—	—	84

Source: www.sportzdomain.com

14.6 ▶▶▶ Solving Systems of Linear Equations by Matrix Methods

OBJECTIVE 1 Define a matrix. An ordered array of numbers such as

Columns
$$\text{Rows} \begin{bmatrix} 2 & 3 & 5 \\ 7 & 1 & 2 \end{bmatrix} \quad \text{Matrix}$$

is called a **matrix.** The numbers are called **elements** of the matrix. *Matrices* (the plural of *matrix*) are named according to the number of **rows** and **columns** they contain. The rows are read horizontally, and the columns are read vertically. For example, the first row in the preceding matrix is 2 3 5 and the first column is $\frac{2}{7}$. This matrix is a 2 × 3 (read "two by three") matrix because it has 2 rows and 3 columns. The number of rows followed by the number of columns gives the **dimensions** of the matrix.

$$\begin{bmatrix} -1 & 0 \\ 1 & -2 \end{bmatrix} \quad \begin{array}{c} 2 \times 2 \\ \text{matrix} \end{array} \qquad \begin{bmatrix} 8 & -1 & -3 \\ 2 & 1 & 6 \\ 0 & 5 & -3 \\ 5 & 9 & 7 \end{bmatrix} \quad \begin{array}{c} 4 \times 3 \\ \text{matrix} \end{array}$$

A **square matrix** is one that has the same number of rows as columns. The 2 × 2 matrix is a square matrix.

🖩 **Calculator Tip** Figure 9 shows how a graphing calculator displays the preceding two matrices. Work with matrices is made much easier by using technology when available. Consult your owner's manual for details.

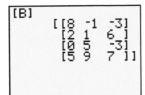

Figure 9

In this section, we discuss a method of solving linear systems that uses matrices. The advantage of this new method is that it can be done by a graphing calculator or a computer, allowing large systems of equations to be solved easily.

OBJECTIVE 2 Write the augmented matrix for a system. To solve a linear system using matrices, we begin by writing an *augmented matrix* for the system. An **augmented matrix** has a vertical bar that separates the columns of the matrix into two groups. For example, to solve the system

$$x - 3y = 1$$
$$2x + y = -5,$$

we start with the augmented matrix

$$\left[\begin{array}{cc|c} 1 & -3 & 1 \\ 2 & 1 & -5 \end{array} \right]. \qquad \text{Augmented matrix}$$

OBJECTIVES

1 Define a matrix.

2 Write the augmented matrix for a system.

3 Use row operations to solve a system with two equations.

4 Use row operations to solve a system with three equations.

5 Use row operations to solve special systems.

System of equations:

$$x - 3y = 1$$
$$2x + y = -5$$

Augmented matrix:

$$\begin{bmatrix} 1 & -3 & | & 1 \\ 2 & 1 & | & -5 \end{bmatrix}$$

Coefficients of the variables   The bar separates the coefficients from the constants.   Constants

Notice that we place the coefficients of the variables to the left of the bar, and the constants to the right. *The matrix is just a shorthand way of writing the system of equations, so the rows of the augmented matrix can be treated the same as the equations of a system of equations.*

We know that exchanging the position of two equations in a system does not change the system. Also, multiplying any equation in a system by a nonzero number does not change the system. Comparable changes to the augmented matrix of a system of equations produce new matrices that correspond to systems with the same solutions as the original system.

The following **row operations** produce new matrices that lead to systems having the same solutions as the original system.

Matrix Row Operations

1. Any two rows of the matrix may be interchanged.
2. The numbers in any row may be multiplied by any nonzero real number.
3. Any row may be transformed by adding to the numbers of the row the product of a real number and the corresponding numbers of another row.

Examples of these row operations follow.

Row operation 1:

$$\begin{bmatrix} 2 & 3 & 9 \\ 4 & 8 & -3 \\ 1 & 0 & 7 \end{bmatrix} \text{ becomes } \begin{bmatrix} 1 & 0 & 7 \\ 4 & 8 & -3 \\ 2 & 3 & 9 \end{bmatrix}.$$

Interchange row 1 and row 3.

Row operation 2:

$$\begin{bmatrix} 2 & 3 & 9 \\ 4 & 8 & -3 \\ 1 & 0 & 7 \end{bmatrix} \text{ becomes } \begin{bmatrix} 6 & 9 & 27 \\ 4 & 8 & -3 \\ 1 & 0 & 7 \end{bmatrix}.$$

Multiply the numbers in row 1 by 3.

Row operation 3:

$$\begin{bmatrix} 2 & 3 & 9 \\ 4 & 8 & -3 \\ 1 & 0 & 7 \end{bmatrix} \text{ becomes } \begin{bmatrix} 0 & 3 & -5 \\ 4 & 8 & -3 \\ 1 & 0 & 7 \end{bmatrix}.$$

Multiply the numbers in row 3 by −2; add them to the corresponding numbers in row 1.

The third row operation corresponds to the way we eliminated a variable from a pair of equations in the previous sections.

OBJECTIVE 3 Use row operations to solve a system with two equations. Row operations can be used to rewrite a matrix. The goal is a matrix in the form

$$\begin{bmatrix} 1 & a & | & b \\ 0 & 1 & | & c \end{bmatrix} \quad \text{or} \quad \begin{bmatrix} 1 & a & b & | & c \\ 0 & 1 & d & | & e \\ 0 & 0 & 1 & | & f \end{bmatrix}$$

for systems with two or three equations, respectively. Notice that there are 1s down the diagonal from upper left to lower right and 0s below the 1s. A matrix written this way is said to be in **row echelon form.** When these matrices are rewritten as systems of equations, the value of one variable is known, and the rest can be found by substitution. The following examples illustrate this method.

> **Example 1** **Using Row Operations to Solve a System with Two Variables**

Use row operations to solve the system.

$$x - 3y = 1$$
$$2x + y = -5$$

We start with the augmented matrix of the system.

$$\begin{bmatrix} 1 & -3 & | & 1 \\ 2 & 1 & | & -5 \end{bmatrix}$$ Augmented matrix

Now we use the various row operations to change this matrix into one that leads to a system that is easier to solve.

It is best to work by columns. We start with the first column and make sure that there is a 1 in the first row, first column position. There is already a 1 in this position. Next, we get 0 in every position below the first. To get a 0 in row two, column one, we use the third row operation and add to the numbers in row two the result of multiplying each number in row one by -2. (We abbreviate this as $-2R_1 + R_2$.) Row one remains unchanged.

$$\begin{bmatrix} 1 & -3 & | & 1 \\ 2 + 1(-2) & 1 + -3(-2) & | & -5 + 1(-2) \end{bmatrix}$$

↑ Original number from row two   ↑ -2 times number from row one

$$\begin{bmatrix} 1 & -3 & | & 1 \\ 0 & 7 & | & -7 \end{bmatrix}$$ $-2R_1 + R_2$

The matrix now has a 1 in the first position of column one, with 0 in every position below the first.

Now we go to column two. An entry of 1 is needed in row two, column two. We get this 1 by using the second row operation, multiplying each number of row two by $\frac{1}{7}$.

Stop here—this matrix is in row echelon form. → $$\begin{bmatrix} 1 & -3 & | & 1 \\ 0 & 1 & | & -1 \end{bmatrix}$$ $\frac{1}{7}R_2$

This augmented matrix leads to the system of equations

$$1x - 3y = 1$$
$$0x + 1y = -1,$$ or $$x - 3y = 1$$
$$y = -1.$$

From the second equation, $y = -1$. We substitute -1 for y in the first equation to get

$$x - 3y = 1$$
$$x - 3(-1) = 1$$ Let $y = -1$.
$$x + 3 = 1$$ Multiply.
$$x = -2.$$ Subtract 3.

Write the values of x and y in the correct order.

The solution set of the system is $\{(-2, -1)\}$. Check this solution by substitution in both equations of the system.

Work Problem ① *at the Side.* ▶

> **①** Use row operations to solve the system.
>
> $$x - 2y = 9$$
> $$3x + y = 13$$

📱 **Calculator Tip** If the augmented matrix of the system in Example 1 is entered as matrix A in a graphing calculator (Figure 10(a)) and the row echelon form of the matrix is found (Figure 10(b)), the system becomes

$$x + \frac{1}{2}y = -\frac{5}{2}$$
$$y = -1.$$

While this system looks different from the one we obtained in Example 1, it is equivalent, since its solution set is also $\{(-2, -1)\}$.

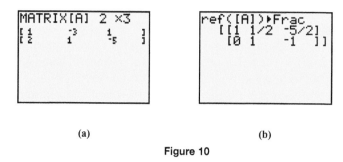

(a)   (b)

Figure 10

OBJECTIVE **4** **Use row operations to solve a system with three equations.** As before, we use row operations to get 1s down the diagonal from left to right and all 0s below each 1.

Example 2 **Using Row Operations to Solve a System with Three Variables**

Use row operations to solve the system.

$$x - y + 5z = -6$$
$$3x + 3y - z = 10$$
$$x + 3y + 2z = 5$$

Start by writing the augmented matrix of the system.

$$\begin{bmatrix} 1 & -1 & 5 & | & -6 \\ 3 & 3 & -1 & | & 10 \\ 1 & 3 & 2 & | & 5 \end{bmatrix} \qquad \text{Augmented matrix}$$

This matrix already has 1 in row one, column one. Next get 0s in the rest of column one. First, add to row two the results of multiplying each number of row one by -3. This gives the matrix

$$\begin{bmatrix} 1 & -1 & 5 & | & -6 \\ 0 & 6 & -16 & | & 28 \\ 1 & 3 & 2 & | & 5 \end{bmatrix}. \qquad -3R_1 + R_2$$

Now add to the numbers in row three the results of multiplying each number of row one by -1.

$$\begin{bmatrix} 1 & -1 & 5 & | & -6 \\ 0 & 6 & -16 & | & 28 \\ 0 & 4 & -3 & | & 11 \end{bmatrix} \qquad -1R_1 + R_3$$

Continued on Next Page

Get 1 in row two, column two by multiplying each number in row two by $\frac{1}{6}$.

$$\begin{bmatrix} 1 & -1 & 5 & \Big| & -6 \\ 0 & 1 & -\frac{8}{3} & \Big| & \frac{14}{3} \\ 0 & 4 & -3 & \Big| & 11 \end{bmatrix} \quad \frac{1}{6}R_2$$

Introduce 0 in row three, column two by adding to row three the results of multiplying each number in row two by -4.

$$\begin{bmatrix} 1 & -1 & 5 & \Big| & -6 \\ 0 & 1 & -\frac{8}{3} & \Big| & \frac{14}{3} \\ 0 & 0 & \frac{23}{3} & \Big| & -\frac{23}{3} \end{bmatrix} \quad -4R_2 + R_3$$

Finally, obtain 1 in row three, column three by multiplying each number in row three by $\frac{3}{23}$.

$$\begin{bmatrix} 1 & -1 & 5 & \Big| & -6 \\ 0 & 1 & -\frac{8}{3} & \Big| & \frac{14}{3} \\ 0 & 0 & 1 & \Big| & -1 \end{bmatrix} \quad \frac{3}{23}R_3$$

This final matrix gives the system of equations

$$x - y + 5z = -6$$
$$y - \frac{8}{3}z = \frac{14}{3}$$
$$z = -1.$$

Substitute -1 for z in the second equation, $y - \frac{8}{3}z = \frac{14}{3}$, to get $y = 2$. Substitute 2 for y and -1 for z in the first equation, $x - y + 5z = -6$, to get $x = 1$. The solution set is $\{(1, 2, -1)\}$. Check by substitution in the original system.

Work Problem **2** *at the Side.* ▶

2 Use row operations to solve the system.

$$2x - y + z = 7$$
$$x - 3y - z = 7$$
$$-x + y - 5z = -9$$

OBJECTIVE 5 Use row operations to solve special systems.

Example 3 **Recognizing Inconsistent Systems or Dependent Equations**

Use row operations to solve each system.

(a) $2x - 3y = 8$
$-6x + 9y = 4$

$$\begin{bmatrix} 2 & -3 & \Big| & 8 \\ -6 & 9 & \Big| & 4 \end{bmatrix} \quad \text{Write the augmented matrix.}$$

$$\begin{bmatrix} 1 & -\frac{3}{2} & \Big| & 4 \\ -6 & 9 & \Big| & 4 \end{bmatrix} \quad \frac{1}{2}R_1$$

$$\begin{bmatrix} 1 & -\frac{3}{2} & \Big| & 4 \\ 0 & 0 & \Big| & 28 \end{bmatrix} \quad 6R_1 + R_2$$

The corresponding system of equations is

$$x - \frac{3}{2}y = 4$$
$$0 = 28, \quad \text{False}$$

which has no solution and is inconsistent. The solution set is $\emptyset$.

ANSWER

2. $\{(2, -2, 1)\}$

Continued on Next Page

3 Use row operations to solve each system.

(a) $\begin{aligned} x - y &= 2 \\ -2x + 2y &= 2 \end{aligned}$

(b) $\begin{aligned} -10x + 12y &= 30 \\ 5x - 6y &= -15 \end{aligned}$

$$\begin{bmatrix} -10 & 12 & | & 30 \\ 5 & -6 & | & -15 \end{bmatrix} \quad \text{Write the augmented matrix.}$$

$$\begin{bmatrix} 1 & -\frac{6}{5} & | & -3 \\ 5 & -6 & | & -15 \end{bmatrix} \quad -\frac{1}{10}R_1$$

$$\begin{bmatrix} 1 & -\frac{6}{5} & | & -3 \\ 0 & 0 & | & 0 \end{bmatrix} \quad -5R_1 + R_2$$

The corresponding system is

$$x - \frac{6}{5}y = -3$$

$$0 = 0, \qquad \text{True}$$

which has dependent equations. Using the second equation of the original system, we write the solution set as

$$\{(x, y) \mid 5x - 6y = -15\}.$$

◀ *Work Problem* **3** *at the Side.*

(b) $\begin{aligned} x - y &= 2 \\ -2x + 2y &= -4 \end{aligned}$

14.6 ▶▶▶ **Exercises**

 FOR EXTRA HELP  Math XL PRACTICE WATCH ⬇ DOWNLOAD READ REVIEW

1. Consider the matrix $\begin{bmatrix} -2 & 3 & 1 \\ 0 & 5 & -3 \\ 1 & 4 & 8 \end{bmatrix}$, and answer the following.

   (a) What are the elements of the second row?

   (b) What are the elements of the third column?

   (c) Is this a square matrix? Explain.

   (d) Give the matrix obtained by interchanging the first and third rows.

   (e) Give the matrix obtained by multiplying the first row by $-\frac{1}{2}$.

   (f) Give the matrix obtained by multiplying the third row by 3 and adding it to the first row.

2. Give the dimensions of each matrix.

   (a) $\begin{bmatrix} 3 & -7 \\ 4 & 5 \\ -1 & 0 \end{bmatrix}$

   (b) $\begin{bmatrix} 4 & 9 & 0 \\ -1 & 2 & -4 \end{bmatrix}$

   (c) $\begin{bmatrix} 6 & 3 \\ -2 & 5 \\ 4 & 10 \\ 1 & -11 \end{bmatrix}$

Complete the steps in the matrix solution of each system by filling in the blanks. Give the final system and the solution set. See Example 1.

3. $4x + 8y = 44$
   $2x - y = -3$

   $\begin{bmatrix} 4 & 8 & | & 44 \\ 2 & -1 & | & -3 \end{bmatrix}$

   $\begin{bmatrix} 1 & \_\_ & | & \_\_ \\ 2 & -1 & | & -3 \end{bmatrix}$ $\quad \frac{1}{4}R_1$

   $\begin{bmatrix} 1 & 2 & | & 11 \\ 0 & \_\_ & | & \_\_ \end{bmatrix}$ $\quad -2R_1 + R_2$

   $\begin{bmatrix} 1 & 2 & | & 11 \\ 0 & 1 & | & \_\_ \end{bmatrix}$ $\quad -\frac{1}{5}R_2$

4. $2x - 5y = -1$
   $3x + y = 7$

   $\begin{bmatrix} 2 & -5 & | & -1 \\ 3 & 1 & | & 7 \end{bmatrix}$

   $\begin{bmatrix} 1 & -\frac{5}{2} & | & \_\_ \\ 3 & 1 & | & 7 \end{bmatrix}$ $\quad \frac{1}{2}R_1$

   $\begin{bmatrix} 1 & -\frac{5}{2} & | & -\frac{1}{2} \\ 0 & \_\_ & | & \_\_ \end{bmatrix}$ $\quad -3R_1 + R_2$

   $\begin{bmatrix} 1 & -\frac{5}{2} & | & -\frac{1}{2} \\ 0 & 1 & | & \_\_ \end{bmatrix}$ $\quad \frac{2}{17}R_2$

Use row operations to solve each system. See Examples 1 and 3.

5. $x + y = 5$
   $x - y = 3$

6. $x + 2y = 7$
   $x - y = -2$

🌐 **7.** $2x + 4y = 6$
   $3x - y = 2$

8. $4x + 5y = -7$
   $x - y = 5$

9. $3x + 4y = 13$
   $2x - 3y = -14$

10. $5x + 2y = 8$
   $3x - y = 7$

🌐 **11.** $-4x + 12y = 36$
   $x - 3y = 9$

12. $2x - 4y = 8$
   $-3x + 6y = 5$

13. $2x + y = 4$
$4x + 2y = 8$

14. $-3x - 4y = 1$
$6x + 8y = -2$

15. $\dfrac{1}{2}x + \dfrac{1}{3}y = 0$
$\dfrac{2}{3}x + \dfrac{3}{4}y = 0$

16. $1.2x + 0.3y = 0$
$2.9x - 0.6y = 0$

Complete the steps in the matrix solution of each system by filling in the blanks. Give the final system and the solution set. See Example 2.

17. $x + y - z = -3$
$2x + y + z = 4$
$5x - y + 2z = 23$

$$\left[\begin{array}{ccc|c} 1 & 1 & -1 & -3 \\ 2 & 1 & 1 & 4 \\ 5 & -1 & 2 & 23 \end{array}\right]$$

$$\left[\begin{array}{ccc|c} 1 & 1 & -1 & -3 \\ 0 & \rule{0.6cm}{0.4pt} & \rule{0.6cm}{0.4pt} & \rule{0.6cm}{0.4pt} \\ 0 & \rule{0.6cm}{0.4pt} & \rule{0.6cm}{0.4pt} & \rule{0.6cm}{0.4pt} \end{array}\right] \begin{array}{l} -2R_1 + R_2 \\ -5R_1 + R_3 \end{array}$$

$$\left[\begin{array}{ccc|c} 1 & 1 & -1 & -3 \\ 0 & 1 & \rule{0.6cm}{0.4pt} & \rule{0.6cm}{0.4pt} \\ 0 & -6 & 7 & 38 \end{array}\right] -1R_2$$

$$\left[\begin{array}{ccc|c} 1 & 1 & -1 & -3 \\ 0 & 1 & -3 & -10 \\ 0 & 0 & \rule{0.6cm}{0.4pt} & \rule{0.6cm}{0.4pt} \end{array}\right] 6R_2 + R_3$$

$$\left[\begin{array}{ccc|c} 1 & 1 & -1 & -3 \\ 0 & 1 & -3 & -10 \\ 0 & 0 & 1 & \rule{0.6cm}{0.4pt} \end{array}\right] -\tfrac{1}{11}R_3$$

18. $2x + y + 2z = 11$
$2x - y - z = -3$
$3x + 2y + z = 9$

$$\left[\begin{array}{ccc|c} 2 & 1 & 2 & 11 \\ 2 & -1 & -1 & -3 \\ 3 & 2 & 1 & 9 \end{array}\right]$$

$$\left[\begin{array}{ccc|c} 1 & \rule{0.6cm}{0.4pt} & \rule{0.6cm}{0.4pt} & \rule{0.6cm}{0.4pt} \\ 2 & -1 & -1 & -3 \\ 3 & 2 & 1 & 9 \end{array}\right] \tfrac{1}{2}R_1$$

$$\left[\begin{array}{ccc|c} 1 & \frac{1}{2} & 1 & \frac{11}{2} \\ 0 & \rule{0.6cm}{0.4pt} & \rule{0.6cm}{0.4pt} & \rule{0.6cm}{0.4pt} \\ 0 & \rule{0.6cm}{0.4pt} & \rule{0.6cm}{0.4pt} & \rule{0.6cm}{0.4pt} \end{array}\right] \begin{array}{l} -2R_1 + R_2 \\ -3R_1 + R_3 \end{array}$$

$$\left[\begin{array}{ccc|c} 1 & \frac{1}{2} & 1 & \frac{11}{2} \\ 0 & 1 & \rule{0.6cm}{0.4pt} & \rule{0.6cm}{0.4pt} \\ 0 & \frac{1}{2} & -2 & -\frac{15}{2} \end{array}\right] -\tfrac{1}{2}R_2$$

$$\left[\begin{array}{ccc|c} 1 & \frac{1}{2} & 1 & \frac{11}{2} \\ 0 & 1 & \frac{3}{2} & 7 \\ 0 & 0 & \rule{0.6cm}{0.4pt} & \rule{0.6cm}{0.4pt} \end{array}\right] -\tfrac{1}{2}R_2 + R_3$$

$$\left[\begin{array}{ccc|c} 1 & \frac{1}{2} & 1 & \frac{11}{2} \\ 0 & 1 & \frac{3}{2} & 7 \\ 0 & 0 & 1 & \rule{0.6cm}{0.4pt} \end{array}\right] -\tfrac{4}{11}R_3$$

Use row operations to solve each system. See Examples 2 and 3.

19. $x + y - 3z = 1$
$2x - y + z = 9$
$3x + y - 4z = 8$

20. $2x + 4y - 3z = -18$
$3x + y - z = -5$
$x - 2y + 4z = 14$

21. $x + y - z = 6$
$2x - y + z = -9$
$x - 2y + 3z = 1$

22. $x + 3y - 6z = 7$
$2x - y + 2z = 0$
$x + y + 2z = -1$

23. $x - y = 1$
$y - z = 6$
$x + z = -1$

24. $x + y = 1$
$2x - z = 0$
$y + 2z = -2$

25. $4x + 8y + 4z = 9$
$x + 3y + 4z = 10$
$5x + 10y + 5z = 12$

26. $x + 2y + 3z = -2$
$2x + 4y + 6z = -5$
$x - y + 2z = 6$

27. $x - 2y + z = 4$
$3x - 6y + 3z = 12$
$-2x + 4y - 2z = -8$

28. $x + 3y + z = 1$
$2x + 6y + 2z = 2$
$3x + 9y + 3z = 3$

29. $5x + 3y - z = 0$
$2x - 3y + z = 0$
$x + 4y - 2z = 0$

30. $4x + 5y - z = 0$
$7x - 5y + z = 0$
$x + 3y - 2z = 0$

15

Factoring

15.1 ▶▶▶ Factors: The Greatest Common Factor

OBJECTIVES

1 Find the greatest common factor of a list of numbers.

2 Find the greatest common factor of a list of variable terms.

3 Factor out the greatest common factor.

4 Factor by grouping.

Recall from **Section 4.2** that to **factor** a number means to write it as the product of two or more numbers. The product is called the **factored form** of the number. Here is an example.

$$\text{Factors}$$
$$12 = \underbrace{6 \cdot 2}_{\text{Factored form}}$$

Factoring is a process that "undoes" multiplying. We multiply $6 \cdot 2$ to get 12, but we factor 12 by writing it as $6 \cdot 2$.

OBJECTIVE 1 Find the greatest common factor of a list of numbers. An integer that is a factor of two or more integers is a **common factor** of those integers. For example, 6 is a common factor of 18 and 24 because 6 is a factor of both 18 and 24. Other common factors of 18 and 24 are 1, 2, and 3. The **greatest common factor (GCF)** of a list of integers is the largest common factor of those integers. This means 6 is the greatest common factor of 18 and 24, since it is the largest of their common factors.

> **Note**
>
> Factors of a number are also divisors of the number. The greatest common factor is the same as the greatest common divisor.

EXAMPLE 1   Finding the Greatest Common Factor for Numbers

Find the greatest common factor for each list of numbers.

(a) 30, 45

First write each number in prime factored form.

$$30 = 2 \cdot 3 \cdot 5$$
$$45 = 3 \cdot 3 \cdot 5$$

Use each prime the *least* number of times it appears in *all* the factored forms. There is no 2 in the prime factored form of 45, so there will be no 2 in the greatest common factor. The least number of times 3 appears in all the factored forms is 1. The least number of times 5 appears is also 1. From this, the

$$\text{GCF} = 3^1 \cdot 5^1 = 3 \cdot 5 = 15.$$

(b) 72, 120, 432

Find the prime factored form of each number.

$$72 = 2 \cdot 2 \cdot 2 \cdot 3 \cdot 3$$
$$120 = 2 \cdot 2 \cdot 2 \cdot 3 \cdot 5$$
$$432 = 2 \cdot 2 \cdot 2 \cdot 2 \cdot 3 \cdot 3 \cdot 3$$

The least number of times 2 appears in all the factored forms is 3, and the least number of times 3 appears is 1. There is no 5 in the prime factored form of either 72 or 432, so the

$$\text{GCF} = 2^3 \cdot 3^1 = 24.$$

Continued on Next Page

(c) 10, 11, 14

Write the prime factored form of each number.

$$10 = 2 \cdot 5$$
$$11 = 11$$
$$14 = 2 \cdot 7$$

There are no primes common to all three numbers, so the GCF is 1.

Work Problem **1** *at the Side.* ▶

OBJECTIVE **2** **Find the greatest common factor of a list of variable terms.**   The terms x^4, x^5, x^6, and x^7 have x^4 as the greatest common factor because the least exponent on the variable x is 4.

$$x^4 = 1 \cdot x^4, \quad x^5 = x \cdot x^4, \quad x^6 = x^2 \cdot x^4, \quad x^7 = x^3 \cdot x^4$$

Note

The exponent on a variable in the GCF is the *least* exponent that appears on that variable in *all* the terms.

EXAMPLE 2   **Finding the Greatest Common Factor for Variable Terms**

Find the greatest common factor for each list of terms.

(a) $21m^7, -18m^6, 45m^8$

$$21m^7 = 3 \cdot 7 \cdot m^7$$
$$-18m^6 = -1 \cdot 2 \cdot 3 \cdot 3 \cdot m^6$$
$$45m^8 = 3 \cdot 3 \cdot 5 \cdot m^8$$

First, 3 is the greatest common factor of the coefficients 21, -18, and 45. The least exponent on m is 6, so the

$$GCF = 3m^6.$$

(b) $x^4y^2, x^7y^5, x^3y^7, y^{15}$

$$x^4y^2, \quad x^7y^5, \quad x^3y^7, \quad y^{15}$$

There is no x in the last term, y^{15}, so x will not appear in the greatest common factor. There is a y in each term, however, and 2 is the least exponent on y. The GCF is y^2.

(c) $-a^2b, -ab^2$

$$-a^2b = -1a^2b = -1 \cdot 1 \cdot a^2b$$
$$-ab^2 = -1ab^2 = -1 \cdot 1 \cdot ab^2$$

The factors of -1 are -1 and 1. Since $1 > -1$, the GCF is $1ab$, or ab.

Note

In a list of negative terms, sometimes a negative common factor is preferable (even though it is not the greatest common factor). In Example 2(c), for instance, we might prefer $-ab$ as the common factor. In factoring exercises like this, either answer will be acceptable.

1 Find the greatest common factor for each list of numbers.

(a) 30, 20, 15

$$30 = 2 \cdot 3 \cdot 5$$
$$20 = 2 \cdot \underline{\quad} \cdot \underline{\quad}$$
$$15 = 3 \cdot \underline{\quad}$$
$$GCF = \underline{\quad}$$

(b) 42, 28, 35

(c) 12, 18, 26, 32

(d) 10, 15, 21

2 Find the greatest common factor for each list of terms.

(a) $6m^4, 9m^2, 12m^5$

$$6m^4 = 2 \cdot \underline{\quad} \cdot m^4$$

$$9m^2 = 3 \cdot \underline{\quad} \cdot \underline{\quad}$$

$$12m^5 = 2 \cdot 2 \cdot \underline{\quad} \cdot \underline{\quad}$$

$$\text{GCF} = \underline{\quad}$$

Finding the Greatest Common Factor (GCF)

Step 1 **Factor.** Write each number in prime factored form.

Step 2 **List common factors.** List each prime number or each variable that is a factor of every term in the list. (If a prime does not appear in one of the prime factored forms, it cannot appear in the greatest common factor.)

Step 3 **Choose least exponents.** Use as exponents on the common prime factors the *least* exponents from the prime factored forms.

Step 4 **Multiply.** Multiply the primes from Step 3. If there are no primes left after Step 3, the greatest common factor is 1.

◀ *Work Problem* **2** *at the Side.*

OBJECTIVE 3 Factor out the greatest common factor. The polynomial

$$3m + 12$$

has two terms, $3m$ and 12. The greatest common factor of these two terms is 3.

(b) $-12p^5, -18q^4$

We can write $3m + 12$ so that each term is a product with 3 as one factor.

$$3m + 12$$
$$= 3 \cdot m + 3 \cdot 4$$
$$= 3(m + 4) \qquad \text{Distributive property}$$

The factored form of $3m + 12$ is $3(m + 4)$. This process is called **factoring out the greatest common factor.**

CAUTION

The polynomial $3m + 12$ is *not* in factored form when written as the *sum*

$$3 \cdot m + 3 \cdot 4. \qquad \text{Not in factored form}$$

(c) y^4z^2, y^6z^8, z^9

The terms are factored, but the polynomial is not. The factored form of $3m + 12$ is the *product*

$$3(m + 4). \qquad \text{In factored form}$$

Writing a polynomial as a product, that is, in factored form, is called **factoring** the polynomial.

(d) $12p^{11}, 17q^5$

EXAMPLE 3 **Factoring Out the Greatest Common Factor**

Factor out the greatest common factor.

(a) $5y^2 + 10y$
$$= 5y(y) + 5y(2) \qquad \text{GCF} = 5y$$
$$= 5y(y + 2) \qquad \text{Distributive property}$$

Check Multiply the factored form.
$$5y(y + 2)$$
$$= 5y(y) + 5y(2) \qquad \text{Distributive property}$$
$$= 5y^2 + 10y \qquad \text{Original polynomial}$$

Continued on Next Page

(b) $20m^5 + 10m^4 - 15m^3$

$\quad = 5m^3(4m^2) + 5m^3(2m) - 5m^3(3) \qquad \text{GCF} = 5m^3$

$\quad = 5m^3(4m^2 + 2m - 3) \qquad\qquad\qquad \text{Factor out } 5m^3.$

Check $\;5m^3(4m^2 + 2m - 3)$

$\qquad\qquad = 20m^5 + 10m^4 - 15m^3 \qquad \text{Original polynomial}$

(c) $x^5 + x^3$

$\quad = x^3(x^2) + x^3(1)$

$\quad = x^3(x^2 + 1) \quad$ ┌ Don't forget
$\qquad\qquad\qquad\qquad$ └ the 1.

(d) $20m^7p^2 - 36m^3p^4$

$\quad = 4m^3p^2(5m^4) - 4m^3p^2(9p^2) \qquad \text{GCF} = 4m^3p^2$

$\quad = 4m^3p^2(5m^4 - 9p^2) \qquad\qquad\qquad \text{Factor out } 4m^3p^2.$

(e) $\dfrac{1}{6}n^2 + \dfrac{5}{6}n$

$\quad = \dfrac{1}{6}n(n) + \dfrac{1}{6}n(5) \qquad \text{GCF} = \frac{1}{6}n$

$\quad = \dfrac{1}{6}n(n + 5)$

CAUTION
Be sure to include the **1** in a problem like Example 3(c). ***Check that the factored form can be multiplied out to give the original polynomial.***

$\qquad\qquad\qquad\qquad$ *Work Problem* **3** *at the Side.* ▶

$\boxed{\text{EXAMPLE 4}}$ **Factoring Out a Negative Common Factor**

Factor $-8x^4 + 16x^3 - 4x^2$.
$\qquad$ We can factor out either $4x^2$ or $-4x^2$ here. We factor out $-4x^2$ so that the coefficient of the first term in the trinomial factor will be positive.

$\qquad\qquad\qquad\qquad\qquad$ ┌ Be careful
$\qquad\qquad\qquad\qquad\qquad$ └ with signs.

$-8x^4 + 16x^3 - 4x^2$

$\quad = -4x^2(2x^2) - 4x^2(-4x) - 4x^2(1) \qquad -4x^2 \text{ is a common factor.}$

$\quad = -4x^2(2x^2 - 4x + 1) \qquad\qquad\qquad \text{Factor out } -4x^2.$

Check $\;-4x^2(2x^2 - 4x + 1)$

$\qquad\quad = -4x^2(2x^2) - 4x^2(-4x) - 4x^2(1) \qquad \text{Distributive property}$

$\qquad\quad = -8x^4 + 16x^3 - 4x^2 \qquad\qquad\qquad \text{Original polynomial}$

$\qquad\qquad\qquad\qquad$ *Work Problem* **4** *at the Side.* ▶

Note
Whenever we factor a polynomial in which the coefficient of the first term of a polynomial is negative, we will factor out the negative common factor, even if it is just -1. However, it would also be correct to factor out $4x^2$ in Example 4 to obtain $4x^2(-2x^2 + 4x - 1)$.

3 Factor out the greatest common factor.

(a) $4x^2 + 6x$

(b) $10y^5 - 8y^4 + 6y^2$

(c) $m^7 + m^9$

(d) $8p^5q^2 + 16p^6q^3 - 12p^4q^7$

(e) $\dfrac{1}{3}b^2 - \dfrac{2}{3}b$

4 Factor

$\qquad -14a^3b^2 - 21a^2b^3 + 7ab$

by factoring out a negative common factor.

ANSWERS

3. (a) $2x(2x + 3)$
$\quad$ **(b)** $2y^2(5y^3 - 4y^2 + 3)$
$\quad$ **(c)** $m^7(1 + m^2)$
$\quad$ **(d)** $4p^4q^2(2p + 4p^2q - 3q^5)$
$\quad$ **(e)** $\dfrac{1}{3}b(b - 2)$

4. $-7ab(2a^2b + 3ab^2 - 1)$

5 Factor out the greatest common factor.

(a) $r(t - 4) + 5(t - 4)$

EXAMPLE 5 **Factoring Out a Common Binomial Factor**

Factor out the greatest common factor.

(a) $a(a + 3) + 4(a + 3)$

Sometimes the GCF has a factor with more than one term. The binomial $a + 3$ is the greatest common factor here.

Same

$$a(a + 3) + 4(a + 3)$$

$$= (a + 3)(a + 4)$$

(b) $x^2(x + 1) - 5(x + 1)$

$$= (x + 1)(x^2 - 5) \qquad \text{Factor out } x + 1.$$

◀ *Work Problem* **5** *at the Side.*

OBJECTIVE **4** **Factor by grouping.** *When a polynomial has four terms, common factors can sometimes be used to factor by grouping.*

(b) $y^2(y + 2) - 3(y + 2)$

EXAMPLE 6 **Factoring by Grouping**

Factor by grouping.

(a) $2x + 6 + ax + 3a$

Group the first two terms and the last two terms, since the first two terms have a common factor of 2 and the last two terms have a common factor of a.

$$2x + 6 + ax + 3a$$

$$= (2x + 6) + (ax + 3a)$$

$$= 2(x + 3) + a(x + 3)$$

The expression is still not in factored form because it is the *sum* of two terms. Now, however, $x + 3$ is a common factor and can be factored out.

$$2x + 6 + ax + 3a$$

(c) $x(x - 1) - 5(x - 1)$

$$= (2x + 6) + (ax + 3a) \qquad \text{Group the terms.}$$

$$= 2(x + 3) + a(x + 3) \qquad \text{Factor each group.}$$

$$= (x + 3)(2 + a) \qquad \text{Factor out } x + 3.$$

The final result is in factored form because it is a **product.** Note that the goal in factoring by grouping is to get a common factor, $x + 3$ here, so that the last step is possible. Check by multiplying the binomials using the FOIL method from **Section 13.3.**

Check $(x + 3)(2 + a)$

$$= 2x + ax + 6 + 3a \qquad \text{FOIL}$$

$$= 2x + 6 + ax + 3a, \qquad \text{Rearrange terms.}$$

which is the original polynomial.

Continued on Next Page

(b) $6ax + 24x + a + 4$

$\quad = (6ax + 24x) + (a + 4)$ Group the terms.

$\quad = 6x(a + 4) + 1(a + 4)$ Factor each group.

> Remember the 1.

$\quad = (a + 4)(6x + 1)$ Factor out $a + 4$.

Check $(a + 4)(6x + 1)$

$\quad\quad = 6ax + a + 24x + 4$ FOIL

$\quad\quad = 6ax + 24x + a + 4,$ Rearrange terms.

which is the original polynomial.

(c) $2x^2 - 10x + 3xy - 15y$

$\quad = (2x^2 - 10x) + (3xy - 15y)$ Group the terms.

$\quad = 2x(x - 5) + 3y(x - 5)$ Factor each group.

$\quad = (x - 5)(2x + 3y)$ Factor out the common factor, $x - 5$.

Check $(x - 5)(2x + 3y)$

$\quad\quad = 2x^2 + 3xy - 10x - 15y$ FOIL

$\quad\quad = 2x^2 - 10x + 3xy - 15y$ Original polynomial

(d) $t^3 + 2t^2 - 3t - 6$

> Be sure to write a $+$ sign between the groups.

$\quad = (t^3 + 2t^2) + (-3t - 6)$ Group the terms.

$\quad = t^2(t + 2) - 3(t + 2)$ Factor out -3 so there is a common factor,

> Be careful with signs.

                        $t + 2; -3(t + 2) = -3t - 6.$

$\quad = (t + 2)(t^2 - 3)$ Factor out $t + 2$.

Check by multiplying.

> **6** Factor by grouping.
>
> **(a)** $pq + 5q + 2p + 10$
>
> **(b)** $2xy + 3y + 2x + 3$
>
> **(c)** $2a^2 - 4a + 3ab - 6b$
>
> **(d)** $x^3 + 3x^2 - 5x - 15$

> **CAUTION**
> *Be careful with signs when grouping* in a problem like Example 6(d). It is wise to check the factoring in the second step, as shown in the example side comment, before continuing.

Work Problem **6** *at the Side.*

Factoring a Polynomial with Four Terms by Grouping

Step 1   **Group terms.** Collect the terms into two groups so that each group has a common factor.

Step 2   **Factor within groups.** Factor out the greatest common factor from each group.

Step 3   **Factor the entire polynomial.** Factor a common binomial factor from the results of Step 2.

Step 4   **If necessary, rearrange terms.** If Step 2 does not result in a common binomial factor, try a different grouping.

7 Factor by grouping.

(a) $6y^2 - 20w + 15y - 8yw$

(b) $9mn - 4 + 12m - 3n$

EXAMPLE 7   **Rearranging Terms Before Factoring by Grouping**

Factor by grouping.

(a) $10x^2 - 12y + 15x - 8xy$

Factoring out the common factor of 2 from the first two terms and the common factor of x from the last two terms gives

$$10x^2 - 12y + 15x - 8xy$$
$$= 2(5x^2 - 6y) + x(15 - 8y).$$

This does not lead to a common factor, so we try rearranging the terms. There is usually more than one way to do this. We try the following.

$$10x^2 - 12y + 15x - 8xy$$
$$= 10x^2 - 8xy - 12y + 15x \qquad \text{Commutative property}$$
$$= (10x^2 - 8xy) + (-12y + 15x) \qquad \text{Group the terms.}$$
$$= 2x(5x - 4y) + 3(-4y + 5x) \qquad \text{Factor each group.}$$
$$= 2x(5x - 4y) + 3(5x - 4y) \qquad \text{Rewrite } -4y + 5x.$$
$$= (5x - 4y)(2x + 3) \qquad \text{Factor out } 5x - 4y.$$

Check $(5x - 4y)(2x + 3)$
$$= 10x^2 + 15x - 8xy - 12y \qquad \text{FOIL}$$
$$= 10x^2 - 12y + 15x - 8xy \qquad \text{Original polynomial}$$

(b) $2xy + 12 - 3y - 8x$

We need to rearrange these terms to get two groups that each have a common factor. Trial and error suggests the following grouping.

$$2xy + 12 - 3y - 8x \qquad \boxed{\text{Always write a } + \text{ sign between the two groups.}}$$
$$= (2xy - 3y) + (-8x + 12) \qquad \text{Group the terms.}$$
$$= y(2x - 3) - 4(2x - 3) \qquad \text{Factor each group.}$$
$$\qquad\qquad \boxed{\text{Be careful with signs.}}$$
$$= (2x - 3)(y - 4) \qquad \text{Factor out } 2x - 3.$$

Since the quantities in parentheses in the second step must be the same, we factored out -4 rather than 4. *Check* by multiplying.

CAUTION
Use negative signs carefully when grouping, as in Example 7(b), or a sign error will occur. ***Always check by multiplying.***

◄ *Work Problem* **7** *at the Side.*

FOR EXTRA HELP   **MyMathLab**   Math XL PRACTICE   WATCH   DOWNLOAD   READ   REVIEW

Find the greatest common factor for each list of numbers. See Example 1.

1. 12, 16   **2.** 18, 24   🌐 **3.** 40, 20, 4   **4.** 50, 30, 5

5. 18, 24, 36, 48   **6.** 15, 30, 45, 75   **7.** 4, 9, 12   **8.** 9, 16, 24

Find the greatest common factor for each list of terms. See Example 2.

9. $16y$, 24   **10.** $18w$, 27   **11.** $30x^3, 40x^6, 50x^7$

12. $60z^4, 70z^8, 90z^9$ 🌐 **13.** $-x^4y^3, -xy^2$ **14.** $-a^4b^5, -a^3b$

15. $42ab^3, -36a, 90b, -48ab$ **16.** $45c^3d, 75c, 90d, -105cd$

Complete each factoring.

17. $9m^4 = 3m^2 (\quad)$ **18.** $12p^5 = 6p^3 (\quad)$ **19.** $-8z^9 = -4z^5 (\quad)$

20. $-15k^{11} = -5k^8 (\quad)$ **21.** $6m^4n^5 = 3m^3n (\quad)$ **22.** $27a^3b^2 = 9a^2b (\quad)$

23. $12y + 24 = 12(\quad)$ **24.** $18p + 36 = 18(\quad)$

25. $10a^2 - 20a = 10a(\quad)$ **26.** $15x^2 - 30x = 15x(\quad)$

27. $8x^2y + 12x^3y^2 = 4x^2y(\quad)$ **28.** $18s^3t^2 + 10st = 2st(\quad)$

Factor out the greatest common factor, or a negative common factor if the coefficient of the term of greatest degree is negative. See Examples 3–5.

29. $x^2 - 4x$ **30.** $m^2 - 7m$ **31.** $6t^2 + 15t$ **32.** $8x^2 + 6x$

33. $\frac{1}{4}d^2 - \frac{3}{4}d$ **34.** $\frac{1}{5}z^2 + \frac{3}{5}z$ **35.** $-12x^3 - 6x^2$ **36.** $-21b^3 + 7b^2$

37. $65y^{10} + 35y^6$ **38.** $100a^5 + 16a^3$ **39.** $11w^3 - 100$

40. $13z^5 - 80$ **41.** $8m^2n^3 + 24m^2n^2$ **42.** $19p^2y - 38p^2y^3$

43. $-4x^3 + 10x^2 - 6x$ **44.** $-9z^3 + 6z^2 - 12z$ **45.** $13y^8 + 26y^4 - 39y^2$

46. $5x^5 + 25x^4 - 20x^3$

47. $45q^4p^5 + 36qp^6 + 81q^2p^3$

48. $125a^3z^5 + 60a^4z^4 - 85a^5z^2$

49. $c(x + 2) + d(x + 2)$

50. $r(5 - x) + t(5 - x)$

51. $a^2(2a + b) - b(2a + b)$

52. $3x(x^2 + 5) - y(x^2 + 5)$

53. $q(p + 4) - 1(p + 4)$

54. $y^2(x - 4) + 1(x - 4)$

Factor by grouping. See Examples 6 and 7.

55. $5m + mn + 20 + 4n$

56. $ts + 5t + 2s + 10$

☉ 57. $6xy - 21x + 8y - 28$

58. $2mn - 8n + 3m - 12$

59. $3xy + 9x + y + 3$

60. $6n + 4mn + 3 + 2m$

61. $7z^2 + 14z - az - 2a$

62. $2b^2 + 3b - 8ab - 12a$

63. $18r^2 + 12ry - 3xr - 2xy$

64. $5m^2 + 15mp - 2mr - 6pr$

65. $w^3 + w^2 + 9w + 9$

66. $y^3 + y^2 + 6y + 6$

67. $3a^3 + 6a^2 - 2a - 4$

68. $10x^3 + 15x^2 - 8x - 12$

69. $16m^3 - 4m^2p^2 - 4mp + p^3$

70. $10t^3 - 2t^2s^2 - 5ts + s^3$

71. $y^2 + 3x + 3y + xy$

72. $m^2 + 14p + 7m + 2mp$

73. $2z^2 + 6w - 4z - 3wz$

74. $2a^2 + 20b - 8a - 5ab$

Relating Concepts (Exercises 75–78) For Individual or Group Work

In many cases, the choice of which pairs of terms to group when factoring by grouping can be made in different ways. To see this for Example 7(b), **work Exercises 75–78 in order.**

75. Start with the polynomial from Example 7(b), $2xy + 12 - 3y - 8x$, and rearrange the terms as follows: $2xy - 8x - 3y + 12$. What property from **Section 1.3** allows this?

76. Group the first two terms and the last two terms of the rearranged polynomial in Exercise 75. Then factor each group.

77. Is your result from Exercise 76 in factored form? Explain your answer.

78. If your answer to Exercise 77 is *no*, factor the polynomial. Is the result the same as the one shown for Example 7(b)?

15.2 ►►► Factoring Trinomials

Using FOIL, the product of the binomials $k - 3$ and $k + 1$ is

$$(k - 3)(k + 1) = k^2 - 2k - 3. \quad \text{Multiplying}$$

Suppose instead that we are given the polynomial $k^2 - 2k - 3$ and want to rewrite it as the product $(k - 3)(k + 1)$. That is,

$$k^2 - 2k - 3 = (k - 3)(k + 1). \quad \text{Factoring}$$

Recall from **Section 15.1** that this process is called *factoring* the polynomial. Factoring reverses or, "undoes," multiplying.

OBJECTIVE 1 Factor trinomials with a coefficient of 1 for the squared term. When factoring polynomials with integer coefficients, we use only integers in the factors. For example, we can factor $x^2 + 5x + 6$ by finding integers m and n such that

$$x^2 + 5x + 6 \quad \text{is written as} \quad (x + m)(x + n).$$

To find these integers m and n, we first use FOIL to multiply the two binomials on the right above:

$$(x + m)(x + n)$$
$$= x^2 + nx + mx + mn$$
$$= x^2 + (n + m)x + mn. \quad \text{Distributive property}$$

Comparing this result with $x^2 + 5x + 6$ shows that we must find integers m and n having a sum of 5 and a product of 6.

$$x^2 + 5x + 6 = x^2 + (n + m)x + mn$$

Product of m and n is 6.

Sum of m and n is 5.

Because many pairs of integers have a sum of 5, it is best to begin by listing those pairs of integers whose product is 6. Both 5 and 6 are positive, so we consider only pairs in which both integers are positive.

Work Problem **1** *at the Side.* ►

From Problem 1 at the side, we see that the numbers 1 and 6 and the numbers 2 and 3 both have a product of 6, but only the pair 2 and 3 has a sum of 5. So 2 and 3 are the required integers, and

$$x^2 + 5x + 6 \quad \text{is factored as} \quad (x + 2)(x + 3).$$

Check by multiplying the binomials using FOIL. *Make sure that the sum of the outer and inner products produces the correct middle term.*

Check
$$(x + 2)(x + 3) = x^2 + 5x + 6 \quad \text{Correct}$$
$$2x$$
$$3x$$
$$\overline{5x} \quad \text{Add.}$$

This method of factoring can be used only for trinomials that have 1 as the coefficient of the squared term.

OBJECTIVES

1 **Factor trinomials with a coefficient of 1 for the squared term.**

2 **Factor trinomials after factoring out the greatest common factor.**

---

1 **(a)** List all pairs of positive integers whose product is 6.

(b) Find the pair from part (a) whose sum is 5.

---

2 Factor each trinomial.

(a) $y^2 + 12y + 20$

First complete the given list of numbers.

Factors of 20	Sums of Factors
20, 1	20 + 1 = 21
10, __	10 + __ = __
5, __	5 + __ = __

(b) $x^2 + 9x + 18$

3 Factor each trinomial.

(a) $t^2 - 12t + 32$

First complete the given list of numbers.

Factors of 32	Sums of Factors
−32, −1	−32 + (−1) = −33
−16, __	−16 + (__) = __
−8, __	−8 + (__) = __

(b) $y^2 - 10y + 24$

EXAMPLE 1   Factoring a Trinomial with All Positive Terms

Factor $m^2 + 9m + 14$.

Look for two integers whose product is 14 and whose sum is 9. List the pairs of integers whose products are 14. Then examine the sums. Only positive integers are needed since all signs in $m^2 + 9m + 14$ are positive.

Factors of 14	Sums of Factors
14, 1	14 + 1 = 15
7, 2	7 + 2 = 9

Sum is 9.

From the list, 7 and 2 are the required integers, since $7 \cdot 2 = 14$ and $7 + 2 = 9$. Thus,

$$m^2 + 9m + 14 \quad \text{factors as} \quad (m + 2)(m + 7).$$

Check $(m + 2)(m + 7)$

$= m^2 + 7m + 2m + 14$ FOIL

$= m^2 + 9m + 14$ Original polynomial

Note

In Example 1, the answer $(m + 2)(m + 7)$ also could have been written

$$(m + 7)(m + 2).$$

Because of the commutative property of multiplication, the order of the factors does not matter. *Always check by multiplying.*

◀ Work Problem **2** at the Side.

EXAMPLE 2   Factoring a Trinomial with a Negative Middle Term

Factor $x^2 - 9x + 20$.

Find two integers whose product is 20 and whose sum is −9. Since the numbers we are looking for have a *positive product* and a *negative sum*, we consider only pairs of negative integers.

Factors of 20	Sums of Factors
−20, −1	−20 + (−1) = −21
−10, −2	−10 + (−2) = −12
−5, −4	−5 + (−4) = −9

Sum is −9.

The required integers are −5 and −4, so

$$x^2 - 9x + 20 \quad \text{factors as} \quad (x - 5)(x - 4).$$

Check $(x - 5)(x - 4)$

$= x^2 - 4x - 5x + 20$ FOIL

$= x^2 - 9x + 20$ Original polynomial

◀ Work Problem **3** at the Side.

EXAMPLE 3   **Factoring a Trinomial with Two Negative Terms**

Factor $p^2 - 2p - 15$.

Find two integers whose product is -15 and whose sum is -2. If these numbers do not come to mind right away, find them (if they exist) by listing all the pairs of integers whose product is -15. Because the last term, -15, is negative, we need pairs of integers with different signs.

Factors of -15	Sums of Factors
$15, -1$	$15 + (-1) = 14$
$-15, 1$	$-15 + 1 = -14$
$5, -3$	$5 + (-3) = 2$
$-5, 3$	$-5 + 3 = -2$ Sum is -2.

The required integers are -5 and 3, so

$$p^2 - 2p - 15 \quad \text{factors as} \quad (p - 5)(p + 3).$$

Check   Multiply $(p - 5)(p + 3)$ to obtain $p^2 - 2p - 15$.

Note

In Examples 1–3, notice that we listed factors in descending order (disregarding sign) when we were looking for the required pair of integers. This helps avoid skipping the correct combination.

Work Problem **4** *at the Side.* ▶

As shown in the next example, some trinomials cannot be factored using only integers. We call such trinomials **prime polynomials.**

EXAMPLE 4   **Deciding Whether Polynomials Are Prime**

Factor each trinomial.

(a) $x^2 - 5x + 12$

As in Example 2, both factors must be negative to give a positive product and a negative sum. First, list all the pairs of negative integers whose product is 12. Then examine the sums.

Factors of 12	Sums of Factors
$-12, -1$	$-12 + (-1) = -13$
$-6, -2$	$-6 + (-2) = -8$
$-4, -3$	$-4 + (-3) = -7$

None of the pairs of integers has a sum of -5. Therefore, the trinomial $x^2 - 5x + 12$ *cannot be factored using only integers; it is a prime polynomial.*

(b) $k^2 - 8k + 11$

There is no pair of integers whose product is 11 and whose sum is -8, so $k^2 - 8k + 11$ is a prime polynomial.

Work Problem **5** *at the Side.* ▶

4 Factor each trinomial.

(a) $a^2 - 9a - 22$

(b) $r^2 - 6r - 16$

5 Factor each trinomial, if possible.

(a) $r^2 - 3r - 4$

(b) $m^2 - 2m + 5$

ANSWERS

4. (a) $(a - 11)(a + 2)$ **(b)** $(r - 8)(r + 2)$
5. (a) $(r - 4)(r + 1)$ **(b)** prime

Guidelines for factoring a trinomial of the form $x^2 + bx + c$ are summarized here.

6 Factor each trinomial.

(a) $b^2 - 3ab - 4a^2$

Factoring $x^2 + bx + c$

Find two integers whose product is c and whose sum is b.

1. Both integers must be positive if b and c are positive.

2. Both integers must be negative if c is positive and b is negative.

3. One integer must be positive and one must be negative if c is negative.

(b) $r^2 - 6rs + 8s^2$

EXAMPLE 5   **Factoring a Trinomial with Two Variables**

Factor $z^2 - 2bz - 3b^2$.

    Here, the coefficient of z in the middle term is $-2b$, so we need to find two expressions whose product is $-3b^2$ and whose sum is $-2b$. The expressions are $-3b$ and b, so

$$z^2 - 2bz - 3b^2 \quad \text{factors as} \quad (z - 3b)(z + b).$$

Check $(z - 3b)(z + b)$

$$= z^2 + zb - 3bz - 3b^2 \qquad \text{FOIL}$$

$$= z^2 + 1bz - 3bz - 3b^2 \qquad \text{Identity and commutative properties}$$

$$= z^2 - 2bz - 3b^2 \qquad \text{Combine like terms.}$$

◀ *Work Problem* **6** *at the Side.*

7 Factor each trinomial completely.

(a) $2p^3 + 6p^2 - 8p$

OBJECTIVE **2** **Factor trinomials after factoring out the greatest common factor.**   The trinomial in the next example does not have a coefficient of 1 for the squared term. (In fact, there is no squared term.) However, there may be a common factor.

EXAMPLE 6   **Factoring a Trinomial with a Common Factor**

Factor $4x^5 - 28x^4 + 40x^3$.

    First, factor out the greatest common factor, $4x^3$.

$$4x^5 - 28x^4 + 40x^3$$

$$= 4x^3(x^2 - 7x + 10)$$

(b) $-3x^4 + 15x^3 - 18x^2$

Now factor $x^2 - 7x + 10$. The integers -5 and -2 have a product of 10 and a sum of -7. The complete factored form is

    Include $4x^3$. $4x^3(x - 5)(x - 2)$.

Check $4x^3(x - 5)(x - 2)$

$$= 4x^3(x^2 - 7x + 10) \qquad \text{FOIL}$$

$$= 4x^5 - 28x^4 + 40x^3 \qquad \text{Distributive property}$$

◀ *Work Problem* **7** *at the Side.*

CAUTION

When factoring, ***always look for a common factor first.*** Remember to include the common factor as part of the answer. As a check, multiplying out the complete factored form should give the original polynomial.

15.2 ▶▶▶ Exercises

1. When factoring a trinomial in x as $(x + a)(x + b)$, what must be true of a and b, if the last term of the trinomial is negative?

2. In Exercise 1, what must be true of a and b if the last term is positive?

3. What is meant by a *prime polynomial*?

4. How can you check your work when factoring a trinomial? Does the check ensure that the trinomial is *completely* factored?

In Exercises 5–8, list all pairs of integers with the given product. Then find the pair whose sum is given. See the tables in Examples 1–4.

5. Product: 12; Sum: 7

6. Product: 18; Sum: 9

7. Product: -24; Sum: -5

8. Product: -36; Sum: -16

9. Which one of the following is the correct factored form of $x^2 - 12x + 32$?

  A. $(x - 8)(x + 4)$ **B.** $(x + 8)(x - 4)$
  C. $(x - 8)(x - 4)$ **D.** $(x + 8)(x + 4)$

10. What would be the first step in factoring
$$2x^3 + 8x^2 - 10x?$$

Complete each factoring.

11. $x^2 + 15x + 44 = (x + 4)(\quad)$

12. $r^2 + 15r + 56 = (r + 7)(\quad)$

13. $x^2 - 9x + 8 = (x - 1)(\quad)$

14. $t^2 - 14t + 24 = (t - 2)(\quad)$

15. $y^2 - 2y - 15 = (y + 3)(\quad)$

16. $t^2 - t - 42 = (t + 6)(\quad)$

17. $x^2 + 9x - 22 = (x - 2)(\quad)$

18. $x^2 + 6x - 27 = (x - 3)(\quad)$

19. $y^2 - 7y - 18 = (y + 2)(\quad)$

20. $y^2 - 2y - 24 = (y + 4)(\quad)$

Factor completely. If a polynomial cannot be factored, write prime. See Examples 1–4.

21. $y^2 + 9y + 8$

22. $a^2 + 9a + 20$

23. $b^2 + 8b + 15$

24. $x^2 + 6x + 8$

25. $m^2 + m - 20$

26. $p^2 + 4p - 5$

27. $x^2 + 3x - 40$

28. $d^2 + 4d - 45$

29. $y^2 - 8y + 15$

30. $y^2 - 6y + 8$

31. $z^2 - 15z + 56$

32. $x^2 - 13x + 36$

33. $r^2 - r - 30$

34. $q^2 - q - 42$

35. $a^2 - 8a - 48$

36. $m^2 - 10m - 24$

37. $x^2 + 4x + 5$

38. $t^2 + 11t + 12$

Factor completely. See Examples 5 and 6.

39. $r^2 + 3ra + 2a^2$

40. $x^2 + 5xa + 4a^2$

41. $x^2 + 4xy + 3y^2$

42. $p^2 + 9pq + 8q^2$

43. $t^2 - tz - 6z^2$

44. $a^2 - ab - 12b^2$

45. $v^2 - 11vw + 30w^2$

46. $v^2 - 11vx + 24x^2$

47. $4x^2 + 12x - 40$

48. $5y^2 - 5y - 30$

49. $2t^3 + 8t^2 + 6t$

50. $3t^3 + 27t^2 + 24t$

51. $-2x^6 - 8x^5 + 42x^4$

52. $-4y^5 - 12y^4 + 40y^3$

53. $a^5 + 3a^4b - 4a^3b^2$

54. $z^{10} - 4z^9y - 21z^8y^2$

55. $m^3n - 10m^2n^2 + 24mn^3$

56. $y^3z + 3y^2z^2 - 54yz^3$

57. Use the FOIL method from **Section 13.3** to show that $(2x + 4)(x - 3) = 2x^2 - 2x - 12$. Why, then, is it incorrect to completely factor $2x^2 - 2x - 12$ as $(2x + 4)(x - 3)$?

58. Why is it incorrect to completely factor $3x^2 + 9x - 12$ as the product $(x - 1)(3x + 12)$?

15.3 ▶▶▶ Factoring Trinomials by Grouping

Trinomials like $2x^2 + 7x + 6$, in which the coefficient of the squared term is *not* 1, are factored with extensions of the methods from the previous sections. One such method uses factoring by grouping from **Section 15.1**.

OBJECTIVE 1 Factor trinomials by grouping when the coefficient of the squared term is not 1. Recall that a trinomial such as $m^2 + 3m + 2$ is factored by finding two integers whose product is 2 and whose sum is 3. To factor $2x^2 + 7x + 6$, we look for two integers whose product is $2 \cdot 6 = 12$ and whose sum is 7.

$$\underbrace{2x^2 + 7x + 6}$$

Sum is 7.

Product is $2 \cdot 6 = 12$.

By considering pairs of positive integers whose product is 12, the necessary integers are found to be 3 and 4. We use these integers to write the middle term, $7x$, as $7x = 3x + 4x$. The trinomial $2x^2 + 7x + 6$ becomes

$$2x^2 + 7x + 6$$
$$= 2x^2 + \underbrace{3x + 4x}_{7x} + 6$$
$$= (2x^2 + 3x) + (4x + 6) \qquad \text{Group the terms.}$$
$$= x(2x + 3) + 2(2x + 3) \qquad \text{Factor each group.}$$

Must be the same

$$= (2x + 3)(x + 2). \qquad \text{Factor out } 2x + 3.$$

Check Multiply $(2x + 3)(x + 2)$ to obtain $2x^2 + 7x + 6$.

In the preceding example, we could have written $7x$ as $4x + 3x$. Factoring by grouping this way would give the same answer.

Work Problem **1** *at the Side.* ▶

EXAMPLE 1 Factoring Trinomials by Grouping

Factor each trinomial.

(a) $6r^2 + r - 1$

We must find two integers with a product of $6(-1) = -6$ and a sum of 1. The integers are -2 and 3. We write the middle term, r, as $-2r + 3r$.

$$6r^2 + r - 1$$
$$= 6r^2 - 2r + 3r - 1 \qquad r = -2r + 3r$$
$$= (6r^2 - 2r) + (3r - 1) \qquad \text{Group the terms.}$$
$$= 2r(3r - 1) + 1(3r - 1) \qquad \text{The binomials must be the same.}$$

Remember the 1.

$$= (3r - 1)(2r + 1) \qquad \text{Factor out } 3r - 1.$$

Check Multiply $(3r - 1)(2r + 1)$ to obtain $6r^2 + r - 1$.

Continued on Next Page

OBJECTIVE

1 **Factor trinomials by grouping when the coefficient of the squared term is not 1.**

1 (a) Factor $2x^2 + 7x + 6$ by writing $7x$ as $4x + 3x$. Complete the following.

$$2x^2 + 7x + 6$$
$$= 2x^2 + 4x + 3x + 6$$
$$= (2x^2 + \underline{\quad}) + (3x + \underline{\quad})$$
$$= 2x(x + \underline{\quad}) + 3(x + \underline{\quad})$$
$$= (\underline{\quad})(2x + 3)$$

(b) Is the answer in part (a) the same as in the example? (Remember that the order of the factors does not matter.)

ANSWERS

1. (a) $4x$; 6; 2; 2; $x + 2$ **(b)** yes

2 Factor each trinomial by grouping.

(a) $2m^2 + 7m + 3$

(b) $5p^2 - 2p - 3$

(c) $15k^2 - km - 2m^2$

(b) $12z^2 - 5z - 2$

Look for two integers whose product is $12(-2) = -24$ and whose sum is -5. The required integers are 3 and -8, so

$$12z^2 - 5z - 2$$

$$= 12z^2 + 3z - 8z - 2 \qquad -5z = 3z - 8z$$

$$= (12z^2 + 3z) + (-8z - 2) \qquad \text{Group the terms.}$$

$$= 3z(4z + 1) - 2(4z + 1) \qquad \text{Factor each group.}$$

> Be careful with signs.

$$= (4z + 1)(3z - 2). \qquad \text{Factor out } 4z + 1.$$

Check Multiply $(4z + 1)(3z - 2)$ to obtain $12z^2 - 5z - 2$.

(c) $10m^2 + mn - 3n^2$

Two integers whose product is $10(-3) = -30$ and whose sum is 1 are -5 and 6. Rewrite the trinomial with four terms.

$$10m^2 + mn - 3n^2$$

$$= 10m^2 - 5mn + 6mn - 3n^2 \qquad mn = -5mn + 6mn$$

$$= 5m(2m - n) + 3n(2m - n) \qquad \text{Group the terms; factor each group.}$$

$$= (2m - n)(5m + 3n) \qquad \text{Factor out } 2m - n.$$

> Check by multiplying.

◀ *Work Problem* **2** *at the Side.*

3 Factor each trinomial completely.

(a) $-4x^2 + 2x + 30$

(b) $18p^4 + 63p^3 + 27p^2$

(c) $6a^2 + 3ab - 18b^2$

> **EXAMPLE 2** **Factoring a Trinomial with a Common Factor by Grouping**

Factor $28x^5 - 58x^4 - 30x^3$.

First factor out the greatest common factor, $2x^3$.

$$28x^5 - 58x^4 - 30x^3$$

$$= 2x^3(14x^2 - 29x - 15)$$

To factor $14x^2 - 29x - 15$, find two integers whose product is $14(-15) = -210$ and whose sum is -29. Factoring 210 into prime factors gives

$$210 = 2 \cdot 3 \cdot 5 \cdot 7.$$

Combine these prime factors in pairs in different ways, using one positive factor and one negative factor to get -210. The factors 6 and -35 have the correct sum, -29. Now rewrite the given trinomial and factor it.

$$28x^5 - 58x^4 - 30x^3$$

> Remember the common factor.

$$= 2x^3(14x^2 - 29x - 15)$$

$$= 2x^3(14x^2 + 6x - 35x - 15)$$

$$= 2x^3[(14x^2 + 6x) + (-35x - 15)]$$

$$= 2x^3[2x(7x + 3) - 5(7x + 3)]$$

$$= 2x^3[(7x + 3)(2x - 5)]$$

$$= 2x^3(7x + 3)(2x - 5)$$

◀ *Work Problem* **3** *at the Side.*

ANSWERS

2. (a) $(2m + 1)(m + 3)$
   (b) $(5p + 3)(p - 1)$
   (c) $(5k - 2m)(3k + m)$
3. (a) $-2(2x + 5)(x - 3)$
   (b) $9p^2(2p + 1)(p + 3)$
   (c) $3(2a - 3b)(a + 2b)$

FOR EXTRA HELP  MyMathLab Math XL PRACTICE WATCH DOWNLOAD READ REVIEW

The middle term of each trinomial has been rewritten. Now factor by grouping.
See Example 1.

1. $m^2 + 8m + 12$
$= m^2 + 6m + 2m + 12$

2. $x^2 + 9x + 14$
$= x^2 + 7x + 2x + 14$

3. $a^2 + 3a - 10$
$= a^2 + 5a - 2a - 10$

4. $y^2 - 2y - 24$
$= y^2 + 4y - 6y - 24$

5. $10t^2 + 9t + 2$
$= 10t^2 + 5t + 4t + 2$

6. $6x^2 + 13x + 6$
$= 6x^2 + 9x + 4x + 6$

7. $15z^2 - 19z + 6$
$= 15z^2 - 10z - 9z + 6$

8. $12p^2 - 17p + 6$
$= 12p^2 - 9p - 8p + 6$

9. $8s^2 + 2st - 3t^2$
$= 8s^2 - 4st + 6st - 3t^2$

10. $3x^2 - xy - 14y^2$
$= 3x^2 - 7xy + 6xy - 14y^2$

11. $15a^2 + 22ab + 8b^2$
$= 15a^2 + 10ab + 12ab + 8b^2$

12. $25m^2 + 25mn + 6n^2$
$= 25m^2 + 15mn + 10mn + 6n^2$

13. Which pair of integers would be used to rewrite the middle term when factoring $12y^2 + 5y - 2$ by grouping?

A. $-8, 3$ **B.** $8, -3$ **C.** $-6, 4$ **D.** $6, -4$

14. Which pair of integers would be used to rewrite the middle term when factoring $20b^2 - 13b + 2$ by grouping?

A. $10, 3$ **B.** $-10, -3$ **C.** $8, 5$ **D.** $-8, -5$

Complete the steps to factor each trinomial by grouping.

15. $2m^2 + 11m + 12$

  (a) Find two integers whose product is

  _____ · _____ = _____ and whose
  sum is _____.

  (b) The required integers are _____ and
  _____.

  (c) Write the middle term $11m$ as _____ +
  _____.

  (d) Rewrite the given trinomial using four terms.

  (e) Factor the polynomial in part (d) by grouping.

  (f) Check by multiplying.

16. $6y^2 - 19y + 10$

  (a) Find two integers whose product is

  _____ · _____ = _____ and whose
  sum is _____.

  (b) The required integers are _____ and
  _____.

  (c) Write the middle term $-19y$ as _____ +
  _____.

  (d) Rewrite the given trinomial using four terms.

  (e) Factor the polynomial in part (d) by grouping.

  (f) Check by multiplying.

Factor each trinomial by grouping. See Examples 1 and 2.

17. $2x^2 + 7x + 3$

18. $3y^2 + 13y + 4$

19. $4r^2 + r - 3$

20. $4r^2 + 3r - 10$

21. $8m^2 - 10m - 3$

22. $20x^2 - 28x - 3$

23. $21m^2 + 13m + 2$

24. $38x^2 + 23x + 2$

25. $6b^2 + 7b + 2$

26. $6w^2 + 19w + 10$

27. $12y^2 - 13y + 3$

28. $15a^2 - 16a + 4$

29. $24x^2 - 42x + 9$

30. $48b^2 - 74b - 10$

31. $2m^3 + 2m^2 - 40m$

32. $3x^3 + 12x^2 - 36x$

33. $-32z^5 + 20z^4 + 12z^3$

34. $-18x^5 - 15x^4 + 75x^3$

35. $12p^2 + 7pq - 12q^2$

36. $6m^2 - 5mn - 6n^2$

37. $6a^2 - 7ab - 5b^2$

38. $25g^2 - 5gh - 2h^2$

39. $5 - 6x + x^2$

40. $7 + 8x + x^2$

41. On a quiz, a student factored $16x^2 - 24x + 5$ by grouping as follows.

$$16x^2 - 24x + 5$$
$$= 16x^2 - 4x - 20x + 5$$
$$= 4x(4x - 1) - 5(4x - 1) \qquad \text{His answer}$$

He thought his answer was correct since it checked by multiplying. Why was his answer marked wrong? What is the correct factored form?

42. On the same quiz, another student factored $3k^3 - 12k^2 - 15k$ by first factoring out the common factor $3k$ to get $3k(k^2 - 4k - 5)$. Then she wrote

$$k^2 - 4k - 5$$
$$= k^2 - 5k + k - 5$$
$$= k(k - 5) + 1(k - 5)$$
$$= (k - 5)(k + 1). \qquad \text{Her answer}$$

Why was her answer marked wrong? What is the correct factored form?

15.4 ▶▶▶ Factoring Trinomials Using FOIL

OBJECTIVE 1 Factor trinomials using FOIL. This section shows an alternative method of factoring trinomials in which the coefficient of the squared term is not 1. This method uses trial and error.

To factor $2x^2 + 7x + 6$ (the same trinomial factored at the beginning of **Section 15.3**) by trial and error, we use FOIL backwards. We want to write $2x^2 + 7x + 6$ as the product of two binomials.

$$(\qquad)(\qquad)$$

The product of the two first terms of the binomials is $2x^2$. The possible factors of $2x^2$ are $2x$ and x or $-2x$ and $-x$. Since all terms of the trinomial are positive, we consider only positive factors. Thus, we have

$$(2x\qquad)(x\qquad).$$

The product of the two last terms, 6, can be factored as $1 \cdot 6, 6 \cdot 1, 2 \cdot 3$, or $3 \cdot 2$. Try each pair to find the pair that gives the correct middle term, $7x$.

Work Problem ① *at the Side.* ▶

In part (b) at the side, since $2x + 6 = 2(x + 3)$, the binomial $2x + 6$ has a common factor of 2, while $2x^2 + 7x + 6$ has no common factor other than 1. The product $(2x + 6)(x + 1)$ cannot be correct. (Part (c) also has one binomial factor with a common factor.)

> **Note**
> If the original polynomial has no common factor, then none of its binomial factors will either.

Now try the remaining numbers 3 and 2 as factors of 6.

$$(2x + 3)(x + 2) = 2x^2 + 7x + 6 \qquad \text{Correct}$$

$$3x$$
$$4x$$
$$7x \qquad \text{Add.}$$

Finally, we see that $2x^2 + 7x + 6$ factors as $(2x + 3)(x + 2)$.

Check Multiply $(2x + 3)(x + 2)$ to obtain $2x^2 + 7x + 6$.

EXAMPLE 1 **Factoring a Trinomial with All Positive Terms Using FOIL**

Factor $8p^2 + 14p + 5$.

The number 8 has several possible pairs of factors, but 5 has only 1 and 5 or -1 and -5. For this reason, it is easier to begin by considering the factors of 5. Ignore the negative factors, since all coefficients in the trinomial are positive. If $8p^2 + 14p + 5$ can be factored, the factors will have the form

$$(\qquad + 5)(\qquad + 1).$$

Continued on Next Page

OBJECTIVE

1 Factor trinomials using FOIL.

① Multiply to decide whether each factored form is correct or incorrect for
$$2x^2 + 7x + 6.$$
(a) $(2x + 1)(x + 6)$

(b) $(2x + 6)(x + 1)$

(c) $(2x + 2)(x + 3)$

2 Factor each trinomial.

(a) $2p^2 + 9p + 9$

(b) $6p^2 + 19p + 10$

(c) $8x^2 + 14x + 3$

3 Factor each trinomial.

(a) $4y^2 - 11y + 6$

(b) $9x^2 - 21x + 10$

When factoring $8p^2 + 14p + 5$, the possible pairs of factors of $8p^2$ are $8p$ and p, or $4p$ and $2p$. Try various combinations, checking to see if the middle term is $14p$ in each case.

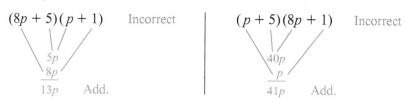

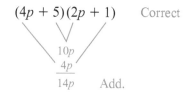

Since $14p$ is the correct middle term,

$$8p^2 + 14p + 5 \quad \text{factors as} \quad (4p + 5)(2p + 1).$$

Check Multiply $(4p + 5)(2p + 1)$ to obtain $8p^2 + 14p + 5$.

◀ *Work Problem* **2** *at the Side.*

EXAMPLE 2 **Factoring a Trinomial with a Negative Middle Term Using FOIL**

Factor $6x^2 - 11x + 3$.

Since 3 has only 1 and 3 or -1 and -3 as factors, it is better here to begin by factoring 3. The last term of the trinomial $6x^2 - 11x + 3$ is positive and the middle term has a negative coefficient, so we consider only negative factors. We need two negative factors because the *product* of two negative factors is positive and their *sum* is negative, as required.

Try -3 and -1 as factors of 3:

$$(\quad - 3)(\quad - 1).$$

The factors of $6x^2$ may be either $6x$ and x, or $2x$ and $3x$.

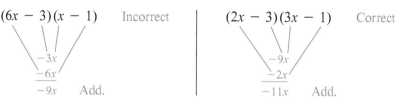

The factors $2x$ and $3x$ produce $-11x$, the correct middle term, so

$$6x^2 - 11x + 3 \quad \text{factors as} \quad (2x - 3)(3x - 1).$$

Check Multiply $(2x - 3)(3x - 1)$ to obtain $6x^2 - 11x + 3$.

Note

In Example 2, we might also realize that our initial attempt to factor $6x^2 - 11x + 3$ as $(6x - 3)(x - 1)$ *cannot* be correct since $6x - 3$ has a common factor of 3 and the original polynomial does not.

◀ *Work Problem* **3** *at the Side.*

EXAMPLE 3   **Factoring a Trinomial with a Negative Last Term Using FOIL**

Factor $8x^2 + 6x - 9$.

The integer 8 has several possible pairs of factors, as does -9. Since the last term is negative, one positive factor and one negative factor of -9 are needed. Since the coefficient of the middle term is small, it is wise to avoid large factors such as 8 or 9. We try 4 and 2 as factors of 8, and 3 and -3 as factors of -9, and check the middle term.

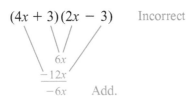

$(4x + 3)(2x - 3)$ Incorrect

$6x$
$-12x$
$-6x$ Add.

Now we try interchanging 3 and -3, since only the sign of the middle term is incorrect.

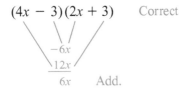

$(4x - 3)(2x + 3)$ Correct

$-6x$
$12x$
$6x$ Add.

This combination produces $6x$, the correct middle term, so

$$8x^2 + 6x - 9 \quad \text{factors as} \quad (4x - 3)(2x + 3).$$

——————— *Work Problem* 4 *at the Side.* ▶

EXAMPLE 4   **Factoring a Trinomial with Two Variables**

Factor $12a^2 - ab - 20b^2$.

There are several pairs of factors of $12a^2$, including

$$12a \text{ and } a, \quad 6a \text{ and } 2a, \quad \text{and} \quad 4a \text{ and } 3a,$$

just as there are many possible pairs of factors of $-20b^2$, including

$$20b \text{ and } -b, \quad -20b \text{ and } b, \quad 10b \text{ and } -2b,$$

$$-10b \text{ and } 2b, \quad 4b \text{ and } -5b, \quad \text{and} \quad -4b \text{ and } 5b.$$

Once again, since the coefficient of the middle term is small, avoid the larger factors. Try the factors $6a$ and $2a$ and $4b$ and $-5b$.

$$(6a + 4b)(2a - 5b)$$

This cannot be correct, as mentioned before, since $6a + 4b$ has 2 as a common factor, while the given trinomial does not. Try $3a$ and $4a$ with $4b$ and $-5b$.

$$(3a + 4b)(4a - 5b)$$

$$= 12a^2 + ab - 20b^2 \quad \text{Incorrect}$$

Here the middle term is ab, rather than $-ab$. Interchange the signs of the last two terms in the factors.

$$(3a - 4b)(4a + 5b)$$

$$= 12a^2 - ab - 20b^2 \quad \text{Correct}$$

——————— *Work Problem* 5 *at the Side.* ▶

4 Factor each trinomial, if possible.

(a) $6x^2 + 5x - 4$

(b) $6m^2 - 11m - 10$

(c) $4x^2 - 3x - 7$

(d) $3y^2 + 8y - 6$

5 Factor each trinomial.

(a) $2x^2 - 5xy - 3y^2$

(b) $8a^2 + 2ab - 3b^2$

ANSWERS

4. (a) $(3x + 4)(2x - 1)$
   (b) $(2m - 5)(3m + 2)$
   (c) $(4x - 7)(x + 1)$
   (d) prime
5. (a) $(2x + y)(x - 3y)$
   (b) $(4a + 3b)(2a - b)$

6 Factor each trinomial.

(a) $36z^3 - 6z^2 - 72z$

(b) $-24x^3 + 32x^2y + 6xy^2$

EXAMPLE 5   **Factoring Trinomials with Common Factors**

Factor each trinomial.

(a) $15y^3 + 55y^2 + 30y$

First factor out the greatest common factor, $5y$.

$$15y^3 + 55y^2 + 30y$$
$$= 5y(3y^2 + 11y + 6)$$

Now factor $3y^2 + 11y + 6$. Try $3y$ and y as factors of $3y^2$ and 2 and 3 as factors of 6.

$$(3y + 2)(y + 3)$$
$$= 3y^2 + 11y + 6 \qquad \text{Correct}$$

The complete factored form of $15y^3 + 55y^2 + 30y$ is

$$5y(3y + 2)(y + 3).$$

Remember the common factor.

Check $5y(3y + 2)(y + 3)$
$$= 5y(3y^2 + 11y + 6) \qquad \text{FOIL}$$
$$= 15y^3 + 55y^2 + 30y \qquad \text{Distributive property}$$

(b) $-24a^3 - 42a^2 + 45a$

The common factor could be $3a$ or $-3a$. If we factor out $-3a$, the first term of the trinomial will be positive, which makes it easier to factor.

$$-24a^3 - 42a^2 + 45a$$
$$= -3a(8a^2 + 14a - 15) \qquad \text{Factor out } -3a.$$
$$= -3a(4a - 3)(2a + 5) \qquad \text{Use trial and error.}$$

Check $-3a(4a - 3)(2a + 5)$
$$= -3a(8a^2 + 14a - 15)$$
$$= -24a^3 - 42a^2 + 45a$$

CAUTION
This caution bears repeating: ***Remember to include the common factor in the final factored form.***

◀ *Work Problem* **6** *at the Side.*

15.4 ▶▶▶ **Exercises**

Decide which is the correct factored form of the given polynomial.

1. $2x^2 - x - 1$
   A. $(2x - 1)(x + 1)$ **B.** $(2x + 1)(x - 1)$

2. $3a^2 - 5a - 2$
   A. $(3a + 1)(a - 2)$ **B.** $(3a - 1)(a + 2)$

3. $4y^2 + 17y - 15$
   A. $(y + 5)(4y - 3)$ **B.** $(2y - 5)(2y + 3)$

4. $12c^2 - 7c - 12$
   A. $(6c - 2)(2c + 6)$ **B.** $(4c + 3)(3c - 4)$

5. $4k^2 + 13mk + 3m^2$
   A. $(4k + m)(k + 3m)$ **B.** $(4k + 3m)(k + m)$

6. $2x^2 + 11x + 12$
   A. $(2x + 3)(x + 4)$ **B.** $(2x + 4)(x + 3)$

Complete each factoring.

7. $6a^2 + 7ab - 20b^2$
   $= (3a - 4b)(\qquad)$

8. $9m^2 - 3mn - 2n^2$
   $= (3m + n)(\qquad)$

9. $2x^2 + 6x - 8$
   $= 2(\qquad\qquad)$
   $= 2(\qquad)(\qquad)$

10. $3x^2 - 9x - 30$
   $= 3(\qquad\qquad)$
   $= 3(\qquad)(\qquad)$

11. $4z^3 - 10z^2 - 6z$
   $= 2z(\qquad\qquad)$
   $= 2z(\qquad)(\qquad)$

12. $15r^3 - 39r^2 - 18r$
   $= 3r(\qquad\qquad)$
   $= 3r(\qquad)(\qquad)$

13. For the polynomial $12x^2 + 7x - 12$, 2 is not a common factor. Explain why the binomial $2x - 6$, then, cannot be a factor of the polynomial.

14. How are the signs of the last terms of the two binomial factors of a trinomial determined?

Factor each trinomial completely. See Examples 1–5.

🌐 **15.** $3a^2 + 10a + 7$

16. $7r^2 + 8r + 1$

17. $2y^2 + 7y + 6$

18. $5z^2 + 12z + 4$

19. $15m^2 + m - 2$

20. $6x^2 + x - 1$

21. $12s^2 + 11s - 5$

22. $20x^2 + 11x - 3$

🌐 **23.** $10m^2 - 23m + 12$

24. $6x^2 - 17x + 12$

25. $8w^2 - 14w + 3$

26. $9p^2 - 18p + 8$

27. $20y^2 - 39y - 11$

28. $10x^2 - 11x - 6$

29. $3x^2 - 15x + 16$

30. $2t^2 + 13t - 18$

31. $20x^2 + 22x + 6$

32. $36y^2 + 81y + 45$

33. $-40m^2q - mq + 6q$

34. $-15a^2b - 22ab - 8b$

35. $15n^4 - 39n^3 + 18n^2$

36. $24a^4 + 10a^3 - 4a^2$

37. $-15x^2y^2 + 7xy^2 + 4y^2$

38. $-14a^2b^3 - 15ab^3 + 9b^3$

39. $5a^2 - 7ab - 6b^2$

40. $6x^2 - 5xy - y^2$

41. $12s^2 + 11st - 5t^2$

42. $25a^2 + 25ab + 6b^2$

⊕ 43. $6m^6n + 7m^5n^2 + 2m^4n^3$

44. $12k^3q^4 - 4k^2q^5 - kq^6$

If a trinomial has a negative coefficient for the squared term, such as $-2x^2 + 11x - 12$, it may be easier to factor by first factoring out the common factor -1:

$$-2x^2 + 11x - 12$$
$$= -1(2x^2 - 11x + 12)$$
$$= -1(2x - 3)(x - 4).$$

Use this method to factor the trinomials in Exercises 45–50.

45. $-x^2 - 4x + 21$

46. $-x^2 + x + 72$

47. $-3x^2 - x + 4$

48. $-5x^2 + 2x + 16$

49. $-2a^2 - 5ab - 2b^2$

50. $-3p^2 + 13pq - 4q^2$

Relating Concepts (Exercises 51–56) For Individual or Group Work

One of the most common problems that beginning algebra students face is this: If an answer obtained doesn't look exactly like the one given in the back of the book, is it necessarily incorrect? Often there are several different equivalent forms of an answer that are all correct. **Work Exercises 51–56 in order,** *to see how and why this is possible for factoring problems.*

51. Factor the integer 35 as the product of two prime numbers.

52. Factor the integer 35 as the product of the negatives of two prime numbers.

53. Verify that $6x^2 - 11x + 4$ factors as $(3x - 4)(2x - 1)$.

54. Verify that $6x^2 - 11x + 4$ factors as $(4 - 3x)(1 - 2x)$.

55. Compare the two valid factored forms in Exercises 53 and 54. How do the factors in each case compare?

56. Suppose you know that the correct factored form of a particular trinomial is $(7t - 3)(2t - 5)$. Based on your observations in Exercises 51–55, what is another valid factored form?

15.5 ▶▶▶ Special Factoring Techniques

By reversing the rules for multiplication of binomials from **Section 13.4**, we obtain rules for factoring polynomials in certain forms.

OBJECTIVE 1 Factor a difference of squares. The formula for the product of the sum and difference of the same two terms is

$$(a + b)(a - b) = a^2 - b^2.$$

Reversing this rule leads to the following special factoring rule.

> **Factoring a Difference of Squares**
> $$a^2 - b^2 = (a + b)(a - b)$$

For example, $m^2 - 16$

$$= m^2 - 4^2$$

$$= (m + 4)(m - 4).$$

As the next examples show, the following conditions must be true for a binomial to be a difference of squares.

1. Both terms of the binomial must be squares, such as

$$x^2, \quad 9y^2, \quad 25, \quad 1, \quad m^4.$$

2. The terms of the binomial must have different signs (one positive and one negative).

EXAMPLE 1   Factoring Differences of Squares

Factor each binomial, if possible. (In part (c), use fractions.)

$$a^2 - b^2 = (a + b)(a - b)$$

(a) $x^2 - 49 = x^2 - 7^2 = (x + 7)(x - 7)$

(b) $y^2 - m^2$

$= (y + m)(y - m)$

(c) $z^2 - \dfrac{9}{16}$

$= \left(z + \dfrac{3}{4}\right)\left(z - \dfrac{3}{4}\right)$ $\frac{9}{16} = \left(\frac{3}{4}\right)^2$

(d) $x^2 - 8$

Because 8 is not the square of an integer, this binomial is not a difference of squares. It is a prime polynomial.

(e) $p^2 + 16$

Since $p^2 + 16$ is a *sum* of squares, it is not equal to $(p + 4)(p - 4)$. Also, using FOIL,

$$(p - 4)(p - 4)$$

$$= p^2 - 8p + 16, \quad \text{not} \quad p^2 + 16,$$

and $(p + 4)(p + 4)$

$$= p^2 + 8p + 16, \quad \text{not} \quad p^2 + 16,$$

so $p^2 + 16$ is a prime polynomial.

1 Factor, if possible. (In part (b), use fractions.)

(a) $p^2 - 100$

(b) $x^2 - \dfrac{25}{36}$

(c) $x^2 + y^2$

(d) $9m^2 - 49$

(e) $64a^2 - 25$

---

2 Factor completely.

(a) $50r^2 - 32$

(b) $27y^2 - 75$

(c) $25a^2 - 64b^2$

(d) $k^4 - 49$

(e) $81r^4 - 16$

ANSWERS

1. **(a)** $(p + 10)(p - 10)$
   (b) $\left(x + \dfrac{5}{6}\right)\left(x - \dfrac{5}{6}\right)$
   (c) prime
   (d) $(3m + 7)(3m - 7)$
   (e) $(8a + 5)(8a - 5)$
2. **(a)** $2(5r + 4)(5r - 4)$
   (b) $3(3y + 5)(3y - 5)$
   (c) $(5a + 8b)(5a - 8b)$
   (d) $(k^2 + 7)(k^2 - 7)$
   (e) $(9r^2 + 4)(3r + 2)(3r - 2)$

> **CAUTION**
>
> As Example 1(e) suggests, *after any common factor is removed, a sum of squares cannot be factored.*

EXAMPLE 2 **Factoring Differences of Squares**

Factor each difference of squares.

$$a^2 \ - \ b^2 \ = \ (a \ + \ b) \ (a \ - \ b)$$

(a) $25m^2 - 16 = (5m)^2 - 4^2 = (5m + 4)(5m - 4)$

(b) $49z^2 - 64$

$$= (7z)^2 - 8^2$$

$$= (7z + 8)(7z - 8)$$

◀ *Work Problem* **1** *at the Side.*

> **Note**
>
> *Always check a factored form by multiplying.*

EXAMPLE 3 **Factoring More Complex Differences of Squares**

Factor completely.

(a) $81y^2 - 36$

$$= 9(9y^2 - 4) \qquad \text{Factor out the GCF, 9.}$$

$$= 9[(3y)^2 - 2^2]$$

$$= 9(3y + 2)(3y - 2) \qquad \text{Difference of squares}$$

(b) $9x^2 - 4z^2$

$$= (3x)^2 - (2z)^2$$

$$= (3x + 2z)(3x - 2z)$$

(c) $p^4 - 36$

$$= (p^2)^2 - 6^2$$

$$= (p^2 + 6)(p^2 - 6)$$

(d) $m^4 - 16$

$$= (m^2)^2 - 4^2$$

$$= (m^2 + 4)(m^2 - 4) \qquad \text{Difference of squares}$$

Don't stop here.

$$= (m^2 + 4)(m + 2)(m - 2) \qquad \text{Difference of squares again}$$

> **CAUTION**
>
> *Factor again when any of the factors is a difference of squares*, as in Example 3(d). Check by multiplying.

◀ *Work Problem* **2** *at the Side.*

OBJECTIVE 2 Factor a perfect square trinomial. The expressions 144, $4x^2$, and $81m^6$ are called *perfect squares* because

$$144 = 12^2, \quad 4x^2 = (2x)^2, \quad \text{and} \quad 81m^6 = (9m^3)^2.$$

A **perfect square trinomial** is a trinomial that is the square of a binomial. For example, $x^2 + 8x + 16$ is a perfect square trinomial because it is the square of the binomial $x + 4$:

$$x^2 + 8x + 16$$
$$= (x + 4)(x + 4)$$
$$= (x + 4)^2.$$

On the one hand, a necessary condition for a trinomial to be a perfect square is that *two of its terms must be perfect squares*. For this reason, $16x^2 + 4x + 15$ is not a perfect square trinomial because only the term $16x^2$ is a perfect square.

On the other hand, even if two of the terms are perfect squares, the trinomial may not be a perfect square trinomial. For example, $x^2 + 6x + 36$ has two perfect square terms, but it is not a perfect square trinomial. (Try to find a binomial that can be squared to give $x^2 + 6x + 36$.)

We can multiply to see that the square of a binomial gives one of the following perfect square trinomials.

> **Factoring Perfect Square Trinomials**
>
> $$a^2 + 2ab + b^2 = (a + b)^2$$
> $$a^2 - 2ab + b^2 = (a - b)^2$$

The middle term of a perfect square trinomial is always twice the product of the two terms in the squared binomial. (See **Section 13.4.**) Use this to check any attempt to factor a trinomial that appears to be a perfect square.

EXAMPLE 4 **Factoring a Perfect Square Trinomial**

Factor $x^2 + 10x + 25$.

The term x^2 is a perfect square, and so is 25. Try to factor the trinomial

$$x^2 + 10x + 25 \quad \text{as} \quad (x + 5)^2.$$

To check, take twice the product of the two terms in the squared binomial.

$$2 \cdot x \cdot 5 = 10x$$

Twice   First term   Last term
of binomial   of binomial

Since $10x$ is the middle term of the trinomial, the trinomial is a perfect square and can be factored as $(x + 5)^2$. Thus,

$$x^2 + 10x + 25 \quad \text{factors as} \quad (x + 5)^2.$$

Work Problem **3** *at the Side.* ▶

EXAMPLE 5 **Factoring Perfect Square Trinomials**

Factor each trinomial.

(a) $x^2 - 22x + 121$

The first and last terms are perfect squares ($121 = 11^2$ or $(-11)^2$). Check to see whether the middle term of $x^2 - 22x + 121$ is twice the product of the first and last terms of the binomial $x - 11$.

Continued on Next Page

3 Factor each trinomial.

(a) $p^2 + 14p + 49$

(b) $m^2 + 8m + 16$

(c) $x^2 + 2x + 1$

4 Factor each trinomial.

(a) $p^2 - 18p + 81$

$$2 \cdot x \cdot (-11) = -22x$$

Twice ——— First term ——— Last term

Since twice the product of the first and last terms of the binomial is the middle term, $x^2 - 22x + 121$ is a perfect square trinomial and

$$x^2 - 22x + 121 \quad \text{factors as} \quad (x - 11)^2.$$

Same sign

Notice that the sign of the second term in the squared binomial is the same as the sign of the middle term in the trinomial.

(b) $16a^2 + 56a + 49$

(b) $9m^2 - 24m + 16 = (3m)^2 + 2(3m)(-4) + (-4)^2 = (3m - 4)^2$

Twice ——— First term ——— Last Term

(c) $25y^2 + 20y + 16$

The first and last terms are perfect squares.

$$25y^2 = (5y)^2 \quad \text{and} \quad 16 = 4^2$$

However, twice the product of the first and last terms of the binomial $5y + 4$ is $2 \cdot 5y \cdot 4 = 40y$, which is not the middle term of $25y^2 + 20y + 16$. This trinomial is not a perfect square. In fact, the trinomial cannot be factored, even with the methods of the previous sections. It is a prime polynomial.

(c) $121p^2 + 110p + 100$

(d) $12z^3 + 60z^2 + 75z$

$= 3z(4z^2 + 20z + 25)$ Factor out $3z$.

$= 3z[(2z)^2 + 2(2z)(5) + 5^2]$ $4z^2 + 20z + 25$ is a perfect square trinomial.

$= 3z(2z + 5)^2$ Factor.

(d) $64x^2 - 48x + 9$

> **Note**
>
> 1. The sign of the second term in the squared binomial is always the same as the sign of the middle term in the trinomial.
> 2. The first and last terms of a perfect square trinomial must be *positive,* because they are squares. For example, the polynomial $x^2 - 2x - 1$ cannot be a perfect square because the last term is negative.
> 3. Perfect square trinomials can also be factored using grouping or FOIL, although using the method of this section is often easier.

(e) $27y^3 + 72y^2 + 48y$

◀ Work Problem **4** at the Side.

The methods of factoring discussed in this section are summarized here.

> **Special Factoring Rules**
>
> Difference of squares $\quad a^2 - b^2 = (a + b)(a - b)$
>
> Perfect square trinomials $\quad a^2 + 2ab + b^2 = (a + b)^2$
>
> $\qquad\qquad\qquad\qquad\qquad\; a^2 - 2ab + b^2 = (a - b)^2$

15.5 ▶▶▶ Exercises

1. To help you factor a difference of squares, complete the following list of squares.

$1^2 =$ _____ $2^2 =$ _____ $3^2 =$ _____ $4^2 =$ _____ $5^2 =$ _____

$6^2 =$ _____ $7^2 =$ _____ $8^2 =$ _____ $9^2 =$ _____ $10^2 =$ _____

$11^2 =$ _____ $12^2 =$ _____ $13^2 =$ _____ $14^2 =$ _____ $15^2 =$ _____

$16^2 =$ _____ $17^2 =$ _____ $18^2 =$ _____ $19^2 =$ _____ $20^2 =$ _____

2. To use the factoring techniques described in this section, you will sometimes need to recognize fourth powers of integers. Complete the following list of fourth powers.

$1^4 =$ _____ $2^4 =$ _____ $3^4 =$ _____ $4^4 =$ _____ $5^4 =$ _____

3. The following powers of x are all perfect squares: $x^2, x^4, x^6, x^8, x^{10}$. Based on this observation, we may make a conjecture (an educated guess) that if the power of a variable is divisible by _____ (with 0 remainder), then it is a perfect square.

4. Which of the following are differences of squares?

A. $x^2 - 4$ **B.** $y^2 + 9$ **C.** $2a^2 - 25$ **D.** $9m^2 - 1$

Factor each binomial completely. In Exercises 7, 8, 13, and 14, use fractions. See Examples 1–3.

5. $y^2 - 25$ **6.** $t^2 - 16$ **7.** $p^2 - \dfrac{1}{9}$ **8.** $q^2 - \dfrac{1}{4}$

9. $m^2 - 12$ **10.** $k^2 - 18$ **11.** $9r^2 - 4$ **12.** $4x^2 - 9$

13. $4m^2 - \dfrac{9}{25}$ **14.** $100b^2 - \dfrac{49}{81}$ **15.** $36x^2 - 16$ **16.** $32a^2 - 8$

17. $196p^2 - 225$ **18.** $361q^2 - 400$ **19.** $16r^2 - 25a^2$ **20.** $49m^2 - 100p^2$

21. $100x^2 + 49$ **22.** $81w^2 + 16$ **23.** $p^4 - 49$ **24.** $r^4 - 25$

25. $x^4 - 1$ **26.** $y^4 - 10,000$ **27.** $p^4 - 256$ **28.** $16k^4 - 1$

29. When a student was directed to factor $x^4 - 81$ completely, his teacher did not give him full credit for the answer $(x^2 + 9)(x^2 - 9)$. The student argued that because his answer does indeed give $x^4 - 81$ when multiplied out, he should be given full credit. **WHAT WENT WRONG?** Give the correct factored form.

30. The binomial $4x^2 + 16$ is a sum of squares that *can* be factored. How is this binomial factored? When can a sum of squares be factored?

31. In the polynomial $9y^2 + 14y + 25$, the first and last terms are perfect squares. Can the polynomial be factored? If it can, factor it. If it cannot, explain why it is not a perfect square trinomial.

32. Which of the following are perfect square trinomials?

    A. $y^2 - 13y + 36$ **B.** $x^2 + 6x + 9$ **C.** $4z^2 - 4z + 1$ **D.** $16m^2 + 10m + 1$

Factor each trinomial completely. It may be necessary to factor out the greatest common factor first. In Exercises 37–40, use fractions or decimals, as appropriate. See Examples 4 and 5.

33. $w^2 + 2w + 1$ **34.** $p^2 + 4p + 4$ **35.** $x^2 - 8x + 16$

36. $x^2 - 10x + 25$ **37.** $t^2 + t + \dfrac{1}{4}$ **38.** $m^2 + \dfrac{2}{3}m + \dfrac{1}{9}$

39. $x^2 - 1.0x + 0.25$ **40.** $y^2 - 1.4y + 0.49$ **41.** $2x^2 + 24x + 72$

42. $3y^2 - 48y + 192$ **43.** $16x^2 - 40x + 25$ **44.** $36y^2 - 60y + 25$

45. $49x^2 - 28xy + 4y^2$ **46.** $4z^2 - 12zw + 9w^2$ **47.** $64x^2 + 48xy + 9y^2$

48. $9t^2 + 24tr + 16r^2$ **49.** $-50h^3 + 40h^2y - 8hy^2$ **50.** $-18x^3 - 48x^2y - 32xy^2$

Relating Concepts (Exercises 51–54)   For Individual or Group Work

*We have seen that multiplication and factoring are reverse processes. We know that multiplication and division are also related. To check a division problem, we multiply the quotient by the divisor to get the dividend. To see how factoring and division are related, **work Exercises 51–54 in order.***

51. Factor $10x^2 + 11x - 6$.

52. Use long division from **Section 13.7** to divide $10x^2 + 11x - 6$ by $2x + 3$.

53. Could we have predicted the result in Exercise 52 from the result in Exercise 51? Explain.

54. Divide $x^3 - 1$ by $x - 1$. Use your answer to factor $x^3 - 1$.

As you factor a polynomial, we suggest asking yourself these questions to decide on a suitable factoring technique.

> **Factoring a Polynomial**
> 1. **Is there a common factor other than 1?** If so, factor out the greatest common factor (GCF) of all terms of the given polynomial.
> 2. **How many terms are in the polynomial?**
>   *Two terms:* Check to see whether it is a difference of squares.
>   *Three terms:* Is it a perfect square trinomial? If the trinomial is not a perfect square, check to see whether the coefficient of the second-degree term is 1. If so, use the method of **Section 15.2.** If the coefficient of the squared term of the trinomial is not 1, use the general factoring methods of **Sections 15.3** and **15.4.**
>   *Four terms:* Try to factor the polynomial by grouping.
> 3. **Can any factors be factored further?** If so, factor them.

> **CAUTION**
> Be careful when checking your answer to a factoring problem.
> 1. *Check* that the product of all the factors does indeed yield the original polynomial.
> 2. *Check* that the original polynomial has been factored *completely*. (See Question 3 above.)
>
> *Checking by multiplication alone will not ensure that you have factored the original polynomial completely.*

Suppose we are asked to completely factor the trinomial

$$6x^2 + 24xy + 24y^2$$

and give

$$(2x + 4y)(3x + 6y)$$

as the answer. If we only check by multiplying, we might conclude that our answer is correct because, by FOIL,

$$(2x + 4y)(3x + 6y)$$
$$= 6x^2 + 24xy + 24y^2.$$

However, we would not have factored the given polynomial *completely* because the binomial $2x + 4y$ has a common factor of 2 and the binomial $3x + 6y$ has a common factor of 3. Rather than factoring out these common factors at the *end* of our work, it is more efficient to factor out the GCF, 6 (which is $2 \cdot 3$), at the beginning, as follows.

$$6x^2 + 24xy + 24y^2$$
$$= 6(x^2 + 4xy + 4y^2) \quad \text{Factor out the GCF, 6.}$$
$$= 6(x + 2y)^2 \quad \text{Factor the perfect square trinomial.}$$

To avoid leaving out common factors in your final answer, *remember to always factor out the GCF first.*

We now use the factoring guidelines given on the preceding page to factor $12x^2 + 26xy + 12y^2$ completely.

Question 1: *Is there a common factor?* Yes, there is a common factor. The GCF is 2, so factor it out.

$$12x^2 + 26xy + 12y^2$$

$$= 2(6x^2 + 13xy + 6y^2)$$

Question 2: *How many terms are in the polynomial?* The polynomial $6x^2 + 13xy + 6y^2$ has three terms, but it is not a perfect square. To factor the trinomial by grouping, as in **Section 15.3,** begin by finding two integers with a product of $6 \cdot 6$, or 36, and a sum of 13. These integers are 4 and 9.

$12x^2 + 26xy + 12y^2$

$\quad = 2(6x^2 + 13xy + 6y^2)$ Factor out the GCF, 2.

$\quad = 2(6x^2 + 4xy + 9xy + 6y^2)$ $4 \cdot 9 = 36; 4 + 9 = 13$

$\quad = 2[(6x^2 + 4xy) + (9xy + 6y^2)]$ Group the terms.

$\quad = 2[2x(3x + 2y) + 3y(3x + 2y)]$ Factor each group.

$\quad = 2(3x + 2y)(2x + 3y)$ Factor out the common factor, $3x + 2y$.

(The trinomial $6x^2 + 13xy + 6y^2$ could also be factored by trial and error, using FOIL backwards, as in **Section 15.4.**)

Question 3: *Can any factors be factored further?* None of the factors can be factored further, so the original polynomial has been factored completely.

Match each polynomial in Column I with the method you would use to factor it in Column II. The choices in Column II may be used once, more than once, or not at all.

I	**II**
1. $12x^2 + 20x + 8$	**A.** Factor out the GCF; no further factoring is possible.
2. $x^2 - 17x + 72$	**B.** Factor a difference of squares once.
3. $-16m^2n + 24mn - 40mn^2$	**C.** Factor a difference of squares twice.
4. $64a^2 - 121b^2$	**D.** Factor a perfect square trinomial.
5. $36p^2 - 60pq + 25q^2$	**E.** Factor by grouping.
6. $z^2 - 4z + 6$	**F.** Factor out the GCF; then factor a trinomial by grouping or trial and error.
7. $625 - r^4$	**G.** Factor into two binomials by finding two integers whose product is the constant in the trinomial and whose sum is the coefficient of the middle term.
8. $x^6 + 4x^4 - 3x^2 - 12$	
9. $4w^2 + 49$	
10. $144 - 24z + z^2$	**H.** The polynomial is prime.

Factor each polynomial completely. In Exercises 26, 32, 64, and 81, use fractions or decimals, as appropriate. Remember to check by multiplying.

11. $32m^9 + 16m^5 + 24m^3$

12. $2m^2 - 10m - 48$

13. $14k^3 + 7k^2 - 70k$

14. $9z^2 + 64$

15. $6z^2 + 31z + 5$

16. $m^2 - 3mn - 4n^2$

17. $49z^2 - 16y^2$

18. $100n^2r^2 + 30nr^3 - 50n^2r$

19. $16x^2 + 20x$

20. $20 + 5m + 12n + 3mn$

21. $10y^2 - 7yz - 6z^2$

22. $y^4 - 81$

23. $m^2 + 2m - 15$

24. $6y^2 - 5y - 4$

25. $32z^3 + 56z^2 - 16z$

26. $p^2 - 2.4p + 1.44$

27. $z^2 - 12z + 36$

28. $9m^2 - 64$

29. $y^2 - 4yk - 12k^2$

30. $16z^2 - 8z + 1$

31. $6y^2 - 6y - 12$

32. $x^2 + \frac{1}{2}x + \frac{1}{16}$

33. $p^2 - 17p + 66$

34. $a^2 + 17a + 72$

35. $k^2 + 100$

36. $108m^2 - 36m + 3$

37. $z^2 - 3za - 10a^2$

38. $2a^3 + a^2 - 14a - 7$

39. $4k^2 - 12k + 9$

40. $a^2 - 3ab - 28b^2$

41. $16r^2 + 24rm + 9m^2$

42. $3k^2 + 4k - 4$

43. $n^2 - 12n - 35$

44. $a^4 - 625$

45. $16k^2 - 48k + 36$

46. $8k^2 - 10k - 3$

47. $36y^6 - 42y^5 - 120y^4$

48. $5z^3 - 45z^2 + 70z$

49. $8p^2 + 23p - 3$

50. $8k^2 - 2kh - 3h^2$

51. $54m^2 - 24z^2$

52. $4k^2 - 20kz + 25z^2$

53. $6a^2 + 10a - 4$

54. $15h^2 + 11hg - 14g^2$

55. $28a^2 - 63b^2$

56. $10z^2 - 7z - 6$

57. $125m^4 - 400m^3n + 195m^2n^2$

58. $9y^2 + 12y - 5$

59. $9u^2 + 66uv + 121v^2$

60. $36x^2 + 32x + 9$

61. $27p^{10} - 45p^9 - 252p^8$

62. $10m^2 + 25m - 60$

63. $4 - 2q - 6p + 3pq$

64. $k^2 - \dfrac{64}{121}$

65. $64p^2 - 100m^2$

66. $m^3 + 4m^2 - 6m - 24$

67. $100a^2 - 81y^2$

68. $8a^2 + 23ab - 3b^2$

69. $a^2 + 8a + 16$

70. $4y^2 - 25$

71. $2x^2 + 5x + 6$

72. $-3x^3 + 12xy^2$

73. $25a^2 - 70ab + 49b^2$

74. $8t^4 - 8$

75. $-4x^2 + 24xy - 36y^2$

76. $100a^2 - 25b^2$

77. $-2x^2 + 26x - 72$

78. $2m^2 - 15n - 5mn + 6m$

79. $12x^2 + 22x - 20$

80. $y^6 + 5y^4 - 3y^2 - 15$

81. $y^2 - 0.64$

82. $12p^3 - 54p^2 - 30p$

15.6 ►►► A General Approach to Factoring

A polynomial is completely factored when **(1)** it is written as a *product* of prime polynomials with integer coefficients, and **(2)** none of the polynomial factors can be factored further.

Factoring a Polynomial

Step 1 **Factor out any common factor.**

Step 2 **If the polynomial is a binomial,** check to see if it is the difference of squares, the difference of cubes, or the sum of cubes.

If the polynomial is a trinomial, check to see if it is a perfect square trinomial. If it is not, factor as in **Section 15.2.**

If the polynomial has more than three terms, try to factor by grouping.

Step 3 **Check the factored form by multiplying.**

OBJECTIVES

1 Factor out any common factor.

2 Factor binomials.

3 Factor trinomials.

4 Factor polynomials with more than three terms.

OBJECTIVE 1 Factor out any common factor. *This step is always the same, regardless of the number of terms in the polynomial.*

EXAMPLE 1 Factoring Out a Common Factor

Factor each polynomial.

(a) $9p + 45$
$= 9(p + 5)$ GCF = 9

(b) $8m^2p^2 + 4mp$
$= 4mp(2mp + 1)$

(c) $5x(a + b) - y(a + b)$
$= (a + b)(5x - y)$ Factor out $a + b$.

Work Problem **1** *at the Side.* ►

OBJECTIVE 2 Factor binomials. Use one of the following rules.

Factoring a Binomial

For a **binomial** (two terms), check for the following patterns.

Difference of squares	$x^2 - y^2 = (x + y)(x - y)$
Difference of cubes	$x^3 - y^3 = (x - y)(x^2 + xy + y^2)$
Sum of cubes	$x^3 + y^3 = (x + y)(x^2 - xy + y^2)$

EXAMPLE 2 Factoring Binomials

Factor each binomial if possible.

(a) $64m^2 - 9n^2$
$= (8m)^2 - (3n)^2$ Difference of squares
$= (8m + 3n)(8m - 3n)$

(b) $8p^3 - 27$ $8p^3 = (2p)^3; 27 = 3^3$
$= (2p - 3)[(2p)^2 + (2p)(3) + 3^2]$
$= (2p - 3)(4p^2 + 6p + 9)$

(c) $1000m^3 + 1$
$= (10m)^3 + 1^3$ Sum of cubes
$= (10m + 1)[(10m)^2 - (10m)(1) + 1^2]$
$= (10m + 1)(100m^2 - 10m + 1)$

(d) $25m^2 + 121$ is prime.
It is the *sum* of squares.

Work Problem **2** *at the Side.* ►

1 Factor each polynomial.

(a) $8x - 80$

(b) $2x^3 + 10x^2 - 2x$

(c) $12m(p - q) - 7n(p - q)$

2 Factor each binomial if possible.

(a) $36x^2 - y^2$

(b) $4t^2 + 1$

(c) $125x^3 - 27y^3$

(d) $x^3 + 343y^3$

ANSWERS

1. **(a)** $8(x - 10)$
   (b) $2x(x^2 + 5x - 1)$
   (c) $(p - q)(12m - 7n)$
2. **(a)** $(6x + y)(6x - y)$
   (b) prime
   (c) $(5x - 3y)(25x^2 + 15xy + 9y^2)$
   (d) $(x + 7y)(x^2 - 7xy + 49y^2)$

3 Factor each trinomial.

(a) $16m^2 + 56m + 49$

(b) $r^2 + 18r + 72$

(c) $8t^2 - 13t + 5$

(d) $6x^2 - 3x - 63$

4 Factor each polynomial.

(a) $p^3 - 2pq^2 + p^2q - 2q^3$

(b) $9x^2 + 24x + 16 - y^2$

(c) $64a^3 + 16a^2 + b^3 - b^2$

Note

The binomial $25m^2 + 625$ is a sum of squares. It *can* be factored, however, as $25(m^2 + 25)$ because it has a common factor, 25.

OBJECTIVE **3** **Factor trinomials.** Consider the following.

Factoring a Trinomial

For a **trinomial** (three terms), decide whether it is a perfect square trinomial of the form

$$x^2 + 2xy + y^2 = (x + y)^2 \quad \text{or} \quad x^2 - 2xy + y^2 = (x - y)^2.$$

If not, use the general factoring methods of **Section 7.2.**

EXAMPLE 3 **Factoring Trinomials**

Factor each trinomial.

(a) $p^2 + 10p + 25$
$= (p + 5)^2$ $2(p)(5) = 10p$

(b) $49z^2 - 42z + 9$
$= (7z - 3)^2$ $2(7z)(3) = 42z$

(c) $y^2 - 5y - 6$ The numbers -6 and 1 have a product of -6 and a sum of -5.
$= (y - 6)(y + 1)$

(d) $2k^2 - k - 6$
$= (2k + 3)(k - 2)$

(e) $28z^2 + 6z - 10$
$= 2(14z^2 + 3z - 5)$
$= 2(7z + 5)(2z - 1)$

◀ *Work Problem* **3** *at the Side.*

OBJECTIVE **4** **Factor polynomials with more than three terms.**
Consider factoring by grouping.

EXAMPLE 4 **Factoring Polynomials with More than Three Terms**

Factor each polynomial.

(a) $20k^3 + 4k^2 - 45k - 9$
$= (20k^3 + 4k^2) - (45k + 9)$ Group the terms.
$= 4k^2(5k + 1) - 9(5k + 1)$ Factor each group.
$= (5k + 1)(4k^2 - 9)$ $5k + 1$ is a common factor.
$= (5k + 1)(2k + 3)(2k - 3)$ Difference of squares

(b) $4a^2 + 4a + 1 - b^2$
$= (4a^2 + 4a + 1) - b^2$ Group the first three terms.
$= (2a + 1)^2 - b^2$ Perfect square trinomial
$= (2a + 1 + b)(2a + 1 - b)$ Difference of squares

(c) $8m^3 + 4m^2 - n^3 - n^2$
$= (8m^3 - n^3) + (4m^2 - n^2)$ Rearrange and group the terms.
$= (2m - n)(4m^2 + 2mn + n^2) + (2m - n)(2m + n)$
     Factor each group.
$= (2m - n)(4m^2 + 2mn + n^2 + 2m + n)$ Factor out $2m - n$.

◀ *Work Problem* **4** *at the Side.*

ANSWERS

3. (a) $(4m + 7)^2$
   (b) $(r + 6)(r + 12)$
   (c) $(8t - 5)(t - 1)$
   (d) $3(2x - 7)(x + 3)$
4. (a) $(p + q)(p^2 - 2q^2)$
   (b) $(3x + 4 + y)(3x + 4 - y)$
   (c) $(4a + b)(16a^2 - 4ab + b^2 + 4a - b)$

FOR EXTRA HELP

MyMathLab Math XL PRACTICE   WATCH   DOWNLOAD READ   REVIEW

Factor each polynomial completely. We have randomly included all the different types of factoring exercises here to give you practice in applying factoring strategies. See Examples 1–4.

1. $100a^2 - 9b^2$

2. $10r^2 + 13r - 3$

3. $18p^5 - 24p^3 + 12p^6$

4. $15x^2 - 20x$

5. $x^2 + 2x - 35$

6. $9 - a^2 + 2ab - b^2$

7. $225p^2 + 256$

8. $x^3 + 1000$

⊕ **9.** $6b^2 - 17b - 3$

10. $k^2 - 6k + 16$

11. $18m^3n + 3m^2n^2 - 6mn^3$

12. $6t^2 + 19tu - 77u^2$

13. $2p^2 + 11pq + 15q^2$

14. $9m^2 - 45m + 18m^3$

15. $4k^2 + 28kr + 49r^2$

16. $54m^3 - 2000$

17. $mn - 2n + 5m - 10$

18. $9m^2 - 30mn + 25n^2 - p^2$

19. $x^3 + 3x^2 - 9x - 27$

20. $56k^3 - 875$

21. $9r^2 + 100$

22. $8p^3 - 125$

23. $6k^2 - k - 1$

24. $27m^2 + 144mn + 192n^2$

25. $x^4 - 625$

26. $125m^6 + 216$

⊕ **27.** $ab + 6b + ac + 6c$

28. $p^3 + 64$

29. $4y^2 - 8y$

30. $6a^4 - 11a^2 - 10$

31. $14z^2 - 3zk - 2k^2$

32. $12z^3 - 6z^2 + 18z$

33. $256b^2 - 400c^2$

34. $z^2 - zp + 20p^2$

35. $1000z^3 + 512$

36. $64m^2 - 25n^2$

37. $10r^2 + 23rs - 5s^2$

38. $12k^2 - 17kq - 5q^2$

39. $32x^2 + 16x^3 - 24x^5$

40. $48k^4 - 243$

41. $14x^2 - 25xq - 25q^2$

42. $5p^2 - 10p$

43. $y^2 + 3y - 10$

44. $b^2 - 7ba - 18a^2$

45. $2a^3 + 6a^2 - 4a$

46. $12m^2rx + 4mnrx + 40n^2rx$

47. $18p^2 + 53pr - 35r^2$

48. $21a^2 - 5ab - 4b^2$

49. $(x - 2y)^2 - 4$

50. $(3m - n)^2 - 25$

51. $(5r + 2s)^2 - 6(5r + 2s) + 9$

52. $(p + 8q)^2 - 10(p + 8q) + 25$

53. $z^4 - 9z^2 + 20$

54. $21m^4 - 32m^2 - 5$

55. $4(p + 2) + m(p + 2)$

56. $kq - 9q + kr - 9r$

57. $50p^2 - 162$

58. $25x^2 - 20xy + 4y^2$

59. $16a^2 + 8ab + b^2$

60. $40p - 32r$

15.7 ▶▶▶ Solving Quadratic Equations by Factoring

Galileo Galilei developed theories to explain physical phenomena and set up experiments to test his ideas. According to legend, Galileo dropped objects of different weights from the Leaning Tower of Pisa to disprove the belief that heavier objects fall faster than lighter objects. He developed a formula for freely falling objects described by $d = 16t^2$, where d is the distance in feet that an object falls (disregarding air resistance) in t seconds, regardless of weight.

The equation $d = 16t^2$ is a *quadratic equation.* A quadratic equation contains a squared term and no terms of higher degree.

OBJECTIVES

1. Solve quadratic equations by factoring.

2. Solve other equations by factoring.

> **Quadratic Equation**
>
> A **quadratic equation** is an equation that can be written in the form
>
> $$ax^2 + bx + c = 0,$$
>
> where a, b, and c are real numbers, with $a \neq 0$. The given form is called **standard form**.

$$x^2 + 5x + 6 = 0, \quad 2t^2 - 5t = 3, \quad y^2 = 4 \qquad \text{Quadratic equations}$$

In these examples, only $x^2 + 5x + 6 = 0$ is in standard form.

Work Problems **1** *and* **2** *at the Side.* ▶

Galileo Galilei (1564–1642)

Up to now, we have factored *expressions,* including many quadratic expressions of the form $ax^2 + bx + c$. In this section, we use factored quadratic expressions to solve quadratic *equations.*

OBJECTIVE **1** **Solve quadratic equations by factoring.** We use the **zero-factor property** to solve a quadratic equation by factoring.

> **Zero-Factor Property**
>
> **If a and b are real numbers and $ab = 0$, then $a = 0$ or $b = 0$.**
>
> In words, if the product of two numbers is 0, then at least one of the numbers must be 0. One number *must* be 0, but both *may* be 0.

EXAMPLE 1 **Using the Zero-Factor Property**

Solve each equation.

(a) $(x + 3)(2x - 1) = 0$

The product $(x + 3)(2x - 1)$ is equal to 0. By the zero-factor property, the only way that the product of these two factors can be 0 is if at least one of the factors equals 0. Therefore, either $x + 3 = 0$ or $2x - 1 = 0$.

$$x + 3 = 0 \quad \text{or} \quad 2x - 1 = 0 \qquad \text{Zero-factor property}$$
$$x = -3 \quad \text{or} \quad 2x = 1 \qquad \text{Solve each equation.}$$
$$x = \frac{1}{2}$$

Continued on Next Page

1 Which of the following equations are quadratic equations?

A. $y^2 - 4y - 5 = 0$

B. $x^3 - x^2 + 16 = 0$

C. $2z^2 + 7z = -3$

D. $x + 2y = -4$

2 Write each quadratic equation in standard form.

(a) $x^2 - 3x = 4$

(b) $y^2 = 9y - 8$

ANSWERS

1. A, C
2. **(a)** $x^2 - 3x - 4 = 0$
   (b) $y^2 - 9y + 8 = 0$

3 Solve each equation. Check your solutions.

(a) $(x - 5)(x + 2) = 0$

(b) $(3x - 2)(x + 6) = 0$

(c) $z(2z + 5) = 0$

The given equation, $(x + 3)(2x - 1) = 0$, has two solutions, -3 and $\frac{1}{2}$. *Check* these solutions by substituting -3 for x in the original equation, $(x + 3)(2x - 1) = 0$. Then start over and substitute $\frac{1}{2}$ for x.

Check   If $x = -3$, then

$$(x + 3)(2x - 1) = 0$$

$$(-3 + 3)[2(-3) - 1] \stackrel{?}{=} 0$$

$$0(-7) = 0. \quad \text{True}$$

If $x = \frac{1}{2}$, then

$$(x + 3)(2x - 1) = 0$$

$$\left(\frac{1}{2} + 3\right)\left(2 \cdot \frac{1}{2} - 1\right) \stackrel{?}{=} 0$$

$$\frac{7}{2}(1 - 1) \stackrel{?}{=} 0$$

$$\frac{7}{2} \cdot 0 = 0. \quad \text{True}$$

Both -3 and $\frac{1}{2}$ result in true equations, so the solution set is $\{-3, \frac{1}{2}\}$.

(b) $$y(3y - 4) = 0$$

$$y = 0 \quad \text{or} \quad 3y - 4 = 0 \quad \text{Zero-factor property}$$

Don't forget that 0 is a solution.

$$3y = 4$$

$$y = \frac{4}{3}$$

Check these solutions by substituting each one in the original equation. The solution set is $\{0, \frac{4}{3}\}$.

◀ *Work Problem* **3** *at the Side.*

> **Note**
>
> The word *or* as used in Example 1 means "one or the other or both."

In Example 1, each equation to be solved was given with the polynomial in factored form. If the polynomial in an equation is not already factored, first make sure that the equation is in standard form. Then factor and solve.

EXAMPLE 2   **Solving Quadratic Equations**

Solve each equation.

(a) $x^2 - 5x = -6$

First, write the equation in standard form by adding 6 to each side.

Don't factor x out at this step.

$$x^2 - 5x = -6$$

$$x^2 - 5x + 6 = 0 \quad \text{Add 6.}$$

Now factor $x^2 - 5x + 6$. Find two numbers whose product is 6 and whose sum is -5. These two numbers are -2 and -3, so the equation becomes

$$(x - 2)(x - 3) = 0. \quad \text{Factor the trinomial.}$$

$$x - 2 = 0 \quad \text{or} \quad x - 3 = 0 \quad \text{Zero-factor property}$$

$$x = 2 \quad \text{or} \qquad x = 3 \quad \text{Solve each equation.}$$

Continued on Next Page

Check   If $x = 2$, then

$$2^2 - 5(2) \stackrel{?}{=} -6$$
$$4 - 10 \stackrel{?}{=} -6$$
$$-6 = -6. \quad \text{True}$$

If $x = 3$, then

$$3^2 - 5(3) \stackrel{?}{=} -6$$
$$9 - 15 \stackrel{?}{=} -6$$
$$-6 = -6. \quad \text{True}$$

Both solutions check, so the solution set is $\{2, 3\}$.

(b)
$$y^2 = y + 20$$

$$y^2 - y - 20 = 0 \qquad \text{Write in standard form.}$$
$$(y - 5)(y + 4) = 0 \qquad \text{Factor the trinomial.}$$
$$y - 5 = 0 \quad \text{or} \quad y + 4 = 0 \qquad \text{Zero-factor property}$$
$$y = 5 \quad \text{or} \qquad y = -4 \qquad \text{Solve each equation.}$$

Check by substituting in the original equation. The solution set is $\{-4, 5\}$.

Work Problem **4** *at the Side.* ▶

4 Solve each equation. Check your solutions.

(a) $m^2 - 3m - 10 = 0$

(b) $r^2 + 2r = 8$

Solving a Quadratic Equation by Factoring

Step 1   **Write the equation in standard form,** that is, with all terms on one side of the equals sign in descending powers of the variable and 0 on the other side.

Step 2   **Factor** completely.

Step 3   **Use the zero-factor property** to set each factor with a variable equal to 0.

Step 4   **Solve** the resulting equations.

Step 5   **Check** each solution in the original equation.

5 Solve each equation. Check your solutions.

(a) $10a^2 - 5a - 15 = 0$

EXAMPLE 3   **Solving a Quadratic Equation (Common Factor)**

Solve $4p^2 + 40 = 26p$.

$$4p^2 - 26p + 40 = 0 \qquad \text{Standard form}$$
$$2(2p^2 - 13p + 20) = 0 \qquad \text{Factor out 2.}$$
$$2p^2 - 13p + 20 = 0 \qquad \text{Divide each side by 2.}$$
$$(2p - 5)(p - 4) = 0 \qquad \text{Factor.}$$
$$2p - 5 = 0 \quad \text{or} \quad p - 4 = 0 \qquad \text{Zero-factor property}$$
$$2p = 5 \quad \text{or} \qquad p = 4 \qquad \text{Solve each equation.}$$
$$p = \frac{5}{2}$$

Check that the solution set is $\{\frac{5}{2}, 4\}$ by substituting in the original equation.

(b) $4x^2 - 2x = 42$

CAUTION
A common error is to include the common factor **2** as a solution in Example 3. *Only factors containing variables lead to solutions.*

Work Problem **5** *at the Side.* ▶

ANSWERS

4. (a) $\{-2, 5\}$ (b) $\{-4, 2\}$

5. (a) $\left\{-1, \frac{3}{2}\right\}$ (b) $\left\{-3, \frac{7}{2}\right\}$

6 Solve each equation. Check your solutions.

(a) $49m^2 - 9 = 0$

EXAMPLE 4 **Solving Quadratic Equations**

Solve each equation.

(a) $16m^2 - 25 = 0$

We can factor the left side of the equation as the difference of squares (**Section 14.5**).

$$16m^2 - 25 = 0$$

$$(4m + 5)(4m - 5) = 0 \qquad \text{Factor the difference of squares.}$$

$$4m + 5 = 0 \quad \text{or} \quad 4m - 5 = 0 \qquad \text{Zero-factor property}$$

$$4m = -5 \quad \text{or} \qquad 4m = 5 \qquad \text{Solve each equation.}$$

$$m = -\frac{5}{4} \quad \text{or} \qquad m = \frac{5}{4}$$

Check the solutions $-\frac{5}{4}$ and $\frac{5}{4}$ in the original equation. The solution set is $\{-\frac{5}{4}, \frac{5}{4}\}$.

(b) $k(2k + 5) = 3$

We need to write this equation in standard form.

$$k(2k + 5) = 3 \qquad \boxed{\text{To be in standard form, 0 must be on one side.}}$$

$$2k^2 + 5k = 3 \qquad \text{Multiply.}$$

$$2k^2 + 5k - 3 = 0 \qquad \text{Subtract 3.}$$

$$(2k - 1)(k + 3) = 0 \qquad \text{Factor.}$$

$$2k - 1 = 0 \quad \text{or} \quad k + 3 = 0 \qquad \text{Zero-factor property}$$

$$2k = 1 \quad \text{or} \qquad k = -3$$

$$k = \frac{1}{2}$$

The solution set is $\{-3, \frac{1}{2}\}$.

(c) $y^2 = 2y$

$$y^2 - 2y = 0 \qquad \text{Standard form}$$

$$\boxed{\text{Don't forget to set the variable factor } y \text{ equal to 0.}} \quad y(y - 2) = 0 \qquad \text{Factor.}$$

$$y = 0 \quad \text{or} \quad y - 2 = 0 \qquad \text{Zero-factor property}$$

$$y = 2$$

The solution set is $\{0, 2\}$.

(b) $p(4p + 7) = 2$

(c) $m^2 = 3m$

CAUTION

In Example 4(b), the zero-factor property could not be used to solve the equation $k(2k + 5) = 3$ in its given form because of the 3 on the right. *The zero-factor property applies only to a product that equals 0.*

In Example 4(c), it is tempting to begin by dividing each side of the equation $y^2 = 2y$ by y to get $y = 2$. Note that we do not get the other solution, 0, if we divide by a variable. (We *may* divide each side of an equation by a *nonzero* real number, however. For instance, in Example 3 we divided each side by 2.)

◀ *Work Problem* **6** *at the Side.*

EXAMPLE 5 **Solving a Quadratic Equation with a Double Solution**

Solve each equation.

(a)
$$z^2 + 121 = 22z$$

$$z^2 - 22z + 121 = 0 \qquad \text{Standard form}$$

Because $121 = 11^2$ and $22z = 2 \cdot z \cdot 11$, the trinomial on the left is a perfect square.

$$(z - 11)^2 = 0 \qquad \text{Factor.}$$

To apply the zero-product property, write $(z - 11)^2$ as two separate factors.

$$(z - 11)(z - 11) = 0 \qquad a^2 = a \cdot a$$

$$z - 11 = 0 \quad \text{or} \quad z - 11 = 0 \qquad \text{Zero-factor property}$$

Because the two factors are identical, they both lead to the same solution. (This is called a **double solution.**) Thus,

$$z - 11 = 0$$

$$z = 11. \qquad \text{Add 11.}$$

Check
$$z^2 + 121 = 22z$$

$$11^2 + 121 \stackrel{?}{=} 22(11) \qquad \text{Let } z = 11.$$

$$121 + 121 \stackrel{?}{=} 242$$

$$242 = 242 \qquad \text{True}$$

The solution set is $\{11\}$.

(b)
$$9t^2 - 30t = -25$$

$$9t^2 - 30t + 25 = 0 \qquad \text{Standard form}$$

$$(3t - 5)^2 = 0 \qquad \text{Factor the perfect square trinomial.}$$

$$3t - 5 = 0 \quad \text{or} \quad 3t - 5 = 0 \qquad \text{Zero-factor property}$$

$$3t = 5 \qquad \text{Solve the equation.}$$

$$t = \frac{5}{3}$$

Check the double solution by substituting $\frac{5}{3}$ in the original equation. The solution set is $\{\frac{5}{3}\}$.

Work Problem 7 *at the Side.* ▶

7 Solve each equation. Check your solutions.

(a) $x^2 + 16x = -64$

(b) $4x^2 - 4x + 1 = 0$

CAUTION
When a trinomial has two identical factors (a perfect square trinomial), as in Examples 5(a) and (b), it is common for students to write the solution of the corresponding quadratic equation twice in the solution set. Each of these equations has only *one* distinct solution. ***There is no need to write the same number more than once in a solution set.***

Note
Not all quadratic equations can be solved by factoring. A more general method for solving such equations is given in **Chapter 17.**

ANSWERS
7. (a) $\{-8\}$ (b) $\left\{\frac{1}{2}\right\}$

8 Solve each equation. Check your solutions.

(a) $r^3 - 16r = 0$

(b) $x^3 - 3x^2 - 18x = 0$

OBJECTIVE **2** **Solve other equations by factoring.** We can extend the zero-factor property to solve equations that involve more than two factors with variables, as shown in Examples 6 and 7. (These equations are *not* quadratic equations. Why not?)

EXAMPLE 6 **Solving an Equation with More Than Two Variable Factors**

Solve $6z^3 - 6z = 0$.

$$6z^3 - 6z = 0$$
$$6z(z^2 - 1) = 0 \qquad \text{Factor out } 6z.$$
$$6z(z + 1)(z - 1) = 0 \qquad \text{Factor } z^2 - 1.$$

By an extension of the zero-factor property, this product can equal 0 only if at least one of the factors equals 0. Write and solve three equations, one for each factor with a variable.

$$6z = 0 \quad \text{or} \quad z + 1 = 0 \quad \text{or} \quad z - 1 = 0$$
$$z = 0 \quad \text{or} \qquad z = -1 \quad \text{or} \qquad z = 1$$

Check by substituting, in turn, 0, −1, and 1 in the original equation. The solution set is $\{-1, 0, 1\}$.

◀ *Work Problem* **8** *at the Side.*

---

9 Solve each equation. Check your solutions.

(a) $(m + 3)(m^2 - 11m + 10) = 0$

EXAMPLE 7 **Solving an Equation with a Quadratic Factor**

Solve $(2x - 1)(x^2 - 9x + 20) = 0$.

$$(2x - 1)(x^2 - 9x + 20) = 0$$
$$(2x - 1)(x - 5)(x - 4) = 0 \qquad \text{Factor } x^2 - 9x + 20.$$
$$2x - 1 = 0 \quad \text{or} \quad x - 5 = 0 \quad \text{or} \quad x - 4 = 0 \qquad \text{Zero-factor property}$$
$$x = \frac{1}{2} \quad \text{or} \qquad x = 5 \quad \text{or} \qquad x = 4$$

Check to verify that the solution set is $\{\frac{1}{2}, 4, 5\}$.

◀ *Work Problem* **9** *at the Side.*

(b) $(2x + 5)(4x^2 - 9) = 0$

CAUTION
In Example 7, it would be unproductive to begin by multiplying the two factors together. Keep in mind that the zero-factor property and its extension requires the product of two or more factors to equal 0. *Always consider first whether an equation is given in the appropriate form to apply the zero-factor property.*

ANSWERS

8. (a) $\{-4, 0, 4\}$ **(b)** $\{-3, 0, 6\}$

9. (a) $\{-3, 1, 10\}$ **(b)** $\left\{-\frac{5}{2}, -\frac{3}{2}, \frac{3}{2}\right\}$

15.7 ▶▶▶ **Exercises**

FOR EXTRA HELP

Math XL
PRACTICE

WATCH

DOWNLOAD

READ

REVIEW

Solve each equation, and check your solutions. See Example 1.

1. $(x + 5)(x - 2) = 0$

2. $(x - 1)(x + 8) = 0$

3. $(2m - 7)(m - 3) = 0$

4. $(6k + 5)(k + 4) = 0$

5. $t(6t + 5) = 0$

6. $w(4w + 1) = 0$

7. $2x(3x - 4) = 0$

8. $6x(4x + 9) = 0$

9. $\left(x + \dfrac{1}{2}\right)\left(2x - \dfrac{1}{3}\right) = 0$

10. $\left(a + \dfrac{2}{3}\right)\left(5a - \dfrac{1}{2}\right) = 0$

11. $(x - 9)(x - 9) = 0$

12. $(2x + 1)(2x + 1) = 0$

13. Look at this "solution." ***WHAT WENT WRONG?***

$$2x(3x - 4) = 0$$
$$x = 2 \quad \text{or} \quad x = 0 \quad \text{or} \quad 3x - 4 = 0$$
$$x = \dfrac{4}{3}$$

The solution set is $\{2, 0, \frac{4}{3}\}$.

14. Look at this "solution." ***WHAT WENT WRONG?***

$$x(7x - 1) = 0$$
$$7x - 1 = 0 \quad \text{Zero-factor property}$$
$$x = \dfrac{1}{7}$$

The solution set is $\{\frac{1}{7}\}$.

Solve each equation, and check your solutions. See Examples 2–7.

15. $y^2 + 3y + 2 = 0$

16. $p^2 + 8p + 7 = 0$

17. $y^2 - 3y + 2 = 0$

18. $r^2 - 4r + 3 = 0$

19. $x^2 = 24 - 5x$

20. $t^2 = 2t + 15$

21. $x^2 = 3 + 2x$

22. $m^2 = 4 + 3m$

23. $z^2 + 3z = -2$

24. $p^2 - 2p = 3$

25. $m^2 + 8m + 16 = 0$

26. $b^2 - 6b + 9 = 0$

27. $3x^2 + 5x - 2 = 0$

28. $6r^2 - r - 2 = 0$

29. $6p^2 = 4 - 5p$

30. $6x^2 = 4 + 5x$

31. $9s^2 + 12s = -4$

32. $36x^2 + 60x = -25$

33. $y^2 - 9 = 0$

34. $m^2 - 100 = 0$

35. $16k^2 - 49 = 0$

36. $4w^2 - 9 = 0$

37. $n^2 = 121$

38. $x^2 = 400$

39. $x^2 = 7x$

40. $t^2 = 9t$

41. $6r^2 = 3r$

42. $10y^2 = -5y$

◉ **43.** $g(g - 7) = -10$

44. $r(r - 5) = -6$

45. $z(2z + 7) = 4$

46. $b(2b + 3) = 9$

47. $2(y^2 - 66) = -13y$

48. $3(t^2 + 4) = 20t$

49. $5x^3 - 20x = 0$

50. $3x^3 - 48x = 0$

51. $9y^3 - 49y = 0$

52. $16r^3 - 9r = 0$

53. $(2r + 5)(3r^2 - 16r + 5) = 0$

54. $(3m + 4)(6m^2 + m - 2) = 0$

55. $(2x + 7)(x^2 + 2x - 3) = 0$
◉

56. $(x + 1)(6x^2 + x - 12) = 0$

57. Galileo's formula for freely falling objects, $d = 16t^2$, was given at the beginning of this section. The distance d in feet an object falls depends on the time elapsed t in seconds. (This is an example of an important mathematical concept, a **function.**)

(a) Use Galileo's formula and complete the following table. (*Hint:* Substitute each given value into the formula and solve for the unknown value.)

t in seconds	0	1	2	3		
d in feet	0	16			256	576

(b) When $t = 0$, $d = 0$. Explain this in the context of the problem.

58. In Exercise 57, when you substituted 256 for d and solved for t, you should have found two solutions: 4 and -4. Why doesn't -4 make sense as an answer?

15.8 ▶▶▶ Applications of Quadratic Equations

We can use factoring to solve quadratic equations that arise in applications. We follow the same basic problem-solving steps used throughout this text.

Solving an Applied Problem

Step 1   **Read** the problem, several times if necessary, until you *understand* what is given and what is to be found.

Step 2   **Assign a variable** to represent the unknown value, using diagrams or tables as needed. Write a statement that tells what the variable represents. Express any other unknown values in terms of the variable.

Step 3   **Write an equation** using the variable expression(s).

Step 4   **Solve** the equation.

Step 5   **State the answer.** Does it seem reasonable?

Step 6   **Check** the answer in the words of the original problem.

OBJECTIVES

1 Solve problems about geometric figures.

2 Solve problems about consecutive integers.

3 Solve problems using the Pythagorean formula.

4 Solve problems using given quadratic models.

OBJECTIVE 1 Solve problems about geometric figures.   Refer to the formulas given on the inside back cover of this text, if necessary.

EXAMPLE 1   Solving an Area Problem

The Monroes want to plant a rectangular garden in their yard. The width of the garden will be 4 ft less than its length, and they want it to have an area of 96 ft². (ft² means square feet.) Find the length and width of the garden.

Step 1   **Read** the problem carefully. We need to find the dimensions of a garden with area 96 ft².

Step 2   **Assign a variable.**

Let x = the length of the garden.

Then $x - 4$ = the width. (The width is 4 ft less than the length.)

See Figure 1.

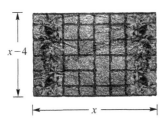

Figure 1

Step 3   **Write an equation.** The area of a rectangle is given by

$$\text{Area} = lw = \text{length} \times \text{width}. \quad \text{Area formula}$$

Substitute 96 for area, x for length, and $x - 4$ for width.

$$A = lw$$

$$96 = x(x - 4) \quad \text{Let } A = 96, l = x, w = x - 4.$$

Continued on Next Page

1 Solve each problem.

(a) The length of a rectangular room is 2 m more than the width. The area of the floor is 48 m². Find the length and width of the room.

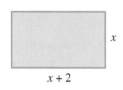

x

$x + 2$

(b) The length of each side of a square is increased by 4 in. The sum of the areas of the original square and the larger square is 106 in². What is the length of a side of the original square?

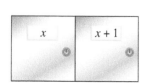

x $x + 1$

Figure 2

Step 4 **Solve.** $96 = x(x - 4)$

$$96 = x^2 - 4x \qquad \text{Distributive property}$$

$$x^2 - 4x - 96 = 0 \qquad \text{Standard form}$$

$$(x - 12)(x + 8) = 0 \qquad \text{Factor.}$$

$$x - 12 = 0 \quad \text{or} \quad x + 8 = 0 \qquad \text{Zero-factor property}$$

$$x = 12 \quad \text{or} \qquad x = -8$$

Step 5 **State the answer.** The solutions are 12 and −8. A rectangle cannot have a side of negative length, so discard −8. The length of the garden will be 12 ft. The width will be 12 − 4 = 8 ft.

Step 6 **Check.** The width of the garden is 4 ft less than the length; the area is 12 · 8 = 96 ft².

> **Problem-Solving Hint**
>
> When solving applied problems, ***always check solutions against physical facts*** and discard any answers that are not appropriate.

◀ *Work Problem* **1** *at the Side.*

OBJECTIVE **2** **Solve problems about consecutive integers.** Two **consecutive integers** are integers that are next to each other on a number line, such as 5 and 6, or −11 and −10. **Consecutive odd integers** are *odd* integers that are next to each other, such as 5 and 7, or −13 and −11. **Consecutive even integers** are defined similarly; 4 and 6 are consecutive even integers, as are −10 and −8. (In this book, we will list consecutive integers in increasing order from left to right.)

> **Problem-Solving Hint**
>
> In consecutive integer problems, if x represents the first integer, then for
> two consecutive integers, use $x, \quad x + 1;$
> three consecutive integers, use $x, \quad x + 1, \quad x + 2;$
> two consecutive even or odd integers, use $x, \quad x + 2;$
> three consecutive even or odd integers, use $x, \quad x + 2, \quad x + 4.$

EXAMPLE 2   **Solving a Consecutive Integer Problem**

The product of the numbers on two consecutive post-office boxes is 210. Find the box numbers.

Step 1 **Read** the problem. Note that the boxes are numbered consecutively.

Step 2 **Assign a variable.**

Let $x =$ the first box number.

Then $x + 1 =$ the next consecutive box number.

See Figure 2.

Step 3 **Write an equation.** The product of the box numbers is 210, so

$$x(x + 1) = 210.$$

Continued on Next Page

Step 4 **Solve.**

$$x(x + 1) = 210$$

$$x^2 + x = 210 \qquad \text{Distributive property}$$

$$x^2 + x - 210 = 0 \qquad \text{Standard form}$$

$$(x + 15)(x - 14) = 0 \qquad \text{Factor.}$$

$$x + 15 = 0 \quad \text{or} \quad x - 14 = 0 \qquad \text{Zero-factor property}$$

$$x = -15 \quad \text{or} \qquad x = 14$$

Step 5 **State the answer.** The solutions are -15 and 14. Discard the solution -15 since a box number cannot be negative. When $x = 14$, then $x + 1 = 15$, so the post-office boxes have the numbers 14 and 15.

Step 6 **Check.** The numbers 14 and 15 are consecutive and their product is $14 \cdot 15 = 210$, as required.

─────── *Work Problem* **2** *at the Side.* ▶

2 Solve the problem.
The product of the numbers on two consecutive lockers at a health club is 132. Find the locker numbers.

EXAMPLE 3 **Solving a Consecutive Integer Problem**

The product of two consecutive odd integers is 1 less than five times their sum. Find the integers.

Step 1 **Read** carefully. This problem is a little more complicated.

Step 2 **Assign a variable.** We must find two consecutive *odd* integers.

$$\text{Let} \qquad x = \text{the lesser integer.}$$

$$\text{Then } x + 2 = \text{the next greater odd integer.}$$

Step 3 **Write an equation.** According to the problem, the product is 1 less than five times the sum.

$$
\begin{array}{ccccc}
\text{The} & & \text{five times} & & \\
\text{product} & \text{is} & \text{the sum} & \text{less 1.} & \\
\downarrow & \downarrow & \downarrow & \downarrow & \\
x(x + 2) & = & 5(x + x + 2) & - & 1
\end{array}
$$

Step 4 **Solve.**

$$x^2 + 2x = 5x + 5x + 10 - 1 \qquad \text{Distributive property}$$

$$x^2 + 2x = 10x + 9 \qquad \text{Combine like terms.}$$

$$x^2 - 8x - 9 = 0 \qquad \text{Standard form}$$

$$(x - 9)(x + 1) = 0 \qquad \text{Factor.}$$

$$x - 9 = 0 \quad \text{or} \quad x + 1 = 0 \qquad \text{Zero-factor property}$$

$$x = 9 \quad \text{or} \qquad x = -1$$

Step 5 **State the answer.** We need to find two consecutive odd integers.

If $x = 9$ is the lesser, then $x + 2 = 9 + 2 = 11$ is the greater.

If $x = -1$ is the lesser, then $x + 2 = -1 + 2 = 1$ is the greater.

There are two sets of answers here since integers can be positive or negative.

Step 6 **Check.** The product of the first pair of integers is $9 \cdot 11 = 99$. One less than five times their sum is $5(9 + 11) - 1 = 99$. Thus 9 and 11 satisfy the problem. Repeat the check with -1 and 1.

─────── *Work Problem* **3** *at the Side.* ▶

3 Solve each problem.

(a) The product of two consecutive even integers is 4 more than two times their sum. Find the integers.

(b) Find three consecutive odd integers such that the product of the least and greatest is 16 more than the middle integer.

CAUTION
Do *not* use $x, x + 1, x + 3$, and so on to represent consecutive odd integers. To see why, let $x = 3$. Then $x + 1 = 3 + 1 = 4$ and $x + 3 = 3 + 3 = 6$, and 3, 4, and 6 are not consecutive odd integers.

OBJECTIVE **3** **Solve problems using the Pythagorean formula.**
The next example uses the Pythagorean formula from **Section 5.8.**

Pythagorean Formula
If a right triangle (a triangle with a 90° angle) has longest side of length c and two other sides of lengths a and b, then

$$a^2 + b^2 = c^2.$$

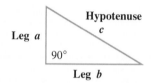

Recall that the longest side, the **hypotenuse,** is opposite the right angle. The two shorter sides are the **legs** of the triangle.

EXAMPLE 4 **Using the Pythagorean Formula**

Amy and Kevin leave their office, with Amy traveling north and Kevin traveling east. When Kevin is 1 mi farther than Amy from the office, the distance between them is 2 mi more than Amy's distance from the office. Find their distances from the office and the distance between them.

Step 1 **Read** the problem again. We must find three distances.

Step 2 **Assign a variable.** Let x represent Amy's distance from the office, $x + 1$ represent Kevin's distance from the office, and $x + 2$ represent the distance between them. Place these on a right triangle, as in Figure 3.

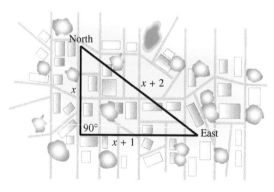

Figure 3

Step 3 **Write an equation.** Substitute into the Pythagorean formula.

$$a^2 + b^2 = c^2$$

$$x^2 + (x + 1)^2 = (x + 2)^2$$

> Be careful to substitute properly.

Continued on Next Page

Step 4 **Solve.** $x^2 + x^2 + 2x + 1 = x^2 + 4x + 4$

$$x^2 - 2x - 3 = 0 \qquad \text{Standard form}$$

$$(x - 3)(x + 1) = 0 \qquad \text{Factor.}$$

$$x - 3 = 0 \quad \text{or} \quad x + 1 = 0 \qquad \text{Zero-factor property}$$

$$x = 3 \quad \text{or} \qquad x = -1$$

Step 5 **State the answer.** Since -1 cannot represent a distance, 3 is the only possible answer. Amy's distance is 3 mi, Kevin's distance is $3 + 1 = 4$ mi, and the distance between them is $3 + 2 = 5$ mi.

Step 6 **Check.** Since $3^2 + 4^2 = 5^2$, the answer is correct.

CAUTION

When solving a problem involving the Pythagorean formula, be sure that the expressions for the sides are properly placed.

$$\mathbf{leg^2 + leg^2 = hypotenuse^2}$$

Work Problem **4** *at the Side.* ▶

OBJECTIVE **4** **Solve problems using given quadratic models.** In Examples 1–4, we wrote quadratic equations to model, or mathematically describe, various situations and then solved the equations. Now we are given the quadratic models and must use them to determine data.

EXAMPLE 5   **Finding the Height of a Ball**

A tennis player can hit a ball 180 ft per sec. If she hits a ball directly upward, the height h of the ball in feet at time t in seconds is modeled by the quadratic equation

$$h = -16t^2 + 180t + 6.$$

When will the ball be 206 ft above the ground?

A height of 206 ft means $h = 206$, so we substitute 206 for h in the equation and then solve for t.

$$206 = -16t^2 + 180t + 6 \qquad \text{Let } h = 206.$$

$$-16t^2 + 180t + 6 = 206 \qquad \text{Interchange sides.}$$

$$-16t^2 + 180t - 200 = 0 \qquad \text{Standard form}$$

$$4t^2 - 45t + 50 = 0 \qquad \text{Divide by } -4.$$

$$(4t - 5)(t - 10) = 0 \qquad \text{Factor.}$$

$$4t - 5 = 0 \quad \text{or} \quad t - 10 = 0 \qquad \text{Zero-factor property}$$

$$t = \frac{5}{4} \quad \text{or} \qquad t = 10$$

Since we found two acceptable answers, the ball will be 206 ft above the ground twice (once on its way up and once on its way down)—at $\frac{5}{4}$ sec and at 10 sec after it is hit. See Figure 4.

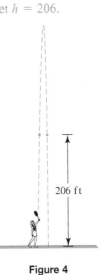

206 ft

Figure 4

Work Problem **5** *at the Side.* ▶

4 Solve the problem.

The hypotenuse of a right triangle is 3 in. longer than the longer leg. The shorter leg is 3 in. shorter than the longer leg. Find the lengths of the sides of the triangle.

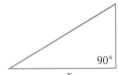

$90°$

x

5 Solve the problem.

The number of impulses fired after a nerve has been stimulated is modeled by

$$I = -x^2 + 2x + 60,$$

where x is in milliseconds (ms) after the stimulation. When will 45 impulses occur? Do you get two solutions? Why is only one answer given?

ANSWERS

4. 9 in., 12 in., 15 in.
5. After 5 ms; There are two solutions, -3 and 5; Only one answer makes sense here because a negative answer is not appropriate.

6 Use the model in Example 6 to find the foreign-born population of the United States in 1990. Give your answer to the nearest tenth of a million. How does it compare to the actual value from the table?

EXAMPLE 6 **Modeling the Foreign-Born Population of the United States**

After decreasing in the middle of the 20th century, the foreign-born population of the United States started to increase in the later part of the century and is now increasing rapidly. The foreign-born population over the years 1930–2004 can be modeled by the quadratic equation

$$y = 0.01036x^2 - 0.5316x + 15.36,$$

where $x = 0$ represents 1930, $x = 10$ represents 1940, and so on, and y is the number of people in millions. (*Source:* U.S. Census Bureau.)

(a) Use the model to find the foreign-born population in 1980 to the nearest tenth of a million.

Since $x = 0$ represents 1930, $x = 50$ represents 1980. Substitute 50 for x in the equation.

$y = 0.01036(50)^2 - 0.5316(50) + 15.36$ Let $x = 50$.

$y = 14.7$ Round to the nearest tenth.

In 1980, the foreign-born population of the United States was about 14.7 million.

(b) Repeat part (a) for 2004.

$y = 0.01036(74)^2 - 0.5316(74) + 15.36$ For 2004, let $x = 74$.

$y = 32.8$ Round to the nearest tenth.

In 2004, the foreign-born population of the United States was about 32.8 million.

(c) The model used in parts (a) and (b) was developed using the data in the table below. How do the results in parts (a) and (b) compare to the actual data from the table?

Year	Foreign-Born Population (millions)
1930	14.2
1940	11.6
1950	10.3
1960	9.7
1970	9.6
1980	14.1
1990	19.8
2000	28.4
2004	34.2

From the table, the actual value for 1980 is 14.1 million. Our answer in part (a), 14.7 million, is slightly high. For 2004, the actual value is 34.2 million, so our answer of 32.8 million in part (b) is somewhat low.

◀ *Work Problem* **6** *at the Side.*

ANSWER

6. 20.8 million; The actual value is 19.8 million, so our answer using the model is somewhat high.

1. To review the six problem-solving steps, complete each statement.

Step 1: _____ the problem, several times if necessary, until you understand what is given and what must be found.

Step 2: Assign a _____ to represent the unknown value.

Step 3: Write a(n) _____ using the variable expression(s).

Step 4: _____ the equation.

Step 5: State the _____.

Step 6: _____ the answer in the words of the _____ problem.

2. A student solves an applied problem and gets 6 or -3 for the length of the side of a square. Which of these answers is reasonable? Explain.

In Exercises 3–6, a figure and a corresponding geometric formula are given. Using x as the variable, complete Steps 3–6 for each problem. (Refer to the steps in Exercise 1 as needed.)

3.

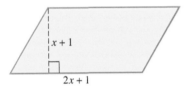

$x + 1$

$2x + 1$

Area of a parallelogram: $A = bh$

The area of this parallelogram is 45 sq. units. Find its base and height.

4.

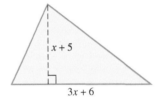

$x + 5$

$3x + 6$

Area of a triangle: $A = \frac{1}{2}bh$

The area of this triangle is 60 sq. units. Find its base and height.

5.

4

$x + 2$ x

Volume of a rectangular Chinese box: $V = lwh$

The volume of this box is 192 cu. units. Find its length and width.

6.

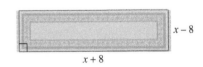

$x - 8$

$x + 8$

Area of a rectangular rug: $A = lw$

The area of this rug is 80 sq. units. Find its length and width.

Solve each problem. Check your answers to be sure they are reasonable. Refer to the formulas on the inside back cover. See Example 1.

7. The length of a standard jewel case is 2 cm more than its width. The area of the rectangular top of the case is 168 cm². Find the length and width of the jewel case.

8. A standard DVD case is 6 cm longer than it is wide. The area of the rectangular top of the case is 247 cm². Find the length and width of the case.

9. The dimensions of an HPf1905 flat-panel monitor are such that its length is 3 in. more than its width. If the length were doubled and if the width were decreased by 1 in., the area would be increased by 150 in.². What are the length and width of the flat panel?

10. The keyboard of the computer in Exercise 9 is 11 in. longer than it is wide. If both its length and width are increased by 2 in., the area of the top of the keyboard is increased by 54 in.². Find the length and width of the keyboard. (*Source:* Author's computer.)

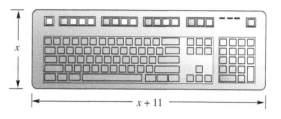

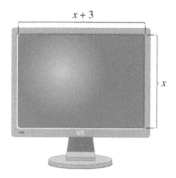

11. A 10-gal aquarium is 3 in. higher than it is wide. Its length is 21 in., and its volume is 2730 in.³. What are the height and width of the aquarium?

12. A toolbox is 2 ft high, and its width is 3 ft less than its length. If its volume is 80 ft³, find the length and width of the box.

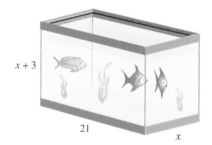

13. A square mirror has sides measuring 2 ft less than the sides of a square painting. If the difference between their areas is 32 ft², find the lengths of the sides of the mirror and the painting.

14. The sides of one square have length 3 m more than the sides of a second square. If the area of the larger square is subtracted from 4 times the area of the smaller square, the result is 36 m². What are the lengths of the sides of each square?

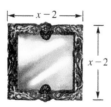

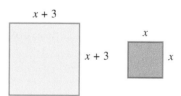

Solve each problem about consecutive integers. See Examples 2 and 3.

15. The product of the numbers on two consecutive volumes of research data is 420. Find the volume numbers.

16. The product of the page numbers on two facing pages of a book is 600. Find the page numbers.

17. The product of two consecutive integers is 11 more than their sum. Find the integers.

18. The product of two consecutive integers is 4 less than four times their sum. Find the integers.

19. Find two consecutive odd integers such that their product is 15 more than three times their sum.

20. Find two consecutive odd integers such that five times their sum is 23 less than their product.

21. Find three consecutive even integers such that the sum of the squares of the lesser two is equal to the square of the greatest.

22. Find three consecutive even integers such that the square of the sum of the lesser two is equal to twice the greatest.

Use the Pythagorean formula to solve each problem. See Example 4.

🌐 23. The hypotenuse of a right triangle is 1 cm longer than the longer leg. The shorter leg is 7 cm shorter than the longer leg. Find the length of the longer leg of the triangle.

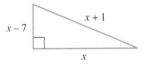

24. The longer leg of a right triangle is 1 m longer than the shorter leg. The hypotenuse is 1 m shorter than twice the shorter leg. Find the length of the shorter leg of the triangle.

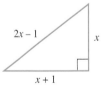

25. Terri works due north of home. Her husband Denny works due east. They leave for work at the same time. By the time Terri is 5 mi from home, the distance between them is 1 mi more than Denny's distance from home. How far from home is Denny?

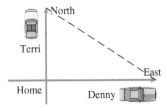

26. Two cars left an intersection at the same time. One traveled north. The other traveled 14 mi farther, but to the east. How far apart were they then, if the distance between them was 4 mi more than the distance traveled east?

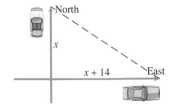

27. A ladder is leaning against a building. The distance from the bottom of the ladder to the building is 4 ft less than the length of the ladder. How high up the side of the building is the top of the ladder if that distance is 2 ft less than the length of the ladder?

28. A lot has the shape of a right triangle with one leg 2 m longer than the other. The hypotenuse is 2 m less than twice the length of the shorter leg. Find the length of the shorter leg.

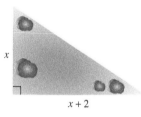

Solve each problem. See Examples 5 and 6.

29. An object projected from a height of 48 ft with an initial velocity of 32 ft per sec after t seconds has height

$$h = -16t^2 + 32t + 48.$$

48 ft

(a) After how many seconds is the height 64 ft? (*Hint:* Let $h = 64$ and solve.)

(b) After how many seconds is the height 60 ft?

(c) After how many seconds does the object hit the ground? (*Hint:* When the object hits the ground, $h = 0$.)

(d) The quadratic equation from part (c) has two solutions, yet only one of them is appropriate for answering the question. Why is this so?

30. If an object is projected upward from ground level with an initial velocity of 64 ft per sec, its height h in feet t seconds later is

$$h = -16t^2 + 64t.$$

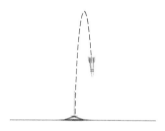

(a) After how many seconds is the height 48 ft?

(b) The object reaches its maximum height 2 sec after it is projected. What is this maximum height?

(c) After how many seconds does the object hit the ground?

(d) The quadratic equation from part (c) has two solutions, yet only one of them is appropriate for answering the question. Why is this so?

31. The table shows the number of cellular phone subscribers (in millions) in the United States.

Year	Subscribers (in millions)
1990	5
1992	11
1994	24
1996	44
1998	69
2000	109
2002	141
2004	182
2006	233

Source: CTIA-The Wireless Association.

We used the data to develop the quadratic equation

$$y = 0.734x^2 + 2.62x + 3.37,$$

which models the number of cellular phone subscribers y (in millions) in the year x, where $x = 0$ represents 1990, $x = 2$ represents 1992, and so on.

(a) Use the model to find the number of cellular phones in 1996 to the nearest million. How does the result compare to the actual data in the table?

(b) What value of x corresponds to 2004?

(c) Use the model to find the number of cellular phones in 2004 to the nearest million. How does the result compare to the actual data in the table?

(d) Assuming that the trend in the data continues, use the quadratic equation to estimate the number of cellular phones in 2009 to the nearest million.

Relating Concepts (Exercises 32—40) For Individual or Group Work

The U.S. trade deficit represents the amount by which exports are less than imports. It provides not only a sign of economic prosperity but also a warning of potential decline. The data in the table shows the U.S. trade deficit in goods and services for 2001 through 2005.

Year	Deficit (in billions of dollars)
2001	365.1
2002	423.7
2003	496.9
2004	612.1
2005	714.4

Source: U.S. Census Bureau.

*Use the data to **work Exercises 32–40 in order.***

32. How much did the trade deficit in goods and services increase from 2001 to 2002? What percent increase is this (to the nearest percent)?

33. The U.S. trade deficit might be approximated by the linear equation

$$y = 88.7x + 256,$$

where y is the deficit in billions of dollars. Here $x = 1$ represents 2001, $x = 2$ represents 2002, and so on. Use this equation to approximate the trade deficits in 2003, 2004, and 2005.

34. How do your answers from Exercise 33 compare to the actual data in the table?

35. The trade deficit y (in billions of dollars) might also be approximated by the quadratic equation

$$y = 9.24x^2 + 33.24x + 321,$$

where $x = 1$ again represents 2001, $x = 2$ represents 2002, and so on. Use this equation to approximate the trade deficits in 2003, 2004, and 2005.

36. Compare your answers from Exercise 35 to the actual data in the table. Which equation, the linear one in Exercise 33 or the quadratic one in Exercise 35, models the data better?

37. Write the data from the table as a set of ordered pairs (x, y), where x represents the years starting with 2001, such that $x = 1$ for 2001, $x = 2$ for 2002, and so on, and y represents the trade deficit in billions of dollars.

Year	Deficit (in billions of dollars)
2001	365.1
2002	423.7
2003	496.9
2004	612.1
2005	714.4

Source: U.S. Census Bureau.

38. Plot the ordered pairs from Exercise 37 on the graph.

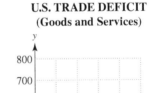

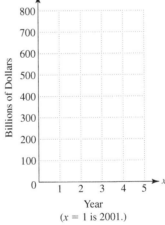

U.S. TRADE DEFICIT
(Goods and Services)

39. Assuming that the trend in the data continues, use the quadratic equation from Exercise 35 to estimate the trade deficit for the year 2006.

40. The actual trade deficit for 2006 was 758.2 billion dollars.

    (a) How does the actual deficit for 2006 compare to your estimate from Exercise 39?

    (b) Should the quadratic equation be used to estimate the U.S. trade deficit for years after 2005? Explain.

16

Rational Expressions

OBJECTIVES

1 Find the values of the variable for which a rational expression is undefined.

2 Find the numerical value of a rational expression.

3 Write rational expressions in lowest terms.

4 Recognize equivalent forms of rational expressions.

The quotient of two integers (with denominator not 0), such as $\frac{2}{3}$ or $-\frac{3}{4}$, is called a *rational number*. In the same way, the quotient of two polynomials with denominator not equal to 0 is called a *rational expression*.

Rational Expression

A **rational expression** is an expression of the form $\frac{P}{Q}$, where P and Q are polynomials, with $Q \neq 0$.

Examples of rational expressions include

$$\frac{-6x}{x^3 + 8}, \quad \frac{9x}{y + 3}, \quad \text{and} \quad \frac{2m^3}{8}. \qquad \text{Rational expressions}$$

Our work with rational expressions will require much of what we learned in **Chapters 5 and 6** on polynomials and factoring, as well as the rules for fractions from **Chapter R.**

OBJECTIVE 1 Find the values of the variable for which a rational expression is undefined. In the definition of a rational expression $\frac{P}{Q}$, Q cannot equal 0. *The denominator of a rational expression cannot equal 0 because division by 0 is undefined.*

For instance, in the rational expression

$$\frac{8x^2}{x - 3}, \quad \leftarrow \text{Denominator cannot equal 0.}$$

the variable x can take on any value except 3. When x is 3, the denominator becomes $3 - 3 = 0$, making the expression undefined. Thus, x cannot equal 3. We can indicate this restriction by writing $x \neq 3$.

To determine the values for which a rational expression is undefined, use the following procedure.

Determining When a Rational Expression Is Undefined

Step 1 Set the denominator of the rational expression equal to 0.

Step 2 Solve this equation.

Step 3 The solutions of the equation are the values that make the rational expression undefined.

EXAMPLE 1 **Finding Values That Make Rational Expressions Undefined**

Find any values of the variable for which each rational expression is undefined.

(a) $\dfrac{p + 5}{3p + 2}$

Remember that the *numerator* may be any number; we must find any value of p that makes the *denominator* equal to 0 since division by 0 is undefined.

Continued on Next Page

Step 1 Set the denominator equal to 0.

$$3p + 2 = 0$$

Step 2 Solve this equation.

$$3p = -2$$

$$p = -\frac{2}{3}$$

Step 3 The given expression is undefined for $-\frac{2}{3}$, since substituting $-\frac{2}{3}$ for p makes the denominator 0. Thus, $p \neq -\frac{2}{3}$.

(b) $\dfrac{9m^2}{m^2 - 5m + 6}$

$$
\begin{array}{ll}
m^2 - 5m + 6 = 0 & \text{Set the denominator equal to 0.} \\
(m - 2)(m - 3) = 0 & \text{Factor.} \\
m - 2 = 0 \quad \text{or} \quad m - 3 = 0 & \text{Zero-factor property} \\
m = 2 \quad \text{or} \qquad m = 3 & \text{Solve.}
\end{array}
$$

The original expression is undefined for 2 and 3, so $m \neq 2$ and $m \neq 3$.

(c) $\dfrac{2r}{r^2 + 1}$

This denominator will not equal 0 for any value of r because r^2 is always greater than or equal to 0, and adding 1 makes the sum greater than 0. Thus, there are no values for which this rational expression is undefined.

——————— *Work Problem* ⓵ *at the Side.* ▶

1 Find any values of the variable for which each rational expression is undefined. Write answers with $\neq$.

(a) $\dfrac{x + 2}{x - 5}$

(b) $\dfrac{3r}{r^2 + 6r + 8}$

OBJECTIVE **2** **Find the numerical value of a rational expression.**
We use substitution to evaluate a rational expression for a given value of the variable.

EXAMPLE 2 **Evaluating Rational Expressions**

Find the numerical value of $\dfrac{3x + 6}{2x - 4}$ for each value of x.

(a) $x = 1$

$$\frac{3x + 6}{2x - 4}$$

$$= \frac{3(1) + 6}{2(1) - 4} \quad \text{Let } x = 1.$$

$$= \frac{9}{-2}$$

$$= -\frac{9}{2} \qquad \frac{a}{-b} = -\frac{a}{b}$$

(b) $x = 0$

$$\frac{3x + 6}{2x - 4}$$

$$= \frac{3(0) + 6}{2(0) - 4} \quad \text{Let } x = 0.$$

$$= \frac{6}{-4}$$

$$= -\frac{3}{2} \qquad \text{Lowest terms}$$

(c) $\dfrac{-5m}{m^2 + 4}$

Continued on Next Page

2 Find the numerical value of each rational expression when $x = -3$, $x = 0$, and $x = 3$.

(a) $\dfrac{x}{2x + 1}$

(c) $x = 2$

$$\dfrac{3x + 6}{2x - 4}$$

$$= \dfrac{3(2) + 6}{2(2) - 4} \qquad \text{Let } x = 2.$$

$$= \dfrac{12}{0}$$

Substituting 2 for x makes the denominator 0, so the expression is undefined when $x = 2$.

(d) $x = -2$

$$\dfrac{3x + 6}{2x - 4}$$

$$= \dfrac{3(-2) + 6}{2(-2) - 4} \qquad \text{Let } x = -2.$$

$$= \dfrac{0}{-8}$$

$$= 0 \qquad\qquad \tfrac{0}{b} = 0$$

> **Note**
>
> *The numerator of a rational expression may be any real number.* If the numerator equals 0 and the denominator does *not* equal 0, then the rational expression equals 0. See Example 2(d).

◀ *Work Problem* **2** *at the Side.*

OBJECTIVE 3 Write rational expressions in lowest terms.
A fraction such as $\frac{2}{3}$ is said to be in *lowest terms*. How can "lowest terms" be defined? We use the idea of greatest common factor for this definition, which applies to all rational expressions.

(b) $\dfrac{2x + 6}{x - 3}$

> **Lowest Terms**
>
> A rational expression $\frac{P}{Q}$ $(Q \neq 0)$ is in **lowest terms** if the greatest common factor of its numerator and denominator is 1.

The properties of rational numbers also apply to rational expressions. We use the **fundamental property of rational expressions** to write a rational expression in lowest terms.

> **Fundamental Property of Rational Expressions**
> If $\frac{P}{Q}$ $(Q \neq 0)$ is a rational expression and if K represents any polynomial, where $K \neq 0$, then
>
> $$\dfrac{PK}{QK} = \dfrac{P}{Q}.$$

This property is based on the identity property of multiplication, which says that multiplying by 1 leaves any number unchanged.

$$\dfrac{PK}{QK} = \dfrac{P}{Q} \cdot \dfrac{K}{K} = \dfrac{P}{Q} \cdot 1 = \dfrac{P}{Q}$$

The next example shows how to write both a rational number and a rational expression in lowest terms. Notice the similarity in the procedures. In both cases, we factor and then divide out the greatest common factor.

EXAMPLE 3 **Writing in Lowest Terms**

Write each expression in lowest terms.

(a) $\dfrac{30}{72}$

Begin by factoring.

$$= \dfrac{2 \cdot 3 \cdot 5}{2 \cdot 2 \cdot 2 \cdot 3 \cdot 3}$$

Group any factors common to the numerator and denominator.

$$= \dfrac{5 \cdot (2 \cdot 3)}{2 \cdot 2 \cdot 3 \cdot (2 \cdot 3)}$$

Use the fundamental property.

$$= \dfrac{5}{2 \cdot 2 \cdot 3}, \quad \text{or} \quad \dfrac{5}{12}$$

(b) $\dfrac{14k^2}{2k^3}$

Write k^2 as $k \cdot k$ and k^3 as $k \cdot k \cdot k$.

$$= \dfrac{2 \cdot 7 \cdot k \cdot k}{2 \cdot k \cdot k \cdot k}$$

$$= \dfrac{7 (2 \cdot k \cdot k)}{k (2 \cdot k \cdot k)}$$

$$= \dfrac{7}{k}$$

3 Write each expression in lowest terms.

(a) $\dfrac{15}{40}$

(b) $\dfrac{5x^4}{15x^2}$

(c) $\dfrac{6p^3}{2p^2}$

Work Problem **3** *at the Side.* ▶

Writing a Rational Expression in Lowest Terms

Step 1 **Factor** the numerator and denominator completely.

Step 2 **Use the fundamental property** to divide out any common factors.

EXAMPLE 4 **Writing in Lowest Terms**

Write each rational expression in lowest terms.

(a) $\dfrac{3x - 12}{5x - 20}$

$$= \dfrac{3 (x - 4)}{5 (x - 4)} \qquad \text{Factor. (Step 1)}$$

$$= \dfrac{3}{5} \qquad \text{Fundamental property (Step 2)}$$

The given expression is equal to $\frac{3}{5}$ for all values of x, where $x \neq 4$ (since the denominator of the original rational expression is 0 when x is 4).

(b) $\dfrac{m^2 + 2m - 8}{2m^2 - m - 6}$

$$= \dfrac{(m + 4)(m - 2)}{(2m + 3)(m - 2)} \qquad \text{Factor. (Step 1)}$$

$$= \dfrac{m + 4}{2m + 3} \qquad \text{Fundamental property (Step 2)}$$

Here $m \neq -\frac{3}{2}$ and $m \neq 2$, since the denominator of the original expression is 0 for these values of m.

ANSWERS

3. **(a)** $\frac{3}{8}$ **(b)** $\frac{x^2}{3}$ **(c)** $3p$

4 Write each rational expression in lowest terms.

(a) $\dfrac{4y + 2}{6y + 3}$

(b) $\dfrac{8p + 8q}{5p + 5q}$

(c) $\dfrac{x^2 + 4x + 4}{4x + 8}$

(d) $\dfrac{a^2 - b^2}{a^2 + 2ab + b^2}$

From now on, we write statements of equality of rational expressions with the understanding that they apply only to those real numbers that make neither denominator equal to 0.

> **CAUTION**
> *Rational expressions cannot be written in lowest terms until after the numerator and denominator have been factored. Only common factors can be divided out, not common terms.* For example,
>
> $$\frac{6x + 9}{4x + 6} = \frac{3\,(2x + 3)}{2\,(2x + 3)} = \frac{3}{2} \qquad \frac{6 + x}{4x} \leftarrow \text{Numerator cannot be factored.}$$
>
>   ↑   ⌣
> Divide out the   This expression is already
> common factor.   in lowest terms.

◀ *Work Problem* **4** *at the Side.*

EXAMPLE 5   **Writing in Lowest Terms (Factors Are Opposites)**

Write $\dfrac{x - y}{y - x}$ in lowest terms.

At first glance, there might not seem to be any way in which $x - y$ and $y - x$ can be factored to get a common factor. However, $y - x$ can be factored as

$$y - x$$

> Be careful with signs.

$$= -1\,(-y + x) \qquad \text{Factor out } -1.$$
$$= -1\,(x - y) \qquad \text{Commutative property}$$

With this result in mind, we simplify as follows.

$$\frac{x - y}{y - x}$$
$$= \frac{1\,(x - y)}{-1\,(x - y)} \qquad y - x = -1\,(x - y) \text{ from above.}$$
$$= \frac{1}{-1}, \quad \text{or} \quad -1 \qquad \text{Fundamental property}$$

◀ *Work Problem* **5** *at the Side.*

5 Write $\dfrac{x - y}{y - x}$ from Example 5 in lowest terms by factoring -1 from the numerator. How does the result compare to the result in Example 5?

In Example 5, notice that $y - x$ is the **opposite** (or **additive inverse**) of $x - y$. A general rule for this situation follows.

> If the numerator and the denominator of a rational expression are opposites, such as in $\frac{x - y}{y - x}$, then the rational expression is equal to -1.

> **CAUTION**
> Although x and y appear in both the numerator and denominator in Example 5, we cannot use the fundamental property right away because they are *terms*, not *factors*. ***Terms are added, while factors are multiplied.***

ANSWERS

4. (a) $\dfrac{2}{3}$ (b) $\dfrac{8}{5}$ (c) $\dfrac{x + 2}{4}$ (d) $\dfrac{a - b}{a + b}$

5. The result is -1, the same as in Example 5.

EXAMPLE 6   **Writing in Lowest Terms (Factors Are Opposites)**

Write each rational expression in lowest terms.

(a) $\dfrac{2 - m}{m - 2}$

Since $2 - m$ and $m - 2$ (or $-2 + m$) are opposites, this expression equals -1.

(b) $\dfrac{4x^2 - 9}{6 - 4x}$

$\quad = \dfrac{(2x + 3)(2x - 3)}{2(3 - 2x)}$ Factor the numerator and denominator.

$\quad = \dfrac{(2x + 3)(2x - 3)}{2(-1)(2x - 3)}$ Write $3 - 2x$ as $-1(2x - 3)$.

$\quad = \dfrac{2x + 3}{2(-1)}$ Fundamental property

$\quad = \dfrac{2x + 3}{-2},\quad$ or $\quad -\dfrac{2x + 3}{2}$ $\dfrac{a}{-b} = -\dfrac{a}{b}$

(c) $\dfrac{3 + r}{3 - r}$

The quantity $3 - r$ *is not* the opposite of $3 + r$. This rational expression is already in lowest terms.

————— *Work Problem* ⑥ *at the Side.* ▶

OBJECTIVE ④ **Recognize equivalent forms of rational expressions.** When working with rational expressions, it is important to be able to recognize equivalent forms of an expression. For example, the common fraction $-\frac{5}{6}$ can also be written as $\frac{-5}{6}$ and as $\frac{5}{-6}$.

Consider the final rational expression from Example 6(b),

$$-\dfrac{2x + 3}{2}.$$

The $-$ sign representing the factor -1 is in front of the expression, even with the fraction bar. As with the common fraction $-\frac{5}{6}$, the factor -1 may instead be placed in the numerator or in the denominator. Some other equivalent forms of this rational expression are

Use parentheses.

$\dfrac{-(2x + 3)}{2}\qquad$ and $\qquad \dfrac{2x + 3}{-2}.$

⟨Multiply *each term* in the parentheses by -1.⟩

By the distributive property,

$\dfrac{-(2x + 3)}{2}\quad$ can also be written $\quad \dfrac{-2x - 3}{2}.$

CAUTION
$\frac{-2x + 3}{2}$ is *not* an equivalent form of $\frac{-(2x + 3)}{2}$. The sign preceding 3 in the numerator of $\frac{-2x + 3}{2}$ should be $-$ rather than $+$. ***Be careful to apply the distributive property correctly.***

⑥ Write each rational expression in lowest terms.

(a) $\dfrac{5 - y}{y - 5}$

(b) $\dfrac{m - n}{n - m}$

(c) $\dfrac{25x^2 - 16}{12 - 15x}$

(d) $\dfrac{9 - k}{9 + k}$

7 Decide whether each rational expression is equivalent to

$$-\frac{2x - 6}{x + 3}.$$

(a) $\dfrac{-(2x - 6)}{x + 3}$

(b) $\dfrac{-2x + 6}{x + 3}$

(c) $\dfrac{-2x - 6}{x + 3}$

(d) $\dfrac{2x - 6}{-(x + 3)}$

(e) $\dfrac{2x - 6}{-x - 3}$

(f) $\dfrac{2x - 6}{x - 3}$

EXAMPLE 7   **Writing Equivalent Forms of a Rational Expression**

Write four equivalent forms of the rational expression

$$-\frac{3x + 2}{x - 6}.$$

If we apply the negative sign to the numerator, we obtain the equivalent forms

$$\frac{-(3x + 2)}{x - 6}, \quad \text{and, by the distributive property,} \quad \frac{-3x - 2}{x - 6}.$$

If we apply the negative sign to the denominator of the given rational expression, we obtain the equivalent forms

$$\frac{3x + 2}{-(x - 6)} \quad \text{and, by distributing again,} \quad \frac{3x + 2}{-x + 6}.$$

CAUTION

Recall that $-\frac{5}{6} \neq \frac{-5}{-6}$. Thus, in Example 7, it would be incorrect to distribute the negative sign in $-\frac{3x + 2}{x - 6}$ to *both* the numerator *and* the denominator. (Doing this would actually lead to the *opposite* of the original expression.)

◀ *Work Problem* **7** *at the Side.*

16.1 ▶▶▶ **Exercises**

1. Fill in each blank with the correct response.

    (a) The rational expression $\dfrac{x+5}{x-3}$ is undefined when $x =$ _____, and is equal to 0 when $x =$ _____.

    (b) The rational expression $\dfrac{p-q}{q-p}$ is undefined when $p =$ _____, and in all other cases when written

    in lowest terms is equal to _____.

2. Make the correct choice for each blank.

    (a) $\dfrac{4-r^2}{4+r^2}$ _____ equal to -1.
    (is/is not)

    (b) $\dfrac{5+2x}{3-x}$ and $\dfrac{-5-2x}{x-3}$ _____ equivalent rational expressions.
                          (are/are not)

3. Define *rational expression* in your own words, and give an example.

4. Why can't the denominator of a rational expression equal 0?

Find any value(s) of the variable for which each rational expression is undefined. Write answers with $\neq$. See Example 1.

5. $\dfrac{2}{5y}$ **6.** $\dfrac{7}{3z}$ **7.** $\dfrac{x+1}{x+6}$ **8.** $\dfrac{m+2}{m+5}$

9. $\dfrac{4x^2}{3x-5}$ **10.** $\dfrac{2x^3}{3x-4}$ **11.** $\dfrac{m+2}{m^2+m-6}$ **12.** $\dfrac{r-5}{r^2-5r+4}$

13. $\dfrac{x^2-3x}{4}$ **14.** $\dfrac{x^2-4x}{6}$ **15.** $\dfrac{3x}{x^2+2}$ **16.** $\dfrac{4q}{q^2+9}$

Find the numerical value of each rational expression when **(a)** $x = 2$ *and* **(b)** $x = -3$. *See Example 2.*

17. $\dfrac{5x-2}{4x}$ **18.** $\dfrac{3x+1}{5x}$ **19.** $\dfrac{x^2-4}{2x+1}$ **20.** $\dfrac{2x^2-4x}{3x-1}$

21. $\dfrac{(-3x)^2}{4x+12}$ **22.** $\dfrac{(-2x)^3}{3x+9}$ **23.** $\dfrac{5x+2}{2x^2+11x+12}$ **24.** $\dfrac{7-3x}{3x^2-7x+2}$

Write each rational expression in lowest terms. See Examples 3 and 4.

25. $\dfrac{18r^3}{6r}$ **26.** $\dfrac{27p^2}{3p}$ **27.** $\dfrac{4(y-2)}{10(y-2)}$

28. $\dfrac{15\,(m-1)}{9\,(m-1)}$

29. $\dfrac{(x+1)(x-1)}{(x+1)^2}$

30. $\dfrac{(t+5)(t-3)}{(t-1)(t+5)}$

31. $\dfrac{7m+14}{5m+10}$

32. $\dfrac{8z-24}{4z-12}$

33. $\dfrac{m^2-n^2}{m+n}$

34. $\dfrac{a^2-b^2}{a-b}$

35. $\dfrac{12m^2-3}{8m-4}$

36. $\dfrac{20p^2-45}{6p-9}$

37. $\dfrac{3m^2-3m}{5m-5}$

38. $\dfrac{6t^2-6t}{2t-2}$

39. $\dfrac{9r^2-4s^2}{9r+6s}$

40. $\dfrac{16x^2-9y^2}{12x-9y}$

41. $\dfrac{2x^2-3x-5}{2x^2-7x+5}$

42. $\dfrac{3x^2+8x+4}{3x^2-4x-4}$

43. $\dfrac{zw+4z-3w-12}{zw+4z+5w+20}$

44. $\dfrac{km+4k+4m+16}{km+4k+5m+20}$

45. $\dfrac{ac-ad+bc-bd}{ac-ad-bc+bd}$

46. Which rational expression can be simplified?

   A. $\dfrac{x^2+2}{x^2}$ **B.** $\dfrac{x^2+2}{2}$ **C.** $\dfrac{x^2+y^2}{y^2}$ **D.** $\dfrac{x^2-5x}{x}$

Write each rational expression in lowest terms. See Examples 5 and 6.

47. $\dfrac{6-t}{t-6}$

48. $\dfrac{2-k}{k-2}$

49. $\dfrac{m^2-1}{1-m}$

50. $\dfrac{a^2-b^2}{b-a}$

51. $\dfrac{q^2-4q}{4q-q^2}$

52. $\dfrac{z^2-5z}{5z-z^2}$

Write four equivalent forms for each rational expression. See Example 7.

53. $-\dfrac{x+4}{x-3}$

54. $-\dfrac{x+6}{x-1}$

55. $-\dfrac{2x-3}{x+3}$

56. $-\dfrac{5x-6}{x+4}$

57. $-\dfrac{3x-1}{5x-6}$

58. $-\dfrac{2x-9}{7x-1}$

59. The area of the rectangle is represented by x^4+10x^2+21. What is the width? $\left(\textit{Hint}\text{: Use } w=\frac{A}{l}.\right)$

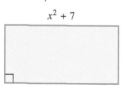

x^2+7

60. The volume of the box is represented by
$$(x^2+8x+15)(x+4).$$
Find the polynomial that represents the area of the bottom of the box.

$x+5$

16.2 ▶▶▶ Multiplying and Dividing Rational Expressions

OBJECTIVE 1 Multiply rational expressions. The product of two fractions is found by multiplying the numerators and multiplying the denominators. Rational expressions are multiplied in the same way.

Multiplying Rational Expressions

The product of the rational expressions $\frac{P}{Q}$ and $\frac{R}{S}$ is shown below.

$$\frac{P}{Q} \cdot \frac{R}{S} = \frac{PR}{QS}$$

In words: To multiply rational expressions, multiply the numerators and multiply the denominators.

OBJECTIVES

1 Multiply rational expressions.

2 Find reciprocals.

3 Divide rational expressions.

EXAMPLE 1 Multiplying Rational Expressions

Multiply. Write each answer in lowest terms.

(a) $\dfrac{3}{10} \cdot \dfrac{5}{9}$ | **(b)** $\dfrac{6}{x} \cdot \dfrac{x^2}{12}$

Indicate the product of the numerators and the product of the denominators.

$= \dfrac{3 \cdot 5}{10 \cdot 9}$ | $= \dfrac{6 \cdot x^2}{x \cdot 12}$

Leave the products in factored form because common factors are needed to write the product in lowest terms. Factor the numerator and denominator to further identify any common factors. Then use the fundamental property to write each product in lowest terms.

$= \dfrac{3 \cdot 5}{2 \cdot 5 \cdot 3 \cdot 3}$ | $= \dfrac{6 \cdot x \cdot x}{2 \cdot 6 \cdot x}$

$= \dfrac{1}{6}$ | $= \dfrac{x}{2}$

Work Problem **1** *at the Side.* ▶

EXAMPLE 2 Multiplying Rational Expressions

Multiply. Write the answer in lowest terms.

$\dfrac{x+y}{2x} \cdot \dfrac{x^2}{(x+y)^2}$

$= \dfrac{(x+y)x^2}{2x(x+y)^2}$ Multiply numerators. Multiply denominators.

$= \dfrac{(x+y)\, x \cdot x}{2x(x+y)(x+y)}$ Factor; identify common factors.

$= \dfrac{x}{2(x+y)}$ $\dfrac{(x+y)x}{x(x+y)} = 1$; lowest terms

Work Problem **2** *at the Side.* ▶

---

1 Multiply. Write each answer in lowest terms.

(a) $\dfrac{2}{7} \cdot \dfrac{5}{10}$

(b) $\dfrac{3m^2}{2} \cdot \dfrac{10}{m}$

(c) $\dfrac{8p^2q}{3} \cdot \dfrac{9}{q^2p}$

2 Multiply. Write each answer in lowest terms.

(a) $\dfrac{a+b}{5} \cdot \dfrac{30}{2(a+b)}$

(b) $\dfrac{3(p-q)}{q^2} \cdot \dfrac{q}{2(p-q)^2}$

ANSWERS

1. (a) $\dfrac{1}{7}$ (b) $15m$ (c) $\dfrac{24p}{q}$

2. (a) 3 (b) $\dfrac{3}{2q(p-q)}$

3 Multiply. Write each answer in lowest terms.

(a)

$$\frac{x^2 + 7x + 10}{3x + 6} \cdot \frac{6x - 6}{x^2 + 2x - 15}$$

(b)

$$\frac{m^2 + 4m - 5}{m + 5} \cdot \frac{m^2 + 8m + 15}{m - 1}$$

4 Find the reciprocal of each rational expression.

(a) $\dfrac{5}{8}$

(b) $\dfrac{6b^5}{3r^2b}$

(c) $\dfrac{t^2 - 4t}{t^2 + 2t - 3}$

EXAMPLE 3   **Multiplying Rational Expressions**

Multiply. Write the answer in lowest terms.

$$\frac{x^2 + 3x}{x^2 - 3x - 4} \cdot \frac{x^2 - 5x + 4}{x^2 + 2x - 3}$$

$$= \frac{(x^2 + 3x)(x^2 - 5x + 4)}{(x^2 - 3x - 4)(x^2 + 2x - 3)} \qquad \text{Definition of multiplication}$$

$$= \frac{x(x + 3)(x - 4)(x - 1)}{(x - 4)(x + 1)(x + 3)(x - 1)} \qquad \text{Factor.}$$

$$= \frac{x}{x + 1} \qquad \text{Divide out the common factors.}$$

The quotients $\frac{x+3}{x+3}, \frac{x-4}{x-4}$, and $\frac{x-1}{x-1}$ are all equal to 1, justifying the final product $\frac{x}{x+1}$.

◀ Work Problem **3** at the Side.

OBJECTIVE 2 Find reciprocals.   If the product of two rational expressions is 1, the rational expressions are called **reciprocals** (or **multiplicative inverses**) of each other. The reciprocal of a rational expression is found by interchanging the numerator and the denominator. For example,

$$\frac{2x - 1}{x - 5} \quad \text{has reciprocal} \quad \frac{x - 5}{2x - 1}.$$

EXAMPLE 4   **Finding Reciprocals of Rational Expressions**

Find the reciprocal of each rational expression.

(a) $\dfrac{4p^3}{9q}$ has reciprocal $\dfrac{9q}{4p^3}$.   Interchange the numerator and denominator.

(b) $\dfrac{k^2 - 9}{k^2 - k - 20}$ has reciprocal $\dfrac{k^2 - k - 20}{k^2 - 9}$.

◀ Work Problem **4** at the Side.

OBJECTIVE 3 Divide rational expressions.   Suppose we have $\frac{7}{8}$ gal of milk and want to find how many quarts we have. Since 1 qt is $\frac{1}{4}$ gal, we ask, "How many $\frac{1}{4}$s are there in $\frac{7}{8}$?" This would be interpreted as

$$\frac{7}{8} \div \frac{1}{4}, \quad \text{or} \quad \frac{\dfrac{7}{8}}{\dfrac{1}{4}} \leftarrow \text{The fraction bar means division.}$$

The fundamental property of rational expressions discussed earlier can be applied to rational number values of P, Q, and K.

$$\frac{P}{Q} = \frac{P \cdot K}{Q \cdot K} = \frac{\dfrac{7}{8} \cdot 4}{\dfrac{1}{4} \cdot 4} = \frac{\dfrac{7}{8} \cdot 4}{1} = \frac{7}{8} \cdot \frac{4}{1}. \qquad \begin{array}{l}\text{Let } P = \frac{7}{8}, Q = \frac{1}{4},\\ \text{and } K = 4 \text{ (the}\\ \text{reciprocal of } Q).\end{array}$$

So, to divide $\frac{7}{8}$ by $\frac{1}{4}$, we multiply $\frac{7}{8}$ by the reciprocal of $\frac{1}{4}$, namely $\frac{4}{1}$, or 4. Since $\frac{7}{8}(4) = \frac{7}{2}$, there are $\frac{7}{2}$ qt, or $3\frac{1}{2}$ qt, in $\frac{7}{8}$ gal.

ANSWERS

3. **(a)** $\dfrac{2(x - 1)}{x - 3}$ **(b)** $(m + 5)(m + 3)$

4. **(a)** $\dfrac{8}{5}$ **(b)** $\dfrac{3r^2b}{6b^5}$ **(c)** $\dfrac{t^2 + 2t - 3}{t^2 - 4t}$

The preceding discussion illustrates dividing common fractions. Division of rational expressions is defined in the same way.

> ### Dividing Rational Expressions
>
> If $\frac{P}{Q}$ and $\frac{R}{S}$ are any two rational expressions, with $\frac{R}{S} \neq 0$, then
>
> $$\frac{P}{Q} \div \frac{R}{S} = \frac{P}{Q} \cdot \frac{S}{R} = \frac{PS}{QR}.$$
>
> In words: To divide one rational expression by another rational expression, multiply the first rational expression (dividend) by the reciprocal of the second rational expression (divisor).

The next example shows the division of two rational numbers and the division of two rational expressions.

EXAMPLE 5 Dividing Rational Expressions

Divide. Write each answer in lowest terms.

(a) $\dfrac{5}{8} \div \dfrac{7}{16}$ **(b)** $\dfrac{y}{y+3} \div \dfrac{4y}{y+5}$

Multiply the first expression by the reciprocal of the second.

$= \dfrac{5}{8} \cdot \dfrac{16}{7}$ ← Reciprocal of $\frac{7}{16}$

$= \dfrac{5 \cdot 16}{8 \cdot 7}$

$= \dfrac{5 \cdot 8 \cdot 2}{8 \cdot 7}$

$= \dfrac{10}{7}$

$= \dfrac{y}{y+3} \cdot \dfrac{y+5}{4y}$ ← Reciprocal of $\frac{4y}{y+5}$

$= \dfrac{y(y+5)}{(y+3)(4y)}$

$= \dfrac{y+5}{4(y+3)}$

Work Problem **5** *at the Side.* ▶

EXAMPLE 6 Dividing Rational Expressions

Divide. Write the answer in lowest terms.

$$\frac{(3m)^2}{(2p)^3} \div \frac{6m^3}{16p^2}$$

$(3m)^2 = 3^2 m^2;$
$(2p)^3 = 2^3 p^3$

$= \dfrac{(3m)^2}{(2p)^3} \cdot \dfrac{16p^2}{6m^3}$ Multiply by the reciprocal.

$= \dfrac{9m^2}{8p^3} \cdot \dfrac{16p^2}{6m^3}$ Power rule for exponents

$= \dfrac{9 \cdot 16m^2 p^2}{8 \cdot 6p^3 m^3}$ Multiply numerators.
Multiply denominators.

$= \dfrac{3}{mp}$ Lowest terms

Work Problem **6** *at the Side.* ▶

5 Divide. Write each answer in lowest terms.

(a) $\dfrac{3}{4} \div \dfrac{5}{16}$

(b) $\dfrac{r}{r-1} \div \dfrac{3r}{r+4}$

(c) $\dfrac{6x-4}{3} \div \dfrac{15x-10}{9}$

6 Divide. Write each answer in lowest terms.

(a) $\dfrac{5a^2b}{2} \div \dfrac{10ab^2}{8}$

(b) $\dfrac{(3t)^2}{w} \div \dfrac{3t^2}{5w^4}$

ANSWERS

5. **(a)** $\dfrac{12}{5}$ **(b)** $\dfrac{r+4}{3(r-1)}$ **(c)** $\dfrac{6}{5}$

6. **(a)** $\dfrac{2a}{b}$ **(b)** $15w^3$

7 Divide. Write each answer in lowest terms.

(a)

$$\frac{y^2 + 4y + 3}{y + 3} \div \frac{y^2 - 4y - 5}{y - 3}$$

(b) $\dfrac{4x(x + 3)}{2x + 1} \div \dfrac{-x^2(x + 3)}{4x^2 - 1}$

8 Divide. Write each answer in lowest terms.

(a) $\dfrac{ab - a^2}{a^2 - 1} \div \dfrac{a - b}{a - 1}$

(b) $\dfrac{x^2 - 9}{2x + 6} \div \dfrac{9 - x^2}{4x - 12}$

EXAMPLE 7 **Dividing Rational Expressions**

Divide. Write the answer in lowest terms.

$$\frac{x^2 - 4}{(x + 3)(x - 2)} \div \frac{(x + 2)(x + 3)}{-2x}$$

$$= \frac{x^2 - 4}{(x + 3)(x - 2)} \cdot \frac{-2x}{(x + 2)(x + 3)} \qquad \text{Multiply by the reciprocal.}$$

$$= \frac{-2x(x^2 - 4)}{(x + 3)(x - 2)(x + 2)(x + 3)} \qquad \begin{array}{l}\text{Multiply numerators.}\\ \text{Multiply denominators.}\end{array}$$

$$= \frac{-2x(x + 2)(x - 2)}{(x + 3)(x - 2)(x + 2)(x + 3)} \qquad \text{Factor the numerator.}$$

$$= \frac{-2x}{(x + 3)^2}, \quad \text{or} \quad -\frac{2x}{(x + 3)^2} \qquad \text{Lowest terms; } \tfrac{-a}{b} = -\tfrac{a}{b}$$

◀ Work Problem **7** at the Side.

EXAMPLE 8 **Dividing Rational Expressions (Factors Are Opposites)**

Divide. Write the answer in lowest terms.

$$\frac{m^2 - 4}{m^2 - 1} \div \frac{2m^2 + 4m}{1 - m}$$

$$= \frac{m^2 - 4}{m^2 - 1} \cdot \frac{1 - m}{2m^2 + 4m} \qquad \text{Multiply by the reciprocal.}$$

$$= \frac{(m^2 - 4)(1 - m)}{(m^2 - 1)(2m^2 + 4m)} \qquad \begin{array}{l}\text{Multiply numerators.}\\ \text{Multiply denominators.}\end{array}$$

$$= \frac{(m + 2)(m - 2)(1 - m)}{(m + 1)(m - 1)(2m)(m + 2)} \qquad \begin{array}{l}\text{Factor; } 1 - m \text{ and } m - 1 \text{ are}\\ \text{opposites.}\end{array}$$

$$= \frac{-1(m - 2)}{2m(m + 1)} \qquad \text{From \textbf{Section 15.1}, } \tfrac{1 - m}{m - 1} = -1.$$

$$= \frac{-m + 2}{2m(m + 1)}, \quad \text{or} \quad \frac{2 - m}{2m(m + 1)} \qquad \text{Distribute } -1 \text{ in the numerator.}$$

◀ Work Problem **8** at the Side.

In summary, follow these steps to multiply or divide rational expressions.

Multiplying or Dividing Rational Expressions

Step 1 **Note the operation.** If the operation is division, use the definition of division to rewrite as multiplication.

Step 2 **Multiply** numerators and multiply denominators.

Step 3 **Factor** all numerators and denominators completely.

Step 4 **Write in lowest terms** using the fundamental property.

Steps 2 and 3 may be interchanged based on personal preference.

ANSWERS

7. (a) $\dfrac{y - 3}{y - 5}$ (b) $-\dfrac{4(2x - 1)}{x}$

8. (a) $\dfrac{-a}{a + 1}$ (b) $\dfrac{-2x + 6}{3 + x}$

16.2 ▶▶▶ **Exercises**

1. Match each multiplication problem in Column I with the correct product in Column II.

I	II
(a) $\dfrac{5x^3}{10x^4} \cdot \dfrac{10x^7}{2x}$	**A.** $\dfrac{2}{5x^5}$
(b) $\dfrac{10x^4}{5x^3} \cdot \dfrac{10x^7}{2x}$	**B.** $\dfrac{5x^5}{2}$
(c) $\dfrac{5x^3}{10x^4} \cdot \dfrac{2x}{10x^7}$	**C.** $\dfrac{1}{10x^7}$
(d) $\dfrac{10x^4}{5x^3} \cdot \dfrac{2x}{10x^7}$	**D.** $10x^7$

2. Match each division problem in Column I with the correct quotient in Column II.

I	II
(a) $\dfrac{5x^3}{10x^4} \div \dfrac{10x^7}{2x}$	**A.** $\dfrac{5x^5}{2}$
(b) $\dfrac{10x^4}{5x^3} \div \dfrac{10x^7}{2x}$	**B.** $10x^7$
(c) $\dfrac{5x^3}{10x^4} \div \dfrac{2x}{10x^7}$	**C.** $\dfrac{2}{5x^5}$
(d) $\dfrac{10x^4}{5x^3} \div \dfrac{2x}{10x^7}$	**D.** $\dfrac{1}{10x^7}$

Multiply. Write each answer in lowest terms. See Examples 1 and 2.

3. $\dfrac{10m^2}{7} \cdot \dfrac{14}{15m}$

4. $\dfrac{36z^3}{6z} \cdot \dfrac{28}{z^2}$

5. $\dfrac{16y^4}{18y^5} \cdot \dfrac{15y^5}{y^2}$

6. $\dfrac{20x^5}{-2x^2} \cdot \dfrac{8x^4}{35x^3}$

7. $\dfrac{2(c+d)}{3} \cdot \dfrac{18}{6(c+d)^2}$

8. $\dfrac{4(y-2)}{x} \cdot \dfrac{3x}{6(y-2)^2}$

Find the reciprocal of each rational expression. See Example 4.

9. $\dfrac{3p^3}{16q}$

10. $\dfrac{6x^4}{9y^2}$

11. $\dfrac{r^2 + rp}{7}$

12. $\dfrac{16}{9a^2 + 36a}$

13. $\dfrac{z^2 + 7z + 12}{z^2 - 9}$

14. $\dfrac{p^2 - 4p + 3}{p^2 - 3p}$

Divide. Write each answer in lowest terms. See Examples 5 and 6.

15. $\dfrac{9z^4}{3z^5} \div \dfrac{3z^2}{5z^3}$

16. $\dfrac{35q^8}{9q^5} \div \dfrac{25q^6}{10q^5}$

17. $\dfrac{4t^4}{2t^5} \div \dfrac{(2t)^3}{-6}$

18. $\dfrac{-12a^6}{3a^2} \div \dfrac{(2a)^3}{27a}$

19. $\dfrac{3}{2y-6} \div \dfrac{6}{y-3}$

20. $\dfrac{4m+16}{10} \div \dfrac{3m+12}{18}$

21. Explain in your own words how to multiply rational expressions.

22. Explain in your own words how to divide rational expressions.

Multiply or divide. Write each answer in lowest terms. See Examples 3, 7, and 8.

23. $\dfrac{5x - 15}{3x + 9} \cdot \dfrac{4x + 12}{6x - 18}$

24. $\dfrac{8r + 16}{24r - 24} \cdot \dfrac{6r - 6}{3r + 6}$

25. $\dfrac{2 - t}{8} \div \dfrac{t - 2}{6}$

26. $\dfrac{4}{m - 2} \div \dfrac{16}{2 - m}$

27. $\dfrac{5 - 4x}{5 + 4x} \cdot \dfrac{4x + 5}{4x - 5}$

28. $\dfrac{5 - x}{5 + x} \cdot \dfrac{x + 5}{x - 5}$

29. $\dfrac{6\,(m - 2)^2}{5\,(m + 4)^2} \cdot \dfrac{15\,(m + 4)}{2\,(2 - m)}$

30. $\dfrac{7\,(q - 1)}{3\,(q + 1)^2} \cdot \dfrac{6\,(q + 1)}{3\,(1 - q)^2}$

31. $\dfrac{p^2 + 4p - 5}{p^2 + 7p + 10} \div \dfrac{p - 1}{p + 4}$

32. $\dfrac{z^2 - 3z + 2}{z^2 + 4z + 3} \div \dfrac{z - 1}{z + 1}$

33. $\dfrac{2k^2 - k - 1}{2k^2 + 5k + 3} \div \dfrac{4k^2 - 1}{2k^2 + k - 3}$

34. $\dfrac{2m^2 - 5m - 12}{m^2 + m - 20} \div \dfrac{4m^2 - 9}{m^2 + 4m - 5}$

35. $\dfrac{2k^2 + 3k - 2}{6k^2 - 7k + 2} \cdot \dfrac{4k^2 - 5k + 1}{k^2 + k - 2}$

36. $\dfrac{2m^2 - 5m - 12}{m^2 - 10m + 24} \div \dfrac{4m^2 - 9}{m^2 - 9m + 18}$

37. $\dfrac{m^2 + 2mp - 3p^2}{m^2 - 3mp + 2p^2} \div \dfrac{m^2 + 4mp + 3p^2}{m^2 + 2mp - 8p^2}$

38. $\dfrac{r^2 + rs - 12s^2}{r^2 - rs - 20s^2} \div \dfrac{r^2 - 2rs - 3s^2}{r^2 + rs - 30s^2}$

39. $\left(\dfrac{x^2 + 10x + 25}{x^2 + 10x} \cdot \dfrac{10x}{x^2 + 15x + 50} \right) \div \dfrac{x + 5}{x + 10}$

40. $\left(\dfrac{m^2 - 12m + 32}{8m} \cdot \dfrac{m^2 - 8m}{m^2 - 8m + 16} \right) \div \dfrac{m - 8}{m - 4}$

41. If the rational expression $\dfrac{5x^2 y^3}{2pq}$ represents the area of a rectangle and $\dfrac{2xy}{p}$ represents the length, what rational expression represents the width?

Width

Length $= \dfrac{2xy}{p}$

The area is $\dfrac{5x^2 y^3}{2pq}$.

42. Consider the division problem $\dfrac{x - 6}{x + 4} \div \dfrac{x + 7}{x + 5}$.

We know that division by 0 is undefined, so the restrictions on x are $x \neq -4$, $x \neq -5$, and $x \neq -7$. Why is the last restriction needed?

16.3 ▶▶▶ Least Common Denominators

OBJECTIVE 1 Find the least common denominator for a list of fractions. Just as with common fractions, adding or subtracting rational expressions (to be discussed in the next section) often requires a **least common denominator (LCD),** the simplest expression that is divisible by all denominators. For example, the least common denominator for $\frac{2}{9}$ and $\frac{5}{12}$ is 36, because 36 is the smallest positive number divisible by both 9 and 12.

We can often find least common denominators by inspection. For example, the LCD for $\frac{1}{6}$ and $\frac{2}{3m}$ is $6m$. In other cases, we find the LCD by a procedure similar to that used in **Section 14.1** for finding the greatest common factor.

OBJECTIVES

1 Find the least common denominator for a list of fractions.

2 Write equivalent rational expressions.

Finding the Least Common Denominator (LCD)

Step 1 **Factor** each denominator into prime factors.

Step 2 **List each different denominator factor** the *greatest* number of times it appears in any of the denominators.

Step 3 **Multiply** the denominator factors from Step 2 to get the LCD.

When each denominator is factored into prime factors, every prime factor must be a factor of the least common denominator.

In Example 1, we find the LCD for both numerical and algebraic denominators.

EXAMPLE 1 **Finding Least Common Denominators**

Find the LCD for each pair of fractions.

(a) $\dfrac{1}{24}, \dfrac{7}{15}$ **(b)** $\dfrac{1}{8x}, \dfrac{3}{10x}$

Step 1 Write each denominator in factored form with numerical coefficients in prime factored form.

$$24 = 2 \cdot 2 \cdot 2 \cdot 3 = 2^3 \cdot 3 \qquad\quad 8x = 2 \cdot 2 \cdot 2 \cdot x = 2^3 \cdot x$$
$$15 = 3 \cdot 5 \qquad\qquad\qquad\qquad\quad 10x = 2 \cdot 5 \cdot x$$

Step 2 We find the LCD by taking each different factor the *greatest* number of times it appears as a factor in any of the denominators.

The factor 2 appears three times in one product and not at all in the other, so the greatest number of times 2 appears is three. The greatest number of times both 3 and 5 appear is one.

Here, 2 appears three times in one product and once in the other, so the greatest number of times 2 appears is three. The greatest number of times 5 appears is one, and the greatest number of times x appears in either product is one.

Step 3
$$\text{LCD} = 2 \cdot 2 \cdot 2 \cdot 3 \cdot 5$$
$$= 2^3 \cdot 3 \cdot 5$$
$$= 120$$

$$\text{LCD} = 2 \cdot 2 \cdot 2 \cdot 5 \cdot x$$
$$= 2^3 \cdot 5 \cdot x$$
$$= 40x$$

Work Problem **1** *at the Side.* ▶

1 Find the LCD for each pair of fractions.

(a) $\dfrac{7}{10}, \dfrac{1}{25}$

(b) $\dfrac{7}{20p}, \dfrac{11}{30p}$

(c) $\dfrac{4}{5x}, \dfrac{12}{10x}$

2 Find the LCD.

(a) $\dfrac{4}{16m^3n}, \dfrac{5}{9m^5}$

(b) $\dfrac{3}{25a^2}, \dfrac{2}{10a^3b}$

EXAMPLE 2 **Finding the LCD**

Find the LCD for $\dfrac{5}{6r^2}$ and $\dfrac{3}{4r^3}$.

Step 1 Factor each denominator.

$$6r^2 = 2 \cdot 3 \cdot r^2$$
$$4r^3 = 2^2 \cdot r^3$$

Step 2 The greatest number of times 2 appears is two, the greatest number of times 3 appears is one, and the greatest number of times r appears is three; therefore,

Step 3 $$\text{LCD} = 2^2 \cdot 3 \cdot r^3 = 12r^3.$$

◀ Work Problem **2** at the Side.

> **CAUTION**
> When finding the LCD, use each factor the *greatest* number of times it appears in any *single* denominator, not the *total* number of times it appears. For instance, the greatest number of times r appears as a factor in one denominator in Example 2 is 3, *not* 5.

---

3 Find the LCD for the fractions in each list.

(a) $\dfrac{7}{3a}, \dfrac{11}{a^2 - 4a}$

(b)
$$\dfrac{2m}{m^2 - 3m + 2}, \dfrac{5m - 3}{m^2 + 3m - 10},$$
$$\dfrac{4m + 7}{m^2 + 4m - 5}$$

(c) $\dfrac{6}{x - 4}, \dfrac{3x - 1}{4 - x}$

EXAMPLE 3 **Finding LCDs**

Find the LCD for the fractions in each list.

(a) $\dfrac{6}{5m}, \dfrac{4}{m^2 - 3m}$

$$\left.\begin{array}{l} 5m = 5 \cdot m \\ m^2 - 3m = m(m - 3) \end{array}\right\} \text{Factor each denominator.}$$

Use each different factor the greatest number of times it appears.

$$\text{LCD} = 5 \cdot m \cdot (m - 3) = 5m(m - 3)$$

> Be sure to include m as a factor in the LCD.

Because m is not a *factor* of $m - 3$, both factors, m and $m - 3$, must appear in the LCD.

(b) $\dfrac{1}{r^2 - 4r - 5}, \dfrac{3}{r^2 - r - 20}, \dfrac{1}{r^2 - 10r + 25}$

$$\left.\begin{array}{l} r^2 - 4r - 5 = (r - 5)(r + 1) \\ r^2 - r - 20 = (r - 5)(r + 4) \\ r^2 - 10r + 25 = (r - 5)^2 \end{array}\right\} \text{Factor each denominator.}$$

Use each different factor the greatest number of times it appears as a factor.

$$\text{LCD} = (r - 5)^2(r + 1)(r + 4)$$

(c) $\dfrac{1}{q - 5}, \dfrac{3}{5 - q}$

The expressions $q - 5$ and $5 - q$ are opposites of each other because

$$-(q - 5) = -q + 5 = 5 - q.$$

Therefore, either $q - 5$ or $5 - q$ can be used as the LCD.

◀ Work Problem **3** at the Side.

OBJECTIVE 2 Write equivalent rational expressions. Once the LCD has been found, the next step in preparing to add or subtract two rational expressions is to use the fundamental property to write equivalent rational expressions. We use the following steps.

Writing a Rational Expression with a Specified Denominator

Step 1 **Factor** both denominators.

Step 2 **Decide what factor(s) the denominator must be multiplied by** in order to equal the specified denominator.

Step 3 **Multiply** the rational expression by that factor divided by itself. (That is, multiply by 1.)

EXAMPLE 4 **Writing Equivalent Rational Expressions**

Write each rational expression as an equivalent expression with the indicated denominator.

(a) $\dfrac{3}{8} = \dfrac{?}{40}$ (b) $\dfrac{9k}{25} = \dfrac{?}{50k}$

Step 1 For each example, first factor the denominator on the right. Then compare the denominator on the left with the one on the right to decide what factors are missing.

$\dfrac{3}{8} = \dfrac{?}{5 \cdot 8}$ $\dfrac{9k}{25} = \dfrac{?}{25 \cdot 2k}$

Step 2 A factor of 5 is missing.   Factors of 2 and k are missing.

Step 3 Multiply $\frac{3}{8}$ by $\frac{5}{5}$.   Multiply $\frac{9k}{25}$ by $\frac{2k}{2k}$.

$\dfrac{3}{8} = \dfrac{3}{8} \cdot \dfrac{5}{5} = \dfrac{15}{40}$ $\dfrac{9k}{25} = \dfrac{9k}{25} \cdot \dfrac{2k}{2k} = \dfrac{18k^2}{50k}$

$\frac{5}{5} = 1 \uparrow$ $\frac{2k}{2k} = 1 \uparrow$

Work Problem **4** *at the Side.* ▶

4 Write each rational expression as an equivalent expression with the indicated denominator.

(a) $\dfrac{3}{4} = \dfrac{?}{36}$

(b) $\dfrac{7k}{5} = \dfrac{?}{30p}$

EXAMPLE 5 **Writing Equivalent Rational Expressions**

Write each rational expression as an equivalent expression with the indicated denominator.

(a)
$$\dfrac{8}{3x + 1} = \dfrac{?}{12x + 4}$$

$$\dfrac{8}{3x + 1} = \dfrac{?}{4(3x + 1)}$$ Factor the denominator on the right.

The missing factor is 4, so multiply the fraction on the left by $\frac{4}{4}$.

$$\dfrac{8}{3x + 1} \cdot \dfrac{4}{4} = \dfrac{32}{12x + 4}$$ Fundamental property

Continued on Next Page

ANSWERS

4. (a) $\dfrac{27}{36}$ (b) $\dfrac{42kp}{30p}$

5 Write each rational expression as an equivalent expression with the indicated denominator.

(a) $\dfrac{9}{2a + 5} = \dfrac{?}{6a + 15}$

(b) $\dfrac{5k + 1}{k^2 + 2k} = \dfrac{?}{k^3 + k^2 - 2k}$

(b) $\dfrac{12p}{p^2 + 8p} = \dfrac{?}{p^3 + 4p^2 - 32p}$

Factor the denominator in each rational expression.

$$\dfrac{12p}{p(p + 8)} = \dfrac{?}{p(p + 8)(p - 4)}$$

$$\begin{aligned} p^3 + 4p^2 - 32p \\ = p(p^2 + 4p - 32) \\ = p(p + 8)(p - 4) \end{aligned}$$

The factor $p - 4$ is missing, so multiply $\dfrac{12p}{p(p + 8)}$ by $\dfrac{p - 4}{p - 4}$.

$$\dfrac{12p}{p^2 + 8p} = \dfrac{12p}{p(p + 8)} \cdot \dfrac{p - 4}{p - 4} \qquad \text{Fundamental property}$$

$$= \dfrac{12p(p - 4)}{p(p + 8)(p - 4)} \qquad \begin{array}{l}\text{Multiply numerators.}\\ \text{Multiply denominators.}\end{array}$$

$$= \dfrac{12p^2 - 48p}{p^3 + 4p^2 - 32p} \qquad \text{Multiply the factors.}$$

Note

In the next section we add and subtract rational expressions, which sometimes requires the steps illustrated in Examples 4 and 5. While it may be beneficial to leave the equivalent expression in factored form, we multiplied out the factors in the numerator and the denominator in Example 5(b),

$$\dfrac{12p(p - 4)}{p(p + 8)(p - 4)},$$

in order to give the answer,

$$\dfrac{12p^2 - 48p}{p^3 + 4p^2 - 32p},$$

in the same form as the original problem.

◀ *Work Problem* **5** *at the Side.*

16.3 ▶▶▶ Exercises

FOR
EXTRA
HELP

MyMathLab

 Math XL
PRACTICE

WATCH

DOWNLOAD

READ

REVIEW

Choose the correct response in Exercises 1–4.

1. Suppose that the greatest common factor of a and b is 1. Then the least common denominator for $\frac{1}{a}$ and $\frac{1}{b}$ is

A. a **B.** b **C.** ab **D.** 1.

2. If a is a factor of b, then the least common denominator for $\frac{1}{a}$ and $\frac{1}{b}$ is

A. a **B.** b **C.** ab **D.** 1.

3. The least common denominator for $\frac{11}{20}$ and $\frac{1}{2}$ is

A. 40   **B.** 2   **C.** 20   **D.** none of these.

4. Suppose that we wish to write the rational expression $\dfrac{1}{(x-4)^2(y-3)}$ with denominator $(x-4)^3(y-3)^2$. We must multiply both the numerator and the denominator by

A. $(x-4)(y-3)$ **B.** $(x-4)^2$
C. $x-4$ **D.** $(x-4)^2(y-3)$.

Find the least common denominator for the fractions in each list. See Examples 1 and 2.

5. $\dfrac{2}{15}, \dfrac{3}{10}, \dfrac{7}{30}$

6. $\dfrac{5}{24}, \dfrac{7}{12}, \dfrac{9}{28}$

7. $\dfrac{3}{x^4}, \dfrac{5}{x^7}$

8. $\dfrac{2}{y^5}, \dfrac{3}{y^6}$

9. $\dfrac{5}{36q}, \dfrac{17}{24q}$

10. $\dfrac{4}{30p}, \dfrac{9}{50p}$

🌐 **11.** $\dfrac{6}{21r^3}, \dfrac{8}{12r^5}$

12. $\dfrac{9}{35t^2}, \dfrac{5}{49t^6}$

13. If the denominators of two fractions in prime factored form are $2^3 \cdot 3$ and $2^2 \cdot 5$, what is the factored form of their LCD?

14. Suppose two rational expressions have denominators $(t+4)^3(t-3)$ and $(t+4)^2(t+8)$. Find the factored form of their LCD. What is the similarity between the answers for this problem and for Exercise 13?

15. If two denominators have greatest common factor equal to 1, how can you easily find their least common denominator?

16. Suppose two fractions have denominators a^k and a^r, where k and r are natural numbers, with $k > r$. What is their least common denominator?

Find the least common denominator for the fractions in each list. See Examples 1–3.

17. $\dfrac{9}{28m^2}, \dfrac{3}{12m-20}$

18. $\dfrac{15}{27a^3}, \dfrac{8}{9a-45}$

19. $\dfrac{7}{5b-10}, \dfrac{11}{6b-12}$

20. $\dfrac{3}{7x^2+21x}, \dfrac{1}{5x^2+15x}$

21. $\dfrac{5}{c-d}, \dfrac{8}{d-c}$

22. $\dfrac{4}{y-x}, \dfrac{7}{x-y}$

23. $\dfrac{3}{k^2 + 5k}, \dfrac{2}{k^2 + 3k - 10}$

24. $\dfrac{1}{z^2 - 4z}, \dfrac{4}{z^2 - 3z - 4}$

25. $\dfrac{5}{p^2 + 8p + 15}, \dfrac{3}{p^2 - 3p - 18}, \dfrac{2}{p^2 - p - 30}$

26. $\dfrac{10}{y^2 - 10y + 21}, \dfrac{2}{y^2 - 2y - 3}, \dfrac{5}{y^2 - 6y - 7}$

Write each rational expression as an equivalent expression with the indicated denominator.
See Examples 4 and 5.

27. ⊕ $\dfrac{4}{11} = \dfrac{?}{55}$

28. $\dfrac{6}{7} = \dfrac{?}{42}$

29. $\dfrac{-5}{k} = \dfrac{?}{9k}$

30. $\dfrac{-3}{q} = \dfrac{?}{6q}$

31. $\dfrac{13}{40y} = \dfrac{?}{80y^3}$

32. $\dfrac{5}{27p} = \dfrac{?}{108p^4}$

33. $\dfrac{5t^2}{6r} = \dfrac{?}{42r^4}$

34. $\dfrac{8y^2}{3x} = \dfrac{?}{30x^3}$

35. $\dfrac{5}{2(m + 3)} = \dfrac{?}{8(m + 3)}$

36. $\dfrac{7}{4(y - 1)} = \dfrac{?}{16(y - 1)}$

37. ⊕ $\dfrac{-4t}{3t - 6} = \dfrac{?}{12 - 6t}$

38. $\dfrac{-7k}{5k - 20} = \dfrac{?}{40 - 10k}$

39. $\dfrac{14}{z^2 - 3z} = \dfrac{?}{z(z - 3)(z - 2)}$

40. $\dfrac{12}{x(x + 4)} = \dfrac{?}{x(x + 4)(x - 9)}$

41. $\dfrac{2(b - 1)}{b^2 + b} = \dfrac{?}{b^3 + 3b^2 + 2b}$

42. $\dfrac{3(c + 2)}{c(c - 1)} = \dfrac{?}{c^3 - 5c^2 + 4c}$

16.4 ▶▶▶ Adding and Subtracting Rational Expressions

To add and subtract rational expressions, we find least common denominators and write equivalent fractions with the LCD.

OBJECTIVE 1 **Add rational expressions having the same denominator.** We find the sum of two such rational expressions with the same procedure that we used in **Section 4.4** for adding two fractions having the same denominator.

Adding Rational Expressions (Same Denominator)

If $\frac{P}{Q}$ and $\frac{R}{Q}$ ($Q \neq 0$) are rational expressions, then

$$\frac{P}{Q} + \frac{R}{Q} = \frac{P+R}{Q}.$$

In words: To add rational expressions with the same denominator, add the numerators and keep the same denominator.

EXAMPLE 1 **Adding Rational Expressions (Same Denominator)**

Add. Write each answer in lowest terms.

(a) $\frac{4}{9} + \frac{2}{9}$ **(b)** $\frac{3x}{x+1} + \frac{3}{x+1}$

The denominators are the same, so the sum is found by adding the two numerators and keeping the same (common) denominator.

$= \frac{4+2}{9}$ Add.

$= \frac{6}{9}$

$= \frac{2 \cdot 3}{3 \cdot 3}$ Factor.

$= \frac{2}{3}$ Lowest terms

$= \frac{3x+3}{x+1}$ Add.

$= \frac{3(x+1)}{x+1}$ Factor.

$= 3$ Lowest terms

Work Problem **1** *at the Side.* ▶

OBJECTIVE 2 **Add rational expressions having different denominators.** As in **Section 4.4**, we use the following steps to add two rational expressions having different denominators.

Adding Rational Expressions (Different Denominators)

Step 1 **Find the least common denominator (LCD).**

Step 2 **Write each rational expression** as an equivalent rational expression with the LCD as the denominator.

Step 3 **Add the numerators** to get the numerator of the sum. The LCD is the denominator of the sum.

Step 4 **Write in lowest terms** using the fundamental property.

OBJECTIVES

1 Add rational expressions having the same denominator.

2 Add rational expressions having different denominators.

3 Subtract rational expressions.

1 Add. Write each answer in lowest terms.

(a) $\frac{7}{15} + \frac{3}{15}$

(b) $\frac{3}{y+4} + \frac{2}{y+4}$

(c) $\frac{x}{x+y} + \frac{1}{x+y}$

(d) $\frac{a}{a+b} + \frac{b}{a+b}$

(e) $\frac{x^2}{x+1} + \frac{x}{x+1}$

ANSWERS

1. **(a)** $\frac{2}{3}$ **(b)** $\frac{5}{y+4}$ **(c)** $\frac{x+1}{x+y}$

    (d) 1   **(e)** x

2 Add. Write each answer in lowest terms.

(a) $\dfrac{1}{10} + \dfrac{1}{15}$

(b) $\dfrac{6}{5x} + \dfrac{9}{2x}$

(c) $\dfrac{m}{3n} + \dfrac{2}{7n}$

EXAMPLE 2 Adding Rational Expressions (Different Denominators)

Add. Write each answer in lowest terms.

(a) $\dfrac{1}{12} + \dfrac{7}{15}$ **(b)** $\dfrac{2}{3y} + \dfrac{1}{4y}$

Step 1 First find the LCD, using the methods of the previous section.

$$12 = 2 \cdot 2 \cdot 3 = 2^2 \cdot 3 \qquad 3y = 3 \cdot y$$
$$15 = 3 \cdot 5 \qquad 4y = 2 \cdot 2 \cdot y = 2^2 \cdot y$$
$$\text{LCD} = 2^2 \cdot 3 \cdot 5 = 60 \qquad \text{LCD} = 2^2 \cdot 3 \cdot y = 12y$$

Step 2 Now write each rational expression as an equivalent expression with the LCD (either 60 or 12y) as the denominator.

$$\dfrac{1}{12} + \dfrac{7}{15} = \dfrac{1(5)}{12(5)} + \dfrac{7(4)}{15(4)} \qquad \dfrac{2}{3y} + \dfrac{1}{4y} = \dfrac{2(4)}{3y(4)} + \dfrac{1(3)}{4y(3)}$$

$$= \dfrac{5}{60} + \dfrac{28}{60} \qquad\qquad = \dfrac{8}{12y} + \dfrac{3}{12y}$$

Step 3 Add the numerators. The LCD is the denominator.

Step 4 Write in lowest terms if necessary.

$$= \dfrac{5 + 28}{60} \qquad\qquad = \dfrac{8 + 3}{12y}$$

$$= \dfrac{33}{60}, \text{ or } \dfrac{11}{20} \qquad\qquad = \dfrac{11}{12y}$$

◀ *Work Problem* **2** *at the Side.*

EXAMPLE 3 Adding Rational Expressions

Add. Write the answer in lowest terms.

$$\dfrac{2x}{x^2 - 1} + \dfrac{-1}{x + 1}$$

Step 1 Since the denominators are different, find the LCD.

$$\left. \begin{array}{l} x^2 - 1 = (x + 1)(x - 1) \\ x + 1 \text{ is prime.} \end{array} \right\} \text{ The LCD is } (x + 1)(x - 1).$$

Step 2 Write each rational expression as an equivalent expression with the LCD as the denominator.

$$\dfrac{2x}{x^2 - 1} + \dfrac{-1}{x + 1} \qquad\qquad \text{The LCD is } (x + 1)(x - 1).$$

$$= \dfrac{2x}{(x + 1)(x - 1)} + \dfrac{-1(x - 1)}{(x + 1)(x - 1)} \qquad \text{Multiply the second fraction by } \frac{x - 1}{x - 1}.$$

$$= \dfrac{2x}{(x + 1)(x - 1)} + \dfrac{-x + 1}{(x + 1)(x - 1)} \qquad \text{Distributive property}$$

Step 3 $= \dfrac{2x - x + 1}{(x + 1)(x - 1)} \qquad \text{Add numerators; keep the same denominator.}$

Continued on Next Page

$$= \frac{x + 1}{(x + 1)(x - 1)}$$ Combine like terms in the numerator.

Step 4 $$= \frac{1(x + 1)}{(x + 1)(x - 1)}$$ Identity property for multiplication

> Remember to write 1 in the numerator.

$$= \frac{1}{x - 1}$$ Divide out the common factors.

Work Problem **3** *at the Side.* ▶

EXAMPLE 4   **Adding Rational Expressions**

Add. Write the answer in lowest terms.

$$\frac{2x}{x^2 + 5x + 6} + \frac{x + 1}{x^2 + 2x - 3}$$

$$= \frac{2x}{(x + 2)(x + 3)} + \frac{x + 1}{(x + 3)(x - 1)}$$ Factor the denominators.

$$= \frac{2x(x - 1)}{(x + 2)(x + 3)(x - 1)} + \frac{(x + 1)(x + 2)}{(x + 2)(x + 3)(x - 1)}$$ The LCD is $(x + 2) \cdot (x + 3)(x - 1)$.

$$= \frac{2x(x - 1) + (x + 1)(x + 2)}{(x + 2)(x + 3)(x - 1)}$$ Add numerators; keep the same denominator.

$$= \frac{2x^2 - 2x + x^2 + 3x + 2}{(x + 2)(x + 3)(x - 1)}$$ Multiply.

$$= \frac{3x^2 + x + 2}{(x + 2)(x + 3)(x - 1)}$$ Combine like terms.

It is usually more convenient to leave the denominator in factored form. The numerator cannot be factored here, so the expression is in lowest terms.

Work Problem **4** *at the Side.* ▶

EXAMPLE 5   **Adding Rational Expressions with Denominators That Are Opposites**

Add. Write the answer in lowest terms.

$$\frac{y}{y - 2} + \frac{8}{2 - y}$$ The denominators are opposites.

$$= \frac{y}{y - 2} + \frac{8(-1)}{(2 - y)(-1)}$$ Multiply $\frac{8}{2 - y}$ by $\frac{-1}{-1}$ to get a common denominator.

$$= \frac{y}{y - 2} + \frac{-8}{-2 + y}$$ Distributive property

$$= \frac{y}{y - 2} + \frac{-8}{y - 2}$$ Rewrite $-2 + y$ as $y - 2$.

$$= \frac{y - 8}{y - 2}$$ Add numerators; keep the same denominator.

If we had chosen to use $2 - y$ as the common denominator, the final answer would be in the form $\frac{8 - y}{2 - y}$, which is equivalent to $\frac{y - 8}{y - 2}$.

Work Problem **5** *at the Side.* ▶

---

3 Add. Write each answer in lowest terms.

(a) $$\frac{2p}{3p + 3} + \frac{5p}{2p + 2}$$

(b) $$\frac{4}{y^2 - 1} + \frac{6}{y + 1}$$

(c) $$\frac{-2}{p + 1} + \frac{4p}{p^2 - 1}$$

4 Add. Write each answer in lowest terms.

(a) $$\frac{2k}{k^2 - 5k + 4} + \frac{3}{k^2 - 1}$$

(b)

$$\frac{4m}{m^2 + 3m + 2} + \frac{2m - 1}{m^2 + 6m + 5}$$

5 Add. Write the answer in lowest terms.

$$\frac{m}{2m - 3n} + \frac{n}{3n - 2m}$$

ANSWERS

3. (a) $\dfrac{19p}{6(p + 1)}$ (b) $\dfrac{2(3y - 1)}{(y + 1)(y - 1)}$

(c) $\dfrac{2}{p - 1}$

4. (a) $\dfrac{(2k - 3)(k + 4)}{(k - 4)(k - 1)(k + 1)}$

(b) $\dfrac{6m^2 + 23m - 2}{(m + 2)(m + 1)(m + 5)}$

5. $\dfrac{m - n}{2m - 3n}$, or $\dfrac{n - m}{3n - 2m}$

6 Subtract. Write each answer in lowest terms.

(a) $\dfrac{3}{m^2} - \dfrac{2}{m^2}$

OBJECTIVE **3** **Subtract rational expressions.** To subtract rational expressions having the same denominator, use the following rule.

> **Subtracting Rational Expressions (Same Denominator)**
>
> If $\frac{P}{Q}$ and $\frac{R}{Q}$ ($Q \neq 0$) are rational expressions, then
>
> $$\frac{P}{Q} - \frac{R}{Q} = \frac{P - R}{Q}.$$
>
> In words: To subtract rational expressions with the same denominator, subtract the numerators and keep the same denominator.

EXAMPLE 6 **Subtracting Rational Expressions (Same Denominator)**

Subtract. Write the answer in lowest terms.

$$\frac{2m}{m-1} - \frac{m+3}{m-1}$$ Use parentheses around the quantity being subtracted.

$$= \frac{2m - (m+3)}{m-1}$$ Subtract numerators; keep the same denominator.

Be careful with signs. $$= \frac{2m - m - 3}{m-1}$$ Distributive property

$$= \frac{m-3}{m-1}$$ Combine like terms.

(b) $\dfrac{x}{2x+3} - \dfrac{3x+4}{2x+3}$

> **CAUTION**
> Sign errors often occur in problems like the one in Example 6. The numerator of the fraction being subtracted must be treated as a single quantity. *Be sure to use parentheses after the subtraction sign.*

◀ Work Problem **6** at the Side.

In the remaining examples, we subtract rational expressions having different denominators.

EXAMPLE 7 **Subtracting Rational Expressions (Different Denominators)**

Subtract. Write the answer in lowest terms.

$$\frac{9}{x-2} - \frac{3}{x}$$ The LCD is $x(x-2)$.

$$= \frac{9x}{x(x-2)} - \frac{3(x-2)}{x(x-2)}$$ Rewrite each expression with the LCD.

$$= \frac{9x - 3(x-2)}{x(x-2)}$$ Subtract numerators; keep the same denominator.

Continued on Next Page

Be careful here.

$$= \frac{9x - 3x + 6}{x(x - 2)} \qquad \text{Distributive property}$$

$$= \frac{6x + 6}{x(x - 2)}, \quad \text{or} \quad \frac{6(x + 1)}{x(x - 2)} \qquad \begin{array}{l}\text{Combine like terms;}\\ \text{factor the numerator.}\end{array}$$

Note

We factored the final numerator in Example 7 to get $\frac{6(x + 1)}{x(x - 2)}$. The fundamental property does not apply, however, since there are no common factors to divide out. The answer is in lowest terms.

Work Problem **7** *at the Side.* ▶

EXAMPLE 8 **Subtracting Rational Expressions with Denominators That Are Opposites**

Subtract. Write the answer in lowest terms.

$$\frac{3x}{x - 5} - \frac{2x - 25}{5 - x} \qquad \begin{array}{l}\text{The denominators are opposites.}\\ \text{We choose } x - 5 \text{ as the common}\\ \text{denominator.}\end{array}$$

$$= \frac{3x}{x - 5} - \frac{(2x - 25)(-1)}{(5 - x)(-1)} \qquad \begin{array}{l}\text{Multiply } \frac{2x - 25}{5 - x} \text{ by } \frac{-1}{-1} \text{ to get a}\\ \text{common denominator.}\end{array}$$

$$= \frac{3x}{x - 5} - \frac{-2x + 25}{x - 5} \qquad (5 - x)(-1) = -5 + x = x - 5$$

$$= \frac{3x - (-2x + 25)}{x - 5} \qquad \boxed{\text{Use parentheses.}} \quad \text{Subtract numerators.}$$

$$= \frac{3x + 2x - 25}{x - 5} \qquad \text{Distributive property}$$

$$= \frac{5x - 25}{x - 5} \qquad \text{Combine like terms.}$$

$$= \frac{5(x - 5)}{x - 5} \qquad \text{Factor.}$$

$$= 5 \qquad \text{Divide out the common factor.}$$

Work Problem **8** *at the Side.* ▶

EXAMPLE 9 **Subtracting Rational Expressions**

Subtract. Write the answer in lowest terms.

$$\frac{6x}{x^2 - 2x + 1} - \frac{1}{x^2 - 1}$$

Begin by factoring the denominators.

$$x^2 - 2x + 1 = (x - 1)^2 \quad \text{and} \quad x^2 - 1 = (x - 1)(x + 1)$$

From the factored denominators, we identify the LCD, $(x - 1)^2(x + 1)$. *We use the factor $x - 1$ twice* because it appears twice in the first denominator.

Continued on Next Page

7 Subtract. Write each answer in lowest terms.

(a) $\dfrac{1}{k + 4} - \dfrac{2}{k}$

(b) $\dfrac{6}{a + 2} - \dfrac{1}{a - 3}$

8 Subtract. Write each answer in lowest terms.

(a) $\dfrac{5}{x - 1} - \dfrac{3x}{1 - x}$

(b) $\dfrac{2y}{y - 2} - \dfrac{1 + y}{2 - y}$

ANSWERS

7. (a) $\dfrac{-k - 8}{k(k + 4)}$ (b) $\dfrac{5(a - 4)}{(a + 2)(a - 3)}$

8. (a) $\dfrac{5 + 3x}{x - 1}$, or $\dfrac{-5 - 3x}{1 - x}$

(b) $\dfrac{3y + 1}{y - 2}$, or $\dfrac{-3y - 1}{2 - y}$

9 Subtract. Write each answer in lowest terms.

(a) $\dfrac{4y}{y^2 - 1} - \dfrac{5}{y^2 + 2y + 1}$

(b) $\dfrac{3r}{r^2 - 5r} - \dfrac{4}{r^2 - 10r + 25}$

$\dfrac{6x}{(x - 1)^2} - \dfrac{1}{(x - 1)(x + 1)}$ The LCD is $(x - 1)^2 (x + 1)$.

$= \dfrac{6x(x + 1)}{(x - 1)^2 (x + 1)} - \dfrac{1(x - 1)}{(x - 1)(x - 1)(x + 1)}$ Fundamental property

$= \dfrac{6x(x + 1) - 1(x - 1)}{(x - 1)^2 (x + 1)}$ Subtract numerators.

$= \dfrac{6x^2 + 6x - x + 1}{(x - 1)^2 (x + 1)}$ Distributive property

$= \dfrac{6x^2 + 5x + 1}{(x - 1)^2 (x + 1)},$ or $\dfrac{(2x + 1)(3x + 1)}{(x - 1)^2 (x + 1)}$ Combine like terms; factor the numerator.

Verify that the final answer is in lowest terms.

◀ *Work Problem* **9** *at the Side.*

EXAMPLE 10   Subtracting Rational Expressions

Subtract. Write the answer in lowest terms.

$$\dfrac{q}{q^2 - 4q - 5} - \dfrac{3}{2q^2 - 13q + 15}$$

To find the LCD, factor each denominator.

$$q^2 - 4q - 5 = (q + 1)(q - 5)$$
$$2q^2 - 13q + 15 = (q - 5)(2q - 3)$$

The LCD here is $(q + 1)(q - 5)(2q - 3)$. Write each rational expression with the LCD, using the fundamental property.

$\dfrac{q}{(q + 1)(q - 5)} - \dfrac{3}{(q - 5)(2q - 3)}$ The LCD is $(q + 1) \cdot (q - 5)(2q - 3)$.

$= \dfrac{q(2q - 3)}{(q + 1)(q - 5)(2q - 3)} - \dfrac{3(q + 1)}{(q + 1)(q - 5)(2q - 3)}$

$= \dfrac{q(2q - 3) - 3(q + 1)}{(q + 1)(q - 5)(2q - 3)}$ Subtract numerators.

$= \dfrac{2q^2 - 3q - 3q - 3}{(q + 1)(q - 5)(2q - 3)}$ Distributive property

$= \dfrac{2q^2 - 6q - 3}{(q + 1)(q - 5)(2q - 3)}$ Combine like terms.

Verify that the final answer is in lowest terms.

◀ *Work Problem* **10** *at the Side.*

10 Subtract. Write each answer in lowest terms.

(a) $\dfrac{2}{p^2 - 5p + 4} - \dfrac{3}{p^2 - 1}$

(b)
$\dfrac{q}{2q^2 + 5q - 3} - \dfrac{3q + 4}{3q^2 + 10q + 3}$

ANSWERS

9. (a) $\dfrac{4y^2 - y + 5}{(y + 1)^2 (y - 1)}$

   (b) $\dfrac{3r - 19}{(r - 5)^2}$

10. (a) $\dfrac{14 - p}{(p - 4)(p - 1)(p + 1)}$

   (b) $\dfrac{-3q^2 - 4q + 4}{(2q - 1)(q + 3)(3q + 1)}$

Match the expression in Column I with the correct sum or difference in Column II.

I

II

1. $\dfrac{x}{x+6} + \dfrac{6}{x+6}$

2. $\dfrac{2x}{x-6} - \dfrac{12}{x-6}$

A. 2

B. $\dfrac{x-6}{x+6}$

3. $\dfrac{6}{x-6} - \dfrac{x}{x-6}$

4. $\dfrac{6}{x+6} - \dfrac{x}{x+6}$

C. -1

D. $\dfrac{6+x}{6x}$

5. $\dfrac{x}{x+6} - \dfrac{6}{x+6}$

6. $\dfrac{1}{x} + \dfrac{1}{6}$

E. 1

F. 0

7. $\dfrac{1}{6} - \dfrac{1}{x}$

8. $\dfrac{1}{6x} - \dfrac{1}{6x}$

G. $\dfrac{x-6}{6x}$

H. $\dfrac{6-x}{x+6}$

Note: When adding and subtracting rational expressions, several different equivalent forms of the answer often exist. If your answer does not look exactly like the one given in the back of the book, check to see whether you have written an equivalent form.

Add or subtract. Write each answer in lowest terms. See Examples 1 and 6.

9. $\dfrac{4}{m} + \dfrac{7}{m}$

10. $\dfrac{5}{p} + \dfrac{11}{p}$

11. $\dfrac{a+b}{2} - \dfrac{a-b}{2}$

12. $\dfrac{x-y}{2} - \dfrac{x+y}{2}$

13. $\dfrac{5}{y+4} - \dfrac{1}{y+4}$

14. $\dfrac{4}{y+3} - \dfrac{1}{y+3}$

15. $\dfrac{5m}{m+1} - \dfrac{1+4m}{m+1}$

16. $\dfrac{4x}{x+2} - \dfrac{2+3x}{x+2}$

17. $\dfrac{x^2}{x+5} + \dfrac{5x}{x+5}$

18. $\dfrac{t^2}{t-3} + \dfrac{-3t}{t-3}$

19. $\dfrac{y^2-3y}{y+3} + \dfrac{-18}{y+3}$

20. $\dfrac{r^2-8r}{r-5} + \dfrac{15}{r-5}$

21. Explain with an example how to add or subtract rational expressions with the same denominator.

22. Explain with an example how to add or subtract rational expressions with different denominators.

Add or subtract. Write each answer in lowest terms. See Examples 2, 3, 4, and 7.

23. $\dfrac{z}{5} + \dfrac{1}{3}$

24. $\dfrac{p}{8} + \dfrac{3}{5}$

25. $\dfrac{5}{7} - \dfrac{r}{2}$

26. $\dfrac{10}{9} - \dfrac{z}{3}$

27. $-\dfrac{3}{4} - \dfrac{1}{2x}$

28. $-\dfrac{5}{8} - \dfrac{3}{2a}$

29. $\dfrac{3}{5x} + \dfrac{9}{4x}$

30. $\dfrac{3}{2x} + \dfrac{4}{7x}$

31. $\dfrac{x+1}{6} + \dfrac{3x+3}{9}$

32. $\dfrac{2x-6}{4} + \dfrac{x+5}{6}$

33. $\dfrac{x+3}{3x} + \dfrac{2x+2}{4x}$

34. $\dfrac{x+2}{5x} + \dfrac{6x+3}{3x}$

35. $\dfrac{2}{x+3} + \dfrac{1}{x}$

36. $\dfrac{3}{x-4} + \dfrac{2}{x}$

37. $\dfrac{1}{k+5} - \dfrac{2}{k}$

38. $\dfrac{3}{m+1} - \dfrac{4}{m}$

39. $\dfrac{x}{x-2} + \dfrac{-8}{x^2-4}$

40. $\dfrac{2x}{x-1} + \dfrac{-4}{x^2-1}$

41. $\dfrac{x}{x-2} + \dfrac{4}{x+2}$

42. $\dfrac{2x}{x-1} + \dfrac{3}{x+1}$

43. $\dfrac{t}{t+2} + \dfrac{5-t}{t} - \dfrac{4}{t^2+2t}$

44. $\dfrac{2p}{p-3} + \dfrac{2+p}{p} - \dfrac{-6}{p^2-3p}$

45. What are the two possible LCDs that could be used for the sum

$$\frac{10}{m-2} + \frac{5}{2-m}?$$

46. If one form of the correct answer to a sum or difference of rational expressions is $\frac{4}{k-3}$, what would be an alternative form of the answer if the denominator is $3 - k$?

Add or subtract. Write each answer in lowest terms. See Examples 5 and 8.

47. $\dfrac{4}{x-5} + \dfrac{6}{5-x}$

48. $\dfrac{10}{m-2} + \dfrac{5}{2-m}$

49. $\dfrac{-1}{1-y} + \dfrac{3-4y}{y-1}$

50. $\dfrac{-4}{p-3} - \dfrac{p+1}{3-p}$

51. $\dfrac{2}{x-y^2} + \dfrac{7}{y^2-x}$

52. $\dfrac{-8}{p-q^2} + \dfrac{3}{q^2-p}$

53. $\dfrac{x}{5x-3y} - \dfrac{y}{3y-5x}$

54. $\dfrac{t}{8t-9s} - \dfrac{s}{9s-8t}$

55. $\dfrac{3}{4p-5} + \dfrac{9}{5-4p}$

56. $\dfrac{8}{3-7y} - \dfrac{2}{7y-3}$

*In each subtraction problem, the rational expression that follows the subtraction sign has a numerator with more than one term. **Be careful with signs** and find each difference. See Examples 6–10.*

57. $\dfrac{2m}{m-n} - \dfrac{5m+n}{2m-2n}$

58. $\dfrac{5p}{p-q} - \dfrac{3p+1}{4p-4q}$

59. $\dfrac{5}{x^2 - 9} - \dfrac{x + 2}{x^2 + 4x + 3}$

60. $\dfrac{1}{a^2 - 1} - \dfrac{a - 1}{a^2 + 3a - 4}$

61. $\dfrac{2q + 1}{3q^2 + 10q - 8} - \dfrac{3q + 5}{2q^2 + 5q - 12}$

62. $\dfrac{4y - 1}{2y^2 + 5y - 3} - \dfrac{y + 3}{6y^2 + y - 2}$

Perform the indicated operations. See Examples 1–10.

63. $\dfrac{4}{r^2 - r} + \dfrac{6}{r^2 + 2r} - \dfrac{1}{r^2 + r - 2}$

64. $\dfrac{6}{k^2 + 3k} - \dfrac{1}{k^2 - k} + \dfrac{2}{k^2 + 2k - 3}$

65. $\dfrac{x + 3y}{x^2 + 2xy + y^2} + \dfrac{x - y}{x^2 + 4xy + 3y^2}$

66. $\dfrac{m}{m^2 - 1} + \dfrac{m - 1}{m^2 + 2m + 1}$

67. $\dfrac{r + y}{18r^2 + 9ry - 2y^2} + \dfrac{3r - y}{36r^2 - y^2}$

68. $\dfrac{2x - z}{2x^2 + xz - 10z^2} - \dfrac{x + z}{x^2 - 4z^2}$

69. Refer to the rectangle in the figure.

  (a) Find an expression that represents its perimeter. Give the simplified form.

  (b) Find an expression that represents its area. Give the simplified form.

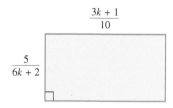

70. Refer to the triangle in the figure. Find an expression that represents its perimeter.

The quotient of two mixed numbers in arithmetic, such as $2\frac{1}{2} \div 3\frac{1}{4}$, can be written as a fraction:

$$2\frac{1}{2} \div 3\frac{1}{4} = \frac{2\frac{1}{2}}{3\frac{1}{4}} = \frac{2 + \frac{1}{2}}{3 + \frac{1}{4}}.$$

The last expression is the quotient of expressions that involve fractions. In algebra, some rational expressions also have fractions in the numerator, or denominator, or both.

OBJECTIVES

1 Simplify a complex fraction by writing it as a division problem (Method 1).

2 Simplify a complex fraction by multiplying numerator and denominator by the least common denominator (Method 2).

Complex Fraction

A rational expression with one or more fractions in the numerator, or denominator, or both, is called a **complex fraction.**

Examples of complex fractions include

$$\frac{2 + \frac{1}{2}}{3 + \frac{1}{4}}, \quad \frac{\frac{3x^2 - 5x}{6x^2}}{2x - \frac{1}{x}}, \quad \text{and} \quad \frac{3 + x}{5 - \frac{2}{x}}. \quad \text{Complex fractions}$$

The parts of a complex fraction are named as follows.

$$\left.\begin{array}{c} \dfrac{2}{p} - \dfrac{1}{q} \\ \hline \dfrac{3}{p} + \dfrac{5}{q} \end{array}\right.$$

$\leftarrow$ Numerator of complex fraction
$\leftarrow$ Main fraction bar
$\leftarrow$ Denominator of complex fraction

OBJECTIVE 1 Simplify a complex fraction by writing it as a division problem (Method 1). Since the main fraction bar represents division in a complex fraction, one method of simplifying a complex fraction involves division. This is the method introduced in **Section 4.6.**

Method 1 for Simplifying a Complex Fraction

Step 1   Write both the numerator and denominator as single fractions.

Step 2   Change the complex fraction to a division problem.

Step 3   Perform the indicated division.

Once again, the first example shows complex fractions from both arithmetic and algebra.

1 Simplify each complex fraction using Method 1.

(a) $\dfrac{\dfrac{2}{5} + \dfrac{1}{4}}{\dfrac{1}{2} + \dfrac{1}{3}}$

(b) $\dfrac{6 + \dfrac{1}{x}}{5 - \dfrac{2}{x}}$

(c) $\dfrac{9 - \dfrac{4}{p}}{\dfrac{2}{p} + 1}$

2 Simplify each complex fraction using Method 1.

(a) $\dfrac{\dfrac{rs^2}{t}}{\dfrac{r^2 s}{t^2}}$

(b) $\dfrac{\dfrac{m^2 n^3}{p}}{\dfrac{m^4 n}{p^2}}$

EXAMPLE 1 **Simplifying Complex Fractions (Method 1)**

Simplify each complex fraction.

(a) $\dfrac{\dfrac{2}{3} + \dfrac{5}{9}}{\dfrac{1}{4} + \dfrac{1}{12}}$

(b) $\dfrac{6 + \dfrac{3}{x}}{\dfrac{x}{4} + \dfrac{1}{8}}$

Step 1 First, write each numerator as a single fraction.

$$\frac{2}{3} + \frac{5}{9} = \frac{2(3)}{3(3)} + \frac{5}{9} \qquad\qquad 6 + \frac{3}{x} = \frac{6}{1} + \frac{3}{x}$$

$$= \frac{6}{9} + \frac{5}{9} = \frac{11}{9} \qquad\qquad = \frac{6x}{x} + \frac{3}{x} = \frac{6x + 3}{x}$$

Do the same thing with each denominator.

$$\frac{1}{4} + \frac{1}{12} = \frac{1(3)}{4(3)} + \frac{1}{12} \qquad\qquad \frac{x}{4} + \frac{1}{8} = \frac{x(2)}{4(2)} + \frac{1}{8}$$

$$= \frac{3}{12} + \frac{1}{12} = \frac{4}{12} \qquad\qquad = \frac{2x}{8} + \frac{1}{8} = \frac{2x + 1}{8}$$

Step 2 Write the equivalent complex fraction as a division problem.

$$\frac{\dfrac{11}{9}}{\dfrac{4}{12}} = \frac{11}{9} \div \frac{4}{12} \qquad\qquad \frac{\dfrac{6x + 3}{x}}{\dfrac{2x + 1}{8}} = \frac{6x + 3}{x} \div \frac{2x + 1}{8}$$

Step 3 Now use the definition of division and multiply by the reciprocal. Then write in lowest terms using the fundamental property.

$$= \frac{11}{9} \cdot \frac{12}{4} \qquad\qquad = \frac{6x + 3}{x} \cdot \frac{8}{2x + 1}$$

$$= \frac{11 \cdot 3 \cdot 4}{3 \cdot 3 \cdot 4} \qquad\qquad = \frac{3(2x + 1)}{x} \cdot \frac{8}{2x + 1}$$

$$= \frac{11}{3} \qquad\qquad = \frac{24}{x}$$

◀ *Work Problem* **1** *at the Side.*

EXAMPLE 2 **Simplifying a Complex Fraction (Method 1)**

Simplify the complex fraction.

$\dfrac{\dfrac{xp}{q^3}}{\dfrac{p^2}{qx^2}}$ The numerator and denominator are single fractions, so use the definition of division and then the fundamental property.

$$\frac{xp}{q^3} \div \frac{p^2}{qx^2}$$

$$= \frac{xp}{q^3} \cdot \frac{qx^2}{p^2}$$

$$= \frac{x^3}{q^2 p}$$

◀ *Work Problem* **2** *at the Side.*

EXAMPLE 3 **Simplifying a Complex Fraction (Method 1)**

Simplify the complex fraction.

$$\dfrac{\dfrac{3}{x+2} - 4}{\dfrac{2}{x+2} + 1}$$

$$= \dfrac{\dfrac{3}{x+2} - \dfrac{4(x+2)}{x+2}}{\dfrac{2}{x+2} + \dfrac{1(x+2)}{x+2}}$$ Write both second terms with a denominator of $x+2$.

$$= \dfrac{\dfrac{3-4(x+2)}{x+2}}{\dfrac{2+1(x+2)}{x+2}}$$ Subtract in the numerator.

Add in the denominator.

$$= \dfrac{\dfrac{3-4x-8}{x+2}}{\dfrac{2+x+2}{x+2}}$$ [Be careful with signs.]

Distributive property

$$= \dfrac{\dfrac{-5-4x}{x+2}}{\dfrac{4+x}{x+2}}$$ Combine like terms.

$$= \dfrac{-5-4x}{x+2} \cdot \dfrac{x+2}{4+x}$$ Multiply by the reciprocal.

$$= \dfrac{-5-4x}{4+x}$$ Lowest terms

3 Simplify using Method 1.

$$\dfrac{\dfrac{2}{x-1} + \dfrac{1}{x+1}}{\dfrac{3}{x-1} - \dfrac{4}{x+1}}$$

CAUTION

$$\dfrac{\dfrac{a}{b} + \dfrac{c}{d}}{\dfrac{e}{f} + \dfrac{g}{h}} \quad \textbf{\textit{does not equal}} \quad \left(\dfrac{a}{b} + \dfrac{c}{d}\right) \cdot \left(\dfrac{f}{e} + \dfrac{h}{g}\right).$$

Work Problem 3 *at the Side.* ▶

OBJECTIVE 2 **Simplify a complex fraction by multiplying numerator and denominator by the least common denominator (Method 2).** Since any expression can be multiplied by a form of 1 to get an equivalent expression, we can multiply both the numerator and the denominator of a complex fraction by the same nonzero expression to get an equivalent complex fraction. If we choose the expression to be the LCD of all the fractions within the complex fraction, the result will no longer be complex. This is Method 2.

ANSWER

3. $\dfrac{3x+1}{-x+7}$

4 Simplify each complex fraction using Method 2.

(a) $\dfrac{\dfrac{2}{3} - \dfrac{1}{4}}{\dfrac{4}{9} + \dfrac{1}{2}}$

(b) $\dfrac{2 - \dfrac{6}{a}}{3 + \dfrac{4}{a}}$

(c) $\dfrac{\dfrac{p}{5 - p}}{\dfrac{4p}{2p + 1}}$

Method 2 for Simplifying a Complex Fraction

Step 1 Find the LCD of all fractions within the complex fraction.

Step 2 Multiply both the numerator and the denominator of the complex fraction by this LCD using the distributive property as necessary. Write in lowest terms.

In the next example, Method 2 is used to simplify the complex fractions from Example 1.

EXAMPLE 4 **Simplifying Complex Fractions (Method 2)**

Simplify each complex fraction.

(a) $\dfrac{\dfrac{2}{3} + \dfrac{5}{9}}{\dfrac{1}{4} + \dfrac{1}{12}}$

(b) $\dfrac{6 + \dfrac{3}{x}}{\dfrac{x}{4} + \dfrac{1}{8}}$

Step 1 Find the LCD for all denominators in the complex fraction.

The LCD for 3, 9, 4, and 12 is 36. | The LCD for x, 4, and 8 is $8x$.

Step 2 Multiply the numerator and denominator of the complex fraction by the LCD.

$\dfrac{\dfrac{2}{3} + \dfrac{5}{9}}{\dfrac{1}{4} + \dfrac{1}{12}}$ $\dfrac{6 + \dfrac{3}{x}}{\dfrac{x}{4} + \dfrac{1}{8}}$

$= \dfrac{36\left(\dfrac{2}{3} + \dfrac{5}{9}\right)}{36\left(\dfrac{1}{4} + \dfrac{1}{12}\right)}$ $= \dfrac{8x\left(6 + \dfrac{3}{x}\right)}{8x\left(\dfrac{x}{4} + \dfrac{1}{8}\right)}$

Multiply each term by 36. $= \dfrac{36\left(\dfrac{2}{3}\right) + 36\left(\dfrac{5}{9}\right)}{36\left(\dfrac{1}{4}\right) + 36\left(\dfrac{1}{12}\right)}$

Multiply each term by $8x$. $= \dfrac{8x(6) + 8x\left(\dfrac{3}{x}\right)}{8x\left(\dfrac{x}{4}\right) + 8x\left(\dfrac{1}{8}\right)}$

$= \dfrac{24 + 20}{9 + 3}$ $= \dfrac{48x + 24}{2x^2 + x}$

$= \dfrac{44}{12}$ $= \dfrac{24(2x + 1)}{x(2x + 1)}$

$= \dfrac{4 \cdot 11}{4 \cdot 3}$ $= \dfrac{24}{x}$

$= \dfrac{11}{3}$

◀ *Work Problem* **4** *at the Side.*

ANSWERS

4. (a) $\dfrac{15}{34}$ (b) $\dfrac{2a - 6}{3a + 4}$ (c) $\dfrac{2p + 1}{4(5 - p)}$

EXAMPLE 5   **Simplifying a Complex Fraction (Method 2)**

Simplify the complex fraction.

$$\frac{\dfrac{3}{5m} - \dfrac{2}{m^2}}{\dfrac{9}{2m} + \dfrac{3}{4m^2}}$$ The LCD for $5m$, m^2, $2m$, and $4m^2$ is $20m^2$.

$$= \frac{20m^2\left(\dfrac{3}{5m} - \dfrac{2}{m^2}\right)}{20m^2\left(\dfrac{9}{2m} + \dfrac{3}{4m^2}\right)}$$ Multiply numerator and denominator by $20m^2$.

$$= \frac{20m^2\left(\dfrac{3}{5m}\right) - 20m^2\left(\dfrac{2}{m^2}\right)}{20m^2\left(\dfrac{9}{2m}\right) + 20m^2\left(\dfrac{3}{4m^2}\right)}$$ Distributive property

$$= \frac{12m - 40}{90m + 15}$$ Multiply and simplify.

Work Problem **5** *at the Side.* ▶

Some students use Method 1 for problems like Example 2, which is the quotient of two fractions, and Method 2 for problems like Examples 1, 3, 4, and 5, which have sums or differences in the numerators or denominators.

EXAMPLE 6   **Simplifying Complex Fractions**

Simplify each complex fraction. Use either method.

(a) $\dfrac{\dfrac{1}{y} + \dfrac{2}{y+2}}{\dfrac{4}{y} - \dfrac{3}{y+2}}$ We use Method 2, since there are sums and differences in the numerator and denominator.

$$= \frac{\left(\dfrac{1}{y} + \dfrac{2}{y+2}\right)y(y+2)}{\left(\dfrac{4}{y} - \dfrac{3}{y+2}\right)y(y+2)}$$ Multiply numerator and denominator by the LCD, $y(y+2)$.

$$= \frac{\left(\dfrac{1}{y}\right)y(y+2) + \left(\dfrac{2}{y+2}\right)y(y+2)}{\left(\dfrac{4}{y}\right)y(y+2) - \left(\dfrac{3}{y+2}\right)y(y+2)}$$ Distributive property

$$= \frac{1(y+2) + 2y}{4(y+2) - 3y}$$ Fundamental property

$$= \frac{y + 2 + 2y}{4y + 8 - 3y}$$ Distributive property

$$= \frac{3y + 2}{y + 8}$$ Combine like terms.

Continued on Next Page

5 Simplify using Method 2.

$$\frac{\dfrac{2}{5x} - \dfrac{3}{x^2}}{\dfrac{7}{4x} + \dfrac{1}{2x^2}}$$

ANSWER

5. $\dfrac{8x - 60}{35x + 10}$

6 Simplify each complex fraction. Use either method.

(a) $\dfrac{\dfrac{1}{x} + \dfrac{2}{x-1}}{\dfrac{2}{x} - \dfrac{4}{x-1}}$

(b) $\dfrac{1 - \dfrac{2}{x} - \dfrac{15}{x^2}}{1 + \dfrac{5}{x} + \dfrac{6}{x^2}}$

(c) $\dfrac{\dfrac{2x+3}{x-4}}{\dfrac{4x^2-9}{x^2-16}}$

(b) $\dfrac{1 - \dfrac{2}{x} - \dfrac{3}{x^2}}{1 - \dfrac{5}{x} + \dfrac{6}{x^2}}$ There are sums and differences in the numerator and denominator, so we use Method 2.

$= \dfrac{\left(1 - \dfrac{2}{x} - \dfrac{3}{x^2}\right)x^2}{\left(1 - \dfrac{5}{x} + \dfrac{6}{x^2}\right)x^2}$ Multiply numerator and denominator by the LCD, x^2.

$= \dfrac{x^2 - 2x - 3}{x^2 - 5x + 6}$ Distributive property

$= \dfrac{(x-3)(x+1)}{(x-3)(x-2)}$ Factor.

$= \dfrac{x+1}{x-2}$ Divide out the common factor.

You may wish to verify that in this example, like the others, *either* method can be used to simplify the complex fractions.

(c) $\dfrac{\dfrac{x+2}{x-3}}{\dfrac{x^2-4}{x^2-9}}$ This is a quotient of two rational expressions, so we use Method 1.

$= \dfrac{x+2}{x-3} \div \dfrac{x^2-4}{x^2-9}$ Write as a division problem.

$= \dfrac{x+2}{x-3} \cdot \dfrac{x^2-9}{x^2-4}$ Multiply by the reciprocal.

$= \dfrac{(x+2)(x+3)(x-3)}{(x-3)(x+2)(x-2)}$ Multiply; factor.

$= \dfrac{x+3}{x-2}$ Divide out the common factors.

◀ *Work Problem* **6** *at the Side.*

16.5 ▶▶▶ **Exercises**

FOR
EXTRA
HELP

Math XL
PRACTICE

WATCH

DOWNLOAD

READ

REVIEW

Note: In many problems involving complex fractions, several different equivalent forms of the answer often exist. If your answer does not look exactly like the one given in the back of the book, check to see whether you have written an equivalent form.

1. Consider the complex fraction $\dfrac{\frac{1}{2} - \frac{1}{3}}{\frac{5}{6} - \frac{1}{12}}$. Answer each part, outlining Method 1 for simplifying this complex fraction.

 (a) To combine the terms in the numerator, we must find the LCD of $\frac{1}{2}$ and $\frac{1}{3}$. What is this LCD? Determine the simplified form of the numerator of the complex fraction.

 (b) To combine the terms in the denominator, we must find the LCD of $\frac{5}{6}$ and $\frac{1}{12}$. What is this LCD? Determine the simplified form of the denominator of the complex fraction.

 (c) Now use the results from parts (a) and (b) to write the complex fraction as a division problem using the symbol ÷.

 (d) Perform the operation from part (c) to obtain the final simplification.

2. Consider the same complex fraction given in Exercise 1, $\dfrac{\frac{1}{2} - \frac{1}{3}}{\frac{5}{6} - \frac{1}{12}}$. Answer each part, outlining Method 2 for simplifying this complex fraction.

 (a) We must determine the LCD of all the fractions within the complex fraction. What is this LCD?

 (b) Multiply every term in the complex fraction by the LCD found in part (a), but at this time do not combine the terms in the numerator and the denominator.

 (c) Now combine the terms from part (b) to obtain the simplified form of the complex fraction.

Simplify each complex fraction. Use either method. See Examples 1–6.

3. $\dfrac{-\dfrac{4}{3}}{\dfrac{2}{9}}$

4. $\dfrac{-\dfrac{5}{6}}{\dfrac{5}{4}}$

5. $\dfrac{\dfrac{p}{q^2}}{\dfrac{p^2}{q}}$

6. $\dfrac{\dfrac{a}{x}}{\dfrac{a^2}{2x}}$

7. $\dfrac{\dfrac{x}{y^2}}{\dfrac{x^2}{y}}$

8. $\dfrac{\dfrac{p^4}{r}}{\dfrac{p^2}{r^2}}$

9. $\dfrac{\dfrac{4a^4b^3}{3a}}{\dfrac{2ab^4}{b^2}}$

10. $\dfrac{\dfrac{2r^4t^2}{3t}}{\dfrac{5r^2t^5}{3r}}$

11. $\dfrac{\dfrac{m+2}{3}}{\dfrac{m-4}{m}}$

12. $\dfrac{\dfrac{q-5}{q}}{\dfrac{q+5}{3}}$

13. $\dfrac{\dfrac{2}{x}-3}{\dfrac{2-3x}{2}}$

14. $\dfrac{6+\dfrac{2}{r}}{\dfrac{3r+1}{4}}$

15. $\dfrac{\dfrac{1}{x}+x}{\dfrac{x^2+1}{8}}$

16. $\dfrac{\dfrac{3}{m}-m}{\dfrac{3-m^2}{4}}$

17. $\dfrac{a-\dfrac{5}{a}}{a+\dfrac{1}{a}}$

18. $\dfrac{q+\dfrac{1}{q}}{q+\dfrac{4}{q}}$

19. $\dfrac{\dfrac{1}{2}+\dfrac{1}{p}}{\dfrac{2}{3}+\dfrac{1}{p}}$

20. $\dfrac{\dfrac{3}{4}-\dfrac{1}{r}}{\dfrac{1}{5}+\dfrac{1}{r}}$

21. $\dfrac{\dfrac{2}{p^2}-\dfrac{3}{5p}}{\dfrac{4}{p}+\dfrac{1}{4p}}$

22. $\dfrac{\dfrac{2}{m^2}-\dfrac{3}{m}}{\dfrac{2}{5m^2}+\dfrac{1}{3m}}$

23. $\dfrac{\dfrac{t}{t+2}}{\dfrac{4}{t^2-4}}$

24. $\dfrac{\dfrac{m}{m+1}}{\dfrac{3}{m^2-1}}$

25. $\dfrac{\dfrac{1}{k+1}-1}{\dfrac{1}{k+1}+1}$

26. $\dfrac{\dfrac{2}{p-1}+2}{\dfrac{3}{p-1}-2}$

27. $\dfrac{2+\dfrac{1}{x}-\dfrac{28}{x^2}}{3+\dfrac{13}{x}+\dfrac{4}{x^2}}$

28. $\dfrac{4-\dfrac{11}{x}-\dfrac{3}{x^2}}{2-\dfrac{1}{x}-\dfrac{15}{x^2}}$

29. $\dfrac{\dfrac{1}{m-1}+\dfrac{2}{m+2}}{\dfrac{2}{m+2}-\dfrac{1}{m-3}}$

30. $\dfrac{\dfrac{5}{r+3}-\dfrac{1}{r-1}}{\dfrac{2}{r+2}+\dfrac{3}{r+3}}$

31. $2-\dfrac{2}{2+\dfrac{2}{2+2}}$

32. $3-\dfrac{2}{4+\dfrac{2}{4-2}}$

16.6 ▶▶▶ Equations with Rational Expressions and Graphs

In **Section 8.1,** we defined the domain of a rational function as the set of all possible values of the variable. (We can also refer to this as "the domain of the variable.") Any value that makes the denominator 0 is excluded.

OBJECTIVE 1 Determine the domain of the variable in a rational equation. The **domain of the variable in a rational equation** is the intersection (overlap) of the domains of the rational expressions in the equation.

EXAMPLE 1   Determining Domains in Rational Equations

Find the domain of the variable in each equation.

(a) $\dfrac{2}{x} - \dfrac{3}{2} = \dfrac{7}{2x}$

The domains of the three rational terms of the equation are, in order, $\{x \mid x \neq 0\}$, $(-\infty, \infty)$, and $\{x \mid x \neq 0\}$. The intersection of these three domains is all real numbers except 0, which may be written $\{x \mid x \neq 0\}$.

(b) $\dfrac{2}{x-3} - \dfrac{3}{x+3} = \dfrac{12}{x^2 - 9}$

The domains of these three terms are, respectively, $\{x \mid x \neq 3\}$, $\{x \mid x \neq -3\}$, and $\{x \mid x \neq \pm 3\}$. ($\pm$ is read "positive or negative," or "plus or minus.") The domain of the variable is the intersection of the three domains, all real numbers except 3 and -3, written $\{x \mid x \neq \pm 3\}$.

Work Problem **1** *at the Side.* ▶

OBJECTIVE 2 Solve rational equations. The easiest way to solve most equations involving rational expressions is to multiply all terms in the equation by the least common denominator. This step will clear the equation of all denominators. *We can do this only with equations, not expressions.*

> **CAUTION**
> When each side of an equation is multiplied by a *variable* expression, the resulting "solutions" may not satisfy the original equation. *You must either determine and observe the domain or check all proposed solutions in the original equation. It is wise to do both.*

EXAMPLE 2   Solving a Rational Equation

Solve $\dfrac{2}{x} - \dfrac{3}{2} = \dfrac{7}{2x}$.

The domain, which excludes 0, was found in Example 1(a).

$$2x\left(\dfrac{2}{x} - \dfrac{3}{2}\right) = 2x\left(\dfrac{7}{2x}\right) \qquad \text{Multiply by the LCD, } 2x.$$

$$2x\left(\dfrac{2}{x}\right) - 2x\left(\dfrac{3}{2}\right) = 2x\left(\dfrac{7}{2x}\right) \qquad \text{Distributive property}$$

$$4 - 3x = 7 \qquad \text{Multiply.}$$

$$-3x = 3 \qquad \text{Subtract 4.}$$

Proposed solution $\longrightarrow$ $x = -1$ $\qquad$ Divide by -3.

Continued on Next Page

OBJECTIVES

1 Determine the domain of the variable in a rational equation.

2 Solve rational equations.

3 Recognize the graph of a rational function.

1 Find the domain of the variable in each equation.

(a) $\dfrac{3}{x} + \dfrac{1}{2} = \dfrac{5}{6x}$

(b)

$\dfrac{4}{x-5} - \dfrac{2}{x+5} = \dfrac{1}{x^2 - 25}$

ANSWERS

1. (a) $\{x \mid x \neq 0\}$ (b) $\{x \mid x \neq \pm 5\}$

2 Solve $-\dfrac{3}{20} + \dfrac{2}{x} = \dfrac{5}{4x}$.

3 Solve each equation.

(a) $\dfrac{3}{x+1} = \dfrac{1}{x-1} - \dfrac{2}{x^2-1}$

(b) $\dfrac{1}{x-3} + \dfrac{1}{x+3} = \dfrac{6}{x^2-9}$

Check Replace x with -1 in the original equation.

$$\dfrac{2}{x} - \dfrac{3}{2} = \dfrac{7}{2x} \qquad \text{Original equation}$$

$$\dfrac{2}{-1} - \dfrac{3}{2} \stackrel{?}{=} \dfrac{7}{2(-1)} \qquad \text{Let } x = -1.$$

$$-2 - \dfrac{3}{2} \stackrel{?}{=} -\dfrac{7}{2}$$

$$-\dfrac{7}{2} = -\dfrac{7}{2} \qquad \text{True}$$

The solution set is $\{-1\}$.

◀ *Work Problem* **2** *at the Side.*

EXAMPLE 3 **Solving a Rational Equation with No Solution**

Solve $\dfrac{2}{x-3} - \dfrac{3}{x+3} = \dfrac{12}{x^2-9}$.

Using the result from Example 1(b), we know that the domain excludes 3 and -3, since these values make one or more of the denominators in the equation equal 0. Multiply each side by the LCD, $(x+3)(x-3)$.

$$(x+3)(x-3)\left(\dfrac{2}{x-3} - \dfrac{3}{x+3}\right) = (x+3)(x-3)\left(\dfrac{12}{x^2-9}\right)$$

$$(x+3)(x-3)\left(\dfrac{2}{x-3}\right) - (x+3)(x-3)\left(\dfrac{3}{x+3}\right)$$

$$= (x+3)(x-3)\left(\dfrac{12}{x^2-9}\right) \quad \begin{array}{l}\text{Distributive}\\\text{property}\end{array}$$

$$2(x+3) - 3(x-3) = 12 \qquad \text{Multiply.}$$

$$2x + 6 - 3x + 9 = 12 \qquad \text{Distributive property}$$

$$-x + 15 = 12 \qquad \text{Combine like terms.}$$

$$-x = -3 \qquad \text{Subtract 15.}$$

$$\text{Proposed solution} \longrightarrow x = 3 \qquad \text{Divide by } -1.$$

Since 3 is not in the domain, it cannot be a solution of the equation. Substituting 3 in the original equation shows why.

Check

$$\dfrac{2}{x-3} - \dfrac{3}{x+3} = \dfrac{12}{x^2-9} \qquad \text{Original equation}$$

$$\dfrac{2}{3-3} - \dfrac{3}{3+3} \stackrel{?}{=} \dfrac{12}{3^2-9} \qquad \text{Let } x = 3.$$

$$\dfrac{2}{0} - \dfrac{3}{6} \stackrel{?}{=} \dfrac{12}{0}$$

Since division by 0 is undefined, the given equation has no solution, and the solution set is $\emptyset$.

◀ *Work Problem* **3** *at the Side.*

EXAMPLE 4   **Solving a Rational Equation**

Solve $\dfrac{3}{p^2 + p - 2} - \dfrac{1}{p^2 - 1} = \dfrac{7}{2(p^2 + 3p + 2)}$.

Factor each denominator to find the LCD, $2(p - 1)(p + 2)(p + 1)$. The domain excludes 1, −2, and −1. Multiply each side by the LCD.

$$2(p - 1)(p + 2)(p + 1)\left(\dfrac{3}{(p + 2)(p - 1)} - \dfrac{1}{(p + 1)(p - 1)}\right)$$

$$= 2(p - 1)(p + 2)(p + 1)\left(\dfrac{7}{2(p + 2)(p + 1)}\right)$$

$2 \cdot 3(p + 1) - 2(p + 2) = 7(p - 1)$ Distributive property

$6p + 6 - 2p - 4 = 7p - 7$ Distributive property

$4p + 2 = 7p - 7$ Combine like terms.

$9 = 3p$ Subtract $4p$; add 7.

Proposed solution ⟶ $3 = p$ Divide by 3.

Note that 3 is in the domain. Substitute 3 for p in the original equation to check that the solution set is $\{3\}$.

——————— *Work Problem* **4** *at the Side.* ▶

4 Solve

$$\dfrac{4}{x^2 + x - 6} - \dfrac{1}{x^2 - 4} = \dfrac{2}{x^2 + 5x + 6}.$$

EXAMPLE 5   **Solving a Rational Equation That Leads to a Quadratic Equation**

Solve $\dfrac{2}{3x + 1} = \dfrac{1}{x} - \dfrac{6x}{3x + 1}$.

Since the denominator $3x + 1$ cannot equal 0, $-\frac{1}{3}$ is excluded from the domain, as is 0. Multiply each side by the LCD, $x(3x + 1)$.

$$x(3x + 1)\left(\dfrac{2}{3x + 1}\right) = x(3x + 1)\left(\dfrac{1}{x} - \dfrac{6x}{3x + 1}\right)$$

$$x(3x + 1)\left(\dfrac{2}{3x + 1}\right) = x(3x + 1)\left(\dfrac{1}{x}\right) - x(3x + 1)\left(\dfrac{6x}{3x + 1}\right)$$

   Distributive property

$$2x = 3x + 1 - 6x^2$$

Write this quadratic equation in standard form with 0 on the right side.

$6x^2 - 3x + 2x - 1 = 0$

$6x^2 - x - 1 = 0$ Standard form

$(3x + 1)(2x - 1) = 0$ Factor.

$3x + 1 = 0$ or $2x - 1 = 0$ Zero-factor property

$x = -\dfrac{1}{3}$ or $x = \dfrac{1}{2}$ Proposed solutions

Because $-\frac{1}{3}$ is not in the domain, it is not a solution. Check that the solution set is $\{\frac{1}{2}\}$.

——————— *Work Problem* **5** *at the Side.* ▶

5 Solve

$$\dfrac{1}{x + 4} + \dfrac{x}{x - 4} = \dfrac{-8}{x^2 - 16}.$$

6 Graph each rational function, and give the equations of the vertical and horizontal asymptotes.

(a) $f(x) = -\dfrac{1}{x}$

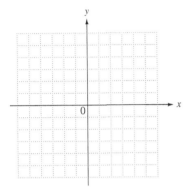

(b) $f(x) = \dfrac{2}{x+3}$

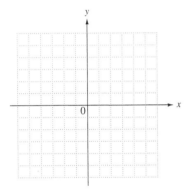

6. (a) vertical asymptote: $x = 0$;
   horizontal asymptote: $y = 0$

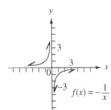

(b) vertical asymptote: $x = -3$;
   horizontal asymptote: $y = 0$

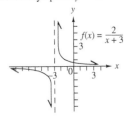

OBJECTIVE 3 Recognize the graph of a rational function. As mentioned in **Section 8.1,** a function defined by a quotient of polynomials is a **rational function.** Because one or more values of x may be excluded from the domain of most rational functions, their graphs are often **discontinuous.** That is, there will be one or more breaks in the graph. For example, we use point plotting and observing the domain to graph the simple rational function defined by

$$f(x) = \frac{1}{x}.$$

The domain of this function includes all real numbers except 0. Thus, there will be no point on the graph with $x = 0$. The vertical line with equation $x = 0$ is called a **vertical asymptote** of the graph. The horizontal line with equation $y = 0$ is called a **horizontal asymptote.** We show some typical ordered pairs in the table for both negative and positive x-values.

x	-3	-2	-1	$-\frac{1}{2}$	$-\frac{1}{4}$	$-\frac{1}{10}$	$\frac{1}{10}$	$\frac{1}{4}$	$\frac{1}{2}$	1	2	3
y	$-\frac{1}{3}$	$-\frac{1}{2}$	-1	-2	-4	-10	10	4	2	1	$\frac{1}{2}$	$\frac{1}{3}$

Notice that the closer positive values of x are to 0, the larger y is. Similarly, the closer negative values of x are to 0, the smaller (more negative) y is. Using this observation, excluding 0 from the domain, and plotting the points in the table, we obtain the graph in Figure 2.

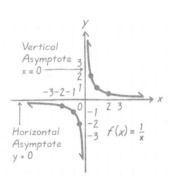

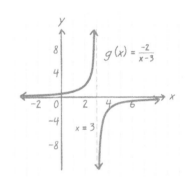

Figure 2   **Figure 3**

The graph of

$$g(x) = \frac{-2}{x - 3}$$

is shown in Figure 3. Some ordered pairs are shown in the table.

x	-2	-1	0	1	2	2.5	2.75	3.25	3.5	4	5	6
y	$\frac{2}{5}$	$\frac{1}{2}$	$\frac{2}{3}$	1	2	4	8	-8	-4	-2	-1	$-\frac{2}{3}$

There is no point on the graph for $x = 3$ because 3 is excluded from the domain. The dashed line $x = 3$ represents the vertical asymptote and is not part of the graph. As suggested by the points from the table, the graph gets closer to the vertical asymptote as the x-values get closer to 3. Again, $y = 0$ is a horizontal asymptote.

◀ *Work Problem* **6** *at the Side.*

16.6 ▶▶▶ Exercises

FOR EXTRA HELP

 Math XL
PRACTICE

WATCH

DOWNLOAD

 READ

 REVIEW

As explained in this section, any values that would cause a denominator to equal 0 must be excluded from the domain and consequently as solutions of an equation that has variable expressions in the denominators. **(a)** *Without actually solving the equation, list all possible numbers that would have to be rejected if they appeared as potential solutions.* **(b)** *Then give the domain using set notation. See Example 1.*

1. $\dfrac{1}{x+1} - \dfrac{1}{x-2} = 0$

2. $\dfrac{3}{x+4} - \dfrac{2}{x-9} = 0$

3. $\dfrac{5}{3x+5} - \dfrac{1}{x} = \dfrac{1}{2x+3}$

4. $\dfrac{6}{4x+7} - \dfrac{3}{x} = \dfrac{5}{6x-13}$

5. $\dfrac{1}{3x} + \dfrac{1}{2x} = \dfrac{x}{3}$

6. $\dfrac{5}{6x} - \dfrac{8}{2x} = \dfrac{x}{4}$

7. $\dfrac{3x+1}{x-4} = \dfrac{6x+5}{2x-7}$

8. $\dfrac{4x-1}{2x+3} = \dfrac{12x-25}{6x-2}$

9. $\dfrac{2}{x^2-x} + \dfrac{1}{x+3} = \dfrac{4}{x-2}$

10. Suppose that in solving the following equation, all of your algebraic steps are correct. Is it possible that your proposed solution would have to be rejected? Explain.

$$\dfrac{x+7}{4} - \dfrac{x+3}{3} = \dfrac{x}{12}$$

Solve each equation. See Examples 2–5.

11. $\dfrac{-5}{2x} + \dfrac{3}{4x} = \dfrac{-7}{4}$

12. $\dfrac{6}{5x} - \dfrac{2}{3x} = \dfrac{-8}{45}$

🌐 **13.** $x - \dfrac{24}{x} = -2$

14. $p + \dfrac{15}{p} = -8$

15. $\dfrac{x - 4}{x + 6} = \dfrac{2x + 3}{2x - 1}$

16. $\dfrac{5x - 8}{x + 2} = \dfrac{5x - 1}{x + 3}$

17. $\dfrac{3x + 1}{x - 4} = \dfrac{6x + 5}{2x - 7}$

18. $\dfrac{4x - 1}{2x + 3} = \dfrac{12x - 25}{6x - 2}$

19. $\dfrac{1}{y - 1} + \dfrac{5}{12} = \dfrac{-2}{3y - 3}$

20. $\dfrac{4}{m + 2} - \dfrac{11}{9} = \dfrac{1}{3m + 6}$

21. $\dfrac{-2}{3t - 6} - \dfrac{1}{36} = \dfrac{-3}{4t - 8}$

22. $\dfrac{3}{4m + 2} = \dfrac{17}{2} - \dfrac{7}{2m + 1}$

23. $\dfrac{3}{k + 2} - \dfrac{2}{k^2 - 4} = \dfrac{1}{k - 2}$

24. $\dfrac{3}{x - 2} + \dfrac{21}{x^2 - 4} = \dfrac{14}{x + 2}$

🌐 **25.** $\dfrac{1}{y + 2} + \dfrac{3}{y + 7} = \dfrac{5}{y^2 + 9y + 14}$

26. $\dfrac{1}{t + 3} + \dfrac{4}{t + 5} = \dfrac{2}{t^2 + 8t + 15}$

27. $\dfrac{9}{x} + \dfrac{4}{6x - 3} = \dfrac{2}{6x - 3}$

28. $\dfrac{5}{n} + \dfrac{4}{6 - 3n} = \dfrac{2n}{6 - 3n}$

29. $\dfrac{6}{w + 3} + \dfrac{-7}{w - 5} = \dfrac{-48}{w^2 - 2w - 15}$

30. $\dfrac{2}{r - 5} + \dfrac{3}{2r + 1} = \dfrac{22}{2r^2 - 9r - 5}$

🌐 **31.** $\dfrac{x}{x - 3} + \dfrac{4}{x + 3} = \dfrac{18}{x^2 - 9}$

32. $\dfrac{2x}{x - 3} + \dfrac{4}{x + 3} = \dfrac{-24}{x^2 - 9}$

33. $\dfrac{6}{x - 4} + \dfrac{5}{x} = \dfrac{-20}{x^2 - 4x}$

34. $\dfrac{7}{x-4} + \dfrac{3}{x} = \dfrac{-12}{x^2-4x}$

35. $\dfrac{2}{4x+7} + \dfrac{x}{3} = \dfrac{6}{12x+21}$

36. $\dfrac{5x+14}{x^2-9} = \dfrac{-2x^2-5x+2}{x^2-9} + \dfrac{2x+4}{x-3}$

37. $\dfrac{4x-7}{4x^2-9} = \dfrac{-2x^2+5x-4}{4x^2-9} + \dfrac{x+1}{2x+3}$

38. What is wrong with the following problem?   "Solve $\dfrac{2x+1}{3x-4} + \dfrac{1}{2x+3}$."

Graph each rational function. Give the equations of the vertical and horizontal asymptotes. See Objective 3 and Figures 2 and 3.

39. $f(x) = \dfrac{2}{x}$

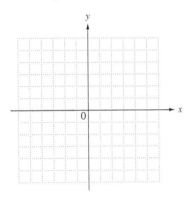

40. $f(x) = \dfrac{3}{x}$

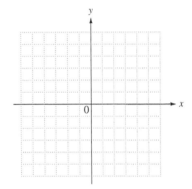

41. $f(x) = \dfrac{1}{x-2}$

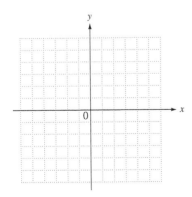

42. $f(x) = \dfrac{1}{x+2}$

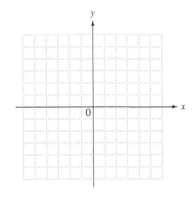

Solve each problem.

43. The average number of vehicles waiting in line to enter a parking area is modeled by the rational function defined by

$$w(x) = \frac{x^2}{2(1-x)},$$

where x is a quantity between 0 and 1 known as the **traffic intensity.** (*Source:* Mannering, F. and W. Kilareski, *Principles of Highway Engineering and Traffic Control,* John Wiley and Sons, 1990.) To the nearest tenth, find the average number of vehicles waiting for each traffic intensity.

(a) 0.1

(b) 0.8

(c) 0.9

(d) What happens to waiting time as traffic intensity increases?

44. The force required to keep a 2000-lb car going 30 mph from skidding on a curve, where r is the radius of the curve in feet, is given by

$$F(r) = \frac{225{,}000}{r}.$$

(a) What radius must a curve have if a force of 450 lb is needed to keep the car from skidding?

(b) As the radius of the curve is lengthened, how is the force affected?

Relating Concepts (Exercises 45–48) For Individual or Group Work

An equation of the form

$$\frac{A}{x+B} + \frac{x}{x-B} = \frac{C}{x^2 - B^2}$$

will have one rejected solution if the relationship $C = -2AB$ holds true. (This can be proved using methods not covered in intermediate algebra.) For example, if $A = 1$ and $B = 2$, then $C = -2AB = -2(1)(2) = -4$, and the equation becomes

$$\frac{1}{x+2} + \frac{x}{x-2} = \frac{-4}{x^2 - 4}.$$

*This equation has solution set $\{-1\}$; the potential solution -2 must be rejected. To further understand this idea, **work Exercises 45–48 in order.***

45. Show that the second equation does indeed have solution set $\{-1\}$ and -2 must be rejected.

46. Let $A = 2$ and let $B = 1$. What is the corresponding value of C? Solve the equation determined by A, B, and C. What is the solution set? What value must be rejected?

47. Let $A = 4$ and let $B = -3$. What is the corresponding value of C? Solve the equation determined by A, B, and C. What is the solution set? What value must be rejected?

48. Choose two numbers of your own, letting one be A and the other be B. Repeat the process described in Exercises 46 and 47.

Summary Exercises on Rational Expressions and Equations

A common student error is to confuse an equation, *such as* $\frac{x}{2} + \frac{x}{3} = -5$, *with an expression, such as* $\frac{x}{2} + \frac{x}{3}$. *Look for the equals sign to distinguish between them. Equations are solved for a numerical answer, while problems involving operations result in simplified expressions.*

Solving an Equation

Solve: $\dfrac{x}{2} + \dfrac{x}{3} = -5.$

Multiply each side by the LCD, 6.

$$6\left(\dfrac{x}{2} + \dfrac{x}{3}\right) = 6(-5)$$

$$6\left(\dfrac{x}{2}\right) + 6\left(\dfrac{x}{3}\right) = 6(-5)$$

$$3x + 2x = -30$$

$$5x = -30$$

$$x = -6$$

Check that the solution set is $\{-6\}$.

Simplifying an Expression Involving an Operation

Add: $\dfrac{x}{2} + \dfrac{x}{3}.$

Write both fractions with the LCD, 6.

$$\dfrac{x}{2} + \dfrac{x}{3}$$

$$= \dfrac{x \cdot 3}{2 \cdot 3} + \dfrac{x \cdot 2}{3 \cdot 2}$$

$$= \dfrac{3x}{6} + \dfrac{2x}{6}$$

$$= \dfrac{3x + 2x}{6}$$

$$= \dfrac{5x}{6}$$

Identify each exercise as an expression *or an* equation. *Then simplify the expression by performing the indicated operation, or solve the given equation, as appropriate.*

1. $\dfrac{x}{2} - \dfrac{x}{4} = 5$

2. $\dfrac{4x - 20}{x^2 - 25} \cdot \dfrac{(x + 5)^2}{10}$

3. $\dfrac{6}{7x} - \dfrac{4}{x}$

4. $\dfrac{\dfrac{1}{x} + \dfrac{1}{y}}{\dfrac{1}{x} - \dfrac{1}{y}}$

5. $\dfrac{5}{7t} = \dfrac{52}{7} - \dfrac{3}{t}$

6. $\dfrac{x - 5}{3} + \dfrac{1}{3} = \dfrac{x - 2}{5}$

7. $\dfrac{7}{6x} + \dfrac{5}{8x}$

8. $\dfrac{4}{x} - \dfrac{8}{x + 1} = 0$

9. $\dfrac{\dfrac{6}{x + 1} - \dfrac{1}{x}}{\dfrac{2}{x} - \dfrac{4}{x + 1}}$

10. $\dfrac{8}{r + 2} - \dfrac{7}{4r + 8}$

11. $\dfrac{x}{x + y} + \dfrac{2y}{x - y}$

12. $\dfrac{3p^2 - 6p}{p + 5} \div \dfrac{p^2 - 4}{8p + 40}$

13. $\dfrac{x-2}{9} \cdot \dfrac{5}{8-4x}$

14. $\dfrac{a-4}{3} + \dfrac{11}{6} = \dfrac{a+1}{2}$

15. $\dfrac{b^2+b-6}{b^2+2b-8} \cdot \dfrac{b^2+8b+16}{3b+12}$

16. $\dfrac{10z^2-5z}{3z^3-6z^2} \div \dfrac{2z^2+5z-3}{z^2+z-6}$

17. $\dfrac{5}{x^2-2x} - \dfrac{3}{x^2-4}$

18. $\dfrac{6}{t+1} + \dfrac{4}{5t+5} = \dfrac{34}{15}$

19. $\dfrac{\dfrac{5}{x} - \dfrac{3}{y}}{\dfrac{9x^2-25y^2}{x^2y}}$

20. $\dfrac{-2}{a^2+2a-3} - \dfrac{5}{3-3a} = \dfrac{4}{3a+9}$

21. $\dfrac{4y^2-13y+3}{2y^2-9y+9} \div \dfrac{4y^2+11y-3}{6y^2-5y-6}$

22. $\dfrac{8}{3k+9} - \dfrac{8}{15} = \dfrac{2}{5k+15}$

23. $\dfrac{3r}{r-2} = 1 + \dfrac{6}{r-2}$

24. $\dfrac{6z^2-5z-6}{6z^2+5z-6} \cdot \dfrac{12z^2-17z+6}{12z^2-z-6}$

25. $\dfrac{-1}{3-x} - \dfrac{2}{x-3}$

26. $\dfrac{\dfrac{t}{4} - \dfrac{1}{t}}{1 + \dfrac{t+4}{t}}$

27. $\dfrac{2}{y+1} - \dfrac{3}{y^2-y-2} = \dfrac{3}{y-2}$

28. $\dfrac{7}{2x^2-8x} + \dfrac{3}{x^2-16}$

29. $\dfrac{3}{y-3} - \dfrac{3}{y^2-5y+6} = \dfrac{2}{y-2}$

30. $\dfrac{2k + \dfrac{5}{k-1}}{3k - \dfrac{2}{k}}$

16.7 ▶▶▶ Applications of Rational Expressions

OBJECTIVE 1 **Find the value of an unknown variable in a formula.** Formulas may contain rational expressions, such as $t = \frac{d}{r}$ and $\frac{1}{f} = \frac{1}{p} + \frac{1}{q}$.

EXAMPLE 1 **Finding the Value of a Variable in a Formula**

In physics, the focal length, f, of a lens is given by the formula

$$\frac{1}{f} = \frac{1}{p} + \frac{1}{q},$$

where p is the distance from the object to the lens and q is the distance from the lens to the image. See Figure 4. Find q if $p = 20$ cm and $f = 10$ cm.

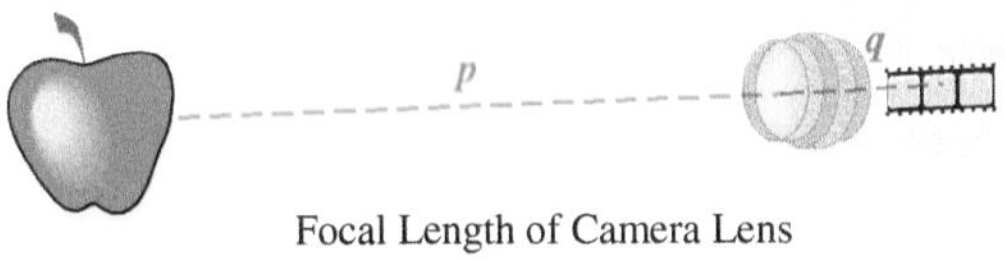

Focal Length of Camera Lens

Figure 4

Replace f with 10 and p with 20.

$$\frac{1}{f} = \frac{1}{p} + \frac{1}{q}$$ Solve this equation for q.

$$\frac{1}{10} = \frac{1}{20} + \frac{1}{q}$$ Let $f = 10, p = 20$.

$$20q \cdot \frac{1}{10} = 20q\left(\frac{1}{20} + \frac{1}{q}\right)$$ Multiply by the LCD, $20q$.

$$20q \cdot \frac{1}{10} = 20q\left(\frac{1}{20}\right) + 20q\left(\frac{1}{q}\right)$$ Distributive property.

$$2q = q + 20$$ Multiply.

$$q = 20$$ Subtract q.

The distance from the lens to the image is 20 cm.

Work Problem **1** *at the Side.* ▶

OBJECTIVE 2 **Solve a formula for a specified variable.** The goal in solving for a specified variable is to isolate it on one side of the equals sign.

EXAMPLE 2 **Solving a Formula for a Specified Variable**

Solve $\frac{1}{f} = \frac{1}{p} + \frac{1}{q}$ for p.

$$\frac{1}{f} = \frac{1}{p} + \frac{1}{q}$$

$$fpq \cdot \frac{1}{f} = fpq\left(\frac{1}{p} + \frac{1}{q}\right)$$ Multiply by the LCD, fpq.

$$pq = fq + fp$$ Distributive property

Continued on Next Page

OBJECTIVES

1 Find the value of an unknown variable in a formula.

2 Solve a formula for a specified variable.

3 Solve applications using proportions.

4 Solve applications about distance, rate, and time.

5 Solve applications about work rates.

---

1 Use the formula given in Example 1 to answer each part.

(a) Find p if $f = 15$ and $q = 25$.

(b) Find f if $p = 6$ and $q = 9$.

(c) Find q if $f = 12$ and $p = 16$.

ANSWERS

1. (a) $\frac{75}{2}$ (b) $\frac{18}{5}$ (c) 48

2 Solve $\dfrac{3}{p} + \dfrac{3}{q} = \dfrac{5}{r}$ for q.

Transform the equation so that the terms with p (the specified variable) are on the same side. One way to do this is to subtract fp from each side.

$$pq = fq + fp$$

$$pq - fp = fq \qquad \text{Subtract } fp.$$

[This is a key step.] $\longrightarrow \quad p(q - f) = fq \qquad \text{Factor out } p.$

$$p = \frac{fq}{q - f} \qquad \text{Divide by } q - f.$$

◀ Work Problem **2** at the Side.

EXAMPLE 3 Solving a Formula for a Specified Variable

Solve $I = \dfrac{nE}{R + nr}$ for n.

$$I = \frac{nE}{R + nr}$$

$$(R + nr)I = (R + nr)\frac{nE}{R + nr} \qquad \text{Multiply by } R + nr.$$

$$RI + nrI = nE$$

$$RI = nE - nrI \qquad \text{Subtract } nrI.$$

$$RI = n(E - rI) \qquad \text{Factor out } n.$$

$$\frac{RI}{E - rI} = n \qquad \text{Divide by } E - rI.$$

3 Solve $A = \dfrac{Rr}{R + r}$ for R.

CAUTION
Refer to the steps in Examples 2 and 3 that factor out the desired variable. *The variable for which you are solving must be a factor on only one side of the equation,* so that each side can be divided by the remaining factor in the last step.

◀ Work Problem **3** at the Side.

We can now solve problems that translate into equations with rational expressions. To do so, we continue to use the six-step problem-solving method from **Section 2.3.**

OBJECTIVE 3 Solve applications using proportions. A **ratio** is a comparison of two quantities. The ratio of a to b may be written in any of the following ways:

$$a \text{ to } b, \quad a : b, \quad \text{or} \quad \frac{a}{b}. \qquad \text{Ratio of } a \text{ to } b$$

Ratios are usually written as quotients in algebra. A **proportion** is a statement that two ratios are equal, such as

$$\frac{a}{b} = \frac{c}{d}. \qquad \text{Proportion}$$

Proportions are a useful and important type of rational equation.

EXAMPLE 4 **Solving a Proportion**

In 2005, about 15 of every 100 Americans had no health insurance coverage. The population at that time was about 296 million. How many million Americans had no health insurance? (*Source:* U.S. Census Bureau.)

Step 1   **Read** the problem.

Step 2   **Assign a variable.** Let x = the number (in millions) who had no health insurance.

Step 3   **Write an equation.** To get an equation, set up a proportion. The ratio 15 to 100 should equal the ratio x to 296.

$$\frac{15}{100} = \frac{x}{296} \qquad \text{Write a proportion.}$$

Step 4   **Solve.** $29{,}600\left(\dfrac{15}{100}\right) = 29{,}600\left(\dfrac{x}{296}\right)$ Multiply by a common denominator.

$$4440 = 100x \qquad \text{Simplify.}$$

$$x = 44.4 \qquad \text{Divide by 100.}$$

Step 5   **State the answer.** There were about 44.4 million Americans with no health insurance in 2005.

Step 6   **Check** that the ratio of 44.4 million to 296 million equals $\frac{15}{100}$.

Work Problem **4** *at the Side.* ▶

4 Solve the problem.
In 2006, approximately 11.7% (that is, 11.7 of every 100) of the 73,740,000 children under 18 yr of age in the United States had no health insurance. How many such children were uninsured? (*Source:* U.S. Census Bureau.)

EXAMPLE 5 **Solving a Proportion Involving Rates**

Marissa's car uses 10 gal of gas to travel 210 mi. She has 5 gal of gas in the car, and she still needs to drive 640 mi. If we assume the car continues to use gas at the same rate, how many more gallons will she need?

Step 1   **Read** the problem.

Step 2   **Assign a variable.** Let x = the additional number of gallons of gas.

Step 3   **Write an equation.** To get an equation, set up a proportion.

$$\text{gallons} \longrightarrow \frac{10}{210} = \frac{5 + x}{640} \longleftarrow \text{gallons}$$
$$\text{miles} \longrightarrow \qquad\qquad\qquad \longleftarrow \text{miles}$$

Step 4   **Solve.** We could multiply by the LCD $10 \cdot 21 \cdot 64$. Instead we use an alternative method that involves *cross products:* For $\frac{a}{b} = \frac{c}{d}$ to be true, then the cross products ad and bc must be equal. Thus,

$$10 \cdot 640 = 210(5 + x) \qquad \text{If } \tfrac{a}{b} = \tfrac{c}{d}, \text{ then } ad = bc.$$

$$6400 = 1050 + 210x \qquad \text{Multiply; distributive property}$$

$$5350 = 210x \qquad \text{Subtract 1050.}$$

$$25.5 \approx x. \qquad \text{Divide by 210.}$$

Step 5   **State the answer.** Marissa will need about 25.5 more gallons of gas.

Step 6   **Check.** The 25.5 gal plus the 5 gal equals 30.5 gal.

$$\frac{30.5}{640} \approx 0.048 \quad \text{and} \quad \frac{10}{210} \approx 0.048$$

Since the ratios are equal, the answer is correct.

Work Problem **5** *at the Side.* ▶

5 Solve the problem.
Lauren's car uses 15 gal of gasoline to drive 495 mi. She has 6 gal of gasoline in the car, and she wants to know how much more gasoline she will need to drive 600 mi. If we assume that the car continues to use gasoline at the same rate, how many more gallons will she need? (Round your answer to the nearest tenth.)

ANSWERS
4. 8,627,580
5. 12.2 more gallons

OBJECTIVE 4 Solve applications about distance, rate, and time.   The next examples use the distance formula $d = rt$ that was first introduced in **Section 2.2.** A familiar example of a rate is speed, which is the ratio of distance to time, or $r = \frac{d}{t}$.

EXAMPLE 6   **Solving a Problem about Distance, Rate, and Time**

A paddle wheeler goes 10 mi against the current in a river in the same time that it goes 15 mi with the current. If the speed of the current is 3 mph, find the speed of the boat in still water.

Step 1   **Read** the problem. We must find the speed of the boat in still water.

Step 2   **Assign a variable.**

Let $x =$ the speed of the boat in still water.

When the boat is traveling *against* the current, the current slows the boat down, and the speed of the boat is the difference between its speed in still water and the speed of the current. So, the speed against the current is $(x - 3)$ mph.

When the boat is traveling *with* the current, the current speeds the boat up, and the speed of the boat is the sum of its speed in still water and the speed of the current, that is, $(x + 3)$ mph.

Thus, $x - 3 =$ the speed of the boat *against* the current,

and $x + 3 =$ the speed of the boat *with* the current.

Because the time is the same going against the current as with the current, find time in terms of distance and rate (speed) for each situation. Start with the distance formula,

$$d = rt,$$

and divide each side by r to get $t = \frac{d}{r}$. Against the current, the distance is 10 mi and the rate is $(x - 3)$ mph, giving

$$t = \frac{d}{r} = \frac{10}{x - 3}. \qquad \text{Time against the current}$$

With the current, the distance is 15 mi and the rate is $(x + 3)$ mph, so

$$t = \frac{d}{r} = \frac{15}{x + 3}. \qquad \text{Time with the current}$$

This information is summarized in the following table.

	Distance	Rate	Time
Against Current	10	$x - 3$	$\dfrac{10}{x - 3}$
With Current	15	$x + 3$	$\dfrac{15}{x + 3}$

Times are equal.

Step 3   **Write an equation.** Because the times are equal,

$$\frac{10}{x - 3} = \frac{15}{x + 3}.$$

Continued on Next Page

Step 4 **Solve.** $\dfrac{10}{x-3} = \dfrac{15}{x+3}$

$(x+3)(x-3)\left(\dfrac{10}{x-3}\right) = (x+3)(x-3)\left(\dfrac{15}{x+3}\right)$ Multiply by the LCD.

$10(x+3) = 15(x-3)$ Multiply.

$10x + 30 = 15x - 45$ Distributive property

$30 = 5x - 45$ Subtract $10x$.

$75 = 5x$ Add 45.

$15 = x$ Divide by 5.

Step 5 **State the answer.** The speed of the boat in still water is 15 mph.

Step 6 **Check** the answer: $\dfrac{10}{15-3} = \dfrac{15}{15+3}$ is true.

Work Problem **6** *at the Side.* ▶

---

6 Solve the problem.
  A plane travels 100 mi against the wind in the same time that it takes to travel 120 mi with the wind. The wind speed is 20 mph.

(a) Complete this table.

	d	r	t
Against Wind	100	$x - 20$	
With Wind	120	$x + 20$	

(b) Find the speed of the plane in still air.

EXAMPLE 7 **Solving a Problem about Distance, Rate, and Time**

At O'Hare International Airport in Chicago, Cheryl and Bill are walking to the gate (at the same speed) to catch their flight to Denver. Bill steps onto the moving sidewalk and continues to walk while Cheryl uses the stationary sidewalk. If the sidewalk moves at 1 m per sec and Bill saves 50 sec covering the 300-m distance, what is their walking speed?

Step 1 **Read** the problem. We must find their walking speed.

Step 2 **Assign a variable.** Let x represent their walking speed in meters per second. Thus Cheryl travels at x meters per second and Bill travels at $(x+1)$ meters per second. Express their times in terms of the known distances and the variable rates. As in Example 6, start with $d = rt$ and divide each side by r to get $t = \frac{d}{r}$. For Cheryl, the distance is 300 m and the rate is x, so Cheryl's time is

$$t = \frac{d}{r} = \frac{300}{x}. \quad \text{Cheryl's time}$$

Bill travels 300 m at a rate of $x + 1$, so his time is

$$t = \frac{d}{r} = \frac{300}{x+1}. \quad \text{Bill's time}$$

This information is summarized in the following table.

	Distance	Rate	Time
Cheryl	300	x	$\dfrac{300}{x}$
Bill	300	$x + 1$	$\dfrac{300}{x+1}$

Step 3 **Write an equation** using the times from the table.

Bill's time   is   Cheryl's time   less 50 seconds.

$$\frac{300}{x+1} = \frac{300}{x} - 50$$

Continued on Next Page

7 Solve the problem.

Kathy Manley drove 300 mi north from San Antonio, mostly on the freeway. She usually averaged 55 mph, but an accident slowed her speed through Dallas to 15 mph. If her trip took 6 hr, how many miles did she drive at reduced speed?

	d	r	t
Normal Speed	$300 - x$	55	
Reduced Speed	x	15	

Step 4 **Solve.**

$$\frac{300}{x + 1} = \frac{300}{x} - 50$$

$$x(x + 1)\left(\frac{300}{x + 1}\right) = x(x + 1)\left(\frac{300}{x} - 50\right) \qquad \text{Multiply by the LCD, } x(x + 1).$$

$$x(x + 1)\left(\frac{300}{x + 1}\right) = x(x + 1)\left(\frac{300}{x}\right) - x(x + 1)(50) \qquad \text{Distributive property}$$

$$300x = 300(x + 1) - 50x(x + 1) \qquad \text{Multiply.}$$

$$300x = 300x + 300 - 50x^2 - 50x \qquad \text{Distributive property}$$

$$50x^2 + 50x - 300 = 0 \qquad \text{Standard form}$$

$$x^2 + x - 6 = 0 \qquad \text{Divide by 50.}$$

$$(x + 3)(x - 2) = 0 \qquad \text{Factor.}$$

$$x + 3 = 0 \quad \text{or} \quad x - 2 = 0 \qquad \text{Zero-factor property}$$

$$x = -3 \quad \text{or} \quad x = 2 \qquad \text{Solve each equation.}$$

Discard the negative answer, since speed cannot be negative.

Step 5 **State the answer.** Their walking speed is 2 m per sec.

Step 6 **Check** the answer in the words of the original problem.

◀ *Work Problem* **7** *at the Side.*

OBJECTIVE 5 Solve applications about work rates. Problems about work are closely related to distance problems.

> **Problem–Solving Hint**
>
> People work at different rates. If the letters r, t, and A represent the rate at which the work is done, the time required, and the amount of work accomplished, respectively, then $A = rt$. Notice the similarity to the distance formula, $d = rt$.
>
> Amount of work can be measured in terms of jobs accomplished. Thus, if 1 job is completed, $A = 1$, and the formula gives the rate as
>
> $$1 = rt$$
> $$r = \frac{1}{t}.$$

To solve a work problem, we begin by using the following fact to express all rates of work.

> **Rate of Work**
> If a job can be accomplished in t units of time, then the rate of work is
>
> $$\frac{1}{t} \text{ job per unit of time.}$$

See if you can identify the six problem-solving steps in the next example.

EXAMPLE 8 **Solving a Problem about Work**

Letitia and Kareem are working on a neighborhood cleanup. Kareem can clean up all the trash in the area in 7 hr, while Letitia can do the same job in 5 hr. How long will it take them if they work together?

Let $x =$ the number of hours it will take the two people working together. Just as we made a table for the distance formula, $d = rt$, make a table here for $A = rt$, with $A = 1$. Since $A = 1$, the rate for each person will be $\frac{1}{t}$, where t is the time it takes the person to complete the job alone. For example, since Kareem can clean up all the trash in 7 hr, his rate is $\frac{1}{7}$ of the job per hour. Similarly, Letitia's rate is $\frac{1}{5}$ of the job per hour.

	Rate	Time Working Together	Fractional Part of the Job Done
Kareem	$\frac{1}{7}$	x	$\frac{1}{7}x$
Letitia	$\frac{1}{5}$	x	$\frac{1}{5}x$

Since together they complete 1 job, the sum of the fractional parts accomplished by them should equal 1.

Part done by Kareem + part done by Letitia is 1 whole job.

$$\frac{1}{7}x + \frac{1}{5}x = 1$$

$$35\left(\frac{1}{7}x + \frac{1}{5}x\right) = 35 \cdot 1 \quad \text{Multiply by the LCD, 35.}$$

$$5x + 7x = 35 \quad \text{Distributive property}$$

$$12x = 35 \quad \text{Combine like terms.}$$

$$x = \frac{35}{12} \quad \text{Divide by 12.}$$

Working together, Kareem and Letitia can do the entire job in $\frac{35}{12}$ hr, or 2 hr, 55 min. Check this result in the original problem.

Work Problem **8** *at the Side.* ▶

There is another way to approach problems about work. For instance, in Example 8, x represents the number of hours it will take the two people working together to complete the entire job. In one hour, $\frac{1}{x}$ of the entire job will be completed. Kareem completes $\frac{1}{7}$ of the job in one hour, and Letitia completes $\frac{1}{5}$ of the job, so the sum of their rates should equal $\frac{1}{x}$. Thus,

$$\frac{1}{7} + \frac{1}{5} = \frac{1}{x}.$$

Multiplying each side of this equation by $35x$ gives $5x + 7x = 35$. This is the same equation we got in Example 8 in the third line from the bottom. Thus, the solution of the equation is the same using either approach.

8 Solve each problem.

(a) Stan needs 45 min to do the dishes, while Deb can do them in 30 min. How long will it take them if they work together?

	Rate	Time Working Together	Fractional Part of the Job Done
Stan	$\frac{1}{45}$	x	
Deb	$\frac{1}{30}$	x	

(b) Suppose it takes Stan 35 min to do the dishes, and together they can do them in 15 min. How long will it take Deb to do them alone?

Math in the Media

A "BIG LEAGUE" APPLICATION OF RATIONAL EXPRESSIONS AND EQUATIONS

In the 1994 movie *Little Big League*, young Billy Heywood (Luke Edwards) inherits the Minnesota Twins baseball team and becomes manager. He leads the team to the Division Championship and then to the playoffs. But before the final playoff game, the biggest game of the year, he can't keep his mind on his job because a homework problem is giving him trouble:

> *If Joe can paint a house in 3 hours and Sam can paint the same house in 5 hours, how long does it take for them to do it together?*

With the help of one of his players, he is able to solve the problem.

1. Use the method described in Example 8 of **Section 8.5** to solve this problem.

2. Before the player was able to solve the problem correctly, Billy got "help" from some of the other players. The incorrect answers they gave him were

   (a) 15 hr   **(b)** 8 hr   **(c)** 4 hr.

   Explain the faulty reasoning behind each of these incorrect answers.

3. The player who gave Billy the correct answer solved the problem as follows:

   > *Using the simple formula a times b over a plus b, we get our answer of one and seven-eighths.*

   Show that if it takes one person a hours to complete one job and another b hours to complete the same job, then the expression stated by the player,

   $$\frac{a \cdot b}{a + b}$$

   actually does give the number of hours it would take them to do the job together. (*Hint:* Refer to Example 8, and use a and b rather than 7 and 5. Then solve the resulting formula for x.)

16.7 ▶▶▶ Exercises

FOR EXTRA HELP

MyMathLab

Math XL
PRACTICE

WATCH

DOWNLOAD

READ

REVIEW

In Exercises 1–4, a familiar formula is given. Give the letter of the choice that is an equivalent form of the given formula.

1. $p = br$ (percent)

A. $b = \dfrac{p}{r}$ **B.** $r = \dfrac{b}{p}$

C. $b = \dfrac{r}{p}$ **D.** $p = \dfrac{r}{b}$

2. $V = LWH$ (geometry)

A. $H = \dfrac{LW}{V}$ **B.** $L = \dfrac{V}{WH}$

C. $L = \dfrac{WH}{V}$ **D.** $W = \dfrac{H}{VL}$

3. $m = \dfrac{F}{a}$ (physics)

A. $a = mF$ **B.** $F = \dfrac{m}{a}$

C. $F = \dfrac{a}{m}$ **D.** $F = ma$

4. $I = \dfrac{E}{R}$ (electricity)

A. $R = \dfrac{I}{E}$ **B.** $R = IE$

C. $E = \dfrac{I}{R}$ **D.** $E = RI$

Solve each problem. See Example 1.

5. A gas law in chemistry says that
$$\frac{PV}{T} = \frac{pv}{t}.$$
Suppose that $T = 300$, $t = 350$, $V = 9$, $P = 50$, and $v = 8$. Find p.

6. In work with electric circuits, the formula
$$\frac{1}{a} = \frac{1}{b} + \frac{1}{c}$$
occurs. Find b if $a = 8$ and $c = 12$.

7. A formula from anthropology says that
$$c = \frac{100b}{L}.$$
Find L if $c = 80$ and $b = 5$.

8. The gravitational force between two masses is given by
$$F = \frac{GMm}{d^2}.$$
Find M to the nearest thousandth if $F = 10$, $G = 6.67 \times 10^{-11}$, $m = 1$, and $d = 3 \times 10^{-6}$.

Solve each formula for the specified variable. See Examples 2 and 3.

9. $F = \dfrac{GMm}{d^2}$ for G (physics)

10. $F = \dfrac{GMm}{d^2}$ for M (physics)

11. $\dfrac{1}{a} = \dfrac{1}{b} + \dfrac{1}{c}$ for a (electricity)

12. $\dfrac{1}{a} = \dfrac{1}{b} + \dfrac{1}{c}$ for b (electricity)

13. $\dfrac{PV}{T} = \dfrac{pv}{t}$ for v (chemistry)

14. $\dfrac{PV}{T} = \dfrac{pv}{t}$ for T (chemistry)

15. $I = \dfrac{nE}{R + nr}$ for r (engineering)

16. $a = \dfrac{V - v}{t}$ for V (physics)

17. $A = \dfrac{1}{2}h(b + B)$ for b (mathematics)

18. $S = \dfrac{n}{2}(a + \ell)d$ for n (mathematics)

19. $\dfrac{E}{e} = \dfrac{R + r}{r}$ for r (engineering)

20. $y = \dfrac{x + z}{a - x}$ for x

21. To solve the equation $m = \dfrac{ab}{a - b}$ for a, what is the first step?

22. Suppose you are asked to solve the equation
$$rp - rq = p + q$$
for r. What is the first step?

Solve each problem mentally. Use proportions in Exercises 23 and 24.

23. In a mathematics class, 3 of every 4 students are girls. If there are 28 students in the class, how many are girls? How many are boys?

24. In a certain southern state, sales tax on a purchase of $1.50 is $0.12. What is the sales tax on a purchase of $9.00?

25. If Marin can mow her yard in 2 hr, what is her rate (in job per hour)?

26. A van traveling from Atlanta to Detroit averages 50 mph and takes 14 hr to make the trip. What is the driving distance from Atlanta to Detroit?

Use a proportion to solve each problem. Give answers to the nearest tenth if an approximation is needed. See Examples 4 and 5.

27. On a map of the United States, the distance between Seattle and Durango is 4.125 in. The two cities are actually 1238 miles apart. On this same map, what would be the distance between Chicago and El Paso, two cities that are actually 1606 mi apart? (*Source:* Universal Map Atlas.)

28. On a map of the United States, the distance between Reno and Phoenix is 2.5 in. The two cities are actually 768 miles apart. On this same map, what would be the distance between St. Louis and Jacksonville, two cities that are actually 919 mi apart? (*Source:* Universal Map Atlas.)

29. On a world globe, the distance between New York and Cairo, two cities that are actually 5619 mi apart, is 8.5 in. On this same globe, how far apart are Madrid and Rio de Janeiro, two cities that are actually 5045 mi apart? (*Source:* Author's globe, *World Almanac and Book of Facts.*)

30. On a world globe, the distance between San Francisco and Melbourne, two cities that are actually 7856 mi apart, is 11.875 in. On this same globe, how far apart are Mexico City and Singapore, two cities that are actually 10,327 mi apart? (*Source:* Author's globe, *World Almanac and Book of Facts.*)

Solve each problem. See Examples 4 and 5.

31. On May 23, 2008, the Boston Red Sox were in first place in the East Division of the American League, having won 31 of their first 50 regular season games. If the team continued to win the same fraction of its games, how many games would the Red Sox win for the complete 162-game season? Round your answer to the nearest whole number. (*Source:* www.mlb.com)

32. During 2004–2005, the ratio of teachers to students in public elementary and secondary schools was approximately 1 to 16. If a public school had 846 students, how many teachers would be at the school if this ratio was valid for that school? Round your answer to the nearest whole number. (*Source*: U.S. National Center for Education Statistics.)

33. Biologists tagged 500 fish in a lake on January 1. On February 1 they returned and collected a random sample of 400 fish, 8 of which had been previously tagged. Approximately how many fish does the lake have based on this experiment?

34. Suppose that in the experiment of Exercise 33, 10 of the previously tagged fish were collected on February 1. What would be the estimate of the fish population?

35. Bruce Johnston's Shelby Cobra uses 5 gal of gasoline to drive 156 mi. He has 3 gal of gasoline in the car, and he wants to know how much more gasoline he will need to drive 300 mi. If we assume that the car continues to use gasoline at the same rate, how many more gallons will he need?

36. Mike Love's T-bird uses 6 gal of gasoline to drive 141 miles. He has 4 gal of gasoline in the car, and he wants to know how much more gasoline he will need to drive 275 mi. If we assume that the car continues to use gasoline at the same rate, how many more gallons will he need?

Nurses use proportions to determine the amount of a drug to administer when the dose of the drug is measured in milligrams but the drug is packaged in a diluted form in milliliters. (Source: Hoyles, Celia, Richard Noss, and Stefano Pozzi, "Proportional Reasoning in Nursing Practice," *Journal for Research in Mathematics Education,* January 2001.) *For example, to find the number of milliliters of fluid needed to administer* 300 mg *of a drug that comes packaged as* 120 mg *in* 2 mL *of fluid, a nurse sets up the proportion*

$$\frac{120 \text{ mg}}{2 \text{ mL}} = \frac{300 \text{ mg}}{x \text{ mL}},$$

where x represents the amount to administer in milliliters. Use this method to find the correct dose for each prescription.

37. 120 mg of Amakacine packaged as 100 mg in 2-mL vials

38. 1.5 mg of morphine packaged as 20 mg ampules diluted in 10 mL of fluid

In geometry, it is shown that two triangles with corresponding angle measures equal, called **similar triangles,** *have corresponding sides proportional. For example, in the figure, angle A = angle D, angle B = angle E, and angle C = angle F, so the triangles are similar. Then the following ratios of corresponding sides are equal.*

$$\frac{4}{6} = \frac{6}{9} = \frac{2x + 1}{2x + 5}$$

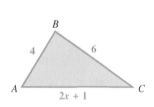 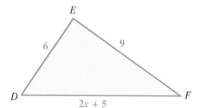

39. Solve for *x* using the given proportion to find the lengths of the third sides of the triangles.

40. Suppose the following triangles are similar. Find *y* and the lengths of the two longest sides of each triangle.

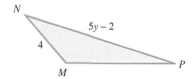 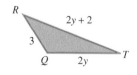

Solve each problem. See Examples 6 and 7.

41. Kellen's boat goes 12 mph. Find the rate of the current of the river if she can go 6 mi upstream in the same amount of time she can go 10 mi downstream.

	Distance	Rate	Time
Downstream	10	$12 + x$	
Upstream	6	$12 - x$	

42. Kasey can travel 8 mi upstream in the same time it takes her to go 12 mi downstream. Her boat goes 15 mph in still water. What is the rate of the current?

	Distance	Rate	Time
Downstream			
Upstream			

43. On his drive from Montpelier, Vermont, to Columbia, South Carolina, Dylan Davis averaged 51 mph. If he had been able to average 60 mph, he would have reached his destination 3 hr earlier. What is the driving distance between Montpelier and Columbia?

44. Leah drove from her apartment to her parents' house for the weekend. Driving to their house on Saturday morning, she was able to average 60 mph because traffic was light. However, returning on Sunday night, she was able to average only 45 mph on the same route, because traffic was heavy. The drive on Sunday took her 1.5 hr longer than the drive on Saturday. What is the distance between Leah's apartment and her parents' house?

45. A private plane traveled from San Francisco to a secret rendezvous. It averaged 200 mph. On the return trip, the average speed was 300 mph. If the total traveling time was 4 hr, how far from San Francisco was the secret rendezvous?

46. Johnny averages 30 mph when he drives on the old highway to his favorite fishing hole, and he averages 50 mph when most of his route is on the interstate. If both routes are the same length, and he saves 2 hr by traveling on the interstate, how far away is the fishing hole?

47. On the first part of a trip to Carmel traveling on the freeway, Marge averaged 60 mph. On the rest of the trip, which was 10 mi longer than the first part, she averaged 50 mph. Find the total distance to Carmel if the second part of the trip took 30 min more than the first part.

48. While on vacation, Jim and Annie decided to drive all day. During the first part of their trip on the highway, they averaged 60 mph. When they got to Houston, traffic caused them to average only 30 mph. The distance they drove in Houston was 100 mi less than their distance on the highway. What was their total driving distance if they spent 50 min more on the highway than they did in Houston?

Solve each problem. See Example 8.

49. Butch and Peggy want to pick up the mess that their grandson, Grant, has made in his playroom. Butch could do it in 15 min working alone. Peggy, working alone, could clean it in 12 min. How long will it take them if they work together?

	Rate	Time Working Together	Fractional Part of the Job Done
Butch	$\frac{1}{15}$	x	
Peggy	$\frac{1}{12}$	x	

50. Lou can groom Jay Beckenstein's dogs in 8 hr, but it takes his business partner, Janet, only 5 hr to groom the same dogs. How long will it take them to groom Jay's dogs if they work together?

	Rate	Time Working Together	Fractional Part of the Job Done
Lou	$\frac{1}{8}$	x	
Janet	$\frac{1}{5}$	x	

51. Jerry and Kuba are laying a hardwood floor. Working alone, Jerry can do the job in 20 hr. If the two of them work together, they can complete the job in 12 hr. How long would it take Kuba to lay the floor working alone?

52. Mrs. Disher is a high school mathematics teacher. She can grade a set of chapter tests in 5 hr working alone. If her student teacher Mr. Howes helps her, it will take 3 hr to grade the tests. How long would it take Mr. Howes to grade the tests if he worked alone?

53. If a vat of acid can be filled by an inlet pipe in 10 hr and emptied by an outlet pipe in 20 hr, how long will it take to fill the vat if both pipes are open?

54. A winery has a vat to hold Chardonnay. An inlet pipe can fill the vat in 9 hr, while an outlet pipe can empty it in 12 hr. How long will it take to fill the vat if both the outlet and the inlet pipes are open?

55. Suppose that Hortense and Mort can clean their entire house in 7 hr, while their toddler, Mimi, just by being around, can completely mess it up in only 2 hr. If Hortense and Mort clean the house while Mimi is at her grandma's, and then start cleaning up after Mimi the minute she gets home, how long does it take from the time Mimi gets home until the whole place is a shambles?

56. An inlet pipe can fill an artificial lily pond in 60 min, while an outlet pipe can empty it in 80 min. Through an error, both pipes are left open. How long will it take for the pond to fill?

17

Roots & Radicals

17.1 ▶▶▶ Evaluating Roots

OBJECTIVES

1 Find square roots.

2 Decide whether a given root is rational, irrational, or not a real number.

3 Find decimal approximations for irrational square roots.

4 Use the Pythagorean formula.

5 Find cube, fourth, and other roots.

In **Section 1.8,** we discussed the idea of the *square* of a number. Recall that squaring a number means multiplying the number by itself.

$$\text{If } a = 8, \quad \text{then} \quad a^2 = 8 \cdot 8 = 64.$$

$$\text{If } a = -4, \quad \text{then} \quad a^2 = (-4)(-4) = 16.$$

$$\text{If } a = -\frac{1}{2}, \quad \text{then} \quad a^2 = \left(-\frac{1}{2}\right)\left(-\frac{1}{2}\right) = \frac{1}{4}.$$

In this chapter, we consider the opposite process.

$$\text{If } a^2 = 64, \quad \text{then} \quad a = ?$$

$$\text{If } a^2 = 16, \quad \text{then} \quad a = ?$$

$$\text{If } a^2 = \frac{1}{4}, \quad \text{then} \quad a = ?$$

OBJECTIVE 1 Find square roots. To find a in the three preceding statements, we must find a number that when multiplied by itself results in the given number. The number a is called a **square root** of the number a^2.

EXAMPLE 1 Finding All Square Roots of a Number

Find all square roots of 49.

To find a square root of 49, think of a number that when multiplied by itself gives 49. One square root is 7 because $7 \cdot 7 = 49$. Another square root of 49 is -7 because $(-7)(-7) = 49$. The number 49 has two square roots, 7 and -7; one is positive, and one is negative.

◀ *Work Problem* **1** *at the Side.*

The **positive** or **principal square root** of a number is written with the symbol $\sqrt{}$. For example, the positive square root of 121 is 11, written

$$\sqrt{121} = 11.$$

The symbol $-\sqrt{}$ is used for the **negative square root** of a number. For example, the negative square root of 121 is -11, written

$$-\sqrt{121} = -11.$$

The symbol $\sqrt{}$, called a **radical sign,** always represents the positive square root (except that $\sqrt{0} = 0$). The number inside the radical sign is called the **radicand,** and the entire expression, radical sign and radicand, is called a **radical.**

Radical sign ↘   ↙ Radicand
$$\sqrt{a}$$
‿‿
Radical

An algebraic expression containing a radical is called a **radical expression.**

Radicals have a long mathematical history. The radical sign $\sqrt{}$ has been used since sixteenth-century Germany and was probably derived from the letter R. The radical symbol in the margin comes from the Latin word for root, *radix.* It was first used by Leonardo da Pisa (Fibonnaci) in 1220.

1 Find all square roots.

(a) 100

(b) 25

(c) 36

(d) $\dfrac{25}{36}$

Early radical symbol

We summarize our discussion of square roots as follows.

Square Roots of a

If a is a positive real number, then

$\quad\quad\quad \sqrt{a}$ is the positive or principal square root of a,

and $\quad\quad -\sqrt{a}$ is the negative square root of a.

For nonnegative a,

$$\sqrt{a} \cdot \sqrt{a} = \left(\sqrt{a}\right)^2 = a \quad \text{and} \quad -\sqrt{a} \cdot \left(-\sqrt{a}\right) = \left(-\sqrt{a}\right)^2 = a.$$

Also, $\sqrt{0} = 0$.

Calculator Tip Recall from **Section 5.8** that most calculators have a square root key, usually labeled $\boxed{\sqrt{x}}$, that allows us to find the square root of a number. On some models, the square root key must be used in conjunction with the key marked $\boxed{\text{INV}}$ or $\boxed{\text{2nd}}$.

EXAMPLE 2 **Finding Square Roots**

Find each square root.

(a) $\sqrt{144}$

The radical $\sqrt{144}$ represents the positive or principal square root of 144. Think of a positive number whose square is 144.

$$12^2 = 144, \quad \text{so} \quad \sqrt{144} = 12.$$

(b) $-\sqrt{1024}$

This symbol represents the negative square root of 1024. A calculator with a square root key can be used to find $\sqrt{1024} = 32$. Then, $-\sqrt{1024} = -32$.

(c) $\sqrt{\dfrac{4}{9}} = \dfrac{2}{3}$ **(d)** $-\sqrt{\dfrac{16}{49}} = -\dfrac{4}{7}$ **(e)** $\sqrt{0.81} = 0.9$

Work Problem **2** *at the Side.* ▶

As noted above, when the square root of a positive real number is squared, the result is that positive real number. $\left(\text{Also, } \left(\sqrt{0}\right)^2 = 0.\right)$

EXAMPLE 3 **Squaring Radical Expressions**

Find the *square* of each radical expression.

(a) $\sqrt{13}$

$\quad \left(\sqrt{13}\right)^2 = 13$ Definition of square root

(b) $-\sqrt{29}$

$\quad \left(-\sqrt{29}\right)^2 = 29$ The square of a *negative* number is positive.

(c) $\sqrt{p^2 + 1}$

$\quad \left(\sqrt{p^2 + 1}\right)^2 = p^2 + 1$

Work Problem **3** *at the Side.* ▶

---

2 Find each square root.

(a) $\sqrt{16}$

(b) $-\sqrt{169}$

(c) $-\sqrt{225}$

(d) $\sqrt{729}$

(e) $\sqrt{\dfrac{36}{25}}$

(f) $\sqrt{0.49}$

3 Find the *square* of each radical expression.

(a) $\sqrt{41}$

(b) $-\sqrt{39}$

(c) $\sqrt{2x^2 + 3}$

ANSWERS

2. **(a)** 4 **(b)** -13 **(c)** -15
   (d) 27 **(e)** $\dfrac{6}{5}$ **(f)** 0.7

3. **(a)** 41 **(b)** 39 **(c)** $2x^2 + 3$

4 Tell whether each square root is *rational, irrational,* or *not a real number.*

(a) $\sqrt{9}$

(b) $\sqrt{7}$

(c) $\sqrt{\dfrac{4}{9}}$

(d) $\sqrt{72}$

(e) $\sqrt{-43}$

OBJECTIVE 2 Decide whether a given root is rational, irrational, or not a real number. All numbers with square roots that are rational are called **perfect squares.**

Perfect squares		Rational square roots
25		$\sqrt{25} = 5$
144	are perfect squares since	$\sqrt{144} = 12$
$\dfrac{4}{9}$		$\sqrt{\dfrac{4}{9}} = \dfrac{2}{3}$

A number that is not a perfect square has a square root that is not a rational number. For example, $\sqrt{5}$ is not a rational number because it cannot be written as the ratio of two integers. Its decimal equivalent (or approximation) neither terminates nor repeats. However, $\sqrt{5}$ is a real number and corresponds to a point on the number line. As mentioned in **Section 10.1,** a real number that is not rational is called an **irrational number.** The number $\sqrt{5}$ is irrational. Many square roots of integers are irrational.

> If a is a *positive* real number that is *not* a perfect square, then
> $$\sqrt{a} \text{ is irrational.}$$

Not every number has a real number square root. For example, there is no real number that can be squared to obtain -36. (The square of a real number can never be negative.) Because of this, $\sqrt{-36}$ *is not a real number.*

> If a is a *negative* real number, then $\sqrt{a}$ is *not* a real number.

CAUTION
Be careful not to confuse $\sqrt{-36}$ and $-\sqrt{36}$. $\sqrt{-36}$ is not a real number since there is no real number that can be squared to obtain -36. However, $-\sqrt{36}$ is the negative square root of 36, which is -6.

EXAMPLE 4   Identifying Types of Square Roots

Tell whether each square root is *rational, irrational,* or *not a real number.*

(a) $\sqrt{17}$
Because 17 is not a perfect square, $\sqrt{17}$ is irrational.

(b) $\sqrt{64}$
The number 64 is a perfect square, 8^2, so $\sqrt{64} = 8$ is a rational number.

(c) $\sqrt{-25}$
There is no real number whose square is -25. Therefore, $\sqrt{-25}$ is not a real number.

◄ Work Problem **4** *at the Side.*

ANSWERS
4. (a) rational **(b)** irrational **(c)** rational
(d) irrational **(e)** not a real number

Note

Not all irrational numbers are square roots of integers. For example, π (approximately 3.14159) is an irrational number that is not a square root of any integer.

OBJECTIVE 3 Find decimal approximations for irrational square roots. Even if a number is irrational, a decimal that approximates the number can be found using a calculator, as we did in **Section 5.8.** For example, if we use a calculator to find $\sqrt{10}$, the display might show 3.16227766, which is only an *approximation* of $\sqrt{10}$, not an exact rational value.

EXAMPLE 5 Approximating Irrational Square Roots

Find a decimal approximation for each square root. Round answers to the nearest thousandth.

(a) $\sqrt{11}$

Using the square root key of a calculator gives $3.31662479 \approx 3.317$, where $\approx$ means "is approximately equal to."

(b) $\sqrt{39} \approx 6.245$ Use a calculator.   **(c)** $-\sqrt{740} \approx -27.203$

Work Problem **5** *at the Side.* ▶

OBJECTIVE 4 Use the Pythagorean formula. Many applications of square roots use the Pythagorean formula. Recall from **Section 14.7** that by this formula if c is the length of the hypotenuse of a right triangle, and a and b are the lengths of the two legs, as shown in Figure 1, then

$$a^2 + b^2 = c^2$$

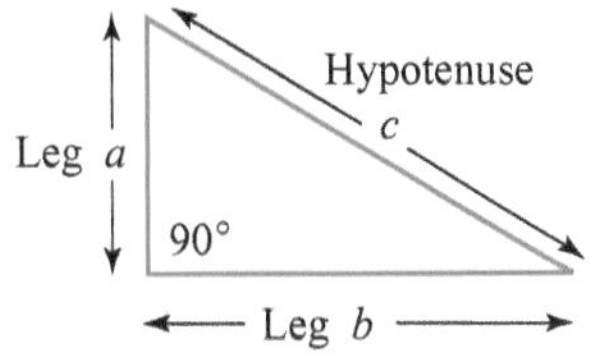

Figure 1

EXAMPLE 6 Using the Pythagorean Formula

Find the length of the unknown side of each right triangle with sides a, b, and c, where c is the hypotenuse.

(a) $a = 3, b = 4$

Use the Pythagorean formula to find c^2 first.

$$c^2 = a^2 + b^2$$
$$c^2 = 3^2 + 4^2 \quad \text{Let } a = 3 \text{ and } b = 4.$$
$$c^2 = 9 + 16 \quad \text{Square.}$$
$$c^2 = 25 \quad \text{Add.}$$

Since the length of a side of a triangle must be a positive number, find the positive square root of 25 to get c.

$$c = \sqrt{25} = 5$$

Continued on Next Page

---

5 Find a decimal approximation for each square root. Round answers to the nearest thousandth.

(a) $\sqrt{28}$

(b) $\sqrt{63}$

(c) $-\sqrt{190}$

(d) $\sqrt{1000}$

ANSWERS

5. (a) 5.292   **(b)** 7.937   **(c)** -13.784
    (d) 31.623

6 Find the length of the unknown side in each right triangle. Give any decimal approximations to the nearest thousandth.

(a) $a = 7, b = 24$

(b) $c = 15, b = 13$

(c)

8   11

?

(b) $c = 9, b = 5$

Substitute the given values in the Pythagorean formula. Then solve for a^2.

$$c^2 = a^2 + b^2$$
$$9^2 = a^2 + 5^2 \qquad \text{Let } c = 9 \text{ and } b = 5.$$
$$81 = a^2 + 25 \qquad \text{Square.}$$
$$56 = a^2 \qquad \text{Subtract 25.}$$

Use a calculator to find the positive square root of 56 to get a.

$$a = \sqrt{56} \approx 7.483$$

CAUTION

Be careful not to make the common mistake of thinking that $\sqrt{a^2 + b^2}$ equals $a + b$. As Example 6(a) shows, $\sqrt{9 + 16} = \sqrt{25} = 5$. However, $\sqrt{9} + \sqrt{16} = 3 + 4 = 7$. Since $5 \neq 7$, in general,

$$\sqrt{a^2 + b^2} \neq a + b.$$

◀ *Work Problem* **6** *at the Side.*

The Pythagorean formula can be used to solve applied problems that involve right triangles. Use the same six problem-solving steps that we have been using throughout the text.

EXAMPLE 7   **Using the Pythagorean Formula to Solve an Application**

A ladder 10 ft long leans against a wall. The foot of the ladder is 6 ft from the base of the wall. How high up the wall does the top of the ladder rest?

Step 1   **Read** the problem again.

Step 2   **Assign a variable.** As shown in Figure 2, a right triangle is formed with the ladder as the hypotenuse. Let a represent the height of the top of the ladder when measured straight down to the ground.

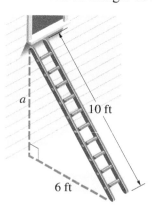

a

10 ft

6 ft

Figure 2

Continued on Next Page

Step 3 **Write an equation** using the Pythagorean formula.

Substitute carefully.

$$c^2 = a^2 + b^2$$

$$10^2 = a^2 + 6^2 \qquad \text{Let } c = 10 \text{ and } b = 6.$$

Step 4 **Solve.**

$$100 = a^2 + 36 \qquad \text{Square.}$$

$$64 = a^2 \qquad \text{Subtract 36.}$$

$$\sqrt{64} = a$$

$$a = 8 \qquad \sqrt{64} = 8$$

Choose the positive square root of 64 since *a* represents a length.

Step 5 **State the answer.** The top of the ladder rests 8 ft up the wall.

Step 6 **Check.** From Figure 2, we see that we must have

$$8^2 + 6^2 \overset{?}{=} 10^2$$

$$64 + 36 = 100. \qquad \text{True}$$

The check confirms that the top of the ladder rests 8 ft up the wall.

Work Problem **7** *at the Side.* ▶

OBJECTIVE 5 Find cube, fourth, and other roots. Finding the square root of a number is the inverse (reverse) of squaring a number. In a similar way, there are inverses to finding the cube of a number, or finding the fourth or higher power of a number. These inverses are the **cube root,** written $\sqrt[3]{a}$, and the **fourth root,** written $\sqrt[4]{a}$. Similar symbols are used for higher roots. In general, we have the following.

$\sqrt[n]{a}$

The *n*th root of *a* is written: $\qquad \sqrt[n]{a}$

In $\sqrt[n]{a}$, the number *n* is the **index,** or **order,** of the radical.

Index

Radical sign $\qquad$ Radicand

$$\sqrt[n]{a}$$

Radical

We could write $\sqrt[2]{a}$ instead of $\sqrt{a}$, but the simpler symbol $\sqrt{a}$ is customary since the square root is the most commonly used root.

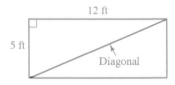

Calculator Tip A calculator that has a key marked $\sqrt[x]{y}$, x^y, or y^x (again perhaps in conjunction with the INV or 2nd key) can be used to find other roots.

When working with cube roots or fourth roots, it is helpful to memorize the first few *perfect cubes* ($1^3 = 1, 2^3 = 8, 3^3 = 27$, and so on) and the first few *perfect fourth powers* ($1^4 = 1, 2^4 = 16, 3^4 = 81$, and so on).

Work Problem **8** *at the Side.* ▶

---

7 A rectangle has dimensions 5 ft by 12 ft. Find the length of its diagonal.

12 ft

5 ft

Diagonal

(Note that the diagonal divides the rectangle into two right triangles with itself as the hypotenuse.)

8 Complete the following list of perfect cubes and perfect fourth powers.

Perfect Cubes	Perfect Fourth Powers
$1^3 = 1$	$1^4 = 1$
$2^3 = 8$	$2^4 = 16$
$3^3 = 27$	$3^4 = 81$
$4^3 = \underline{\quad}$	$4^4 = \underline{\quad}$
$5^3 = \underline{\quad}$	$5^4 = \underline{\quad}$
$6^3 = \underline{\quad}$	$6^4 = \underline{\quad}$
$7^3 = \underline{\quad}$	$7^4 = \underline{\quad}$
$8^3 = \underline{\quad}$	$8^4 = \underline{\quad}$
$9^3 = \underline{\quad}$	$9^4 = \underline{\quad}$
$10^3 = \underline{\quad}$	$10^4 = \underline{\quad}$

ANSWERS

7. 13 ft
8. Perfect cubes: 64; 125; 216; 343; 512; 729; 1000
Perfect fourth powers: 256; 625; 1296; 2401; 4096; 6561; 10,000

9 Find each cube root.

(a) $\sqrt[3]{27}$

(b) $\sqrt[3]{64}$

(c) $\sqrt[3]{-125}$

---

10 Find each root.

(a) $\sqrt[4]{81}$

(b) $\sqrt[4]{-81}$

(c) $-\sqrt[4]{81}$

(d) $\sqrt[5]{243}$

(e) $\sqrt[5]{-243}$

EXAMPLE 8   Finding Cube Roots

Find each cube root.

(a) $\sqrt[3]{8}$
Look for a number that can be cubed to give 8. Because $2^3 = 8, \sqrt[3]{8} = 2$.

(b) $\sqrt[3]{-8} = -2$ because $(-2)^3 = -8$.

(c) $\sqrt[3]{216} = 6$ because $6^3 = 216$.

Notice in Example 8(b) that we can find the cube root of a negative number. (Contrast this with the square root of a negative number, which is not real.) In fact, the cube root of a positive number is positive, and the cube root of a negative number is negative. **There is only one real number cube root for each real number.**

◀ *Work Problem* **9** *at the Side.*

When a radical has an **even index** (square root, fourth root, and so on), **the radicand must be nonnegative** to yield a real number root. Also,

$$\sqrt{a},\ \sqrt[4]{a},\ \sqrt[6]{a},\ \textbf{and so on are positive (principal) roots;}$$

$$-\sqrt{a},\ -\sqrt[4]{a},\ -\sqrt[6]{a},\ \textbf{and so on are negative roots.}$$

EXAMPLE 9   Finding Other Roots

Find each root.

(a) $\sqrt[4]{16} = 2$ because 2 is positive and $2^4 = 16$.

(b) $-\sqrt[4]{16}$
From part (a), $\sqrt[4]{16} = 2$, so the negative root is $-\sqrt[4]{16} = -2$.

(c) $\sqrt[4]{-16}$
For a real number fourth root, the radicand must be nonnegative. There is no real number that equals $\sqrt[4]{-16}$.

(d) $-\sqrt[5]{32}$
First find $\sqrt[5]{32}$. Because 2 is the number whose fifth power is 32, $\sqrt[5]{32} = 2$. Since $\sqrt[5]{32} = 2$, it follows that
$$-\sqrt[5]{32} = -2.$$

(e) $\sqrt[5]{-32}$
Because $(-2)^5 = -32$, $\sqrt[5]{-32} = -2$.

◀ *Work Problem* **10** *at the Side.*

ANSWERS

9. (a) 3   (b) 4   (c) −5
10. (a) 3   (b) not a real number
     (c) −3   (d) 3   (e) −3

17.1 ▶▶▶ **Exercises**

FOR
EXTRA
HELP
PRACTICE   WATCH   DOWNLOAD   READ   REVIEW

Decide whether each statement is true *or* false. *If* false, *tell why.*

1. Every positive number has two real square roots.

2. A negative number has negative square roots.

3. Every nonnegative number has two real square roots.

4. The positive square root of a positive number is its principal square root.

5. The cube root of every real number has the same sign as the number itself.

6. Every positive number has three real cube roots.

Find all square roots of each number. See Example 1.

7. 9

8. 16

9. 64

10. 100

11. 169

12. 225

13. $\dfrac{25}{196}$

14. $\dfrac{81}{400}$

15. 900

16. 1600

Find each square root. See Examples 2 and 4(c).

17. $\sqrt{1}$

18. $\sqrt{4}$

19. $\sqrt{49}$

20. $\sqrt{81}$

21. $-\sqrt{256}$

22. $-\sqrt{196}$

23. $-\sqrt{\dfrac{144}{121}}$

24. $-\sqrt{\dfrac{49}{36}}$

25. $\sqrt{0.64}$

26. $\sqrt{0.16}$

27. $\sqrt{-121}$

28. $\sqrt{-64}$

29. $-\sqrt{-49}$

30. $-\sqrt{-100}$

Find the square of each radical expression. See Example 3.

31. $\sqrt{100}$

32. $\sqrt{36}$

33. $-\sqrt{19}$

34. $-\sqrt{99}$

35. $\sqrt{\dfrac{2}{3}}$

36. $\sqrt{\dfrac{5}{7}}$

37. $\sqrt{3x^2 + 4}$

38. $\sqrt{9y^2 + 3}$

What must be true about the value of a for each statement in Exercises 39–42 to be true?

39. $\sqrt{a}$ represents a positive number.

40. $-\sqrt{a}$ represents a negative number.

41. $\sqrt{a}$ is not a real number.

42. $-\sqrt{a}$ is not a real number.

Write rational, irrational, or not a real number for each number. If a number is rational, give its exact value. If a number is irrational, give a decimal approximation to the nearest thousandth. Use a calculator as necessary. See Examples 4 and 5.

43. $\sqrt{25}$

44. $\sqrt{169}$

45. $\sqrt{29}$

46. $\sqrt{33}$

47. $-\sqrt{64}$

48. $-\sqrt{81}$

49. $-\sqrt{300}$

50. $-\sqrt{500}$

51. $\sqrt{-29}$

52. $\sqrt{-47}$

53. $\sqrt{1200}$

54. $\sqrt{1500}$

Work Exercises 55 and 56 without using a calculator.

55. Choose the best estimate for the length and width (in meters) of this rectangle.

   A. 11 by 6   **B.** 11 by 7   **C.** 10 by 7   **D.** 10 by 6

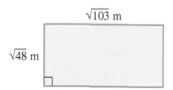

56. Choose the best estimate for the base and height (in feet) of this triangle.

   A. $b = 8, h = 5$ **B.** $b = 8, h = 4$

   C. $b = 9, h = 5$ **D.** $b = 9, h = 4$

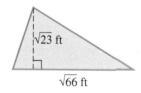

Find the length of the unknown side of each right triangle with sides a, b, and c, where c is the hypotenuse. See Figure 1 and Example 6. Give any decimal approximations to the nearest thousandth.

57. $a = 8, b = 15$

58. $a = 24, b = 10$

59. $a = 6, c = 10$

60. $b = 12, c = 13$

61. $a = 11, b = 4$

62. $a = 13, b = 9$

 *Solve each problem. See Example 7.*

63. The diagonal of a rectangle measures 25 cm. The width of the rectangle is 7 cm. Find the length of the rectangle.

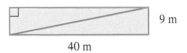

64. The length of a rectangle is 40 m, and the width is 9 m. Find the measure of the diagonal of the rectangle.

65. Tyler is flying a kite on 100 ft of string. How high is it above his hand (vertically) if the horizontal distance between Tyler and the kite is 60 ft?

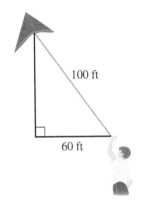

66. A guy wire is attached to the mast of a short-wave transmitting antenna. It is attached 96 ft above ground level. If the wire is staked to the ground 72 ft from the base of the mast, how long is the wire?

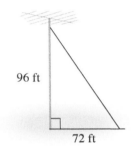

67. A surveyor measured the distances shown in the figure. Find the distance across the lake between points *R* and *S*.

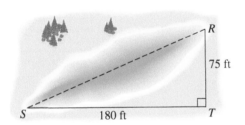

68. A boat is being pulled toward a dock with a rope attached at water level. When the boat is 24 ft from the dock, 30 ft of rope is extended. What is the height of the dock above the water?

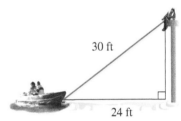

69. A surveyor wants to find the height of a building. At a point 110.0 ft from the base of the building he sights to the top of the building and finds the distance to be 193.0 ft. How high is the building (to the nearest tenth)?

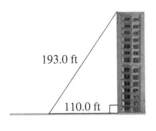

70. Two towns are separated by a dense forest. To go from Town B to Town A, it is necessary to travel due west for 19.0 mi, then turn due north and travel for 14.0 mi. How far apart are the towns (to the nearest tenth)?

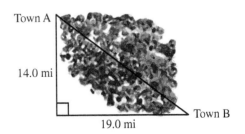

71. Following Hurricane Katrina, thousands of pine trees in southeastern Louisiana formed right triangles as shown in the photo. Suppose that, for a small such tree, the vertical distance from the base of the broken tree to the point of the break is 4.5 ft. The length of the broken part is 12.0 ft. How far along the ground (to the nearest tenth) is it from the base of the tree to the point where the broken part touches the ground?

72. One of the authors of this text purchased a new rear-projection Toshiba 51H84 television. A television set is "sized" according to the diagonal measurement of the viewing screen. The author purchased a 51-in. TV, so the TV measures 51 in. from one corner of the viewing screen diagonally to the other corner. The viewing screen is 44.5 in. wide. Find the height of the viewing screen (to the nearest tenth).

73. What is the value of x (to the nearest thousandth) in the figure?

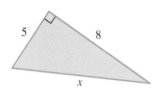

74. What is the value of y (to the nearest thousandth) in the figure?

Find each root. See Examples 8 and 9.

75. $\sqrt[3]{1}$

76. $\sqrt[3]{729}$

77. $\sqrt[3]{125}$

78. $\sqrt[3]{1000}$

79. $\sqrt[3]{-27}$

80. $\sqrt[3]{-64}$

81. $\sqrt[3]{-216}$

82. $\sqrt[3]{-343}$

83. $-\sqrt[3]{-8}$

84. $-\sqrt[3]{-216}$

85. $\sqrt[4]{256}$

86. $\sqrt[4]{625}$

87. $\sqrt[4]{1296}$

88. $\sqrt[4]{10,000}$

89. $\sqrt[4]{-1}$

90. $\sqrt[4]{-625}$

91. $-\sqrt[4]{625}$

92. $-\sqrt[4]{256}$

93. $\sqrt[5]{-1024}$

94. $\sqrt[5]{-100,000}$

17.2 ▶▶▶ Radical Expressions and Graphs

OBJECTIVES

1. **Find roots of numbers.**
2. **Find principal roots.**
3. **Graph functions defined by radical expressions.**
4. **Find *n*th roots of *n*th powers.**
5. **Use a calculator to find roots.**

OBJECTIVE 1 Find roots of numbers. Recall from **Section 1.3** that $6^2 = 36$; that is, 6 *squared* is 36. The opposite (or inverse) of *squaring* a number is taking its *square root*. Thus,

It is customary to write $\sqrt{}$, rather than $\sqrt[2]{}$.

$$\sqrt{36} = 6, \quad \text{because} \quad 6^2 = 36.$$

We now extend our discussion of roots to *cube roots* $\sqrt[3]{}$, *fourth roots* $\sqrt[4]{}$, and higher roots. In general, $\sqrt[n]{a}$ is a number whose *n*th power equals *a*. That is,

$$\sqrt[n]{a} = b \quad \text{means} \quad b^n = a.$$

The number *a* is the **radicand**, *n* is the **index**, or **order**, and the expression $\sqrt[n]{a}$ is a **radical.**

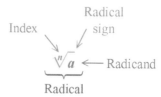

1 Simplify.

(a) $\sqrt[3]{27}$

Example 1 **Simplifying Higher Roots**

Simplify.

(a) $\sqrt[3]{64} = 4$, because $4^3 = 64$.
(b) $\sqrt[3]{125} = 5$, because $5^3 = 125$.

(c) $\sqrt[4]{16} = 2$, because $2^4 = 16$.
(d) $\sqrt[5]{32} = 2$, because $2^5 = 32$.

(e) $\sqrt[3]{\dfrac{8}{27}} = \dfrac{2}{3}$, because $\left(\dfrac{2}{3}\right)^3 = \dfrac{8}{27}$.
(f) $\sqrt[4]{0.0016} = 0.2$, because $(0.2)^4 = 0.0016$.

◀ *Work Problem* 1 *at the Side.*

(b) $\sqrt[3]{1000}$

(c) $\sqrt[4]{256}$

OBJECTIVE 2 Find principal roots. If *n* is even, positive numbers have two *n*th roots. For example, both 4 and −4 are square roots of 16, and 2 and −2 are fourth roots of 16. The notation $\sqrt[n]{a}$ represents the positive root, called the **principal root**, and $-\sqrt[n]{a}$ represents the negative root.

(d) $\sqrt[5]{243}$

---

nth Root

Case 1 If *n* is ***even*** and *a* is ***positive or 0,*** then

$\sqrt[n]{a}$ represents the **principal *n*th root** of *a*, and
$-\sqrt[n]{a}$ represents the **negative *n*th root** of *a*.

(e) $\sqrt[4]{\dfrac{16}{81}}$

Case 2 If *n* is ***even*** and *a* is ***negative,*** then

$\sqrt[n]{a}$ is not a real number.

Case 3 If *n* is ***odd,*** then

there is exactly one *n*th root of *a*, written $\sqrt[n]{a}$.

(f) $\sqrt[3]{0.064}$

ANSWERS

1. **(a)** 3 **(b)** 10 **(c)** 4 **(d)** 3
   (e) $\dfrac{2}{3}$ **(f)** 0.4

If *n* is even, then the two *n*th roots of *a* are often written together as $\pm\sqrt[n]{a}$, with $\pm$ read "positive or negative," or "plus or minus."

Example 2 **Finding Roots**

Find each root.

(a) $\sqrt{100} = 10$
While 100 has two square roots, $\sqrt{100}$ represents the principal square root, which is 10.

(b) $-\sqrt{100} = -10$
Here, we want the negative square root, -10.

(c) $\sqrt[4]{81} = 3$ Principal 4th root

(d) $-\sqrt[4]{81} = -3$ Negative 4th root

Parts (a)–(d) illustrate Case 1 in the preceding box.

(e) $\sqrt[4]{-81}$
The index is *even* and the radicand is *negative,* so $\sqrt[4]{-81}$ is not a real number. This is Case 2 in the preceding box.

(f) $\sqrt[3]{8} = 2$, because $2^3 = 8$.

(g) $\sqrt[3]{-8} = -2$, because $(-2)^3 = -8$.

Parts (f) and (g) illustrate Case 3 in the box. The index is *odd,* so each radical represents exactly one *n*th root (regardless of whether the radicand is positive, negative, or 0).

Work Problem **2** *at the Side.* ▶

OBJECTIVE **3** **Graph functions defined by radical expressions.**
A **radical expression** is an algebraic expression that contains radicals.

$$3 - \sqrt{x}, \quad \sqrt[3]{x}, \quad \text{and} \quad \sqrt{2x - 1} \quad \text{Radical expressions}$$

In earlier chapters we graphed functions defined by polynomial and rational expressions. Now we examine the graphs of functions defined by the radical expressions $f(x) = \sqrt{x}$ and $f(x) = \sqrt[3]{x}$.

Figure 1 shows the graph of the **square root function** defined by $f(x) = \sqrt{x}$, together with a table of selected points. Only nonnegative values can be used for x, so the domain is $[0, \infty)$. Because $\sqrt{x}$ is the principal square root of x, it always has a nonnegative value, so the range is also $[0, \infty)$.

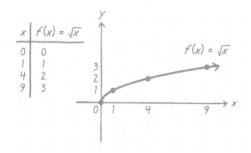

Figure 1

Figure 2 on the next page shows the graph of the **cube root function** defined by $f(x) = \sqrt[3]{x}$, together with a table of selected points. Since any real number (positive, negative, or 0) can be used for x in the cube root function, $\sqrt[3]{x}$ can be positive, negative, or 0. Thus, both the domain and the range of the cube root function are $(-\infty, \infty)$.

2 Find each root.
(a) $\sqrt{36}$

(b) $-\sqrt{36}$

(c) $\sqrt[4]{16}$

(d) $-\sqrt[4]{16}$

(e) $\sqrt[4]{-16}$

(f) $\sqrt[5]{1024}$

(g) $\sqrt[5]{-1024}$

ANSWERS

2. **(a)** 6 **(b)** −6 **(c)** 2 **(d)** −2
(e) not a real number
(f) 4 **(g)** −4

3 Graph each function by creating a table of values. Give the domain and range.

(a) $f(x) = \sqrt{x} + 2$

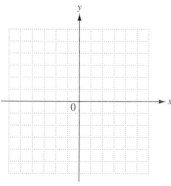

(b) $f(x) = \sqrt[3]{x} - 1$

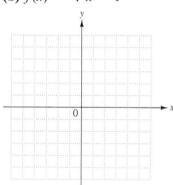

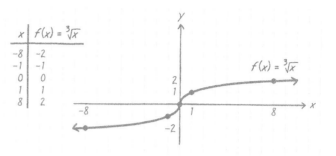

Figure 2

Example 3   **Graphing Functions Defined with Radicals**

Graph each function by creating a table of values. Give the domain and the range.

(a) $f(x) = \sqrt{x - 3}$

A table of values is shown. The x-values were chosen so that the function values are all integers. For the radicand to be nonnegative, we must have $x - 3 \geq 0$, or $x \geq 3$. Therefore, the domain is $[3, \infty)$. Again, function values are positive or 0, so the range is $[0, \infty)$. See the graph in Figure 3.

x	$f(x) = \sqrt{x - 3}$
3	$\sqrt{3 - 3} = 0$
4	$\sqrt{4 - 3} = 1$
7	$\sqrt{7 - 3} = 2$

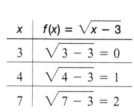

Figure 3

(b) $f(x) = \sqrt[3]{x} + 2$

See the table and Figure 4. Both the domain and the range are $(-\infty, \infty)$.

x	$f(x) = \sqrt[3]{x} + 2$
-8	$\sqrt[3]{-8} + 2 = 0$
-1	$\sqrt[3]{-1} + 2 = 1$
0	$\sqrt[3]{0} + 2 = 2$
1	$\sqrt[3]{1} + 2 = 3$
8	$\sqrt[3]{8} + 2 = 4$

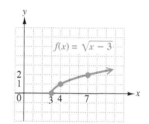

Figure 4

◀ *Work Problem* **3** *at the Side.*

ANSWERS

3. (a) domain: $[0, \infty)$; range: $[2, \infty)$

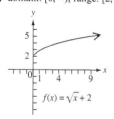

(b) domain: $(-\infty, \infty)$; range: $(-\infty, \infty)$

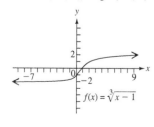

OBJECTIVE **4** **Find nth roots of nth powers.**   What does $\sqrt{a^2}$ equal? Your first answer might be a, but this is not necessarily true. For example, consider the following:

If $a = 6$,   then $\sqrt{a^2} = \sqrt{6^2} = \sqrt{36} = 6$.

If $a = -6$,   then $\sqrt{a^2} = \sqrt{(-6)^2} = \sqrt{36} = 6$.← Instead of -6, we get 6, the *absolute value* of -6.

Since the symbol $\sqrt{a^2}$ represents the *nonnegative* square root, we write $\sqrt{a^2}$ with absolute value bars, as $|a|$, because a may be a negative number.

$$\boxed{\sqrt{a^2}}$$

For any real number a, $\sqrt{a^2} = |a|.$

In words, the principal square root of a^2 is the absolute value of a.

4 Find each square root that is a real number.

(a) $\sqrt{15^2}$

Example 4   **Simplifying Square Roots Using Absolute Value**

Find each square root that is a real number.

(a) $\sqrt{7^2} = |7| = 7$

(b) $\sqrt{(-7)^2} = |-7| = 7$

(c) $\sqrt{k^2} = |k|$

(d) $\sqrt{(-k)^2} = |-k| = |k|$

(b) $\sqrt{(-12)^2}$

Work Problem **4** *at the Side.* ▶

We can generalize this idea to any nth root.

(c) $\sqrt{r^2}$

$$\boxed{\sqrt[n]{a^n}}$$

If n is an *even* positive integer, then $\sqrt[n]{a^n} = |a|.$

If n is an *odd* positive integer, then $\sqrt[n]{a^n} = a.$

In words, use absolute value when n is even; absolute value is not necessary when n is odd.

(d) $\sqrt{(-r)^2}$

5 Simplify.

(a) $\sqrt[4]{(-5)^4}$

Example 5   **Simplifying Higher Roots Using Absolute Value**

Simplify each root.

(a) $\sqrt[6]{(-3)^6} = |-3| = 3$ *n is even; use absolute value.*

(b) $\sqrt[5]{(-4)^5} = -4$ *n is odd.*

(c) $-\sqrt[4]{(-9)^4} = -|-9| = -9$ *n is even; use absolute value.*

(d) $-\sqrt{m^4} = -|m^2| = -m^2$ *For all m, $|m^2| = m^2$.*
    No absolute value bars are needed here because m^2 is nonnegative for any real number value of m.

(e) $\sqrt[3]{a^{12}} = a^4$, because $a^{12} = (a^4)^3$.

(f) $\sqrt[4]{x^{12}} = |x^3|$
    We use absolute value bars to guarantee that the result is not negative (because x^3 can be either positive or negative, depending on x). If desired, $|x^3|$ can be written as $x^2 \cdot |x|$.

(b) $\sqrt[5]{(-7)^5}$

(c) $-\sqrt[6]{(-3)^6}$

(d) $-\sqrt[4]{m^8}$

(e) $\sqrt[3]{x^{24}}$

Work Problem **5** *at the Side.* ▶

OBJECTIVE 5 Use a calculator to find roots.   Radical expressions often represent irrational numbers. To find approximations of such radicals, we usually use a calculator. For example,

$\sqrt{15} \approx 3.872983346$, $\sqrt[3]{10} \approx 2.15443469$,   and $\sqrt[4]{2} \approx 1.189207115$,

where the symbol $\approx$ means "is approximately equal to." In this book, we often give approximations rounded to three decimal places. Thus,

$$\sqrt{15} \approx 3.873,   \sqrt[3]{10} \approx 2.154,   \text{and}   \sqrt[4]{2} \approx 1.189.$$

(f) $\sqrt[6]{y^{18}}$

ANSWERS
4. (a) 15   (b) 12   (c) $|r|$ (d) $|r|$
5. (a) 5   (b) -7 (c) -3
   (d) $-m^2$ (e) x^8 (f) $|y^3|$

6 Use a calculator to approximate each radical to three decimal places.

(a) $\sqrt{17}$

> 📇 **Calculator Tip**   The methods for finding approximations differ among makes and models, and you should always consult your owner's manual for keystroke instructions. Be aware that graphing calculators often differ from scientific calculators in the order in which keystrokes are made.

(b) $-\sqrt{362}$

Figure 5 shows how the preceding approximations are displayed on a TI-83/84 Plus graphing calculator. In Figure 5(a), eight or nine decimal places are shown, while in Figure 5(b), the number of decimal places is fixed at three.

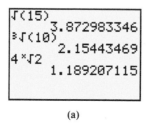

| (a) | (b) |

Figure 5

There is a simple way to check that a calculator approximation is "in the ballpark." Because 16 is a little larger than 15, $\sqrt{16} = 4$ should be a little larger than $\sqrt{15}$. Thus, 3.873 is a reasonable approximation for $\sqrt{15}$.

(c) $\sqrt[3]{9482}$

Example 6   Finding Approximations for Roots

Use a calculator to verify that each approximation is correct.

(a) $\sqrt{39} \approx 6.245$ (b) $-\sqrt{72} \approx -8.485$

(c) $\sqrt[3]{93} \approx 4.531$ (d) $\sqrt[4]{39} \approx 2.499$

(d) $\sqrt[4]{6825}$

◀ *Work Problem* **6** *at the Side.*

Example 7   Using Roots to Calculate Resonant Frequency

In electronics, the resonant frequency f of a circuit may be found by the formula

$$f = \frac{1}{2\pi\sqrt{LC}},$$

7 Use the formula in Example 7 to approximate f to the nearest thousand if

$$L = 6 \times 10^{-5}$$
and $C = 4 \times 10^{-9}$.

where f is in cycles per second, L is in henrys, and C is in farads.* Find the resonant frequency f if $L = 5 \times 10^{-4}$ henry and $C = 3 \times 10^{-10}$ farad. Give your answer to the nearest thousand.

Find the value of f when $L = 5 \times 10^{-4}$ and $C = 3 \times 10^{-10}$.

$$f = \frac{1}{2\pi\sqrt{LC}} \qquad \text{Given formula}$$

$$f = \frac{1}{2\pi\sqrt{(5 \times 10^{-4})(3 \times 10^{-10})}} \qquad \text{Substitute for } L \text{ and } C.$$

$$f \approx 411,000 \qquad \text{Use a calculator.}$$

The resonant frequency f is approximately 411,000 cycles per sec.

◀ *Work Problem* **7** *at the Side.*

*Henrys and farads are units of measure in electronics.

17.2 ▶▶▶ Exercises

FOR
EXTRA
HELP

Math XL
PRACTICE

WATCH

DOWNLOAD

READ

REVIEW

*Match each expression from Column I with the equivalent choice from Column II. Answers
may be used once, more than once, or not at all. See Examples 1 and 2.*

I

1. $-\sqrt{16}$

2. $\sqrt{-16}$

3. $\sqrt[3]{-27}$

4. $\sqrt[5]{-32}$

5. $\sqrt[4]{16}$

6. $-\sqrt[3]{64}$

II

A. 3

B. -2

C. 2

D. -3

E. -4

F. Not a real number

Choose the closest approximation of each square root.

7. $\sqrt{123.5}$

    A. 9   **B.** 10   **C.** 11   **D.** 12

8. $\sqrt{67.8}$

    A. 7   **B.** 8   **C.** 9   **D.** 10

Refer to the figure to answer the questions in Exercises 9–10.

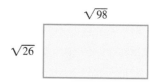

$\sqrt{98}$

$\sqrt{26}$

9. Which one of the following is the best estimate of
its area?

    A. 2500   **B.** 250   **C.** 50   **D.** 100

10. Which one of the following is the best estimate of
its perimeter?

    A. 15   **B.** 250   **C.** 100   **D.** 30

11. Consider the expression $-\sqrt{-a}$. Decide whether it
is positive, negative, 0, or not a real number if
  (a) $a > 0$,   **(b)** $a < 0$,   **(c)** $a = 0$.

12. If n is odd, under what conditions is $\sqrt[n]{a}$
  (a) positive,   **(b)** negative,   **(c)** 0?

Find each root that is a real number. Use a calculator as necessary. See Examples 1 and 2.

13. $-\sqrt{81}$

14. $-\sqrt{121}$

15. $\sqrt[3]{216}$

16. $\sqrt[3]{343}$

17. $\sqrt[3]{-64}$

18. $\sqrt[3]{-125}$

19. $-\sqrt[3]{512}$

20. $-\sqrt[3]{1000}$

21. $\sqrt[4]{1296}$

22. $\sqrt[4]{625}$

23. $-\sqrt[4]{16}$

24. $-\sqrt[4]{256}$

25. $\sqrt[4]{-625}$ **26.** $\sqrt[4]{-256}$ **27.** $\sqrt[6]{729}$ **28.** $\sqrt[6]{64}$

29. $\sqrt[6]{-64}$ **30.** $\sqrt[6]{-1}$ **31.** $\sqrt{\dfrac{64}{81}}$ **32.** $\sqrt{\dfrac{100}{9}}$

33. $\sqrt{0.49}$ **34.** $\sqrt{0.81}$ **35.** $\sqrt[3]{\dfrac{64}{27}}$ **36.** $\sqrt[4]{\dfrac{81}{16}}$

37. $-\sqrt[6]{\dfrac{1}{64}}$ **38.** $-\sqrt[5]{\dfrac{1}{32}}$ **39.** $\sqrt[3]{0.001}$ **40.** $\sqrt[3]{0.125}$

Graph each function and give its domain and range. See Example 3.

41. $f(x) = \sqrt{x + 3}$

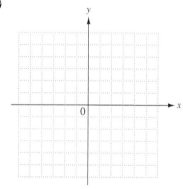

42. $f(x) = \sqrt{x - 5}$

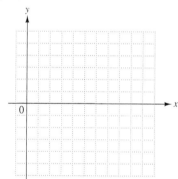

43. $f(x) = \sqrt{x} - 2$

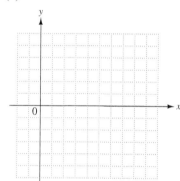

44. $f(x) = \sqrt{x} + 4$

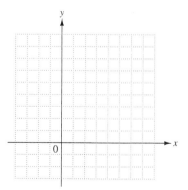

45. $f(x) = \sqrt[3]{x} - 3$

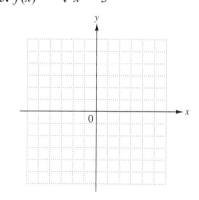

46. $f(x) = \sqrt[3]{x} + 1$

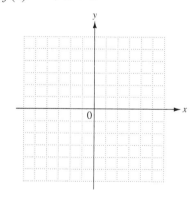

Simplify each root. See Examples 4 and 5.

47. $\sqrt{12^2}$

48. $\sqrt{19^2}$

49. $\sqrt{(-10)^2}$

50. $\sqrt{(-13)^2}$

51. $\sqrt[6]{(-2)^6}$

52. $\sqrt[6]{(-4)^6}$

53. $\sqrt[5]{(-9)^5}$

54. $\sqrt[5]{(-8)^5}$

55. $-\sqrt[6]{(-5)^6}$

56. $-\sqrt[6]{(-7)^6}$

57. $\sqrt{x^2}$

58. $-\sqrt{x^2}$

59. $\sqrt{(-z)^2}$

60. $\sqrt{(-q)^2}$

61. $\sqrt[3]{x^3}$

62. $-\sqrt[3]{x^3}$

63. $\sqrt[3]{x^{15}}$

64. $\sqrt[3]{m^9}$

65. $\sqrt[6]{x^{30}}$

66. $\sqrt[4]{k^{20}}$

Use a calculator to find a decimal approximation for each radical. Round answers to three decimal places. See Example 6.

67. $\sqrt{9483}$

68. $\sqrt{6825}$

69. $\sqrt{284.361}$

70. $\sqrt{846.104}$

71. $-\sqrt{82}$

72. $-\sqrt{91}$

73. $\sqrt[3]{423}$

74. $\sqrt[3]{555}$

75. $\sqrt[4]{100}$

76. $\sqrt[4]{250}$

77. $\sqrt[5]{23.8}$

78. $\sqrt[5]{98.4}$

Solve each problem. See Example 7.

79. Use the formula in Example 7 to calculate the resonant frequency of a circuit to the nearest thousand if $L = 7.237 \times 10^{-5}$ henry and $C = 2.5 \times 10^{-10}$ farad.

80. The threshold weight T for a person is the weight above which the risk of death increases greatly. The threshold weight in pounds for men aged 40–49 is related to height in inches by the formula

$$h = 12.3\sqrt[3]{T}.$$

What height corresponds to a threshold weight of 216 lb for a 43-yr-old man? Round your answer to the nearest inch, and then to the nearest tenth of a foot.

81. According to an article in *The World Scanner Report,* the distance D, in miles, to the horizon from an observer's point of view over water or "flat" earth is given by

$$D = \sqrt{2H},$$

where H is the height of the point of view, in feet. If a person whose eyes are 6 ft above ground level is standing at the top of a hill 44 ft above "flat" earth, approximately how far to the horizon will she be able to see?

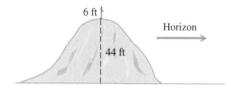

82. The time for one complete swing of a simple pendulum is

$$t = 2\pi\sqrt{\frac{L}{g}},$$

where t is time in seconds, L is the length of the pendulum in feet, and g, the force due to gravity, is about 32 ft per sec^2. Find the time of a complete swing of a 2-ft pendulum to the nearest tenth of a second.

83. Heron's formula gives a method of finding the area of a triangle if the lengths of its sides are known. Suppose that a, b, and c are the lengths of the sides. Let s denote one-half of the perimeter of the triangle (called the **semiperimeter**); that is,

$$s = \frac{1}{2}(a + b + c).$$

Then the area of the triangle is

$$A = \sqrt{s(s - a)(s - b)(s - c)}.$$

Find the area of the Bermuda Triangle, if the "sides" of this triangle measure approximately 850 mi, 925 mi, and 1300 mi. Give your answer to the nearest thousand square miles.

84. The Vietnam Veterans' Memorial in Washington, D.C., is in the shape of an unenclosed isosceles triangle with equal sides of length 246.75 ft. If the triangle were enclosed, the third side would have length 438.14 ft. Use Heron's formula from the previous exercise to find the area of this enclosure to the nearest hundred square feet. (*Source:* Information pamphlet obtained at the Vietnam Veterans' Memorial.)

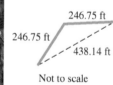

Not to scale

The coefficient of self-induction L (in henrys), the energy P stored in an electronic circuit (in joules), and the current I (in amps) are related by the formula

$$I = \sqrt{\frac{2P}{L}}.$$

Round your answers in Exercises 85 and 86 to the nearest thousandth.

85. Find I if $P = 120$ and $L = 80$.

86. Find I if $P = 100$ and $L = 40$.

17.3 ▷▷▷ Rational Exponents

OBJECTIVE 1 Use exponential notation for nth roots. We now look at exponents that are rational numbers of the form $\frac{1}{n}$, or $1/n$, where n is a natural number.

Consider the product $(3^{1/2})^2 = 3^{1/2} \cdot 3^{1/2}$. Using the rules of exponents from **Section 6.1,** extended to rational exponents, we can simplify this product as follows:

$$(3^{1/2})^2 = 3^{1/2} \cdot 3^{1/2}$$
$$= 3^{1/2+1/2} \qquad \text{Product rule: } a^m \cdot a^n = a^{m+n}$$
$$= 3^1 \qquad \text{Add exponents.}$$
$$= 3.$$

Also, by definition,

$$\left(\sqrt{3}\right)^2 = \sqrt{3} \cdot \sqrt{3} = 3.$$

Since both $(3^{1/2})^2$ and $\left(\sqrt{3}\right)^2$ are equal to 3, it seems reasonable to define

$$3^{1/2} = \sqrt{3}.$$

This suggests the following generalization.

$a^{1/n}$

If $\sqrt[n]{a}$ is a real number, then $\qquad a^{1/n} = \sqrt[n]{a}.$

Example 1 Evaluating Exponentials of the Form $a^{1/n}$

Evaluate each exponential.

The denominator is the index.

(a) $64^{1/3} = \sqrt[3]{64} = 4$

The denominator is the index. $\sqrt{}$ means $\sqrt[2]{}$.

(b) $100^{1/2} = \sqrt{100} = 10$

(c) $-256^{1/4} = -\sqrt[4]{256} = -4$

(d) $(-256)^{1/4} = \sqrt[4]{-256}$ is not a real number, because the radicand, -256, is negative and the index is even.

(e) $(-32)^{1/5} = \sqrt[5]{-32} = -2$

(f) $\left(\frac{1}{8}\right)^{1/3} = \sqrt[3]{\frac{1}{8}} = \frac{1}{2}$

CAUTION
Notice the difference between parts (c) and (d) in Example 1. The radical in part (c) is the *negative fourth root of a positive number,* while the radical in part (d) is the *principal fourth root of a negative number, which is not a real number.*

Work Problem **1** at the Side. ▶

OBJECTIVES

1 Use exponential notation for nth roots.

2 Define and use expressions of the form $a^{m/n}$.

3 Convert between radicals and rational exponents.

4 Use the rules for exponents with rational exponents.

1 Evaluate each exponential.

(a) $8^{1/3}$

(b) $9^{1/2}$

(c) $-81^{1/4}$

(d) $(-81)^{1/4}$

(e) $(-64)^{1/3}$

(f) $\left(\frac{1}{32}\right)^{1/5}$

ANSWERS

1. (a) 2 (b) 3 (c) -3
   (d) not a real number (e) -4 (f) $\frac{1}{2}$

2 Evaluate each exponential.

(a) $25^{3/2}$

(b) $27^{2/3}$

(c) $-16^{3/2}$

(d) $(-64)^{2/3}$

(e) $(-36)^{3/2}$

OBJECTIVE 2 Define and use expressions of the form $a^{m/n}$.
We know that $8^{1/3} = \sqrt[3]{8}$. How should we define a number like $8^{2/3}$? For past rules of exponents to be valid,

$$8^{2/3} = 8^{(1/3)2} = (8^{1/3})^2.$$

Since $8^{1/3} = \sqrt[3]{8}$,

$$8^{2/3} = \left(\sqrt[3]{8}\right)^2 = 2^2 = 4.$$

Generalizing from this example, we define $a^{m/n}$ as follows.

$a^{m/n}$

If m and n are positive integers with m/n in lowest terms, then

$$a^{m/n} = (a^{1/n})^m,$$

provided that $a^{1/n}$ is a real number. If $a^{1/n}$ is not a real number, then $a^{m/n}$ is not a real number.

Example 2   Evaluating Exponentials of the Form $a^{m/n}$

Evaluate each exponential.

Think:
$36^{1/2} = \sqrt{36} = 6$

Think:
$125^{1/3} = \sqrt[3]{125} = 5$

(a) $36^{3/2} = (36^{1/2})^3 = 6^3 = 216$ (b) $125^{2/3} = (125^{1/3})^2 = 5^2 = 25$

Be careful.
The base is 4.

(c) $-4^{5/2} = -(4^{5/2}) = -(4^{1/2})^5 = -(2)^5 = -32$
    Because the base here is 4, the negative sign is *not* affected by the exponent.

(d) $(-27)^{2/3} = [(-27)^{1/3}]^2 = (-3)^2 = 9$

Notice how the $-$ sign is used in parts (c) and (d). In part (c), we first evaluate the exponential and then find its negative. In part (d), the $-$ sign is part of the base, -27.

(e) $(-100)^{3/2} = [(-100)^{1/2}]^3$, which is not a real number, since $(-100)^{1/2}$, or $\sqrt{-100}$, is not a real number.

◀ Work Problem **2** at the Side.

Recall from **Section 6.1** that for any natural number n,

$$a^{-n} = \frac{1}{a^n} \quad (a \neq 0).$$

When a rational exponent is negative, we apply this interpretation of negative exponents.

$a^{-m/n}$

If $a^{m/n}$ is a real number, then

$$a^{-m/n} = \frac{1}{a^{m/n}} \quad (a \neq 0).$$

Example 3 **Evaluating Exponentials with Negative Rational Exponents**

Evaluate each exponential.

(a) $16^{-3/4} = \dfrac{1}{16^{3/4}} = \dfrac{1}{(16^{1/4})^3} = \dfrac{1}{\left(\sqrt[4]{16}\right)^3} = \dfrac{1}{2^3} = \dfrac{1}{8}$

> The denominator of 3/4 is the index and the numerator is the exponent.

(b) $25^{-3/2} = \dfrac{1}{25^{3/2}} = \dfrac{1}{(25^{1/2})^3} = \dfrac{1}{\left(\sqrt{25}\right)^3} = \dfrac{1}{5^3} = \dfrac{1}{125}$

(c) $\left(\dfrac{8}{27}\right)^{-2/3} = \dfrac{1}{\left(\dfrac{8}{27}\right)^{2/3}} = \dfrac{1}{\left(\sqrt[3]{\dfrac{8}{27}}\right)^2} = \dfrac{1}{\left(\dfrac{2}{3}\right)^2} = \dfrac{1}{\dfrac{4}{9}} = \dfrac{9}{4}$

> $\dfrac{1}{\frac{4}{9}} = 1 \div \dfrac{4}{9} = 1 \cdot \dfrac{9}{4}$

We could also use the rule $\left(\frac{b}{a}\right)^{-m} = \left(\frac{a}{b}\right)^{m}$ here, as follows:

$$\left(\dfrac{8}{27}\right)^{-2/3} = \left(\dfrac{27}{8}\right)^{2/3} = \left(\sqrt[3]{\dfrac{27}{8}}\right)^2 = \left(\dfrac{3}{2}\right)^2 = \dfrac{9}{4}.$$

> Take the reciprocal only of the base, *not* the exponent.

Work Problem **3** *at the Side.* ▶

3 Evaluate each exponential.

(a) $36^{-3/2}$

(b) $32^{-4/5}$

(c) $\left(\dfrac{4}{9}\right)^{-5/2}$

CAUTION

Be careful to distinguish between exponential expressions such as

$16^{-1/4}$, which equals $\dfrac{1}{2}$; $-16^{1/4}$, which equals -2;   and

$-16^{-1/4}$, which equals $-\dfrac{1}{2}$.

A negative exponent does not necessarily lead to a negative result. Negative exponents lead to reciprocals, which may be positive.

We obtain an alternative definition of $a^{m/n}$ by applying the power rule a little differently than earlier. If all indicated roots are real numbers, then

$$a^{m/n} = a^{m(1/n)} = (a^m)^{1/n}, \qquad \text{so} \qquad a^{m/n} = (a^m)^{1/n}.$$

$a^{m/n}$

If all indicated roots are real numbers, then

$$a^{m/n} = (a^{1/n})^m = (a^m)^{1/n}.$$

We can now evaluate an expression such as $27^{2/3}$ in two ways:

$$27^{2/3} = (27^{1/3})^2 = 3^2 = 9$$

> The result is the same.

or $27^{2/3} = (27^2)^{1/3} = 729^{1/3} = 9.$

In most cases, it is easier to use $(a^{1/n})^m$.

Answers

3. **(a)** $\dfrac{1}{216}$ **(b)** $\dfrac{1}{16}$ **(c)** $\dfrac{243}{32}$

4 Write each exponential as a radical. Assume that all variables represent positive real numbers. Use the definition that takes the root first.

(a) $19^{1/2}$

(b) $5^{2/3}$

(c) $4k^{3/5}$

(d) $5x^{3/5} - (2x)^{3/5}$

(e) $x^{-5/7}$

(f) $(m^3 + n^3)^{1/3}$

5 Write each radical as an exponential and simplify. Assume that all variables represent positive real numbers.

(a) $\sqrt{37}$

(b) $\sqrt[4]{9^8}$

(c) $\sqrt[4]{t^4}$

4. (a) $\sqrt{19}$ **(b)** $\left(\sqrt[3]{5}\right)^2$ **(c)** $4\left(\sqrt[5]{k}\right)^3$

(d) $5\left(\sqrt[5]{x}\right)^3 - \left(\sqrt[5]{2x}\right)^3$

(e) $\dfrac{1}{\left(\sqrt[7]{x}\right)^5}$ **(f)** $\sqrt[3]{m^3 + n^3}$

5. (a) $37^{1/2}$ **(b)** 9^2, or 81 **(c)** t

This rule can also be expressed with radicals as follows.

Radical Form of $a^{m/n}$

If all indicated roots are real numbers, then

$$a^{m/n} = \sqrt[n]{a^m} = \left(\sqrt[n]{a}\right)^m.$$

In words, raise a to the mth power and then take the nth root, or take the nth root of a and then raise to the mth power.

For example,

$$8^{2/3} = \sqrt[3]{8^2} = \sqrt[3]{64} = 4, \quad \text{and} \quad 8^{2/3} = \left(\sqrt[3]{8}\right)^2 = 2^2 = 4,$$

so

$$8^{2/3} = \sqrt[3]{8^2} = \left(\sqrt[3]{8}\right)^2.$$

OBJECTIVE 3 **Convert between radicals and rational exponents.** Using the definition of rational exponents, we can simplify many problems involving radicals by converting the radicals to numbers with rational exponents. After simplifying, we convert the answer back to radical form.

Example 4 **Converting between Rational Exponents and Radicals**

In (a)–(f), write each exponential as a radical. Assume that all variables represent positive real numbers. Use the definition that takes the root first.

(a) $13^{1/2} = \sqrt{13}$ **(b)** $6^{3/4} = \left(\sqrt[4]{6}\right)^3$ **(c)** $9m^{5/8} = 9\left(\sqrt[8]{m}\right)^5$

(d) $6x^{2/3} - (4x)^{3/5} = 6\left(\sqrt[3]{x}\right)^2 - \left(\sqrt[5]{4x}\right)^3$

(e) $r^{-2/3} = \dfrac{1}{r^{2/3}} = \dfrac{1}{\left(\sqrt[3]{r}\right)^2}$

(f) $(a^2 + b^2)^{1/2} = \sqrt{a^2 + b^2}$ $\quad\boxed{\sqrt{a^2+b^2} \neq a+b}$

In (g)–(i), write each radical as an exponential. Simplify. Assume that all variables represent positive real numbers.

(g) $\sqrt{10} = 10^{1/2}$

(h) $\sqrt[4]{3^8} = 3^{8/4} = 3^2 = 9$

(i) $\sqrt[6]{z^6} = z^{6/6} = z^1 = z$, since z is positive.

◀ *Work Problem* **4** *at the Side.*

Note

In Example 4(i), it was not necessary to use absolute value bars, since the directions specifically stated that the variable represents a positive real number. Because the absolute value of the positive real number z is z itself, the answer is simply z.

◀ *Work Problem* **5** *at the Side.*

OBJECTIVE 4 Use the rules for exponents with rational exponents. The definition of rational exponents allows us to apply the rules for exponents first introduced in **Section 6.1.**

Rules for Rational Exponents

Let r and s be rational numbers. For all real numbers a and b for which the indicated expressions exist:

$$a^r \cdot a^s = a^{r+s} \qquad a^{-r} = \frac{1}{a^r} \qquad \frac{a^r}{a^s} = a^{r-s} \qquad \left(\frac{a}{b}\right)^{-r} = \frac{b^r}{a^r}$$

$$(a^r)^s = a^{rs} \qquad (ab)^r = a^r b^r \qquad \left(\frac{a}{b}\right)^r = \frac{a^r}{b^r} \qquad a^{-r} = \left(\frac{1}{a}\right)^r.$$

Example 5 Applying Rules for Rational Exponents

Write with only positive exponents. Assume that all variables represent positive real numbers.

(a) $2^{1/2} \cdot 2^{1/4}$

$= 2^{1/2 + 1/4}$ Product rule

$= 2^{3/4}$ Add exponents.

(b) $\dfrac{5^{2/3}}{5^{7/3}}$

$= 5^{2/3 - 7/3}$ Quotient rule

$= 5^{-5/3}$ Subtract exponents.

$= \dfrac{1}{5^{5/3}}$ $a^{-r} = \frac{1}{a^r}$

(c) $\dfrac{(x^{1/2}y^{2/3})^4}{y}$

$= \dfrac{(x^{1/2})^4 (y^{2/3})^4}{y}$ Power rule

$= \dfrac{x^2 y^{8/3}}{y^1}$ Power rule

$= x^2 y^{8/3 - 1}$ Quotient rule

$= x^2 y^{5/3}$ $\frac{8}{3} - 1 = \frac{8}{3} - \frac{3}{3} = \frac{5}{3}$

(d) $\left(\dfrac{x^4 y^{-6}}{x^{-2} y^{1/3}}\right)^{-2/3}$

$= \dfrac{(x^4)^{-2/3} (y^{-6})^{-2/3}}{(x^{-2})^{-2/3} (y^{1/3})^{-2/3}}$ Power rule

$= \dfrac{x^{-8/3} y^4}{x^{4/3} y^{-2/9}}$ Power rule

$= x^{-8/3 - 4/3} y^{4 - (-2/9)}$ Quotient rule

$= x^{-4} y^{38/9}$ [Use parentheses to avoid errors.] $4 - \left(-\frac{2}{9}\right) = \frac{36}{9} + \frac{2}{9} = \frac{38}{9}$

$= \dfrac{y^{38/9}}{x^4}$ Definition of negative exponent

Continued on Next Page

6 Write with only positive exponents. Assume that all variables represent positive real numbers.

(a) $11^{3/4} \cdot 11^{5/4}$

(b) $\dfrac{7^{3/4}}{7^{7/4}}$

(c) $\dfrac{9^{2/3} (x^{1/3})^4}{9^{-1/3}}$

(d) $\left(\dfrac{a^3 b^{-4}}{a^{-2} b^{1/5}} \right)^{-1/2}$

(e) $a^{2/3} (a^{7/3} + a^{1/3})$

The same result is obtained if we simplify within the parentheses first.

$$\left(\dfrac{x^4 y^{-6}}{x^{-2} y^{1/3}} \right)^{-2/3}$$

$= (x^{4-(-2)} y^{-6-1/3})^{-2/3}$ Quotient rule

$= (x^6 y^{-19/3})^{-2/3}$ $-6 - \frac{1}{3} = -\frac{18}{3} - \frac{1}{3} = -\frac{19}{3}$

$= (x^6)^{-2/3} (y^{-19/3})^{-2/3}$ Power rule

$= x^{-4} y^{38/9}$ Power rule

$= \dfrac{y^{38/9}}{x^4}$ Definition of negative exponent

(e) $m^{3/4} (m^{5/4} - m^{1/4})$

$= m^{3/4} (m^{5/4}) - m^{3/4} (m^{1/4})$ Distributive property

$= m^{3/4 + 5/4} - m^{3/4 + 1/4}$ Product rule

$= m^{8/4} - m^{4/4}$

$= m^2 - m$

Do not make the common mistake of multiplying exponents in the first step.

◀ *Work Problem* **6** *at the Side.*

CAUTION
Use the rules of exponents in problems like those in Example 5. Do not convert the expressions to radical form.

Example 6   **Applying Rules for Rational Exponents**

Write all radicals as exponentials, and then apply the rules for rational exponents. Give answers in exponential form. Assume that all variables represent positive real numbers.

(a) $\sqrt[3]{x^2} \cdot \sqrt[4]{x}$

$= x^{2/3} \cdot x^{1/4}$ Convert to rational exponents.

$= x^{2/3 + 1/4}$ Product rule

$= x^{8/12 + 3/12}$ Write exponents with a common denominator.

$= x^{11/12}$

(b) $\dfrac{\sqrt{x^3}}{\sqrt[3]{x^2}}$

$= \dfrac{x^{3/2}}{x^{2/3}}$ Convert to rational exponents.

$= x^{3/2 - 2/3}$ Quotient rule

$= x^{5/6}$ $\frac{3}{2} - \frac{2}{3} = \frac{9}{6} - \frac{4}{6} = \frac{5}{6}$

(c) $\sqrt{\sqrt[4]{z}}$

$= \sqrt{z^{1/4}}$ Convert the inside radical to rational exponents.

$= (z^{1/4})^{1/2}$ Convert to rational exponents.

$= z^{1/8}$ Power rule

◀ *Work Problem* **7** *at the Side.*

7 Write all radicals as exponentials, and then apply the rules for rational exponents. Give answers in exponential form. Assume that all variables represent positive real numbers.

(a) $\sqrt[5]{m^3} \cdot \sqrt{m}$

(b) $\dfrac{\sqrt[3]{p^5}}{\sqrt{p^3}}$

(c) $\sqrt[4]{\sqrt[3]{x}}$

ANSWERS

6. (a) 11^2, or 121   **(b)** $\dfrac{1}{7}$ **(c)** $9x^{4/3}$

(d) $\dfrac{b^{21/10}}{a^{5/2}}$ **(e)** $a^3 + a$

7. (a) $m^{11/10}$ **(b)** $p^{1/6}$ **(c)** $x^{1/12}$

Match each expression from Column I with the equivalent choice from Column II.

I		II	
1. $2^{1/2}$	**2.** $(-27)^{1/3}$	**A.** -4	**B.** 8
3. $-16^{1/2}$	**4.** $(-16)^{1/2}$	**C.** $\sqrt{2}$	**D.** $-\sqrt{6}$
5. $(-32)^{1/5}$	**6.** $(-32)^{2/5}$	**E.** -3	**F.** $\sqrt{6}$
7. $4^{3/2}$	**8.** $6^{2/4}$	**G.** 4	**H.** -2
9. $-6^{2/4}$	**10.** $36^{0.5}$	**I.** 6	**J.** Not a real number

Evaluate each exponential. See Examples 1–3.

11. $169^{1/2}$ **12.** $121^{1/2}$ **13.** $729^{1/3}$ **14.** $512^{1/3}$ **15.** $16^{1/4}$

16. $625^{1/4}$ **17.** $\left(\dfrac{64}{81}\right)^{1/2}$ **18.** $\left(\dfrac{8}{27}\right)^{1/3}$ **19.** $(-27)^{1/3}$ **20.** $(-32)^{1/5}$

21. $(-144)^{1/2}$ **22.** $(-36)^{1/2}$ **23.** $100^{3/2}$ **24.** $64^{3/2}$

25. $81^{3/4}$ **26.** $216^{2/3}$ **27.** $-16^{5/2}$ **28.** $-32^{3/5}$

29. $(-8)^{4/3}$ **30.** $(-243)^{2/5}$ **31.** $32^{-3/5}$ **32.** $27^{-4/3}$

33. $64^{-3/2}$ **34.** $81^{-3/2}$ **35.** $\left(\dfrac{125}{27}\right)^{-2/3}$ **36.** $\left(\dfrac{64}{125}\right)^{-2/3}$

Write with radicals. Assume that all variables represent positive real numbers. Use the definition that takes the root first. See Example 4.

37. $12^{1/2}$

38. $3^{1/2}$

39. $8^{3/4}$

40. $7^{2/3}$

⊛ **41.** $(9q)^{5/8} - (2x)^{2/3}$

42. $(3p)^{3/4} + (4x)^{1/3}$

43. $(2m)^{-3/2}$

44. $(5y)^{-3/5}$

45. $(2y + x)^{2/3}$

46. $(r + 2z)^{3/2}$

47. $(3m^4 + 2k^2)^{-2/3}$

48. $(5x^2 + 3z^3)^{-5/6}$

49. Show that, in general, $\sqrt{a^2 + b^2} \neq a + b$ by replacing a with 3 and b with 4.

50. Suppose someone claims that $\sqrt[n]{a^n + b^n}$ must equal $a + b$, since when $a = 1$ and $b = 0$, a true statement results:

$$\sqrt[n]{a^n + b^n} = \sqrt[n]{1^n + 0^n} = \sqrt[n]{1^n} = 1 = 1 + 0 = a + b.$$

Explain why this is faulty reasoning.

Simplify by first converting to rational exponents. Assume that all variables represent positive real numbers. See Example 4.

51. $\sqrt{2^{12}}$

52. $\sqrt{5^{10}}$

⊛ **53.** $\sqrt[3]{4^9}$

54. $\sqrt[4]{6^8}$

55. $\sqrt{x^{20}}$

56. $\sqrt{r^{50}}$

57. $\sqrt[3]{x} \cdot \sqrt{x}$

58. $\sqrt[4]{y} \cdot \sqrt[5]{y^2}$

59. $\dfrac{\sqrt[3]{t^4}}{\sqrt[5]{t^4}}$

60. $\dfrac{\sqrt[4]{w^3}}{\sqrt[6]{w}}$

Simplify each expression. Write all answers with positive exponents. Assume that all variables represent positive real numbers. See Example 5.

61. $3^{1/2} \cdot 3^{3/2}$
⊛

62. $6^{4/3} \cdot 6^{2/3}$

63. $\dfrac{64^{5/3}}{64^{4/3}}$

64. $\dfrac{125^{7/3}}{125^{5/3}}$

65. $y^{7/3} \cdot y^{-4/3}$

66. $r^{-8/9} \cdot r^{17/9}$

67. $x^{2/3} \cdot x^{-1/4}$

68. $x^{2/5} \cdot x^{-1/3}$

69. $\dfrac{k^{1/3}}{k^{2/3} \cdot k^{-1}}$

70. $\dfrac{z^{3/4}}{z^{5/4} \cdot z^{-2}}$

71. $\dfrac{(x^{1/4}y^{2/5})^{20}}{x^2}$

72. $\dfrac{(r^{1/5}s^{2/3})^{15}}{r^2}$

73. $\dfrac{(x^{2/3})^2}{(x^2)^{7/3}}$

74. $\dfrac{(p^3)^{1/4}}{(p^{5/4})^2}$

75. $\dfrac{m^{3/4}n^{-1/4}}{(m^2n)^{1/2}}$

76. $\dfrac{(a^2b^5)^{-1/4}}{(a^{-3}b^2)^{1/6}}$

77. $\dfrac{p^{1/5}p^{7/10}p^{1/2}}{(p^3)^{-1/5}}$

78. $\dfrac{z^{1/3}z^{-2/3}z^{1/6}}{(z^{-1/6})^3}$

79. $\left(\dfrac{b^{-3/2}}{c^{-5/3}}\right)^2 (b^{-1/4}c^{-1/3})^{-1}$

80. $\left(\dfrac{m^{-2/3}}{a^{-3/4}}\right)^4 (m^{-3/8}a^{1/4})^{-2}$

81. $\left(\dfrac{p^{-1/4}q^{-3/2}}{3^{-1}p^{-2}q^{-2/3}}\right)^{-2}$

82. $\left(\dfrac{2^{-2}w^{-3/4}x^{-5/8}}{w^{3/4}x^{-1/2}}\right)^{-3}$

83. $p^{2/3}(p^{1/3} + 2p^{4/3})$

84. $z^{5/8}(3z^{5/8} + 5z^{11/8})$

85. $k^{1/4}(k^{3/2} - k^{1/2})$

86. $r^{3/5}(r^{1/2} + r^{3/4})$

87. $6a^{7/4}(a^{-7/4} + 3a^{-3/4})$

88. $4m^{5/3}(m^{-2/3} - 4m^{-5/3})$

89. $5m^{-2/3}(m^{2/3} + m^{-7/3})$

Write radicals as exponentials, and then apply the rules for rational exponents. Give answers in exponential form. Assume that all radicands represent positive real numbers. See Example 6.

90. $\sqrt[5]{x^3} \cdot \sqrt[4]{x}$

91. $\sqrt[6]{y^5} \cdot \sqrt[3]{y^2}$

92. $\dfrac{\sqrt{x^5}}{\sqrt{x^8}}$

93. $\dfrac{\sqrt[3]{k^5}}{\sqrt[3]{k^7}}$

94. $\sqrt{y} \cdot \sqrt[3]{yz}$

95. $\sqrt[3]{xz} \cdot \sqrt{z}$

96. $\sqrt[4]{\sqrt[3]{m}}$

97. $\sqrt[3]{\sqrt{k}}$

98. $\sqrt{\sqrt[3]{\sqrt[4]{x}}}$

99. $\sqrt[3]{\sqrt[5]{\sqrt{y}}}$

100. $\sqrt{y^{5/4}}$

101. $\sqrt[3]{x^{5/9}}$

Solve each problem.

102. Meteorologists can determine the duration of a storm by using the function defined by

$$T(D) = 0.07D^{3/2},$$

where D is the diameter of the storm in miles and T is the time in hours. Find the duration of a storm with a diameter of 16 mi. Round your answer to the nearest tenth of an hour.

103. The threshold weight T, in pounds, for a person is the weight above which the risk of death increases greatly. The threshold weight in pounds for men aged 40–49 is related to height in inches by the function defined by

$$h(T) = (1860.867T)^{1/3}.$$

What height corresponds to a threshold weight of 200 lb for a 46-yr-old man? Round your answer to the nearest inch, and then to the nearest tenth of a foot.

*The **windchill factor** is a measure of the cooling effect that the wind has on a person's skin. It calculates the equivalent cooling temperature if there were no wind. The National Weather Service uses the formula*

$$\text{Windchill temperature} = 35.74 + 0.6215T - 35.75V^{4/25} + 0.4275TV^{4/25},$$

where T is the temperature in °F and V is the wind speed in miles per hour, to calculate windchill. The chart gives the windchill factor for various wind speeds and temperatures at which frostbite is a risk, and how quickly it may occur.

		Temperature (°F)								
Calm	40	30	20	10	0	−10	−20	−30	−40
5	36	25	13	1	−11	−22	−34	−46	−57
10	34	21	9	−4	−16	−28	−41	−53	−66
15	32	19	6	−7	−19	−32	−45	−58	−71
20	30	17	4	−9	−22	−35	−48	−61	−74
25	29	16	3	−11	−24	−37	−51	−64	−78
30	28	15	1	−12	−26	−39	−53	−67	−80
35	28	14	0	−14	−27	−41	−55	−69	−82
40	27	13	−1	−15	−29	−43	−57	−71	−84

(Left axis label: **Wind speed (mph)**)

Frostbites times: ☐ 30 minutes ◼ 10 minutes ◼ 5 minutes

Source: National Oceanic and Atmospheric Administration, National Weather Service.

Use the formula to determine the windchill to the nearest tenth of a degree, given the following conditions. Compare your answers with the appropriate entries in the table.

104. 30°F, 15-mph wind

105. 10°F, 30-mph wind

17.4 ▶▶▶ Simplifying Radical Expressions

OBJECTIVE 1 Use the product rule for radicals. Is the product of two *n*th-root radicals equal to the *n*th root of the product of the radicands? For example, are $\sqrt{36 \cdot 4}$ and $\sqrt{36} \cdot \sqrt{4}$ equal?

$$\sqrt{36 \cdot 4} = \sqrt{144} = 12$$

$$\sqrt{36} \cdot \sqrt{4} = 6 \cdot 2 = 12$$

The result is the same.

This is an example of the **product rule for radicals.**

> **Product Rule for Radicals**
>
> If $\sqrt[n]{a}$ and $\sqrt[n]{b}$ are real numbers and *n* is a natural number, then
>
> $$\sqrt[n]{a} \cdot \sqrt[n]{b} = \sqrt[n]{ab}.$$
>
> In words, the product of two *n*th roots is the *n*th root of the product.

We justify the product rule using the rules for rational exponents. Since $\sqrt[n]{a} = a^{1/n}$ and $\sqrt[n]{b} = b^{1/n}$,

$$\sqrt[n]{a} \cdot \sqrt[n]{b} = a^{1/n} \cdot b^{1/n} = (ab)^{1/n} = \sqrt[n]{ab}.$$

> **CAUTION**
> *Use the product rule only when the radicals have the same index.*

Example 1 Using the Product Rule

Multiply. Assume that all variables represent positive real numbers.

(a) $\sqrt{5} \cdot \sqrt{7}$

$= \sqrt{5 \cdot 7}$

$= \sqrt{35}$

(b) $\sqrt{2} \cdot \sqrt{19}$

$= \sqrt{2 \cdot 19}$

$= \sqrt{38}$

(c) $\sqrt{11} \cdot \sqrt{p}$

$= \sqrt{11p}$

(d) $\sqrt{7} \cdot \sqrt{11xyz}$

$= \sqrt{77xyz}$

Work Problem 1 at the Side. ▶

Example 2 Using the Product Rule

Multiply. Assume that all variables represent positive real numbers.

(a) $\sqrt[3]{3} \cdot \sqrt[3]{12}$

$= \sqrt[3]{3 \cdot 12}$

$= \sqrt[3]{36}$

(b) $\sqrt[4]{8y} \cdot \sqrt[4]{3r^2}$

$= \sqrt[4]{24yr^2}$

(c) $\sqrt[6]{10m^4} \cdot \sqrt[6]{5m}$

$= \sqrt[6]{50m^5}$

(d) $\sqrt[4]{2} \cdot \sqrt[5]{2}$ cannot be simplified using the product rule for radicals, because the indexes (4 and 5) are different.

Work Problem 2 at the Side. ▶

OBJECTIVES

1. Use the product rule for radicals.
2. Use the quotient rule for radicals.
3. Simplify radicals.
4. Simplify products and quotients of radicals with different indexes.
5. Use the Pythagorean formula.
6. Use the distance formula.

1 Multiply. Assume that all variables represent positive real numbers.

(a) $\sqrt{5} \cdot \sqrt{13}$

(b) $\sqrt{10y} \cdot \sqrt{3k}$

2 Multiply. Assume that all variables represent positive real numbers.

(a) $\sqrt[3]{2} \cdot \sqrt[3]{7}$

(b) $\sqrt[6]{8r^2} \cdot \sqrt[6]{2r^3}$

(c) $\sqrt[5]{9y^2x} \cdot \sqrt[5]{8xy^2}$

(d) $\sqrt{7} \cdot \sqrt[3]{5}$

ANSWERS

1. **(a)** $\sqrt{65}$ **(b)** $\sqrt{30yk}$
2. **(a)** $\sqrt[3]{14}$ **(b)** $\sqrt[6]{16r^5}$ **(c)** $\sqrt[5]{72y^4x^2}$
   (d) cannot be simplified using the product rule

3 Simplify. Assume that all variables represent positive real numbers.

(a) $\sqrt{\dfrac{100}{81}}$

(b) $\sqrt{\dfrac{11}{25}}$

(c) $\sqrt[3]{-\dfrac{125}{216}}$

(d) $\sqrt{\dfrac{y^8}{16}}$

(e) $-\sqrt[3]{\dfrac{x^2}{r^{12}}}$

OBJECTIVE 2 Use the quotient rule for radicals.   The **quotient rule for radicals** is similar to the product rule.

> **Quotient Rule for Radicals**
>
> If $\sqrt[n]{a}$ and $\sqrt[n]{b}$ are real numbers, $b \neq 0$, and n is a natural number, then
>
> $$\sqrt[n]{\dfrac{a}{b}} = \dfrac{\sqrt[n]{a}}{\sqrt[n]{b}}.$$
>
> In words, the nth root of a quotient is the quotient of the nth roots.

Example 3   Using the Quotient Rule

Simplify. Assume that all variables represent positive real numbers.

(a) $\sqrt{\dfrac{16}{25}} = \dfrac{\sqrt{16}}{\sqrt{25}} = \dfrac{4}{5}$

(b) $\sqrt{\dfrac{7}{36}} = \dfrac{\sqrt{7}}{\sqrt{36}} = \dfrac{\sqrt{7}}{6}$

(c) $\sqrt[3]{-\dfrac{8}{125}} = \sqrt[3]{\dfrac{-8}{125}} = \dfrac{\sqrt[3]{-8}}{\sqrt[3]{125}} = \dfrac{-2}{5} = -\dfrac{2}{5}$ $\quad \dfrac{-a}{b} = -\dfrac{a}{b}$

(d) $\sqrt[3]{\dfrac{7}{216}} = \dfrac{\sqrt[3]{7}}{\sqrt[3]{216}} = \dfrac{\sqrt[3]{7}}{6}$

(e) $\sqrt[5]{\dfrac{x}{32}} = \dfrac{\sqrt[5]{x}}{\sqrt[5]{32}} = \dfrac{\sqrt[5]{x}}{2}$

Think: $\sqrt[3]{m^6} = m^{6/3} = m^2$

(f) $-\sqrt[3]{\dfrac{m^6}{125}} = -\dfrac{\sqrt[3]{m^6}}{\sqrt[3]{125}} = -\dfrac{m^2}{5}$

◀ *Work Problem* **3** *at the Side.*

OBJECTIVE 3 Simplify radicals.   We use the product and quotient rules to simplify radicals. A radical is **simplified** if the following four conditions are met.

> **Conditions for a Simplified Radical**
>
> 1. The radicand has no factor raised to a power greater than or equal to the index.
> 2. The radicand has no fractions.
> 3. No denominator has a radical.
> 4. Exponents in the radicand and the index of the radical have greatest common factor 1.

ANSWERS

3. **(a)** $\dfrac{10}{9}$ **(b)** $\dfrac{\sqrt{11}}{5}$ **(c)** $-\dfrac{5}{6}$

  (d) $\dfrac{y^4}{4}$ **(e)** $-\dfrac{\sqrt[3]{x^2}}{r^4}$

Example 4   **Simplifying Roots of Numbers**

Simplify.

(a) $\sqrt{24}$

Check to see whether 24 is divisible by a perfect square (the square of a natural number) such as 4, 9, 16, ... The largest perfect square that divides into 24 is 4.

$$\sqrt{24}$$
$$= \sqrt{4 \cdot 6} \qquad \text{Factor; 4 is a perfect square.}$$
$$= \sqrt{4} \cdot \sqrt{6} \qquad \text{Product rule}$$
$$= 2\sqrt{6} \qquad \sqrt{4} = 2$$

(b) $\sqrt{108}$

As shown on the left, the number 108 is divisible by the perfect square 36. If this perfect square is not immediately clear, try factoring 108 into its prime factors, as shown on the right.

$\sqrt{108}$	$\sqrt{108}$	
$= \sqrt{36 \cdot 3}$	$= \sqrt{2^2 \cdot 3^3}$	
$= \sqrt{36} \cdot \sqrt{3}$	$= \sqrt{2^2 \cdot 3^2 \cdot 3}$	
$= 6\sqrt{3}$	$= \sqrt{2^2} \cdot \sqrt{3^2} \cdot \sqrt{3}$	Product rule
	$= 2 \cdot 3 \cdot \sqrt{3}$	$\sqrt{2^2} = 2, \sqrt{3^2} = 3$
	$= 6\sqrt{3}$	Multiply.

(c) $\sqrt{10}$ No perfect square (other than 1) divides into 10, so $\sqrt{10}$ cannot be simplified further.

(d) $\sqrt[3]{16}$

The largest perfect *cube* that divides into 16 is 8, so factor 16 as $8 \cdot 2$.

$$\sqrt[3]{16} \qquad \boxed{\text{Remember to write the index.}}$$
$$= \sqrt[3]{8 \cdot 2} \qquad \text{8 is a perfect cube.}$$
$$= \sqrt[3]{8} \cdot \sqrt[3]{2} \qquad \text{Product rule}$$
$$= 2\sqrt[3]{2} \qquad \sqrt[3]{8} = 2$$

(e) $\qquad -\sqrt[4]{162}$

$$= -\sqrt[4]{81 \cdot 2} \qquad \text{81 is a perfect 4th power.}$$

$\boxed{\text{Remember the negative sign in each line.}}$
$$= -\sqrt[4]{81} \cdot \sqrt[4]{2} \qquad \text{Product rule}$$
$$= -3\sqrt[4]{2} \qquad \sqrt[4]{81} = 3$$

Work Problem **4** *at the Side.* ▶

CAUTION
Be careful with which factors belong outside the radical sign and which belong inside. Note in Example 4(b) how $2 \cdot 3$ is written outside because $\sqrt{2^2} = 2$ and $\sqrt{3^2} = 3$. The remaining 3 is left inside the radical.

---

4 Simplify.

(a) $\sqrt{32}$

(b) $\sqrt{45}$

(c) $\sqrt{300}$

(d) $\sqrt{35}$

(e) $-\sqrt[3]{54}$

(f) $\sqrt[4]{243}$

Answers

4. **(a)** $4\sqrt{2}$ **(b)** $3\sqrt{5}$ **(c)** $10\sqrt{3}$
   (d) cannot be simplified further
   (e) $-3\sqrt[3]{2}$ **(f)** $3\sqrt[4]{3}$

5 Simplify. Assume that all variables represent positive real numbers.

(a) $\sqrt{25p^7}$

(b) $\sqrt{72y^3x}$

(c) $\sqrt[3]{-27y^7x^5z^6}$

(d) $-\sqrt[4]{32a^5b^7}$

Example 5 Simplifying Radicals Involving Variables

Simplify. Assume that all variables represent positive real numbers.

(a) $\sqrt{16m^3}$

$\quad = \sqrt{16m^2 \cdot m}$ Factor.

$\quad = \sqrt{16m^2} \cdot \sqrt{m}$ Product rule

$\quad = 4m\sqrt{m}$

Absolute value bars are not needed around the m in color because of the assumption that all the variables represent *positive* real numbers.

(b) $\sqrt{200k^7q^8}$

$\quad = \sqrt{10^2 \cdot 2 \cdot (k^3)^2 \cdot k \cdot (q^4)^2}$ Factor.

$\quad = 10k^3q^4\sqrt{2k}$ Remove perfect square factors.

(c) $\sqrt[3]{-8x^4y^5}$

$\quad = \sqrt[3]{(-8x^3y^3)\,(xy^2)}$ Choose $-8x^3y^3$ as the perfect cube that divides into $-8x^4y^5$.

$\quad = \sqrt[3]{-8x^3y^3} \cdot \sqrt[3]{xy^2}$ Product rule

$\quad = -2xy\sqrt[3]{xy^2}$

(d) $-\sqrt[4]{32y^9}$

$\quad = -\sqrt[4]{(16y^8)(2y)}$ $16y^8$ is the largest 4th power that divides into $32y^9$.

$\quad = -\sqrt[4]{16y^8} \cdot \sqrt[4]{2y}$ Product rule

$\quad = -2y^2\sqrt[4]{2y}$

◀ Work Problem **5** at the Side.

Note

From Example 5 we see that if a variable is raised to a power with an exponent divisible by 2, it is a perfect square. If it is raised to a power with an exponent divisible by 3, it is a perfect cube. ***In general, if it is raised to a power with an exponent divisible by n, it is a perfect nth power.***

The conditions for a simplified radical given earlier state that an exponent in the radicand and the index of the radical should have greatest common factor 1. The next example applies this condition.

Example 6 Simplifying Radicals by Using Lesser Indexes

Simplify. Assume that all variables represent positive real numbers.

(a) $\sqrt[9]{5^6}$

We can write this radical using rational exponents and then write the exponent in lowest terms. We then express the answer as a radical.

$$\sqrt[9]{5^6} = 5^{6/9} = 5^{2/3} = \sqrt[3]{5^2}, \quad \text{or} \quad \sqrt[3]{25}$$

(b) $\sqrt[4]{p^2} = p^{2/4} = p^{1/2} = \sqrt{p}$ (Recall the assumption that $p > 0$.)

These examples suggest the following rule.

> If m is an integer, n and k are natural numbers, and all indicated roots exist, then
> $$\sqrt[kn]{a^{km}} = \sqrt[n]{a^{m}}.$$

Work Problem **6** *at the Side.* ▶

OBJECTIVE **4** **Simplify products and quotients of radicals with different indexes.** Since the product and quotient rules for radicals apply only when they have the same index, we multiply and divide radicals with different indexes by using rational exponents.

Example 7 **Multiplying Radicals with Different Indexes**

Simplify $\sqrt{7} \cdot \sqrt[3]{2}$.

Because the different indexes, 2 and 3, have a least common index of 6, we use rational exponents to write each radical as a sixth root.

$$\sqrt{7} = 7^{1/2} = 7^{3/6} = \sqrt[6]{7^3} = \sqrt[6]{343}$$

$$\sqrt[3]{2} = 2^{1/3} = 2^{2/6} = \sqrt[6]{2^2} = \sqrt[6]{4}$$

Therefore,

$$\sqrt{7} \cdot \sqrt[3]{2}$$

$$= \sqrt[6]{343} \cdot \sqrt[6]{4} \quad \text{Substitute; } \sqrt{7} = \sqrt[6]{343}, \sqrt[3]{2} = \sqrt[6]{4}$$

$$= \sqrt[6]{1372}. \quad \text{Product rule}$$

Work Problem **7** *at the Side.* ▶

OBJECTIVE **5** **Use the Pythagorean formula.** The **Pythagorean formula** relates the lengths of the three sides of a right triangle.

> **Pythagorean Formula**
>
> If a and b are the lengths of the shorter sides of a right triangle and c is the length of the longest side, then
>
> $$a^2 + b^2 = c^2.$$
>
>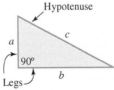
>
> The two shorter sides are the **legs** of the triangle, and the longest side is the **hypotenuse.** The hypotenuse is the side opposite the right angle. Thus,
>
> $$\text{leg}^2 + \text{leg}^2 = \text{hypotenuse}^2.$$

In **Section 10.1,** we will see that an equation such as $x^2 = 7$ has two solutions: $\sqrt{7}$ (the principal, or positive, square root of 7) and $-\sqrt{7}$. Similarly, $c^2 = 52$ has two solutions, $\pm\sqrt{52}$, or $\pm 2\sqrt{13}$. In applications we often choose only the positive square root.

---

6 Simplify. Assume that all variables represent positive real numbers.

(a) $\sqrt[12]{2^3}$

(b) $\sqrt[6]{t^2}$

7 Simplify $\sqrt{5} \cdot \sqrt[3]{4}$.

1272 Chapter 17 Roots & Radicals

 8 Find the length of the unknown side in each triangle.

(a)

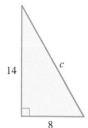

14

c

8

(b)

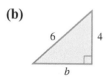

6   4

b

(Hint: Write the Pythagorean formula as $b^2 = c^2 - a^2$ here.)

Example 8   Using the Pythagorean Formula

Use the Pythagorean formula to find the length of the hypotenuse in the triangle in Figure 6.

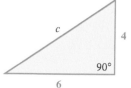

c

4

90°

6

Figure 6

To find the length of the hypotenuse c, let $a = 4$ and $b = 6$. Then, use the formula.

$$a^2 + b^2 = c^2$$

| Substitute carefully. | $4^2 + 6^2 = c^2$ | Let $a = 4$ and $b = 6$. |

$$16 + 36 = c^2 \qquad \text{Apply the exponents.}$$

$$c^2 = 52 \qquad \text{Add; interchange sides.}$$

$$c = \sqrt{52} \qquad \text{Choose the principal root.}$$

$$c = \sqrt{4 \cdot 13} \qquad \text{Factor.}$$

$$c = \sqrt{4} \cdot \sqrt{13} \qquad \text{Product rule}$$

$$c = 2\sqrt{13} \qquad \text{Simplify.}$$

The length of the hypotenuse is $2\sqrt{13}$.

◀ *Work Problem* **8** *at the Side.*

CAUTION
When substituting in the Pythagorean formula $a^2 + b^2 = c^2$, be sure that the lengths of the legs are substituted for a and b and the length of the hypotenuse is substituted for c.

OBJECTIVE 6 Use the distance formula. The *distance formula* allows us to find the distance between two points in the coordinate plane, or the length of the line segment joining those two points.

Figure 7 shows the points $(3, -4)$ and $(-5, 3)$. The vertical line through $(-5, 3)$ and the horizontal line through $(3, -4)$ intersect at the point $(-5, -4)$. Thus, the point $(-5, -4)$ becomes the vertex of the right angle in a right triangle. By the Pythagorean formula, the sum of the squares of the lengths of the two legs a and b of the right triangle in Figure 7 is equal to the square of the length of the hypotenuse, d:

$$a^2 + b^2 = d^2, \qquad \text{or} \qquad d^2 = a^2 + b^2.$$

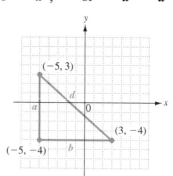

y

(−5, 3)

d

a

0   x

(3, −4)

(−5, −4)   b

Figure 7

The length a is the difference between the y-coordinates of the endpoints. Since the x-coordinate of both of these points in Figure 7 is -5, the side is vertical, and we can find a by finding the difference between the y-coordinates. We subtract -4 from 3 to get a positive value for a.

$$a = 3 - (-4) = 7$$

8. (a) $2\sqrt{65}$ **(b)** $2\sqrt{5}$

Similarly, we find b by subtracting -5 from 3.

$$b = 3 - (-5) = 8$$

Substituting these values into the formula, we have

$$d^2 = a^2 + b^2$$

$$d^2 = 7^2 + 8^2 \qquad \text{Let } a = 7 \text{ and } b = 8.$$

$$d^2 = 49 + 64 \qquad \text{Apply the exponents.}$$

$$d^2 = 113 \qquad \text{Add.}$$

$$d = \sqrt{113}. \qquad \text{Choose the principal root.}$$

We choose the principal root since distance cannot be negative. Therefore, the distance between $(-5, 3)$ and $(3, -4)$ is $\sqrt{113}$.

> **Note**
>
> It is customary to leave the distance in radical form. Do not use a calculator to get an approximation, unless you are specifically directed to do so.

This result can be generalized. Figure 8 shows the two points (x_1, y_1) and (x_2, y_2). The distance a between (x_1, y_1) and (x_2, y_1) is

$$a = x_2 - x_1,$$

and the distance b between (x_2, y_2) and (x_2, y_1) is

$$b = y_2 - y_1.$$

From the Pythagorean formula,

$$d^2 = a^2 + b^2$$

$$d^2 = (x_2 - x_1)^2 + (y_2 - y_1)^2.$$

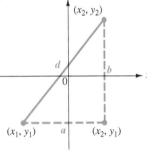

Figure 8

Choosing the principal square root gives the **distance formula.**

> **Distance Formula**
>
> The distance between the points (x_1, y_1) and (x_2, y_2) is
>
> $$d = \sqrt{(x_2 - x_1)^2 + (y_2 - y_1)^2}.$$

Example 9   **Using the Distance Formula**

Find the distance between $(-3, 5)$ and $(6, 4)$.

When using the distance formula to find the distance between two points, designating the points as (x_1, y_1) and (x_2, y_2) is arbitrary. We choose $(x_1, y_1) = (-3, 5)$ and $(x_2, y_2) = (6, 4)$.

$$d = \sqrt{(x_2 - x_1)^2 + (y_2 - y_1)^2} \qquad \text{Distance formula}$$

$$d = \sqrt{(6 - (-3))^2 + (4 - 5)^2} \qquad x_2 = 6, y_2 = 4, x_1 = -3, y_1 = 5$$

$$d = \sqrt{9^2 + (-1)^2} \qquad \text{Substitute carefully.}$$

$$d = \sqrt{82} \qquad \text{Leave in radical form.}$$

Work Problem **9** *at the Side.* ▶

9 Find the distance between each pair of points.

(a) $(2, -1)$ and $(5, 3)$

(b) $(-3, 2)$ and $(0, -4)$

ANSWERS

9. (a) 5   **(b)** $\sqrt{45}$, or $3\sqrt{5}$

Math in the Media

Probably the most famous mathematical statement in the history of motion pictures is heard in the 1939 classic *The Wizard of Oz*. Ray Bolger's character, the Scarecrow, wants a brain. When the Wizard grants him his "Th.D." (Doctor of Thinkology), the Scarecrow replies with a statement that has made mathematics teachers shudder for 70 years.

Scarecrow: *The sum of the square roots of any two sides of an isosceles triangle is equal to the square root of the remaining side.*

His statement is quite impressive and sounds like the formula for the *Pythagorean Theorem* (page 531). Let's see why it is incorrect.

1. To what kind of triangle does the Scarecrow refer in his statement? To what kind of triangle does the Pythagorean Theorem actually refer?

2. In the Scarecrow's statement, he refers to square roots. In applying the formula for the Pythagorean Theorem, do you find square roots of the sides? If not, what do you find?

3. An isosceles triangle has two sides of equal length. Draw an isosceles triangle with two sides of length 9 units and remaining side of length 4 units. Now show that this triangle does not satisfy the Scarecrow's statement.

   (This is called a *counterexample* and is sufficient to show that his statement is false in general.)

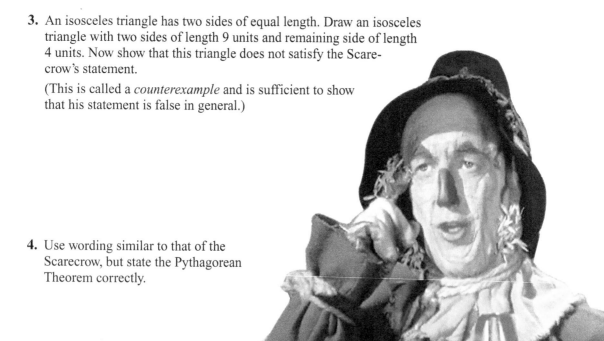

4. Use wording similar to that of the Scarecrow, but state the Pythagorean Theorem correctly.

17.4 ▶▶▶ **Exercises**

FOR
EXTRA
HELP

 MyMathLab   *Math XL*
PRACTICE   WATCH   DOWNLOAD READ   REVIEW

Decide whether each statement is true *or* false *by using the product rule explained in this section. Then support your answer by finding a calculator approximation for each expression.*

1. $2\sqrt{12} = \sqrt{48}$

2. $\sqrt{72} = 2\sqrt{18}$

3. $3\sqrt{8} = 2\sqrt{18}$

4. $5\sqrt{72} = 6\sqrt{50}$

5. Explain why $\sqrt[3]{x} \cdot \sqrt[3]{x}$ is not equal to x. What is it equal to?

6. Explain why $\sqrt[4]{x} \cdot \sqrt[4]{x}$ is not equal to x, but *is* equal to $\sqrt{x}$, for $x \geq 0$.

7. Which one of the following is *not* equal to $\sqrt{\frac{1}{2}}$? (Do not use calculator approximations.)

   A. $\sqrt{0.5}$ **B.** $\sqrt{\frac{2}{4}}$ **C.** $\sqrt{\frac{3}{6}}$ **D.** $\frac{\sqrt{4}}{\sqrt{16}}$

8. Use the π key on your calculator to get a value for π. Now find an approximation for $\sqrt[4]{\dfrac{2143}{22}}$. Does the result mean that π is actually equal to $\sqrt[4]{\dfrac{2143}{22}}$? Why or why not?

Multiply using the product rule. Assume all variables represent positive real numbers. See Examples 1 and 2.

9. $\sqrt{5} \cdot \sqrt{6}$

10. $\sqrt{10} \cdot \sqrt{3}$

11. $\sqrt{14} \cdot \sqrt{x}$

12. $\sqrt{23} \cdot \sqrt{t}$

13. $\sqrt{14} \cdot \sqrt{3pqr}$

14. $\sqrt{7} \cdot \sqrt{5xt}$

15. $\sqrt[3]{7x} \cdot \sqrt[3]{2y}$

16. $\sqrt[3]{9x} \cdot \sqrt[3]{4y}$

17. $\sqrt[4]{11} \cdot \sqrt[4]{3}$

18. $\sqrt[4]{6} \cdot \sqrt[4]{9}$

19. $\sqrt[4]{2x} \cdot \sqrt[4]{3y^2}$

20. $\sqrt[4]{3y^2} \cdot \sqrt[4]{6yz}$

21. $\sqrt[3]{7} \cdot \sqrt[4]{3}$

22. $\sqrt[5]{8} \cdot \sqrt[6]{12}$

Simplify. Assume that all variables represent positive real numbers. See Example 3.

23. $\sqrt{\dfrac{64}{121}}$

24. $\sqrt{\dfrac{16}{49}}$

25. $\sqrt{\dfrac{3}{25}}$

26. $\sqrt{\dfrac{13}{49}}$

27. $\sqrt{\dfrac{x}{25}}$

28. $\sqrt{\dfrac{k}{100}}$

29. $\sqrt{\dfrac{p^6}{81}}$

30. $\sqrt{\dfrac{w^{10}}{36}}$

31. $\sqrt[3]{-\dfrac{27}{64}}$

32. $\sqrt[3]{-\dfrac{216}{125}}$

33. $\sqrt[3]{\dfrac{r^2}{8}}$

34. $\sqrt[3]{\dfrac{t}{125}}$

35. $-\sqrt[4]{\dfrac{81}{x^4}}$

36. $-\sqrt[4]{\dfrac{625}{y^4}}$

37. $\sqrt[5]{\dfrac{1}{x^{15}}}$

38. $\sqrt[5]{\dfrac{32}{y^{20}}}$

Express each radical in simplified form. See Example 4.

39. $\sqrt{12}$

40. $\sqrt{18}$

41. $\sqrt{288}$

42. $\sqrt{72}$

43. $-\sqrt{32}$

44. $-\sqrt{48}$

45. $-\sqrt{28}$

46. $-\sqrt{24}$

47. $\sqrt{30}$

48. $\sqrt{46}$

49. $\sqrt[3]{128}$

50. $\sqrt[3]{24}$

51. $\sqrt[3]{-16}$

52. $\sqrt[3]{-250}$

53. $\sqrt[3]{40}$

54. $\sqrt[3]{375}$

55. $-\sqrt[4]{512}$

56. $-\sqrt[4]{1250}$

57. $\sqrt[5]{64}$

58. $\sqrt[5]{128}$

59. A student claimed that $\sqrt[3]{14}$ is not in simplified form, since $14 = 8 + 6$, and 8 is a perfect cube. Was his reasoning correct? Why or why not?

60. Explain in your own words why $\sqrt[3]{k^4}$ is not a simplified radical.

Express each radical in simplified form. Assume that all variables represent positive real numbers. See Example 5.

61. $\sqrt{72k^2}$

62. $\sqrt{18m^2}$

63. $\sqrt{144x^3y^9}$

64. $\sqrt{169s^5t^{10}}$

65. $\sqrt{121x^6}$

66. $\sqrt{256z^{12}}$

67. $-\sqrt[3]{27t^{12}}$

68. $-\sqrt[3]{64y^{18}}$

69. $-\sqrt{100m^8z^4}$

70. $-\sqrt{25t^6s^{20}}$

71. $-\sqrt[3]{-125a^6b^9c^{12}}$

72. $-\sqrt[3]{-216y^{15}x^6z^3}$

73. $\sqrt[4]{\dfrac{1}{16}r^8t^{20}}$

74. $\sqrt[4]{\dfrac{81}{256}t^{12}u^8}$

⊙ **75.** $\sqrt{50x^3}$

76. $\sqrt{300z^3}$

77. $-\sqrt{500r^{11}}$

78. $-\sqrt{200p^{13}}$

79. $\sqrt{13x^7y^8}$

80. $\sqrt{23k^9p^{14}}$

81. $\sqrt[3]{8z^6w^9}$ **82.** $\sqrt[3]{64a^{15}b^{12}}$ **83.** $\sqrt[3]{-16z^5t^7}$ **84.** $\sqrt[3]{-81m^4n^{10}}$

85. $\sqrt[4]{81x^{12}y^{16}}$ **86.** $\sqrt[4]{81t^8u^{28}}$ **87.** $-\sqrt[4]{162r^{15}s^{10}}$ **88.** $-\sqrt[4]{32k^5m^{10}}$

89. $\sqrt{\dfrac{y^{11}}{36}}$ **90.** $\sqrt{\dfrac{v^{13}}{49}}$ **91.** $\sqrt[3]{\dfrac{x^{16}}{27}}$ **92.** $\sqrt[3]{\dfrac{y^{17}}{125}}$

Simplify. Assume that $x \geq 0$. See Example 6.

93. $\sqrt[4]{48^2}$ **94.** $\sqrt[4]{50^2}$ **95.** $\sqrt[4]{25}$

96. $\sqrt[6]{8}$ **97.** $\sqrt[10]{x^{25}}$ **98.** $\sqrt[12]{x^{44}}$

Simplify by first writing the radicals as radicals with the same index. Then multiply. Assume that $x \geq 0$. See Example 7.

99. $\sqrt[3]{4} \cdot \sqrt{3}$ **100.** $\sqrt[3]{5} \cdot \sqrt{6}$ **101.** $\sqrt[4]{3} \cdot \sqrt[3]{4}$

102. $\sqrt[3]{2} \cdot \sqrt[5]{3}$ **103.** $\sqrt{x} \cdot \sqrt[3]{x}$ **104.** $\sqrt[3]{x} \cdot \sqrt[4]{x}$

Find the unknown length in each right triangle. Simplify the answer if necessary.
See Example 8.

105.

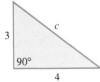

106.

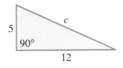

107.

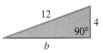

108.

109.

110.

Find the distance between each pair of points. See Example 9.

111. $(6, 13)$ and $(1, 1)$

112. $(8, 13)$ and $(2, 5)$

113. $(-6, 5)$ and $(3, -4)$

114. $(-1, 5)$ and $(-7, 7)$

115. $(-8, 2)$ and $(-4, 1)$

116. $(-1, 2)$ and $(5, 3)$

117. $(4.7, 2.3)$ and $(1.7, -1.7)$

118. $(-2.9, 18.2)$ and $(2.1, 6.2)$

119. $\left(\sqrt{2}, \sqrt{6}\right)$ and $\left(-2\sqrt{2}, 4\sqrt{6}\right)$

120. $\left(\sqrt{7}, 9\sqrt{3}\right)$ and $\left(-\sqrt{7}, 4\sqrt{3}\right)$

121. $(x + y, y)$ and $(x - y, x)$

122. $(c, c - d)$ and $(d, c + d)$

Solve each problem.

123. A Sanyo color television, model AVM-2755, has a rectangular screen with a 21.7-in. width. Its height is 16 in. What is the diagonal of the screen to the nearest tenth of an inch? (*Source:* Actual measurements of the author's television.)

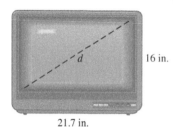

16 in.

21.7 in.

124. The length of the diagonal of a box is given by

$$D = \sqrt{L^2 + W^2 + H^2},$$

where L, W, and H are the length, width, and height of the box. Find the length of the diagonal, D, of a box that is 4 ft long, 3 ft high, and 2 ft wide. Give the exact value, and then round to the nearest tenth of a foot.

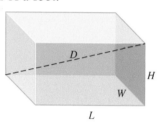

125. A formula from electronics dealing with impedance of parallel resonant circuits is

$$I = \frac{E}{\sqrt{R^2 + \omega^2 L^2}},$$

where the variables are in appropriate units. Find I if $E = 282$, $R = 100$, $L = 264$, and $\omega = 120\pi$. Give your answer to the nearest thousandth.

126. In the study of sound, one version of the law of tensions is

$$f_1 = f_2 \sqrt{\frac{F_1}{F_2}}.$$

If $F_1 = 300$, $F_2 = 60$, and $f_2 = 260$, find f_1 to the nearest unit.

127. The following letter appeared in the column "Ask Tom Why," written by Tom Skilling of the *Chicago Tribune.*

Dear Tom,
  I cannot remember the formula to calculate the distance to the horizon. I have a stunning view from my 14th floor condo, 150 feet above the ground. How far can I see?
      Ted Fleischaker; Indianapolis, Ind.

Skilling's answer was as follows.

  To find the distance to the horizon in miles, take the square root of the height of your view in feet and multiply that result by 1.224. Your answer will be the number of miles to the horizon. (*Source: Chicago Tribune*, August 17, 2002.)

Assuming Ted's eyes are 6 ft above the ground, the total height from the ground is $150 + 6 = 156$ ft. To the nearest tenth of a mile, how far can he see to the horizon?

17.5 ▶▶▶ Adding and Subtracting Radical Expressions

OBJECTIVE 1 Simplify radical expressions involving addition and subtraction. Expressions such as $4\sqrt{2} + 3\sqrt{2}$ and $2\sqrt{3} - 5\sqrt{3}$ can be simplified by using the distributive property.

$$4\sqrt{2} + 3\sqrt{2}$$
$$= (4 + 3)\sqrt{2} = 7\sqrt{2}$$
This is similar to simplifying $4x + 3x$ as $7x$.

$$2\sqrt{3} - 5\sqrt{3}$$
$$= (2 - 5)\sqrt{3} = -3\sqrt{3}$$
This is similar to simplifying $2x - 5x$ as $-3x$.

> **CAUTION**
> *Only radical expressions with the same index and the same radicand may be combined.* Expressions such as $5\sqrt{3} + 2\sqrt{2}$ or $3\sqrt{3} + 2\sqrt[3]{3}$ cannot be simplified by combining terms.

Example 1 Adding and Subtracting Radicals

Add or subtract to simplify each radical expression.

(a) $3\sqrt{24} + \sqrt{54}$

  Simplify each radical; then use the distributive property to combine terms.

$$3\sqrt{24} + \sqrt{54}$$
$$= 3\sqrt{4}\cdot\sqrt{6} + \sqrt{9}\cdot\sqrt{6} \qquad \text{Product rule}$$
$$= 3\cdot2\sqrt{6} + 3\sqrt{6}$$
$$= 6\sqrt{6} + 3\sqrt{6}$$
$$= 9\sqrt{6} \qquad\qquad \text{Combine like terms.}$$

(b) $2\sqrt{20x} - \sqrt{45x}, \quad x \geq 0$

$$= 2\sqrt{4}\cdot\sqrt{5x} - \sqrt{9}\cdot\sqrt{5x} \qquad \text{Product rule}$$
$$= 2\cdot2\sqrt{5x} - 3\sqrt{5x}$$
$$= 4\sqrt{5x} - 3\sqrt{5x}$$
$$= \sqrt{5x} \qquad\qquad \text{Combine like terms.}$$

(c) $2\sqrt{3} - 4\sqrt{5}$

  Here the radicals differ and are already simplified, so $2\sqrt{3} - 4\sqrt{5}$ cannot be simplified further.

Work Problem **1** *at the Side.* ▶

> **CAUTION**
> Do not confuse the product rule with combining like terms. *The root of a sum does not equal the sum of the roots.* For example,
> $$\sqrt{9 + 16} \neq \sqrt{9} + \sqrt{16},$$
> since $\sqrt{9 + 16} = \sqrt{25} = 5$, but $\sqrt{9} + \sqrt{16} = 3 + 4 = 7$.

OBJECTIVE

1 Simplify radical expressions involving addition and subtraction.

1 Add or subtract to simplify each radical expression.

(a) $3\sqrt{5} + 7\sqrt{5}$

(b) $2\sqrt{11} - \sqrt{11} + 3\sqrt{44}$

(c) $5\sqrt{12y} + 6\sqrt{75y}, \ y \geq 0$

(d) $3\sqrt{8} - 6\sqrt{50} + 2\sqrt{200}$

(e) $9\sqrt{5} - 4\sqrt{10}$

ANSWERS

1. (a) $10\sqrt{5}$ (b) $7\sqrt{11}$
   (c) $40\sqrt{3y}$ (d) $-4\sqrt{2}$
   (e) cannot be simplified further

2 Simplify. Assume that all variables represent positive real numbers.

(a) $7\sqrt[3]{81} + 3\sqrt[3]{24}$

(b) $-2\sqrt[4]{32} - 7\sqrt[4]{162}$

(c) $\sqrt[3]{p^4q^7} - \sqrt[3]{64pq}$

3 Simplify. Assume that all variables represent positive real numbers.

(a) $2\sqrt{\dfrac{8}{9}} - 2\dfrac{\sqrt{27}}{\sqrt{108}}$

(b) $\sqrt{\dfrac{80}{y^4}} + \sqrt{\dfrac{81}{y^{10}}}$

Example 2 **Adding and Subtracting Radicals**

Simplify. Assume that all variables represent positive real numbers.

(a) $2\sqrt[3]{16} - 5\sqrt[3]{54}$ Remember to write the index with each radical.

$$= 2\sqrt[3]{8 \cdot 2} - 5\sqrt[3]{27 \cdot 2} \qquad \text{Factor.}$$
$$= 2\sqrt[3]{8} \cdot \sqrt[3]{2} - 5\sqrt[3]{27} \cdot \sqrt[3]{2} \qquad \text{Product rule}$$
$$= 2 \cdot 2 \cdot \sqrt[3]{2} - 5 \cdot 3 \cdot \sqrt[3]{2}$$
$$= 4\sqrt[3]{2} - 15\sqrt[3]{2}$$
$$= (4 - 15)\sqrt[3]{2} \qquad \text{Distributive property}$$
$$= -11\sqrt[3]{2} \qquad \text{Combine like terms.}$$

(b)
$$2\sqrt[3]{x^2y} + \sqrt[3]{8x^5y^4}$$
$$= 2\sqrt[3]{x^2y} + \sqrt[3]{(8x^3y^3)x^2y} \qquad \text{Factor.}$$
$$= 2\sqrt[3]{x^2y} + \sqrt[3]{8x^3y^3} \cdot \sqrt[3]{x^2y} \qquad \text{Product rule}$$
$$= 2\sqrt[3]{x^2y} + 2xy\sqrt[3]{x^2y}$$

This result cannot be simplified further.

$$= (2 + 2xy)\sqrt[3]{x^2y} \qquad \text{Distributive property}$$

◀ *Work Problem* **2** *at the Side.*

Example 3 **Adding and Subtracting Radicals with Fractions**

Simplify. Assume that all variables represent positive real numbers.

(a) $2\sqrt{\dfrac{75}{16}} + 4\dfrac{\sqrt{8}}{\sqrt{32}}$

$$= 2\dfrac{\sqrt{25 \cdot 3}}{\sqrt{16}} + 4\dfrac{\sqrt{4 \cdot 2}}{\sqrt{16 \cdot 2}} \qquad \text{Quotient rule; factor.}$$
$$= 2\left(\dfrac{5\sqrt{3}}{4}\right) + 4\left(\dfrac{2\sqrt{2}}{4\sqrt{2}}\right) \qquad \text{Product rule; take square roots.}$$
$$= \dfrac{5\sqrt{3}}{2} + 2 \qquad \text{Multiply; } \tfrac{\sqrt{2}}{\sqrt{2}} = 1.$$
$$= \dfrac{5\sqrt{3}}{2} + \dfrac{4}{2} \qquad \text{Write with a common denominator.}$$
$$= \dfrac{5\sqrt{3} + 4}{2} \qquad \text{Add fractions.}$$

(b) $10\sqrt[3]{\dfrac{5}{x^6}} - 3\sqrt[3]{\dfrac{4}{x^9}}$

$$= 10\dfrac{\sqrt[3]{5}}{\sqrt[3]{x^6}} - 3\dfrac{\sqrt[3]{4}}{\sqrt[3]{x^9}} \qquad \text{Quotient rule}$$
$$= \dfrac{10\sqrt[3]{5}}{x^2} - \dfrac{3\sqrt[3]{4}}{x^3} \qquad \text{Simplify denominators.}$$
$$= \dfrac{10\sqrt[3]{5} \cdot x}{x^2 \cdot x} - \dfrac{3\sqrt[3]{4}}{x^3} \qquad \text{Write with a common denominator.}$$
$$= \dfrac{10x\sqrt[3]{5} - 3\sqrt[3]{4}}{x^3} \qquad \text{Subtract fractions.}$$

◀ *Work Problem* **3** *at the Side.*

1. Which one of the following sums could be simplified without first simplifying the individual radical expressions?

   A. $\sqrt{50} + \sqrt{32}$ **B.** $3\sqrt{6} + 9\sqrt{6}$ **C.** $\sqrt[3]{32} - \sqrt[3]{108}$ **D.** $\sqrt[5]{6} - \sqrt[5]{192}$

2. Let $a = 1$ and $b = 64$.

   (a) Evaluate $\sqrt{a} + \sqrt{b}$. Then find $\sqrt{a + b}$. Are they equal?

   (b) Evaluate $\sqrt[3]{a} + \sqrt[3]{b}$. Then find $\sqrt[3]{a + b}$. Are they equal?

   (c) Complete the following: In general, $\sqrt[n]{a} + \sqrt[n]{b} \neq$ _____, based on the observations in parts (a) and (b) of this exercise.

3. Even though the indexes of the terms are not equal, the sum $\sqrt{64} + \sqrt[3]{125} + \sqrt[4]{16}$ can be simplified quite easily. What is this sum? Why can these terms be combined so easily?

4. Explain why $28 - 4\sqrt{2}$ *is not equal to* $24\sqrt{2}$. (This is a common error among algebra students.)

Simplify. Assume that all variables represent positive real numbers. See Examples 1 and 2.

5. $\sqrt{36} - \sqrt{100}$

6. $\sqrt{25} - \sqrt{81}$

7. $-2\sqrt{48} + 3\sqrt{75}$

8. $4\sqrt{32} - 2\sqrt{8}$

9. $\sqrt[3]{16} + 4\sqrt[3]{54}$

10. $3\sqrt[3]{24} - 2\sqrt[3]{192}$

11. $\sqrt[4]{32} + 3\sqrt[4]{2}$

12. $\sqrt[4]{405} - 2\sqrt[4]{5}$

13. $6\sqrt{18} - \sqrt{32} + 2\sqrt{50}$

14. $5\sqrt{8} + 3\sqrt{72} - 3\sqrt{50}$

15. $5\sqrt{6} + 2\sqrt{10}$

16. $3\sqrt{11} - 5\sqrt{13}$

17. $2\sqrt{5} + 3\sqrt{20} + 4\sqrt{45}$

18. $5\sqrt{54} - 2\sqrt{24} - 2\sqrt{96}$

19. $8\sqrt{2x} - \sqrt{8x} + \sqrt{72x}$

20. $4\sqrt{18k} - \sqrt{72k} + \sqrt{50k}$

21. $3\sqrt{72m^2} - 5\sqrt{32m^2}$

22. $9\sqrt{27p^2} - 14\sqrt{108p^2}$

23. $-\sqrt[3]{54} + 2\sqrt[3]{16}$

24. $15\sqrt[3]{81} - 4\sqrt[3]{24}$

25. $2\sqrt[3]{27x} - 2\sqrt[3]{8x}$

26. $6\sqrt[3]{128m} + 3\sqrt[3]{16m}$

27. $\sqrt[3]{x^2y} - \sqrt[3]{8x^2y}$

28. $3\sqrt[3]{x^2y^2} - 2\sqrt[3]{64x^2y^2}$

29. $3x\sqrt[3]{xy^2} - 2\sqrt[3]{8x^4y^2}$

30. $6q^2\sqrt[3]{5q} - 2q\sqrt[3]{40q^4}$

31. $5\sqrt[4]{32} + 3\sqrt[4]{162}$

32. $2\sqrt[4]{512} + 4\sqrt[4]{32}$

33. $3\sqrt[4]{x^5y} - 2x\sqrt[4]{xy}$

34. $2\sqrt[4]{m^9p^6} - 3m^2p\sqrt[4]{mp^2}$

35. $2\sqrt[4]{32a^3} + 5\sqrt[4]{2a^3}$

36. $-\sqrt[4]{16r} + 5\sqrt[4]{r}$

Simplify. Assume that all variables represent positive real numbers. See Example 3.

37. $\dfrac{2\sqrt{5}}{3} + \dfrac{\sqrt{5}}{6}$

38. $\dfrac{4\sqrt{3}}{3} + \dfrac{2\sqrt{3}}{9}$

39. $\sqrt{\dfrac{8}{9}} + \sqrt{\dfrac{18}{36}}$

40. $\sqrt{\dfrac{12}{16}} + \sqrt{\dfrac{48}{64}}$

41. $\dfrac{\sqrt{32}}{3} + \dfrac{2\sqrt{2}}{3} - \dfrac{\sqrt{2}}{\sqrt{9}}$

42. $\dfrac{\sqrt{27}}{2} - \dfrac{3\sqrt{3}}{2} + \dfrac{\sqrt{3}}{\sqrt{4}}$

43. $3\sqrt{\dfrac{50}{9}} + 8\dfrac{\sqrt{2}}{\sqrt{8}}$

44. $9\sqrt{\dfrac{48}{25}} - 2\dfrac{\sqrt{2}}{\sqrt{98}}$

45. $\sqrt{\dfrac{25}{x^8}} - \sqrt{\dfrac{9}{x^6}}$

46. $\sqrt{\dfrac{100}{y^4}} + \sqrt{\dfrac{81}{y^{10}}}$

47. $3\sqrt[3]{\dfrac{m^5}{27}} - 2m\sqrt[3]{\dfrac{m^2}{64}}$

48. $2a\sqrt[4]{\dfrac{a}{16}} - 5a\sqrt[4]{\dfrac{a}{81}}$

49. $3\sqrt[3]{\dfrac{2}{x^6}} - 4\sqrt[3]{\dfrac{5}{x^9}}$

50. $-4\sqrt[3]{\dfrac{4}{t^9}} + 3\sqrt[3]{\dfrac{9}{t^{12}}}$

Solve each problem. Give answers as simplified radical expressions.

51. Find the perimeter of the triangle.

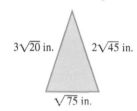

$3\sqrt{20}$ in. $2\sqrt{45}$ in.

$\sqrt{75}$ in.

52. Find the perimeter of the rectangle.

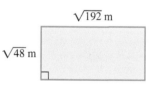

$\sqrt{192}$ m

$\sqrt{48}$ m

53. What is the perimeter of the computer graphic?

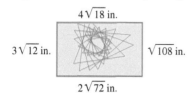

$4\sqrt{18}$ in.

$3\sqrt{12}$ in. $\sqrt{108}$ in.

$2\sqrt{72}$ in.

54. Find the area of the trapezoid.

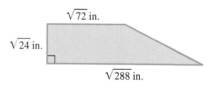

$\sqrt{72}$ in.

$\sqrt{24}$ in.

$\sqrt{288}$ in.

17.6 ▶▶▶ Multiplying and Dividing Radical Expressions

OBJECTIVE 1 Multiply radical expressions. We multiply binomial expressions involving radicals by using the FOIL method from **Section 6.4.** For example, we find the product of $\sqrt{5} + 3$ and $\sqrt{6} + 1$ as follows:

$$\left(\sqrt{5} + 3\right)\left(\sqrt{6} + 1\right)$$

$$\overset{\text{First}}{} \quad \overset{\text{Outer}}{} \quad \overset{\text{Inner}}{} \quad \overset{\text{Last}}{}$$

$$= \sqrt{5} \cdot \sqrt{6} + \sqrt{5} \cdot 1 + 3 \cdot \sqrt{6} + 3 \cdot 1$$

This result cannot be simplified further.

$$= \sqrt{30} + \sqrt{5} + 3\sqrt{6} + 3.$$

OBJECTIVES

1. **Multiply radical expressions.**

2. **Rationalize denominators with one radical term.**

3. **Rationalize denominators with binomials involving radicals.**

4. **Write radical quotients in lowest terms.**

Example 1 **Multiplying Binomials Involving Radical Expressions**

Multiply, using the FOIL method.

(a) $\left(7 - \sqrt{3}\right)\left(\sqrt{5} + \sqrt{2}\right)$

$$\overset{F}{} \quad \overset{O}{} \quad \overset{I}{} \quad \overset{L}{}$$

$$= 7\sqrt{5} + 7\sqrt{2} - \sqrt{3} \cdot \sqrt{5} - \sqrt{3} \cdot \sqrt{2}$$

$$= 7\sqrt{5} + 7\sqrt{2} - \sqrt{15} - \sqrt{6}$$

(b) $\left(\sqrt{10} + \sqrt{3}\right)\left(\sqrt{10} - \sqrt{3}\right)$

$$= \sqrt{10} \cdot \sqrt{10} - \sqrt{10} \cdot \sqrt{3} + \sqrt{3} \cdot \sqrt{10} - \sqrt{3} \cdot \sqrt{3}$$

$$= 10 - 3$$

$$= 7$$

The product $\left(\sqrt{10} + \sqrt{3}\right)\left(\sqrt{10} - \sqrt{3}\right) = \left(\sqrt{10}\right)^2 - \left(\sqrt{3}\right)^2$ is the difference of squares:

$$(x + y)(x - y) = x^2 - y^2. \quad \text{Here, } x = \sqrt{10} \text{ and } y = \sqrt{3}.$$

(c) $\left(\sqrt{7} - 3\right)^2$

$$= \left(\sqrt{7} - 3\right)\left(\sqrt{7} - 3\right)$$

$$= \sqrt{7} \cdot \sqrt{7} - 3\sqrt{7} - 3\sqrt{7} + 3 \cdot 3$$

$$= 7 - 6\sqrt{7} + 9$$

$$= 16 - 6\sqrt{7}$$

Be careful! These terms cannot be combined.

(d) $\left(5 - \sqrt[3]{3}\right)\left(5 + \sqrt[3]{3}\right)$

$$= 5 \cdot 5 + 5\sqrt[3]{3} - 5\sqrt[3]{3} - \sqrt[3]{3} \cdot \sqrt[3]{3}$$

$$= 25 - \sqrt[3]{3^2}$$

Remember to write the index 3 in *each* radical.

$$= 25 - \sqrt[3]{9}$$

(e) $\left(\sqrt{k} + \sqrt{y}\right)\left(\sqrt{k} - \sqrt{y}\right)$

$$= \left(\sqrt{k}\right)^2 - \left(\sqrt{y}\right)^2 \quad \text{Difference of squares}$$

$$= k - y, \quad k \geq 0 \text{ and } y \geq 0$$

1 Multiply, using the FOIL method.

(a) $\left(2 + \sqrt{3}\right)\left(1 + \sqrt{5}\right)$

(b) $\left(4 + \sqrt{3}\right)\left(4 - \sqrt{3}\right)$

(c) $\left(\sqrt{13} - 2\right)^2$

(d) $\left(4 + \sqrt[3]{7}\right)\left(4 - \sqrt[3]{7}\right)$

(e) $\left(\sqrt{p} + \sqrt{s}\right)\left(\sqrt{p} - \sqrt{s}\right),$
    $p \geq 0$ and $s \geq 0$

> **Note**
> In Example 1(c) we could have used the formula for the square of a binomial,
> $$(x - y)^2 = x^2 - 2xy + y^2,$$
> to obtain the same result:
> $$\left(\sqrt{7} - 3\right)^2$$
> $$= \left(\sqrt{7}\right)^2 - 2\left(\sqrt{7}\right)(3) + 3^2$$
> $$= 7 - 6\sqrt{7} + 9$$
> $$= 16 - 6\sqrt{7}.$$

◀ *Work Problem* **1** *at the Side.*

OBJECTIVE **2** **Rationalize denominators with one radical term.** As defined earlier, a simplified radical expression will have no radical in the denominator. The origin of this agreement no doubt occurred before the days of high-speed calculation, when computation was a tedious process performed by hand.

For example, consider the radical expression $\frac{1}{\sqrt{2}}$. To find a decimal approximation by hand, it would be necessary to divide 1 by a decimal approximation for $\sqrt{2}$, such as 1.414. It would be much easier if the divisor were a whole number. This can be accomplished by multiplying $\frac{1}{\sqrt{2}}$ by 1 in the form $\frac{\sqrt{2}}{\sqrt{2}}$. *Multiplying by 1 in any form does not change the value of the original expression.*

$$\frac{1}{\sqrt{2}} \cdot \frac{\sqrt{2}}{\sqrt{2}} = \frac{\sqrt{2}}{2} \qquad \text{Multiply by 1; } \frac{\sqrt{2}}{\sqrt{2}} = 1.$$

Now the computation would require dividing 1.414 by 2 to obtain 0.707, a much easier task.

With current technology, either form of this fraction can be approximated with the same number of keystrokes. See Figure 9, which shows how a calculator gives the same approximation for both forms of the expression.

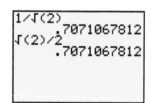

Figure 9

> **Rationalizing a Denominator**
> A common way of "standardizing" the form of a radical expression is to have the denominator contain no radicals. The process of removing radicals from a denominator so that the denominator contains only rational numbers is called **rationalizing the denominator.**

ANSWERS
1. **(a)** $2 + 2\sqrt{5} + \sqrt{3} + \sqrt{15}$
   (b) 13   **(c)** $17 - 4\sqrt{13}$
   (d) $16 - \sqrt[3]{49}$ **(e)** $p - s$

Example 2   **Rationalizing Denominators with Square Roots**

Rationalize each denominator.

(a) $\dfrac{3}{\sqrt{7}}$

Multiply by $\dfrac{\sqrt{7}}{\sqrt{7}}$. This is an application of the multiplicative identity property.

$$\dfrac{3}{\sqrt{7}} = \dfrac{3 \cdot \sqrt{7}}{\sqrt{7} \cdot \sqrt{7}} = \dfrac{3\sqrt{7}}{7}$$ In the denominator, $\sqrt{7} \cdot \sqrt{7} = \sqrt{7 \cdot 7} = \sqrt{49} = 7$. The final denominator is now a rational number.

(b) $\dfrac{5\sqrt{2}}{\sqrt{5}} = \dfrac{5\sqrt{2} \cdot \sqrt{5}}{\sqrt{5} \cdot \sqrt{5}} = \dfrac{5\sqrt{10}}{5} = \sqrt{10}$

(c) $\dfrac{-6}{\sqrt{12}}$

Less work is involved if the radical in the denominator is simplified first.

$$\dfrac{-6}{\sqrt{12}} = \dfrac{-6}{\sqrt{4 \cdot 3}} = \dfrac{-6}{2\sqrt{3}} = \dfrac{-3}{\sqrt{3}}$$

Now rationalize the denominator.

$$\dfrac{-3}{\sqrt{3}} = \dfrac{-3 \cdot \sqrt{3}}{\sqrt{3} \cdot \sqrt{3}} = \dfrac{-3\sqrt{3}}{3} = -\sqrt{3}$$

Work Problem 2 *at the Side.* ▶

Example 3   **Rationalizing Denominators in Roots of Fractions**

Simplify each radical. Assume that all variables represent positive real numbers.

(a) $\sqrt{\dfrac{18}{125}}$

$= \dfrac{\sqrt{18}}{\sqrt{125}}$ Quotient rule

$= \dfrac{\sqrt{9 \cdot 2}}{\sqrt{25 \cdot 5}}$ Factor.

$= \dfrac{3\sqrt{2}}{5\sqrt{5}}$ Product rule

$= \dfrac{3\sqrt{2} \cdot \sqrt{5}}{5\sqrt{5} \cdot \sqrt{5}}$ Multiply by $\dfrac{\sqrt{5}}{\sqrt{5}}$.

$= \dfrac{3\sqrt{10}}{5 \cdot 5}$ Product rule

$= \dfrac{3\sqrt{10}}{25}$ Multiply.

Continued on Next Page

2 Rationalize each denominator.

(a) $\dfrac{8}{\sqrt{3}}$

(b) $\dfrac{5\sqrt{6}}{\sqrt{5}}$

(c) $\dfrac{3}{\sqrt{48}}$

(d) $\dfrac{-16}{\sqrt{32}}$

ANSWERS

2. (a) $\dfrac{8\sqrt{3}}{3}$ (b) $\sqrt{30}$

   (c) $\dfrac{\sqrt{3}}{4}$ (d) $-2\sqrt{2}$

3 Simplify each radical. Assume that all variables represent positive real numbers.

(a) $\sqrt{\dfrac{8}{45}}$

(b) $\sqrt{\dfrac{72}{y}}$

(c) $\sqrt{\dfrac{200k^6}{y^7}}$

4 Simplify.

(a) $\sqrt[3]{\dfrac{15}{32}}$

(b) $\sqrt[3]{\dfrac{m^{12}}{n}}, \quad n \neq 0$

(c) $\sqrt[4]{\dfrac{6y}{w^2}}, \quad y \geq 0, w \neq 0$

(b) $\sqrt{\dfrac{50m^4}{p^5}}$

$= \dfrac{\sqrt{50m^4}}{\sqrt{p^5}}$ Quotient rule

$= \dfrac{\sqrt{25m^4 \cdot 2}}{\sqrt{p^4 \cdot p}}$ Factor.

$= \dfrac{5m^2\sqrt{2}}{p^2\sqrt{p}}$ Product rule

$= \dfrac{5m^2\sqrt{2} \cdot \sqrt{p}}{p^2\sqrt{p} \cdot \sqrt{p}}$ Multiply by $\dfrac{\sqrt{p}}{\sqrt{p}}$.

$= \dfrac{5m^2\sqrt{2p}}{p^2 \cdot p}$ Product rule

$= \dfrac{5m^2\sqrt{2p}}{p^3}$ Multiply.

◀ *Work Problem* **3** *at the Side.*

Example 4   **Rationalizing Denominators with Higher Roots**

Simplify.

(a) $\sqrt[3]{\dfrac{27}{16}}$

Use the quotient rule and simplify the numerator and denominator.

$$\sqrt[3]{\dfrac{27}{16}} = \dfrac{\sqrt[3]{27}}{\sqrt[3]{16}} = \dfrac{3}{\sqrt[3]{8} \cdot \sqrt[3]{2}} = \dfrac{3}{2\sqrt[3]{2}}$$

To get a rational denominator, multiply the numerator and denominator by a number that will result in a perfect cube in the radicand in the denominator. Since $2 \cdot 4 = 8$, a perfect cube, apply the multiplicative identity property and multiply the numerator and denominator by $\sqrt[3]{4}$.

$$\sqrt[3]{\dfrac{27}{16}} = \dfrac{3}{2\sqrt[3]{2}} = \dfrac{3 \cdot \sqrt[3]{4}}{2\sqrt[3]{2} \cdot \sqrt[3]{4}} = \dfrac{3\sqrt[3]{4}}{2\sqrt[3]{8}} = \dfrac{3\sqrt[3]{4}}{2 \cdot 2} = \dfrac{3\sqrt[3]{4}}{4}$$

(b) $\sqrt[4]{\dfrac{5x}{z}} = \dfrac{\sqrt[4]{5x} \cdot \sqrt[4]{z^3}}{\sqrt[4]{z} \cdot \sqrt[4]{z^3}} = \dfrac{\sqrt[4]{5xz^3}}{\sqrt[4]{z^4}} = \dfrac{\sqrt[4]{5xz^3}}{z}, \quad x \geq 0, z > 0$

CAUTION

In Example 4(a), a typical error is to multiply the numerator and denominator by $\sqrt[3]{2}$, forgetting that $\sqrt[3]{2} \cdot \sqrt[3]{2} = \sqrt[3]{2^2}$, which does **not** equal 2. We need **three** factors of 2 to get 2^3 under the radical.

$$\sqrt[3]{2} \cdot \sqrt[3]{2} \cdot \sqrt[3]{2} = \sqrt[3]{2^3}, \quad \text{which does equal} \quad 2.$$

ANSWERS

3. (a) $\dfrac{2\sqrt{10}}{15}$ (b) $\dfrac{6\sqrt{2y}}{y}$ (c) $\dfrac{10k^3\sqrt{2y}}{y^4}$

4. (a) $\dfrac{\sqrt[3]{30}}{4}$ (b) $\dfrac{m^4\sqrt[3]{n^2}}{n}$ (c) $\dfrac{\sqrt[4]{6yw^2}}{w}$

◀ *Work Problem* **4** *at the Side.*

OBJECTIVE 3 **Rationalize denominators with binomials involving radicals.** Recall the special product

$$(x + y)(x - y) = x^2 - y^2.$$

To rationalize a denominator that contains a binomial expression (one that contains exactly two terms) involving radicals, such as

$$\frac{3}{1 + \sqrt{2}},$$

we must use *conjugates*. The conjugate of $1 + \sqrt{2}$ is $1 - \sqrt{2}$. In general, $x + y$ and $x - y$ are **conjugates.**

Rationalizing a Binomial Denominator

If a radical expression has a sum or difference with square root radicals in the denominator, rationalize the denominator by multiplying both the numerator and denominator by the conjugate of the denominator.

For $\frac{3}{1 + \sqrt{2}}$, we rationalize the denominator by multiplying both the numerator and denominator by $1 - \sqrt{2}$, the conjugate of the denominator.

$$\frac{3}{1 + \sqrt{2}}$$

$$= \frac{3\left(1 - \sqrt{2}\right)}{\left(1 + \sqrt{2}\right)\left(1 - \sqrt{2}\right)}$$

$$\begin{aligned} \left(1 + \sqrt{2}\right)\left(1 - \sqrt{2}\right) \\ = 1^2 - \left(\sqrt{2}\right)^2 \\ = 1 - 2 = -1 \end{aligned}$$

$$= \frac{3\left(1 - \sqrt{2}\right)}{-1} \qquad \text{The denominator is now a rational number.}$$

$$= \frac{3}{-1}\left(1 - \sqrt{2}\right)$$

$$= -3\left(1 - \sqrt{2}\right), \quad \text{or} \quad -3 + 3\sqrt{2}$$

Example 5 **Rationalizing Binomial Denominators**

Rationalize each denominator.

(a) $\dfrac{5}{4 - \sqrt{3}}$

$$= \frac{5\left(4 + \sqrt{3}\right)}{\left(4 - \sqrt{3}\right)\left(4 + \sqrt{3}\right)} \qquad \text{Multiply the numerator and denominator by } 4 + \sqrt{3}.$$

$$= \frac{5\left(4 + \sqrt{3}\right)}{16 - 3} \qquad \text{Multiply in the denominator.}$$

$$= \frac{5\left(4 + \sqrt{3}\right)}{13} \qquad \text{Subtract.}$$

Notice that the numerator is left in factored form. This makes it easier to determine whether the expression is written in lowest terms.

Continued on Next Page

5 Rationalize each denominator.

(a) $\dfrac{-4}{\sqrt{5} + 2}$

(b) $\dfrac{15}{\sqrt{7} + \sqrt{2}}$

(c) $\dfrac{\sqrt{3} + \sqrt{5}}{\sqrt{2} - \sqrt{7}}$

(d) $\dfrac{2}{\sqrt{k} + \sqrt{z}}$,

$k \ne z, k > 0, z > 0$

(b) $\dfrac{\sqrt{2} - \sqrt{3}}{\sqrt{5} + \sqrt{3}}$

$= \dfrac{\left(\sqrt{2} - \sqrt{3}\right)\left(\sqrt{5} - \sqrt{3}\right)}{\left(\sqrt{5} + \sqrt{3}\right)\left(\sqrt{5} - \sqrt{3}\right)}$ Multiply the numerator and denominator by $\sqrt{5} - \sqrt{3}$.

$= \dfrac{\sqrt{10} - \sqrt{6} - \sqrt{15} + 3}{5 - 3}$ Multiply.

$= \dfrac{\sqrt{10} - \sqrt{6} - \sqrt{15} + 3}{2}$ Subtract in the denominator.

(c) $\dfrac{3}{\sqrt{5m} - \sqrt{p}}$, $5m \ne p, m > 0, p > 0$

$= \dfrac{3\left(\sqrt{5m} + \sqrt{p}\right)}{\left(\sqrt{5m} - \sqrt{p}\right)\left(\sqrt{5m} + \sqrt{p}\right)}$

$= \dfrac{3\left(\sqrt{5m} + \sqrt{p}\right)}{5m - p}$

◀ *Work Problem* **5** *at the Side.*

OBJECTIVE **4** **Write radical quotients in lowest terms.**

Example 6 **Writing Radical Quotients in Lowest Terms**

Write each quotient in lowest terms.

(a) $\dfrac{6 + 2\sqrt{5}}{4}$

$= \dfrac{2\left(3 + \sqrt{5}\right)}{2 \cdot 2}$ (This is a key step.)   Factor the numerator and denominator.

$= \dfrac{3 + \sqrt{5}}{2}$ Divide out the common factor.

Here is an alternative method for writing this expression in lowest terms.

$$\dfrac{6 + 2\sqrt{5}}{4} = \dfrac{6}{4} + \dfrac{2\sqrt{5}}{4} = \dfrac{3}{2} + \dfrac{\sqrt{5}}{2} = \dfrac{3 + \sqrt{5}}{2}$$

6 Write each quotient in lowest terms.

(a) $\dfrac{24 - 36\sqrt{7}}{16}$

(b) $\dfrac{2x + \sqrt{32x^2}}{6x}$, $x > 0$

(b) $\dfrac{5y - \sqrt{8y^2}}{6y}$, $y > 0$

$= \dfrac{5y - 2y\sqrt{2}}{6y}$ $\sqrt{8y^2} = \sqrt{4y^2 \cdot 2} = 2y\sqrt{2}$

$= \dfrac{y\left(5 - 2\sqrt{2}\right)}{6y}$ Factor the numerator.

$= \dfrac{5 - 2\sqrt{2}}{6}$ Divide out the common factor.

◀ *Work Problem* **6** *at the Side.*

ANSWERS

5. (a) $-4\left(\sqrt{5} - 2\right)$ (b) $3\left(\sqrt{7} - \sqrt{2}\right)$

(c) $\dfrac{-\left(\sqrt{6} + \sqrt{21} + \sqrt{10} + \sqrt{35}\right)}{5}$

(d) $\dfrac{2\left(\sqrt{k} - \sqrt{z}\right)}{k - z}$

6. (a) $\dfrac{6 - 9\sqrt{7}}{4}$ (b) $\dfrac{1 + 2\sqrt{2}}{3}$

17.6 ▶▶▶ **Exercises**

Match each part of a rule for a special product in Column I with the part it equals in Column II.

I

1. $\left(x + \sqrt{y}\right)\left(x - \sqrt{y}\right)$

2. $\left(\sqrt{x} + y\right)\left(\sqrt{x} - y\right)$

3. $\left(\sqrt{x} + \sqrt{y}\right)\left(\sqrt{x} - \sqrt{y}\right)$

4. $\left(\sqrt{x} + \sqrt{y}\right)^2$

5. $\left(\sqrt{x} - \sqrt{y}\right)^2$

6. $\left(\sqrt{x} + y\right)^2$

II

A. $x - y$

B. $x + 2y\sqrt{x} + y^2$

C. $x - y^2$

D. $x - 2\sqrt{xy} + y$

E. $x^2 - y$

F. $x + 2\sqrt{xy} + y$

Multiply, and then simplify each product. Assume that all variables represent positive real numbers. See Example 1.

7. $\sqrt{3}\left(\sqrt{12} - 4\right)$

8. $\sqrt{5}\left(\sqrt{125} - 6\right)$

9. $\sqrt{2}\left(\sqrt{18} - \sqrt{3}\right)$

10. $\sqrt{5}\left(\sqrt{15} + \sqrt{5}\right)$

11. $\left(\sqrt{6} + 2\right)\left(\sqrt{6} - 2\right)$

12. $\left(\sqrt{7} + 8\right)\left(\sqrt{7} - 8\right)$

13. $\left(\sqrt{12} - \sqrt{3}\right)\left(\sqrt{12} + \sqrt{3}\right)$

14. $\left(\sqrt{18} + \sqrt{8}\right)\left(\sqrt{18} - \sqrt{8}\right)$

15. $\left(\sqrt{3} + 2\right)\left(\sqrt{6} - 5\right)$

16. $\left(\sqrt{7} + 1\right)\left(\sqrt{2} - 4\right)$

17. $\left(\sqrt{3x} + 2\right)\left(\sqrt{3x} - 2\right)$

18. $\left(\sqrt{6y} - 4\right)\left(\sqrt{6y} + 4\right)$

19. $\left(2\sqrt{x} + \sqrt{y}\right)\left(2\sqrt{x} - \sqrt{y}\right)$

20. $\left(\sqrt{p} + 5\sqrt{s}\right)\left(\sqrt{p} - 5\sqrt{s}\right)$

21. $\left(4\sqrt{x} + 3\right)^2$

22. $\left(5\sqrt{p} - 6\right)^2$

23. $\left(9 - \sqrt[3]{2}\right)\left(9 + \sqrt[3]{2}\right)$

24. $\left(7 + \sqrt[3]{6}\right)\left(7 - \sqrt[3]{6}\right)$

25. The correct answer to Exercise 7 is $6 - 4\sqrt{3}$. Explain why this is not equal to $2\sqrt{3}$.

26. When we rationalize the denominator in the radical expression $\frac{1}{\sqrt{2}}$, we multiply both the numerator and denominator by $\sqrt{2}$. What property of real numbers covered in **Section 1.4** justifies this procedure?

Rationalize the denominator in each expression. Assume that all variables represent positive real numbers. See Example 2.

27. $\dfrac{7}{\sqrt{7}}$

28. $\dfrac{11}{\sqrt{11}}$

29. $\dfrac{15}{\sqrt{3}}$

30. $\dfrac{12}{\sqrt{6}}$

31. $\dfrac{\sqrt{3}}{\sqrt{2}}$

32. $\dfrac{\sqrt{7}}{\sqrt{6}}$

33. $\dfrac{9\sqrt{3}}{\sqrt{5}}$

34. $\dfrac{3\sqrt{2}}{\sqrt{11}}$

35. $\dfrac{-6}{\sqrt{18}}$

36. $\dfrac{-5}{\sqrt{24}}$

37. $\dfrac{-8\sqrt{3}}{\sqrt{k}}$

38. $\dfrac{-4\sqrt{13}}{\sqrt{m}}$

39. $\dfrac{6\sqrt{3y}}{\sqrt{y^3}}$

40. $\dfrac{-8\sqrt{5y}}{\sqrt{y^5}}$

41. Explain why $\dfrac{1}{\sqrt[3]{2}}$ would not be written with the denominator rationalized if you begin by multiplying both the numerator and denominator by $\sqrt[3]{2}$. By what should you multiply them both to achieve the desired result?

42. Look again at the expression in Exercise 39. Start by multiplying both the numerator and the denominator by $\sqrt{y}$, to obtain the final answer. Then start over, multiplying both the numerator and denominator by $\sqrt{y^3}$, to obtain the same answer. Which method do you prefer? Why?

Simplify. Assume that all variables represent positive real numbers. See Examples 3 and 4.

43. $\sqrt{\dfrac{7}{2}}$

44. $\sqrt{\dfrac{10}{3}}$

45. $-\sqrt{\dfrac{7}{50}}$

46. $-\sqrt{\dfrac{13}{75}}$

47. $\sqrt{\dfrac{24}{x}}$

48. $\sqrt{\dfrac{52}{y}}$

49. $-\sqrt{\dfrac{98r^3}{s}}$

50. $-\sqrt{\dfrac{150m^5}{n}}$

51. $\sqrt{\dfrac{288x^7}{y^9}}$

52. $\sqrt{\dfrac{242t^9}{u^{11}}}$

53. $\sqrt[3]{\dfrac{2}{3}}$　　　**54.** $\sqrt[3]{\dfrac{4}{5}}$　　　 ● **55.** $\sqrt[3]{\dfrac{4}{9}}$　　　**56.** $\sqrt[3]{\dfrac{5}{16}}$　　　**57.** $-\sqrt[3]{\dfrac{2p}{r^2}}$

58. $-\sqrt[3]{\dfrac{6x}{y^2}}$　　　**59.** $\sqrt[4]{\dfrac{16}{x}}$　　　**60.** $\sqrt[4]{\dfrac{81}{y}}$　　　**61.** $\sqrt[4]{\dfrac{2y}{z}}$　　　**62.** $\sqrt[4]{\dfrac{7t}{s^2}}$

Rationalize the denominator in each expression. Assume that all variables represent positive real numbers and that no denominators are 0. See Example 5.

63. $\dfrac{2}{4 + \sqrt{3}}$　　　**64.** $\dfrac{6}{5 + \sqrt{2}}$　　　 ● **65.** $\dfrac{6}{\sqrt{5} + \sqrt{3}}$　　　**66.** $\dfrac{12}{\sqrt{6} + \sqrt{3}}$

67. $\dfrac{-4}{\sqrt{3} - \sqrt{7}}$　　　**68.** $\dfrac{-3}{\sqrt{2} + \sqrt{5}}$　　　**69.** $\dfrac{1 - \sqrt{2}}{\sqrt{7} + \sqrt{6}}$　　　**70.** $\dfrac{-1 - \sqrt{3}}{\sqrt{6} + \sqrt{5}}$

71. $\dfrac{\sqrt{2} - \sqrt{3}}{\sqrt{6} - \sqrt{5}}$　　　**72.** $\dfrac{\sqrt{5} + \sqrt{6}}{\sqrt{3} - \sqrt{2}}$　　　**73.** $\dfrac{4}{\sqrt{x} - 2\sqrt{y}}$

74. $\dfrac{5}{3\sqrt{r} + \sqrt{s}}$　　　**75.** $\dfrac{\sqrt{x} - \sqrt{y}}{\sqrt{2x} + \sqrt{3y}}$　　　**76.** $\dfrac{\sqrt{a} + \sqrt{b}}{\sqrt{5a} - \sqrt{2b}}$

Write each quotient in lowest terms. Assume that all variables represent positive real numbers. See Example 6.

77. $\dfrac{25 + 10\sqrt{6}}{20}$

78. $\dfrac{12 - 6\sqrt{2}}{24}$

79. $\dfrac{16 + 4\sqrt{8}}{12}$

80. $\dfrac{12 + 9\sqrt{72}}{18}$

81. $\dfrac{6x + \sqrt{24x^3}}{3x}$

82. $\dfrac{11y + \sqrt{242y^5}}{22y}$

Relating Concepts (Exercises 83–86) For Individual or Group Work

*Sometimes it is desirable to **rationalize the numerator** in an expression. The procedure is similar to rationalizing the denominator. For example, to rationalize the numerator in the following expression, we multiply both the numerator and denominator by the conjugate of the numerator, $6 + \sqrt{2}$.*

$$\frac{6 - \sqrt{2}}{3}$$

$$= \frac{\left(6 - \sqrt{2}\right)\left(6 + \sqrt{2}\right)}{3\left(6 + \sqrt{2}\right)}$$

$$= \frac{36 - 2}{3\left(6 + \sqrt{2}\right)}$$

$$= \frac{34}{3\left(6 + \sqrt{2}\right)}$$

In the final expression, the numerator is rationalized. **Work Exercises 83–86 in order.**

83. Rationalize the numerator of $\dfrac{8\sqrt{5} - 1}{6}$.

84. Rationalize the numerator of $\dfrac{3\sqrt{a} + \sqrt{b}}{\sqrt{b} - \sqrt{a}}$. Assume a and b are positive and $a \neq b$.

85. Rationalize the denominator of the expression in Exercise 84.

86. Describe the difference in the procedures used in Exercises 84 and 85.

Summary Exercises on Operations with Radicals and Rational Exponents

Recall that a simplified radical satisfies the following conditions.

Conditions for a Simplified Radical

1. The radicand has no factor raised to a power greater than or equal to the index.

2. The radicand has no fractions.

3. No denominator has a radical.

4. Exponents in the radicand and the index of the radical have greatest common factor 1.

Perform all indicated operations, and express each answer in simplest form with positive exponents. Assume that all variables represent positive real numbers.

1. $6\sqrt{10} - 12\sqrt{10}$

2. $\sqrt{7}\left(\sqrt{7} - \sqrt{2}\right)$

3. $\left(1 - \sqrt{3}\right)\left(2 + \sqrt{6}\right)$

4. $\sqrt{50} - \sqrt{98} + \sqrt{72}$

5. $\left(3\sqrt{5} + 2\sqrt{7}\right)^2$

6. $\dfrac{-3}{\sqrt{6}}$

7. $\dfrac{8}{\sqrt{7} + \sqrt{5}}$

8. $\sqrt[3]{16x^2} - \sqrt[3]{54x^2} + \sqrt[3]{128x^2}$

9. $\dfrac{1 - \sqrt{2}}{1 + \sqrt{2}}$

10. $\left(1 - \sqrt[3]{3}\right)\left(1 + \sqrt[3]{3} + \sqrt[3]{9}\right)$

11. $\left(\sqrt{5} + 7\right)\left(\sqrt{5} - 7\right)$

12. $\dfrac{1}{\sqrt{x} - \sqrt{5}}, \quad x \neq 5$

13. $\sqrt[3]{8a^3b^5c^9}$

14. $\dfrac{15}{\sqrt[3]{9}}$

15. $\dfrac{3}{\sqrt{5} + 2}$

16. $\sqrt{\dfrac{3}{5x}}$

17. $\dfrac{16\sqrt{3}}{5\sqrt{12}}$

18. $\dfrac{2\sqrt{25}}{8\sqrt{50}}$

19. $\dfrac{-10}{\sqrt[3]{10}}$

20. $\dfrac{\sqrt{6}+\sqrt{5}}{\sqrt{6}-\sqrt{5}}$

21. $\sqrt{12x}-\sqrt{75x}$

22. $\left(5-3\sqrt{3}\right)^2$

23. $\left(\sqrt{74}-\sqrt{73}\right)\left(\sqrt{74}+\sqrt{73}\right)$

24. $\sqrt[3]{\dfrac{13}{81}}$

25. $-t^2\sqrt[4]{t}+3\sqrt[4]{t^9}-t\sqrt[4]{t^5}$

26. $\dfrac{\sqrt{3}+\sqrt{7}}{\sqrt{6}-\sqrt{5}}$

27. $\dfrac{6}{\sqrt[4]{3}}$

28. $\dfrac{1}{1-\sqrt[3]{3}}$

29. $\sqrt[3]{\dfrac{x^2 y}{x^{-3}y^4}}$

30. $\sqrt{12}-\sqrt{108}-\sqrt[3]{27}$

31. $\dfrac{x^{-2/3}y^{4/5}}{x^{-5/3}y^{-2/5}}$

32. $\left(\dfrac{x^{3/4}y^{2/3}}{x^{1/3}y^{5/8}}\right)^{24}$

33. $(125x^3)^{-2/3}$

34. $(3x^{-2/3}y^{1/2})(-2x^{5/8}y^{-1/3})$

35. $\dfrac{4^{1/2}+3^{1/2}}{4^{1/2}-3^{1/2}}$

36. $\left(\sqrt{6}-\sqrt{5}\right)^2\left(\sqrt{6}+\sqrt{5}\right)^2$

17.7 ▶▶▶ Solving Equations with Radicals

An equation that includes one or more radical expressions with a variable is called a **radical equation.** Some examples of radical equations are

$$\sqrt{x-4} = 8, \quad \sqrt{5x+12} = 3\sqrt{2x-1}, \quad \text{and} \quad \sqrt[3]{6+x} = 27.$$

Radical equations

OBJECTIVE 1 **Solve radical equations using the power rule.** The equation $x = 1$ has only one solution. Its solution set is $\{1\}$. If we square both sides of this equation, we get $x^2 = 1$. This new equation has two solutions: -1 and 1. Notice that the solution of the original equation is also a solution of the squared equation. However, the squared equation has another solution, -1, that is *not* a solution of the original equation. When solving equations with radicals, we use this idea of raising both sides to a power. This is an application of the **power rule.**

> **Power Rule for Solving Equations with Radicals**
> If both sides of an equation are raised to the same power, all solutions of the original equation are also solutions of the new equation.

Read the power rule carefully; it does not say that all solutions of the new equation are solutions of the original equation. They may or may not be. Solutions that do not satisfy the original equation are called **extraneous solutions;** they must be discarded.

> **CAUTION**
> When the power rule is used to solve an equation, *every solution of the new equation* **must** *be checked in the original equation.*

Example 1 Using the Power Rule

Solve $\sqrt{3x+4} = 8$.

Use the power rule and square both sides to get

$$\left(\sqrt{3x+4}\right)^2 = 8^2$$

$$3x + 4 = 64$$

$$3x = 60 \qquad \text{Subtract 4.}$$

$$x = 20. \qquad \text{Divide by 3.}$$

To check, substitute the proposed solution in the *original* equation.

Check

$$\sqrt{3x+4} = 8 \qquad \text{Original equation}$$

$$\sqrt{3 \cdot 20 + 4} \stackrel{?}{=} 8 \qquad \text{Let } x = 20.$$

$$\sqrt{64} \stackrel{?}{=} 8$$

$$8 = 8 \qquad \text{True}$$

Since 20 satisfies the *original* equation, the solution set is $\{20\}$.

Work Problem ① *at the Side.* ▶

OBJECTIVES

① Solve radical equations using the power rule.

② Solve radical equations that require additional steps.

③ Solve radical equations with indexes greater than 2.

---

① Solve each equation.

(a) $\sqrt{r} = 3$

(b) $\sqrt{5x+1} = 4$

The solution of the equation in Example 1 can be generalized.

2 Solve each equation.

(a) $\sqrt{5x + 3} + 2 = 0$

> **Solving an Equation with Radicals**
>
> *Step 1*   **Isolate the radical.** Make sure that one radical term is alone on one side of the equation.
>
> *Step 2*   **Apply the power rule.** Raise both sides of the equation to a power that is the same as the index of the radical.
>
> *Step 3*   **Solve.** Solve the resulting equation; if it still contains a radical, repeat Steps 1 and 2.
>
> *Step 4*   **Check** all proposed solutions in the original equation.

> **CAUTION**
> Remember to check (Step 4) or you may get an incorrect solution set.

> **Example 2**   **Using the Power Rule**
>
> Solve $\sqrt{5x - 1} + 3 = 0$.
>
> *Step 1*   To isolate the radical on one side, subtract 3 from each side.
>
> $$\sqrt{5x - 1} = -3$$
>
> *Step 2*   Now square both sides.
>
> $$\left(\sqrt{5x - 1}\right)^2 = (-3)^2$$
>
> *Step 3* $5x - 1 = 9$
>
> $5x = 10$ Add 1.
>
> $x = 2$ Divide by 5.
>
> *Step 4*   Check the proposed solution, 2, by substituting it in the original equation.
>
> **Check** $\sqrt{5x - 1} + 3 = 0$ Original equation
>
> $\sqrt{5 \cdot 2 - 1} + 3 \overset{?}{=} 0$ Let $x = 2$.
>
> $3 + 3 = 0$ False
>
> This false result shows that 2 is *not* a solution of the original equation; it is extraneous. The solution set is $\emptyset$.

(b) $\sqrt{x - 9} - 3 = 0$

> **Note**
> We could have determined after Step 1 that the equation in Example 2 has no solution because the expression on the left cannot equal a negative number.

◀ *Work Problem* **2** *at the Side.*

OBJECTIVE **2** **Solve radical equations that require additional steps.**   The next examples involve finding the square of a binomial. Recall that

$$(x + y)^2 = x^2 + 2xy + y^2.$$

Example 3 Using the Power Rule; Squaring a Binomial

Solve $\sqrt{4-x} = x + 2$.

Step 1 The radical is alone on the left side of the equation.

Step 2 Square both sides. On the right, $(x+2)^2 = x^2 + 2(x)(2) + 2^2$.

$$\left(\sqrt{4-x}\right)^2 = (x+2)^2 \qquad \boxed{\text{Remember the middle term.}}$$

$$4 - x = x^2 + 4x + 4$$

$\boxed{\text{Pay careful attention here.}}$ $\quad$ Twice the product of 2 and x

Step 3 The new equation is quadratic, so get 0 on one side.

$$0 = x^2 + 5x \qquad \text{Subtract 4; add } x.$$

$$0 = x(x+5) \qquad \text{Factor.}$$

$\boxed{\text{Set } \textit{each} \text{ factor equal to 0.}}$ $\quad x = 0 \quad$ or $\quad x + 5 = 0 \qquad$ Zero-factor property

$$x = -5 \qquad \text{Solve.}$$

Step 4 Check each proposed solution in the original equation.

Check If $x = 0$, then

$$\sqrt{4-x} = x + 2$$

$$\sqrt{4-0} \overset{?}{=} 0 + 2$$

$$\sqrt{4} \overset{?}{=} 2$$

$$2 = 2. \qquad \text{True}$$

If $x = -5$, then

$$\sqrt{4-x} = x + 2$$

$$\sqrt{4-(-5)} \overset{?}{=} -5 + 2$$

$$\sqrt{9} \overset{?}{=} -3$$

$$3 = -3. \qquad \text{False}$$

The solution set is $\{0\}$. The other proposed solution, -5, is extraneous.

Work Problem **3** *at the Side.* ▶

3 Solve.

(a) $\sqrt{3x-5} = x - 1$

(b) $x + 1 = \sqrt{-2x-2}$

Example 4 Using the Power Rule; Squaring a Binomial

Solve $\sqrt{x^2 - 4x + 9} = x - 1$.

Square both sides. On the right, $(x-1)^2 = x^2 - 2(x)(1) + 1^2$.

$$\left(\sqrt{x^2 - 4x + 9}\right)^2 = (x-1)^2 \qquad \boxed{\text{Remember the middle term.}}$$

$$x^2 - 4x + 9 = x^2 - 2x + 1$$

$\quad$ Twice the product of x and -1

$$-2x = -8 \qquad \text{Subtract } x^2 \text{ and 9; add } 2x.$$

$$x = 4 \qquad \text{Divide by } -2.$$

Check $\quad \sqrt{x^2 - 4x + 9} = x - 1 \qquad$ Original equation

$$\sqrt{4^2 - 4 \cdot 4 + 9} \overset{?}{=} 4 - 1 \qquad \text{Let } x = 4.$$

$$3 = 3 \qquad \text{True}$$

The solution set of the original equation is $\{4\}$.

Work Problem **4** *at the Side.* ▶

4 Solve.

$$\sqrt{4x^2 + 2x - 3} = 2x + 7$$

CAUTION

When a radical equation requires squaring a binomial, as in Examples 3 and 4, *remember to include the middle term.*

ANSWERS

3. **(a)** $\{2, 3\}$ **(b)** $\{-1\}$
4. $\{-2\}$

5 **(a)** Verify that 15 is an extraneous solution of the equation in Example 5 and must be discarded.

Example 5 **Using the Power Rule; Squaring Twice**

Solve $\sqrt{5x + 6} + \sqrt{3x + 4} = 2$.

Start by isolating one radical on one side of the equation. Do this by subtracting $\sqrt{3x + 4}$ from each side.

$$\sqrt{5x + 6} = 2 - \sqrt{3x + 4} \qquad \text{Subtract } \sqrt{3x + 4}.$$

$$\left(\sqrt{5x + 6}\right)^2 = \left(2 - \sqrt{3x + 4}\right)^2 \qquad \text{Square both sides.}$$

$$5x + 6 = 4 - 4\sqrt{3x + 4} + (3x + 4) \qquad \boxed{\text{Be careful here.}}$$

Remember the middle term. ⎯ Twice the product of 2 and $-\sqrt{3x + 4}$

This equation still contains a radical, so isolate the radical term on the right and square both sides again.

$$5x + 6 = 8 + 3x - 4\sqrt{3x + 4} \qquad \text{Combine like terms.}$$

$$2x - 2 = -4\sqrt{3x + 4} \qquad \text{Subtract 8 and } 3x.$$

Divide each term by 2. ⎯ $x - 1 = -2\sqrt{3x + 4}$ Divide by 2 to make the numbers smaller.

$$(x - 1)^2 = \left(-2\sqrt{3x + 4}\right)^2 \qquad \text{Square both sides again.}$$

$$x^2 - 2x + 1 = (-2)^2\left(\sqrt{3x + 4}\right)^2 \qquad \text{On the right, } (ab)^2 = a^2 b^2.$$

$$x^2 - 2x + 1 = 4(3x + 4) \qquad \text{Apply the exponents.}$$

$$x^2 - 2x + 1 = 12x + 16 \qquad \text{Distributive property}$$

$$x^2 - 14x - 15 = 0 \qquad \text{Standard form}$$

$$(x + 1)(x - 15) = 0 \qquad \text{Factor.}$$

$$x + 1 = 0 \quad \text{or} \quad x - 15 = 0 \qquad \text{Zero-factor property}$$

$$x = -1 \quad \text{or} \quad x = 15 \qquad \text{Solve each equation.}$$

Check each of these proposed solutions in the original equation. Only -1 satisfies the equation, so the solution set, $\{-1\}$, has only one element.

◀ Work Problem 5 at the Side.

(b) Solve.

$$\sqrt{2x + 3} + \sqrt{x + 1} = 1$$

---

6 Solve each equation.

(a) $\sqrt[3]{2x + 7} = \sqrt[3]{3x - 2}$

OBJECTIVE 3 **Solve radical equations with indexes greater than 2.** The power rule also works for powers greater than 2.

Example 6 **Using the Power Rule for a Power Greater than 2**

Solve $\sqrt[3]{x + 5} = \sqrt[3]{2x - 6}$.

Raise both sides to the third power.

$$\left(\sqrt[3]{x + 5}\right)^3 = \left(\sqrt[3]{2x - 6}\right)^3$$

$$x + 5 = 2x - 6$$

$$11 = x \qquad \text{Subtract } x; \text{ add 6.}$$

Check $\sqrt[3]{x + 5} = \sqrt[3]{2x - 6}$ Original equation

$$\sqrt[3]{11 + 5} \overset{?}{=} \sqrt[3]{2 \cdot 11 - 6} \qquad \text{Let } x = 11.$$

$$\sqrt[3]{16} = \sqrt[3]{16} \qquad \text{True}$$

The solution set is $\{11\}$.

(b) $\sqrt[4]{2x + 5} + 1 = 0$

◀ Work Problem 6 at the Side.

17.7 ▶▶▶ **Exercises**

Check each equation to see if the given value for x is a solution.

1. $\sqrt{3x + 18} = x$

    (a) 6   **(b)** −3

2. $\sqrt{3x - 3} = x - 1$

    (a) 1   **(b)** 4

3. $\sqrt{x + 2} = \sqrt{9x - 2} - 2\sqrt{x - 1}$

    (a) 2   **(b)** 7

4. $\sqrt{8x - 3} = 2x$

    (a) $\dfrac{3}{2}$ **(b)** $\dfrac{1}{2}$

5. Is 9 a solution of the equation $\sqrt{x} = -3$? If not, what is the solution of this equation? Explain.

6. Before even attempting to solve $\sqrt{3x + 18} = x$, how can you be sure that the equation cannot have a negative solution?

Solve each equation. See Examples 1–4.

7. $\sqrt{x - 2} = 3$

8. $\sqrt{x + 1} = 7$

9. $\sqrt{6x - 1} = 1$

10. $\sqrt{7x - 3} = 5$

11. $\sqrt{4x + 3} + 1 = 0$

12. $\sqrt{5x - 3} + 2 = 0$

13. $\sqrt{3k + 1} - 4 = 0$

14. $\sqrt{5z + 1} - 11 = 0$

15. $4 - \sqrt{x - 2} = 0$

16. $9 - \sqrt{4k + 1} = 0$

17. $\sqrt{9a - 4} = \sqrt{8a + 1}$

18. $\sqrt{4p - 2} = \sqrt{3p + 5}$

19. $2\sqrt{x} = \sqrt{3x + 4}$

20. $2\sqrt{m} = \sqrt{5m - 16}$

21. $3\sqrt{z - 1} = 2\sqrt{2z + 2}$

22. $5\sqrt{4x + 1} = 3\sqrt{10x + 25}$

23. $k = \sqrt{k^2 + 4k - 20}$

24. $p = \sqrt{p^2 - 3p + 18}$

25. $x = \sqrt{x^2 + 3x + 9}$

26. $z = \sqrt{z^2 - 4z - 8}$

27. $\sqrt{9 - x} = x + 3$

28. $\sqrt{5 - x} = x + 1$

29. $\sqrt{k^2 + 2k + 9} = k + 3$

30. $\sqrt{x^2 - 3x + 3} = x - 1$

31. $\sqrt{r^2 + 9r + 3} = -r$

32. $\sqrt{p^2 - 15p + 15} = p - 5$

33. $\sqrt{z^2 + 12z - 4} + 4 - z = 0$

34. $\sqrt{m^2 + 3m + 12} - m - 2 = 0$

35. A student wrote the following as his first step in solving $\sqrt{3x + 4} = 8 - x$.

$$3x + 4 = 64 + x^2$$

WHAT WENT WRONG? Solve the given equation correctly.

36. A student wrote the following as her first step in solving $\sqrt{5x + 6} = \sqrt{x + 3} + 3$.

$$5x + 6 = x + 3 + 9$$

WHAT WENT WRONG? Solve the given equation correctly.

Solve each equation. See Examples 5 and 6.

37. $\sqrt[3]{2x + 5} = \sqrt[3]{6x + 1}$

38. $\sqrt[3]{p - 1} = 2$

39. $\sqrt[3]{a^2 + 5a + 1} = \sqrt[3]{a^2 + 4a}$

40. $\sqrt[3]{r^2 + 2r + 8} = \sqrt[3]{r^2}$

41. $\sqrt[3]{2m - 1} = \sqrt[3]{m + 13}$

42. $\sqrt[3]{2k - 11} - \sqrt[3]{5k + 1} = 0$

43. $\sqrt[4]{a + 8} = \sqrt[4]{2a}$

44. $\sqrt[4]{z + 11} = \sqrt[4]{2z + 6}$

45. $\sqrt[3]{x - 8} + 2 = 0$

46. $\sqrt[3]{r + 1} + 1 = 0$

47. $\sqrt[4]{2k - 5} + 4 = 0$

48. $\sqrt[4]{8z - 3} + 2 = 0$

49. $\sqrt{k + 2} - \sqrt{k - 3} = 1$

50. $\sqrt{r + 6} - \sqrt{r - 2} = 2$

51. $\sqrt{2r + 11} - \sqrt{5r + 1} = -1$

52. $\sqrt{3x - 2} - \sqrt{x + 3} = 1$

53. $\sqrt{3p + 4} - \sqrt{2p - 4} = 2$

54. $\sqrt{4x + 5} - \sqrt{2x + 2} = 1$

55. $\sqrt{3 - 3p} - 3 = \sqrt{3p + 2}$

56. $\sqrt{4x + 7} - 4 = \sqrt{4x - 1}$

57. $\sqrt{2\sqrt{x + 11}} = \sqrt{4x + 2}$

58. $\sqrt{1 + \sqrt{24 - 10x}} = \sqrt{3x + 5}$

For each equation, rewrite the expressions with rational exponents as radical expressions, and then solve using the procedures explained in this section.

59. $(2x - 9)^{1/2} = 2 + (x - 8)^{1/2}$

60. $(3w + 7)^{1/2} = 1 + (w + 2)^{1/2}$

61. $(2w - 1)^{2/3} - w^{1/3} = 0$

62. $(x^2 - 2x)^{1/3} - x^{1/3} = 0$

Solve each formula from electricity and radio for the indicated variable. (Source: Cooke, Nelson M., and Joseph B. Orleans, Mathematics Essential to Electricity and Radio, McGraw-Hill, 1943.)

63. $V = \sqrt{\dfrac{2K}{m}}$ for K

64. $V = \sqrt{\dfrac{2K}{m}}$ for m

65. $Z = \sqrt{\dfrac{L}{C}}$ for C

66. $Z = \sqrt{\dfrac{L}{C}}$ for L

67. $f = \dfrac{1}{2\pi\sqrt{LC}}$ for L

68. $r = \sqrt{\dfrac{Mm}{F}}$ for F

A number of useful formulas involve radicals or radical expressions. Many occur in the mathematics needed for working with objects in space. The formula

$$N = \frac{1}{2\pi}\sqrt{\frac{a}{r}}$$

is used to find the rotational rate N of a space station. Here a is the acceleration and r represents the radius of the space station in meters. To find the value of r that will make N simulate the effect of gravity on Earth, the equation must be solved for r, using the required value of N. (Source: Kastner, Bernice, Space Mathematics, NASA, 1972.)

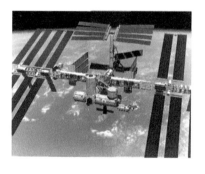

69. Solve the equation for r.

70. If $a = 9.8$ m per sec^2, find the value of r (to the nearest tenth) using each value of N.

    (a) $N = 0.063$ rotation per sec

    (b) $N = 0.04$ rotation per sec

17.8 ▶▶▶ Complex Numbers

OBJECTIVES

1 Simplify numbers of the form $\sqrt{-b}$, where $b > 0$.

2 Recognize subsets of the complex numbers.

3 Add and subtract complex numbers.

4 Multiply complex numbers.

5 Divide complex numbers.

6 Find powers of i.

As we saw in **Section 1.1,** the set of real numbers includes many other number sets (the rational numbers, integers, and natural numbers, for example). In this section, a new set of numbers is introduced that includes the set of real numbers, as well as numbers that are even roots of negative numbers, like $\sqrt{-2}$.

OBJECTIVE 1 Simplify numbers of the form $\sqrt{-b}$, where $b > 0$. The equation $x^2 + 1 = 0$ has no real number solution since any solution must be a number whose square is -1. In the set of real numbers, all squares are nonnegative numbers because the product of two positive numbers or two negative numbers is positive and $0^2 = 0$. To provide a solution for the equation $x^2 + 1 = 0$, we introduce a new number i.

Imaginary Unit i

The **imaginary unit** i is defined as

$$i = \sqrt{-1}, \quad \text{where} \quad i^2 = -1.$$

In words, i is the principal square root of -1.

This definition of i makes it possible to define any square root of a negative number as follows.

$\sqrt{-b}$

For any positive number b, $\quad \sqrt{-b} = i\sqrt{b}.$

Example 1 Simplifying Square Roots of Negative Numbers

Write each number as a product of a real number and i.

(a) $\sqrt{-100} = i\sqrt{100} = 10i$

(b) $-\sqrt{-36} = -i\sqrt{36} = -6i$

(c) $\sqrt{-2} = i\sqrt{2}$

(d) $\sqrt{-8} = i\sqrt{8} = i\sqrt{4 \cdot 2} = 2i\sqrt{2}$

CAUTION

It is easy to mistake $\sqrt{2}i$ for $\sqrt{2i}$, with the i under the radical. For this reason, we usually write $\sqrt{2}i$ as $i\sqrt{2}$, as in the definition of $\sqrt{-b}$.

Work Problem **1** *at the Side.* ▶

When finding a product such as $\sqrt{-4} \cdot \sqrt{-9}$, we cannot use the product rule for radicals because it applies only to nonnegative radicands. *For this reason, we change $\sqrt{-b}$ to the form $i\sqrt{b}$ before performing any multiplications or divisions.*

1 Write each number as a product of a real number and i.

(a) $\sqrt{-16}$

(b) $-\sqrt{-81}$

(c) $\sqrt{-7}$

(d) $\sqrt{-32}$

2 Multiply.

(a) $\sqrt{-7} \cdot \sqrt{-5}$

For example, $\sqrt{-4} \cdot \sqrt{-9}$

| First write all square roots in terms of i. | $= i\sqrt{4} \cdot i\sqrt{9}$ $\quad \sqrt{-b} = i\sqrt{b}$ |

$= i \cdot 2 \cdot i \cdot 3$

$= 6i^2$

$= 6(-1) \qquad$ Substitute: $i^2 = -1$.

$= -6$.

(b) $\sqrt{-5} \cdot \sqrt{-10}$

> **CAUTION**
> Using the product rule for radicals *before* using the definition of $\sqrt{-b}$ gives a *wrong* answer. The preceding example shows that
>
> $$\sqrt{-4} \cdot \sqrt{-9} = -6, \qquad \text{Correct}$$
>
> but $\qquad \sqrt{-4(-9)} = \sqrt{36} = 6, \qquad$ Incorrect
>
> so $\qquad \sqrt{-4} \cdot \sqrt{-9} \neq \sqrt{-4(-9)}$.

(c) $\sqrt{-15} \cdot \sqrt{2}$

Example 2 **Multiplying Square Roots of Negative Numbers**

Multiply.

(a) $\qquad \sqrt{-3} \cdot \sqrt{-7}$

| First write all square roots in terms of i. | $= i\sqrt{3} \cdot i\sqrt{7} \quad \sqrt{-b} = i\sqrt{b}$ |

$= i^2\sqrt{3 \cdot 7} \qquad$ Product rule

$= (-1)\sqrt{21} \qquad$ Substitute: $i^2 = -1$.

$= -\sqrt{21}$

3 Divide.

(a) $\dfrac{\sqrt{-32}}{\sqrt{-2}}$

(b) $\sqrt{-2} \cdot \sqrt{-8}$

$= i\sqrt{2} \cdot i\sqrt{8}$

$= i^2\sqrt{2 \cdot 8}$

$= (-1)\sqrt{16}$

$= (-1)4, \quad$ or $\quad -4$

(c) $\sqrt{-5} \cdot \sqrt{6}$

$= i\sqrt{5} \cdot \sqrt{6}$

$= i\sqrt{30}$

(b) $\dfrac{\sqrt{-27}}{\sqrt{-3}}$

◀ *Work Problem* **2** *at the Side.*

Example 3 **Dividing Square Roots of Negative Numbers**

Divide.

(a) $\dfrac{\sqrt{-75}}{\sqrt{-3}}$

(c) $\dfrac{\sqrt{-40}}{\sqrt{10}}$

| First write all square roots in terms of i. |

$= \dfrac{i\sqrt{75}}{i\sqrt{3}}$

$= \sqrt{\dfrac{75}{3}} \qquad$ Quotient rule

$= \sqrt{25} \qquad$ Divide.

$= 5$

(b) $\dfrac{\sqrt{-32}}{\sqrt{8}}$

$= \dfrac{i\sqrt{32}}{\sqrt{8}}$

$= i\sqrt{\dfrac{32}{8}}$

$= i\sqrt{4}$

$= 2i$

ANSWERS

2. (a) $-\sqrt{35}$ (b) $-5\sqrt{2}$ (c) $i\sqrt{30}$
3. (a) 4 (b) 3 (c) 2i

◀ *Work Problem* **3** *at the Side.*

OBJECTIVE 2 **Recognize subsets of the complex numbers.**
With the imaginary unit i and the real numbers, a new set of numbers can be
formed that includes the real numbers as a subset. The *complex numbers* are
defined as follows.

Complex Number

If a and b are real numbers, then any number of the form $a + bi$ is
called a **complex number.** In the complex number $a + bi$, the number a
is called the **real part** and b is called the **imaginary part.***

For a complex number $a + bi$, if $b = 0$, then $a + bi = a$, which is a real
number. ***Thus, the set of real numbers is a subset of the set of complex
numbers.*** If $a = 0$ and $b \neq 0$, the complex number is said to be a **pure
imaginary number.** For example, $3i$ is a pure imaginary number. A number
such as $7 + 2i$ is a **nonreal complex number.** These numbers are very useful in applications, particularly in work with electricity.
   The relationships among the sets of numbers are shown in Figure 10.

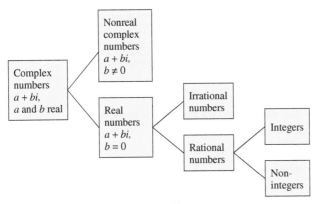

Figure 10

OBJECTIVE 3 **Add and subtract complex numbers.**   The commutative, associative, and distributive properties for real numbers are also
valid for complex numbers. ***Thus, to add complex numbers, we add their
real parts and add their imaginary parts.***

Example 4   **Adding Complex Numbers**

Add.

(a) $(2 + 3i) + (6 + 4i)$

$\qquad = (2 + 6) + (3 + 4)i$ Commutative, associative, and distributive properties

$\qquad = 8 + 7i$ Add real parts; add imaginary parts.

(b) $5 + (9 - 3i)$

$\qquad = (5 + 9) - 3i$ Associative property

$\qquad = 14 - 3i$ Add real parts.

Work Problem **4** at the Side. ▶

---

4 Add.

(a) $(4 + 6i) + (-3 + 5i)$

(b) $(-1 + 8i) + (9 - 3i)$

ANSWERS

4. **(a)** $1 + 11i$ **(b)** $8 + 5i$

5 Subtract.

(a) $(7 + 3i) - (4 + 2i)$

(b) $(-6 - i) - (-5 - 4i)$

(c) $8 - (3 - 2i)$

To subtract complex numbers, we subtract their real parts and subtract their imaginary parts.

> **Example 5** **Subtracting Complex Numbers**
>
> Subtract.
>
> **(a)** $(6 + 5i) - (3 + 2i)$
>
> $\quad = (6 - 3) + (5 - 2)i$ Properties of real numbers
>
> $\quad = 3 + 3i$ Subtract real parts; subtract imaginary parts.
>
> **(b)** $(7 - 3i) - (8 - 6i)$ **(c)** $(-9 + 4i) - (-9 + 8i)$
>
> $\quad = (7 - 8) + [-3 - (-6)]i$ $= (-9 + 9) + (4 - 8)i$
>
> $\quad = -1 + 3i$ $= 0 - 4i$
>
> $= -4i$

◀ *Work Problem* **5** *at the Side.*

In Example 5(c), the answer was written as $0 - 4i$ and then as just $-4i$. A complex number written in the form $a + bi$, like $0 - 4i$, is in **standard form**. In this section, most answers will be given in standard form, but if a or b is 0, we consider answers such as a or bi to be in standard form.

OBJECTIVE **4** **Multiply complex numbers.** We multiply complex numbers as we multiply polynomials.

> **Example 6** **Multiplying Complex Numbers**
>
> Multiply.
>
> **(a)** $4i(2 + 3i)$
>
> $\quad = 4i(2) + 4i(3i)$ Distributive property
>
> $\quad = 8i + 12i^2$ Multiply.
>
> $\quad = 8i + 12(-1)$ Substitute: $i^2 = -1$.
>
> $\quad = -12 + 8i$ Standard form
>
> **(b)** $(3 + 5i)(4 - 2i)$
>
> $\quad = \underbrace{3(4)}_{\text{First}} + \underbrace{3(-2i)}_{\text{Outer}} + \underbrace{5i(4)}_{\text{Inner}} + \underbrace{5i(-2i)}_{\text{Last}}$ Use the FOIL method for multiplying binomials. **(Section 6.4)**
>
> $\quad = 12 - 6i + 20i - 10i^2$ Multiply.
>
> $\quad = 12 + 14i - 10(-1)$ Combine imaginary terms; $i^2 = -1$.
>
> $\quad = 12 + 14i + 10$ Multiply.
>
> $\quad = 22 + 14i$ Combine real terms.
>
> **(c)** $(2 + 3i)(1 - 5i)$
>
> $\quad = 2(1) + 2(-5i) + 3i(1) + 3i(-5i)$ FOIL
>
> $\quad = 2 - 10i + 3i - 15i^2$
>
> $\quad = 2 - 7i - 15(-1)$ Use parentheses around -1 to avoid errors.
>
> $\quad = 2 - 7i + 15$
>
> $\quad = 17 - 7i$

6 Multiply.

(a) $6i(4 + 3i)$

(b) $(6 - 4i)(2 + 4i)$

(c) $(3 - 2i)(3 + 2i)$

ANSWERS

5. **(a)** $3 + i$ **(b)** $-1 + 3i$ **(c)** $5 + 2i$
6. **(a)** $-18 + 24i$ **(b)** $28 + 16i$ **(c)** 13

◀ *Work Problem* **6** *at the Side.*

The two complex numbers $a + bi$ and $a - bi$ are called *complex conjugates,* or simply *conjugates,* of each other. ***The product of a complex number and its conjugate is always a real number,*** as shown here.

$$(a + bi)(a - bi) = a^2 - abi + abi - b^2 i^2$$
$$= a^2 - b^2(-1)$$
$$(a + bi)(a - bi) = a^2 + b^2$$

The product eliminates i.

For example, $(3 + 7i)(3 - 7i) = 3^2 + 7^2 = 9 + 49 = 58$.

OBJECTIVE 5 Divide complex numbers. The quotient of two complex numbers should be a complex number. To write the quotient as a complex number, we need to eliminate i in the denominator. We use conjugates and a process like that for rationalizing a denominator to do this.

Example 7 Dividing Complex Numbers

Find each quotient.

(a) $\dfrac{8 + 9i}{5 + 2i}$

Multiply both the numerator and denominator by the conjugate of the denominator. The conjugate of $5 + 2i$ is $5 - 2i$.

$$\frac{8 + 9i}{5 + 2i}$$

$$= \frac{(8 + 9i)(5 - 2i)}{(5 + 2i)(5 - 2i)} \qquad \tfrac{5 - 2i}{5 - 2i} = 1$$

$$= \frac{40 - 16i + 45i - 18i^2}{5^2 + 2^2} \qquad \begin{array}{l}\text{In the denominator,}\\ (a + bi)(a - bi) = a^2 + b^2.\end{array}$$

$$= \frac{58 + 29i}{29} \qquad \begin{array}{l}-18i^2 = -18(-1) = 18;\\ \text{Combine like terms.}\end{array}$$

$$= \frac{29(2 + i)}{29} \qquad \text{Factor the numerator.}$$

Factor first; then divide out the common factor.

$$= 2 + i \qquad \text{Lowest terms}$$

(b) $\dfrac{1 + i}{i}$

$$= \frac{(1 + i)(-i)}{i(-i)} \qquad \begin{array}{l}\text{Multiply numerator and denominator by } -i,\\ \text{the conjugate of } i.\end{array}$$

$$= \frac{-i - i^2}{-i^2} \qquad \text{Distributive property; multiply.}$$

$$= \frac{-i - (-1)}{-(-1)} \qquad \text{Substitute: } i^2 = -1.$$

$$= \frac{-i + 1}{1} \qquad \begin{array}{l}\text{Use parentheses}\\ \text{to avoid errors.}\end{array}$$

$$= 1 - i$$

Work Problem **7** *at the Side.* ▶

---

7 Find each quotient.

(a) $\dfrac{2 + i}{3 - i}$

(b) $\dfrac{8 - 4i}{1 - i}$

(c) $\dfrac{5}{3 - 2i}$

(d) $\dfrac{5 - i}{i}$

8 Find each power of i.

(a) i^{21}

(b) i^{36}

(c) i^{50}

(d) i^{-9}

▦ **Calculator Tip** In Examples 4–7, we showed how complex numbers can be added, subtracted, multiplied, and divided algebraically. Many current models of graphing calculators can perform these operations. Figure 11 shows how the computations in parts of Examples 4–7 are displayed on a TI-83/84 Plus calculator. Be sure to use parentheses as shown.

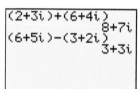
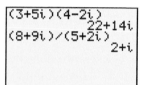

Figure 11

OBJECTIVE 6 Find powers of i. Because i^2 is defined to be -1, we can find higher powers of i as shown in the following examples.

$$i^3 = i \cdot i^2 = i(-1) = -i \qquad i^6 = i^2 \cdot i^4 = (-1) \cdot 1 = -1$$

$$i^4 = i^2 \cdot i^2 = (-1)(-1) = 1 \qquad i^7 = i^3 \cdot i^4 = (-i) \cdot 1 = -i$$

$$i^5 = i \cdot i^4 = i \cdot 1 = i \qquad i^8 = i^4 \cdot i^4 = 1 \cdot 1 = 1$$

As these examples suggest, the powers of i rotate through the four numbers i, -1, $-i$, and 1. Larger powers of i can be simplified by using the fact that $i^4 = 1$. For example,

$$i^{75} = (i^4)^{18} \cdot i^3 = 1^{18} \cdot i^3 = 1 \cdot i^3 = i^3 = -i.$$

Example 8 **Simplifying Powers of i**

Find each power of i.

(a) $i^{12} = (i^4)^3 = 1^3 = 1$

(b) $i^{39} = i^{36} \cdot i^3 = (i^4)^9 \cdot i^3 = 1^9 \cdot (-i) = -i$

(c) $i^{-2} = \dfrac{1}{i^2} = \dfrac{1}{-1} = -1$

(d) $i^{-1} = \dfrac{1}{i} = \dfrac{1(-i)}{i(-i)} = \dfrac{-i}{-i^2} = \dfrac{-i}{-(-1)} = \dfrac{-i}{1} = -i$

◀ *Work Problem* **8** *at the Side.*

17.8 ▶▶▶ **Exercises**

FOR EXTRA HELP

MyMathLab

Math XL
PRACTICE

WATCH

DOWNLOAD

READ

REVIEW

Decide whether each expression is equal to $1, -1, i,$ *or* $-i$.

1. $\sqrt{-1}$

2. $-i^2$

3. $\dfrac{1}{i}$

4. $(-i)^2$

5. Every real number is a complex number. Explain why this is so.

6. Not every complex number is a real number. Give an example of this, and explain why this statement is true.

Write each number as a product of a real number and i. Simplify all radical expressions. See Example 1.

⊙ **7.** $\sqrt{-169}$

8. $\sqrt{-225}$

9. $-\sqrt{-144}$

10. $-\sqrt{-196}$

11. $\sqrt{-5}$

12. $\sqrt{-21}$

13. $\sqrt{-48}$

14. $\sqrt{-96}$

Multiply or divide as indicated. See Examples 2 and 3.

15. $\sqrt{-15} \cdot \sqrt{-15}$

16. $\sqrt{-19} \cdot \sqrt{-19}$

17. $\sqrt{-3} \cdot \sqrt{-19}$

18. $\sqrt{-7} \cdot \sqrt{-15}$

19. $\sqrt{-4} \cdot \sqrt{-25}$

20. $\sqrt{-9} \cdot \sqrt{-81}$

21. $\sqrt{-3} \cdot \sqrt{11}$

22. $\sqrt{-5} \cdot \sqrt{13}$

23. $\dfrac{\sqrt{-300}}{\sqrt{-100}}$

24. $\dfrac{\sqrt{-40}}{\sqrt{-10}}$

⊙ **25.** $\dfrac{\sqrt{-75}}{\sqrt{3}}$

26. $\dfrac{\sqrt{-160}}{\sqrt{10}}$

Add or subtract as indicated. Write your answers in standard form. See Examples 4 and 5.

⊙ **27.** $(3 + 2i) + (-4 + 5i)$

28. $(7 + 15i) + (-11 + 14i)$

29. $(5 - i) + (-5 + i)$

30. $(-2 + 6i) + (2 - 6i)$

⊙ **31.** $(4 + i) - (-3 - 2i)$

32. $(9 + i) - (3 + 2i)$

33. $(-3 - 4i) - (-1 - 4i)$

34. $(-2 - 3i) - (-5 - 3i)$

35. $(-4 + 11i) + (-2 - 4i) + (7 + 6i)$

36. $(-1 + i) + (2 + 5i) + (3 + 2i)$

37. $[(7 + 3i) - (4 - 2i)] + (3 + i)$

38. $[(7 + 2i) + (-4 - i)] - (2 + 5i)$

39. Fill in the blank with the correct response: Because $(4 + 2i) - (3 + i) = 1 + i$, using the definition of subtraction we can check this to find that

$$(1 + i) + (3 + i) = \underline{\hspace{1cm}}.$$

40. Fill in the blank with the correct response: Because $\frac{-5}{2 - i} = -2 - i$, using the definition of division we can check this to find that

$$(-2 - i)(2 - i) = \underline{\hspace{1cm}}.$$

Multiply. See Example 6.

41. $(3i)(27i)$

42. $(5i)(125i)$

43. $(-8i)(-2i)$

44. $(-32i)(-2i)$

45. $5i(-6 + 2i)$

46. $3i(4 + 9i)$

47. $(4 + 3i)(1 - 2i)$

48. $(7 - 2i)(3 + i)$

49. $(4 + 5i)^2$

50. $(3 + 2i)^2$

51. $(12 + 3i)(12 - 3i)$

52. $(6 + 7i)(6 - 7i)$

53. (a) What is the conjugate of $a + bi$?

(b) If we multiply $a + bi$ by its conjugate, we get, _____ + _____, which is always a real number.

54. Explain the procedure you would use to find the quotient

$$\frac{-1 + 5i}{3 + 2i}.$$

Write each quotient in the form $a + bi$. See Example 7.

55. $\dfrac{2}{1 - i}$

56. $\dfrac{29}{5 + 2i}$

57. $\dfrac{-7 + 4i}{3 + 2i}$

58. $\dfrac{-38 - 8i}{7 + 3i}$

59. $\dfrac{8i}{2 + 2i}$

60. $\dfrac{-8i}{1 + i}$

61. $\dfrac{2 - 3i}{2 + 3i}$

62. $\dfrac{-1 + 5i}{3 + 2i}$

Relating Concepts (Exercises 63–68) For Individual or Group Work

Consider these expressions:

Binomials	**Complex Numbers**
$x + 2, \quad 3x - 1$	$1 + 2i, \quad 3 - i.$

*When we add, subtract, or multiply complex numbers in standard form, the rules are the same as those for the corresponding operations on binomials. That is, we add or subtract like terms, and we use FOIL to multiply. Division, however, is comparable to division by the sum or difference of radicals, where we multiply by the conjugate of the denominator to get a rational denominator. To express the quotient of two complex numbers in standard form, we also multiply by the conjugate of the denominator. **Work Exercises 63–68 in order,** to better understand these ideas.*

63. (a) Add the two binomials.

(b) Add the two complex numbers.

64. (a) Subtract the second binomial from the first.

(b) Subtract the second complex number from the first.

65. (a) Multiply the two binomials.

(b) Multiply the two complex numbers.

66. (a) Rationalize the denominator: $\dfrac{\sqrt{3} - 1}{1 + \sqrt{2}}$.

(b) Write in standard form: $\dfrac{3 - i}{1 + 2i}$.

67. Explain why the answers for parts (a) and (b) in Exercise 65 do not correspond as the answers in Exercises 63 and 64 do.

68. Explain why the answers for parts (a) and (b) in Exercise 66 do not correspond as the answers in Exercises 63 and 64 do.

69. Recall that if $a \neq 0$, then $\frac{1}{a}$ is called the reciprocal of a. Use this definition to express the reciprocal of $5 - 4i$ in the form $a + bi$.

70. Recall that if $a \neq 0$, then a^{-1} is defined to be $\frac{1}{a}$. Use this definition to express $(4 - 3i)^{-1}$ in the form $a + bi$.

Find each power of i. See Example 8.

71. i^{18}

72. i^{26}

73. i^{89}

74. i^{45}

75. i^{96}

76. i^{48}

77. i^{-5}

78. i^{-17}

79. A student simplified i^{-18} as follows:

$$i^{-18} = i^{-18} \cdot i^{20} = i^{-18+20} = i^2 = -1.$$

Explain the mathematical justification for this correct work.

80. Explain why

$$(46 + 25i)(3 - 6i) \quad \text{and} \quad (46 + 25i)(3 - 6i)i^{12}$$

must be equal. (Do not actually perform the computation.)

Ohm's law *for the current I in a circuit with voltage E, resistance R, capacitance reactance*
X_c, *and inductive reactance* X_L *is*

$$I = \frac{E}{R + (X_L - X_c)i}.$$

Use this law to work Exercises 81 and 82.

81. Find I if $E = 2 + 3i$, $R = 5$, $X_L = 4$, and $X_c = 3$. 　　**82.** Find E if $I = 1 - i$, $R = 2$, $X_L = 3$, and $X_c = 1$.

83. Show that $1 + 5i$ is a solution of

$$x^2 - 2x + 26 = 0.$$

84. Show that $3 + 2i$ is a solution of

$$x^2 - 6x + 13 = 0.$$

18

Quadratics

OBJECTIVES

1 Solve equations of the form $x^2 = k$, where $k > 0$.

2 Solve equations of the form $(ax + b)^2 = k$, where $k > 0$.

3 Use formulas involving squared variables.

A **quadratic equation** is an equation that can be written in the form

$$ax^2 + bx + c = 0 \qquad \text{Standard form}$$

for real numbers a, b, and c, with $a \neq 0$. As we saw in **Section 14.6**, we can solve a quadratic equation such as $x^2 + 4x + 3 = 0$ by first factoring and then applying the zero-factor property.

$$x^2 + 4x + 3 = 0$$

$$(x + 3)(x + 1) = 0 \qquad \text{Factor.}$$

$$x + 3 = 0 \quad \text{or} \quad x + 1 = 0 \qquad \text{Zero-factor property}$$

$$x = -3 \quad \text{or} \qquad x = -1 \qquad \text{Solve each equation.}$$

The solution set is $\{-3, -1\}$.

◀ Work Problem **1** at the Side.

1 Solve each equation by factoring.

(a) $x^2 - 2x - 15 = 0$

OBJECTIVE 1 Solve equations of the form $x^2 = k$, where $k > 0$.
We can solve an equation such as $x^2 = 9$ by factoring as follows.

$$x^2 = 9$$

$$x^2 - 9 = 0 \qquad \text{Subtract 9.}$$

$$(x + 3)(x - 3) = 0 \qquad \text{Factor.}$$

$$x + 3 = 0 \quad \text{or} \quad x - 3 = 0 \qquad \text{Zero-factor property}$$

$$x = -3 \quad \text{or} \qquad x = 3 \qquad \text{Solve each equation.}$$

We might also solve $x^2 = 9$ by noticing that x must be a number whose square is 9. Thus, $x = \sqrt{9} = 3$ or $x = -\sqrt{9} = -3$. This approach is generalized as the **square root property.**

> **Square Root Property**
> If k is a positive number and if $x^2 = k$, then
> $$x = \sqrt{k} \quad \text{or} \quad x = -\sqrt{k}$$

(b) $2x^2 - 3x + 1 = 0$

EXAMPLE 1 Solving Quadratic Equations of the Form $x^2 = k$

Solve each equation. Write radicals in simplified form.

(a) $x^2 = 16$
By the square root property, if $x^2 = 16$, then

$$x = \sqrt{16} = 4 \quad \text{or} \quad x = -\sqrt{16} = -4.$$

An abbreviation for $x = 4$ or $x = -4$ is $x = \pm 4$ (read "positive or negative 4"). Check each solution by substituting it for x in the original equation. The solution set is $\{-4, 4\}$, or $\{\pm 4\}$.

(b) $z^2 = 5$
The solutions are $z = \sqrt{5}$ or $z = -\sqrt{5}$, so the solution set is $\{-\sqrt{5}, \sqrt{5}\}$, or $\{\pm\sqrt{5}\}$.

Continued on Next Page

(c)
$$5m^2 - 32 = 8$$

$$5m^2 = 40 \qquad \text{Add 32.}$$

$$m^2 = 8 \qquad \text{Divide by 5.}$$

> Don't stop here. Simplify the radicals.

$$m = \sqrt{8} \quad \text{or} \quad m = -\sqrt{8} \qquad \text{Square root property}$$

$$m = 2\sqrt{2} \quad \text{or} \quad m = -2\sqrt{2} \qquad \sqrt{8} = \sqrt{4}\cdot\sqrt{2} = 2\sqrt{2}$$

The solution set is $\left\{-2\sqrt{2}, 2\sqrt{2}\right\}$, or $\left\{\pm 2\sqrt{2}\right\}$.

(d) $x^2 = -4$

Because -4 is a negative number and because the square of a real number cannot be negative, **there is no real number solution** of this equation. (In this book, we are concerned with finding only *real number* solutions. To use the square root property to find both real number solutions, k must be positive.) The solution set is $\emptyset$.

Work Problem (2) *at the Side.* ▶

OBJECTIVE 2 **Solve equations of the form $(ax + b)^2 = k$, where $k > 0$.** In each equation in Example 1, the exponent 2 had a single variable as its base. We can extend the square root property to solve equations in which the base is a binomial, as shown in the next example.

EXAMPLE 2 | **Solving Quadratic Equations of the Form $(x + b)^2 = k$**

Solve each equation.

(a) Use $x - 3$ as the base. → $(x - 3)^2 = 16$

$$x - 3 = \sqrt{16} \quad \text{or} \quad x - 3 = -\sqrt{16} \qquad \text{Square root property}$$

$$x - 3 = 4 \quad \text{or} \quad x - 3 = -4 \qquad \sqrt{16} = 4$$

$$x = 7 \quad \text{or} \quad x = -1 \qquad \text{Add 3.}$$

Check   Substitute each solution in the original equation.

$$(x - 3)^2 = 16 \qquad\qquad (x - 3)^2 = 16$$

$$(7 - 3)^2 \overset{?}{=} 16 \quad \text{Let } x = 7. \qquad (-1 - 3)^2 \overset{?}{=} 16 \quad \text{Let } x = -1.$$

$$4^2 \overset{?}{=} 16 \qquad\qquad\qquad (-4)^2 \overset{?}{=} 16$$

$$16 = 16 \quad \text{True} \qquad\qquad 16 = 16 \quad \text{True}$$

The solutions are 7 and -1, and the solution set is $\{-1, 7\}$.

(b)
$$(x + 1)^2 = 6$$

$$x + 1 = \sqrt{6} \quad \text{or} \quad x + 1 = -\sqrt{6} \qquad \text{Square root property}$$

$$x = -1 + \sqrt{6} \quad \text{or} \quad x = -1 - \sqrt{6} \qquad \text{Add } -1.$$

Check
$$\left(-1 + \sqrt{6} + 1\right)^2 = \left(\sqrt{6}\right)^2 = 6;$$

$$\left(-1 - \sqrt{6} + 1\right)^2 = \left(-\sqrt{6}\right)^2 = 6.$$

The solution set is $\left\{-1 + \sqrt{6}, -1 - \sqrt{6}\right\}$, or $\left\{-1 \pm \sqrt{6}\right\}$.

Work Problem (3) *at the Side.* ▶

---

2 Solve each equation. Write radicals in simplified form.

(a) $x^2 = 49$

(b) $x^2 = 11$

(c) $2x^2 + 8 = 32$

(d) $x^2 = -9$

3 Solve each equation.

(a) $(x + 2)^2 = 36$

(b) $(x - 4)^2 = 3$

ANSWERS

2. (a) $\{-7, 7\}$ **(b)** $\left\{-\sqrt{11}, \sqrt{11}\right\}$
  (c) $\left\{-2\sqrt{3}, 2\sqrt{3}\right\}$ **(d)** $\emptyset$

3. (a) $\{-8, 4\}$ **(b)** $\left\{4 + \sqrt{3}, 4 - \sqrt{3}\right\}$

4 Solve $(2x - 5)^2 = 18$.

5 Solve each equation.

(a) $(5x + 1)^2 = 7$

(b) $(7x - 1)^2 = -1$

6 Use the formula in Example 5 to approximate the length of a bass weighing 2.80 lb and having a girth of 11 in.

EXAMPLE 3 **Solving a Quadratic Equation of the Form $(ax + b)^2 = k$**

Solve $(3r - 2)^2 = 27$.

$$3r - 2 = \sqrt{27} \qquad \text{or} \quad 3r - 2 = -\sqrt{27} \qquad \text{Square root property}$$

$\qquad\qquad\qquad\qquad\qquad\qquad\qquad\qquad\qquad\quad \sqrt{27} = \sqrt{9} \cdot \sqrt{3}$
$\qquad\qquad\qquad\qquad\qquad\qquad\qquad\qquad\qquad\qquad\quad = 3\sqrt{3}$

$$3r - 2 = 3\sqrt{3} \qquad \text{or} \quad 3r - 2 = -3\sqrt{3}$$

$$3r = 2 + 3\sqrt{3} \quad \text{or} \qquad 3r = 2 - 3\sqrt{3} \qquad \text{Add 2.}$$

$$r = \frac{2 + 3\sqrt{3}}{3} \quad \text{or} \qquad r = \frac{2 - 3\sqrt{3}}{3} \qquad \text{Divide by 3.}$$

The solution set is $\left\{ \dfrac{2 + 3\sqrt{3}}{3}, \dfrac{2 - 3\sqrt{3}}{3} \right\}$.

◀ *Work Problem* **4** *at the Side.*

> **CAUTION**
> The solutions in Example 3 are fractions that cannot be simplified. Note that 3 is *not* a common factor in the numerator.

EXAMPLE 4 **Recognizing When There Is No Real Solution**

Solve $(x + 3)^2 = -9$.

Because the square root of -9 is not a real number, there is no real number solution for this equation. The solution set is $\emptyset$.

◀ *Work Problem* **5** *at the Side.*

OBJECTIVE **3** **Use formulas involving squared variables.**

EXAMPLE 5 **Finding the Length of a Bass**

We can approximate the weight of a bass, in pounds, given its length L and its girth (distance around) g, where both are measured in inches, using this formula.

$$w = \frac{L^2 g}{1200}$$

Approximate the length of a bass weighing 2.20 lb and having a girth of 10 in. (*Source: Sacramento Bee.*)

$$w = \frac{L^2 g}{1200} \qquad \text{Given formula}$$

$$2.20 = \frac{L^2 \cdot 10}{1200} \qquad w = 2.20, g = 10$$

$$2640 = 10L^2 \qquad \text{Multiply by 1200.}$$

$$L^2 = 264 \qquad \text{Divide by 10; interchange the sides.}$$

$$L = \sqrt{264} \quad \text{or} \quad L = -\sqrt{264} \qquad \text{Square root property}$$

A calculator shows that $\sqrt{264} \approx 16.25$, so the length of the bass is a little more than 16 in. (We discard the negative solution $-\sqrt{264} \approx -16.25$, since L represents length.)

◀ *Work Problem* **6** *at the Side.*

18.1 ▶▶▶ **Exercises**

FOR
EXTRA
HELP

MyMathLab

Math XL
PRACTICE

WATCH

DOWNLOAD

READ

REVIEW

Decide whether each statement is true *or* false. *If* false, *tell why.*

1. If k is a prime number, then $x^2 = k$ has two irrational solutions.

2. If k is a positive perfect square, then $x^2 = k$ has two rational solutions.

3. If k is a positive integer, then $x^2 = k$ must have two rational solutions.

4. If $-10 < k < 0$, then $x^2 = k$ has no real solution.

5. If $-10 < k < 10$, then $x^2 = k$ has no real solution.

6. If k is an integer greater than 24 and less than 26, then $x^2 = k$ has two solutions, -5 and 5.

Solve each equation by using the square root property. Write all radicals in simplest form. See Example 1.

7. $x^2 = 81$

8. $x^2 = 121$

⏺ **9.** $k^2 = 14$

10. $m^2 = 22$

11. $t^2 = 48$

12. $x^2 = 54$

13. $x^2 = \dfrac{25}{4}$

14. $m^2 = \dfrac{36}{121}$

15. $x^2 = -100$

16. $x^2 = -64$

17. $z^2 = 2.25$

18. $w^2 = 56.25$

19. $r^2 - 3 = 0$

20. $x^2 - 13 = 0$

21. $7x^2 = 4$

22. $3x^2 = 10$

23. $4x^2 - 72 = 0$

24. $5z^2 - 200 = 0$

25. $3x^2 - 8 = 64$

26. $2x^2 + 7 = 61$

27. $5x^2 + 4 = 8$

28. $4x^2 - 3 = 7$

Solve each equation by using the square root property. Express all radicals in simplest form. See Examples 2–4.

29. $(x - 3)^2 = 25$

30. $(x - 7)^2 = 16$

31. $(x + 5)^2 = -13$

32. $(x + 2)^2 = -17$

33. $(x - 8)^2 = 27$

34. $(x - 5)^2 = 40$

35. $(3x + 2)^2 = 49$

36. $(5x + 3)^2 = 36$

37. $(4x - 3)^2 = 9$

38. $(7x - 5)^2 = 25$

39. $(5 - 2x)^2 = 30$

40. $(3 - 2x)^2 = 70$

🌐 **41.** $(3x + 1)^2 = 18$

42. $(5x + 6)^2 = 75$

43. $\left(\dfrac{1}{2}x + 5\right)^2 = 12$

44. $\left(\dfrac{1}{3}x + 4\right)^2 = 27$

45. $(4x - 1)^2 - 48 = 0$

46. $(2x - 5)^2 - 180 = 0$

47. Johnny solved the equation in Exercise 39 and wrote his answer as $\left\{\dfrac{5 + \sqrt{30}}{2}, \dfrac{5 - \sqrt{30}}{2}\right\}$.

Terry solved the same equation and wrote her answer as $\left\{\dfrac{-5 + \sqrt{30}}{-2}, \dfrac{-5 - \sqrt{30}}{-2}\right\}$.

The teacher gave them both full credit. Explain why both students were correct, although their answers seem to differ.

48. In the solutions found in Example 3 of this section, why is it not valid to simplify by dividing out the 3s in the numerators and denominators?

Solve each problem. See Example 5.

49. One expert at marksmanship can hold a silver dollar at forehead level, drop it, draw his gun, and shoot the coin as it passes waist level. The distance traveled by a falling object is given by

$$d = 16t^2,$$

where d is the distance (in feet) the object falls in t seconds. If the coin falls about 4 ft, use the formula to estimate the time that elapses between the dropping of the coin and the shot.

50. The illumination produced by a light source depends on the distance from the source. For a particular light source, this relationship can be expressed as

$$d^2 = \frac{4050}{I},$$

where d is the distance from the source (in feet) and I is the amount of illumination in foot-candles. How far from the source is the illumination equal to 50 foot-candles?

51. The area A of a circle with radius r is given by the formula

$$A = \pi r^2.$$

If a circle has area 81π in.², what is its radius?

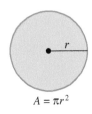

$A = \pi r^2$

52. The surface area S of a sphere with radius r is given by the formula

$$S = 4\pi r^2.$$

If a sphere has surface area 36π ft², what is its radius?

$S = 4\pi r^2$

The amount A that P dollars invested at an annual rate of interest r will grow to in 2 yr is
$A = P(1 + r)^2.$

53. At what interest rate will $100 grow to $110.25 in 2 yr?

54. At what interest rate will $500 grow to $572.45 in 2 yr?

55. At what interest rate will $200 grow to $208.08 in 2 yr?

18.2 ▶▶▶ Solving Quadratic Equations by Completing the Square

OBJECTIVE **1** **Solve quadratic equations by completing the square when the coefficient of the second-degree term is 1.** The methods we have studied so far are not enough to solve this equation.

$$x^2 + 6x + 7 = 0$$

If we could write the equation in the form $(x + 3)^2$ equals a constant, we could solve it with the square root property discussed in **Section 18.1.** To do that, we need to have a perfect square trinomial on one side of the equation. Recall from **Section 14.5** that a perfect square trinomial has the form

$$x^2 + 2kx + k^2 \quad \text{or} \quad x^2 - 2kx + k^2,$$

where k represents a positive number.

EXAMPLE 1 **Creating Perfect Square Trinomials**

Complete each trinomial so that it is a perfect square. Then factor the trinomial.

(a) $x^2 + 8x +$ _____

The perfect square trinomial will have the form $x^2 + 2kx + k^2$. Thus, the middle term, $8x$, must equal $2kx$.

$$8x = 2kx \quad \longleftarrow \text{ Solve this equation for } k.$$
$$4 = k \qquad \text{Divide each side by } 2x.$$

Therefore, $k = 4$ and $k^2 = 4^2 = 16$. The required perfect square trinomial is

$$x^2 + 8x + 16, \quad \text{which factors as} \quad (x + 4)^2.$$

(b) $x^2 - 18x +$ _____

Here the perfect square trinomial will have the form $x^2 - 2kx + k^2$. The middle term, $-18x$, must equal $-2kx$.

$$-18x = -2kx \quad \longleftarrow \text{ Solve this equation for } k.$$
$$9 = k \qquad \text{Divide each side by } -2x.$$

Thus, $k = 9$ and $k^2 = 9^2 = 81$. The required perfect square trinomial is

$$x^2 - 18x + 81, \quad \text{which factors as} \quad (x - 9)^2.$$

Work Problem **1** *at the Side.* ▶

EXAMPLE 2 **Rewriting an Equation to Use the Square Root Property**

Solve $x^2 + 6x + 7 = 0$.

$$x^2 + 6x = -7 \qquad \text{Subtract 7 from each side.}$$

To solve this equation with the square root property, the quantity on the left side, $x^2 + 6x$, must be written as a perfect square trinomial in the form $x^2 + 2kx + k^2$.

$$x^2 + 6x +$ _____

Here, $2kx = 6x$, so $k = 3$ and $k^2 = 9$. The required perfect square trinomial is

$$x^2 + 6x + 9, \quad \text{which factors as} \quad (x + 3)^2.$$

Continued on Next Page

OBJECTIVES

1 Solve quadratic equations by completing the square when the coefficient of the second-degree term is 1.

2 Solve quadratic equations by completing the square when the coefficient of the second-degree term is not 1.

3 Simplify the terms of an equation before solving.

4 Solve applied problems that require quadratic equations.

1 Complete each trinomial so that it is a perfect square. Then factor the trinomial.

(a) $x^2 + 12x +$ _____

(b) $x^2 - 14x +$ _____

(c) $x^2 - 2x +$ _____

ANSWERS

1. **(a)** 36; $(x + 6)^2$
   (b) 49; $(x - 7)^2$
   (c) 1; $(x - 1)^2$

2 Solve $x^2 - 4x - 1 = 0$.

Therefore, if we add 9 to *each* side of $x^2 + 6x = -7$, the equation will have a perfect square trinomial on the left side, as needed.

> This is a key step.

$$x^2 + 6x + 9 = -7 + 9 \qquad \text{Add 9.}$$
$$(x + 3)^2 = 2 \qquad \text{Factor; add.}$$

Now use the square root property to complete the solution.

$$x + 3 = \sqrt{2} \qquad \text{or} \quad x + 3 = -\sqrt{2}$$
$$x = -3 + \sqrt{2} \quad \text{or} \qquad x = -3 - \sqrt{2}$$

Check by substituting $-3 + \sqrt{2}$ and $-3 - \sqrt{2}$ for x in the original equation. The solution set is $\left\{-3 + \sqrt{2}, -3 - \sqrt{2}\right\}$.

◀ *Work Problem* **2** *at the Side.*

The process of changing the form of the equation in Example 2 from

$$x^2 + 6x + 7 = 0 \quad \text{to} \quad (x + 3)^2 = 2$$

is called **completing the square.** Completing the square changes only the form of the equation. To see this, multiply out the left side of $(x + 3)^2 = 2$. Then write the equation in standard form to get $x^2 + 6x + 7 = 0$.

3 Solve each equation by completing the square.

(a) $x^2 + 4x = 1$

Look again at the original equation in Example 2,

$$x^2 + 6x + 7 = 0.$$

If we take half of 6, the coefficient of x, and square it, we get 9.

$$\frac{1}{2} \cdot 6 = 3 \quad \text{and} \quad 3^2 = 9$$

Coefficient of x Quantity added to each side

To complete the square in Example 2, we added 9 to each side.

EXAMPLE 3 **Completing the Square to Solve a Quadratic Equation**

Complete the square to solve $x^2 - 8x = 5$.

(b) $z^2 + 6z - 3 = 0$

To complete the square on $x^2 - 8x$, take half of -8, the coefficient of x, and square it.

$$\frac{1}{2}(-8) = -4 \quad \text{and} \quad (-4)^2 = 16$$

Coefficient of x

Add the result, 16, to each side of the equation.

$$x^2 - 8x = 5 \qquad\qquad \text{Given equation}$$
$$x^2 - 8x + 16 = 5 + 16 \qquad \text{Add 16.}$$
$$(x - 4)^2 = 21 \qquad\qquad \text{Factor; add.}$$
$$x - 4 = \sqrt{21} \qquad \text{or} \quad x - 4 = -\sqrt{21} \qquad \text{Square root property}$$
$$x = 4 + \sqrt{21} \quad \text{or} \qquad x = 4 - \sqrt{21} \qquad \text{Add 4.}$$

A check indicates that the solution set is $\left\{4 + \sqrt{21}, 4 - \sqrt{21}\right\}$.

◀ *Work Problem* **3** *at the Side.*

ANSWERS

2. $\left\{2 + \sqrt{5}, 2 - \sqrt{5}\right\}$

3. (a) $\left\{-2 + \sqrt{5}, -2 - \sqrt{5}\right\}$

  (b) $\left\{-3 + 2\sqrt{3}, -3 - 2\sqrt{3}\right\}$

OBJECTIVE **2** **Solve quadratic equations by completing the square when the coefficient of the second-degree term is not 1.**
If a quadratic equation has the form

$$ax^2 + bx + c = 0, \quad \text{where } a \neq 1,$$

then to obtain 1 as the coefficient of x^2, we first divide each side of the equation by a.

4 Solve each equation by completing the square.

(a) $9x^2 + 18x = -5$

EXAMPLE 4 **Solving a Quadratic Equation by Completing the Square**

Solve $4x^2 + 16x = 9$.
 Before completing the square, the coefficient of x^2 must be 1, not 4. We get 1 as the coefficient of x^2 here by dividing each side by 4.

$$4x^2 + 16x = 9$$

The coefficient of x^2 must be 1. ⟶ $\quad x^2 + 4x = \dfrac{9}{4} \quad$ Divide by 4.

Next, we begin to complete the square by taking half the coefficient of x, and squaring it:

$$\frac{1}{2}(4) = 2 \quad \text{and} \quad 2^2 = 4.$$

We add the result, 4, to each side of the equation.

$$x^2 + 4x + 4 = \frac{9}{4} + 4 \quad \text{Add 4.}$$

$$(x + 2)^2 = \frac{25}{4} \quad \text{Factor; } \tfrac{9}{4} + 4 = \tfrac{9}{4} + \tfrac{16}{4} = \tfrac{25}{4}.$$

(b) $4t^2 - 24t + 11 = 0$

$$x + 2 = \sqrt{\frac{25}{4}} \quad \text{or} \quad x + 2 = -\sqrt{\frac{25}{4}} \quad \text{Square root property}$$

$$x + 2 = \frac{5}{2} \quad \text{or} \quad x + 2 = -\frac{5}{2} \quad \text{Take square roots.}$$

$$x = -2 + \frac{5}{2} \quad \text{or} \quad x = -2 - \frac{5}{2} \quad \text{Subtract 2.}$$

$$x = \frac{1}{2} \quad \text{or} \quad x = -\frac{9}{2} \quad {-2 = -\tfrac{4}{2}}$$

Check

$$4x^2 + 16x = 9 \qquad\qquad\qquad 4x^2 + 16x = 9$$

$$4\left(\frac{1}{2}\right)^2 + 16\left(\frac{1}{2}\right) \stackrel{?}{=} 9 \qquad 4\left(-\frac{9}{2}\right)^2 + 16\left(-\frac{9}{2}\right) \stackrel{?}{=} 9$$

$$4\left(\frac{1}{4}\right) + 8 \stackrel{?}{=} 9 \qquad\qquad 4\left(\frac{81}{4}\right) - 72 \stackrel{?}{=} 9$$

$$1 + 8 \stackrel{?}{=} 9 \qquad\qquad\qquad 81 - 72 \stackrel{?}{=} 9$$

$$9 = 9 \quad \text{True} \qquad\qquad\qquad 9 = 9 \quad \text{True}$$

The two solutions, $\frac{1}{2}$ and $-\frac{9}{2}$, check, so the solution set is $\left\{-\frac{9}{2}, \frac{1}{2}\right\}$.

Work Problem **4** *at the Side.* ▶

The steps used to solve a quadratic equation $ax^2 + bx + c = 0$ by completing the square are summarized here.

5 Solve each equation by completing the square.

(a) $3x^2 + 5x - 2 = 0$

Solving a Quadratic Equation by Completing the Square

Step 1 **Be sure the second-degree term has coefficient 1.** If the coefficient of the second-degree term is 1, proceed to Step 2. If it is not 1, but some other nonzero number a, divide each side of the equation by a.

Step 2 **Write in correct form.** Make sure that all terms with variables are on one side of the equals sign and that all constant terms are on the other side.

Step 3 **Complete the square.** Take half the coefficient of the first-degree term, and square it. Add the square to each side of the equation. Factor the variable side, and simplify on the other side.

Step 4 **Solve** the equation by using the square root property.

EXAMPLE 5 **Solving a Quadratic Equation by Completing the Square**

Solve $2x^2 - 7x - 9 = 0$.

Step 1 Get 1 as the coefficient of the x^2-term.

$$x^2 - \frac{7}{2}x - \frac{9}{2} = 0 \qquad \text{Divide by 2.}$$

(b) $2x^2 - 4x - 1 = 0$

Step 2 Add $\frac{9}{2}$ to each side to get the variable terms on the left and the constant on the right.

$$x^2 - \frac{7}{2}x = \frac{9}{2} \qquad \text{Add } \tfrac{9}{2}.$$

Step 3 To complete the square, take half the coefficient of x and square it: $\left[\frac{1}{2}\left(-\frac{7}{2}\right)\right]^2 = \left(-\frac{7}{4}\right)^2 = \frac{49}{16}$.

$$x^2 - \frac{7}{2}x + \frac{49}{16} = \frac{9}{2} + \frac{49}{16} \qquad \text{Be sure to add } \tfrac{49}{16} \text{ to each side.}$$

$$\left(x - \frac{7}{4}\right)^2 = \frac{121}{16} \qquad \text{Factor; } \tfrac{9}{2} + \tfrac{49}{16} = \tfrac{72}{16} + \tfrac{49}{16} = \tfrac{121}{16}.$$

Step 4 Solve by using the square root property.

$$x - \frac{7}{4} = \sqrt{\frac{121}{16}} \quad \text{or} \quad x - \frac{7}{4} = -\sqrt{\frac{121}{16}} \qquad \text{Square root property}$$

$$x = \frac{7}{4} + \frac{11}{4} \quad \text{or} \quad x = \frac{7}{4} - \frac{11}{4} \qquad \text{Add } \tfrac{7}{4}; \sqrt{\tfrac{121}{16}} = \tfrac{11}{4}.$$

$$x = \frac{18}{4} = \frac{9}{2} \quad \text{or} \quad x = -\frac{4}{4} = -1 \qquad \text{Simplify.}$$

A check confirms that the solution set is $\left\{-1, \frac{9}{2}\right\}$.

ANSWERS

5. (a) $\left\{-2, \frac{1}{3}\right\}$ (b) $\left\{\dfrac{2 + \sqrt{6}}{2}, \dfrac{2 - \sqrt{6}}{2}\right\}$

EXAMPLE 6 Solving a Quadratic Equation by Completing the Square

Solve $4p^2 + 8p + 5 = 0$.

$$4p^2 + 8p + 5 = 0$$

> The coefficient of the second-degree term must be 1.

$$p^2 + 2p + \frac{5}{4} = 0 \qquad \text{Divide by 4.}$$

$$p^2 + 2p = -\frac{5}{4} \qquad \text{Subtract } \tfrac{5}{4}.$$

The coefficient of p is 2. Take half of 2; square the result: $\left[\frac{1}{2}(2)\right]^2 = 1^2 = 1$. Add this result to each side. Then write the left side as a perfect square.

$$p^2 + 2p + 1 = -\frac{5}{4} + 1 \qquad \text{Add 1.}$$

$$(p + 1)^2 = -\frac{1}{4} \qquad \text{Factor; add.}$$

We cannot use the square root property to solve this equation, because the square root of $-\frac{1}{4}$ is not a real number. This equation has no real number solution.* The solution set is $\emptyset$.

Work Problem **6** *at the Side.* ▶

OBJECTIVE **3** Simplify the terms of an equation before solving.

EXAMPLE 7 Simplifying before Completing the Square

Solve $(x + 3)(x - 1) = 2$.

$$(x + 3)(x - 1) = 2 \qquad \text{Given equation}$$
$$x^2 + 2x - 3 = 2 \qquad \text{Multiply using the FOIL method.}$$
$$x^2 + 2x = 5 \qquad \text{Add 3.}$$
$$x^2 + 2x + 1 = 5 + 1 \qquad \text{Complete the square—add } [\tfrac{1}{2}(2)]^2 = 1.$$
$$(x + 1)^2 = 6 \qquad \text{Factor on the left; add on the right.}$$

$$x + 1 = \sqrt{6} \qquad \text{or} \qquad x + 1 = -\sqrt{6} \qquad \text{Square root property}$$
$$x = -1 + \sqrt{6} \quad \text{or} \qquad x = -1 - \sqrt{6} \qquad \text{Add } -1.$$

The solution set is $\{-1 + \sqrt{6}, -1 - \sqrt{6}\}$.

Work Problem **7** *at the Side.* ▶

Note
The solutions $-1 \pm \sqrt{6}$ given in Example 7 are *exact*. In applications, decimal solutions are more appropriate. Using the square root key of a calculator, $\sqrt{6} \approx 2.449$. Approximating the two solutions gives

$$x \approx 1.449 \quad \text{and} \quad x \approx -3.449.$$

6 Solve $5x^2 + 3x + 1 = 0$ by completing the square.

7 Solve each equation.

   (a) $r(r - 3) = -1$

   (b) $(x + 2)(x + 1) = 5$

---

*The equation in Example 6 has no solution over the *real number system*. In the **complex number system,** however, this equation does have solutions. The complex numbers include numbers whose squares are negative. These numbers are discussed in intermediate and college algebra courses.

8 Suppose a ball is projected upward from ground level with an initial velocity of 128 ft per sec. Its height at time t (in seconds) is given by

$$s = -16t^2 + 128t,$$

where s is in feet. At what times will it be 48 ft above the ground? Give answers to the nearest tenth.

OBJECTIVE **4** **Solve applied problems that require quadratic equations.** There are many practical applications of quadratic equations. The next example illustrates an application from physics.

EXAMPLE 8   **Solving a Velocity Problem**

If a ball is projected into the air from ground level with an initial velocity of 64 ft per sec, its altitude (height) s in feet in t seconds is given by the formula

$$s = -16t^2 + 64t.$$

How long will it take the ball to be 48 ft above the ground?

Since s represents the height, we substitute **48** for s in the formula and then solve this equation for time t by completing the square.

$48 = -16t^2 + 64t$	Let $s = 48$.
$-3 = t^2 - 4t$	Divide by -16.
$t^2 - 4t = -3$	Interchange the sides.
$t^2 - 4t + 4 = -3 + 4$	Add $\left[\frac{1}{2}(-4)\right]^2 = 4$.
$(t - 2)^2 = 1$	Factor; add.
$t - 2 = 1 \quad \text{or} \quad t - 2 = -1$	Square root property
$t = 3 \quad \text{or} \quad\quad t = 1$	Add 2.

The ball reaches a height of 48 ft twice, once on the way up and again on the way down. It takes 1 sec to reach 48 ft on the way up, and then after 3 sec, the ball reaches 48 ft again on the way down.

◀ *Work Problem* **8** *at the Side.*

18.2 ▶▶▶ **Exercises**

FOR
EXTRA
HELP

Complete each trinomial so that it is a perfect square. Then factor the trinomial.
See Example 1.

1. $x^2 + 10x +$ _____

2. $x^2 + 16x +$ _____

3. $x^2 + 2x +$ _____

4. $m^2 - 2m +$ _____

5. $p^2 - 5p +$ _____

6. $x^2 + 3x +$ _____

7. Which step is an appropriate way to begin solving the quadratic equation

$$2x^2 - 4x = 9$$

by completing the square?

A. Add 4 to each side of the equation.
B. Factor the left side as $2x(x - 2)$.
C. Factor the left side as $x(2x - 4)$.
D. Divide each side by 2.

8. In Example 3 of **Section 14.6,** we solved the quadratic equation

$$4p^2 - 26p + 40 = 0$$

by factoring. If we were to solve by completing the square, would we get the same solutions, $\frac{5}{2}$ and 4?

Solve each equation by completing the square. See Examples 2 and 3.

9. $x^2 - 4x = -3$

10. $x^2 - 2x = 8$

11. $x^2 + 5x + 6 = 0$

12. $x^2 + 6x + 5 = 0$

13. $x^2 + 2x - 5 = 0$

14. $x^2 + 4x + 1 = 0$

15. $x^2 - 8x = -4$

16. $m^2 - 4m = 14$

17. $t^2 + 6t + 9 = 0$

18. $k^2 - 8k + 16 = 0$

19. $x^2 + x - 1 = 0$

20. $x^2 + x - 3 = 0$

Solve each equation by completing the square. See Examples 4–7.

21. $4x^2 + 4x - 3 = 0$

22. $9x^2 + 3x - 2 = 0$

23. $2x^2 - 4x = 5$

24. $2x^2 - 6x = 3$

25. $2p^2 - 2p + 3 = 0$

26. $3q^2 - 3q + 4 = 0$

27. $3k^2 + 7k = 4$

28. $2k^2 + 5k = 1$

29. $(x + 3)(x - 1) = 5$

30. $(y - 8)(y + 2) = 24$

31. $(r - 3)(r - 5) = 2$

32. $(k - 1)(k - 7) = 1$

33. $-x^2 + 2x = -5$

34. $-r^2 + 3r = -2$

Solve each problem. See Example 8.

35. If an object is projected upward from ground level on Earth with an initial velocity of 96 ft per sec, its altitude (height) s in feet in t seconds is given by the formula $s = -16t^2 + 96t$. At what times will the object be 80 ft above the ground?

36. At what times will the object described in Exercise 35 be 100 ft above the ground? Round your answers to the nearest tenth.

37. If an object is projected upward on the surface of Mars from ground level with an initial velocity of 104 ft per sec, its altitude (height) s in feet in t seconds is given by the formula $s = -13t^2 + 104t$. At what times will the object be 195 ft above the surface?

38. After how many seconds will the object in Exercise 37 return to the surface? (*Hint:* When it returns to the surface, $s = 0$.)

39. A farmer has a rectangular cattle pen with perimeter 350 ft and area 7500 ft². What are the dimensions of the pen? (*Hint:* Use the figure to set up the equation.)

$175 - x$

40. The base of a triangle measures 1 m more than three times the height of the triangle. Its area is 15 m². Find the lengths of the base and the height.

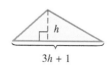

$3h + 1$

18.3 ▶▶▶ The Quadratic Formula

In this section, we complete the square to solve the general quadratic equation

$$ax^2 + bx + c = 0,$$

where a, b, and c are complex numbers and $a \neq 0$. The solution of this general equation gives a formula for finding the solution of *any* specific quadratic equation.

OBJECTIVE 1 Derive the quadratic formula. To solve the general quadratic equation $ax^2 + bx + c = 0$ by completing the square (assuming $a > 0$), we follow the steps given in **Section 10.1**.

$$ax^2 + bx + c = 0$$

$$x^2 + \frac{b}{a}x + \frac{c}{a} = 0 \qquad \text{Divide by } a. \text{ (Step 1)}$$

$$x^2 + \frac{b}{a}x = -\frac{c}{a} \qquad \text{Subtract } \tfrac{c}{a}. \text{ (Step 2)}$$

$$\left[\frac{1}{2}\left(\frac{b}{a}\right)\right]^2 = \left(\frac{b}{2a}\right)^2 = \frac{b^2}{4a^2} \qquad \text{(Step 3)}$$

$$x^2 + \frac{b}{a}x + \frac{b^2}{4a^2} = -\frac{c}{a} + \frac{b^2}{4a^2} \qquad \text{Add } \frac{b^2}{4a^2} \text{ to each side. (Step 4)}$$

Write the left side as a perfect square, and rearrange the right side.

$$\left(x + \frac{b}{2a}\right)^2 = \frac{b^2}{4a^2} + \frac{-c}{a} \qquad \text{(Step 5)}$$

$$\left(x + \frac{b}{2a}\right)^2 = \frac{b^2}{4a^2} + \frac{-4ac}{4a^2} \qquad \text{Write with a common denominator.}$$

$$\left(x + \frac{b}{2a}\right)^2 = \frac{b^2 - 4ac}{4a^2} \qquad \text{Add fractions.}$$

$$x + \frac{b}{2a} = \sqrt{\frac{b^2 - 4ac}{4a^2}} \quad \text{or} \quad x + \frac{b}{2a} = -\sqrt{\frac{b^2 - 4ac}{4a^2}} \qquad \begin{array}{l}\text{Square root}\\\text{property}\\\text{(Step 6)}\end{array}$$

Since

$$\sqrt{\frac{b^2 - 4ac}{4a^2}} = \frac{\sqrt{b^2 - 4ac}}{\sqrt{4a^2}} = \frac{\sqrt{b^2 - 4ac}}{2a},$$

the right sides of these equations can be expressed as

$$x + \frac{b}{2a} = \frac{\sqrt{b^2 - 4ac}}{2a} \qquad \text{or} \quad x + \frac{b}{2a} = \frac{-\sqrt{b^2 - 4ac}}{2a}$$

$$x = \frac{-b}{2a} + \frac{\sqrt{b^2 - 4ac}}{2a} \qquad \text{or} \qquad x = \frac{-b}{2a} - \frac{\sqrt{b^2 - 4ac}}{2a}$$

$$x = \frac{-b + \sqrt{b^2 - 4ac}}{2a} \qquad \text{or} \qquad x = \frac{-b - \sqrt{b^2 - 4ac}}{2a}.$$

If $a < 0$, the same two solutions are obtained. The result is the **quadratic formula,** which is abbreviated as shown on the next page.

OBJECTIVES

1 **Derive the quadratic formula.**

2 **Solve quadratic equations by using the quadratic formula.**

3 **Use the discriminant to determine the number and type of solutions.**

1 Identify the values of a, b, and c. (*Hint:* If necessary, first write the equation in standard form with 0 on the right side.) *Do not actually solve.*

(a) $-3x^2 + 9x - 4 = 0$

> **Quadratic Formula**
>
> The solutions of $ax^2 + bx + c = 0 \ (a \neq 0)$ are given by
> $$x = \frac{-b \pm \sqrt{b^2 - 4ac}}{2a}.$$

> **CAUTION**
>
> In the quadratic formula, $x = \dfrac{-b \pm \sqrt{b^2 - 4ac}}{2a}$, *the square root is added to or subtracted from the value of $-b$ before dividing by $2a$.* A common student error is to fail to divide **all** of the expression $-b \pm \sqrt{b^2 - 4ac}$ by $2a$.

OBJECTIVE 2 Solve quadratic equations by using the quadratic formula. To use the quadratic formula, first write the equation in standard form

$$ax^2 + bx + c = 0.$$

(b) $3x^2 = 6x + 2$

Then identify the values of a, b, and c and substitute them into the quadratic formula.

◀ *Work Problem* **1** *at the Side.*

Example 1 **Using the Quadratic Formula (Rational Solutions)**

Solve $6x^2 - 5x - 4 = 0$.

Here a, the coefficient of the second-degree term, is 6, while b, the coefficient of the first-degree term, is -5, and the constant c is -4. Substitute these values into the quadratic formula.

$$x = \frac{-b \pm \sqrt{b^2 - 4ac}}{2a} \qquad \text{Quadratic formula}$$

2 Solve $4x^2 - 11x - 3 = 0$ using the quadratic formula.

$$x = \frac{-(-5) \pm \sqrt{(-5)^2 - 4(6)(-4)}}{2(6)} \qquad a = 6, b = -5, c = -4$$

Use parentheses and substitute carefully to avoid errors.

$$x = \frac{5 \pm \sqrt{25 + 96}}{12}$$

$$x = \frac{5 \pm \sqrt{121}}{12}$$

$$x = \frac{5 \pm 11}{12}$$

This last statement leads to two solutions, one from the $+$ sign and one from the $-$ sign.

$$x = \frac{5 + 11}{12} = \frac{16}{12} = \frac{4}{3} \quad \text{or} \quad x = \frac{5 - 11}{12} = \frac{-6}{12} = -\frac{1}{2}$$

Check each solution in the original equation. The solution set is $\left\{-\frac{1}{2}, \frac{4}{3}\right\}$.

◀ *Work Problem* **2** *at the Side.*

We could have used factoring to solve the equation in Example 1.

$$6x^2 - 5x - 4 = 0$$

$(3x - 4)(2x + 1) = 0$ Factor.

$3x - 4 = 0$ or $2x + 1 = 0$ Zero-factor property

$3x = 4$ or $2x = -1$ Solve each equation.

$x = \dfrac{4}{3}$ or $x = -\dfrac{1}{2}$ Same solutions as in Example 1

When solving quadratic equations, it is a good idea to try factoring first. If the equation cannot be factored or if factoring is difficult, then use the quadratic formula. Later in this section, we will show a way to determine whether factoring can be used to solve a quadratic equation.

Example 2 **Using the Quadratic Formula (Irrational Solutions)**

Solve $4x^2 = 8x - 1$.

Write the equation in standard form as $4x^2 - 8x + 1 = 0$.

$$x = \frac{-b \pm \sqrt{b^2 - 4ac}}{2a}$$ Quadratic formula

$$x = \frac{-(-8) \pm \sqrt{(-8)^2 - 4(4)(1)}}{2(4)}$$ $a = 4, b = -8, c = 1$

$$x = \frac{8 \pm \sqrt{64 - 16}}{8}$$

$$x = \frac{8 \pm \sqrt{48}}{8}$$

$$x = \frac{8 \pm 4\sqrt{3}}{8}$$ $\sqrt{48} = \sqrt{16} \cdot \sqrt{3} = 4\sqrt{3}$

$$x = \frac{4(2 \pm \sqrt{3})}{4(2)}$$ $\boxed{\text{Factor first; then divide out the common factor.}}$ Factor.

$$x = \frac{2 \pm \sqrt{3}}{2}$$ Lowest terms

The solution set is $\left\{ \dfrac{2 + \sqrt{3}}{2}, \dfrac{2 - \sqrt{3}}{2} \right\}$.

---

3 Solve each equation using the quadratic formula.

(a) $6x^2 + 4x - 1 = 0$

(b) $2x^2 + 19 = 14x$

CAUTION

1. *Every quadratic equation must be written in standard form* $ax^2 + bx + c = 0$ *before we begin to solve it,* whether we use factoring or the quadratic formula.

2. *When writing solutions in lowest terms, be sure to factor first; then divide out the common factor,* as shown in the last two steps in Example 2.

ANSWERS

3. (a) $\left\{ \dfrac{-2 + \sqrt{10}}{6}, \dfrac{-2 - \sqrt{10}}{6} \right\}$

(b) $\left\{ \dfrac{7 + \sqrt{11}}{2}, \dfrac{7 - \sqrt{11}}{2} \right\}$

4 Solve each equation using the quadratic formula.

(a) $x^2 + x + 1 = 0$

(b) $(x + 2)(x - 6) = -17$

Example 3 **Using the Quadratic Formula (Nonreal Complex Solutions)**

Solve $(9x + 3)(x - 1) = -8$.

To write this equation in standard form, we first multiply and collect all nonzero terms on the left.

$$(9x + 3)(x - 1) = -8$$

$$9x^2 - 6x - 3 = -8 \qquad \text{Multiply.}$$

$$9x^2 - 6x + 5 = 0 \qquad \text{Add 8.}$$

From the equation $9x^2 - 6x + 5 = 0$, we identify $a = 9$, $b = -6$, and $c = 5$.

$$x = \frac{-b \pm \sqrt{b^2 - 4ac}}{2a} \qquad \text{Quadratic formula}$$

$$x = \frac{-(-6) \pm \sqrt{(-6)^2 - 4(9)(5)}}{2(9)} \qquad \text{Substitute.}$$

$$x = \frac{6 \pm \sqrt{-144}}{18}$$

$$x = \frac{6 \pm 12i}{18} \qquad \sqrt{-144} = 12i$$

$$x = \frac{6(1 \pm 2i)}{6(3)} \qquad \text{Factor.}$$

$$x = \frac{1 \pm 2i}{3} \qquad \text{Lowest terms}$$

$$x = \frac{1}{3} \pm \frac{2}{3}i \qquad \begin{array}{l}\text{Standard form } a + bi \text{ for a}\\ \text{complex number}\end{array}$$

The solution set is $\left\{ \dfrac{1}{3} + \dfrac{2}{3}i, \dfrac{1}{3} - \dfrac{2}{3}i \right\}$.

◀ *Work Problem* **4** *at the Side.*

OBJECTIVE **3** **Use the discriminant to determine the number and type of solutions.** The solutions of the quadratic equation $ax^2 + bx + c = 0$ are given by

$$x = \frac{-b \pm \sqrt{b^2 - 4ac}}{2a}. \quad \leftarrow \text{Discriminant}$$

If a, b, and c are integers, the type of solutions of a quadratic equation—that is, rational, irrational, or nonreal complex—is determined by the expression under the radical sign, $b^2 - 4ac$. Because it distinguishes among the three types of solutions, $b^2 - 4ac$ is called the *discriminant*. By calculating the discriminant before solving a quadratic equation, we can predict whether the solutions will be rational numbers, irrational numbers, or nonreal complex numbers.

ANSWERS

4. **(a)** $\left\{ -\dfrac{1}{2} + \dfrac{\sqrt{3}}{2}i, -\dfrac{1}{2} - \dfrac{\sqrt{3}}{2}i \right\}$

(b) $\{2 + i, 2 - i\}$

Discriminant

The **discriminant** of $ax^2 + bx + c = 0$ is $b^2 - 4ac$. If a, b, and c are integers, then the number and type of solutions are determined as follows.

Discriminant	Number and Type of Solutions
Positive, and the square of an integer	Two rational solutions
Positive, but not the square of an integer	Two irrational solutions
Zero	One rational solution
Negative	Two nonreal complex solutions

Calculating the discriminant can also help you decide whether to solve a quadratic equation by factoring or by using the quadratic formula. *If the discriminant is a perfect square (including 0), then the equation can be solved by factoring. Otherwise, the quadratic formula (or completing the square) should be used.*

Example 4 **Using the Discriminant**

Find the discriminant. Use it to predict the number and type of solutions for each equation. Tell whether the equation can be solved by factoring or whether the quadratic formula should be used.

(a) $6x^2 - x - 15 = 0$

First identify the values of a, b, and c. Because $-x = -1x$, the value of b is -1. We find the discriminant by evaluating $b^2 - 4ac$.

$$b^2 - 4ac$$
$$= (-1)^2 - 4\,(6)\,(-15) \qquad a = 6, b = -1, c = -15$$
$$= 1 + 360 \qquad \text{Use parentheses and substitute carefully.}$$
$$= 361$$

A calculator shows that $361 = 19^2$, a perfect square. Since a, b, and c are integers and the discriminant is a perfect square, there will be two rational solutions and the equation can be solved by factoring.

(b) $3x^2 - 4x = 5$

Write the equation in standard form as

$$3x^2 - 4x - 5 = 0 \qquad \text{Subtract 5.}$$

to find $a = 3$, $b = -4$, and $c = -5$. The discriminant is

$$b^2 - 4ac$$
$$= (-4)^2 - 4\,(3)\,(-5)$$
$$= 16 + 60$$
$$= 76.$$

Because 76 is positive but *not* the square of an integer and a, b, and c are integers, the equation will have two irrational solutions and is best solved using the quadratic formula.

Continued on Next Page

5 Find the discriminant. Use it to predict the number and type of solutions for each equation.

(a) $2x^2 + 3x = 4$

(b) $2x^2 + 3x + 4 = 0$

(c) $x^2 + 20x + 100 = 0$

(d) $15x^2 + 11x = 14$

(e) Which of the equations in parts (a)–(d) can be solved by factoring?

(c) $4x^2 + x + 1 = 0$

Since $a = 4$, $b = 1$, and $c = 1$, the discriminant is

$$b^2 - 4ac$$
$$= 1^2 - 4\,(4)\,(1)$$
$$= 1 - 16$$
$$= -15.$$

Since the discriminant is negative and a, b, and c are integers, this quadratic equation will have two nonreal complex solutions. The quadratic formula should be used to solve it.

(d) $4x^2 + 9 = 12x$

Write the equation in standard form as

$$4x^2 - 12x + 9 = 0 \qquad \text{Subtract } 12x.$$

to find $a = 4$, $b = -12$, and $c = 9$. The discriminant is

$$b^2 - 4ac$$
$$= (-12)^2 - 4\,(4)\,(9)$$
$$= 144 - 144$$
$$= 0.$$

Because the discriminant is 0, the quantity under the radical in the quadratic formula is 0, and there is only one rational solution. Again, the equation can be solved by factoring.

◀ *Work Problem* **5** *at the Side.*

Note

In **Section 18.6** we will see how the discriminant can be used to determine the number of x-intercepts of the graph of a quadratic function.

18.3 ▶▶▶ **Exercises**

FOR EXTRA HELP

 MyMathLab

Math XL
PRACTICE

WATCH

DOWNLOAD

READ

REVIEW

1. A student wrote the following as the quadratic formula for solving $ax^2 + bx + c = 0, a \neq 0$:

$$x = -b \pm \frac{\sqrt{b^2 - 4ac}}{2a}.$$

This is incorrect. **WHAT WENT WRONG?**

2. A student attempted to solve the equation $5x^2 - 5x + 1 = 0$ as follows.

$$x = \frac{5 \pm \sqrt{25 - 4(5)(1)}}{2(5)} \qquad a = 5, b = -5, c = 1$$

$$x = \frac{5 \pm \sqrt{5}}{10}$$

$$x = \frac{1}{2} \pm \sqrt{5}$$

This is incorrect. **WHAT WENT WRONG?**

Use the quadratic formula to solve each equation. (All solutions for these equations are real numbers.) See Examples 1 and 2.

3. $x^2 - 8x + 15 = 0$

4. $x^2 + 3x - 28 = 0$

5. $2x^2 + 4x + 1 = 0$

6. $2x^2 + 3x - 1 = 0$

7. $2x^2 - 2x = 1$

8. $9x^2 + 6x = 1$

9. $x^2 + 18 = 10x$

10. $x^2 - 4 = 2x$

11. $4k^2 + 4k - 1 = 0$

12. $4r^2 - 4r - 19 = 0$

13. $2 - 2x = 3x^2$

14. $26r - 2 = 3r^2$

15. $\dfrac{x^2}{4} - \dfrac{x}{2} = 1$

(*Hint:* First clear the fractions.)

16. $p^2 + \dfrac{p}{3} = \dfrac{1}{6}$

(*Hint:* First clear the fractions.)

17. $-2t(t+2) = -3$

18. $-3x(x+2) = -4$

19. $(r-3)(r+5) = 2$

20. $(k+1)(k-7) = 1$

Use the quadratic formula to solve each equation. (All solutions for these equations are nonreal complex numbers.) See Example 3.

21. $x^2 - 3x + 17 = 0$

22. $x^2 - 5x + 20 = 0$

23. $r^2 - 6r + 14 = 0$

24. $t^2 + 4t + 11 = 0$

25. $4x^2 - 4x = -7$

26. $9x^2 - 6x = -7$

27. $x(3x+4) = -2$

28. $p(2p+3) = -2$

Use the discriminant to determine whether the solutions for each equation are

    A. *two rational numbers,*   **B.** *one rational number,*

    C. *two irrational numbers,*   **D.** *two nonreal complex numbers.*

Do not actually solve. See Example 4.

29. $25x^2 + 70x + 49 = 0$

30. $4k^2 - 28k + 49 = 0$

31. $x^2 + 4x + 2 = 0$

32. $9x^2 - 12x - 1 = 0$

33. $3x^2 = 5x + 2$

34. $4x^2 = 4x + 3$

35. $3m^2 - 10m + 15 = 0$

36. $18x^2 + 60x + 82 = 0$

37. Using the discriminant, which equations in Exercises 29–36 can be solved by factoring?

38. Based on your answer in Exercise 37, solve the equation given in each exercise.

    (a) Exercise 29   **(b)** Exercise 33

18.4 ▶▶▶ Equations Quadratic in Form

OBJECTIVE 1 Solve an equation with fractions by writing it in quadratic form. A variety of nonquadratic equations can be written in the form of a quadratic equation and solved by using one of the methods from **Sections 10.1 and 18.3.**

Example 1 Solving an Equation with Fractions That Leads to a Quadratic Equation

Solve $\dfrac{1}{x} + \dfrac{1}{x-1} = \dfrac{7}{12}$.

Clear fractions by multiplying each side by the least common denominator, $12x(x-1)$. (Note that the domain must be restricted to $x \neq 0$ and $x \neq 1$.)

$$12x(x-1)\left(\frac{1}{x} + \frac{1}{x+1}\right) = 12x(x-1)\left(\frac{7}{12}\right)$$

$$12x(x-1)\frac{1}{x} + 12x(x-1)\frac{1}{x-1} = 12x(x-1)\left(\frac{7}{12}\right) \quad \text{Distributive property}$$

$$12(x-1) + 12x = 7x(x-1)$$

$$12x - 12 + 12x = 7x^2 - 7x \quad \text{Distributive property}$$

$$24x - 12 = 7x^2 - 7x \quad \text{Combine like terms.}$$

$$7x^2 - 31x + 12 = 0 \quad \text{Standard form}$$

$$(7x-3)(x-4) = 0 \quad \text{Factor.}$$

$$7x - 3 = 0 \quad \text{or} \quad x - 4 = 0 \quad \text{Zero-factor property}$$

$$x = \frac{3}{7} \quad \text{or} \quad x = 4 \quad \text{Solve each equation.}$$

Check by substituting these solutions in the original equation. The solution set is $\left\{\frac{3}{7}, 4\right\}$.

Work Problem 1 *at the Side.* ▶

OBJECTIVE 2 Use quadratic equations to solve applied problems. In **Sections 2.4 and 8.5** we solved distance-rate-time (or motion) problems that led to linear equations or rational equations. Now we can extend that work to motion problems that lead to quadratic equations. We continue to use the six-step problem-solving method from **Section 2.3.**

Example 2 Solving a Motion Problem

A riverboat for tourists averages 12 mph in still water. It takes the boat 1 hr, 4 min to go 6 mi upstream and return. Find the speed of the current.

Step 1 **Read** the problem carefully.

Step 2 **Assign a variable.** Let $x =$ the speed of the current.

The current slows down the boat when it is going upstream, so the rate (or speed) upstream is the speed of the boat in still water less the speed of the current, or $(12 - x)$ mph. See Figure 1 on the next page.

Continued on Next Page

Continued on Next Page

OBJECTIVES

1. Solve an equation with fractions by writing it in quadratic form.
2. Use quadratic equations to solve applied problems.
3. Solve an equation with radicals by writing it in quadratic form.
4. Solve an equation that is quadratic in form by substitution.

1. Solve each equation. Check your solutions.

(a) $\dfrac{5}{m} + \dfrac{12}{m^2} = 2$

(b) $\dfrac{2}{x} + \dfrac{1}{x-2} = \dfrac{5}{3}$

(c) $\dfrac{4}{m-1} + 9 = -\dfrac{7}{m}$

Riverboat traveling *upstream*—the current slows it down.

Figure 1

Similarly, the current speeds up the boat as it travels downstream, so its speed downstream is $(12 + x)$ mph. Thus,

$12 - x =$ the rate upstream in miles per hour;

$12 + x =$ the rate downstream in miles per hour.

This information can be used to complete a table. We use the distance formula, $d = rt$, solved for time t, $t = \frac{d}{r}$, to write expressions for t.

	d	r	t
Upstream	6	$12 - x$	$\dfrac{6}{12 - x}$
Downstream	6	$12 + x$	$\dfrac{6}{12 + x}$

Times in hours

Step 3   **Write an equation.** The total time, 1 hr and 4 min, can be written as

$$1 + \frac{4}{60} = 1 + \frac{1}{15} = \frac{16}{15} \text{ hr.}$$

Because the time upstream plus the time downstream equals $\frac{16}{15}$ hr,

Time upstream $+$ time downstream $=$ total time.

$$\frac{6}{12 - x} \quad + \quad \frac{6}{12 + x} \quad = \quad \frac{16}{15}.$$

Step 4   **Solve** the equation. Multiply each side by $15(12 - x)(12 + x)$, the LCD, and solve the resulting quadratic equation.

$$15(12 + x)6 + 15(12 - x)6 = 16(12 - x)(12 + x)$$

$$90(12 + x) + 90(12 - x) = 16(144 - x^2)$$

$$1080 + 90x + 1080 - 90x = 2304 - 16x^2 \qquad \text{Distributive property}$$

$$2160 = 2304 - 16x^2 \qquad \text{Combine like terms.}$$

$$16x^2 = 144$$

$$x^2 = 9 \qquad \text{Divide by 16.}$$

$$x = 3 \quad \text{or} \quad x = -3 \qquad \text{Square root property}$$

Step 5   **State the answer.** The speed of the current cannot be -3, so the answer is 3 mph.

Step 6   **Check** that this value satisfies the original problem.

CAUTION
As shown in Example 2, when a quadratic equation is used to solve an applied problem, sometimes only *one* answer satisfies the application. ***Always check each answer in the words of the original problem.***

Work Problem **2** *at the Side.* ▶

Recall from **Section 8.5** that a person's work rate is $\frac{1}{t}$ part of the job per hour, where t is the time in hours required to do the complete job. Thus, the part of the job the person will do in x hours is $\frac{1}{t}x$.

Example 3 **Solving a Work Problem**

It takes two carpet layers 4 hr to carpet a room. If each worked alone, one of them could do the job in 1 hr less time than the other. How long would it take each carpet layer to complete the job alone?

Step 1 **Read** the problem again. There will be two answers.

Step 2 **Assign a variable.** Let $x =$ the number of hours for the slower carpet layer to complete the job alone. Then the faster carpet layer could do the entire job in $(x - 1)$ hours. The slower person's rate is $\frac{1}{x}$, and the faster person's rate is $\frac{1}{x - 1}$. Together, they can do the job in 4 hr. Complete a table as shown.

	Rate	Time Working Together	Fractional Part of the Job Done
Slower Worker	$\frac{1}{x}$	4	$\frac{1}{x}(4)$
Faster Worker	$\frac{1}{x - 1}$	4	$\frac{1}{x - 1}(4)$

Sum is 1 whole job.

Step 3 **Write an equation.** The sum of the fractional parts done by the workers should equal 1 (the whole job).

Part done by slower worker + part done by faster worker = 1 whole job.

$$\frac{4}{x} + \frac{4}{x - 1} = 1$$

Step 4 **Solve** the equation. Multiply by $x(x - 1)$, the LCD.

$$x(x - 1)\left(\frac{4}{x} + \frac{4}{x - 1}\right) = x(x - 1)(1) \quad \text{Multiply by the LCD.}$$

$$4(x - 1) + 4x = x(x - 1) \quad \text{Distributive property}$$

$$4x - 4 + 4x = x^2 - x \quad \text{Distributive property}$$

$$x^2 - 9x + 4 = 0 \quad \text{Standard form}$$

Continued on Next Page

2 Solve each problem.

(a) In 4 hr, Kerrie can go 15 mi upriver and come back. The speed of the current is 5 mph. Complete this table.

	d	r	t
Up			
Down			

(b) Find the speed of the boat from part (a) in still water.

(c) In $1\frac{3}{4}$ hr, Ken rows his boat 5 mi upriver and comes back. The speed of the current is 3 mph. How fast does Ken row?

ANSWERS

2. (a) row 1: $15; x - 5; \dfrac{15}{x - 5}$

row 2: $15; x + 5; \dfrac{15}{x + 5}$

(b) 10 mph **(c)** 7 mph

3 Solve each problem. Round answers to the nearest tenth.

(a) Carlos can complete a certain lab test in 2 hr less time than Jaime can. If they can finish the job together in 2 hr, how long would it take each of them working alone?

	Rate	Time Working Together	Fractional Part of the Job Done
Carlos			
Jaime			

The resulting equation $x^2 - 9x + 4 = 0$ cannot be solved by factoring, so use the quadratic formula.

$$x = \frac{-b \pm \sqrt{b^2 - 4ac}}{2a} \qquad \text{Quadratic formula}$$

$$x = \frac{-(-9) \pm \sqrt{(-9)^2 - 4(1)(4)}}{2(1)} \qquad a = 1, b = -9, c = 4$$

$$x = \frac{9 \pm \sqrt{65}}{2} \qquad \text{Simplify.}$$

$$x = \frac{9 + \sqrt{65}}{2} \approx 8.5 \quad \text{or} \quad x = \frac{9 - \sqrt{65}}{2} \approx 0.5 \qquad \text{Use a calculator.}$$

Step 5 **State the answer.** Only the solution 8.5 makes sense in the original problem. (Why?) Thus, the slower worker can do the job in about 8.5 hr and the faster in about $8.5 - 1 = 7.5$ hr.

Step 6 **Check** that these results satisfy the original problem.

◀ *Work Problem* **3** *at the Side.*

OBJECTIVE **3** Solve an equation with radicals by writing it in quadratic form.

Example 4 **Solving Radical Equations That Lead to Quadratic Equations**

Solve each equation.

(a) $k = \sqrt{6k - 8}$

This equation is not quadratic. However, squaring both sides of the equation gives a quadratic equation that can be solved by factoring.

$$k^2 = 6k - 8 \qquad \text{Square each side.}$$
$$k^2 - 6k + 8 = 0 \qquad \text{Standard form}$$
$$(k - 4)(k - 2) = 0 \qquad \text{Factor.}$$
$$k - 4 = 0 \quad \text{or} \quad k - 2 = 0 \qquad \text{Zero-factor property}$$
$$k = 4 \quad \text{or} \qquad k = 2 \qquad \text{Potential solutions}$$

Recall from **Section 9.6** that squaring both sides of a radical equation can introduce extraneous solutions that do not satisfy the original equation. *All proposed solutions must be checked in the original (not the squared) equation.*

(b) Two chefs are preparing a banquet. One chef could prepare the banquet in 2 hr less time than the other. Together, they complete the job in 5 hr. How long would it take the faster chef working alone?

If $k = 4$, then

$$k = \sqrt{6k - 8}$$
$$4 \overset{?}{=} \sqrt{6(4) - 8}$$
$$4 \overset{?}{=} \sqrt{16}$$
$$4 = 4. \qquad \text{True}$$

If $k = 2$, then

$$k = \sqrt{6k - 8}$$
$$2 \overset{?}{=} \sqrt{6(2) - 8}$$
$$2 \overset{?}{=} \sqrt{4}$$
$$2 = 2. \qquad \text{True}$$

Both solutions check, so the solution set is $\{2, 4\}$.

Continued on Next Page

(b) $x + \sqrt{x} = 6$

$(a - b)^2 = a^2 - 2ab + b^2$

$\sqrt{x} = 6 - x$ Isolate the radical on one side.

$x = 36 - 12x + x^2$ Square each side.

$0 = x^2 - 13x + 36$ Standard form

$0 = (x - 4)(x - 9)$ Factor.

$x - 4 = 0$ or $x - 9 = 0$ Zero-factor property

$x = 4$ or $x = 9$ Proposed solutions

Check both proposed solutions in the *original* equation.

If $x = 4$, then	If $x = 9$, then
$x + \sqrt{x} = 6$	$x + \sqrt{x} = 6$
$4 + \sqrt{4} \overset{?}{=} 6$	$9 + \sqrt{9} \overset{?}{=} 6$
$6 = 6.$ True	$12 = 6.$ False

Only the solution 4 checks, so the solution set is $\{4\}$.

Work Problem **4** *at the Side.* ▶

OBJECTIVE **4** **Solve an equation that is quadratic in form by substitution.** A nonquadratic equation that can be written in the form

$$au^2 + bu + c = 0,$$

for $a \neq 0$ and an algebraic expression u, is called **quadratic in form.**

Many equations that are quadratic in form can be solved more easily by defining and substituting a "temporary" variable u for an expression involving the variable in the original equation. The first step is to define this temporary variable u.

Example 5 **Defining Substitution Variables**

Define a variable u, and write each equation in the form $au^2 + bu + c = 0$.

(a) $x^4 - 13x^2 + 36 = 0$

Look at the two terms involving the variable x, ignoring their coefficients. Try to find one variable expression that is the square of the other. We see that $x^4 = (x^2)^2$, so we define $u = x^2$, and rewrite the original equation as the quadratic equation

$$u^2 - 13u + 36 = 0. \quad \text{Here, } u = x^2.$$

(b) $2(4m - 3)^2 + 7(4m - 3) + 5 = 0$

Because this equation involves both $(4m - 3)^2$ and $(4m - 3)$, choose $u = 4m - 3$. Substituting u for $4m - 3$ gives the quadratic equation

$$2u^2 + 7u + 5 = 0. \quad \text{Here, } u = 4m - 3.$$

(c) $2x^{2/3} - 11x^{1/3} + 12 = 0$

Here we apply one of the power rules for exponents from **Section 6.1:** $(a^m)^n = a^{mn}$. Because $(x^{1/3})^2 = x^{2/3}$, we define $u = x^{1/3}$. With this substitution, the original equation becomes

$$2u^2 - 11u + 12 = 0. \quad \text{Here, } u = x^{1/3}.$$

Work Problem **5** *at the Side.* ▶

---

4 Solve each equation. Check your solutions.

(a) $x = \sqrt{7x - 10}$

(b) $2x = \sqrt{x + 1}$

5 Define a variable u, and write each equation in the form $au^2 + bu + c = 0$.

(a) $2x^4 + 5x^2 - 12 = 0$

(b) $2(x + 5)^2 - 7(x + 5) + 6 = 0$

(c) $x^{4/3} - 8x^{2/3} + 16 = 0$

ANSWERS

4. **(a)** $\{2, 5\}$ **(b)** $\{1\}$

5. **(a)** $u = x^2; \ 2u^2 + 5u - 12 = 0$

    (b) $u = x + 5; \ 2u^2 - 7u + 6 = 0$

    (c) $u = x^{2/3}; \ u^2 - 8u + 16 = 0$

| Example 6 | **Solving Equations That Are Quadratic in Form** |

Solve each equation.

(a) $x^4 - 13x^2 + 36 = 0$

From Example 5(a), we write this equation in quadratic form by substituting u for x^2.

$$x^4 - 13x^2 + 36 = 0$$

$$(x^2)^2 - 13x^2 + 36 = 0 \qquad x^4 = (x^2)^2$$

$$u^2 - 13u + 36 = 0 \qquad \text{Let } u = x^2.$$

$$(u - 4)(u - 9) = 0 \qquad \text{Factor.}$$

$$u - 4 = 0 \quad \text{or} \quad u - 9 = 0 \qquad \text{Zero-factor property}$$

Don't stop here. ⟶ $\quad u = 4 \quad \text{or} \quad u = 9 \qquad \text{Solve.}$

$$x^2 = 4 \quad \text{or} \quad x^2 = 9 \qquad \text{Substitute } x^2 \text{ for } u.$$

$$x = \pm 2 \quad \text{or} \quad x = \pm 3 \qquad \text{Square root property}$$

The equation $x^4 - 13x^2 + 36 = 0$, a fourth-degree equation, has four solutions.* The solution set is $\{-3, -2, 2, 3\}$. Check each of the four solutions by substitution.

(b)

$$4x^4 + 1 = 5x^2$$

$$4(x^2)^2 + 1 = 5x^2 \qquad x^4 = (x^2)^2$$

$$4u^2 + 1 = 5u \qquad \text{Let } u = x^2.$$

$$4u^2 - 5u + 1 = 0 \qquad \text{Standard form}$$

$$(4u - 1)(u - 1) = 0 \qquad \text{Factor.}$$

$$4u - 1 = 0 \quad \text{or} \quad u - 1 = 0 \qquad \text{Zero-factor property}$$

$$u = \frac{1}{4} \quad \text{or} \quad u = 1 \qquad \text{Solve.}$$

This is a key step. ⟶ $\quad x^2 = \dfrac{1}{4} \quad \text{or} \quad x^2 = 1 \qquad \text{Substitute } x^2 \text{ for } u.$

$$x = \pm\frac{1}{2} \quad \text{or} \quad x = \pm 1 \qquad \text{Square root property}$$

Check that the solution set is $\left\{-1, -\frac{1}{2}, \frac{1}{2}, 1\right\}$.

(c) $x^4 = 6x^2 - 3$

First write the equation as

$$x^4 - 6x^2 + 3 = 0 \qquad \text{or} \qquad (x^2)^2 - 6x^2 + 3 = 0,$$

which is quadratic in form with $u = x^2$. Substitute u for x^2 and u^2 for x^4 to get

$$u^2 - 6u + 3 = 0.$$

Since this equation cannot be solved by factoring, use the quadratic formula.

Continued on Next Page

---

*In general, an equation in which an nth-degree polynomial equals 0 has n solutions, although some of them may be repeated.

$$u = \frac{-(-6) \pm \sqrt{(-6)^2 - 4(1)(3)}}{2(1)} \qquad a = 1, b = -6, c = 3$$

$$u = \frac{6 \pm \sqrt{24}}{2} \qquad \text{Simplify.}$$

$$u = \frac{6 \pm 2\sqrt{6}}{2} \qquad \sqrt{24} = \sqrt{4} \cdot \sqrt{6} = 2\sqrt{6}$$

$$u = \frac{2(3 \pm \sqrt{6})}{2} \qquad \text{Factor.}$$

$$u = 3 \pm \sqrt{6} \qquad \text{Lowest terms}$$

Find *both* square roots in each case.

$$x^2 = 3 + \sqrt{6} \quad \text{or} \quad x^2 = 3 - \sqrt{6} \qquad \begin{array}{l}\text{Substitute } x^2 \\ \text{for } u.\end{array}$$

$$x = \pm\sqrt{3 + \sqrt{6}} \quad \text{or} \quad x = \pm\sqrt{3 - \sqrt{6}} \qquad \begin{array}{l}\text{Square root} \\ \text{property}\end{array}$$

The solution set contains four numbers:

$$\left\{ \sqrt{3 + \sqrt{6}}, -\sqrt{3 + \sqrt{6}}, \sqrt{3 - \sqrt{6}}, -\sqrt{3 - \sqrt{6}} \right\}.$$

6 Solve each equation. Check your solutions.

(a) $m^4 - 10m^2 + 9 = 0$

(b) $9k^4 - 37k^2 + 4 = 0$

Note

Some students prefer to solve equations like those in Examples 6(a) and (b) by factoring directly. For example,

$$x^4 - 13x^2 + 36 = 0 \qquad \text{Example 6(a) equation}$$
$$(x^2 - 9)(x^2 - 4) = 0 \qquad \text{Factor.}$$
$$(x + 3)(x - 3)(x + 2)(x - 2) = 0. \qquad \text{Factor again.}$$

Using the zero-factor property gives the same solutions obtained in Example 6(a). Equations that cannot be solved by factoring (as in Example 6(c)) must be solved by substitution and the quadratic formula.

(c) $x^4 - 4x^2 = -2$

Work Problem **6** *at the Side.* ▶

The method used in Example 6 can be generalized.

Solving an Equation That Is Quadratic in Form by Substitution

Step 1 Define a temporary variable u, based on the relationship between the variable expressions in the given equation. Substitute u in the original equation and rewrite the equation in the form $au^2 + bu + c = 0$.

Step 2 **Solve the quadratic equation obtained in Step 1** by factoring or the quadratic formula.

Step 3 **Replace u with the expression it defined in Step 1.**

Step 4 **Solve the resulting equations for the original variable.**

Step 5 **Check all solutions by substituting them in the original equation.**

Answers

6. (a) $\{-3, -1, 1, 3\}$ **(b)** $\left\{-2, -\frac{1}{3}, \frac{1}{3}, 2\right\}$

(c) $\{\sqrt{2 + \sqrt{2}}, -\sqrt{2 + \sqrt{2}},$
$\sqrt{2 - \sqrt{2}}, -\sqrt{2 - \sqrt{2}}\}$

7 Solve each equation. Check your solutions.

(a) $5(r + 3)^2 + 9(r + 3) = 2$

Example 7 **Solving Equations That Are Quadratic in Form**

Solve each equation.

(a) $2(4m - 3)^2 + 7(4m - 3) + 5 = 0$

Step 1 Because of the repeated quantity $4m - 3$, substitute u for $4m - 3$ as in Example 5(b).

$$2(4m - 3)^2 + 7(4m - 3) + 5 = 0$$

$$2u^2 + 7u + 5 = 0 \qquad \text{Let } u = 4m - 3.$$

Step 2 $\qquad\qquad (2u + 5)(u + 1) = 0 \qquad$ Factor.

$$2u + 5 = 0 \quad \text{or} \quad u + 1 = 0 \qquad \text{Zero-factor property}$$

Don't stop here. $\qquad u = -\dfrac{5}{2} \quad \text{or} \qquad u = -1 \qquad$ Solve for u.

Step 3 $\quad 4m - 3 = -\dfrac{5}{2} \quad \text{or} \quad 4m - 3 = -1 \qquad$ Substitute $4m - 3$ for u.

Step 4 $\qquad 4m = \dfrac{1}{2} \quad \text{or} \qquad 4m = 2 \qquad$ Solve for m.

$$m = \dfrac{1}{8} \quad \text{or} \qquad m = \dfrac{1}{2}$$

Step 5 Check that the solution set of the original equation is $\left\{\frac{1}{8}, \frac{1}{2}\right\}$.

(b) $2x^{2/3} - 11x^{1/3} + 12 = 0$

From Example 5(c), substitute u for $x^{1/3}$.

$$2u^2 - 11u + 12 = 0 \qquad \text{Let } x^{1/3} = u; x^{2/3} = u^2.$$

$$(2u - 3)(u - 4) = 0 \qquad \text{Factor.}$$

$$2u - 3 = 0 \quad \text{or} \quad u - 4 = 0 \qquad \text{Zero-factor property}$$

$$u = \dfrac{3}{2} \qquad \text{or} \qquad u = 4 \qquad \text{Solve for } u.$$

$$x^{1/3} = \dfrac{3}{2} \qquad \text{or} \qquad x^{1/3} = 4 \qquad u = x^{1/3}$$

$$(x^{1/3})^3 = \left(\dfrac{3}{2}\right)^3 \quad \text{or} \quad (x^{1/3})^3 = 4^3 \qquad \text{Cube each side.}$$

$$x = \dfrac{27}{8} \qquad \text{or} \qquad x = 64$$

Check that the solution set is $\left\{\frac{27}{8}, 64\right\}$.

(b) $4m^{2/3} = 3m^{1/3} + 1$

CAUTION
A common error when solving problems like those in Examples 6 and 7 is to stop too soon. ***Once you have solved for u, remember to substitute and solve for the values of the original variable.*** Keep in mind that u is just a temporary variable that helps you solve the given equation. As in any equation, you must solve for the variable in the *original* equation.

◀ *Work Problem* **7** *at the Side.*

Answers

7. **(a)** $\left\{-5, -\dfrac{14}{5}\right\}$ **(b)** $\left\{-\dfrac{1}{64}, 1\right\}$

Based on the discussion and examples of this section, write a sentence describing the first step you would take to solve each equation. Do not actually solve.

1. $\dfrac{14}{x} = x - 5$

2. $\sqrt{1 + x} + x = 5$

3. $(r^2 + r)^2 - 8(r^2 + r) + 12 = 0$

4. $3t = \sqrt{16 - 10t}$

5. Read this incorrect "solution" carefully. ***WHAT WENT WRONG?***

$$x = \sqrt{3x + 4}$$
$$x^2 = 3x + 4 \qquad \text{Square both sides.}$$
$$x^2 - 3x - 4 = 0$$
$$(x - 4)(x + 1) = 0$$
$$x - 4 = 0 \quad \text{or} \quad x + 1 = 0$$
$$x = 4 \quad \text{or} \quad x = -1$$

Solution set: $\{4, -1\}$

6. Read this incorrect "solution" carefully. ***WHAT WENT WRONG?***

$$2(m - 1)^2 - 3(m - 1) + 1 = 0$$
$$2u^2 - 3u + 1 = 0 \qquad \text{Let } u = m - 1.$$
$$(2u - 1)(u - 1) = 0$$
$$2u - 1 = 0 \quad \text{or} \quad u - 1 = 0$$
$$u = \frac{1}{2} \quad \text{or} \quad u = 1$$

Solution set: $\left\{\frac{1}{2}, 1\right\}$

Solve each equation. Check your solutions. See Example 1.

7. $1 - \dfrac{3}{x} - \dfrac{28}{x^2} = 0$

8. $4 - \dfrac{7}{r} - \dfrac{2}{r^2} = 0$

9. $3 - \dfrac{1}{t} = \dfrac{2}{t^2}$

10. $1 + \dfrac{2}{k} = \dfrac{3}{k^2}$

◐ 11. $\dfrac{1}{x} + \dfrac{2}{x + 2} = \dfrac{17}{35}$

12. $\dfrac{2}{m} + \dfrac{3}{m + 9} = \dfrac{11}{4}$

13. $\dfrac{2}{x + 1} + \dfrac{3}{x + 2} = \dfrac{7}{2}$

14. $\dfrac{4}{3 - p} + \dfrac{2}{5 - p} = \dfrac{26}{15}$

15. $\dfrac{3}{2x} - \dfrac{1}{2(x + 2)} = 1$

16. $\dfrac{4}{3x} - \dfrac{1}{2(x + 1)} = 1$

17. $\dfrac{6}{p} = 2 + \dfrac{p}{p + 1}$

18. $\dfrac{k}{2 - k} + \dfrac{2}{k} = 5$

19. A boat goes 20 mph in still water, and the rate of the current is *t* mph.

    (a) What is the rate of the boat when it travels upstream?

    (b) What is the rate of the boat when it travels downstream?

20. It takes *m* hours to grade a set of papers.

    (a) What is the grader's rate (in job per hour)?

    (b) How much of the job will the grader do in 2 hr?

Solve each problem. See Examples 2 and 3.

21. On a windy day Yoshiaki found that he could go 16 mi downstream and then 4 mi back upstream at top speed in a total of 48 min. What was the top speed of Yoshiaki's boat if the current was 15 mph?

	d	r	t
Upstream	4	x − 15	
Downstream	16		

22. Lekesha flew her plane for 6 hr at a constant speed. She traveled 810 mi with the wind, then turned around and traveled 720 mi against the wind. The wind speed was a constant 15 mph. Find the speed of the plane.

	d	r	t
With Wind	810		
Against Wind	720		

23. In Canada, Medicine Hat and Cranbrook are 300 km apart. Harry rides his Honda 20 km per hr faster than Yoshi rides his Yamaha. Find Harry's average speed if he travels from Cranbrook to Medicine Hat in $1\frac{1}{4}$ hr less time than Yoshi. (*Source: State Farm Road Atlas.*)

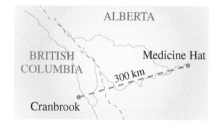

24. In California, the distance from Jackson to Lodi is about 40 mi, as is the distance from Lodi to Manteca. Rico drove from Jackson to Lodi during the rush hour, stopped in Lodi for a root beer, and then drove on to Manteca at 10 mph faster. Driving time for the entire trip was 88 min. Find his speed from Jackson to Lodi. (*Source: State Farm Road Atlas.*)

25. Working together, two people can cut a large lawn in 2 hr. One person can do the job alone in 1 hr less time than the other. How long (to the nearest tenth) would it take the faster person to do the job? (*Hint: x* is the time of the faster person.)

	Rate	Time Working Together	Fractional Part of the Job Done
Faster Worker	$\frac{1}{x}$	2	
Slower Worker		2	

26. A janitorial service provides two people to clean an office building. Working together, the two can clean the building in 5 hr. One person is new to the job and would take 2 hr longer than the other person to clean the building alone. How long (to the nearest tenth) would it take the new worker to clean the building alone?

	Rate	Time Working Together	Fractional Part of the Job Done
Faster Worker			
Slower Worker			

27. A washing machine can be filled in 6 min if both the hot and cold water taps are fully opened. Filling the washer with hot water alone takes 9 min longer than filling it with cold water alone. How long does it take to fill the washer with cold water?

28. Two pipes together can fill a large tank in 2 hr. One of the pipes, used alone, takes 3 hr longer than the other to fill the tank. How long would each pipe take to fill the tank alone?

Solve each equation. Check your solutions. See Example 4.

29. $z = \sqrt{5z - 4}$

30. $x = \sqrt{9x - 14}$

31. $2x = \sqrt{11x + 3}$

32. $4x = \sqrt{6x + 1}$

33. $3x = \sqrt{16 - 10x}$

34. $4t = \sqrt{8t + 3}$

35. $p - 2\sqrt{p} = 8$

36. $k + \sqrt{k} = 12$

37. $m = \sqrt{\dfrac{6 - 13m}{5}}$

38. $r = \sqrt{\dfrac{20 - 19r}{6}}$

Solve each equation. Check your solutions. See Examples 5–7.

39. $t^4 - 18t^2 + 81 = 0$

40. $x^4 - 8x^2 + 16 = 0$

41. $4k^4 - 13k^2 + 9 = 0$

42. $9x^4 - 25x^2 + 16 = 0$

43. $x^4 + 48 = 16x^2$

44. $z^4 = 17z^2 - 72$

45. $2x^4 - 9x^2 = -2$

46. $8x^4 + 1 = 11x^2$

🌐 **47.** $(x + 3)^2 + 5(x + 3) + 6 = 0$

48. $(k - 4)^2 + (k - 4) - 20 = 0$

49. $(t + 5)^2 + 6 = 7(t + 5)$

50. $3(m + 4)^2 - 8 = 2(m + 4)$

51. $2 + \dfrac{5}{3k - 1} = \dfrac{-2}{(3k - 1)^2}$

52. $3 - \dfrac{7}{2p + 2} = \dfrac{6}{(2p + 2)^2}$

53. $x^{2/3} + x^{1/3} - 2 = 0$

54. $x^{2/3} - 2x^{1/3} - 3 = 0$

55. $r^{2/3} + r^{1/3} - 12 = 0$

56. $3x^{2/3} - x^{1/3} - 24 = 0$

57. $2\left(1 + \sqrt{r}\right)^2 = 13\left(1 + \sqrt{r}\right) - 6$

58. $(k^2 + k)^2 + 12 = 8(k^2 + k)$

Relating Concepts (Exercises 59–64) For Individual or Group Work

Consider the following equation, which contains variable expressions in the denominators.
Work Exercises 59–64 in order.

$$\frac{x^2}{(x-3)^2} + \frac{3x}{x-3} - 4 = 0$$

59. Why must 3 be excluded from the domain of this equation?

60. Multiply each side of the equation by the LCD, $(x - 3)^2$, and solve. There is only one solution—what is it?

61. Write the equation in a different manner so that it is quadratic in form using the expression $\frac{x}{x-3}$.

62. In your own words, explain why the expression $\frac{x}{x-3}$ cannot equal 1.

63. Solve the equation from Exercise 61 by making the substitution $t = \frac{x}{x-3}$. You should get two values for t. Why is one of them impossible for this equation?

64. Solve the equation $x^2(x-3)^{-2} + 3x(x-3)^{-1} - 4 = 0$ by letting $s = (x-3)^{-1}$. You should get two values for s. Why is this impossible for this equation?

Summary Exercises on Solving Quadratic Equations

We have introduced four methods for solving quadratic equations written in standard form $ax^2 + bx + c = 0$. The following table lists some advantages and disadvantages of each method.

METHODS FOR SOLVING QUADRATIC EQUATIONS

Method	Advantages	Disadvantages
Factoring	This is usually the fastest method.	Not all polynomials are factorable; some factorable polynomials are hard to factor.
Square root property	This is the simplest method for solving equations of the form $(ax + b)^2 = c$.	Few equations are given in this form.
Completing the square	This method can always be used, although many people prefer the quadratic formula.	It requires more steps than other methods.
Quadratic formula	This method can always be used.	It is more difficult than factoring because of the square root, although calculators can simplify its use.

Refer to the preceding box. Decide whether factoring, the square root property, *or* the quadratic formula *is most appropriate for solving each quadratic equation. Do not actually solve the equations.*

1. $(2x + 3)^2 = 4$

2. $4x^2 - 3x = 1$

3. $z^2 + 5z - 8 = 0$

4. $2k^2 + 3k = 1$

5. $3m^2 = 2 - 5m$

6. $p^2 = 5$

Solve each quadratic equation by the method of your choice. Check your solutions.

7. $p^2 = 47$

8. $6x^2 - x - 15 = 0$

9. $n^2 + 8n + 6 = 0$

10. $(x - 4)^2 = 49$

11. $\dfrac{9}{m} + \dfrac{5}{m^2} = 2$

12. $3m^2 = 3 - 8m$

13. $3x^2 - 9x + 4 = 0$ ***14.** $x^2 = -12$ **15.** $x\sqrt{2} = \sqrt{5x - 2}$

16. $12x^4 - 11x^2 + 2 = 0$ **17.** $(2k + 5)^2 = 12$ **18.** $\dfrac{2}{x} + \dfrac{1}{x - 2} - \dfrac{5}{3} = 0$

19. $t^4 + 14 = 9t^2$ **20.** $2x^2 + 4x = 5$ ***21.** $z^2 + z + 2 = 0$

22. $x^4 - 8x^2 = -1$ **23.** $4t^2 - 12t + 9 = 0$ **24.** $x\sqrt{3} = \sqrt{2 - x}$

25. $r^2 - 72 = 0$ **26.** $-3x^2 + 4x = -4$ **27.** $x^2 - 5x - 36 = 0$

28. $w^2 = 169$ ***29.** $3p^2 = 6p - 4$ **30.** $z = \sqrt{\dfrac{5z + 3}{2}}$

31. $2(3k - 1)^2 + 5(3k - 1) = -2$ ***32.** $\dfrac{4}{r^2} + 3 = \dfrac{1}{r}$ **33.** $x - \sqrt{15 - 2x} = 0$

34. $3 = \dfrac{1}{t + 2} + \dfrac{2}{(t + 2)^2}$ ***35.** $4k^4 + 5k^2 + 1 = 0$ **36.** $(x + 1)^{2/3} - (x + 1)^{1/3} = 2$

---

*This exercise requires knowledge of complex numbers.

18.5 ▶▶▶ Formulas and Further Applications

OBJECTIVE **1** **Solve formulas for variables involving squares and square roots.**   The methods presented earlier in this chapter and the previous one can be used to solve formulas with squares and square roots.

OBJECTIVES

1 Solve formulas for variables involving squares and square roots.

2 Solve applied problems using the Pythagorean formula.

3 Solve applied problems using area formulas.

4 Solve applied problems using quadratic functions as models.

Example 1   **Solving for Variables Involving Squares or Square Roots**

Solve each formula for the given variable.

(a) $w = \dfrac{kFr}{v^2}$ for v

$$w = \dfrac{kFr}{v^2} \qquad \text{The goal is to isolate } v \text{ on one side.}$$

$$v^2 w = kFr \qquad \text{Multiply by } v^2.$$

$$v^2 = \dfrac{kFr}{w} \qquad \text{Divide by } w.$$

$$v = \pm\sqrt{\dfrac{kFr}{w}} \qquad \text{Square root property}$$

$$v = \dfrac{\pm\sqrt{kFr}}{\sqrt{w}} \cdot \dfrac{\sqrt{w}}{\sqrt{w}} = \dfrac{\pm\sqrt{kFrw}}{w} \qquad \text{Rationalize the denominator.}$$

(b) $d = \sqrt{\dfrac{4A}{\pi}}$ for A

$$d = \sqrt{\dfrac{4A}{\pi}} \qquad \text{The goal is to isolate } A \text{ on one side.}$$

$$d^2 = \dfrac{4A}{\pi} \qquad \text{Square both sides.}$$

$$\pi d^2 = 4A \qquad \text{Multiply by } \pi.$$

$$\dfrac{\pi d^2}{4} = A \qquad \text{Divide by 4.}$$

Work Problem **1** *at the Side.* ▶

1 Solve each formula for the given variable.

(a) $A = \pi r^2$ for r

Note
In formulas like $v = \dfrac{\pm\sqrt{kFrw}}{w}$ in Example 1(a), we will include both positive and negative values.

(b) $s = 30\sqrt{\dfrac{a}{p}}$ for a

Example 2   **Solving for a Second-Degree Variable**

Solve $s = 2t^2 + kt$ for t.
    Since the equation has terms with t^2 and t, write it in standard form $ax^2 + bx + c = 0$, with t as the variable instead of x.

$$s = 2t^2 + kt$$

$$0 = 2t^2 + kt - s \qquad \text{Subtract } s.$$

$$2t^2 + kt - s = 0 \qquad \text{Standard form}$$

Continued on Next Page

ANSWERS

1. (a) $r = \dfrac{\pm\sqrt{A\pi}}{\pi}$ **(b)** $a = \dfrac{ps^2}{900}$

2 Solve $2t^2 - 5t + k = 0$ for t.

Now solve $2t^2 + kt - s = 0$ for t using the quadratic formula.

$$t = \frac{-k \pm \sqrt{k^2 - 4(2)(-s)}}{2(2)}$$ Let $a = 2$, $b = k$, and $c = -s$.

$$t = \frac{-k \pm \sqrt{k^2 + 8s}}{4}$$ Simplify.

The solutions are $t = \dfrac{-k + \sqrt{k^2 + 8s}}{4}$ and $t = \dfrac{-k - \sqrt{k^2 + 8s}}{4}$.

◀ Work Problem **2** at the Side.

OBJECTIVE 2 Solve applied problems using the Pythagorean formula.   The Pythagorean formula

$$a^2 + b^2 = c^2,$$

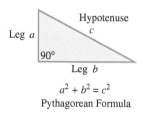
Pythagorean Formula

illustrated by the figure in the margin, was introduced in **Section 9.3** and is used to solve applications involving right triangles. Such problems often require solving quadratic equations.

Example 3   Using the Pythagorean Formula

Two cars left an intersection at the same time, one heading due north, the other due west. Some time later, they were exactly 100 mi apart. The car headed north had gone 20 mi farther than the car headed west. How far had each car traveled?

3 Solve the problem.
    A 13-ft ladder is leaning against a house. The distance from the bottom of the ladder to the house is 7 ft less than the distance from the top of the ladder to the ground. How far is the bottom of the ladder from the house?

Step 1 **Read** the problem carefully.

Step 2 **Assign a variable.**

Let x = the distance traveled by the car headed west.

Then $x + 20$ = the distance traveled by the car headed north.

See Figure 2. The cars are 100 mi apart, so the hypotenuse of the right triangle equals 100.

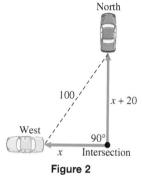
Figure 2

Step 3 **Write an equation.** Use the Pythagorean formula.

$$a^2 + b^2 = c^2$$

$(x + y)^2 = x^2 + 2xy + y^2$ $x^2 + (x + 20)^2 = 100^2$

Step 4 **Solve.** $x^2 + x^2 + 40x + 400 = 10{,}000$ Square the binomial.

$$2x^2 + 40x - 9600 = 0$$ Standard form

$$x^2 + 20x - 4800 = 0$$ Divide by 2.

$$(x + 80)(x - 60) = 0$$ Factor.

$$x + 80 = 0 \quad \text{or} \quad x - 60 = 0$$ Zero-factor property

$$x = -80 \quad \text{or} \qquad x = 60$$ Solve for x.

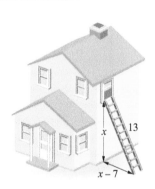

Step 5 **State the answer.** Distance cannot be negative, so discard the negative solution. The distances are 60 mi and $60 + 20 = 80$ mi.

Step 6 **Check.** Since $60^2 + 80^2 = 100^2$, the answers are correct.

◀ Work Problem **3** at the Side.

ANSWERS

2. $t = \dfrac{5 + \sqrt{25 - 8k}}{4}$, $t = \dfrac{5 - \sqrt{25 - 8k}}{4}$

3. 5 ft

OBJECTIVE 3 Solve applied problems using area formulas.

Example 4   Solving an Area Problem

A rectangular reflecting pool in a park is 20 ft wide and 30 ft long. The park gardener wants to plant a strip of grass of uniform width around the edge of the pool. She has enough seed to cover 336 ft². How wide will the strip be?

Step 1   **Read** the problem carefully.

Step 2   **Assign a variable.** The pool is shown in Figure 3. If x represents the unknown width of the grass strip, the width of the large rectangle is given by $20 + 2x$ (the width of the pool plus two grass strips), and the length is given by $30 + 2x$.

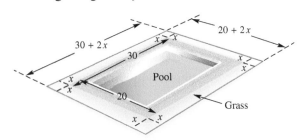

Figure 3

Step 3   **Write an equation.** The area of the large rectangle is given by the product of its length and width, $(30 + 2x)(20 + 2x)$. The area of the pool is $30 \cdot 20 = 600$ ft². The area of the large rectangle, minus the area of the pool, should equal the area of the grass strip. Since the area of the grass strip is to be 336 ft², the equation is

$$\underset{\underset{\text{rectangle}}{\downarrow}}{\text{Area of}} - \underset{\underset{\text{pool}}{\downarrow}}{\text{area of}} = \underset{\underset{\text{grass.}}{\downarrow}}{\text{area of}}$$

$$(30 + 2x)(20 + 2x) - 600 = 336.$$

Step 4   **Solve.**

$600 + 100x + 4x^2 - 600 = 336$	Multiply.
$4x^2 + 100x - 336 = 0$	Standard form
$x^2 + 25x - 84 = 0$	Divide by 4.
$(x + 28)(x - 3) = 0$	Factor.
$x = -28 \quad \text{or} \quad x = 3$	Zero-factor property

Step 5   **State the answer.** The width cannot be -28 ft, so the grass strip should be 3 ft wide.

Step 6   **Check.** If $x = 3$, then the area of the large rectangle is

$(30 + 2 \cdot 3)(20 + 2 \cdot 3) = 36 \cdot 26 = 936$ ft².   Area of pool and strip

The area of the pool is $30 \cdot 20 = 600$ ft². So, the area of the grass strip is $936 - 600 = 336$ ft², as required. The answer is correct.

Work Problem **4** *at the Side.* ▶

---

4 Solve the problem.
   Suppose the pool in Example 4 is 20 ft by 40 ft and there is enough seed to cover 700 ft². How wide should the grass strip be?

OBJECTIVE 4 Solve applied problems using quadratic functions as models. Some applied problems can be modeled by *quadratic functions,* which can be written in the form

$$f(x) = ax^2 + bx + c,$$

for real numbers a, b, and c, with $a \neq 0$.

ANSWER

4. 5 ft

5 Solve the problem.

A ball is projected vertically upward from the ground. Its distance in feet from the ground at t seconds is

$$s(t) = -16t^2 + 64t.$$

At what times will the ball be 32 ft from the ground? Use a calculator and round answers to the nearest tenth. (*Hint:* There are two answers.)

6 Use a calculator to evaluate

$$\frac{-14.8 \pm \sqrt{14.8^2 - 4(-0.065)(-301)}}{2(-0.065)}$$

for both solutions. Round to the nearest whole number. Which solution is valid for this problem?

Example 5 **Solving an Applied Problem Using a Quadratic Function**

If an object is projected upward from the top of a 144-ft building at 112 ft per sec, its position (in feet above the ground) is given by

$$s(t) = -16t^2 + 112t + 144,$$

where t is time in seconds after it was propelled. When does it hit the ground?

When the object hits the ground, its distance above the ground is 0. We must find the value of t that makes $s(t) = 0$.

$$0 = -16t^2 + 112t + 144 \quad \text{Let } s(t) = 0.$$
$$0 = t^2 - 7t - 9 \quad \text{Divide by } -16.$$
$$t = \frac{-(-7) \pm \sqrt{(-7)^2 - 4(1)(-9)}}{2(1)} = \frac{7 \pm \sqrt{85}}{2} \approx \frac{7 \pm 9.2}{2} \quad \text{Use the quadratic formula and a calculator.}$$

The solutions are $t \approx 8.1$ or $t \approx -1.1$. Since time cannot be negative, discard the negative solution. The object will hit the ground about 8.1 sec after it is projected.

◀ Work Problem **5** at the Side.

Example 6 **Using a Quadratic Function to Model the CPI**

The Consumer Price Index (CPI) is used to measure trends in prices for a "basket" of goods purchased by typical American families. This index uses a base year of 1967, which means that the index number for 1967 is 100. The quadratic function defined by

$$f(x) = -0.065x^2 + 14.8x + 249$$

approximates the CPI for the years 1980–2005, where x is the number of years that have elapsed since 1980. (*Source:* Bureau of Labor Statistics.)

(a) Use the model to approximate the CPI for 1995.

For 1995, $x = 1995 - 1980 = 15$, so find $f(15)$.

$$f(x) = -0.065x^2 + 14.8x + 249 \quad \text{Given model}$$
$$f(15) = -0.065(15)^2 + 14.8(15) + 249 \quad \text{Let } x = 15.$$
$$f(15) \approx 456 \quad \text{Nearest whole number}$$

The CPI for 1995 was about 456.

(b) In what year did the CPI reach 550?

Find the value of x that makes $f(x) = 550$.

$$f(x) = -0.065x^2 + 14.8x + 249 \quad \text{Given model}$$
$$550 = -0.065x^2 + 14.8x + 249 \quad \text{Let } f(x) = 550.$$
$$0 = -0.065x^2 + 14.8x - 301 \quad \text{Standard form}$$

Now use $a = -0.065$, $b = 14.8$, and $c = -301$ in the quadratic formula.

◀ Work Problem **6** at the Side.

The first solution is $x \approx 23$. Rounding up to the next whole number, the CPI first reached 550 in $1980 + 23 = 2003$. (Reject the solution $x \approx 205$, as this corresponds to a year far beyond the period covered by the model.)

FOR
EXTRA
HELP

1. What is the first step in solving a formula like $gw^2 = 2r$ for w?

2. What is the first step in solving a formula like $gw^2 = kw + 24$ for w?

In Exercises 3 and 4, solve for m in terms of the other variables ($m > 0$).

3.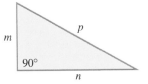

4.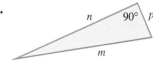

Solve each equation for the indicated variable. (Leave $\pm$ in your answers.) See Examples 1 and 2.

5. $d = kt^2$ for t

6. $s = kwd^2$ for d

🌐 7. $I = \dfrac{ks}{d^2}$ for d

8. $R = \dfrac{k}{d^2}$ for d

9. $F = \dfrac{kA}{v^2}$ for v

10. $L = \dfrac{kd^4}{h^2}$ for h

11. $V = \dfrac{1}{3}\pi r^2 h$ for r

12. $V = \pi(r^2 + R^2)h$ for r

💿 13. $At^2 + Bt = -C$ for t

14. $S = 2\pi rh + \pi r^2$ for r

15. $D = \sqrt{kh}$ for h

16. $F = \dfrac{k}{\sqrt{d}}$ for d

17. $p = \sqrt{\dfrac{k\ell}{g}}$ for ℓ

18. $p = \sqrt{\dfrac{k\ell}{g}}$ for g

Solve each problem. When appropriate, round answers to the nearest tenth. See Example 3.

19. Find the lengths of the sides of the triangle.

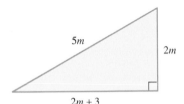

5m

2m

2m + 3

20. Find the lengths of the sides of the triangle.

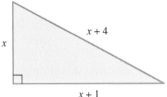

x + 4

x

x + 1

21. Two ships leave port at the same time, one heading due south and the other heading due east. Several hours later, they are 170 mi apart. If the ship traveling south traveled 70 mi farther than the other, how many miles did they each travel?

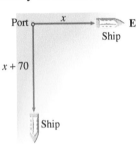

Port   x   E
Ship

x + 70

Ship

S

22. Faith Varnado is flying a kite that is 30 ft farther above her hand than its horizontal distance from her. The string from her hand to the kite is 150 ft long. How high is the kite?

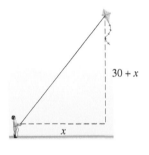

30 + x

x

Solve each problem. See Example 4.

23. A couple wants to buy a rug for a room that is 20 ft long and 15 ft wide. They want to leave an even strip of flooring uncovered around the edges of the room. How wide a strip will they have if they buy a rug with an area of 234 ft²?

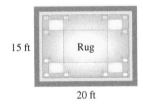

15 ft   Rug

20 ft

24. A club swimming pool is 30 ft wide and 40 ft long. The club members want an exposed aggregate border in a strip of uniform width around the pool. They have enough material for 296 ft². How wide can the strip be?

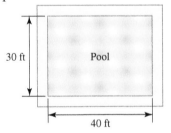

30 ft   Pool

40 ft

25. A rectangular piece of sheet metal has a length that is 4 in. less than twice the width. A square piece 2 in. on a side is cut from each corner. The sides are then turned up to form an uncovered box of volume 256 in.³. Find the length and width of the original piece of metal.

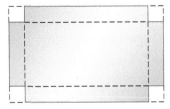

26. Another rectangular piece of sheet metal is 2 in. longer than it is wide. A square piece 3 in. on a side is cut from each corner. The sides are then turned up to form an uncovered box of volume 765 in.³. Find the dimensions of the original piece of metal.

⊞ *Solve each problem. Round answers to the nearest tenth. See Example 5.*

27. A ball is projected upward from the ground. Its distance in feet from the ground in t seconds is given by

$$s(t) = -16t^2 + 128t.$$

At what times will the ball be 213 ft from the ground?

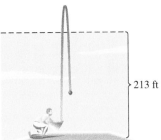

213 ft

28. A toy rocket is launched from ground level. Its distance in feet from the ground in t seconds is given by

$$s(t) = -16t^2 + 208t.$$

At what times will the rocket be 550 ft from the ground?

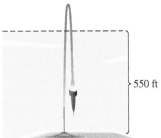

550 ft

29. The function defined by

$$D(t) = 13t^2 - 100t$$

gives the distance in feet a car going approximately 68 mph will skid in t seconds. Find the time it would take for the car to skid 180 ft.

D

30. The function given in Exercise 29 becomes

$$D(t) = 13t^2 - 73t$$

for a car going 50 mph. Find the time for this car to skid 218 ft.

A ball is projected upward from ground level, and its distance in feet from the ground in t seconds is given by $s(t) = -16t^2 + 160t$. Use algebra and a short explanation to answer Exercises 31 and 32.

31. After how many seconds does it reach a height of 400 ft? How would you describe in words its position at this height?

32. After how many seconds does it reach a height of 425 ft? How would you interpret the mathematical result here?

⊞ *Solve each problem using a quadratic equation.*

33. A certain bakery has found that the daily demand for blueberry muffins is $\frac{3200}{p}$, where p is the price of a muffin in cents. The daily supply is $3p - 200$. Find the price at which supply and demand are equal.

34. In one area the demand for compact discs is $\frac{700}{P}$ per day, where P is the price in dollars per disc. The supply is $5P - 1$ per day. At what price, to the nearest cent, does supply equal demand?

The total number of miles traveled by all motor vehicles in the United States for the years 1994–2003 are shown in the bar graph and can be modeled by the quadratic function defined by

$$f(x) = -1.705x^2 + 75.93x + 2351.$$

Here, $x = 0$ represents 1994, $x = 1$ represents 1995, and so on. Use the graph and the model to work Exercises 35–38. See Example 6.

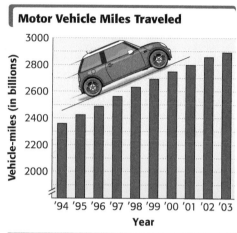

Motor Vehicle Miles Traveled

Source: U.S. Federal Highway Administration.

35. (a) Use the graph to estimate miles traveled in 2000 to the nearest ten billion.

(b) Use the model to approximate miles traveled in 2000 to the nearest ten billion. How does this result compare to your estimate from part (a)?

36. Based on the model, in what year did miles traveled reach 2600 billion? (Round down to the nearest year.) How does this result compare to the vehicle-miles shown in the graph?

37. Based on the model, in what year did miles traveled reach 2800 billion? (Round down to the nearest year.) How does this result compare to the vehicle-miles shown in the graph?

38. If these data were modeled by a *linear* function defined by $f(x) = ax + b$, would the value of a be positive or negative? Explain.

William Froude was a 19th-century naval architect who used the expression

$$\frac{v^2}{g\ell}$$

in shipbuilding. This expression, known as the **Froude number,** was also used by R. McNeill Alexander in his research on dinosaurs. (Source: "How Dinosaurs Ran," Scientific American, *April 1991.*) In Exercises 39 and 40, find to the nearest tenth the value of v (in meters per second), given that g = 9.8 m per sec^2.

39. Rhinoceros: $\ell = 1.2$; Froude number $= 2.57$

40. Triceratops: $\ell = 2.8$; Froude number $= 0.16$

Recall from the **Section 8.5** exercises that corresponding sides of similar triangles are proportional. Use this fact to find the lengths of the indicated sides of each pair of similar triangles. Check all possible solutions in both triangles. Sides of a triangle cannot be negative (and are not drawn to scale here).

41. Side *AC*

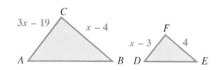

42. Side *RQ*

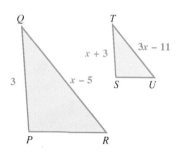

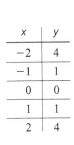

18.6 ▷▷▷ Graphs of Quadratic Functions

OBJECTIVE 1 Graph a quadratic function. Figure 4 gives a graph of the simplest *quadratic function,* defined by $y = x^2$.

x	y
-2	4
-1	1
0	0
1	1
2	4

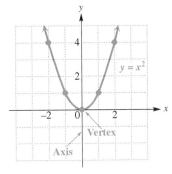

Figure 4

OBJECTIVES

1. Graph a quadratic function.

2. Graph parabolas with horizontal and vertical shifts.

3. Use the coefficient of x^2 to predict the shape and direction in which a parabola opens.

4. Find a quadratic function to model data.

As mentioned in **Section 6.3,** this graph is called a **parabola.** The point $(0, 0)$, the lowest point on the curve, is the **vertex** of this parabola. The vertical line through the vertex is the **axis** of the parabola, here $x = 0$. A parabola is **symmetric about its axis;** that is, if the graph were folded along the axis, the two portions of the curve would coincide. As Figure 4 suggests, x can be any real number, so the domain of the function defined by $y = x^2$ is $(-\infty, \infty)$. Since y is always nonnegative, the range is $[0, \infty)$.

In **Section 18.5,** we solved applications modeled by quadratic functions.

Quadratic Function

A function that can be written in the form

$$f(x) = ax^2 + bx + c$$

for real numbers a, b, and c, with $a \neq 0$, is a **quadratic function.**

The graph of any quadratic function is a parabola with a vertical axis.

Note

We use the variable y and function notation $f(x)$ interchangeably. Although we use the letter f most often to name quadratic functions, other letters can be used. We use the capital letter F to distinguish between different parabolas graphed on the same coordinate axes.

Parabolas, which are a type of *conic section* **(Chapter 12),** have many applications. Cross sections of telescopes, satellite dishes and automobile headlights form parabolas, as do the cables that support suspension bridges.

OBJECTIVE 2 Graph parabolas with horizontal and vertical shifts. Parabolas need not have their vertices at the origin, as does the graph of $f(x) = x^2$. To graph a parabola of the form

$$F(x) = x^2 + k, \quad \text{Vertical shift } k$$

select sample values of x like those that were used to graph $f(x) = x^2$. The corresponding values of $F(x)$ in $F(x) = x^2 + k$ differ by k from those of $f(x) = x^2$. For this reason, the graph of $F(x) = x^2 + k$ is *shifted,* or *translated,* k units vertically compared with that of $f(x) = x^2$.

1 Graph each parabola. Give the vertex, domain, and range.

(a) $f(x) = x^2 + 3$

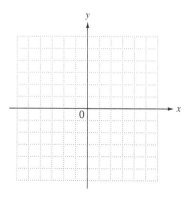

(b) $f(x) = x^2 - 1$

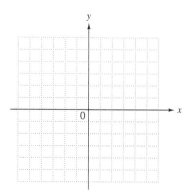

1. (a)

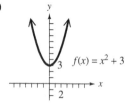

vertex: $(0, 3)$; domain: $(-\infty, \infty)$; range: $[3, \infty)$

(b)

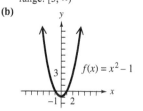

vertex: $(0, -1)$; domain: $(-\infty, \infty)$; range: $[-1, \infty)$

Example 1 **Graphing a Parabola with a Vertical Shift**

Graph $F(x) = x^2 - 2$.

This graph has the same shape as that of $f(x) = x^2$, but since k here is -2, the graph is shifted 2 units down, with vertex $(0, -2)$. Every function value is 2 less than the corresponding function value of $f(x) = x^2$. Plotting points on both sides of the vertex gives the graph in Figure 5.

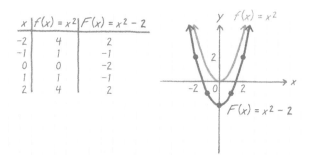

Figure 5

Notice that since the parabola is symmetric about its axis $x = 0$, the plotted points are "mirror images" of each other. Since x can be any real number, the domain is still $(-\infty, \infty)$. The value of y (or $F(x)$) is always greater than or equal to -2, so the range is $[-2, \infty)$. The graph of $f(x) = x^2$ is shown for comparison.

Vertical Shift

The graph of $F(x) = x^2 + k$ is a parabola with the same shape as the graph of $f(x) = x^2$. The parabola is shifted vertically: k units up if $k > 0$, and $|k|$ units down if $k < 0$. The vertex is $(0, k)$.

◀ Work Problem 1 at the Side.

The graph of the function defined by

$$F(x) = (x - h)^2 \qquad \text{Horizontal shift } h$$

is also a parabola with the same shape as that of $f(x) = x^2$. Because $(x - h)^2 \geq 0$ for all x, the vertex of $F(x) = (x - h)^2$ is the lowest point on the parabola. The lowest point occurs here when $F(x)$ is 0. To get $F(x)$ equal to 0, let $x = h$ so the vertex of $F(x) = (x - h)^2$ is $(h, 0)$. Based on this, the graph of $F(x) = (x - h)^2$ is shifted h units horizontally compared with that of $f(x) = x^2$.

Example 2 **Graphing a Parabola with a Horizontal Shift**

Graph $F(x) = (x - 2)^2$.

If $x = 2$, then $F(x) = 0$, which gives the vertex $(2, 0)$. The graph of $F(x) = (x - 2)^2$ has the same shape as that of $f(x) = x^2$ but is shifted 2 units to the right. Plotting several points on one side of the vertex and using symmetry about the axis $x = 2$ to find corresponding points on the other side of the vertex gives the graph in Figure 6 on the next page. Again, the domain is $(-\infty, \infty)$; the range is $[0, \infty)$.

Continued on Next Page

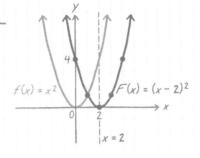

x	$F(x) = (x - 2)^2$
0	4
1	1
2	0
3	1
4	4

$f(x) = x^2$ $F(x) = (x - 2)^2$

$x = 2$

Figure 6

Horizontal Shift

The graph of $F(x) = (x - h)^2$ is a parabola with the same shape as the graph of $f(x) = x^2$. The parabola is shifted h units horizontally: h units to the right if $h > 0$, and $|h|$ units to the left if $h < 0$. The vertex is $(h, 0)$.

CAUTION

Errors frequently occur when horizontal shifts are involved. To determine the direction and magnitude of a horizontal shift, find the value that would cause the expression $x - h$ to equal 0. For example, the graph of $F(x) = (x - 5)^2$ would be shifted 5 units to the *right,* because $+5$ would cause $x - 5$ to equal 0. On the other hand, the graph of $F(x) = (x + 5)^2$ would be shifted 5 units to the *left,* because -5 would cause $x + 5$ to equal 0.

Work Problem *at the Side.* ▶

A parabola can have both horizontal and vertical shifts.

Example 3 **Graphing a Parabola with Horizontal and Vertical Shifts**

Graph $F(x) = (x + 3)^2 - 2$.

This graph has the same shape as that of $f(x) = x^2$, but is shifted 3 units to the left (since $x + 3 = 0$ if $x = -3$) and 2 units down (because of the -2). See Figure 7. The vertex is $(-3, -2)$, with axis $x = -3$. This function has domain $(-\infty, \infty)$ and range $[-2, \infty)$.

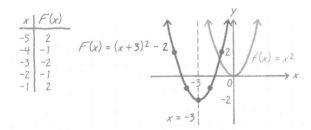

x	$F(x)$
-5	2
-4	-1
-3	-2
-2	-1
-1	2

$F(x) = (x + 3)^2 - 2$ $f(x) = x^2$

$x = -3$

Figure 7

2 Graph each parabola. Give the vertex, axis, domain, and range.

(a) $f(x) = (x - 3)^2$

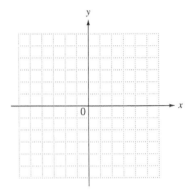

(b) $f(x) = (x + 2)^2$

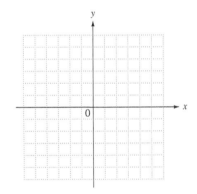

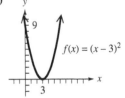
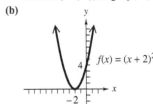

3 Graph each parabola. Give the vertex, axis, domain, and range.

(a) $f(x) = (x + 2)^2 - 1$

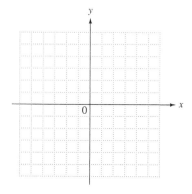

(b) $f(x) = (x - 2)^2 + 5$

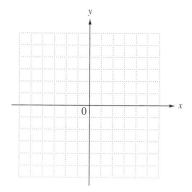

The characteristics of the graph of a parabola with equation of the form $F(x) = (x - h)^2 + k$ are summarized as follows.

Vertex and Axis of a Parabola

The graph of $F(x) = (x - h)^2 + k$ is a parabola with the same shape as the graph of $f(x) = x^2$ with vertex (h, k). The axis is the vertical line $x = h$.

◀ *Work Problem* **3** *at the Side.*

OBJECTIVE 3 Use the coefficient of x^2 to predict the shape and direction in which a parabola opens. Not all parabolas open up, and not all parabolas have the same shape as the graph of $f(x) = x^2$.

Example 4   **Graphing a Parabola That Opens Down**

Graph $f(x) = -\dfrac{1}{2}x^2$.

This parabola is shown in Figure 8. The coefficient $-\frac{1}{2}$ affects the shape of the graph; the $\frac{1}{2}$ makes the parabola wider (since the values of $\frac{1}{2}x^2$ increase more slowly than those of x^2), and the negative sign makes the parabola open down. The graph is not shifted in any direction; the vertex is still $(0, 0)$ and the axis has equation $x = 0$. Unlike the parabolas graphed in Examples 1–3, the vertex here has the *greatest* function value of any point on the graph. The domain is $(-\infty, \infty)$; the range is $(-\infty, 0]$.

x	$f(x)$
-2	-2
-1	$-\frac{1}{2}$
0	0
1	$-\frac{1}{2}$
2	-2

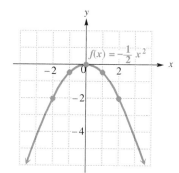

Figure 8

Some general principles concerning the graph of $F(x) = a(x - h)^2 + k$ are summarized as follows.

General Principles

1. The graph of the quadratic function defined by
$$F(x) = a(x - h)^2 + k, \quad a \neq 0,$$
is a parabola with vertex (h, k) and the vertical line $x = h$ as axis.

2. The graph opens up if a is positive and down if a is negative.

3. The graph is wider than that of $f(x) = x^2$ if $0 < |a| < 1$. The graph is narrower than that of $f(x) = x^2$ if $|a| > 1$.

ANSWERS

3. (a)

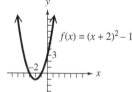

vertex: $(-2, -1)$; axis: $x = -2$; domain: $(-\infty, \infty)$; range: $[-1, \infty)$

(b)

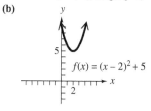

vertex: $(2, 5)$; axis: $x = 2$; domain: $(-\infty, \infty)$; range: $[5, \infty)$

Work Problems **4** *and* **5** *at the Side.* ▶

Example 5   **Using the General Principles to Graph a Parabola**

Graph $F(x) = -2(x + 3)^2 + 4$. Give the domain and the range.

The parabola opens down (because $a < 0$), and is narrower than the graph of $f(x) = x^2$, since $|-2| = 2 > 1$, causing values of $F(x)$ to decrease more quickly than those of $f(x) = -x^2$. This parabola has vertex $(-3, 4)$ as shown in Figure 9. To complete the graph, we plotted the ordered pairs $(-4, 2)$ and, by symmetry, $(-2, 2)$. Symmetry can be used to find additional ordered pairs that satisfy the equation, if desired. The domain is $(-\infty, \infty)$ and the range is $(-\infty, 4]$.

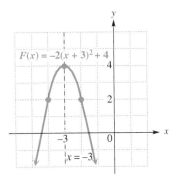

$F(x) = -2(x + 3)^2 + 4$

Figure 9

Work Problem **6** *at the Side.* ▶

OBJECTIVE 4 **Find a quadratic function to model data.**

Example 6   **Modeling the Number of Multiple Births**

After rising steadily over several decades, the number of higher-order multiple births (triplets or more) in the United States started to decline during the first decade of the 21st century. Let x represent the number of years since 1995 and y represent the number of higher-order multiple births. Data for selected years are shown in the table.

Year	x	y
1995	0	4973
1996	1	5939
1997	2	6737
1999	4	7321
2001	6	7471
2003	8	7663
2004	9	7275
2005	10	6694

Source: National Center for Health Statistics.

Find a quadratic function that models the data.

A scatter diagram of the ordered pairs (x, y) is shown in Figure 10 on the next page. The general shape suggested by the scatter diagram indicates that a parabola should approximate these points, as shown by the dashed curve in Figure 11. The equation for such a parabola would have a negative coefficient for x^2 since the graph opens down.

Continued on Next Page

---

4 Decide whether each parabola opens up or down.

(a) $f(x) = -\dfrac{2}{3}x^2$

(b) $f(x) = \dfrac{3}{4}x^2 + 1$

(c) $f(x) = -2x^2 - 3$

(d) $f(x) = 3x^2 + 2$

5 Decide whether each parabola in Problem 4 is wider or narrower than the graph of $f(x) = x^2$.

6 Graph
$$f(x) = \frac{1}{2}(x - 2)^2 + 1.$$

Give the domain and the range.

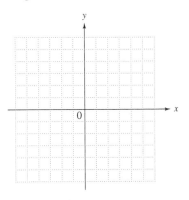

ANSWERS

4. **(a)** down   **(b)** up   **(c)** down   **(d)** up
5. **(a)** wider   **(b)** wider   **(c)** narrower
   (d) narrower
6.

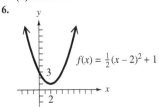

$f(x) = \frac{1}{2}(x - 2)^2 + 1$

domain: $(-\infty, \infty)$
range: $[1, \infty)$

7 Tell whether a linear or quadratic function would be a more appropriate model for each set of graphed data. If linear, tell whether the slope should be positive or negative. If quadratic, tell whether the coefficient a of x^2 should be positive or negative.

(a) **AVERAGE DAILY E-MAIL VOLUME**

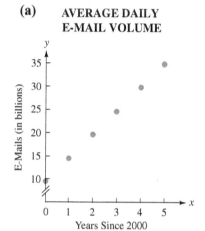

Years Since 2000

Source: General Accounting Office.

(b) **MP3 PLAYER SALES IN U.S.**

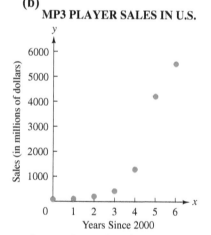

Years Since 2000

Source: Consumer Electronics Association.

8 Using the points (1, 5939), (6, 7471), and (10, 6694), find another quadratic model for the data on higher-order multiple births in Example 6.

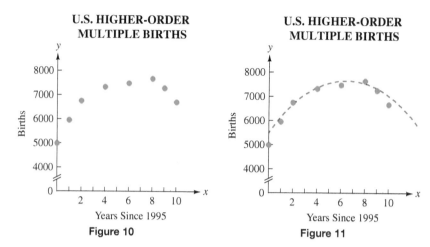

U.S. HIGHER-ORDER MULTIPLE BIRTHS

Years Since 1995

Figure 10

U.S. HIGHER-ORDER MULTIPLE BIRTHS

Years Since 1995

Figure 11

To find a quadratic function of the form

$$y = ax^2 + bx + c$$

that models, or *fits,* these data, we choose three representative ordered pairs and use them to write a system of three equations. Using (0, 4973), (4, 7321), and (10, 6694), we substitute the x- and y-values from the ordered pairs into the quadratic form $y = ax^2 + bx + c$ to get the three equations

$a(0)^2 + b(0) + c = 4973$	or	$c = 4973$ (1)
$a(4)^2 + b(4) + c = 7321$	or	$16a + 4b + c = 7321$ (2)
$a(10)^2 + b(10) + c = 6694$	or	$100a + 10b + c = 6694.$ (3)

We can find the values of a, b, and c by solving this system of three equations in three variables using the methods of **Section 5.2.** From equation (1), $c = 4973$. Substitute 4973 for c in equations (2) and (3) to obtain the equations

$16a + 4b + 4973 = 7321,$	or	$16a + 4b = 2348$ (4)
$100a + 10b + 4973 = 6694,$	or	$100a + 10b = 1721.$ (5)

We can eliminate b from this system of equations in two variables by multiplying equation (4) by -5 and equation (5) by 2, and adding the results to get

$$120a = -8298$$

$$a = -69.15.$$ Divide by 120; use a calculator.

We substitute -69.15 for a in equation (4) or (5) to find that $b = 863.6$. Using the values we have found for a, b, and c, our model is defined by

$$y = -69.15x^2 + 863.6b + 4973.$$

◀ Work Problems **7** and **8** at the Side.

Note
If we had chosen three different ordered pairs of data in Example 6, a slightly different model would have resulted, as in Problem 8 at the side.

🔢 **Calculator Tip** The *quadratic regression* feature on a graphing calculator can be used to generate a quadratic model that fits given data. See your owner's manual for details on how to do this.

ANSWERS

7. **(a)** linear; positive   **(b)** quadratic; positive
8. $y = -55.63x^2 + 695.80x + 5299$

18.6 ▶▶▶ **Exercises**

FOR EXTRA HELP

MyMathLab    *Math XL* PRACTICE   WATCH   DOWNLOAD   READ   REVIEW

1. Match each quadratic function with its graph from choices A–D.

    (a) $f(x) = (x + 2)^2 - 1$ **(b)** $f(x) = (x + 2)^2 + 1$ **(c)** $f(x) = (x - 2)^2 - 1$ **(d)** $f(x) = (x - 2)^2 + 1$

A. 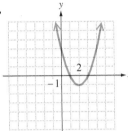   **B.** 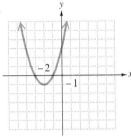   **C.** 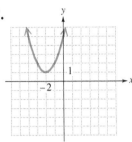   **D.**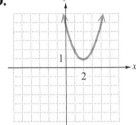

2. Match each quadratic function with its graph from choices A–D.

    (a) $f(x) = -x^2 + 2$ **(b)** $f(x) = -x^2 - 2$ **(c)** $f(x) = -(x + 2)^2$ **(d)** $f(x) = -(x - 2)^2$

A. 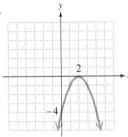   **B.** 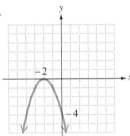   **C.** 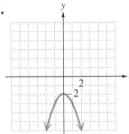   **D.**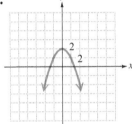

Identify the vertex of each parabola. See Examples 1–4.

3. $f(x) = -3x^2$ **4.** $f(x) = \dfrac{1}{2}x^2$ **5.** $f(x) = x^2 + 4$

6. $f(x) = x^2 - 4$ **7.** $f(x) = (x - 1)^2$ **8.** $f(x) = (x + 3)^2$

9. $f(x) = (x + 3)^2 - 4$ **10.** $f(x) = (x - 5)^2 - 8$

11. Describe how each of the parabolas in Exercises 9 and 10 is shifted compared to the graph of $f(x) = x^2$.

12. What does the value of a in $F(x) = a(x - h)^2 + k$ tell you about the graph of the equation compared to the graph of $f(x) = x^2$?

For each quadratic function, tell whether the graph opens up or down and whether the graph is wider, narrower, or the same shape as the graph of $f(x) = x^2$. See Examples 4 and 5.

13. $f(x) = -\dfrac{2}{5}x^2$

14. $f(x) = -2x^2$

15. $f(x) = 3x^2 + 1$

16. $f(x) = \dfrac{2}{3}x^2 - 4$

17. For $f(x) = a(x - h)^2 + k$, in what quadrant is the vertex if

(a) $h > 0, k > 0$; (b) $h > 0, k < 0$;

(c) $h < 0, k > 0$; (d) $h < 0, k < 0$?

18. Match each quadratic function with the description of the parabola that is its graph.

(a) $f(x) = (x - 4)^2 - 2$ A. Vertex $(2, -4)$, opens down

(b) $f(x) = (x - 2)^2 - 4$ B. Vertex $(2, -4)$, opens up

(c) $f(x) = -(x - 4)^2 - 2$ C. Vertex $(4, -2)$, opens down

(d) $f(x) = -(x - 2)^2 - 4$ D. Vertex $(4, -2)$, opens up

Sketch the graph of each parabola. Plot at least two points in addition to the vertex. In Exercises 25–32, give the vertex, axis, domain, and range of the parabola. See Examples 1–5.

19. $f(x) = -2x^2$

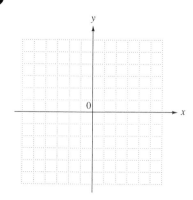

20. $f(x) = \dfrac{1}{3}x^2$

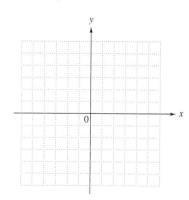

21. $f(x) = x^2 - 1$

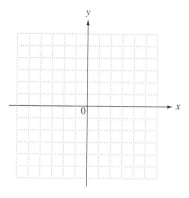

22. $f(x) = x^2 + 3$

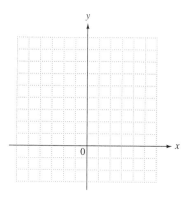

23. $f(x) = -x^2 + 2$

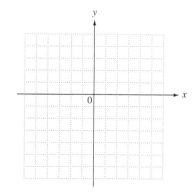

24. $f(x) = 2x^2 - 2$

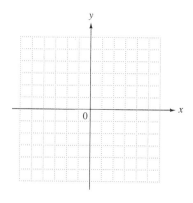

25. $f(x) = \dfrac{1}{2}(x - 4)^2$

    vertex:
    axis:
    domain:
    range:

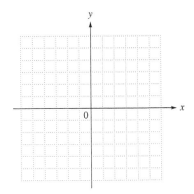

26. $f(x) = -2(x + 1)^2$

    vertex:
    axis:
    domain:
    range:

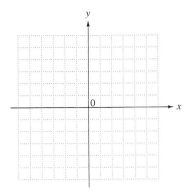

27. $f(x) = (x + 2)^2 - 1$

    vertex:
    axis:
    domain:
    range:

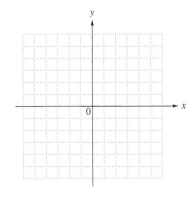

28. $f(x) = (x - 1)^2 + 2$

    vertex:
    axis:
    domain:
    range:

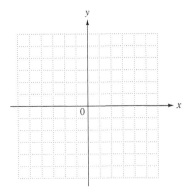

29. $f(x) = -2(x + 3)^2 + 4$

    vertex:
    axis:
    domain:
    range:

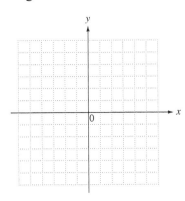

30. $f(x) = 2(x - 2)^2 - 3$

    vertex:
    axis:
    domain:
    range:

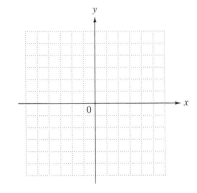

31. $f(x) = -\dfrac{2}{3}(x + 2)^2 + 1$

    vertex:
    axis:
    domain:
    range:

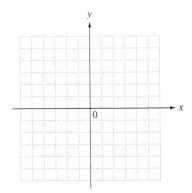

32. $f(x) = -\dfrac{1}{2}(x + 1)^2 + 2$

    vertex:
    axis:
    domain:
    range:

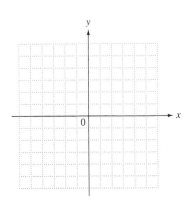

Relating Concepts (Exercises 33–38) For Individual or Group Work

*The procedures described in this section that allow the graph of $f(x) = x^2$ to be shifted vertically and horizontally are applicable to other types of functions. In **Section 4.5** we introduced linear functions of the form $g(x) = ax + b$. Consider the graph of the simplest linear function defined by $g(x) = x$, shown here, and then **work Exercises 33–38 in order.***

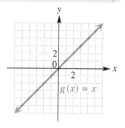

33. Based on the concepts of this section, how does the graph of $F(x) = x^2 + 6$ compare to the graph of $f(x) = x^2$ if a *vertical* shift is considered?

34. Graph the linear function defined by $G(x) = x + 6$.

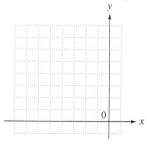

35. Based on the concepts of **Chapter 4**, how does the graph of $G(x) = x + 6$ compare to the graph of $g(x) = x$ if a *vertical* shift is considered? (*Hint:* Look at the *y*-intercept.)

36. Based on the concepts of this section, how does the graph of $F(x) = (x - 6)^2$ compare to the graph of $f(x) = x^2$ if a *horizontal* shift is considered?

37. Graph the linear function defined by $G(x) = x - 6$.

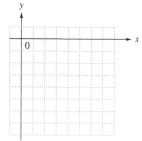

38. Based on the concepts of **Chapter 4,** how does the graph of $G(x) = x - 6$ compare to the graph of $g(x) = x$ if a *horizontal* shift is considered? (*Hint:* Look at the *x*-intercept.)

In Exercises 39–44, tell whether a linear or quadratic function would be a more appropriate model for each set of graphed data. If linear, tell whether the slope should be positive or negative. If quadratic, tell whether the coefficient of x^2 should be positive or negative. See Example 6.

39.   **PLASMA TV SALES IN U.S.**

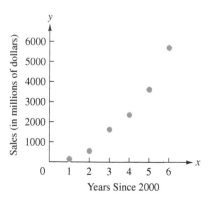

Source: Consumer Electronics Association.

40.   **AVERAGE DAILY VOLUME OF FIRST-CLASS MAIL**

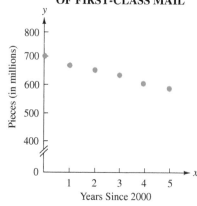

Source: General Accounting Office.

41.   **SOCIAL SECURITY ASSETS***

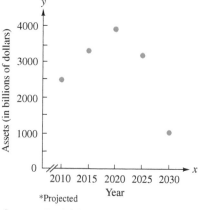

*Projected

Source: Social Security Administration.

42.

**FOOD ASSISTANCE
SPENDING IN IOWA**

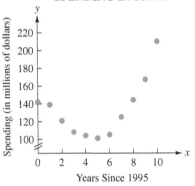

Source: Iowa Department of Human
Services.

43.

**TIME SPENT PLAYING
VIDEO GAMES***

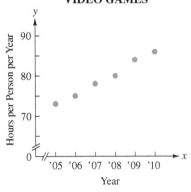

*Later years projected
Source: Veronis Suhler Stevenson.

44.

**SALES OF MUSIC
CASSETTE TAPES**

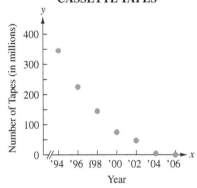

Source: Recording Industry Association
of America.

Solve each problem. See Example 6.

45. Sales of digital cameras in the United States (in millions of dollars) between 2000 and 2006
are shown in the table. In the year column, 0 represents 2000, 1 represents 2001, and so on.

SALES OF DIGITAL CAMERAS

Year	Sales
0	1825
1	1972
2	2794
3	3921
4	4739
5	5611
6	7805

Source: Consumer Electronics
Association.

(a) Use the ordered pairs (year, sales) to make a
scatter diagram of the data.

DIGITAL CAMERA SALES IN U.S.

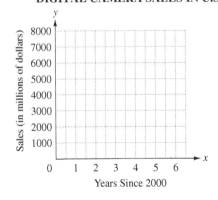

(b) Use the scatter diagram to decide whether a linear or quadratic function would better model the
data. If quadratic, should the coefficient a of x^2
be positive or negative?

(c) Use the ordered pairs (0, 1825), (3, 3921), and
(6, 7805) to find a quadratic function that models the data. Round the values of a, b, and c in
your model to the nearest tenth, as necessary.

(d) Use your model from part (c) to approximate
the sales of digital cameras in the United States
in 2007. Round your answer to the nearest
whole number (of millions).

(e) Sales of digital cameras were projected to be
$6945 million in 2007. Based on this, is the
model valid for 2007? Explain.

46. The percent of U.S. high school students in grades 9–12 who smoke is shown in the table for selected years. In the year column, 1 represents 1991, 3 represents 1993, and so on.

HIGH SCHOOL STUDENTS WHO SMOKE

Year	Percent of Students
1	28
3	31
5	35
7	36
9	35
11	29
13	22

Source: Centers for Disease Control and Prevention.

(a) Use the ordered pairs (year, percent of students) to make a scatter diagram of the data.

PERCENT OF HIGH SCHOOL STUDENTS WHO SMOKE

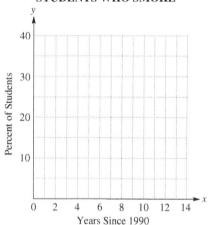

(b) Would a linear or quadratic function better model the data?

(c) Should the coefficient a of x^2 in a quadratic model be positive or negative?

(d) Use the ordered pairs (1, 28), (7, 36), and (11, 29) to find a quadratic function that models the data. Round the values of a, b, and c in your model to the nearest tenth, as necessary.

(e) Use your model from part (d) to approximate the percent of high school students who smoked during 1995 and 2003 to the nearest percent. How well does the model approximate the actual data from the table?

47. In Exercise 46(d), we determined that the quadratic function defined by

$$y = -0.3x^2 + 3.8x + 24.5$$

modeled the percent of U.S. high school students who smoked in the years 1991–2003.

(a) Use this model to approximate the number of high school students who smoked in 2005 and 2007.

(b) The actual smoking rates for high school students were 23% in 2005 and 20% in 2007. (*Source:* Centers for Disease Control and Prevention.) How do the approximations using the model compare to the actual rates for these two years?

48. Should the model from Exercise 46(d) be used to approximate the smoking rate for high school students in years after 2003? Explain.

18.7 ▶▶▶ More about Parabolas and Their Applications

OBJECTIVE **1** **Find the vertex of a vertical parabola.** When the equation of a parabola is given in the form $f(x) = ax^2 + bx + c$, we need to locate the vertex in order to sketch an accurate graph. There are two ways to do this:

1. Complete the square, as shown in Examples 1 and 2, or
2. Use a formula derived by completing the square, as shown in Example 3.

Example 1 **Completing the Square to Find the Vertex ($a = 1$)**

Find the vertex of the graph of $f(x) = x^2 - 4x + 5$.

To find the vertex, we need to write the expression $x^2 - 4x + 5$ in the form $(x - h)^2 + k$. We do this by completing the square on $x^2 - 4x$, as in **Section 10.1.** The process is slightly different here because we want to keep $f(x)$ alone on one side of the equation. Instead of adding the appropriate number to each side, we *add and subtract* it on the right. This is equivalent to adding 0.

$$f(x) = x^2 - 4x + 5$$

$$f(x) = (x^2 - 4x \qquad) + 5 \qquad \text{Group the variable terms.}$$

$$\left[\frac{1}{2}(-4)\right]^2 = (-2)^2 = 4$$

$$f(x) = (x^2 - 4x + 4 - 4) + 5 \qquad \text{Add and subtract 4.}$$

$$f(x) = (x^2 - 4x + 4) - 4 + 5 \qquad \text{Bring } -4 \text{ outside the parentheses.}$$

$$f(x) = (x - 2)^2 + 1 \qquad \text{Factor; combine like terms.}$$

The vertex of this parabola is $(2, 1)$.

Work Problem **1** *at the Side.* ▶

Example 2 **Completing the Square to Find the Vertex ($a \neq 1$)**

Find the vertex of the graph of $f(x) = -3x^2 + 6x - 1$.

We must complete the square on $-3x^2 + 6x$. Because the x^2-term has a coefficient other than 1, we factor that coefficient out of the first two terms and then proceed as in Example 1.

$$f(x) = -3x^2 + 6x - 1$$

$$f(x) = -3(x^2 - 2x) - 1 \qquad \text{Factor out } -3.$$

$$\left[\frac{1}{2}(-2)\right]^2 = (-1)^2 = 1$$

$$f(x) = -3(x^2 - 2x + 1 - 1) - 1 \qquad \text{Add and subtract 1.}$$

Now bring -1 outside the parentheses; be sure to multiply it by -3.

$$f(x) = -3(x^2 - 2x + 1) + (-3)(-1) - 1 \qquad \text{Distributive property}$$

$$f(x) = -3(x^2 - 2x + 1) + 3 - 1 \qquad \boxed{\text{This is a key step.}}$$

$$f(x) = -3(x - 1)^2 + 2 \qquad \text{Factor; combine like terms.}$$

The vertex is $(1, 2)$.

Work Problem **2** *at the Side.* ▶

OBJECTIVES

1 Find the vertex of a vertical parabola.

2 Graph a quadratic function.

3 Use the discriminant to find the number of x-intercepts of a parabola with a vertical axis.

4 Use quadratic functions to solve problems involving maximum or minimum value.

5 Graph parabolas with horizontal axes.

---

1 Find the vertex of the graph of each quadratic function.

(a) $f(x) = x^2 - 6x + 7$

(b) $f(x) = x^2 + 4x - 9$

2 Find the vertex of the graph of each quadratic function.

(a) $f(x) = 2x^2 - 4x + 1$

(b) $f(x) = -\frac{1}{2}x^2 + 2x - 3$

ANSWERS

1. **(a)** $(3, -2)$ **(b)** $(-2, -13)$
2. **(a)** $(1, -1)$ **(b)** $(2, -1)$

3 Use the formula to find the vertex of the graph of each quadratic function.

(a) $f(x) = -2x^2 + 3x - 1$

To derive a formula for the vertex of the graph of the quadratic function defined by $f(x) = ax^2 + bx + c$, complete the square.

$$f(x) = ax^2 + bx + c \quad (a \neq 0) \qquad \text{Standard form}$$

$$f(x) = a\left(x^2 + \frac{b}{a}x\right) + c \qquad \text{Factor } a \text{ from the first two terms.}$$

$$\left[\frac{1}{2}\left(\frac{b}{a}\right)\right]^2 = \left(\frac{b}{2a}\right)^2 = \frac{b^2}{4a^2}$$

$$f(x) = a\left(x^2 + \frac{b}{a}x + \frac{b^2}{4a^2} - \frac{b^2}{4a^2}\right) + c \qquad \text{Add and subtract } \frac{b^2}{4a^2}.$$

$$f(x) = a\left(x^2 + \frac{b}{a}x + \frac{b^2}{4a^2}\right) + a\left(-\frac{b^2}{4a^2}\right) + c \qquad \text{Distributive property}$$

$$f(x) = a\left(x^2 + \frac{b}{a}x + \frac{b^2}{4a^2}\right) - \frac{b^2}{4a} + c \qquad -\frac{ab^2}{4a^2} = -\frac{b^2}{4a}$$

$$f(x) = a\left(x + \frac{b}{2a}\right)^2 + \frac{4ac - b^2}{4a} \qquad \text{Factor; rewrite terms with a common denominator.}$$

$$f(x) = a\left[x - \left(\frac{-b}{2a}\right)\right]^2 + \frac{4ac - b^2}{4a} \qquad f(x) = (x - h)^2 + k$$

$$\underbrace{\phantom{x - \left(\frac{-b}{2a}\right)}}_{h} \qquad \underbrace{\phantom{\frac{4ac-b^2}{4a}}}_{k}$$

Thus, the vertex (h, k) can be expressed in terms of a, b, and c. It is not necessary to remember the expression for k, since it can be found by replacing x with $\frac{-b}{2a}$. Using function notation, if $y = f(x)$, then the y-value of the vertex is $f\left(\frac{-b}{2a}\right)$.

(b) $f(x) = 4x^2 - x + 5$

> **Vertex Formula**
>
> The graph of the quadratic function defined by $f(x) = ax^2 + bx + c$ has vertex
>
> $$\left(\frac{-b}{2a}, f\left(\frac{-b}{2a}\right)\right).$$
>
> The axis of the parabola is the line
>
> $$x = \frac{-b}{2a}.$$

Example 3   Using the Formula to Find the Vertex

Use the vertex formula to find the vertex of the graph of $f(x) = x^2 - x - 6$.
   For this function, $a = 1$, $b = -1$, and $c = -6$. The x-coordinate of the vertex of the parabola is given by

$$\frac{-b}{2a} = \frac{-(-1)}{2(1)} = \frac{1}{2}.$$

The y-coordinate is $f\left(\frac{-b}{2a}\right) = f\left(\frac{1}{2}\right)$.

$$f\left(\frac{1}{2}\right) = \left(\frac{1}{2}\right)^2 - \frac{1}{2} - 6 = \frac{1}{4} - \frac{1}{2} - 6 = -\frac{25}{4}$$

The vertex is $\left(\frac{1}{2}, -\frac{25}{4}\right)$.

ANSWERS

3. **(a)** $\left(\frac{3}{4}, \frac{1}{8}\right)$ **(b)** $\left(\frac{1}{8}, \frac{79}{16}\right)$

◀ Work Problem **3** at the Side.

OBJECTIVE 2 Graph a quadratic function.

> **Graphing a Quadratic Function f**
>
> *Step 1* **Determine whether the graph opens up or down.** If $a > 0$, the parabola opens up; if $a < 0$, it opens down.
>
> *Step 2* **Find the vertex.** Use either the vertex formula or completing the square.
>
> *Step 3* **Find any intercepts.** To find the x-intercepts (if any), solve $f(x) = 0$. To find the y-intercept, evaluate $f(0)$.
>
> *Step 4* **Complete the graph.** Plot the points found so far. Find and plot additional points as needed, using symmetry about the axis.

Example 4   Graphing a Quadratic Function

Graph the quadratic function defined by $f(x) = x^2 - x - 6$.

Step 1 From the equation, $a = 1$, so the graph of the function opens up.

Step 2 The vertex, $\left(\frac{1}{2}, -\frac{25}{4}\right)$, was found in Example 3 by substituting the values $a = 1$, $b = -1$, and $c = -6$ in the vertex formula.

Step 3 Now find any intercepts. Since the vertex, $\left(\frac{1}{2}, -\frac{25}{4}\right)$, is in quadrant IV and the graph opens up, there will be two x-intercepts. To find them, let $f(x) = 0$ and solve the equation.

$$f(x) = x^2 - x - 6$$
$$0 = x^2 - x - 6 \qquad \text{Let } f(x) = 0.$$
$$0 = (x - 3)(x + 2) \qquad \text{Factor.}$$
$$x - 3 = 0 \quad \text{or} \quad x + 2 = 0 \qquad \text{Zero-factor property}$$
$$x = 3 \quad \text{or} \qquad x = -2 \qquad \text{Solve each equation.}$$

The x-intercepts are $(3, 0)$ and $(-2, 0)$. Find the y-intercept.

$$f(x) = x^2 - x - 6$$
$$f(0) = 0^2 - 0 - 6 \qquad \text{Let } x = 0.$$
$$f(0) = -6$$

The y-intercept is $(0, -6)$.

Step 4 Plot the points found so far and additional points as needed using symmetry about the axis $x = \frac{1}{2}$. The graph is shown in Figure 12. The domain is $(-\infty, \infty)$, and the range is $\left[-\frac{25}{4}, \infty\right)$.

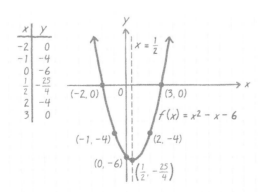

Figure 12

Work Problem **4** *at the Side.* ▶

4 Graph the quadratic function defined by

$$f(x) = x^2 - 6x + 5.$$

Give the vertex, axis, domain, and range.

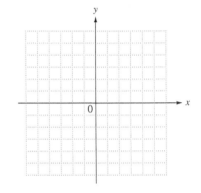

ANSWER

4.

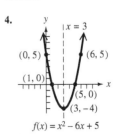

$$f(x) = x^2 - 6x + 5$$

vertex: $(3, -4)$; axis: $x = 3$; domain: $(-\infty, \infty)$; range: $[-4, \infty)$

5 Use the discriminant to determine the number of x-intercepts of the graph of each quadratic function.

(a) $f(x) = 4x^2 - 20x + 25$

(b) $f(x) = 2x^2 + 3x + 5$

(c) $f(x) = -3x^2 - x + 2$

OBJECTIVE **3** **Use the discriminant to find the number of x-intercepts of a parabola with a vertical axis.** Recall from Section 18.3 that the expression $b^2 - 4ac$ is called the **discriminant** of the quadratic *equation* $ax^2 + bx + c = 0$ and that we can use it to determine the number of real solutions of a quadratic equation.

In a similar way, we can use the discriminant of a quadratic *function* to determine the number of x-intercepts of its graph. See Figure 13. If the discriminant is positive, the parabola will have two x-intercepts. If the discriminant is 0, there will be only one x-intercept, and it will be the vertex of the parabola. If the discriminant is negative, the graph will have no x-intercepts.

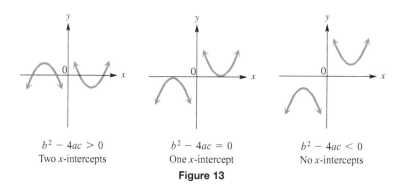

| $b^2 - 4ac > 0$ | $b^2 - 4ac = 0$ | $b^2 - 4ac < 0$ |
| Two x-intercepts | One x-intercept | No x-intercepts |

Figure 13

Example 5 **Using the Discriminant to Determine the Number of x-Intercepts**

Use the discriminant to determine the number of x-intercepts of the graph of each quadratic function.

(a) $f(x) = 2x^2 + 3x - 5$

The discriminant is $b^2 - 4ac$. Here $a = 2$, $b = 3$, and $c = -5$, so

$$b^2 - 4ac$$
$$= 3^2 - 4(2)(-5) \quad \text{Substitute.}$$
$$= 9 - (-40) \quad \text{Apply the exponent; multiply.}$$
$$= 49. \quad \text{Subtract.}$$

Since the discriminant is positive, the parabola has two x-intercepts.

(b) $f(x) = -3x^2 - 1$

In this equation, $a = -3$, $b = 0$, and $c = -1$. The discriminant is

$$b^2 - 4ac$$
$$= 0^2 - 4(-3)(-1)$$
$$= -12.$$

The discriminant is negative, so the graph has no x-intercepts.

(c) $f(x) = 9x^2 + 6x + 1$

Here, $a = 9$, $b = 6$, and $c = 1$. The discriminant is

$$b^2 - 4ac$$
$$= 6^2 - 4(9)(1)$$
$$= 0.$$

The parabola has only one x-intercept (its vertex) because the value of the discriminant is 0.

◀ *Work Problem* **5** *at the Side.*

OBJECTIVE 4 Use quadratic functions to solve problems involving maximum or minimum value. The vertex of a parabola is either the highest or the lowest point on the parabola. The *y*-value of the vertex gives the maximum or minimum value of *y*, while the *x*-value tells where that maximum or minimum occurs.

6 Solve Example 6 if the farmer has only 100 ft of fencing.

> **Problem-Solving Hint**
>
> In many applied problems we must find the least or greatest value of some quantity. When we can express that quantity as a quadratic function, the value of *k* in the vertex (h, k) gives that optimum value.

Example 6 Finding the Maximum Area of a Rectangular Region

A farmer has 120 ft of fencing to enclose a rectangular area next to a building. See Figure 14. Find the maximum area he can enclose and the width required to produce this maximum area.

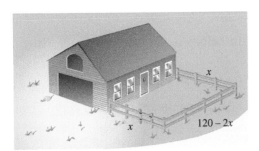

Figure 14

Let *x* represent the width of the rectangle. Since he has 120 ft of fencing,

$$x + x + \text{length} = 120 \qquad \text{Sum of the sides is 120 ft.}$$
$$2x + \text{length} = 120 \qquad \text{Combine like terms.}$$
$$\text{length} = 120 - 2x. \qquad \text{Subtract } 2x.$$

The area $A(x)$ is given by the product of the width and length, so

$$A(x) = x(120 - 2x)$$
$$A(x) = 120x - 2x^2.$$

To determine the maximum area, find the vertex of the parabola given by $A(x) = 120x - 2x^2$ using the vertex formula. Writing the equation in standard form as

$$A(x) = -2x^2 + 120x$$

gives $a = -2$, $b = 120$, and $c = 0$, so

$$h = \frac{-b}{2a} = \frac{-120}{2(-2)} = \frac{-120}{-4} = 30;$$

$$A(30) = -2(30)^2 + 120(30) = -2(900) + 3600 = 1800.$$

The graph is a parabola that opens down, and its vertex is $(30, 1800)$. Thus, the maximum area will be 1800 ft². This area will occur if *x*, the width of the rectangle, is 30 ft.

Work Problem **6** *at the Side.* ▶

ANSWER

6. The rectangle should be 25 ft by 50 ft with a maximum area of 1250 ft².

7 Solve the problem.

A toy rocket is launched from the ground so that its distance in feet above the ground after t seconds is

$$s(t) = -16t^2 + 208t.$$

Find the maximum height it reaches and the number of seconds it takes to reach that height.

> **CAUTION**
> *Be careful when interpreting the meanings of the coordinates of the vertex.* The first coordinate, x, gives the value for which the *function value* is a maximum or a minimum. Be sure to read the problem carefully to determine whether you are asked to find the value of the independent variable, the function value, or both.

Example 7 **Finding the Maximum Height Attained by a Projectile**

If air resistance is neglected, a projectile on Earth shot straight upward with an initial velocity of 40 m per sec will be at a height s in meters given by

$$s(t) = -4.9t^2 + 40t,$$

where t is the number of seconds elapsed after projection. After how many seconds will it reach its maximum height, and what is this maximum height? For this function, $a = -4.9$, $b = 40$, and $c = 0$. Use the vertex formula.

$$h = \frac{-b}{2a} = \frac{-40}{2(-4.9)} \approx 4.1 \quad \text{Use a calculator.}$$

Thus, the maximum height is attained at 4.1 sec. To find this maximum height, calculate $s(4.1)$.

$$s(4.1) = -4.9(4.1)^2 + 40(4.1) \approx 81.6 \quad \text{Use a calculator.}$$

The projectile will attain a maximum height of approximately 81.6 m.

◀ *Work Problem* **7** *at the Side.*

OBJECTIVE **5** **Graph parabolas with horizontal axes.** If x and y are interchanged in the equation $y = ax^2 + bx + c$, the equation becomes

$$x = ay^2 + by + c.$$

Because of the interchange of the roles of x and y, these parabolas are horizontal (with horizontal lines as axes).

> **Graph of a Horizontal Parabola**
> The graph of
> $$x = ay^2 + by + c \quad \text{or} \quad x = a(y - k)^2 + h$$
> is a parabola with vertex (h, k) and the horizontal line $y = k$ as axis. The graph opens to the right if $a > 0$ and to the left if $a < 0$.

Example 8 **Graphing a Horizontal Parabola**

Graph $x = (y - 2)^2 - 3$. Give the vertex, axis, domain, and range.

This graph has its vertex at $(-3, 2)$, since the roles of x and y are reversed. It opens to the right, the positive x-direction, and has the same shape as $y = x^2$. Plotting a few additional points gives the graph shown in Figure 15 on the next page. Note that the graph is symmetric about its axis, $y = 2$. The domain is $[-3, \infty)$, and the range is $(-\infty, \infty)$.

Continued on Next Page

ANSWER

7. 676 ft; 6.5 sec

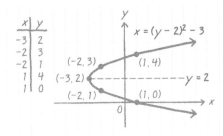

Figure 15

Work Problem **8** at the Side. ▶

When a quadratic equation is given in the form $x = ay^2 + by + c$, completing the square on y will allow us to find the vertex.

Example 9 **Completing the Square to Graph a Horizontal Parabola**

Graph $x = -2y^2 + 4y - 3$. Give the vertex, axis, domain, and range.

$x = -2y^2 + 4y - 3$

$x = -2(y^2 - 2y) - 3$ Factor out -2.

$x = -2(y^2 - 2y + 1 - 1) - 3$ Complete the square within the parentheses; add and subtract 1.

$x = -2(y^2 - 2y + 1) + (-2)(-1) - 3$ Distributive property

> Be careful here.

$x = -2(y - 1)^2 - 1$ Factor; simplify.

Because of the negative coefficient (-2) in $x = -2(y - 1)^2 - 1$, the graph opens to the left (the negative x-direction). The graph is narrower than the graph of $y = x^2$ because $|-2| > 1$. As shown in Figure 16, the vertex is $(-1, 1)$ and the axis is $y = 1$. The domain is $(-\infty, -1]$, and the range is $(-\infty, \infty)$.

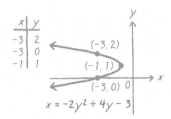

Figure 16

Work Problem **9** at the Side. ▶

CAUTION
Only quadratic equations solved for y (whose graphs are vertical parabolas) are examples of functions. The horizontal parabolas in Examples 8 and 9 are *not* graphs of functions, because they do not satisfy the vertical line test.

8 Graph $x = (y + 1)^2 - 4$. Give the vertex, axis, domain, and range.

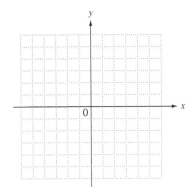

9 Graph $x = -y^2 + 2y + 5$. Give the vertex, axis, domain, and range.

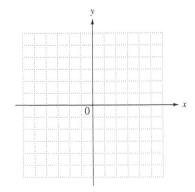

ANSWERS

8.

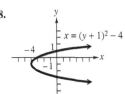

vertex: $(-4, -1)$; axis: $y = -1$;
domain: $[-4, \infty)$; range: $(-\infty, \infty)$

9.

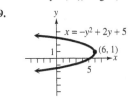

vertex: $(6, 1)$; axis: $y = 1$;
domain: $(-\infty, 6]$; range: $(-\infty, \infty)$

10 Find the vertex of each parabola. Tell whether the graph opens to the right or to the left. Give the domain and range.

(a) $x = 2y^2 - 6y + 5$

(b) $x = -y^2 + 2y + 5$

In summary, the graphs of parabolas studied in **Sections 18.6 and 18.7** fall into the following categories.

GRAPHS OF PARABOLAS

Equation	Graph
$y = ax^2 + bx + c$ $y = a(x - h)^2 + k$	(h, k) $a > 0$ These graphs represent functions. $a < 0$
$x = ay^2 + by + c$ $x = a(y - k)^2 + h$	(h, k) $a > 0$ These graphs are not graphs of functions. $a < 0$

◀ *Work Problems* **10** *and* **11** *at the Side.*

11 (a) Tell whether each of the following equations has a vertical or horizontal parabola as its graph.

A. $y = -x^2 + 20x + 80$

B. $x = 2y^2 + 6y + 5$

C. $x + 1 = (y + 2)^2$

D. $f(x) = (x - 4)^2$

(b) Which of the equations in part (a) represent functions?

ANSWERS

10. (a) $\left(\dfrac{1}{2}, \dfrac{3}{2}\right)$; right; domain: $\left[\dfrac{1}{2}, \infty\right)$;
range: $(-\infty, \infty)$
(b) $(6, 1)$; left; domain; $(-\infty, 6]$;
range: $(-\infty, \infty)$
11. (a) A, D are vertical parabolas; B, C are horizontal parabolas.
(b) A, D

18.7 ▶▶▶ **Exercises**

1. How can you determine just by looking at the equation of a parabola whether it has a vertical or a horizontal axis?

2. Why can't the graph of a quadratic function be a horizontal parabola?

3. How can you determine the number of x-intercepts of the graph of a quadratic function without graphing the function?

4. If the vertex of the graph of a quadratic function is $(1, -3)$ and the graph opens down, how many x-intercepts does the graph have?

Find the vertex of each parabola. For each equation, decide whether the graph opens up, down, to the left, or to the right, and whether it is wider, narrower, or the same shape as the graph of $y = x^2$. If it is a vertical parabola, use the discriminant to determine the number of x-intercepts. See Examples 1–3, 5, 8, and 9.

 5. $y = 2x^2 + 4x + 5$

6. $y = 3x^2 - 6x + 4$

7. $y = -x^2 + 5x + 3$

8. $x = -y^2 + 7y - 2$

9. $x = \frac{1}{3}y^2 + 6y + 24$

10. $x = \frac{1}{2}y^2 + 10y - 5$

Graph each parabola. Give the vertex, axis, domain, and range. See Examples 4, 8, and 9.

11. $f(x) = x^2 + 4x + 3$
vertex:
axis:
domain:
range:

12. $f(x) = x^2 + 2x - 2$
vertex:
axis:
domain:
range:

 13. $f(x) = -2x^2 + 4x - 5$
vertex:
axis:
domain:
range:

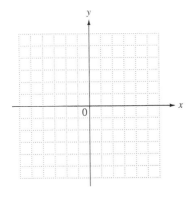

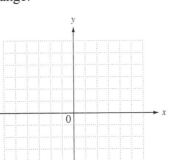

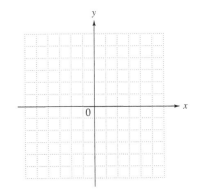

14. $f(x) = -3x^2 + 12x - 8$
   vertex:
   axis:
   domain:
   range:

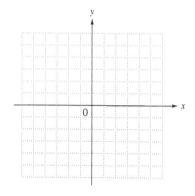

15. $x = -\dfrac{1}{5}y^2 + 2y - 4$
   vertex:
   axis:
   domain:
   range:

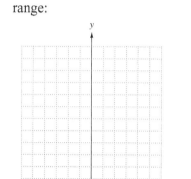

16. $x = -\dfrac{1}{2}y^2 - 4y - 6$
   vertex:
   axis:
   domain:
   range:

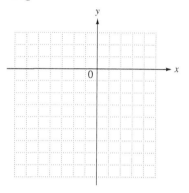

17. $x = 3y^2 + 12y + 5$
   vertex:
   axis:
   domain:
   range:

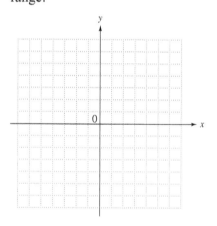

18. $x = 4y^2 + 16y + 11$
   vertex:
   axis:
   domain:
   range:

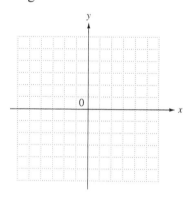

Use the concepts of this section to match each equation with its graph.

19. $y = 2x^2 + 4x - 3$

20. $y = -x^2 + 3x + 5$

21. $y = -\dfrac{1}{2}x^2 - x + 1$

22. $x = y^2 + 6y + 3$

23. $x = -y^2 - 2y + 4$

24. $x = 3y^2 + 6y + 5$

A.

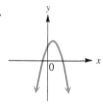

B.

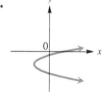

C.

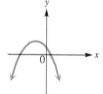

D.

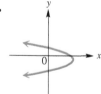

E.

F.

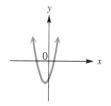

Solve each problem. See Examples 6 and 7.

25. Find the pair of numbers whose sum is 60 and whose product is a maximum. (*Hint:* Let x and $60 - x$ represent the two numbers.)

26. Find the pair of numbers whose sum is 10 and whose product is a maximum.

27. Palo Alto College is planning to construct a rectangular parking lot on land bordered on one side by a highway. The plan is to use 640 ft of fencing to fence off the other three sides. What should the dimensions of the lot be if the enclosed area is to be a maximum?

28. Keisha Hughes has 100 m of fencing material to enclose a rectangular exercise run for her dog. What width will give the enclosure the maximum area?

29. If an object on Earth is projected upward with an initial velocity of 32 ft per sec, then its height (in feet) after t seconds is given by

$$h(t) = 32t - 16t^2.$$

Find the maximum height attained by the object and the number of seconds it takes to hit the ground.

30. A projectile on Earth is fired straight upward so that its distance (in feet) above the ground t seconds after firing is given by

$$s(t) = -16t^2 + 400t.$$

Find the maximum height it reaches and the number of seconds it takes to reach that height.

31. A charter flight charges a fare of $200 per person, plus $4 per person for each unsold seat on the plane. If the plane holds 100 passengers and if x represents the number of unsold seats, find the following.

(a) A function defined by $R(x)$ that describes the total revenue received for the flight (*Hint:* Multiply the number of people flying, $100 - x$, by the price per ticket, $200 + 4x$.)

(b) The number of unsold seats that will produce the maximum revenue

(c) The maximum revenue

32. For a trip, a charter bus company charges a fare of $48 per person, plus $2 per person for each unsold seat on the bus. If the bus has 42 seats and x represents the number of unsold seats, find the following.

(a) A function defined by $R(x)$ that describes the total revenue from the trip (*Hint:* Multiply the total number riding, $42 - x$, by the price per ticket, $48 + 2x$.)

(b) The number of unsold seats that produces the maximum revenue

(c) The maximum revenue

33. The percent of births in the United States to teenage mothers in the years 1990–2002 can be modeled by the quadratic function defined by

$$f(x) = -0.0334x^2 + 0.2351x + 12.79,$$

where $x = 0$ represents 1990, $x = 1$ represents 1991, and so on. (*Source:* U.S. National Center for Health Statistics.)

(a) Since the coefficient of x^2 in the model is negative, the graph of this quadratic function is a parabola that opens down. Will the y-value of the vertex of this graph be a maximum or a minimum?

(b) In what year during this period was the percent of births in the United States to teenage mothers a maximum? (Round down to the nearest year.) Use the actual y-value of the vertex, to the nearest tenth, to find this percent.

35. The graph shows how Social Security assets are expected to change as the number of retirees receiving benefits increases.

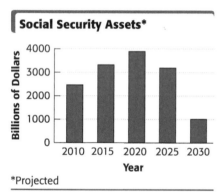

Social Security Assets*

*Projected

Source: Social Security Administration.

The graph suggests that a quadratic function would be a good fit to the data. The data are approximated by the function defined by

$$f(x) = -20.57x^2 + 758.9x - 3140.$$

In the model, $x = 10$ represents 2010, $x = 15$ represents 2015, and so on, and $f(x)$ is in billions of dollars.

(a) Explain why the coefficient of x^2 in the model is negative, based on the graph.

(b) Algebraically determine the vertex of the graph, with coordinates to four significant digits.

(c) Interpret the answer to part (b) as it applies to the application.

34. The total receipts from individual income taxes by the U.S. Treasury in the years 2002–2006 can be modeled by the quadratic function defined by

$$f(x) = 33.79x^2 - 83.44x + 1036,$$

where $x = 0$ represents 2002, $x = 1$ represents 2003, and so on, and $f(x)$ is in billions of dollars. (*Source:* Internal Revenue Service.)

(a) Since the coefficient of x^2 given in the model is positive, the graph of this quadratic function is a parabola that opens up. Will the y-value of the vertex of this graph be a maximum or minimum?

(b) In what year during this period were total receipts from individual taxes a minimum? Use the actual x-value of the vertex, to the nearest tenth, to find this amount.

36. The graph shows the performance of investment portfolios with different mixtures of U.S. and foreign investments over a 25-yr period.

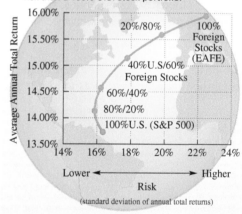

LOOKING FOR THE RIGHT MIX
A portfolio that includes international investments potentially can produce higher returns with lower risk than a 100% U.S. stock portfolio.

Source: *Financial Ink* Newsletter, Investment Management and Research, Inc., Feb. 1998. Thanks to David Van Geffen for this information.

(a) Is this the graph of a function? Explain.

(b) What investment mixture shown on the graph appears to represent the vertex? What relative amount of risk does this point represent? What return on investment does it provide?

(c) Which point on the graph represents the riskiest investment mixture? What return on investment does it provide?

Answers to Selected Exercises

Chapter 1   Whole Numbers

Taken from *Basic College Mathematics* by Lial, Salzman & Hestwood, (0321557123)

Section 1.1 (pages 2–10)

1. 3; 6   **3.** 1; 0   **5.** 8; 2   **7.** 3; 561; 435   **9.** 60; 000; 502; 109
11. Evidence suggests that this is true. It is common to count using fingers.   **13.** twenty-three thousand, one hundred fifteen
15. three hundred forty-six thousand, nine   **17.** twenty-five million, seven hundred fifty-six thousand, six hundred sixty-five
19. 63,163   **21.** 10,000,223   **23.** 3,200,000   **25.** 50,051,507
27. 35,079,448   **29.** 800,000,621,020,215   **31.** public transportation; six million, sixty-nine thousand, five hundred eighty-nine   **33.** seven million, eight hundred ninety-four thousand, nine hundred eleven

Section 1.2 (pages 11–20)

1. 97   **3.** 89   **5.** 889   **7.** 889   **9.** 7785   **11.** 1589   **13.** 7676
15. 78,446   **17.** 8928   **19.** 59,224   **21.** 150   **23.** 155
25. 121   **27.** 145   **29.** 102   **31.** 1651   **33.** 1154   **35.** 413
37. 1771   **39.** 1410   **41.** 6391   **43.** 11,624   **45.** 17,611
47. 15,954   **49.** 10,648   **51.** 15,594   **53.** 11,557   **55.** 12,078
57. 4250   **59.** 12,268   **61.** correct   **63.** incorrect; should be 769
65. correct   **67.** incorrect; should be 11,577   **69.** correct
71. Changing the order in which numbers are added does not change the sum. You can add from bottom to top when checking addition.   **73.** 33 miles   **75.** 38 miles   **77.** $16,342
79. 699 people   **81.** 20,157 students   **83.** 970 ft   **85.** 72 ft
87. 9421   **88.** 1249   **89.** 77,762   **90.** 22,267   **91.** 9,994,433
92. 3,334,499   **93.** Write the largest digits on the left, using the smaller digits as you move right.   **94.** Write the smallest digits on the left, using the larger digits as you move right.

Section 1.3 (pages 21–30)

1. 16   **3.** 33   **5.** 17   **7.** 213   **9.** 101   **11.** 7111   **13.** 3412
15. 2111   **17.** 13,160   **19.** 41,110   **21.** correct   **23.** incorrect; should be 62   **25.** incorrect; should be 121   **27.** correct
29. incorrect; should be 7222   **31.** 38   **33.** 45   **35.** 19
37. 281   **39.** 519   **41.** 7059   **43.** 7589   **45.** 8859   **47.** 3
49. 23   **51.** 19   **53.** 2833   **55.** 7775   **57.** 503   **59.** 156
61. 2184   **63.** 5687   **65.** 19,038   **67.** 31,556   **69.** 6584
71. correct   **73.** correct   **75.** correct   **77.** correct   **79.** Possible answers are 1. 3 + 2 = 5 could be changed to 5 − 2 = 3 or 5 − 3 = 2 2. 6 − 4 = 2 could be changed to 2 + 4 = 6 or 4 + 2 = 6.
81. 47 calories   **83.** 367 ft   **85.** 467 passengers   **87.** 3270 jobs eliminated   **89.** 9539 flags   **91.** $263   **93.** 758 more people visited on Tuesday   **95.** $57,500   **97.** 330 fewer calories; 27 fewer fat grams   **99.** 380 calories; 10 fat grams

Section 1.4 (pages 31–40)

1. 24   **3.** 48   **5.** 0   **7.** 24   **9.** 40   **11.** 0   **13.** Factors may be multiplied in any order to get the same answer. They are the same; you may add or multiply numbers in any order.   **15.** 210   **17.** 238
19. 3210   **21.** 1872   **23.** 8612   **25.** 10,084   **27.** 20,488
29. 258,447   **31.** 280   **33.** 480   **35.** 2220   **37.** 3600   **39.** 3750
41. 65,400   **43.** 270,000   **45.** 86,000,000   **47.** 48,500   **49.** 720,000
51. 1,940,000   **53.** 476   **55.** 2400   **57.** 3735   **59.** 2378   **61.** 6164
63. 15,792   **65.** 21,665   **67.** 15,730   **69.** 82,320   **71.** 183,996
73. 2,468,928   **75.** 66,005   **77.** 86,028   **79.** 19,422,180
81. 2,278,410   **83.** To multiply by 10, 100, or 1000, just add one, two, or three zeros, respectively, to the number you are multiplying and that's your answer.   **85.** 3000 balls   **87.** 540 eggs   **89.** 24,090 gallons
91. $600   **93.** $1560   **95.** $112,888   **97.** 50,568   **99.** 38,250 trees
101. 7,623,663 people   **103.** $7390   **105. (a)** 452   **(b)** 452

106. commutative   **107. (a)** 281   **(b)** 281   **108.** associative
109. (a) 15,840   **(b)** 15,840   **110.** commutative   **111. (a)** 6552
(b) 6552   **112.** associative   **113.** No. Some examples are 1. 7 − 5 = 2, but 5 − 7 does not equal 2   2. 12 − 6 = 6, but 6 − 12 does not equal 6 3. (8 − 2) − 5 = 1, but 8 − (2 − 5) does not equal 1.   **114.** No. Some examples are 1. 10 ÷ 2 = 5, but 2 ÷ 10 does not equal 5 2. (16 ÷ 8) ÷ 2 = 1, but 16 ÷ (8 ÷ 2) does not equal 1.

Section 1.5 (pages 41–54)

1. $4\overline{)24}$ $\frac{\overset{6}{24}}{4} = 6$ **3.** $9\overline{)45}$ $45 ÷ 9 = 5$ **5.** $16 ÷ 2 = 8$ $\frac{\overset{5}{16}}{2} = 8$
7. 1   **9.** 7   **11.** undefined   **13.** 24   **15.** 0   **17.** undefined   **19.** 15
21. 8   **23.** 25   **25.** 18   **27.** 304   **29.** 627 R1   **31.** 1522 R5   **33.** 309
35. 3005   **37.** 5006   **39.** 811 R1   **41.** 2589 R2   **43.** 7324 R2
45. 3157 R2   **47.** 2630   **49.** 12,458 R3   **51.** 10,253 R5   **53.** 18,377 R6
55. correct   **57.** incorrect; should be 1908 R1   **59.** incorrect; should be 670 R2   **61.** incorrect; should be 3568 R1   **63.** correct
65. correct   **67.** incorrect; should be 9628 R3   **69.** correct
71. Multiply the quotient by the divisor and add any remainder. The result should be the dividend.   **73.** 328 tables   **75.** 9600 each hour   **77.** $48,500   **79.** 135 acres   **81.** $1,137,500   **83.** $5429
85. ✓ ✓ ✓ ✓   **87.** ✓ X X X   **89.** X X ✓ X
91. X ✓ X X   **93.** ✓ ✓ X X   **95.** X X X X

Section 1.6 (pages 55–66)

1. 53   **3.** 250   **5.** 120 R7   **7.** 1105 R5   **9.** 7134 R12   **11.** 900 R100
13. 73 R5   **15.** 476 R15   **17.** 2407 R1   **19.** 1146 R15   **21.** 3331 R82
23. 850   **25.** incorrect; should be 101 R14   **27.** incorrect; should be 658
29. incorrect; should be 62   **31.** When dividing by 10, 100, or 1000, drop the same number of zeros from the dividend as there are in the divisor to get the quotient. One example is 2500 ÷ 100 = 25.   **33.** 50 miles
35. 56 floor clocks   **37.** $355   **39.** 43,200 rings   **41.** $39 per week
43. $0   **44.** 0   **45.** undefined   **46.** impossible; if you have 6 cookies, it is not possible to divide them among 0 people.   **47. (a)** 14   **(b)** 17
(c) 38   **48.** Yes. Some examples are 18 • 1 = 18; 26 • 1 = 26; 43 • 1 = 43.   **49. (a)** 3200   **(b)** 320   **(c)** 32   **50.** Drop the same number of zeros that appear in the divisor. The result is the quotient. With the divisor 10, drop one 0; with 100, drop two zeros; with 1000, drop three zeros.

Summary Exercises on Whole Numbers (pages 65–66)

1. 3; 4   **2.** 6; 0   **3.** 1; 6   **4.** eighty-six thousand, two   **5.** four hundred twenty-five million, two hundred eight thousand, seven hundred thirty-three
6. 97   **7.** 905   **8.** 21   **9.** 409   **10.** 17,573   **11.** 82,164   **12.** 677
13. 37,674   **14.** 35,889   **15.** 560   **16.** 5600   **17.** 350,000
18. 252,000   **19.** 6,617,418,351   **20.** 24,657   **21.** 1   **22.** 0
23. undefined   **24.** 15   **25.** 56   **26.** 0   **27.** 96   **28.** 304
29. 2750 R2   **30.** 761 R3   **31.** 3380   **32.** 220,545   **33.** 2016
34. 1476   **35.** 78   **36.** 210   **37.** 18,038,816   **38.** 506 R28
39. 52   **40.** 1208 R3   **41.** 573 R3   **42.** 41   **43.** 208,530
44. 1,101,744

Section 1.7 (pages 67–76)

1. 620   **3.** 860   **5.** 6800   **7.** 86,800   **9.** 28,500   **11.** 6000
13. 16,000   **15.** 78,000   **17.** 8,000,000,000   **19.** 10,000   **21.** 600,000
23. 5,000,000   **25.** 4480; 4500; 4000   **27.** 3370; 3400; 3000
29. 6050; 6000; 6000   **31.** 5340; 5300; 5000   **33.** 19,540; 19,500; 20,000   **35.** 26,290; 26,300; 26,000   **37.** 93,710; 93,700; 94,000
39. 1. Locate the place to be rounded and underline it.   2. Look only at the next digit to the right. If this digit is 5 or more, increase the underlined digit by 1.   3. Change all digits to the right of the underlined place to zeros.   **41.** 30 60 50 80 220; 219   **43.** 80 40 40; 35   **45.** 70 30 2100;

2278 **47.** 900 700 400 800 2800; 2828 **49.** 900 400 500; 435 **51.** 800 400 320,000; 282,000 **53.** 8000 60 700 4000 12,760; 12,605 **55.** 700 500 200; 158 **57.** 900 30 27,000; 27,231 **59.** Perhaps the best explanation is that 3492 is closer to 3500 than 3400, but 3492 is closer to 3000 than 4000. **61.** 80 million people; 300 million people **63.** 349,000; 350,000 **65.** 1,670,000 pounds; 1,700,000 pounds; 2,000,000 pounds **67.** $25,765,500,000; $25,800,000,000; $26,000,000,000 **69.** 71,500 **70.** 72,499 **71.** 7500 **72.** 8499 **73.** 3930; 11,240; 15,970; 17,920; 534,880; 2,788,000 **74.** 4000; 10,000; 20,000; 20,000; 500,000; 3,000,000 **75. (a)** When using front end rounding, all digits are 0 except the first digit. These numbers are easier to work with when estimating answers. **(b)** When using front end rounding to estimate an answer, the estimated answer can vary greatly from the exact answer.

Section 1.8 (pages 77–84)

1. 2; 3; 9 **3.** 2; 5; 25 **5.** 2; 8; 64 **7.** 2; 15; 225 **9.** 4 **11.** 8 **13.** 10 **15.** 12 **17.** 36; 36 **19.** 400; 400 **21.** 1225; 1225 **23.** 625; 625 **25.** 10,000; 10,000 **27.** A perfect square is the square of a whole number. The number 25 is the square of 5 because $5 \cdot 5 = 25$. The number 50 is not a perfect square. There is no whole number that can be squared to get 50. **29.** 12 **31.** 15 **33.** 4 **35.** 20 **37.** 45 **39.** 63 **41.** 118 **43.** 22 **45.** 30 **47.** 102 **49.** 9 **51.** 63 **53.** 33 **55.** 70 **57.** 7 **59.** 17 **61.** 55 **63.** 108 **65.** 26 **67.** 26 **69.** 27 **71.** 16 **73.** 16 **75.** 21 **77.** 7 **79.** 20 **81.** 14 **83.** 25 **85.** 16 **87.** 23 **89.** 233

Section 1.9 (pages 85–92)

1. *Estimate:* $600 + 900 + 1000 + 800 + 2000 = 5300$ sandwiches; *Exact:* 5208 sandwiches **3.** *Estimate:* $70 - 60 = 10$ more recalls; *Exact:* 13 more recalls **5.** *Estimate:* $200 \times 20 = 4000$ kits; *Exact:* 5664 kits **7.** *Estimate:* $3000 \div 700 \approx 4$ toys; *Exact:* 4 toys **9.** *Estimate:* $8000 - 4000 = 4000$ people; *Exact:* 4174 people **11.** *Estimate:* $\$30 \times 5 = \$150$; *Exact:* $170 **13.** *Estimate:* $\$50,000 - \$40,000 = \$10,000$; *Exact:* $14,100 **15. (a)** *Estimate:* $\$50,000 + \$40,000 = \$90,000$ White; $\$40,000 + \$50,000 = \$90,000$ Easterly; *Exact:* $86,950 White; $93,370, Easterly; Mr. and Mrs. Easterly **(b)** *Estimate:* $\$90,000 - \$90,000 = \$0$; *Exact:* $6420 **17.** *Estimate:* $\$2000 - \$700 - \$300 - \$400 - \$200 - \$200 = \$200$; *Exact:* $350 **19.** *Estimate:* $40,000 \times 100 = 4,000,000$ square feet; *Exact:* 6,011,280 square feet **21.** *Estimate:* $\$400 + \$1000 + \$200 + \$400 + \$200 + \$200 = \$2400$; *Exact:* $2680 **23.** *Estimate:* $\$400 + \$200 + \$200 + \$400 = \$1200$; $\$1200 - \$1000 = \$200$; *Exact:* $140 **25.** *Estimate:* $(\$1000 \times 6) + (\$900 \times 20) = \$24,000$; *Exact:* $20,961 **27.** Possible answers are Addition: more; total; gain of Subtraction: less; loss of; decreased by Multiplication: twice; of; product Division: divided by; goes into; per Equals: is; are **29.** Estimating the answer can help you avoid careless mistakes like decimal or calculation errors. Examples of reasonable answers in daily life might be a $35 bag of groceries, $50 to fill the gas tank, or $45 for a phone bill. **31.** $20,009 **33.** 2477 pounds **35.** $378 **37.** $375 **39.** 20 seats

Chapter 2 Fractions

Taken from *Basic College Mathematics* by Lial, Salzman & Hestwood, (0321557123)

Section 2.1 (pages 94–100)

1. $\frac{3}{4}; \frac{1}{4}$ **3.** $\frac{1}{3}; \frac{2}{3}$ **5.** $\frac{7}{5}; \frac{3}{5}$ **7.** $\frac{5}{6}; \frac{4}{6}; \frac{2}{6}$ **9.** $\frac{8}{25}$ **11.** $\frac{303}{520}$ **13.** 4; 5

15. 9; 8 **17.** Proper $\frac{1}{3}, \frac{5}{8}, \frac{7}{16}$ Improper $\frac{8}{5}, \frac{6}{6}, \frac{12}{2}$

19. Proper $\frac{3}{4}, \frac{9}{11}, \frac{7}{15}$ Improper $\frac{3}{2}, \frac{5}{5}, \frac{19}{18}$

21. One possibility is

$\dfrac{3}{4} \begin{matrix} \leftarrow \text{Numerator} \\ \leftarrow \text{Denominator} \end{matrix}$

The denominator shows the number of equal parts in the whole and the numerator shows how many of the parts are being considered.

23. 3; 8 **25.** 5; 24

Section 2.2 (pages 101–106)

1. $\frac{5}{4}$ **3.** $\frac{23}{5}$ **5.** $\frac{13}{2}$ **7.** $\frac{33}{4}$ **9.** $\frac{18}{11}$ **11.** $\frac{19}{3}$ **13.** $\frac{81}{8}$ **15.** $\frac{43}{4}$ **17.** $\frac{27}{8}$ **19.** $\frac{43}{5}$ **21.** $\frac{54}{11}$ **23.** $\frac{131}{4}$ **25.** $\frac{221}{12}$ **27.** $\frac{269}{15}$ **29.** $\frac{187}{24}$ **31.** $1\frac{1}{3}$ **33.** $2\frac{1}{4}$ **35.** 8 **37.** $7\frac{3}{5}$ **39.** $4\frac{7}{8}$ **41.** 9 **43.** $15\frac{3}{4}$ **45.** $5\frac{2}{9}$ **47.** $8\frac{1}{8}$ **49.** $16\frac{4}{5}$ **51.** 28 **53.** $26\frac{1}{7}$

55. Multiply the denominator by the whole number and add the numerator. The result becomes the new numerator, which is placed over the original denominator.

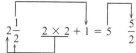

57. $\frac{501}{2}$ **59.** $\frac{1000}{3}$ **61.** $\frac{4179}{8}$ **63.** $154\frac{1}{4}$ **65.** 171 **67.** $122\frac{13}{32}$ **69.** $\frac{2}{3}, \frac{4}{5}, \frac{3}{4}, \frac{7}{10}$ **70. (a)** numerator; denominator

(b)

(c) less **71.** $\frac{5}{5}, \frac{10}{3}, \frac{6}{5}$ **72. (a)** numerator; denominator

(b)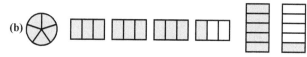

(c) greater **73.** $\frac{5}{3} = 1\frac{2}{3}; \frac{7}{7} = 1; \frac{11}{6} = 1\frac{5}{6}$

74. (a) improper; greater than or equal to

(b)

(c) Divide the numerator by the denominator. Use the quotient as the whole number and place the remainder over the denominator.

Section 2.3 (pages 107–112)

1. 1, 2, 4, 8 **3.** 1, 3, 5, 15 **5.** 1, 2, 3, 4, 6, 8, 12, 16, 24, 48 **7.** 1, 2, 3, 4, 6, 9, 12, 18, 36 **9.** 1, 2, 4, 5, 8, 10, 20, 40 **11.** 1, 2, 4, 8, 16, 32, 64 **13.** composite **15.** prime **17.** composite **19.** prime **21.** prime **23.** composite **25.** composite **27.** composite **29.** 2^3 **31.** $2^2 \cdot 5$ **33.** $2^2 \cdot 3^2$ **35.** 5^2 **37.** $2^2 \cdot 17$ **39.** $2^3 \cdot 3^2$ **41.** $2^2 \cdot 11$ **43.** $2^2 \cdot 5^2$ **45.** 5^3 **47.** $2^2 \cdot 3^2 \cdot 5$ **49.** $2^6 \cdot 5$ **51.** $2^3 \cdot 3^2 \cdot 5$ **53.** A composite number has a factor(s) other than itself or 1. Examples include 4, 6, 8, 9, 10. A prime number is a whole number that has exactly two *different* factors, itself and 1. Examples include 2, 3, 5, 7, 11. The numbers 0 and 1 are neither prime nor composite. **55.** All the possible factors of 24 are 1, 2, 3, 4, 6, 8, 12, and 24. This list includes both prime numbers and composite numbers. The prime factors of 24 include only prime numbers. The prime factorization of 24 is $2 \cdot 2 \cdot 2 \cdot 3 = 2^3 \cdot 3$ **57.** $2 \cdot 5^2 \cdot 7$ **59.** $2^6 \cdot 3 \cdot 5$ **61.** $2^3 \cdot 3 \cdot 5 \cdot 13$ **63.** $2^2 \cdot 3^2 \cdot 5 \cdot 7$

65. 2, 3, 5, 7, 11, 13, 17, 19, 23, 29, 31, 37, 41, 43, 47
66. A prime number is a whole number that is evenly divisible by itself and 1 only.   **67.** No. Every other even number is divisible by 2 in addition to being divisible by itself and 1.   **68.** No. A multiple of a prime number can never be prime because it will always be divisible by the prime number.   **69.** $2 \cdot 2 \cdot 3 \cdot 5 \cdot 5 \cdot 7$ **70.** $2^2 \cdot 3 \cdot 5^2 \cdot 7$

Section 2.4 (pages 113–120)

1. ✓ ✓ ✓ ✓   **3.** ✓ ✓ ✗ ✗   **5.** ✓ ✗ ✓ ✓   **7.** ✓ ✓ ✗ ✗   **9.** $\dfrac{3}{4}$

11. $\dfrac{1}{4}$ **13.** $\dfrac{3}{5}$ **15.** $\dfrac{6}{7}$ **17.** $\dfrac{7}{8}$ **19.** $\dfrac{6}{7}$ **21.** $\dfrac{4}{7}$ **23.** $\dfrac{1}{50}$ **25.** $\dfrac{8}{11}$

27. $\dfrac{5}{9}$ **29.** $\dfrac{\cancel{2} \cdot \cancel{3} \cdot 3}{\cancel{2} \cdot 2 \cdot 2 \cdot \cancel{3}} = \dfrac{3}{4}$ **31.** $\dfrac{\cancel{3} \cdot 7}{2 \cdot 2 \cdot 2 \cdot \cancel{3}} = \dfrac{7}{8}$

33. $\dfrac{\cancel{2} \cdot \cancel{3} \cdot \cancel{3} \cdot \cancel{3}}{\cancel{2} \cdot 2 \cdot \cancel{3} \cdot \cancel{3} \cdot \cancel{3}} = \dfrac{1}{2}$ **35.** $\dfrac{\cancel{2} \cdot \cancel{2} \cdot \cancel{3} \cdot 3}{\cancel{2} \cdot \cancel{2} \cdot \cancel{3}} = 3$

37. $\dfrac{2 \cdot 2 \cdot 2 \cdot \cancel{3} \cdot \cancel{3}}{\cancel{3} \cdot \cancel{3} \cdot 5 \cdot 5} = \dfrac{8}{25}$ **39.** $\dfrac{1}{2} = \dfrac{1}{2}$; equivalent

41. $\dfrac{5}{12} \neq \dfrac{2}{5}$; not equivalent   **43.** $\dfrac{5}{8} \neq \dfrac{35}{52}$; not equivalent

45. $\dfrac{7}{8} = \dfrac{7}{8}$; equivalent   **47.** $8 \neq 9$; not equivalent

49. $\dfrac{5}{6} = \dfrac{5}{6}$; equivalent   **51.** A fraction is in lowest terms when the numerator and the denominator have no common factors other than 1. Some examples are $\dfrac{1}{2}, \dfrac{3}{8},$ and $\dfrac{2}{3}$.   **53.** $\dfrac{5}{8}$ **55.** $\dfrac{2}{1} = 2$

Summary Exercises on Fraction Basics (pages 121–122)

1. $\dfrac{5}{6}; \dfrac{1}{6}$ **2.** $\dfrac{1}{3}; \dfrac{2}{3}$ **3.** $\dfrac{5}{8}; \dfrac{3}{8}$ **4.** 3; 4   **5.** 8; 5   **6.** Proper $\dfrac{3}{5}, \dfrac{4}{25}, \dfrac{1}{32}$
Improper $\dfrac{8}{2}, \dfrac{16}{7}, \dfrac{8}{8}$ **7.** $\dfrac{7}{22}$ **8.** $\dfrac{8}{22}$ **9.** $\dfrac{5}{22}$ **10.** $\dfrac{15}{22}$ **11.** $2\dfrac{1}{2}$ **12.** $1\dfrac{3}{8}$

13. $1\dfrac{2}{7}$ **14.** $2\dfrac{2}{3}$ **15.** 8   **16.** 5   **17.** $7\dfrac{1}{5}$ **18.** $4\dfrac{7}{10}$ **19.** $\dfrac{10}{3}$

20. $\dfrac{43}{8}$ **21.** $\dfrac{34}{5}$ **22.** $\dfrac{53}{5}$ **23.** $\dfrac{51}{4}$ **24.** $\dfrac{62}{13}$ **25.** $\dfrac{71}{6}$ **26.** $\dfrac{189}{8}$

27. $2 \cdot 5$ **28.** $5 \cdot 11$ **29.** $2^2 \cdot 3^2$ **30.** 3^4 **31.** $2^3 \cdot 5 \cdot 7$

32. $2^3 \cdot 3^2 \cdot 5$ **33.** $\dfrac{1}{3}$ **34.** $\dfrac{1}{2}$ **35.** $\dfrac{1}{4}$ **36.** $\dfrac{3}{5}$ **37.** $\dfrac{3}{4}$ **38.** $\dfrac{5}{6}$

39. $\dfrac{7}{8}$ **40.** $\dfrac{1}{50}$ **41.** $\dfrac{1}{8}$ **42.** $\dfrac{5}{9}$ **43.** $\dfrac{4}{7}$ **44.** $\dfrac{5}{9}$

45. $\dfrac{\cancel{2} \cdot \cancel{2} \cdot 2 \cdot \cancel{3}}{\cancel{2} \cdot \cancel{2} \cdot 3 \cdot \cancel{3}} = \dfrac{2}{3}$ **46.** $\dfrac{\cancel{2} \cdot \cancel{2} \cdot \cancel{2} \cdot \cancel{2} \cdot \cancel{3}}{\cancel{2} \cdot \cancel{2} \cdot \cancel{2} \cdot \cancel{2} \cdot 2 \cdot \cancel{3}} = \dfrac{1}{2}$

47. $\dfrac{\cancel{2} \cdot \cancel{3} \cdot 3 \cdot \cancel{7}}{\cancel{2} \cdot \cancel{3} \cdot \cancel{7}} = 3$ **48.** $\dfrac{\cancel{2} \cdot \cancel{2} \cdot \cancel{2} \cdot \cancel{2} \cdot 2 \cdot 3}{\cancel{2} \cdot \cancel{2} \cdot \cancel{2} \cdot \cancel{2} \cdot 7} = \dfrac{6}{7}$

Section 2.5 (pages 123–132)

1. $\dfrac{1}{4}$ **3.** $\dfrac{2}{35}$ **5.** $\dfrac{3}{4}$ **7.** $\dfrac{1}{4}$ **9.** $\dfrac{5}{12}$ **11.** $\dfrac{9}{32}$ **13.** $\dfrac{2}{5}$ **15.** $\dfrac{13}{32}$ **17.** $\dfrac{21}{128}$

19. 4   **21.** 40   **23.** 24   **25.** $13\dfrac{1}{2}$ **27.** $31\dfrac{1}{2}$ **29.** 80   **31.** $94\dfrac{2}{3}$

33. 400   **35.** 810   **37.** $\dfrac{1}{4}$ mi²   **39.** 9 m²   **41.** $\dfrac{3}{10}$ in.²

43. Multiply the numerators and multiply the denominators. An example is $\dfrac{3}{4} \cdot \dfrac{1}{2} = \dfrac{3 \cdot 1}{4 \cdot 2} = \dfrac{3}{8}$ **45.** $1\dfrac{1}{2}$ yd²   **47.** $3\dfrac{1}{2}$ mi²   **49.** They are both the same size: $\dfrac{3}{64}$ mi²   **51.** 60,000 stores   **52.** 64,615 stores

53. Estimate: $\dfrac{2}{3} \cdot 9000 = 6000$; Exact: 6267 stores (rounded)

54. Estimate: $\dfrac{2}{5} \cdot 8000 = 3200$; Exact: 3013 stores (rounded)

55. $\dfrac{2}{3} \cdot 9300 = 6200$ stores

56. $\dfrac{2}{5} \cdot 7500 = 3000$ stores

Section 2.6 (pages 133–140)

1. $\dfrac{1}{2}$ yd²   **3.** $\dfrac{8}{9}$ ft²   **5.** $\dfrac{3}{10}$ yd²   **7.** \$2568   **9.** \$36

11. 910 women   **13.** Don't know; 50 people
15. 100 much less + 250 somewhat less = 350 people
17. Because everyone is included and fractions are given for *all* groups, the sum of the fractions must be *1* or *all* of the people.
19. \$58,000   **21.** \$11,600   **23.** \$3625

25. The correct solution is $\dfrac{9}{10} \times \dfrac{20}{21} = \dfrac{\overset{3}{\cancel{9}}}{\underset{1}{\cancel{10}}} \times \dfrac{\overset{2}{\cancel{20}}}{\underset{7}{\cancel{21}}} = \dfrac{6}{7}$

27. \$750   **29.** 2 ft   **31.** 9000 votes   **33.** $\dfrac{1}{32}$ of the estate

Section 2.7 (pages 141–150)

1. $\dfrac{8}{3}$ **3.** $\dfrac{6}{5}$ **5.** $\dfrac{5}{8}$ **7.** $\dfrac{1}{4}$ **9.** $\dfrac{2}{3}$ **11.** $2\dfrac{5}{8}$ **13.** $\dfrac{9}{20}$ **15.** 4   **17.** 6

19. $\dfrac{13}{16}$ **21.** $\dfrac{4}{5}$ **23.** 18   **25.** 24   **27.** $\dfrac{1}{14}$ **29.** $\dfrac{2}{9}$ quart   **31.** 15 times

33. 88 dispensers   **35.** 60 trips   **37.** You can divide two fractions by using the reciprocal of the second fraction (divisor) and then multiplying
39. 12 pounds   **41.** 208 homes   **43.** 124 visits   **45.** 2432 towels
47. double, twice, times, product, twice as much   **48.** goes into, divide, per, quotient, divided by   **49.** reciprocal   **50.** $\dfrac{4}{3}; \dfrac{8}{7}; \dfrac{1}{5}; \dfrac{19}{12}$

51. (a) Multiply the length of one side by 3, 4, 5, or 6.

(b) $\dfrac{15}{16} \times 4 = \dfrac{15}{\underset{4}{\cancel{16}}} \times \dfrac{\cancel{4}}{1} = \dfrac{15}{4} = 3\dfrac{3}{4}$ in.

52. $\dfrac{225}{256}$ in.²; Multiply the length by the width.

Section 2.8 (pages 151–162)

1. Exact: $7\dfrac{7}{8}$;   Estimate: $5 \cdot 2 = 10$ **3.** Exact: $4\dfrac{1}{2}$; Estimate: $2 \cdot 3 = 6$ **5.** Exact: 4;   Estimate: $3 \cdot 1 = 3$

7. Exact: 50;   Estimate: $8 \cdot 6 = 48$ **9.** Exact: $49\dfrac{1}{2}$; Estimate: $5 \cdot 2 \cdot 5 = 50$ **11.** Exact: 12; Estimate: $3 \cdot 2 \cdot 3 = 18$ **13.** Exact: $\dfrac{1}{3}$;   Estimate: $1 \div 4 = \dfrac{1}{4}$

15. Exact: $\dfrac{5}{6}$;   Estimate: $3 \div 3 = 1$ **17.** Exact: $3\dfrac{3}{5}$; Estimate: $9 \div 3 = 3$ **19.** Exact: $\dfrac{5}{12}$;   Estimate: $1 \div 2 = \dfrac{1}{2}$

21. Exact: $\dfrac{3}{10}$;   Estimate: $2 \div 6 = \dfrac{1}{3}$ **23.** Exact: $\dfrac{17}{18}$;   Estimate: $6 \div 6 = 1$ **25. (a)** Estimate: $1 \cdot 3 = 3$ cups;   Exact: $1\dfrac{7}{8}$ cups of applesauce   **(b)** Estimate: $1 \cdot 3 = 3$ teaspoons; Exact: $1\dfrac{1}{4}$ teaspoons of salt   **(c)** Estimate: $2 \cdot 3 = 6$ cups; Exact: $4\dfrac{3}{8}$ cups of flour   **27. (a)** Estimate: $1 \div 2 = \dfrac{1}{2}$ teaspoon; Exact: $\dfrac{1}{4}$ teaspoon vanilla extract   **(b)** Estimate: $1 \div 2 = \dfrac{1}{2}$ cup;

Exact: $\frac{3}{8}$ cup applesauce   **(c)** *Estimate:* $2 \div 2 = 1$ cup;

Exact: $\frac{7}{8}$ cup of flour   **29.** *Estimate:* $1316 \div 12 \approx 110$ units;

Exact: 112 units   **31.** *Estimate:* $135 \cdot 20 = 2700$ in.;

Exact: $2632\frac{1}{2}$ in.   **33.** The answer should include *Step 1* Change mixed numbers to improper fractions. *Step 2* Multiply the fractions. *Step 3* Write the answer in lowest terms, changing to mixed or whole numbers where possible.   **35.** *Estimate:* $51,460 \div 20 = 2573$ tires;   *Exact:* 2480 tires   **37.** *Estimate:* $10 \div 1 = 10$ spacers;   *Exact:* 13 spacers   **39.** *Estimate:* **(a)** $18 \cdot 4 = 72$ in.;   *Exact:* 71 in.   **(b)** No, because 6 ft = 72 in.   **41.** *Estimate:* $7 \cdot 26 = 182$ gallons;   *Exact:* $172\frac{1}{8}$ gallons

Section 2.9 (pages 163–169)

1. $\frac{5}{8}$ **3.** $\frac{5}{6}$ **5.** $\frac{1}{2}$ **7.** $1\frac{1}{5}$ **9.** $\frac{1}{3}$ **11.** $\frac{13}{20}$ **13.** $\frac{11}{15}$ **15.** $1\frac{1}{2}$ **17.** $\frac{11}{27}$ **19.** $\frac{3}{8}$ **21.** $\frac{6}{11}$ **23.** $\frac{3}{5}$ **25.** $1\frac{1}{7}$ **27.** $\frac{1}{5}$ **29.** $1\frac{1}{6}$ **31.** $1\frac{1}{10}$ **33.** Three steps to add like fractions are: 1. Add the numerators of the fractions to find the numerator of the sum (the answer).   2. Use the denominator of the fractions as the denominator of the sum.   3. Write the answer in lowest terms.   **35.** $\frac{7}{9}$ **37.** $\frac{5}{7}$ **39.** $\frac{1}{2}$ acre

Section 2.10 (pages 170–179)

1. 6   **3.** 15   **5.** 36   **7.** 14   **9.** 30   **11.** 100   **13.** 20   **15.** 60   **17.** 36   **19.** 120   **21.** 180   **23.** 720   **25.** $\frac{16}{24}$ **27.** $\frac{18}{24}$ **29.** $\frac{20}{24}$ **31.** 3   **33.** 12   **35.** 28   **37.** 12   **39.** 32   **41.** 72   **43.** 84   **45.** 96   **47.** 27   **49.** It probably depends on how large the numbers are. If the numbers are small, the method using multiples of the largest number seems best. If the numbers are larger, or there are more than two numbers, then the factorization method will be better.   **51.** 3600   **53.** 10,584   **55.** like; unlike   **56.** numerators; denominator; lowest   **57.** least; smallest   **58.** 40 is the least common multiple.   **59.** 70   **60.** 450   **61.** 240 is a common multiple but twice as large as the least common multiple; 120 is the LCM.   **62.** The least common multiple can be no smaller than the largest number in a group and the number 1760 is a multiple of 55.

Section 2.11 (pages 180–189)

1. $\frac{7}{8}$ **3.** $\frac{8}{9}$ **5.** $\frac{3}{4}$ **7.** $\frac{39}{40}$ **9.** $\frac{23}{36}$ **11.** $\frac{14}{15}$ **13.** $\frac{29}{36}$ **15.** $\frac{17}{20}$ **17.** $\frac{23}{30}$ **19.** $\frac{3}{8}$ **21.** $\frac{23}{48}$ **23.** $\frac{1}{2}$ **25.** $\frac{1}{2}$ **27.** $\frac{7}{15}$ **29.** $\frac{1}{6}$ **31.** $\frac{19}{45}$ **33.** $\frac{3}{40}$ **35.** $\frac{17}{48}$ **37.** $\frac{1}{4}$ in.   **39.** $\frac{17}{40}$ for reserved seating   **41.** $\frac{31}{40}$ in.   **43.** $\frac{1}{24}$ of the tank   **45.** You cannot add or subtract until all the fractional pieces are the same size. For example, halves are larger than fourths, so you cannot add $\frac{1}{2} + \frac{1}{4}$ until you rewrite $\frac{1}{2}$ as $\frac{2}{4}$.   **47.** $\frac{7}{24}$ **49.** work and travel; 8 hr; $\frac{1}{2}$ **51.** $\frac{3}{16}$ in.

Section 2.12 (pages 190–201)

1. *Estimate:* $6 + 3 = 9$; *Exact:* $8\frac{5}{6}$

3. *Estimate:* $7 + 4 = 11$; *Exact:* $11\frac{1}{2}$

5. *Estimate:* $1 + 4 = 5$; *Exact:* $4\frac{5}{24}$

7. *Estimate:* $25 + 19 = 44$; *Exact:* $43\frac{2}{3}$

9. *Estimate:* $34 + 19 = 53$; *Exact:* $52\frac{1}{10}$

11. *Estimate:* $23 + 15 = 38$; *Exact:* $38\frac{5}{28}$

13. *Estimate:* $13 + 19 + 15 = 47$; *Exact:* $45\frac{5}{6}$

15. *Estimate:* $15 - 12 = 3$; *Exact:* $2\frac{5}{8}$

17. *Estimate:* $13 - 1 = 12$; *Exact:* $11\frac{7}{15}$

19. *Estimate:* $28 - 6 = 22$; *Exact:* $22\frac{7}{30}$

21. *Estimate:* $17 - 7 = 10$; *Exact:* $10\frac{3}{8}$

23. *Estimate:* $19 - 6 = 13$; *Exact:* $12\frac{19}{20}$

25. *Estimate:* $20 - 12 = 8$; *Exact:* $7\frac{11}{12}$

27. $9\frac{1}{8}$ **29.** $11\frac{1}{2}$ **31.** $3\frac{5}{6}$ **33.** $6\frac{11}{12}$ **35.** $8\frac{1}{8}$ **37.** $\frac{5}{6}$ **39.** $2\frac{7}{8}$ **41.** $2\frac{7}{12}$ **43.** $5\frac{9}{20}$ **45.** $3\frac{16}{21}$ **47.** Find the least common denominator. Change the fraction parts so that they have the same denominator. Add the fraction parts. Add the whole number parts. Write the answer as a mixed number.

49. *Estimate:* $26 - 15 = 11$ ft; *Exact:* $11\frac{1}{4}$ ft

51. *Estimate:* $23 - 19 = 4$ in.; *Exact:* $4\frac{1}{8}$ in.

53. *Estimate:* $23 + 22 + 21 = 66$ in.; *Exact:* 66 in.

55. *Estimate:* $3 - 1 = 2$ in.; *Exact:* $2\frac{3}{16}$ in.

57. *Estimate:* $16 + 19 + 24 + 31 = 90$ ft; *Exact:* $87\frac{8}{4} = 89$ ft

59. *Estimate:* $24 + 35 + 24 + 35 = 118$ in.; *Exact:* $116\frac{1}{2}$ in.

61. *Estimate:* $100 - 10 - 14 - 9 - 19 - 12 - 10 - 14 = 12$ gallons; *Exact:* $12\frac{5}{8}$ gallons

63. *Estimate:* $527 - 108 - 151 - 139 = 129$ ft; *Exact:* 130 ft

65. *Estimate:* $59 + 24 + 17 + 29 + 58 = 187$ tons; *Exact:* $186\frac{13}{24}$ tons

67. $4\frac{11}{16}$ in.   **69.** $21\frac{3}{8}$ in.   **71. (a)** 30   **(b)** 28   **(c)** 25   **(d)** 264

72. least common denominator   **73. (a)** $\frac{23}{24}$ **(b)** $\frac{8}{15}$ **(c)** $\frac{43}{48}$ **(d)** $\frac{4}{21}$

74. fraction parts   **75.** improper; large

76. (a) $4\frac{5}{8} + 3\frac{6}{8} = 7\frac{11}{8} = 8\frac{3}{8}$; $\frac{37}{8} + \frac{30}{8} = \frac{67}{8} = 8\frac{3}{8}$

(b) $11\frac{56}{40} - 8\frac{35}{40} = 3\frac{21}{40}$; $\frac{496}{40} - \frac{355}{40} = \frac{141}{40} = 3\frac{21}{40}$

Section 2.13 (pages 202–209)

1.–12. $\frac{1}{4}$ $\frac{1}{2}$ $\frac{7}{8}$ $\frac{5}{4}$ $\frac{3}{2}$ $1\frac{7}{8}$ $2\frac{1}{6}$ $\frac{7}{3}$ $\frac{11}{4}$ $3\frac{1}{4}$ $\frac{7}{2}$ $3\frac{4}{5}$

2. 1.   **10.**   4.   3.   12.   7. 5.   6.   11. 9.   8.

13. >   **15.** <   **17.** >   **19.** <   **21.** >   **23.** >   **25.** $\frac{1}{9}$ **27.** $\frac{25}{64}$

29. $\frac{9}{16}$ **31.** $\frac{64}{125}$ **33.** $\frac{81}{16} = 5\frac{1}{16}$ **35.** $\frac{81}{256}$

37. A number line is a horizontal line with a range of equally spaced whole numbers placed on it. The lowest number is on the left and the greatest number is on the right. It can be used to compare the size or value of numbers.

$$0 \quad \frac{1}{2} \quad 1 \quad 1\frac{1}{2} \quad 2 \quad 2\frac{1}{2} \quad 3$$

39. 4 **41.** 10 **43.** 1 **45.** $\frac{3}{16}$ **47.** $\frac{4}{9}$ **49.** $\frac{1}{3}$ **51.** $\frac{1}{2}$ **53.** $\frac{3}{8}$

55. $\frac{1}{4}$ **57.** $1\frac{1}{2}$ **59.** $\frac{1}{12}$ **61.** 3 **63.** $\frac{5}{16}$ **65.** $\frac{1}{4}$ **67.** $\frac{1}{32}$

69. $\frac{5}{30}$ in Atlanta is greater. **71.** $<; >$ **72. (a)** like; numerators; numerator **(b)** Answers will vary. **73.** parentheses; exponents; square; multiply; divide; add; subtract **74.** $\frac{2}{45}$

75.–80.

77. 75. $\frac{27}{125}$ $\frac{4}{9}$ **78. 79. 76.** $1\frac{9}{16}$ 2 $2\frac{1}{4}$ **80.** $2\frac{57}{64}$

$$0 \quad 1 \quad 2 \quad 3$$

Summary Exercises on Fractions (pages 210–211)

1. proper **2.** improper **3.** improper **4.** proper **5.** $\frac{5}{6}$ **6.** $\frac{7}{8}$

7. $\frac{3}{7}$ **8.** $\frac{23}{47}$ **9.** $\frac{1}{2}$ **10.** $\frac{3}{8}$ **11.** 35 **12.** $\frac{5}{6}$ **13.** $1\frac{1}{6}$ **14.** 56

15. $1\frac{13}{24}$ **16.** $1\frac{13}{16}$ **17.** $2\frac{1}{12}$ **18.** $\frac{1}{12}$ **19.** $\frac{11}{24}$ **20.** $\frac{2}{15}$

21. *Exact:* $7\frac{7}{8}$; *Estimate:* $4 \cdot 2 = 8$

22. *Exact:* $17\frac{15}{32}$; *Estimate:* $5 \cdot 3 = 15$

23. *Exact:* $107\frac{2}{3}$; *Estimate:* $8 \cdot 6 \cdot 2 = 96$

24. *Exact:* $1\frac{1}{6}$; *Estimate:* $4 \div 4 = 1$

25. *Exact:* $3\frac{7}{16}$; *Estimate:* $7 \div 2 = 3\frac{1}{2}$

26. *Exact:* $6\frac{1}{6}$; *Estimate:* $5 \div 1 = 5$

27. *Estimate:* $6 + 4 = 10$; *Exact:* $9\frac{11}{12}$

28. *Estimate:* $18 + 10 = 28$; *Exact:* $28\frac{1}{6}$

29. *Estimate:* $15 + 11 = 26$; *Exact:* $25\frac{4}{15}$

30. *Estimate:* $9 - 4 = 5$; *Exact:* $4\frac{19}{20}$

31. *Estimate:* $14 - 7 = 7$; *Exact:* $6\frac{5}{8}$

32. *Estimate:* $32 - 23 = 9$; *Exact:* $9\frac{1}{4}$

33. $\frac{1}{12}$ **34.** $\frac{9}{10}$ **35.** $\frac{5}{18}$ **36.** 40 **37.** 72 **38.** 84 **39.** 35 **40.** 12 **41.** 55 **42.** $<$ **43.** $>$ **44.** $>$

Chapter 2 Review Exercises (pages 216–221)

1. $\frac{6}{7}$ **2.** $\frac{7}{9}$ **3.** $\frac{3}{4}$ **4.** $\frac{1}{8}$ **5.** $\frac{4}{5}$ **6.** $\frac{1}{6}$ **7.** $\frac{13}{31}$ **8.** $\frac{1}{3}$

9. $\frac{11}{12}$ of his total income **10.** $\frac{1}{4}$ Web page less **11.** 10 **12.** 12

13. 60 **14.** 24 **15.** 120 **16.** 180 **17.** 8 **18.** 21 **19.** 10

20. 45 **21.** 32 **22.** 20 **23.** $\frac{5}{6}$ **24.** $\frac{7}{8}$ **25.** $\frac{5}{8}$ **26.** $\frac{5}{12}$ **27.** $\frac{13}{24}$

28. $\frac{17}{36}$ **29.** $\frac{9}{10}$ of the students **30.** $\frac{23}{24}$ of her business

31. *Estimate:* $19 + 14 = 33$; *Exact:* $32\frac{3}{8}$

32. *Estimate:* $23 + 15 = 38$; *Exact:* $38\frac{1}{9}$

33. *Estimate:* $13 + 9 + 10 = 32$; *Exact:* $31\frac{43}{80}$

34. *Estimate:* $32 - 15 = 17$; *Exact:* $17\frac{1}{12}$

35. *Estimate:* $34 - 16 = 18$; *Exact:* $18\frac{1}{3}$

36. *Estimate:* $215 - 136 = 79$; *Exact:* $79\frac{7}{16}$

37. $9\frac{1}{10}$ **38.** $10\frac{5}{12}$ **39.** $3\frac{1}{4}$ **40.** $1\frac{2}{3}$ **41.** $5\frac{1}{2}$ **42.** $2\frac{19}{24}$

43. *Estimate:* $19 - 6 - 7 = 6$ miles; *Exact:* $5\frac{19}{24}$ miles

44. *Estimate:* $29 + 25 = 54$ tons; *Exact:* $53\frac{5}{12}$ tons

45. *Estimate:* $9 + 10 + 7 = 26$ pounds; *Exact:* $25\frac{1}{8}$ pounds

46. *Estimate:* $9 - 2 - 3 = 4$ acres; *Exact:* $4\frac{1}{16}$ acres

47.–50.

$$\frac{3}{8} \quad \frac{7}{4} \quad \frac{8}{3} \quad 3\frac{1}{5}$$
$$0 \quad 1 \quad 2 \quad 3 \quad 4$$
47. 48. 49. 50.

51. $<$ **52.** $<$ **53.** $>$ **54.** $>$ **55.** $<$ **56.** $>$ **57.** $<$

58. $>$ **59.** $\frac{1}{4}$ **60.** $\frac{4}{9}$ **61.** $\frac{27}{1000}$ **62.** $\frac{81}{4096}$ **63.** $\frac{1}{2}$ **64.** $6\frac{3}{4}$

65. $\frac{1}{16}$ **66.** 1 **67.** $\frac{3}{16}$ **68.** $1\frac{25}{64}$ **69.** $\frac{3}{4}$ **70.** $\frac{2}{5}$ **71.** $\frac{19}{32}$

72. $\frac{11}{16}$ **73.** $2\frac{1}{6}$ **74.** $26\frac{1}{4}$ **75.** $5\frac{3}{8}$ **76.** $11\frac{43}{80}$ **77.** $15\frac{5}{12}$

78. $\frac{8}{11}$ **79.** $\frac{1}{250}$ **80.** $\frac{1}{2}$ **81.** $\frac{2}{9}$ **82.** $\frac{11}{27}$ **83.** $>$ **84.** $<$ **85.** $<$

86. $>$ **87.** 36 **88.** 120 **89.** 126 **90.** 18 **91.** 108 **92.** 60

93. *Estimate:* $93 - 14 - 22 = 57$ ft; *Exact:* $56\frac{7}{8}$ ft

94. *Estimate:* $4 \cdot 50 = 200$ pounds of sugar; $200 - 69 - 77 - 33 = 21$ pounds; *Exact:* $21\frac{5}{8}$ pounds

Chapter 2 Test (pages 222–223)

1. $\frac{3}{4}$ **2.** $\frac{1}{2}$ **3.** $\frac{2}{5}$ **4.** $\frac{1}{6}$ **5.** 12 **6.** 30 **7.** 108 **8.** $\frac{5}{8}$

9. $\frac{23}{36}$ **10.** $\frac{5}{24}$ **11.** $\frac{1}{40}$

12. *Estimate:* $8 + 5 = 13$; *Exact:* $12\frac{1}{2}$

13. *Estimate:* $16 - 12 = 4$; *Exact:* $4\frac{11}{15}$

14. *Estimate:* $19 + 9 + 12 = 40$; *Exact:* $40\frac{29}{60}$

15. *Estimate:* $24 - 18 = 6$; *Exact:* $5\frac{5}{8}$

16. Answers will vary. Probably addition and subtraction of fractions is more difficult because you have to find the least common denominator and then change the fractions to the same denominator. **17.** Answers will vary. Round mixed numbers to the nearest whole number. Then add or subtract to estimate the answer. The estimate may vary from the exact answer but it lets you know if your answer is reasonable.

18. *Estimate:* $10 + 85 + 37 + 8 = 140$ pounds; *Exact:* $140\frac{1}{24}$ pounds

19. *Estimate:* $148 - 69 - 37 - 6 = 36$ gal; *Exact:* $35\frac{7}{8}$ gal

20. $>$ **21.** $>$ **22.** 2   **23.** $\frac{13}{48}$ **24.** $1\frac{3}{4}$ **25.** $1\frac{1}{3}$

Cumulative Review Exercises: Chapters 1–2 (pages 226–227)

1. 5, 3, 9, 2   **2.** 59,800; 59,800; 60,000
3. *Estimate:* $20,000 - 10,000 = 10,000$;
Exact: 14,389   **4.** *Estimate:* $100,000 \div 40 = 2500$; *Exact:* 3211
5. 1,255,609   **6.** 2,801,695   **7.** 160   **8.** 369,408   **9.** 135   **10.** 2693 R2
11. *Estimate:* $20 + 9 + 5 + 20 + 9 + 5 = 68$ ft; *Exact:* 64 ft
12. *Estimate:* $20 \cdot 10 = 200$ ft²; *Exact:* 252 ft²

13. *Estimate:* $2 \cdot 3 = 6$ yd²; *Exact:* $4\frac{2}{3}$ yd²

14. *Estimate:* $70 \cdot 130 = 9100$ in.; *Exact:* $9132\frac{1}{2}$ in.

15. 144   **16.** 9   **17.** 44   **18.** $\frac{4}{45}$

19. $\frac{9}{10}$ **20.** $1\frac{1}{16}$ **21.** $\frac{1}{2}$ **22.** $36\frac{3}{4}$ **23.** $2\frac{3}{16}$ **24.** $13\frac{1}{2}$

25. *Estimate:* $3 + 5 = 8$; *Exact:* $7\frac{7}{8}$

26. *Estimate:* $22 + 4 = 26$; *Exact:* $26\frac{7}{24}$

27. *Estimate:* $5 - 2 = 3$; *Exact:* $2\frac{5}{8}$

28.–31.   **32.** $<$ **33.** $>$ **34.** $<$

29.   30. 28. 31.

Chapter 3 Real Number System

Taken from *Prealgebra & Introductory Algebra* by Lial, et. al. (0321578732)

Section 3.1 (pages 231–238)

1. $^+29{,}035$ feet or 29,035 feet   **3.** $^-128.6$ degrees   **5.** $^-18$ yards

7. $^+\$100$ or $\$100$ **9.** $^-6\frac{1}{2}$ pounds

11.
$^-5\ ^-4\ ^-3\ ^-2\ ^-1\ 0\ 1\ 2\ 3\ 4\ 5$

13.
$^-5\ ^-4\ ^-3\ ^-2\ ^-1\ 0\ 1\ 2\ 3\ 4\ 5$

15.
$^-9\ ^-8\ ^-7\ ^-6\ ^-5\ ^-4\ ^-3\ ^-2\ ^-1\ 0\ 1$

17. $>$ **19.** $<$ **21.** $<$ **23.** $>$ **25.** $<$ **27.** $>$ **29.** $>$
31. $<$ **33.** 15   **35.** 3   **37.** 0   **39.** 200   **41.** 75   **43.** 8042
45.
A C   D B

$^-2\quad ^-1\quad 0\quad 1$

46. $^-1.5, ^-1, 0, 0.5$ **47.** A: may be at risk; B: above normal;
C: normal; D: normal   **48. (a)** The patient would think the
interpretation was "above normal" and wouldn't get treatment.
(b) Patient D's score of 0; zero is neither positive nor negative.

Section 3.2 (pages 239–248)

1. 3

5

$^-2$

$^-7\ ^-6\ ^-5\ ^-4\ ^-3\ ^-2\ ^-1\ 0\ 1\ 2\ 3$

3. $^-7$

$^-2$ $^-5$

$^-7\ ^-6\ ^-5\ ^-4\ ^-3\ ^-2\ ^-1\ 0\ 1\ 2\ 3$

5. $^-1$

$^-4$

3

$^-7\ ^-6\ ^-5\ ^-4\ ^-3\ ^-2\ ^-1\ 0\ 1\ 2\ 3$

7. (a) $^-10$ **(b)** 10   **9. (a)** 12   **(b)** $^-12$ **11. (a)** $^-50$ **(b)** 50
13. (a) 158   **(b)** $^-158$ **15.** The absolute values are the same in each
pair of answers, so the only difference in the sums is the common sign.
17. (a) 2   **(b)** $^-2$ **19. (a)** $^-7$ **(b)** 7   **21. (a)** $^-5$ **(b)** 5
23. (a) 150   **(b)** $^-150$ **25.** Each pair of answers differs only in the sign
of the answer. This occurs because the signs of the addends are reversed.
27. $^-3$ **29.** 7   **31.** $^-7$ **33.** 1   **35.** $^-8$ **37.** $^-20$ **39.** $^-17$
41. $^-22$ **43.** $^-19$ **45.** 6   **47.** $^-5$ **49.** 0   **51.** 5   **53.** $^-32$
55. $13 + ^-17 = ^-4$ yards   **57.** $^-62 + 50 = ^-\$12$
59. $^-88 + 35 = ^-\$53$ **61.** Jeff: $^-20 + 75 + ^-55 = 0$ points;
Terry: $42 + ^-15 + 20 = 47$ points   **63.** $^-2$ **65.** 2   **67.** $^-5 + ^-18$;
$^-23$ **69.** $15 + ^-4; 11$ **71.** $6 + (^-14 + 14); 6 + 0 = 6$
73. $(^-14 + ^-6) + ^-7; ^-20 + ^-7 = ^-27$ **75.** Answers will vary.
Some possibilities are: $^-6 + 0 = ^-6; 10 + 0 = 10; 0 + 3 = 3$
77. $^-4116$ **79.** 8686   **81.** $^-96{,}077$

Section 3.3 (pages 249–252)

1. $^-6; 6 + ^-6 = 0$ **3.** $13; ^-13 + 13 = 0$ **5.** $0; 0 + 0 = 0$
7. 14   **9.** $^-2$ **11.** $^-12$ **13.** $^-25$ **15.** $^-23$ **17.** 5   **19.** 20
21. 11   **23.** $^-60$ **25.** 0   **27.** 0   **29.** $^-6$ **31. (a)** 8   **(b)** $^-2$
(c) 2   **(d)** $^-8$ **33. (a)** $^-3$ **(b)** 11   **(c)** $^-11$ **(d)** 3   **35.** $^-6$
37. $^-5$ **39.** 3   **41.** $^-10$ **43.** 12   **45.** $^-5$ **47. (a)** $21\,°F$;
$30 - 21 = 9$ degrees difference   **(b)** $0\,°F; 15 - 0 = 15$ degrees
difference   **(c)** $^-17\,°F; 5 - ^-17 = 22$ degrees difference
(d) $^-41\,°F; ^-10 - ^-41 = 31$ degrees difference   **49.** The student
forgot to change 6 to its opposite, $^-6$. It should be $^-6 + ^-6 = ^-12$.
51. $^-11$ **53.** $^-5$ **55.** $^-10$ **57.** Answers on left: $^-8; 8$. On right:
$^-1; 1$ Subtraction is *not* commutative; the absolute value of the answer is
the same, but the sign changes.   **58.** Subtracting 0 from a number does
not change the number. For example $^-5 - 0 = ^-5$. But subtracting a
number from 0 *does* change the number to its opposite. For example,
$0 - ^-5 = 5$.

Section 3.4 (pages 253–262)

1. 630   **3.** $^-1080$ **5.** 7900   **7.** $^-86{,}800$ **9.** 42,500   **11.** $^-6000$
13. $^-78{,}000$ **15.** 6000   **17.** 600,000   **19.** $^-9{,}000{,}000$
21. 140,000,000   **23.** 20,000,000,000   **25.** 9,000,000,000
27. 30,000 miles   **29.** $^-60$ degrees   **31.** $\$10{,}000$ **33.** 60,000,000
Americans   **35.** $^-300$ feet   **37.** 700,000 people in Alaska; 40,000,000
people in California   **39.** Answers will vary but should mention looking
only at the second digit, rounding first digit up when second digit is 5 or
more, leaving first digit unchanged when second digit is 4 or less. Examples will vary.   **41.** *Estimate:* $^-40 + 90 = 50$; *Exact:* $^-42 + 89 = 47$
43. *Estimate:* $20 + ^-100 = ^-80$; *Exact:* $16 + ^-97 = ^-81$
45. *Estimate:* $^-300 + ^-400 = ^-700$; *Exact:* $^-273 + ^-399 = ^-672$
47. *Estimate:* $3000 + 7000 = 10{,}000$; *Exact:* $3081 + 6826 = 9907$
49. *Estimate:* $20 + ^-80 = ^-60$; *Exact:* $23 - 81 = 23 + ^-81 = ^-58$
51. *Estimate:* $^-40 + ^-40 = ^-80$; *Exact:* $^-39 - 39 =$
$^-39 + ^-39 = ^-78$ **53.** *Estimate:* $^-100 + 30 + ^+70 = 0$;
Exact: $^-106 + 34 - ^-72 = ^-106 + 34 + ^+72 = 0$ **55.** *Estimate:*
$80{,}000 - 50{,}000 = \$30{,}000$; *Exact:* $78{,}650 - 52{,}882 = \$25{,}768$
57. *Estimate:* $2000 - 800 - 300 - 400 - 200 - 200 = \$100$;
Exact: $2120 - 845 - 325 - 365 - 182 - 240 = \$163$
59. *Estimate:* $^-100 + 40 + 50 = ^-10$ degrees; *Exact:*
$^-102 + 37 + 52 = ^-13$ degrees   **61.** *Estimate:* $400 + 100 = 500$
doors and windows; *Exact:* $412 + 147 = 559$ doors and windows

Section 3.5 (pages 263–272)

1. (a) 63 **(b)** 63 **(c)** $^-$63 **(d)** $^-$63 **3. (a)** $^-$56 **(b)** $^-$56 **(c)** 56 **(d)** 56 **5.** $^-$35 **7.** $^-$45 **9.** $^-$18 **11.** $^-$50 **13.** $^-$40 **15.** $^-$56 **17.** 32 **19.** 77 **21.** 0 **23.** 133 **25.** 13 **27.** 0 **29.** 48 **31.** $^-$56 **33.** $^-$160 **35.** 5 **37.** $^-$3 **39.** $^-$1 **41.** 0 **43.** 5 **45.** $^-$4 **47.** Commutative property: changing the *order* of the factors does not change the product.   Associative property: changing the *grouping* of the factors does not change the product. Examples will vary.   **49.** Examples will vary. Some possibilities are: **(a)** $6 \cdot ^-1 = ^-6; 2 \cdot ^-1 = ^-2; 15 \cdot ^-1 = ^-15$ **(b)** $^-6 \cdot ^-1 = 6; ^-2 \cdot ^-1 = 2; ^-15 \cdot ^-1 = 15$ The result of multiplying any nonzero number times $^-1$ is the number with the opposite sign.   **50.** The products are 4, $^-8$, 16, $^-32$. The absolute value doubles each time and the sign changes. The next three products are 64, $^-128$, and 256.   **51.** $= 9 \cdot ^-3 + 9 \cdot 5$ Both results are 18. **53.** $= 8 \cdot 25$ Both products are 200.   **55.** $= (^-3 \cdot 2) \cdot 5$ Both products are $^-30$.   **57.** *Estimate:* $300 \cdot 50 = \$15,000$; *Exact:* $324 \cdot 52 = \$16,848$ **59.** *Estimate:* $^-10,000 \cdot 10 = ^-\$100,000$; *Exact:* $^-9950 \cdot 12 = ^-\$119,400$ **61.** *Estimate:* $200 \cdot 10 = \$2000$; *Exact:* $182 \cdot 13 = \$2366$ **63.** *Estimate:* $20 \cdot 400 = 8000$ hours; *Exact:* $24 \cdot 365 = 8760$ hours   **65.** $^-512$ **67.** 0 **69.** $^-355,299$ **71.** \$247 **73.** $^-22$ degrees **75.** 772 points

Section 3.6 (pages 273–282)

1. (a) 7 **(b)** 7 **(c)** $^-7$ **(d)** $^-7$ **3. (a)** $^-7$ **(b)** 7 **(c)** $^-7$ **(d)** 7 **5. (a)** 1 **(b)** 35 **(c)** $^-13$ **(d)** 1 **7. (a)** 0 **(b)** undefined **(c)** undefined **(d)** 0 **9.** $^-4$ **11.** $^-3$ **13.** 6 **15.** $^-11$ **17.** undefined **19.** $^-14$ **21.** 10 **23.** 4 **25.** $^-1$ **27.** 0 **29.** 191 **31.** $^-499$ **33.** 2 **35.** $^-4$ **37.** 40 **39.** $^-48$ **41.** 5 **43.** 0 **45.** $2 \div 1 = 2$ but $1 \div 2 = 0.5$, so division is not commutative.   **46.** $(12 \div 6) \div 2 = 2 \div 2 = 1$; $12 \div (6 \div 2) = 12 \div 3 = 4$; different quotients. Division is not associative. **47.** Similar: If the signs match, the result is positive. If the signs are different, the result is negative. Different: Multiplication is commutative, division is not. You can multiply by 0, but dividing by 0 is undefined. **48.** Examples will vary. The properties are: Any nonzero number divided by itself is 1. Any number divided by 1 is the number. Division by 0 is undefined. Zero divided by any other number (except 0) is 0. **49. (a)** $\dfrac{^-6}{^-1} = 6; \dfrac{^-2}{^-1} = 2; \dfrac{^-15}{^-1} = 15$ **(b)** $\dfrac{6}{^-1} = ^-6; \dfrac{2}{^-1} = ^-2; \dfrac{15}{^-1} = ^-15$ When dividing by $^-1$, change the sign of the dividend to its opposite to get the quotient. **50.** Division is not commutative. $\dfrac{0}{^-3} = 0$ because $0 \cdot ^-3 = 0$. But $\dfrac{^-3}{0}$ is undefined because when $\dfrac{^-3}{0} = ?$ is rewritten as $? \cdot 0 = ^-3$, no number can replace ? and make a true statement.   **51.** *Estimate:* $^-40,000 \div 20 = ^-2000$ feet; *Exact:* $^-35,836 \div 17 = ^-2108$ feet **53.** *Estimate:* $^-200 + 500 = \$300$; *Exact:* $^-238 + 450 = \$212$ **55.** *Estimate:* $400 - 100 = 300$ days; *Exact:* $365 - 106 = 259$ days **57.** *Estimate:* $^-700 \cdot 40 = ^-28,000$ feet; *Exact:* $^-730 \cdot 37 = ^-27,010$ feet **59.** *Estimate:* $300 \div 5 = 60$ miles; *Exact:* $315 \div 5 = 63$ miles **61.** Average score of 168 **63.** The back shows 520 grams, which is 10 grams more than the front. **65.** $^-\$15$ **67.** 16 hours, with 40 minutes left over **69.** 33 rooms, with space for 2 people unused. **71.** $^-10$ **73.** undefined **75.** 31.70979198 rounds to 32 years.

Summary Exercises on Operations with Integers (pages 283–284)

1. $^-6$ **2.** 0 **3.** $^-7$ **4.** $^-7$ **5.** 63 **6.** $^-1$ **7.** $^-56$ **8.** $^-22$ **9.** 12 **10.** 8 **11.** $^-13$ **12.** 0 **13.** 0 **14.** $^-17$ **15.** $^-48$ **16.** $^-10$ **17.** $^-50$ **18.** undefined **19.** $^-14$ **20.** $^-6$ **21.** 0 **22.** 16 **23.** $^-30$ **24.** undefined **25.** 48 **26.** $^-19$ **27.** 2

28. $^-20$ **29.** 0 **30.** 16 **31.** $^-3$ **32.** $^-36$ **33.** 6 **34.** $^-7$ **35.** $^-5$ **36.** $^-31$ **37.** $^-2$ **38.** $^-32$ **39.** $^-5$ **40.** $^-4$ **41.** $^-9732$ **42.** 100 **43.** 4 **44.** $^-343$ **45.** 5 **46.** $^-6$ **47.** $^-10$ **48.** $^-5$ **49. (a)** The quotient is 0. **(b)** The product is 0. **(c)** The quotient is 1. **50. (a)** The quotient is $^-1$. *Adding* $15 + ^-15$ would give a *sum* of 0. **(b)** Dividing by zero cannot be done; the correct answer is "undefined." **(c)** Work with two numbers at a time: $^-10 \div ^-2$ is 5; then $5 \div ^-5$ is $^-1$, *not* positive 1.

Section 3.7 (pages 285–294)

1. $4 \cdot 4 \cdot 4$; 4 cubed or 4 to the third power **3.** 2^7; 128; 2 to the seventh power **5.** 5^4; 625; 5 to the fourth power **7.** 7^2; $7 \cdot 7$; 49 **9.** 10^1; 10; 10 **11. (a)** 10 **(b)** 100 **(c)** 1000 **(d)** 10,000 **13. (a)** 4 **(b)** 16 **(c)** 64 **(d)** 256 **15.** 9,765,625 **17.** 4096 **19.** 4 **21.** 25 **23.** $^-64$ **25.** 81 **27.** $^-1000$ **29.** 1 **31.** 108 **33.** 200 **35.** $^-750$ **37.** $^-32$ **39. (a)** The answers are 4, $^-8$, 16, $^-32$, 64, $^-128$, 256, $^-512$. When a negative number is raised to an even power, the answer is positive; when raised to an odd power, the answer is negative. **(b)** negative; positive **41.** $^-6$ **43.** 0 **45.** $^-39$ **47.** 16 **49.** 23 **51.** $^-43$ **53.** 7 **55.** $^-3$ **57.** 0 **59.** $^-38$ **61.** 41 **63.** $^-2$ **65.** 13 **67.** 126 **69.** 8 **71.** $\dfrac{27}{^-3} = ^-9$ **73.** $\dfrac{^-48}{^-4} = 12$ **75.** $\dfrac{^-60}{^-1} = 60$ **77.** $^-4050$ **79.** 7 **81.** $\dfrac{27}{0}$ is undefined.

Chapter 4   Introduction to Variables/ Solving Equations

Taken from *Prealgebra & Introductory Algebra* by Lial, et. al. (0321578732)

Section 4.1 (pages 296–308)

1. c is the variable; 4 is the constant. **3.** m is the variable; $^-3$ is the constant. **5.** h is the variable; 5 is the coefficient. **7.** c is the variable; 2 is the coefficient; 10 is the constant. **9.** x and y are variables. **11.** g is the variable; $^-6$ is the coefficient; 9 is the constant **13. (a)** $654 + 10$ is 664 robes. **(b)** $208 + 10$ is 218 robes. **(c)** $95 + 10$ is 105 robes. **15. (a)** $3 \cdot 11$ inches is 33 inches. **(b)** $3 \cdot 3$ feet is 9 feet. **17. (a)** $3 \cdot 12 - 5$ is 31 brushes. **(b)** $3 \cdot 16 - 5$ is 43 brushes. **19. (a)** $\dfrac{332}{4}$ is 83 points. **(b)** $\dfrac{637}{7}$ is 91 points. **21.** $12 + 12 + 12 + 12$ is 48, $4 \cdot 12$ is 48; $0 + 0 + 0 + 0$ is 0, $4 \cdot 0$ is 0; $^-5 + ^-5 + ^-5 + ^-5 = ^-20$, $4 \cdot ^-5$ is $^-20$ **23.** $^-2(^-4) + 5$ is $8 + 5$, or 13; $^-2(^-6) + ^-2$ is $12 + ^-2$, or 10; $^-2(0) + ^-8$ is $0 + ^-8$, or $^-8$ **25.** A variable is a letter that represents the part of a rule that varies or changes depending on the situation. An expression expresses, or tells, the rule for doing something. For example, $c + 5$ is an expression, and c is the variable. **27.** $b \cdot 1 = b$ or $1 \cdot b = b$ **29.** $\dfrac{b}{0}$ is undefined or $b \div 0$ is undefined. **31.** $c \cdot c \cdot c \cdot c \cdot c \cdot c$ **33.** $x \cdot x \cdot x \cdot x \cdot y \cdot y \cdot y$ **35.** $^-3 \cdot a \cdot a \cdot a \cdot b$ **37.** $9 \cdot x \cdot y \cdot y$ **39.** $^-2 \cdot c \cdot c \cdot c \cdot c \cdot c \cdot d$ **41.** $a \cdot a \cdot a \cdot b \cdot c \cdot c$ **43.** 16 **45.** $^-24$ **47.** $^-18$ **49.** $^-128$ **51.** $^-18,432$ **53.** 311,040 **55.** 56 **57.** $\dfrac{36}{0}$ is undefined. **59. (a)** 3 miles **(b)** 2 miles **(c)** 1 mile **60. (a)** $\dfrac{1}{2}$ mile; take half of the distance for 5 seconds **(b)** $7\dfrac{1}{2}$ seconds; find the number halfway between 5 seconds and 10 seconds **(c)** $12\dfrac{1}{2}$ seconds; find the number halfway between 10 seconds and 15 seconds

Section 4.2 (pages 309–322)

1. $2b^2$ and b^2; The coefficients are 2 and 1. **3.** ^-xy and $2xy$; The coefficients are $^-1$ and 2. **5.** 7, 3, and $^-4$; The like terms are constants. **7.** $12r$ **9.** $6x^2$ **11.** ^-4p **13.** $^-3a^3$ **15.** 0

17. xy **19.** $6t^4$ **21.** $4y^2$ **23.** ^-8x **25.** $12a + 4b$ **27.** $7rs + 14$
29. $a + 2ab^2$ **31.** $^-2x + 2y$ **33.** $7b^2$ **35.** cannot be simplified
37. $^-15r + 5s + t$ **39.** $30a$ **41.** $^-8x^2$ **43.** $^-20y^3$ **45.** $18cd$
47. $21a^2bc$ **49.** $12w$ **51.** $6b + 36$ **53.** $7x - 7$ **55.** $21t + 3$
57. $^-10r - 6$ **59.** $^-9k - 36$ **61.** $50m - 300$ **63.** $8y + 16$
65. $6a^2 + 3$ **67.** $9m - 34$ **69.** $^-25$ **71.** $24x$ **73.** $5n + 13$
75. $11p - 1$ **77.** A simplified expression still has variables, but is written in a simpler way. When evaluating an expression, the variables are all replaced by specific numbers and the final result is a numerical answer.
79. Like terms have matching variable parts, that is, matching letters and exponents. The coefficients do not have to match. Examples will vary.
81. Keep the variable part unchanged when combining like terms. The correct answer is $5x + 8$. **83.** $^-2y + 9$ **85.** 0 **87.** ^-9x

Summary Exercises on Variables and Expressions (pages 323–324)

1. m is the variable; $^-10$ is the constant. **2.** c and d are the variables; $^-8$ is the coefficient. **3.** x is the variable; 4 is the coefficient; 6 is the constant. **4. (a)** 32 yards **(b)** 120 inches **5. (a)** \$13,080
(b) \$22,342 **6.** $a \cdot d \cdot d \cdot d \cdot d$ **7.** $b \cdot b \cdot b \cdot c \cdot d$
8. $^-7 \cdot a \cdot b \cdot b \cdot b \cdot b \cdot c \cdot c$ **9.** 625 **10.** 0 **11.** 0 **12.** 60
13. $^-8$ **14.** 120 **15.** $^-216$ **16.** $^-800$ **17.** 120,960 **18.** $24b$
19. $7x + 7$ **20.** $^-8c - 32$ **21.** 0 **22.** $12c^2d$ **23.** ^-6f
24. $6w + 8$ **25.** $^-2a - 6b$ **26.** $50x^3y^2$ **27.** $5r^3 + 3r^2 + 2r$
28. $7h^2$ **29.** $^-9$ **30.** $^-32y + 25$ **31.** $36x - 10$ **32.** $19n + 1$
33. (a) Forgot to multiply $6 \cdot 2$; correct answer is $6n + 12$.
(b) Two negative factors give a *positive* product; correct answer is $20a$.
(c) Keep the variable part unchanged; correct answer is $5y - 10$.
34. In the last step, do not change the sign of the first term; keep ^-7x as ^-7x. The correct answer is $^-7x - 9$.

Section 4.3 (pages 325–336)

1. 58 is the solution. **3.** $^-16$ is the solution. **5.** $^-12$ is the solution.
7. $p = 4$ **Check** $\underbrace{4 + 5}_{9} = 9$
$9 = 9$

9. $r = 10$ **Check** $8 = \underbrace{10 - 2}_{8}$
$8 = 8$

11. $n = ^-8$ **Check** $^-5 = n + 3$
$^-5 = \underbrace{^-8 + 3}$
$^-5 = ^-5$

13. $k = 18$ **Check** $^-4 + k = 14$
$\underbrace{^-4 + 18} = 14$
$14 = 14$

15. $y = 6$ **Check** $y - 6 = 0$
$\underbrace{6 - 6} = 0$
$0 = 0$

17. $r = ^-6$ **Check** $7 = r + 13$
$7 = \underbrace{^-6 + 13}$
$7 = 7$

19. $x = 11$ **Check** $x - 12 = ^-1$
$\underbrace{11 + ^-12} = ^-1$
$^-1 = ^-1$

21. $t = ^-3$ **Check** $^-5 = ^-2 + t$
$^-5 = \underbrace{^-2 + ^-3}$
$^-5 = ^-5$

23.
$\underbrace{^-2 + ^-5}_{^-7} = 3$
Does not balance $\quad ^-7 \neq 3$
The correct solution is 8. $\quad \underbrace{8 - 5}_{3} = 3$
Balances $\quad 3 = 3$

25.
$7 + x = ^-11$
$\downarrow$
$\underbrace{7 + ^-18} = ^-11$
Balances $\quad ^-11 = ^-11$
$^-18$ is the correct solution.

27.
$^-10 = ^-10 + b$
$\downarrow$
$^-10 = \underbrace{^-10 + 10}$
Does not balance $\quad ^-10 \neq 0$
The correct solution is 0. $\quad ^-10 = \underbrace{^-10 + 0}$
Balances $\quad ^-10 = ^-10$

29. $c = 6$; see *Student's Solutions Manual* for **Checks** of odd-numbered Exercises 29–37; Exercise 39 is in the Solutions section in the back of this book. **31.** $y = 5$ **33.** $b = ^-30$ **35.** $t = 0$ **37.** $z = ^-7$
39. $w = 3$ **41.** $x = ^-10$ **43.** $a = 0$ **45.** $y = ^-25$ **47.** $x = 15$
49. $k = 113$ **51.** $b = 18$ **53.** $r = ^-5$ **55.** $n = ^-105$ **57.** $h = ^-5$
59. No, the solution is $^-14$, the number used to replace x in the original equation. **61.** $g = 295$ graduates **63.** $c = 55$ chirps **65.** $p = \$110$ per month in winter **67.** $m = ^-19$ **69.** $x = 2$ **71. (a)** Equations will vary. Some possibilities are $n - 1 = ^-3$ and $8 = x + 10$.
(b) Equations will vary. Some possibilities are $y + 6 = 6$ and
$^-5 = ^-5 + b$. **72. (a)** $x = \frac{1}{2}$ **(b)** $y = \frac{5}{4}$ **(c)** $n = \$0.85$
(d) Equations will vary.

Section 4.4 (pages 337–344)

1. $z = 2$ **Check** $\underbrace{6 \cdot 2}_{12} = 12$
$12 = 12$

3. $r = 4$ **Check** $48 = 12r$
$48 = \underbrace{12 \cdot 4}$
$48 = 48$

5. $y = 0$ **Check** $3y = 0$
$\downarrow$
$\underbrace{3 \cdot 0} = 0$
$0 = 0$

7. $k = ^-10$ **Check** $^-7k = 70$
$\underbrace{^-7 \cdot ^-10} = 70$
$70 = 70$

9. $r = 6$ **Check** $^-54 = ^-9r$
$^-54 = \underbrace{^-9 \cdot 6}$
$^-54 = ^-54$

11. $b = ^-5$ **Check** $^-25 = 5b$
$^-25 = \underbrace{5 \cdot ^-5}$
$^-25 = ^-25$

13. $r = 3$ **Check** $\underbrace{2 \cdot 3}_{6} = 6$
$6 = 6$

15. $p = ^-3$ **Check** $^-12 = 5p - p$
$^-12 = \underbrace{5 \cdot ^-3} - ^-3$
$^-12 = \underbrace{^-15 + {}^+3}$
$^-12 = ^-12$

17. $a = ^-5$ **19.** $x = ^-10$ **21.** $w = 0$ **23.** $t = 3$ **25.** $t = 0$
27. $m = 9$ **29.** $y = ^-1$ **31.** $z = ^-5$ **33.** $p = ^-2$ **35.** $k = 7$

37. $b = {}^-3$ **39.** $x = {}^-32$ **41.** $w = 2$ **43.** $n = 50$ **45.** $p = {}^-10$
47. Each solution is the opposite of the number in the equation. So the rule is: When you change the sign of the variable from negative to positive, then change the number in the equation to its opposite. In $^-x = 5$, the opposite of 5 is $^-5$, so $x = {}^-5$.   **49.** Divide by the coefficient of x, which is 3, *not* by the opposite of 3. The correct solution is 5.
51. $s = 15$ ft   **53.** $s = 24$ meters   **55.** $y = 27$ **57.** $x = 1$

Section 4.5 (pages 345–354)

1. $p = 1$ **Check** $\underbrace{7(1)} + 5 = 12$
$$\underbrace{7 + 5} = 12$$
$$12 \ = 12$$

3. $y = 1$ **Check** $2 = 8y - 6$
$$2 = \underbrace{8(1)} - 6$$
$$2 = \underbrace{8 \ - 6}$$
$$2 = \ 2$$

5. $m = 0$ **Check** $^-3m + 1 = 1$
$$\underbrace{^-3(0)} + 1 = 1$$
$$\underbrace{0 \ + 1} = 1$$
$$1 \ = 1$$

7. $a = {}^-2$ **Check** $28 = \ {}^-9a + 10$
$$28 = \underbrace{^-9(^-2)} + 10$$
$$28 = \underbrace{18 \ + 10}$$
$$28 = \ 28$$

9. $x = {}^-4$ **Check** $^-5x - 4 = 16$
$$\underbrace{^-5(^-4)} - 4 = 16$$
$$\underbrace{20 \ - 4} = 16$$
$$16 \ = 16$$

11. $p = 4; 4 = p$ **Check** $6(4) - 2 = 4(4) + 6$
$$\underbrace{24} - 2 = \underbrace{16 \ + 6}$$
$$22 \ = \ 22$$

13. $k = {}^-2; {}^-2 = k$ **Check** $^-2k - 6 = \ 6k + 10$
$$\underbrace{^-2(^-2)} - 6 = 6(^-2) + 10$$
$$\underbrace{4 \ + \ ^-6} = \underbrace{^-12 \ + 10}$$
$$^-2 \ = \ ^-2$$

15. $a = 5; 5 = a$ **Check** $^-18 + \ 7a \ = \ 2a \ + 7$
$$^-18 + 7(5) \ = 2(5) + 7$$
$$\underbrace{^-18 + \ 35} = \underbrace{10 + 7}$$
$$17 \ = \ 17$$

17. $w = 6$ **19.** $y = {}^-9$ **21.** $t = {}^-5$ **23.** $x = 0$ **25.** $h = 1$
27. $y = {}^-2$ **29.** $m = {}^-3$ **31.** $w = 2$ **33.** $x = 5$ **35.** $a = 3$
37. $b = {}^-3$ **39.** $k = 4$ **41.** $c = 0$ **43.** $y = {}^-5$ **45.** $n = 21$
47. $c = 30$ **49.** $p = {}^-2$ **51.** $b = {}^-2$
53. The series of steps may vary. One possibility is:

$^-2t - \ 10 = 3t + 5$	Change subtraction to adding the opposite.
$^-2t + \ ^-10 = 3t + 5$	Add $2t$ to both sides
$\underline{2t \qquad\qquad 2t}$	(addition property).
$0 + \ ^-10 = 5t + 5$	Add $^-5$ to both sides
$\underline{\quad ^-5 \qquad\quad ^-5}$	(addition property).
$\dfrac{^-15}{5} = \dfrac{5t}{5}$	Divide both sides by 5 (division property).
$^-3 = t$	

55. Check $^-8 + \underline{4(3)} = \underline{2(3)} + 2$
$$\underbrace{^-8 + \ 12} = \underbrace{6 \ + 2}$$
$$4 \ \neq \ 8$$
The check does not balance, so 3 is not the correct solution. The student added ^-2a to $^-8$ on the left side, instead of adding ^-2a to $4a$. The correct solution is 5.   **57. (a)** It must be negative.   **(b)** The sum of x and a positive number is negative, so x must be negative.
58. (a) It must be positive.   **(b)** The sum of d and a negative number is positive, so d must be positive.   **59. (a)** It must be positive; when the signs are different, the product is negative.   **(b)** The product of n and a negative number is negative, so n must be positive.   **60. (a)** It must be negative also; when the signs match, the product is positive.   **(b)** The product of y and a negative number is positive, so y must be negative.

Chapter 4 Review Exercises (pages 361–362)

1. (a) Variable is k; coefficient is 4; constant is $^-3$.   **(b)** $^-9y + 20$
2. (a) 70 test tubes   **(b)** 106 test tubes   **3. (a)** $x \cdot x \cdot y \cdot y \cdot y \cdot y$
(b) $5 \cdot a \cdot b \cdot b \cdot b$ **4. (a)** 9   **(b)** $^-27$ **(c)** $^-128$ **(d)** 720
5. $ab^2 + 3ab$ **6.** $^-4x + 2y - 7$ **7.** $16g^3$ **8.** $12r^2t$ **9.** $5k + 10$
10. $^-6b - 8$ **11.** $6y$ **12.** $20x + 2$ **13.** Expressions will vary. One possibility is $6a^3 + a^2 + 3a - 6$.
14. $n = {}^-11$ **Check** $16 + \ n = 5$
$$\underbrace{16 + \ ^-11} = 5$$
$$5 \ = 5$$

15. $a = 4$ **Check** $^-4 + 2 = 2a - \ 6 - \ 4$
$$^-4 + 2 = 2(4) - \ 6 - \ 4$$
$$\underbrace{^-2 \ = \ 8} + \ ^-6 + \ ^-4$$
$$^-2 = \qquad ^-2$$

16. $m = {}^-8$ **17.** $k = 10$ **18.** $t = 0$ **19.** $p = {}^-6$ **20.** $r = 2$
21. $h = {}^-12$ **22.** $w = 4$ **23.** $c = {}^-2$ **24.** $n = 15$ employees
25. $a = {}^-5$ **26.** $p = 10$ **27.** $y = 5$ **28.** $m = 3$ **29.** $x = 9$
30. $b = 7$ **31.** $z = {}^-3$ **32.** $n = 4$ **33.** $t = 0$ **34.** $d = 5$
35. $b = {}^-2$

Chapter 4 Test (pages 363–364)

1. $^-7$ is the coefficient; w is the variable; 6 is the constant.
2. Buy 177 hot dogs.   **3.** $x \cdot x \cdot x \cdot x \cdot x \cdot y \cdot y \cdot y$
4. $4 \cdot a \cdot b \cdot b \cdot b \cdot b$ **5.** $^-200$ **6.** $^-4w^3$ **7.** 0   **8.** c
9. cannot be simplified   **10.** $^-40b^2$ **11.** $15k$ **12.** $21t + 28$
13. $^-4a - 24$ **14.** $6x - 15$ **15.** $^-9b + c + 6$
16. $x = 5$ **Check** $^-4 = x - 9$
$$^-4 = \underbrace{5 - 9}$$
$$^-4 = \ ^-4$$

17. $w = {}^-11$ **Check** $^-7w = 77$
$$\underbrace{^-7(^-11)} = 77$$
$$77 \ = 77$$

18. $p = {}^-14$ **Check** $^-p = 14$
$$\underbrace{^-1(^-14)} = 14$$
$$14 \ = 14$$

19. $a = 3$ **Check** $^-15 = \ ^-3(a + 2)$
$$^-15 = \ ^-3(3 + 2)$$
$$^-15 = \ ^-3(5)$$
$$^-15 = \ ^-15$$

20. $n = {}^-8$ **21.** $m = 15$ **22.** $x = {}^-1$ **23.** $m = 2$
24. $b = 54$ **25.** $c = 0$ **26.** Equations will vary. Two possibilities are $x - 5 = {}^-9$ and $^-24 = 6y$.

Section 4.6 (pages 365–373)

1. $P = 36$ cm   **3.** $P = 100$ in.   **5.** $P = 4$ miles   **7.** $P = 88$ mm
9. $s = 30$ ft   **11.** $s = 1$ mm   **13.** $s = 23$ yards   **15.** $s = 2$ ft
17. $P = 28$ yd   **19.** $P = 70$ cm   **21.** $P = 72$ ft   **23.** $P = 26$ in.

25. $l = 9$ cm   **Check** 9 cm + 9 cm + 6 cm + 6 cm = 30 cm
27. $w = 1$ mile   **Check** 4 mi + 4 mi + 1 mi + 1 mi = 10 mi
29. $w = 2$ ft   **Check** 6 ft + 6 ft + 2 ft + 2 ft = 16 ft
31. $l = 2$ m   **Check** 2 m + 2 m + 1 m + 1 m = 6 m
33. $P = 208$ m   **35.** $P = 320$ ft   **37.** $P = 54$ mm   **39.** $P = 48$ ft
41. $P = 78$ in.   **43.** $P = 125$ m   **45.** ? = 40 cm   **47.** ? = 12 in.
49. (a) Sketches will vary.   **(b)** Formula for perimeter of an
equilateral triangle is $P = 3s$, where s is the length of one side.
(c) The formula will *not* work for other kinds of triangles because
the sides will have different lengths.   **51. (a)** 140 miles
(b) 350 miles   **(c)** 560 miles   **52. (a)** 70 miles
(b) 175 miles   **(c)** 280 miles   **(d)** The rate is half of 70 miles
per hour, so the distance will be half as far; divide each result in
Exercise 51 by 2.   **53. (a)** 50 hours   **(b)** 60 hours   **(c)** 150 hours
54. (a) 61 miles per hour   **(b)** 57 miles per hour
(c) 65 miles per hour

Section 4.7 (pages 374–383)

1. $A = 77$ ft^2 **3.** $A = 100$ m^2 **5.** $A = 775$ mm^2 **7.** $A = 36$ in.^{2}
9. $A = 105$ cm^2 **11.** $A = 72$ ft^2 **13.** $A = 625$ mi^2
15. $A = 1$ m^2 **17.** $l = 6$ ft   **Check** $A = 6$ ft • 3 ft; $A = 18$ ft^2
19. $w = 80$ yd   **Check** $A = 90$ yd • 80 yd; $A = 7200$ yd^2
21. $l = 14$ in.   **Check** $A = 14$ in. • 11 in.; $A = 154$ in.^{2}
23. $s = 6$ m   **25.** $s = 2$ ft   **27.** $h = 20$ cm
Check $A = 25$ cm • 20 cm; $A = 500$ cm^2 **29.** $b = 17$ in.
Check $A = 17$ in. • 13 in. ; $A = 221$ in.^{2} **31.** $h = 1$ m
Check $A = 9$ m • 1 m; $A = 9$ m^2 **33.** Height is not part of
perimeter. Square units are used for area, not perimeter.
$P = 25$ cm + 25 cm + 25 cm + 25 cm; $P = 100$ cm
35. Square; $P = 180$ in.; $A = 2025$ in.^{2} **37.** Rectangle; $P = 96$ ft;
$A = 351$ ft^2 **39.** Parallelogram; $P = 60$ cm; $A = 180$ cm^2
41. $P = 48$ m; $A = 144$ m^2 **43.** $108   **45.** $725   **47.** 53 yd
49. $P = 52$ ft; $A = 169$ ft^2; 21 ft^2 for each camper (rounded)
51.
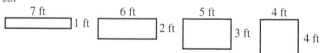
52. (a) 5 ft by 1 ft has area of 5 ft^2; 4 ft by 2 ft has area of 8 ft^2; 3 ft by 3 ft
has area of 9 ft^2 **(b)** The square plot 3 ft by 3 ft has the greatest area.
53.

54. (a) 7 ft^2, 12 ft^2, 15 ft^2, 16 ft^2 **(b)** Square plots have the greatest area.

Summary Exercises on Perimeter and Area (pages 381–385)

1. Rectangle; $P = 32$ m; $A = 39$ m^2
2. Square; $P = 104$ ft; $A = 676$ ft^2
3. Parallelogram; $P = 34$ yd; $A = 56$ yd^2
4. Rectangle; $P = 36$ cm; $A = 80$ cm^2
5. Square; $P = 36$ in.; $A = 81$ in.^{2}
6. Parallelogram; $P = 30$ m; $A = 45$ m^2
7. Rectangle; $P = 26$ ft; $A = 36$ ft^2
8. Parallelogram; $P = 188$ ft; $A = 2100$ ft^2
9. $w = 1$ ft

7 ft
1 ft ⌐———————————⌐ 1 ft
7 ft
Check 7 ft + 7 ft + 1 ft + 1 ft = 16 ft

10. $b = 5$ yd

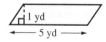
1 yd
5 yd
Check $A = 5$ yd • 1 yd
$A = 5$ yd^2

11. $s = 6$ in.

6 in.
6 in.
Check $A = 6$ in. • 6 in.
$A = 36$ in.^{2}

12. $w = 2$ m

42 m
2 m
Check $A = 42$ m • 2 m
$A = 84$ m^2

13. $s = 16$ cm

16 cm
16 cm   16 cm
16 cm
Check $P = 16$ cm + 16 cm +
16 cm + 16 cm = 64 cm

14. $l = 15$ ft

9 ft
15 ft
Check $P = 15$ ft + 15 ft + 9 ft + 9 ft
= 48 ft

15. 504 meters of fencing   **16.** 13,000 yd^2 − 5000 yd^2 = 8000 yd^2
17. 9 inches   **18.** 176 cm of braid   **19.** 7(15 ft^2) = 105 ft^2 of fabric;
7(16 ft) = 112 ft of binding   **20.** 48 ft

Section 4.8 (pages 386–396)

1. $14 + x$ or $x + 14$ **3.** $^-5 + x$ or $x + ^-5$ **5.** $20 - x$
7. $x - 9$ **9.** $x - 4$ **11.** ^-6x **13.** $2x$ **15.** $\frac{x}{2}$ **17.** $2x + 8$ or
$8 + 2x$ **19.** $7x - 10$ **21.** $2x + x$ or $x + 2x$
23. $4n - 2 = 26$; $n = 7$ **Check** $4 • 7 - 2$ does equal 26
$\underbrace{28} - 2$
26
25. $2n + n = ^-15$ or $n + 2n = ^-15$; $n = ^-5$
Check $2 • ^-5 + ^-5$ does equal $^-15$
$\underbrace{^-10} + ^-5$
$^-15$
27. $5n + 12 = 7n$; $n = 6$ **Check** $5 • 6 + 12 = 7 • 6$
$\underbrace{30} + 12 = \underbrace{42}$
$42 = 42$
29. $30 - 3n = 2 + n$; $n = 7$ **Check** $30 - 3 • 7 = 2 + 7$
$30 - \underbrace{21} = \underbrace{9}$
$9 = 9$
31. Let w be Ricardo's original weight. $w + 15 - 28 + 5 = 177$.
He weighed 185 pounds originally.   **33.** Let c be the number of
cookies the children ate. $18 - c + 36 = 49$. Her children ate
5 cookies.   **35.** Let p be the number of pens in each box.
$6p - 32 - 35 = 5$. There were 12 pens in each box.   **37.** Let d be
each member's dues. $14d + 340 - 575 = ^-25$. Each member
paid $15.   **39.** Let a be Tamu's age. $4a - 75 = a$. Tamu is
25 years old.   **41.** Let m be the amount Brenda spent. $2m - 3 = 81$.
Brenda spent $42.   **43.** Let b be the number of pieces in each bag.
$5b - 3 • 48 = b$. There were 36 pieces of candy in each bag.
45. Let d be the daily amount for an infant. $2d - 4 = 18$. An infant
should receive 11 mg of iron.

Section 4.9 (pages 396–401)

1. a is my age; $a + 9$ is my sister's age. $a + a + 9 = 51$. I am 21;
my sister is 30.   **3.** m is husband's earnings; $m + 1500$ is Lien's.
$m + m + 1500 = 37,500$. Husband earned $18,000; Lien earned
$19,500.   **5.** m is printer's cost; $5m$ is computer's cost;
$5m + m = 1320. Printer cost $220; computer cost $1100.
7. Shorter piece is x; longer piece is $x + 10$. So, $x + x + 10 = 78$.
Shorter piece is 34 cm; longer piece is 44 cm.   **9.** Longer piece is x;

shorter piece is $x - 7$. So, $x + x - 7 = 31$. Longer piece is 19 ft; shorter piece is 12 ft. **11.** s is number of Senators; $5s - 65$ is number of Representatives. $s + 5s - 65 = 535$. 100 Senators; 435 Representatives **13.** First part is x; second part is x; third part is $x + 25$. So, $x + x + x + 25 = 706$. First part is 227 m; second part is 227 m; third part is 252 m. **15.** Length is 19 yd. **17.** Length is 12 ft; width is 6 ft. **19.** Length is 13 in.; width is 5 in. **21.** $P = 52$ in.; $A = 168$ in.^{2}

Chapter 5   Positive and Negative Fractions

Taken from *Prealgebra & Introductory Algebra* by Lial, et. al. (0321578732)

Section 5.1 (pages 404–414)

1. $\frac{5}{8}, \frac{3}{8}$ **3.** $\frac{2}{3}, \frac{1}{3}$ **5.** $\frac{3}{2}, \frac{1}{2}$ **7.** $\frac{11}{6}, \frac{1}{6}$ **9.** $\frac{2}{11}, \frac{3}{11}, \frac{4}{11}$ **11.** $\frac{13}{71}, \frac{58}{71}$

13. (a) $\frac{6}{20}$; (b) $\frac{19}{20}$ **15.** N: 3; D: 4; 4 equal parts **17.** N: 12; D: 7; 7 equal parts **19.** Proper: $\frac{1}{3}, \frac{5}{8}, \frac{7}{16}$; Improper: $\frac{8}{5}, \frac{6}{6}, \frac{12}{2}$

21.

23.

25.

27. $-\frac{3}{4}$ pound **29.** $\frac{3}{10}$ mile **31.** $\frac{2}{5}$ **33.** 0 **35.** (a) $\frac{12}{24}$ (b) $\frac{8}{24}$ (c) $\frac{16}{24}$ (d) $\frac{6}{24}$ (e) $\frac{18}{24}$ (f) $\frac{4}{24}$ (g) $\frac{20}{24}$ (h) $\frac{3}{24}$ (i) $\frac{9}{24}$ (j) $\frac{15}{24}$

37. (a) $-\frac{1}{3}$ (b) $-\frac{2}{3}$ (c) $-\frac{2}{3}$ (d) $-\frac{1}{3}$ (e) $-\frac{2}{3}$ (f) Some possibilities are: $-\frac{4}{12} = -\frac{1}{3}; -\frac{8}{24} = -\frac{1}{3}; -\frac{20}{30} = -\frac{2}{3}; -\frac{24}{36} = -\frac{2}{3}.$

39. (a) $\frac{1467}{3912}$ (b) Divide 3912 by 8 to get 489; multiply 3 by 489 to get 1467. **40.** (a) $\frac{4256}{5472}$ (b) Divide 5472 by 9 to get 608; multiply 7 by 608 to get 4256. **41.** (a) $-\frac{1}{5}$ (b) Divide 3485 by 2, by 3, and by 5 to see that dividing by 5 gives 697. Or divide 3485 by 697 to get 5. **42.** (a) $-\frac{1}{6}$ (b) Divide 4902 by 4, by 6, and by 8 to see that dividing by 6 gives 817. Or divide 4902 by 817 to get 6. **43.** You cannot do it if you want the numerator to be a whole number, because 5 does not divide into 18 evenly. You could use multiples of 5 as the denominator, such as 10, 15, 20, etc. **45.** 10 **47.** -1 **49.** -6 **51.** 3 **53.** 2 **55.** -9 **57.** 1 **59.** -8

61. $\frac{2}{5}$ is unshaded. **63.** $\frac{5}{8}$ is unshaded.

65. One possibility is shown. ○▢▨▢▢▢▢△△△

67. One possibility is shown.(!!)! ! !, . . . ? ? ?

Section 5.2 (pages 415–426)

1. (a) yes (b) No, 5 is a common factor. (c) yes (d) yes (e) No, 3 is a common factor. (f) No, 7 is a common factor. **3.** (a) $\frac{2}{3}$ (b) $\frac{2}{3}$ (c) $-\frac{1}{4}$ (d) $-\frac{1}{2}$ (e) $\frac{8}{9}$ (f) $-\frac{2}{5}$

5. comp. prime comp. neither prime prime comp. comp. **7.** $2 \cdot 3$ **9.** $2 \cdot 2 \cdot 5$ **11.** $5 \cdot 5$ **13.** $2 \cdot 2 \cdot 3 \cdot 3$ **15.** (a) $2 \cdot 2 \cdot 11$ (b) $2 \cdot 2 \cdot 2 \cdot 11$ **17.** (a) $3 \cdot 5 \cdot 5$ (b) $2 \cdot 2 \cdot 17$ (c) $3 \cdot 3 \cdot 3 \cdot 7$

19. $\frac{\cancel{2} \cdot \cancel{2} \cdot \cancel{2}}{\cancel{2} \cdot \cancel{2} \cdot \cancel{2} \cdot 2} = \frac{1}{2}$ **21.** $\frac{\cancel{2} \cdot \cancel{2} \cdot \cancel{2} \cdot \cancel{2} \cdot 2}{\cancel{2} \cdot \cancel{2} \cdot \cancel{2} \cdot \cancel{2} \cdot 3} = \frac{2}{3}$ **23.** $\frac{2 \cdot \cancel{7}}{3 \cdot \cancel{7}} = \frac{2}{3}$

25. $\frac{\cancel{2} \cdot 2 \cdot \cancel{3} \cdot 3}{\cancel{2} \cdot \cancel{3} \cdot 7} = \frac{6}{7}$ **27.** $\frac{2 \cdot 5 \cdot 5}{3 \cdot 3 \cdot 7}$ already in lowest terms

29. $\frac{\cancel{3} \cdot \cancel{3} \cdot 3}{\cancel{3} \cdot \cancel{3} \cdot 5} = \frac{3}{5}$ **31.** $\frac{\cancel{2} \cdot 2 \cdot \cancel{3}}{\cancel{2} \cdot \cancel{3} \cdot 3} = \frac{2}{3}$ **33.** $\frac{\cancel{5} \cdot 7}{2 \cdot 2 \cdot 2 \cdot \cancel{5}} = \frac{7}{8}$

35. $\frac{\cancel{2} \cdot \cancel{3} \cdot \cancel{3} \cdot \cancel{5}}{2 \cdot 2 \cdot \cancel{3} \cdot \cancel{3} \cdot \cancel{5}} = \frac{1}{2}$ **37.** $\frac{2 \cdot \cancel{3} \cdot \cancel{5} \cdot \cancel{7}}{3 \cdot \cancel{3} \cdot \cancel{5} \cdot \cancel{7}} = \frac{2}{3}$

39. $\frac{\cancel{3} \cdot \cancel{11} \cdot 13}{\cancel{3} \cdot 3 \cdot 5 \cdot \cancel{11}} = \frac{13}{15}$ **41.** (a) $\frac{1}{4}$ (b) $\frac{1}{2}$ (c) $\frac{1}{10}$ (d) $\frac{60}{60} = 1$

43. (a) $\frac{1}{3}$ (b) $\frac{1}{6}$ (c) $\frac{1}{2}$ **45.** (a) $\frac{5}{24}$ (b) $\frac{2}{3}$ (c) $\frac{1}{8}$ **47.** (a) The result of dividing 3 by 3 is 1, so 1 should be written above and below all the slashes. The numerator is $1 \cdot 1$, so the correct answer is $\frac{1}{4}$. (b) You must divide numerator and denominator by the *same* number. The fraction is already in lowest terms because 9 and 16 have no common factor besides 1. **49.** $\frac{2c}{5}$ **51.** $\frac{4}{7}$ **53.** $\frac{6r}{5s}$ **55.** $\frac{1}{7n^2}$ **57.** already in lowest terms **59.** $\frac{7}{9y}$ **61.** $\frac{7k}{2}$ **63.** $\frac{1}{3}$ **65.** $\frac{c}{d}$ **67.** $\frac{6ab}{c}$ **69.** already in lowest terms **71.** $3eg^2$

Section 5.3 (pages 427–438)

1. $-\frac{3}{16}$ **3.** $\frac{9}{10}$ **5.** $\frac{1}{2}$ **7.** -6 **9.** 36 **11.** $\frac{15}{4y}$ **13.** $\frac{1}{2}$ **15.** $\frac{6}{5}$ **17.** -9 **19.** $-\frac{1}{6}$ **21.** $\frac{11}{15d}$ **23.** b **25.** (a) Forgot to write 1s in numerator when dividing out common factors. Answer is $\frac{1}{6}$. (b) Used reciprocal of $\frac{2}{3}$ in multiplication, but the reciprocal is used only in division. Correct answer is $\frac{16}{9}$. **27.** (a) Forgot to use reciprocal of $\frac{4}{1}$; correct answer is $\frac{1}{6}$. (b) Used reciprocal of $\frac{5}{6}$ instead of reciprocal of $\frac{10}{9}$; correct answer is $\frac{3}{4}$. **29.** Rewrite division as multiplication. Leave the first number (dividend) the same. Change the second number (divisor) to its reciprocal by "flipping" it. Then multiply.

31. $\frac{4}{15}$ **33.** $-\frac{9}{32}$ **35.** 21 **37.** 15 **39.** undefined **41.** $-\frac{55}{12}$ **43.** $8b$ **45.** $\frac{3}{5d}$ **47.** $\frac{2x^2}{w}$ **49.** $\frac{3}{10}$ yd^2 **51.** 80 dispensers **53.** earn \$9300; borrow \$3100 **55.** 9 trips **57.** About 78 infield players **59.** 3200 times **61.** (a) \$58,000 (b) \$11,600 **63.** \$25,375 **65.** 7 million horses **67.** 154 million dogs and cats

Section 5.4 (pages 439–452)

1. $\frac{7}{8}$ **3.** $-\frac{1}{2}$ **5.** $\frac{1}{2}$ **7.** $-\frac{9}{40}$ **9.** $-\frac{13}{24}$ **11.** $-\frac{3}{5}$ **13.** $-\frac{7}{18}$ **15.** $\frac{8}{7}$

17. $-\frac{3}{8}$ **19.** $\frac{3 + 5c}{15}$ **21.** $\frac{10 - m}{2m}$ **23.** $\frac{8}{b^2}$ **25.** $\frac{bc + 21}{7b}$

27. $\frac{-4 - cd}{c^2}$ **29.** $-\frac{44}{105}$ **31.** You cannot add or subtract until all the fractional pieces are the same size. **33.** (a) $\frac{15}{20} + \frac{8}{20} = \frac{23}{20}$ Cannot add fractions with unlike denominators; use 20 as the LCD. (b) When rewriting fractions with 18 as the denominator, you must multiply denominator and numerator by the same number. The correct answer is $\frac{15}{18} - \frac{8}{18} = \frac{7}{18}$.

35. (a) $\frac{1}{12}$; $\frac{1}{12}$ Addition is commutative. (b) $\frac{1}{3}$; $-\frac{1}{3}$ Subtraction is *not* commutative. (c) $-\frac{3}{5}$; $-\frac{3}{5}$ Multiplication is commutative. (d) 6; $\frac{1}{6}$ Division is *not* commutative. **36.** (a) 0; 0; The sum of a number and its opposite is 0. (b) 1; 1; When a nonzero number is divided by itself, the quotient is 1. (c) $\frac{5}{6}$; $-\frac{17}{20}$; Multiplying by 1 leaves a number unchanged. (d) 1; 1; A number times its reciprocal is 1. **37.** $\frac{47}{60}$ in. **39.** $\frac{23}{24}$ cubic yard **41.** $\frac{3}{4}$ acre **43.** $\frac{23}{50}$ of workers **45.** $\frac{4}{25}$ of workers **47.** $\frac{7}{24}$ of the day; 7 hours **49.** $\frac{1}{8}$ of the day **51.** $\frac{5}{16}$ inch **53.** $\frac{1}{12}$ mile

Section 5.5 (pages 453–466)

1.

$-2\frac{1}{3}$ $2\frac{1}{3}$

3.

$-\frac{3}{2}$ $\frac{3}{2}$

5. $\frac{9}{2}$ **7.** $-\frac{8}{5}$ **9.** $\frac{19}{8}$ **11.** $-\frac{57}{10}$ **13.** $\frac{161}{15}$ **15.** $4\frac{1}{3}$ **17.** $-2\frac{1}{2}$ **19.** $3\frac{2}{3}$

21. $-5\frac{2}{3}$ **23.** $11\frac{3}{4}$ **25.** $7\frac{7}{8}$; $2 \cdot 4 = 8$ **27.** $1\frac{5}{21}$; $3 \div 3 = 1$

29. $5\frac{1}{2}$; $4 + 2 = 6$ **31.** $3\frac{2}{3}$; $4 - 1 = 3$ **33.** $\frac{17}{18}$; $6 \div 6 = 1$

35. $6\frac{1}{5}$; $8 - 2 = 6$ **37.** $P = 7$ in.; $A = 3\frac{1}{16}$ in.^{2}

39. $P = 19\frac{1}{2}$ yd; $A = 21\frac{1}{8}$ yd^2 **41.** $13 + 9 = 22$ ft; $21\frac{1}{6}$ ft

43. $2 \cdot 6 = 12$ ounces; $9\frac{5}{8}$ ounces **45.** $4 - 2 = 2$ miles;

$2\frac{3}{10}$ miles **47.** $4 \cdot 5 = 20$ yd; $18\frac{3}{4}$ yd **49.** $\frac{5}{8}$ mile; **51.** $6\frac{3}{8}$ miles

53. $21\frac{3}{8}$ in. **55.** $24 + 35 + 24 + 35 = 118$ in.; $116\frac{1}{2}$ in.

57. $25,730 \div 10 = 2573$ anchors; 2480 anchors

59. $(4 \cdot 22) + (5 \cdot 23) + (3 \cdot 24) + (12 \cdot 1) = 287$ in.; $280\frac{1}{8}$ in.

Summary Exercises on Fractions (pages 467–486)

1. (a) $\frac{3}{8}$; $\frac{5}{8}$ (b) $\frac{4}{5}$; $\frac{1}{5}$ **2.**

$-\frac{2}{3}$ $\frac{2}{3}$

3. (a) 24 (b) 4

4. (a) 1 (b) -4 (c) 9 **5.** (a) $2 \cdot 2 \cdot 2 \cdot 3 \cdot 3$ (b) $3 \cdot 5 \cdot 7$

6. (a) $\frac{4}{5}$ (b) $\frac{7}{8}$ **7.** $\frac{1}{2}$ **8.** $-\frac{5}{24}$ **9.** $\frac{17}{16}$ **10.** $\frac{5}{6}$ **11.** $-\frac{2}{15}$ **12.** $-\frac{3}{8}$

13. 56 **14.** $\frac{11}{24}$ **15.** $-\frac{7}{6}$ **16.** $-\frac{19}{12}$ **17.** $\frac{25}{12}$ **18.** 35 **19.** $7\frac{7}{12}$;

$5 + 3 = 8$ **20.** $11\frac{3}{7}$; $2 \cdot 5 = 10$ **21.** $3\frac{3}{10}$; $6 - 3 = 3$

22. $\frac{16}{35}$; $2 \div 4 = \frac{2}{4}$ or $\frac{1}{2}$ **23.** 4; $5 \div 1 = 5$ **24.** $2\frac{2}{3}$; $3 - 1 = 2$

25. (a) $2\frac{1}{16}$ in. (b) $\frac{5}{16}$ in. **26.** $P = 3\frac{1}{2}$ in.; $A = \frac{49}{64}$ in.^{2}

27. 12 batches **28.** 6¢ **29.** Not sure, 225 adults; Real, 675 adults; Imaginary, 600 adults **30.** diameter $= \frac{1}{4}$ in.; $P = 4\frac{1}{2}$ in.

31. 23 bottles **32.** 11 lots

Section 5.6 (pages 469–476)

1. $\frac{9}{16}$ **3.** $\frac{8}{125}$ **5.** $-\frac{1}{27}$ **7.** $\frac{1}{32}$ **9.** $\frac{49}{100}$ **11.** $\frac{36}{25}$ or $1\frac{11}{25}$

13. $\frac{12}{25}$ **15.** $\frac{1}{100}$ **17.** $-\frac{3}{2}$ or $-1\frac{1}{2}$ **19.** (a) The answers are

$\frac{1}{4}$, $-\frac{1}{8}$, $\frac{1}{16}$, $-\frac{1}{32}$, $\frac{1}{64}$, $-\frac{1}{128}$, $\frac{1}{256}$, $-\frac{1}{512}$. (b) When a negative number is raised to an even power, the answer is positive. When a negative number is raised to an odd power, the answer is negative. **20.** (a) Ask yourself, "What number, times itself, is 4?" This is the numerator. Then ask, "What number, times itself, is 9?" This is the denominator. The number under the ketchup is either $\frac{2}{3}$ or $-\frac{2}{3}$. (b) The number under the ketchup is $-\frac{1}{3}$. because $\left(-\frac{1}{3}\right)\left(-\frac{1}{3}\right)\left(-\frac{1}{3}\right) = -\frac{1}{27}$. (c) Either $\frac{1}{2}$ or $-\frac{1}{2}$. (d) No real number works, because both $\left(\frac{3}{4}\right)^2$ and $\left(-\frac{3}{4}\right)^2$ give a *positive* result.

(e) Either $\frac{1}{3}$ or $-\frac{1}{3}$ inside one set of parentheses and $\frac{1}{2}$ or $-\frac{1}{2}$ inside the other. **21.** -4 **23.** $\frac{5}{16}$ **25.** $\frac{1}{3}$ **27.** $\frac{1}{6}$ **29.** $-\frac{17}{24}$ **31.** $-\frac{4}{27}$

33. $\frac{1}{36}$ **35.** $\frac{9}{64}$ in.^{2} **37.** $\frac{19}{10}$ or $1\frac{9}{10}$ miles **39.** 4 **41.** $-\frac{25}{2}$ or $-12\frac{1}{2}$

43. $\frac{1}{14}$ **45.** $\frac{5}{18}$ **47.** -8 **49.** $\frac{9}{100}$

Section 5.7 (pages 477–486)

1. $a = 30$ **Check** $\frac{1}{3}(30) = 10$

$10 = 10$

3. $b = -24$ **Check** $-20 = \frac{5}{6}(-24)$

$-20 = -20$

5. $c = 6$ **Check** $-\frac{7}{2}(6) = -21$

$-21 = -21$

7. $m = \frac{3}{4}$ **Check** $\frac{9}{16} = \frac{3}{4}\left(\frac{3}{4}\right)$

$\frac{9}{16} = \frac{9}{16}$

9. $d = -\frac{6}{5}$ **Check** $\frac{3}{10} = -\frac{1}{4}\left(-\frac{6}{5}\right)$

$\frac{3}{10} = \frac{3}{10}$

11. $n = 12$ **Check** $\frac{1}{6}(12) + 7 = 9$

$2 + 7 = 9$

$9 = 9$

13. $r = -9$ **Check** $-10 = \frac{5}{3}(-9) + 5$

$-10 = -15 + 5$

$-10 = -10$

15. $x = 24$ **Check** $\frac{3}{8}(24) - 9 = 0$

$9 - 9 = 0$

$0 = 0$

17. $y = 45$ **19.** $n = -18$ **21.** $x = \frac{1}{12}$ **23.** $b = -\frac{1}{8}$

25. (a) $\frac{1}{6}(18) + 1 = -2$

$$3 + 1 = -2$$
$$4 \neq -2$$

Does *not* balance; correct solution is -18.

(b) $-\frac{3}{2} = \frac{9}{4}\left(-\frac{2}{3}\right)$

$$-\frac{3}{2} = -\frac{3}{2}$$

Balances, so $-\frac{2}{3}$ is correct solution.

27. Some possibilities are: $\frac{1}{2}x = 4$; $-\frac{1}{4}a = -2$; $\frac{3}{4}b = 6$.

29. Let a be the man's age.

$$109 = 100 + \frac{a}{2}$$

The man is 18 years old.

31. Let a be the woman's age.

$$122 = 100 + \frac{a}{2}$$

The woman is 44 years old.

33. Let p be the penny size. $\frac{p}{4} + \frac{1}{2} = 3$. The penny size is 10.

35. Let p be the penny size. $\frac{p}{4} + \frac{1}{2} = \frac{5}{2}$. The penny size is 8.   **37.** Let h be the man's height. $\frac{11}{2}h - 220 = 209$. The man is 78 in. tall.   **39.** Let h be the woman's height. $\frac{11}{2}h - 220 = 132$. The woman is 64 in. tall.

Section 5.8 (pages 487–494)

1. $P = 202$ m; $A = 1914$ m^2 **3.** $P = 5$ ft; $A = \frac{27}{32}$ ft^2

5. $P = 26\frac{1}{4}$ yd; $A = 30\frac{3}{4}$ yd^2 **7.** $P = \frac{454}{15}$ yd or $30\frac{4}{15}$ yd; $A = \frac{115}{3}$ yd^2 or $38\frac{1}{3}$ yd^2 **9.** $A = 1716$ m^2 **11.** $A = \frac{63}{8}$ ft^2 or $7\frac{7}{8}$ ft^2

13. 132 m of curbing; 726 m^2 of sod   **15.** Rectangular solid; $V = 528$ cm^3

17. Rectangular solid or cube; $V = 15\frac{5}{8}$ in.^{3} **19.** Pyramid; $V = 800$ cm^3

21. $V = 106\frac{2}{3}$ ft^3 **23.** $V = 18$ in.^{3} **25.** $V = 651,775$ m^3

Chapter 5 Review Exercises (pages 503–504)

1. $\frac{2}{5}$; $\frac{1}{5}$ **2.** $\frac{3}{10}$; $\frac{7}{10}$ **3.**

4. (a) -4 **(b)** 8 **(c)** -1 **5.** $\frac{7}{8}$ **6.** $\frac{3}{5}$ **7.** already in lowest terms

8. $\frac{3x}{8}$ **9.** $\frac{1}{5b}$ **10.** $\frac{4n}{7m^2}$ **11.** $\frac{1}{16}$ **12.** -12 **13.** $\frac{8}{27}$ **14.** $\frac{1}{6x}$ **15.** $2a^2$

16. $\frac{6}{7k}$ **17.** $\frac{5}{24}$ **18.** $-\frac{2}{15}$ **19.** $\frac{19}{6}$ or $3\frac{1}{6}$ **20.** $\frac{3}{2}$ or $1\frac{1}{2}$ **21.** $\frac{4n+15}{20}$

22. $\frac{3y-70}{10y}$ **23.** $1\frac{5}{13}$; $2 \div 2 = 1$ **24.** $2\frac{1}{2}$; $7 - 5 = 2$ **25.** $4\frac{1}{20}$; $2 + 2 = 4$ **26.** $-\frac{27}{64}$ **27.** $\frac{1}{36}$ **28.** $-\frac{4}{5}$ **29.** $\frac{7}{6}$ or $1\frac{1}{6}$ **30.** 10

31. $-\frac{4}{27}$ **32.** $w = 20$ **33.** $r = -15$ **34.** $x = \frac{1}{2}$ **35.** $A = 14$ ft^2

36. Rectangular solid; $V = 32\frac{1}{2}$ in.^{3} **37.** Pyramid; $V = 93\frac{1}{3}$ yd^3

38. $\frac{1}{4}$ pound; $7\frac{1}{2}$ pounds   **39.** $\frac{5}{6}$ hour; $10\frac{11}{12}$ hours   **40.** 12 preschoolers, 40 toddlers, 8 infants   **41.** $P = 2\frac{1}{10}$ miles; $A = \frac{9}{40}$ mi^2

Chapter 5 Test (pages 505–506)

1. $\frac{5}{6}$; $\frac{1}{6}$ **2.**

3. $\frac{1}{4}$

4. already in lowest terms   **5.** $\frac{2a^2}{3b}$ **6.** $\frac{13}{15}$ **7.** -2 **8.** $-\frac{7}{40}$ **9.** 14

10. $-\frac{2}{27}$ **11.** $\frac{25}{8}$ or $3\frac{1}{8}$ **12.** $\frac{4}{9}$ **13.** $\frac{9}{16}$ **14.** $\frac{4}{7y}$ **15.** $\frac{24-n}{4n}$

16. $\frac{10+3a}{15}$ **17.** $\frac{1}{18b}$ **18.** $-\frac{1}{18}$ **19.** $-\frac{31}{30}$ or $-1\frac{1}{30}$

20. $5 \div 1 = 5$; $\frac{64}{15}$ or $4\frac{4}{15}$ **21.** $3 - 2 = 1$; $\frac{3}{2}$ or $1\frac{1}{2}$ **22.** $d = 35$

23. $t = -\frac{15}{7}$ or $-2\frac{1}{7}$ **24.** $b = 8$ **25.** $x = -15$ **26.** $A = 52$ m^2

27. $A = \frac{117}{2}$ yd^2 or $58\frac{1}{2}$ yd^2 **28.** Rectangular solid; $V = 6480$ m^3

29. Pyramid; $V = 16$ yd^3 **30.** $14\frac{3}{4}$ hours; $1\frac{5}{6}$ hours

31. $\frac{7}{2}$ days or $3\frac{1}{2}$ days   **32.** 7392 students work

Chapter 6 Positive and Negative Decimals/Statistics

Taken from *Prealgebra & Introductory Algebra* by Lial, et. al. (0321578732)

Section 6.1 (pages 516–538)

1. 7; 0; 4   **3.** 5; 1; 8   **5.** 4; 7; 0   **7.** 1; 6; 3   **9.** 1; 8; 9   **11.** 6; 2; 1

13. 410.25   **15.** 6.5432   **17.** 5406.045   **19.** $\frac{7}{10}$ **21.** $13\frac{2}{5}$ **23.** $\frac{7}{20}$

25. $\frac{33}{50}$ **27.** $10\frac{17}{100}$ **29.** $\frac{3}{50}$ **31.** $\frac{41}{200}$ **33.** $5\frac{1}{500}$ **35.** $\frac{343}{500}$

37. five tenths   **39.** seventy-eight hundredths   **41.** one hundred five thousandths   **43.** twelve and four hundredths   **45.** one and seventy-five thousandths   **47.** 6.7   **49.** 0.32   **51.** 420.008   **53.** 0.0703   **55.** 75.030

57. Anne should not say "and" because that denotes a decimal point.

59. ten thousandths inch; $\frac{10}{1000} = \frac{1}{100}$ inch   **61.** 12 pounds   **63.** 3-C

65. 4-A   **67.** one and six hundred two thousandths centimeters

69. millionths, ten-millionths, hundred-millionths, billionths; these match the words on the left side of the chart with "ths" attached.

70. First place to the left of the decimal point is ones. "Oneths" would mean a fraction with a denominator of 1, which would equal 1 or more. Anything that is 1 or more is to the *left* of the decimal point.

71. seventy-two million four hundred thirty-six thousand nine hundred fifty-five hundred-millionths   **72.** six hundred seventy-eight thousand five hundred fifty-four billionths   **73.** eight thousand six and five hundred thousand one millionths   **74.** twenty thousand sixty and five hundred five millionths   **75.** 0.0302040   **76.** 9,876,543,210.100200300

Section 6.2 (pages 517–524)

1. 16.9   **3.** 0.956   **5.** 0.80   **7.** 3.661   **9.** 794.0   **11.** 0.0980

13. 49   **15.** 9.09   **17.** 82.0002   **19.** $0.82   **21.** $1.22   **23.** $0.50

25. $48,650   **27.** $310   **29.** $849   **31.** $500   **33.** $1.00   **35.** $1000

37. (a) 322 miles per hour **(b)** 107 miles per hour **39. (a)** 186.0 miles per hour **(b)** 763.0 miles per hour **41.** Rounds to $0 (zero dollars) because $0.499 is closer to $0 than to $1. **42.** Round $0.499 to the nearest cent to get $0.50. Guideline: Round amounts less than $1.00 to the nearest cent instead of the nearest dollar. **43.** Rounds to $0.00 (zero cents) because $0.0015 is closer to $0.00 than to $0.01. **44.** Both round to $0.60. Rounding to the nearest thousandth (tenth of a cent) would allow you to identify $0.597 as less than $0.601.

Section 6.3 (pages 525–534)

1. 17.72 **3.** 11.98 **5.** 115.861 **7.** 59.323 **9.** 6 should be written 6.00; sum is 46.22 **11.** $0.3000 = \frac{3000 \div 1000}{10,000 \div 1000} = \frac{3}{10} = 0.3$ **13.** 89.7 **15.** 0.109 **17.** 0.91 **19.** 6.661 **21.** The student subtracted in the wrong order; 15.32 should be on top; correct answer is 7.87 **23. (a)** 24.75 in. **(b)** 3.95 in. **25. (a)** 62.27 in. **(b)** 0.39 in. **27.** 23.013 **29.** −45.75 **31.** −6.69 **33.** −6.99 **35.** −4.279 **37.** −0.0035 **39.** 5.37 **41.** *Estimate:* 20 − 10 = 10; *Exact:* 6.275 **43.** *Estimate:* −7 + 1 = −6; *Exact:* −5.8 **45.** *Estimate:* −40 + (−200) = −240; *Exact:* −237.571 **47.** *Estimate:* 8 + (+50) = 58; *Exact:* 59.23 **49.** *Estimate:* 30 − 20 = 10 million people; *Exact:* 12.1 million people **51.** *Estimate:* 200 + 100 + 90 + 50 + 30 + 20 + 20 = 510 million people; *Exact:* 527.0 million people **53.** *Estimate:* 2 + 2 + 2 = 6 m; *Exact:* 6.09 m, which is 0.31 m less than the rhino's height. **55.** *Estimate:* $20 − $9 = $11; *Exact:* $10.88 **57.** *Estimate:* $5 − 5 = $0; *Exact:* $0.30 **59.** *Estimate:* $19 + 2 + 2 + 10 + 2 = $35; *Exact:* $35.25 **61.** $1939.36 **63.** $3.97 **65.** b = 1.39 cm **67.** q = 7.943 ft

Section 6.4 (pages 535–342)

1. 0.1344 **3.** −159.10 **5.** 15.444 **7.** $34,500.20 **9.** −43.2 **11.** 0.432 **13.** 0.0432 **15.** 0.00432 **17.** 0.0000312 **19.** 0.000009 **21.** 59.6; 4.76; 7226; 32; 803.5; 9. Multiplying by 10, decimal point moves one place to the right; by 100, two places to the right; by 1000, three places to the right. **22.** 5.96; 0.0476; 6.5; 0.32; 8.035; 52.3. Multiplying by 0.1, decimal point moves one place to the left; by 0.01, two places to the left; by 0.001, three places to the left. **23.** *Estimate:* 40 × 5 = 200; *Exact:* 190.08 **25.** *Estimate:* 40 × 40 = 1600; *Exact:* 1558.2 **27.** *Estimate:* 7 × 5 = 35; *Exact:* 30.038 **29.** *Estimate:* 3 × 7 = 21; *Exact:* 19.24165 **31.** unreasonable; $289.00 **33.** reasonable **35.** unreasonable; $4.19 **37.** unreasonable; 9.5 pounds **39.** $945.87 (rounded) **41.** $2.45 (rounded) **43.** $81.61 (rounded) **45.** $20,265 **47. (a)** Area before 1929 ≈ 23.2 in.²; Area today ≈ 16.0 in.² **(b)** 7.2 in.² **49. (a)** 0.43 inch **(b)** 4.3 inches **51.** $984.04; $2207.80 **53.** $76.50 **55.** $4.09 (rounded) **57.** $129.25 **59. (a)** $70.05 **(b)** $25.80

Section 6.5 (pages 543–554)

1. −3.9 **3.** 0.47 **5.** 400.2 **7.** 36 **9.** 0.06 **11.** 6000 **13.** 60 **15.** 0.0006 **17.** 25.3 **19.** 516.67 (rounded) **21.** −26.756 (rounded) **23.** 10,082.647 (rounded) **25.** 0.377; 0.0886; 40.65; 0.91; 3.019; 662.57 **(a)** Dividing by 10, decimal point moves one place to the left; by 100, two places to the left; by 1000, three places to the left. **(b)** The decimal point moved to the *right* when multiplying by 10, by 100, or by 1000; here it moves to the *left* when dividing by 10, by 100, or by 1000. **26.** 402; 3.39; 460; 71; 157.7; 8730 **(a)** Dividing by 0.1, decimal point moves one place to the right; by 0.01, two places to the right; by 0.001, three places to the right. **(b)** The decimal point moved to the *left* when multiplying by 0.1, 0.01, or 0.001; here it moves to the *right* when dividing by 0.1, 0.01, or 0.001. **27.** unreasonable; *Estimate:* 40 ÷ 8 = 5; $8)\overline{37.8}$ with quotient 4.725 **29.** reasonable; *Estimate:* 50 ÷ 50 = 1 **31.** unreasonable; *Estimate:* 300 ÷ 5 = 60; $5.1)\overline{307.02}$ with quotient 60.2 **33.** unreasonable; *Estimate:* 9 ÷ 1 = 9; $1.25)\overline{9.30}$

35. $4.00 (rounded) **37.** $67.08 **39.** $0.30 **41.** $11.92 per hour **43.** 21.2 miles per gallon (rounded) **45.** 7.37 meters (rounded) **47.** 0.08 meter **49.** 22.49 meters **51.** 14.25 **53.** 3.8 **55.** −16.155 **57.** 3.714 **59.** $0.03 (rounded) **61. (a)** 1,583,333 pieces (rounded) **(b)** 26,389 pieces (rounded) **(c)** 440 pieces (rounded) **63.** 100,000 box tops **65.** 2632 box tops (rounded)

Summary Exercises on Decimals (pages 555–556)

1. $\frac{4}{5}$ **2.** $6\frac{1}{250}$ **3.** $\frac{7}{20}$ **4.** ninety-four and five tenths **5.** two and three ten-thousandths **6.** seven hundred six thousandths **7.** 0.05 **8.** 0.0309 **9.** 10.7 **10.** 6.19 **11.** 1.0 **12.** 0.420 **13.** $0.89 **14.** $3.00 **15.** $100 **16.** −0.945 **17.** 49.6199 **18.** −50 **19.** 15.03 **20.** 0.00488 **21.** −2.15 **22.** 9.055 **23.** 18.4009 **24.** −6.995 **25.** −808.9 **26.** 2.12 **27.** 0.04 **28.** P = 52.1 in. **29.** P = 9.735 meters **30.** $1.80 **31.** $87.28 **32. (a)** 169 ft² **(b)** $0.75 (rounded) **33.** 144 ft²; $0.69 (rounded) **34. (a)** 9 days (rounded) **(b)** 15.6 pounds (rounded) **35.** Average weight of food eaten by bee is 0.32 ounce. **36.** 0.112 ounce

Section 6.6 (pages 557–564)

1. 0.5 **3.** 0.75 **5.** 0.3 **7.** 0.9 **9.** 0.6 **11.** 0.875 **13.** 2.25 **15.** 14.7 **17.** 3.625 **19.** 6.333 (rounded) **21.** 0.833 (rounded) **23.** 1.889 (rounded) **25. (a)** A proper fraction like $\frac{5}{9}$ is less than 1, so $\frac{5}{9}$ cannot be equivalent to a decimal number that is greater than 1. **(b)** $\frac{5}{9}$ means $5 \div 9$ or $9)\overline{5}$ so correct answer is 0.556 (rounded). This makes sense because both the fraction and decimal are less than 1. **26. (a)** $2.035 = 2\frac{35}{1000} = 2\frac{7}{200}$, not $2\frac{7}{20}$ **(b)** Adding the whole number part gives 2 + 0.35, which is 2.35 not 2.035. To check, $2.35 = 2\frac{35}{100} = 2\frac{7}{20}$ but $2.035 = 2\frac{35}{1000} = 2\frac{7}{200}$ **27.** Just add the whole number part to 0.375. So $1\frac{3}{8} = 1.375$; $3\frac{3}{8} = 3.375$; $295\frac{3}{8} = 295.375$ **28.** It works only when the fraction part has a one-digit numerator and a denominator of 10, or a two-digit numerator and a denominator of 100, and so on. **29.** $\frac{2}{5}$ **31.** $\frac{5}{8}$ **33.** $\frac{7}{20}$ **35.** 0.35 **37.** $\frac{1}{25}$ **39.** $\frac{3}{20}$ **41.** 0.2 **43.** $\frac{9}{100}$ **45.** shorter; 0.72 inch **47.** too much; 0.005 gram **49.** 0.9991 cm, 1.0007 cm **51.** more; 0.05 inch **53. (a)** < **(b)** = **(c)** > **(d)** < **55.** 0.5399, 0.54, 0.5455 **57.** 5.0079, 5.79, 5.8, 5.804 **59.** 0.6009, 0.609, 0.628, 0.62812 **61.** 2.8902, 3.88, 4.876, 5.8751 **63.** 0.006, 0.043, $\frac{1}{20}$, 0.051 **65.** 0.37, $\frac{3}{8}, \frac{2}{5}$, 0.4001 **67. (a)** red box; green box **(b)** 0.01 inch **69.** 1.4 in. (rounded) **71.** 0.3 in. (rounded) **73.** 0.4 in. (rounded)

Section 6.7 (pages 565–572)

1. 4 **3.** 8 **5.** 3.317 (rounded) **7.** 2.236 (rounded) **9.** 8.544 (rounded) **11.** 10.050 (rounded) **13.** 19 **15.** 31.623 (rounded) **17.** 30 is about halfway between 25 and 36, so $\sqrt{30}$ should be about halfway between 5 and 6, or about 5.5. Using a calculator, $\sqrt{30} \approx 5.477$ Similarly, $\sqrt{26}$ should be a little more than $\sqrt{25}$; by calculator $\sqrt{26} \approx 5.099$ And $\sqrt{35}$ should be a little less than $\sqrt{36}$; by calculator $\sqrt{35} \approx 5.916$ **19.** $\sqrt{1521} = 39$ ft **21.** $\sqrt{289} = 17$ in. **23.** $\sqrt{144} = 12$ mm **25.** $\sqrt{73} \approx 8.5$ in. **27.** $\sqrt{65} \approx 8.1$ yd **29.** $\sqrt{195} \approx 14.0$ cm **31.** $\sqrt{7.94} \approx 2.8$ m **33.** $\sqrt{65.01} \approx 8.1$ cm **35.** $\sqrt{292.32} \approx 17.1$ km **37.** hypotenuse = $\sqrt{65} \approx 8.1$ ft **39.** leg = $\sqrt{360,000} = 600$ m

41. hypotenuse $= \sqrt{48.5} \approx 7.0$ ft   **43.** leg $= \sqrt{135} \approx 11.6$ ft.
45. The student used the formula for finding the hypotenuse but the unknown side is a leg, so use leg $= \sqrt{(20)^2 - (13)^2}$. Also, the final answer should be m, not m². Correct answer is $\sqrt{231} \approx 15.2$ m.   **47.** $\sqrt{16,200} \approx 127.3$ ft
48. (a)

```
              Second
               60 ft
   Third            First
               60 ft
              Home
```

(b) $\sqrt{7200} \approx 84.9$ ft

49. The distance from third to first is the same as the distance from home to second because the baseball diamond is a square.
50. (a) The side length is less than 60 ft.   **(b)** $80^2 = 6400$; $6400 \div 2 = 3200$; $\sqrt{3200} \approx 56.6$ ft

Section 6.8 (pages 573–578)

Please see *Solutions* section for sample *checks* of some odd-numbered exercises. **1.** $h = 4.47$ **3.** $n = -1.4$ **5.** $b = 0.008$
7. $a = 0.29$ **9.** $p = -120$ **11.** $t = 0.7$ **13.** $x = -0.82$
15. $z = 0$ **17.** $c = 0.45$ **19.** $w = 28$ **21.** $p = -40.5$
23. Let d be the adult dose. $0.3\,d = 9$; The adult dose is 30 milligrams.
25. Let d be the number of days. $65.95d + 12 = 275.80$; The saw was rented for 4 days.   **27.** $0.7(220 - a) = 140$; The person is 20 years old.   **28.** $0.7(220 - a) = 126$; The person is 40 years old.
29. $0.7(220 - a) = 134$; $a \approx 28.57$, which rounds to 29. The person is about 29 years old.   **30.** $0.7(220 - a) = 117$; $a \approx 52.86$, which rounds to 53. The person is about 53 years old.

Chapter 7 Ratio/Percent

Taken from *Prealgebra & Introductory Algebra* by Lial, et. al. (0321578732)

Section 7.1 (pages 580–586)

1. $\dfrac{8}{9}$ **3.** $\dfrac{2}{1}$ **5.** $\dfrac{1}{3}$ **7.** $\dfrac{9}{7}$ **9.** $\dfrac{5}{6}$ **11.** $\dfrac{8}{5}$ **13.** $\dfrac{1}{12}$ **15.** $\dfrac{4}{1}$
17. $\dfrac{1}{2}$ **19.** $\dfrac{36}{1}$ **21.** Answers will vary. One possibility is stocking cards of various types in the same ratios as those in the table.
23. *White Christmas* to *It's Now or Never*; *White Christmas* to *I Will Always Love You*; *Candle in the Wind* to *I Want to Hold Your Hand*
25. $\dfrac{6}{1}$ **27.** $\dfrac{38}{17}$ **29.** $\dfrac{1}{4}$ **31.** $\dfrac{34}{35}$

Section 7.2 (pages 587–594)

1. $\dfrac{5 \text{ cups}}{3 \text{ people}}$ **3.** $\dfrac{3 \text{ feet}}{7 \text{ seconds}}$ **5.** $\dfrac{1 \text{ person}}{2 \text{ dresses}}$ **7.** $\dfrac{5 \text{ letters}}{1 \text{ minute}}$ **9.** $\dfrac{21 \text{ dollars}}{2 \text{ visits}}$
11. $\dfrac{18 \text{ miles}}{1 \text{ gallon}}$ **13.** \$12 per hour or \$12/hour   **15.** 5 eggs per chicken or 5 eggs/chicken   **17.** 1.25 pounds/person   **19.** \$103.30/day
21. 325.9; 21.0 (rounded)   **23.** 338.6; 20.9 (rounded)   **25.** 4 ounces for \$3.65, about \$0.913/ounce   **27.** 14 ounces for \$2.89, about \$0.206/ounce
29. 18 ounces for \$1.79, about \$0.099/ounce   **31.** Answers will vary. For example, you might choose Brand B because you like more chicken, so the cost per chicken chunk may actually be the same or less than Brand A.
33. 1.75 pounds/week   **35.** \$12.26/hour   **37. (a)** Radiant \$0.44; IDT \$0.25; Access \$0.235   **(b)** Radiant \$0.088/min, IDT \$0.05/min, Access \$0.047/min; Access America is the best buy.   **39.** For a 15-minute call: Radiant \$0.036/min; IDT \$0.031/min; Access \$0.047/min; IDT is the best buy. For a 20-minute call: Radiant \$0.030/min; IDT \$0.029/min; Access \$0.047/min; IDT is the best buy.   **41.** 0.11 second/meter; 9.09 or 9.1 meters/second (rounded)   **43.** One battery for \$1.79; like getting 3 batteries so \$1.79 $\div$ 3 $\approx$ \$0.597 per battery   **45.** Brand P with the 50¢ coupon is the best buy. (\$3.39 $-$ \$0.50 $=$ \$2.89, \$2.89 $\div$ 16.5 ounces $\approx$ \$0.175 per ounce)   **47.** \$2.92 (rounded) per month for Verizon, T-Mobile, and Nextel; \$3 per month for Sprint.   **48.** Average weekdays per month is

about 21.7; Verizon $\approx$ 18 min/weekday; T-Mobile $\approx$ 28 min/weekday; Nextel and Sprint $\approx$ 23 min/weekday.   **49.** Round to hundredths (nearest cent) to see that T-Mobile is the best buy at \$0.07 per "anytime minute"; Verizon $\approx$ \$0.16; Sprint $\approx$ \$0.12; Nextel $\approx$ \$0.10
50. Verizon $\approx$ \$1.65 per "anytime minute"; T-Mobile $\approx$ \$1.57; Nextel $\approx$ \$1.63; Sprint = \$1.48

Section 7.3 (pages 595–606)

1. $\dfrac{\$9}{12 \text{ cans}} = \dfrac{\$18}{24 \text{ cans}}$ **3.** $\dfrac{200 \text{ adults}}{450 \text{ children}} = \dfrac{4 \text{ adults}}{9 \text{ children}}$ **5.** $\dfrac{120}{150} = \dfrac{8}{10}$
7. $\dfrac{2.2}{3.3} = \dfrac{3.2}{4.8}$ **9.** $\dfrac{3}{5} = \dfrac{3}{5}$; true   **11.** $\dfrac{5}{8} = \dfrac{5}{8}$; true   **13.** $\dfrac{3}{4} \neq \dfrac{2}{3}$; false
15. $54 = 54$; true   **17.** $336 \neq 320$; false   **19.** $2880 \neq 2970$; false
21. $28 = 28$; true   **23.** $42\frac{1}{2} \neq 45$; false   **25.** $66 = 66$; true
27. $\dfrac{17 \text{ hits}}{50 \text{ at bats}} = \dfrac{153 \text{ hits}}{450 \text{ at bats}}$

$50 \cdot 153 = 7650$
$17 \cdot 450 = 7650$ Cross products are equal so the proportion is *true;* they hit equally well.   **29.** $x = 4$ **31.** $x = 2$ **33.** $x = 88$ **35.** $x = 91$
37. $x = 5$ **39.** $x = 10$ **41.** $x \approx 24.44$ (rounded)   **43.** $x = 50.4$ **45.** $x \approx 17.64$ (rounded)   **47.** $x = 1$
49. $x = 3\frac{1}{2}$ **51.** $x = 0.2$ or $x = \dfrac{1}{5}$ **53.** $x = 0.005$ or $x = \dfrac{1}{200}$
55. Find the cross products: $20 \neq 30$, so the proportion is false.
$\dfrac{6\frac{2}{3}}{4} = \dfrac{5}{3}$ or $\dfrac{10}{6} = \dfrac{5}{3}$ or $\dfrac{10}{4} = \dfrac{7.5}{3}$ or $\dfrac{10}{4} = \dfrac{5}{2}$
56. Find the cross products: $192 \neq 180$, so the proportion is false.
$\dfrac{6.4}{8} = \dfrac{24}{30}$ or $\dfrac{6}{7.5} = \dfrac{24}{30}$ or $\dfrac{6}{8} = \dfrac{22.5}{30}$ or $\dfrac{6}{8} = \dfrac{24}{32}$

Summary Exercises on Ratios, Rates, and Proportions (pages 607–608)

1. $\dfrac{6}{5}$ **2.** $\dfrac{2}{7}$ **3.** $\dfrac{2}{1}$ **4.** $\dfrac{13}{11}$ **5.** Comparing the violin to piano, guitar, organ, clarinet and drums gives ratios of $\dfrac{1}{11}, \dfrac{1}{10}, \dfrac{1}{3}, \dfrac{1}{2}$, and $\dfrac{2}{3}$, respectively.
6. (a) guitar to clarinet   **(b)** organ to drums, or clarinet to violin
7. 2.1 points/min; 0.5 min/point   **8.** 1.6 points/min; 0.6 min/point
9. \$16.32/hour; \$24.48/hour for overtime   **10.** \$0.50/channel; \$0.39/channel; \$0.32/channel   **11.** 12 ounces for \$7.24, about \$0.60 per ounce   **12.** Brand P with the \$2 coupon is the best buy at \$0.57 per pound.   **13.** $\dfrac{4}{3} = \dfrac{4}{3}$ or $924 = 924$; true   **14.** $2.0125 \neq 2.07$; false
15. $68\frac{1}{4} = 68\frac{1}{4}$; true   **16.** $x = 28$ **17.** $x = 3.2$ **18.** $x = 182$
19. $x \approx 3.64$ (rounded)   **20.** $x \approx 0.93$ (rounded)   **21.** $x = 1.56$
22. $x \approx 0.05$ (rounded)   **23.** $x = 1$ **24.** $x = \dfrac{3}{4}$

Section 7.4 (pages 609–616)

1. 22.5 hours   **3.** \$7.20   **5.** 42 pounds   **7.** \$403.68   **9.** 10 ounces (rounded)   **11.** 5 quarts   **13.** 14 ft, 10 ft   **15.** 14 ft, 8 ft   **17.** 96 pieces of chicken; 33.6 pounds lasagna; 10.8 pounds deli meats; $5\frac{3}{5}$ pounds cheese; 7.2 dozen (about 86) buns; 14.4 pounds potato salad.   **19.** 2065 students (reasonable); about 4214 students with incorrect setup (only 2950 students in the group)   **21.** about 79 people (reasonable); about 714 people with incorrect setup (only 238 people attended)   **23.** 110,838,000 households (reasonable); about 115,408,163 households with incorrect setup (only 113,100,000 U.S. households)   **25.** 625 stocks   **27.** 4.06 meters (rounded)   **29.** 311 calories (rounded)   **31.** 10.53 meters (rounded)
33. You cannot solve this problem using a proportion because the ratio

of age to weight is not constant. As Jim's age increases, his weight may decrease, stay the same, or increase.   **35.** 5050 students use cream.

37. 120 calories and 12 grams of fiber   **39.** $1\frac{3}{4}$ cups water, 3 tablespoons margarine, $\frac{3}{4}$ cup milk, 2 cups flakes   **40.** $5\frac{1}{4}$ cups water, 9 tablespoons margarine, $2\frac{1}{4}$ cups milk, 6 cups flakes   **41.** $\frac{7}{8}$ cup water, $1\frac{1}{2}$ tablespoons margarine, $\frac{3}{8}$ cup milk, 1 cup flakes   **42.** $2\frac{5}{8}$ cups water, $4\frac{1}{2}$ tablespoons margarine, $1\frac{1}{8}$ cups milk, 3 cups flakes

Section 7.5 (pages 617–630)

1. line named $\overleftrightarrow{CD}$ or $\overleftrightarrow{DC}$ **3.** line segment named $\overline{GF}$ or $\overline{FG}$
5. ray named $\overrightarrow{PQ}$ **7.** perpendicular   **9.** parallel   **11.** intersecting
13. $\angle AOS$ or $\angle SOA$ **15.** $\angle CRT$ or $\angle TRC$ **17.** $\angle AQC$ or $\angle CQA$
19. right (90°)   **21.** acute   **23.** straight (180°)   **25.** $\angle EOD$ and $\angle COD$; $\angle AOB$ and $\angle BOC$ **27.** $\angle HNE$ and $\angle ENF$; $\angle ACB$ and $\angle KOL$
29. 50°   **31.** 4°   **33.** 50°   **35.** 90°   **37.** $\angle SON \cong \angle TOM$; $\angle TOS \cong \angle MON$ **39.** $\angle GOH$ measures 63°; $\angle EOF$ measures 37°; $\angle AOC$ and $\angle GOF$ both measure 80°.   **41.** True, because $\overrightarrow{UQ}$ is perpendicular to $\overleftrightarrow{ST}$.   **42.** True, because they form a 90° angle, as indicated by the small red square.   **43.** False; the angles have the same measure (both are 180°).   **44.** False; $\overleftrightarrow{ST}$ and $\overleftrightarrow{PR}$ are parallel.   **45.** False; $\overleftrightarrow{QU}$ and $\overleftrightarrow{TS}$ are perpendicular.   **46.** True, because both angles are formed by perpendicular lines, so they both measure 90°.   **47.** corresponding angles; $\angle 1$ and $\angle 8$, $\angle 2$ and $\angle 5$, $\angle 3$ and $\angle 6$, $\angle 4$ and $\angle 7$; alternate interior angles; $\angle 4$ and $\angle 5$, $\angle 3$ and $\angle 8$.   **49.** $\angle 2$, $\angle 4$, $\angle 6$, $\angle 8$ all measure 130°; $\angle 1$, $\angle 3$, $\angle 5$, $\angle 7$ all measure 50°.   **51.** $\angle 6$, $\angle 1$, $\angle 3$, $\angle 8$ all measure 47°; $\angle 5$, $\angle 2$, $\angle 7$, $\angle 4$ all measure 133°.   **53.** $\angle 6$, $\angle 8$, $\angle 4$, $\angle 2$ all measure 114°; $\angle 7$, $\angle 5$, $\angle 3$, $\angle 1$ all measure 66°.
55. $\angle 1 \cong \angle 3$, both are 138°; $\angle 2 \cong \angle ABC$, both are 42°.

Section 7.6 (pages 631–645)

1. 0.25   **3.** 0.30 or 0.3   **5.** 0.06   **7.** 1.40 or 1.4   **9.** 0.078
11. 1.00 or 1   **13.** 0.005   **15.** 0.0035   **17.** 50%   **19.** 62%
21. 3%   **23.** 12.5%   **25.** 62.9%   **27.** 200%   **29.** 260%
31. 3.12%   **33.** $\frac{1}{5}$ **35.** $\frac{1}{2}$ **37.** $\frac{11}{20}$ **39.** $\frac{3}{8}$ **41.** $\frac{1}{16}$ **43.** $\frac{1}{6}$
45. $1\frac{3}{10}$ **47.** $2\frac{1}{2}$ **49.** 25%   **51.** 30%   **53.** 60%   **55.** 37%
57. $37\frac{1}{2}$% or 37.5%   **59.** 5%   **61.** exactly $55\frac{5}{9}$%, or 55.6% (rounded)   **63.** exactly $14\frac{2}{7}$%, or 14.3% (rounded)   **65.** 0.08
67. 0.42   **69.** 3.5%   **71.** 200%   **73.** $\frac{95}{100}$ or 95% shaded; $\frac{5}{100}$ or 5% unshaded   **75.** $\frac{3}{10}$ or 30% shaded; $\frac{7}{10}$ or 70% unshaded
77. $\frac{3}{4}$ or 75% shaded; $\frac{1}{4}$ or 25% unshaded   **79.** 0.01; 1%
81. $\frac{1}{5}$; 20%   **83.** $\frac{3}{10}$; 0.3   **85.** 0.5; 50%   **87.** $\frac{9}{10}$; 0.9   **89.** $1\frac{1}{2}$; 150%
91. 0.08; $\frac{2}{25}$ **93.** 5%; 0.05; $\frac{1}{20}$ **95.** $\frac{1}{4}$; 0.25; 25%   **97.** $\frac{3}{8}$; 0.375;
37.5%   **99.** $\frac{1}{7}$; exactly $14\frac{2}{7}$%, or 14.3% (rounded)   **101. (a)** The student forgot to move the decimal point in 0.35 two places to the right. So $\frac{7}{20} = 35\%$.   **(b)** The student did the division in the wrong order. Enter $16 \div 25$ to get 0.64 and then move the decimal point two places to the right. So $\frac{16}{25} = 0.64 = 64\%$.   **103. (a)** $78   **(b)** $39

105. (a) 15 inches   **(b)** $7\frac{1}{2}$ inches   **107. (a)** 2.8 miles   **(b)** 1.4 miles
109. 20 children   **111.** 60 credits   **113. (a)** $142.50   **(b)** 50%
(c) $142.50   **115. (a)** 4100 students   **(b)** 50%   **117. (a)** 35 problems
(b) 0 problems   **119.** 50% means 50 out of 100 parts. That's half of the number. A shortcut for finding 50% of a number is to divide the number by 2. Examples will vary.

Section 7.7 (pages 646–653)

1. (a) 10%   **(b)** 3000 runners   **(c)** unknown   **(d)** $\frac{10}{100} = \frac{n}{3000}$;
300 runners   **3. (a)** 4%   **(b)** 120 ft   **(c)** unknown   **(d)** $\frac{4}{100} = \frac{n}{120}$;
4.8 feet   **5. (a)** unknown   **(b)** 32 pizzas   **(c)** 16 pizzas
(d) $\frac{p}{100} = \frac{16}{32}$; 50%   **7. (a)** unknown   **(b)** 200 calories
(c) 16 calories   **(d)** $\frac{p}{100} = \frac{16}{200}$; 8%   **9. (a)** 90%   **(b)** unknown
(c) 495 students   **(d)** $\frac{90}{100} = \frac{495}{n}$; 550 students   **11. (a)** $12\frac{1}{2}$%
(b) unknown   **(c)** $3.50   **(d)** $\frac{12.5}{100} = \frac{3.50}{n}$; $28   **13.** $\frac{250}{100} = \frac{n}{7}$;
17.5 hours   **15.** $\frac{p}{100} = \frac{32}{172}$; 18.6% (rounded)
17. $\frac{110}{100} = \frac{748}{n}$; 680 books   **19.** $\frac{14.7}{100} = \frac{n}{274}$; $40.28 (rounded)
21. $\frac{p}{100} = \frac{105}{54}$; 194.4% (rounded)   **23.** $\frac{4}{100} = \frac{0.33}{n}$; $8.25
25. 150% of $30 cannot be *less* than $30; 25% of $16 cannot be *greater than* $16.   **27.** The correct proportion is $\frac{p}{100} = \frac{14}{8}$. The answer should be labeled with the % symbol. Correct answer is 175%.

Section 7.8 (pages 654–663)

1. 1500 patients   **3.** $15   **5.** 4.5 pounds   **7.** $7.00   **9.** 52 students
11. 870 phones   **13.** 4.75 hours   **15. (a)** 10% means $\frac{10}{100}$ or $\frac{1}{10}$.
The denominator tells you to divide the whole by 10. The shortcut for dividing by 10 is to move the decimal point one place to the left.
(b) Once you find 10% of a number, multiply the result by 2 for 20% and by 3 for 30%.   **17.** 231 programs   **19.** 50%   **21.** 680 circuits
23. 1080 people   **25.** 845 species   **27.** $20.80   **29.** 76%
31. 125%   **33.** 4700 employees   **35.** 83.2 quarts   **37.** 2%
39. 700 tablets   **41.** 325 salads   **43.** 1.5%   **45.** 5 gallons
47. 1029.2 meters   **49. (a)** Multiply 0.2 by 100% to change it from a decimal to a percent. So, $0.20 = 20\%$.   **(b)** The correct equation is $50 = p \cdot 20$, so the solution is 250%.   **51. (a)** $\frac{1}{3} \cdot 162 = n$; the solution is $54.   **(b)** $(0.333333333)(162) = n$; depending upon how your calculator rounds numbers, the solution is either $54 or $53.99999995.
(c) There is no difference or the difference is insignificant.
52. (a) $22 = \frac{2}{3} \cdot n$; the solution is 33 cans.   **(b)** $22 = (0.666666667)(n)$; depending upon how your calculator rounds numbers, the solution is either 33 cans or 32.99999998 cans.   **(c)** There is no difference or the difference is insignificant.

Summary Exercises on Percent (pages 664–665)

1. (a) 0.03; 3%   **(b)** $\frac{3}{10}$; 0.3   **(c)** $\frac{3}{8}$; 37.5%   **(d)** $1\frac{3}{5}$; 1.6
(e) 0.0625; 6.25%   **(f)** $\frac{1}{20}$; 0.05   **(g)** 2; 200%   **(h)** 0.8; 80%
(i) $\frac{9}{125}$; 7.2%   **2. (a)** 3.5 ft   **(b)** 19 miles   **(c)** 105 cows
(d) $0.08   **(e)** 500 women   **(f)** $45   **(g)** $87.50   **(h)** 12 pounds

ANSWERS

(i) 95 students   **3.** $12\frac{1}{2}$% or 12.5%   **4.** 75 DVDs   **5.** $0.53 (rounded)
6. 175%   **7.** 5.9 pounds (rounded)   **8.** 600 hours   **9.** 50%
10. 500 camp sites   **11.** 98 golf balls   **12.** 2.7% (rounded)
13. 2300 apartments   **14.** 0.63 ounce   **15.** 145%   **16.** 244 voters
(rounded)   **17.** 0.021 inch   **18.** 400%   **19.** 8%   **20.** $0.68
21. Invitations; $840   **22.** $2604   **23.** (a) $3830.40
(b) $4166.40   **24.** (a) $14,784   (b) $89.60

Section 7.9 (pages 666–675)

1. $37.80   **3.** (a) 10%   (b) 5%   (c) 2%   (d) 1%   **5.** (a) 101.6
pounds (rounded)   **(b)** 10.1 pounds (rounded)   **7.** 13.1% female;
86.9% male (both rounded)   **9.** 300 million people (rounded)
11. 138%   **13.** 40 problems   **15.** 1340 shots (rounded)   **17.** 23.7 miles
per gallon (rounded)   **19.** March; 24.5 million cans, or 24,500,000 cans
21. 52.5 million cans (January); 38.5 million cans (February)   **23.** 64.8%
(rounded)   **25.** 9.1% (rounded)   **27.** 40%   **29.** 678% (rounded)
31. No. 100% is the entire price, so a decrease of 100% would take
the price down to 0. Therefore, 100% is the maximum possible
decrease in the price of something.   **33.** George ate more than
65 grams, so the percent must be >100%. Use $p \cdot 65 = 78$ to get
120%.   **34.** The team won more than half the games, so the percent
must be >50%. Correct solution is $0.72 = 72\%$.   **35.** The brain could
not weigh 375 pounds, which is more than the person weighs.
$2\frac{1}{2}$%, = 2.5% = 0.025, so $(0.025)(150) = n$ and $n = 3.75$ pounds
36. If 80% were absent, then only 20% made it to class. $800 - 640 = 160$
students, or use $(0.20)(800) = n$.

Section 7.10 (pages 676–687)

1. $6; $106   **3.** 3%; $70.04   **5.** $29.28 (rounded); $395.26   **7.** $0.12
(rounded); $2.22   **9.** $4\frac{1}{2}$%; $13,167   **11.** $3 + $1.50 = $4.50; $4.83
(rounded); 2($3) = $6; $6.43 (rounded)   **13.** $8 + $4 = $12; $11.75
(rounded); 2($8) = $16; $15.67 (rounded)   **15.** $1 + $0.50 = $1.50;
$1.43 (rounded); 2($1) = $2; $1.91   **17.** $15; $85   **19.** 30%; $126
21. $4.38 (rounded); $13.12   **23.** $3.79 (rounded); $34.09   **25.** $42;
$342   **27.** $33.30; $773.30   **29.** $213.75; $1713.75   **31.** $919.67
(rounded); $18,719.67   **33.** $1170   **35.** $7978.13 (rounded)
37. $26.61 (rounded)   **39.** 5%   **41.** $74.25   **43.** $25.13   **45.** $216.00
(rounded); $983.99   **47.** $2016.38 (rounded)   **49.** $21 (rounded)
51. $92.38   **53.** $230.12   **55.** (a) $18.43 (rounded to nearest cent)
(b) When calculating the discount, the *whole* is $18.50. But when calcu-
lating the sales tax, the *whole* is only $17.39 (the discounted price).
56. (a) $396.05 (rounded to nearest cent).   (b) 7.53% sales tax
(rounded to the nearest hundredth) would give a final cost of $398.01.

Chapter 8   Measurement

Taken from *Prealgebra & Introductory Algebra* by Lial, et. al. (0321578732)

Section 8.1 (pages 690–700)

1. 3; 12   **3.** 8; 2   **5.** 5280; 3   **7.** 2000; 16   **9.** 60; 60   **11.** (a) 2;
(b) 240   **13.** (a) $\frac{1}{2}$ or 0.5   (b) 78   **15.** 14,000 to 16,000 lb
17. 27   **19.** 112   **21.** 10   **23.** $1\frac{1}{2}$ or 1.5   **25.** $\frac{1}{4}$ or 0.25
27. $1\frac{1}{2}$ or 1.5   **29.** $2\frac{1}{2}$ or 2.5   **31.** snowmobile/ATV; person
walking   **33.** 5000   **35.** 17   **37.** 4 to 8 in.   **39.** 216   **41.** 28
43. 518,400   **45.** 48,000   **47.** (a) pound/ounces   (b) quarts/pints or
pints/cups   (c) minutes/hours or seconds/minutes   (d) feet/inches
(e) pounds/tons   (f) days/weeks   **49.** 174,240   **51.** 800

53. 0.75 or $\frac{3}{4}$ **55.** $1.83 (rounded)   **57.** $140   **59.** (a) 1056 sec;
(b) 17.6 min   **61.** (a) $12\frac{1}{2}$ qt   (b) 4 containers, because you can't buy
part of a container   **63.** (a) 0.8 mi (rounded)   (b) 13,031 ft   (c) 2.5 mi
(rounded)   **64.** (a) 183 yd (rounded)   (b) 6600 in.   (c) 0.1 mi (rounded)
(d) 9 ft (rounded)   **65.** (a) $1\frac{1}{2}$ to $2\frac{1}{2}$ ft, or 1.5 to 2.5 ft   (b) 8400 months
(c) 140 more years, for a total of 840 years in all   **66.** (a) 283 mi (rounded)
(b) 377 mi (rounded)

Section 8.2 (pages 701–708)

1. 1000; 1000   **3.** $\frac{1}{1000}$ or 0.001; $\frac{1}{1000}$ or 0.001   **5.** $\frac{1}{100}$ or 0.01;
$\frac{1}{100}$ or 0.01   **7.** Answers will vary; about 8 to 10 cm.   **9.** Answers will
vary; about 20 to 25 mm.   **11.** cm   **13.** m   **15.** km   **17.** mm
19. cm   **21.** m   **23.** Some possible answers are: track and field events,
metric auto parts, and lead refills for mechanical pencils.   **25.** 700 cm
27. 0.040 m or 0.04 m   **29.** 9400 m   **31.** 5.09 m   **33.** 40 cm
35. 910 mm   **37.** less; 18 cm or 0.18 m
39.   5 mm = 0.5 cm
       ← 1 mm = 0.1 cm
41. 0.018 km   **43.** 164 cm; 1640 mm   **45.** 0.0000056 km

Section 8.3 (pages 709–718)

1. mL   **3.** L   **5.** kg   **7.** g   **9.** mL   **11.** mg   **13.** L   **15.** kg
17. unreasonable; too much   **19.** unreasonable; too much   **21.** reasonable
23. reasonable   **25.** Some capacity examples are 2 L bottles of soda and
shampoo bottles marked in mL; weight examples are grams of fat listed
on food packages and vitamin doses in milligrams.   **27.** Unit for your
answer (g) is in numerator; unit being changed (kg) is in denominator so
it will divide out. The unit fraction is $\frac{1000 \text{ g}}{1 \text{ kg}}$.   **29.** 15,000 mL   **31.** 3 L
33. 0.925 L   **35.** 0.008 L   **37.** 4150 mL   **39.** 8 kg   **41.** 5200 g
43. 850 mg   **45.** 30 g   **47.** 0.598 g   **49.** 0.06 L   **51.** 0.003 kg
53. 990 mL   **55.** mm   **57.** mL   **59.** cm   **61.** mg   **63.** 0.3 L
65. 1340 g   **67.** 0.9 L   **69.** 3 kg to 4 kg   **71.** greater; 5 mg or 0.005 g
73. 200 nickels   **75.** (a) 1,000,000
(b) $\dfrac{3.5 \text{ Mm}}{1} \cdot \dfrac{1,000,000 \text{ m}}{1 \text{ Mm}} = 3,500,000 \text{ m}$
76. (a) 1,000,000,000
(b) $\dfrac{2500 \text{ m}}{1} \cdot \dfrac{1 \text{ Gm}}{1,000,000,000 \text{ m}} = 0.0000025 \text{ Gm}$
77. (a) 1,000,000,000,000   (b) 1000; 1,000,000
78. 1,000,000; 1,000,000,000; $2^{20} = 1,048,576$; $2^{30} = 1,073,741,824$

Summary Exercises on U.S. Customary and Metric Units (pages 719–720)

1. Length: inch, foot, yard, mile; Weight: ounce, pound, ton; Capacity:
fluid ounce, cup, pint, quart, gallon.   **2.** Length: millimeter, centimeter,
meter, kilometer; Weight: milligram, gram, kilogram; Capacity: milliliter,
liter   **3.** (a) ft   (b) yd   (c) 5280   **4.** (a) min   (b) 60   (c) 24
5. (a) 8   (b) gal   (c) 2   **6.** (a) lb   (b) 2000   (c) 16   **7.** mL   **8.** m
9. kg   **10.** mg   **11.** cm   **12.** mm   **13.** L   **14.** g   **15.** 0.45 m
16. 45 sec   **17.** 600 mL   **18.** 8000 mg   **19.** 30 cm   **20.** $3\frac{3}{4}$ or 3.75 ft
21. 0.050 or 0.05 L   **22.** $4\frac{1}{2}$ or 4.5 gal   **23.** 7280 g   **24.** 36 oz
25. 0.009 kg   **26.** 180 in.   **27.** 272 cm; 2720 mm   **28.** 2.64 m;
0.00264 km   **29.** 0.04 m; 4 cm; 40 mm   **30.** 14 cm; 0.14 m; 140 mm
31. $4.65 (rounded)   **32.** 10.3 ft (rounded)

Section 8.4 (pages 721–724)

1. $0.83 (rounded) **3.** 89.5 kg **5.** 71 beats (rounded) **7.** 180 cm;
$0.02/cm (rounded) **9.** 5.03 m **11.** 4 bottles; 175 mL or 0.175 L
13. 1.89 g **15. (a)** 10 km **(b)** 600 km **(c)** 36,000 km
17. 215 g; 4.3 g; 4300 mg **18.** 330 g; 0.33 g; 330 mg
19. 1550 g; 1500 g; 3 g **20.** 55 g; 50 g; 0.5 g

Section 8.5 (pages 725–732)

1. 21.8 yd **3.** 262.4 ft **5.** 4.8 m **7.** 5.3 oz **9.** 111.6 kg
11. 30.3 qt **13. (a)** about 0.2 oz **(b)** probably not **15.** about 31.8 L
17. about 1.3 cm **19.** 3.5 kg ≈ 7.7 lb so the baby is heavy enough. But
53 cm ≈ 20.7 in., so the baby is not long enough to be in the carrier.
21. −8 °C **23.** 40 °C **25.** 150 °C **27.** 16 °C (rounded) **29.** −20 °C
31. 46 °F (rounded) **33.** 23 °F **35.** 58 °C (rounded); −89 °C (rounded)
37. 10 °C and 41 °C (rounded) **39. (a)** pleasant weather, above freezing
but not hot **(b)** 75 °F to 39 °F (rounded) **(c)** Answers will vary.
In Minnesota, it's 0 °C to −40 °C; in California, 24 °C to 0 °C.
41. about 1.8 m **42.** about 5.0 kg **43.** about 3040.2 km
44. 38 hr 23 min **45.** about 300 m **46.** less than 3790 mL
47. about 59.4 mL **48.** about 1.6%

Chapter 9 Graphs

Taken from *Prealgebra & Introductory Algebra* by Lial, et. al. (0321578732)

Section 9.1 (pages 734–740)

1. (a) 31,419 points **(b)** Michael Jordan **3. (a)** Michael Jordan
(b) Allen Iverson **5.** 11,468 points **7.** West, 27.0; Pettit, 26.4;
O'Neal, 25.9; round to nearest tenth. **9.** The asterisks next to O'Neal's
and Iverson's names mean that they are still actively playing in the NBA.
11. (a) 255 calories **(b)** moderate jogging **13. (a)** moderate jogging,
aerobic dance, racquetball **(b)** moderate jogging, moderate bicycling,
aerobic dance, racquetball, tennis **15.** 370 calories **17. (a)** 366 calories
(rounded) **(b)** 239 calories **19.** about 39 calories **21. (a)** 80 million
or 80,000,000 **(b)** 35 million or 35,000,000 **23.** 165 million or
165,000,000 **25.** 5 million or 5,000,000 **27.** 305 million or 305,000,000
29. Answers will vary. One possibility: choose Southwest because it has
the best on-time performance. **30.** Answers will vary. Possibilities include
planning more time between each flight, or doing some or all of your
business via conference calls or e-mail. **31.** Answers will vary. One
possibility: choose Airtran because it has the fewest luggage problems.
32. Answers will vary. Possibilities include buying heavy-duty luggage
or shipping the golf clubs via a delivery service. **33.** Answers will vary.
Possibilities include a lot of bad weather, maintenance problems, new
computer system. **34.** Answers will vary. Possibilities include availability of nonstop flights, convenience of departure times, type and size of
aircraft, availability of low-cost fares.

Section 9.2 (pages 741–750)

1. (a) $48,000 **(b)** carpentry, $18,000 **3. (a)** $\frac{\$18,000}{\$48,000} = \frac{3}{8}$

(b) $\frac{\$15,000}{\$3000} = \frac{5}{1}$ **5. (a)** $\frac{\$4800}{\$48,000} = \frac{1}{10}$ **(b)** $\frac{\$57,600}{\$48,000} = \frac{6}{5}$

7. (a) don't know **(b)** quicker **9.** $\frac{720}{6000} = \frac{3}{25}$ **11.** $\frac{1020}{1200} = \frac{17}{20}$

13. $\frac{1740}{180} = \frac{29}{3}$ **15.** 140 people **17.** raids the buffet table; 16 people

19. 64 fewer people **21.** 160 people **23.** mustard; 960 people
25. 64 more people **27.** First, find the percent of the total that is
represented by each item. Next, multiply the percent by 360° to find the
size of each sector. Finally, use a protractor to draw each sector.
29. (a) 90° **(b)** 20% **(c)** 10%; 36° **(d)** 10%; 36° **(e)** 15%; 54°
(f) 5%; 18° **(g)** 15%; 54° **(h)** See circle graph below.

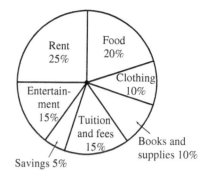

31. (a) $200,000 **(b)** 6.25%; 20%; 30%; 25%; 18.75%
(c) 22.5°; 72°; 108°; 90°; 67.5°
(d) See circle graph below.

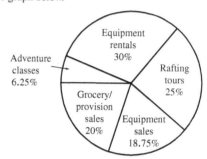

Section 9.3 (pages 751–758)

1. can shop during off hours; 74% **3.** 57%; 342 people **5.** $\frac{1}{2}$, compare

products more easily; nearly $\frac{3}{4}$, shop during off hours **7.** May; 10,000

unemployed **9.** 1500 workers **11.** 2500 workers; 45% increase (rounded)
13. 150,000 gallons **15.** 2004; 250,000 gallons **17.** 550,000 gallons;
367% increase (rounded) **19.** 24.1 million or 24,100,000 PCs
21. 185.6 million or 185,600,000 more PCs **23.** 82.3 million or
82,300,000 PCs; 132% increase (rounded) **25. (a)** 3,000,000 DVDs
(b) 1,500,000 DVDs **27. (a)** 2,500,000 DVDs **(b)** 3,000,000 DVDs
29. Answers will vary. Possibilities include: Both stores had decreased
sales from 2004 to 2005 and increased sales from 2006 to 2008; Store B
had lower sales than Store A in 2004–05 but higher sales than Store A in
2006–2008. **31.** 2006; $25,000 **33.** 2005, 29% (rounded); 2006,
20%; 2007, 17% (rounded); 2008, 38% (rounded) **35.** Answers will
vary. Possibilities include: The decrease in sales may have resulted from
poor service or greater competition; the increase in sales may have been a
result of more advertising or better service. **37.** Shipments have increased at a rapid rate since 1985. **38.** Answers will vary. Some possibilities are lower prices; more uses and applications for students, home
use, and businesses; improved technology. **39. (a)** 104% (rounded)
(b) 159% (rounded) **(c)** 132% (rounded) **(d)** 37% (rounded)
(e) 46% (rounded) **40.** Since 2000, the percent of increase for each
5-year period has been much lower than in earlier periods. **41.** Answers
will vary. Some possibilities are: More people will already own a computer
and not want to buy another; some new invention will replace computers.
42. (a) no change; 0% **(b)** 167% increase (rounded) **43. (a)** Answers
will vary; perhaps 3,500,000 DVDs in 2009. **(b)** Answers will vary;
perhaps 4,500,000 DVDs in 2009. **(c)** Answers will vary; One possibility
is predicting a continuing increase based on the increase from 2006 to 2008.
44. (a) Most people will probably pick Store B because of its greater
sales and more consistent upward trend. **(b)** Answers will vary. Some
possibilities include: age and physical condition of the store, annual
expenses, sales of other products, annual profit.

Section 9.4 (pages 759–764)

1. 69.8 (rounded) **3.** $39,622 **5.** $58.24 **7.** 6.1 (rounded) **9.** 2.60
11. (a) 2.80 **(b)** 2.93 (rounded) **(c)** 3.13 (rounded) **13.** 15 messages
15. 516 students **17.** 48.5 pounds of shrimp **19.** 4142 miles (rounded)
21. 4050 miles **23.** 8 samples **25.** 68 and 74 years (bimodal)
27. no mode **29.** −10 degrees; 4 degrees; 14 degrees warmer

Section 9.5 (pages 765–770)

1.

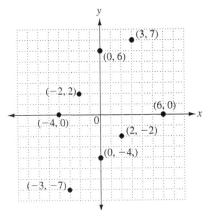

3.

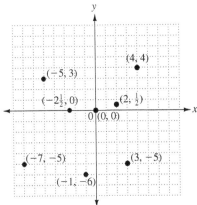

5. A is (3, 4); B is (5, −5); C is (−4, −2); D is approximately $\left(4, \frac{1}{2}\right)$;

E is (0, −7); F is (−5, 5); G is (−2, 0); H is (0,0).   **7.** III, none, IV, II
9. (a) any positive number   **(b)** any negative number   **(c)** 0   **(d)** any
negative number   **(e)** any positive number   **11.** Starting at the origin,
move left or right along the x-axis to the number a; then move up if b is
positive or move down if b is negative.

Section 9.6 (pages 771–784)

1. 4; (0, 4); 3; (1, 3); 2; (2, 2);
All points on the line are solutions.

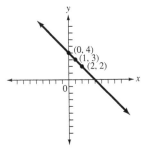

3. −1; (0, −1); −2; (1, −2); −3; (2, −3);
All points on the line are solutions.

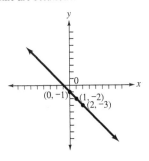

5. 4; −1; −6; 99

7.

x	y	(x, y)
1	−1	(1, −1)
2	0	(2, 0)
3	1	(3, 1)

9.

x	y	(x, y)
0	2	(0, 2)
−1	1	(−1, 1)
−2	0	(−2, 0)

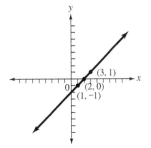 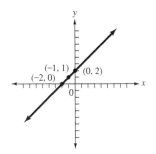

11.

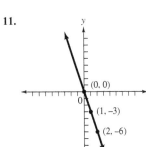

x	y	(x, y)
0	0	(0, 0)
1	−3	(1, −3)
2	−6	(2, −6)

13. The lines in Exercises 7 and 9 have a positive slope. The lines in
Exercises 1, 3, and 11 have a negative slope.

15.

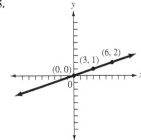

x	y	(x, y)
0	0	(0, 0)
3	1	(3, 1)
6	2	(6, 2)

17.

x	y	(x, y)
−1	−1	(−1, −1)
−2	−2	(−2, −2)
−3	−3	(−3, −3)

19.

x	y	(x, y)
0	3	(0, 3)
1	1	(1, 1)
2	−1	(2, −1)

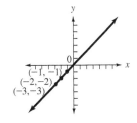 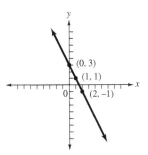

21.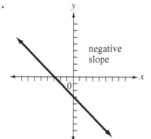

23.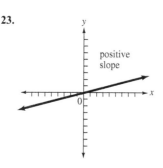

25.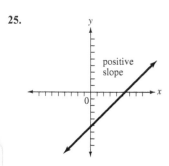

27.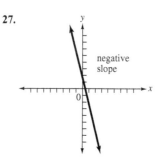

Chapter 10 Solving Equations/Variation

Taken from *Prealgebra & Introductory Algebra* by
Lial, et. al. (0321578732) and
Intermediate Algebra (0321574974)

Section 10.1 (pages 786–794)

1. rational because it terminates   **3.** irrational because decimal form
never ends or repeats in a fixed block   **5.** rational because it's the
quotient of integers   **7.** rational because digits repeat in a fixed block
9. irrational because decimal form never ends or repeats in a
fixed block   **11. (a)** $3, 7$ **(b)** $0, 3, 7$ **(c)** $-9, 0, 3, 7$
(d) $-9, -1\frac{1}{4}, -\frac{3}{5}, 0, 3, 5.9, 7$ **(e)** $-\sqrt{7}, \sqrt{5}$
(f) All are real numbers.

13. "75 hundredths does not equal three-fourths." False; $0.75 = \frac{3}{4}$.

15. "Negative 4 is less than or equal to negative 5." False; $-4 > -5$
and $-4 \neq -5$.   **17.** "Zero is greater than or equal to zero." True,
because $0 = 0$.   **19.** $19 > 12$ **21.** $\frac{1}{2} \leq \frac{4}{5}$ **23.** $-17 \leq -17$; True
25. $-3 \geq 0$; False   **27.** $-6 \neq 6$; True   **29.** $45 \leq 40$; False
31. $1 \geq 1$; True   **33.** $0 \neq$ undefined; True   **35. (a)** *Titanic* and
The Dark Knight   **(b)** *Titanic, The Dark Knight,* and *Star Wars*
36. (a) *The Phantom Menace*   **(b)** *E.T.* and *The Phantom Menace*
37. Answers will vary. One possibility is: gross receipts ≤ 436.5
million dollars.   **38.** Answers will vary. One possibility is: gross
receipts ≥ 436.5 million dollars.   **39.** $-4t - 5m$ **41.** $5c + 4d$
43. $-6h + n$ **45.** $3q - 5r + 8s$ **47.** $-19p + 16$
49. $-4y + 22$ **51.** $y^2 + y - 12$ **53.** $6b^2 - 6b + 8$
55. $a + 1$ **57.** $24k - 4$

Section 10.2 (pages 795–801)

1. A and C   **3.** Both sides are evaluated as 30, so 6 is a solution.
5. Any number is a solution. For example, if the last name is Lincoln,
then $x = 7$. Both sides are evaluated as -48.   **7. (a)** equation
(b) expression   **(c)** equation   **(d)** expression   **9.** The student made a
sign error when the distributive property was applied. The left side of the
second line should be $8x - 4x + 6$. The correct solution is 1.

11. $\{-1\}$ **13.** $\{-4\}$ **15.** $\{-7\}$ **17.** $\{0\}$ **19.** $\{4\}$ **21.** $\left\{-\frac{7}{8}\right\}$

23. $\left\{-\frac{5}{3}\right\}$ **25.** $\left\{-\frac{1}{2}\right\}$ **27.** $\{2\}$ **29.** $\{-2\}$ **31.** $\{-1\}$ **33.** $\{7\}$
35. $\{2\}$ **37.** $\{-8\}$ **39.** 12 **41. (a)** 10^2, or 100   **(b)** 10^3, or 1000
43. $\{12\}$ **45.** $\{4\}$ **47.** $\{-30\}$ **49.** $\{0\}$ **51.** $\{3\}$ **53.** $\{0\}$
55. $\{2000\}$ **57.** $\{25\}$ **59.** $\{40\}$ **61.** $\{3\}$ **63.** A conditional
equation is true only for certain value(s), an identity has infinitely many
solutions, and a contradiction has no solution.   **65. (a)** B   **(b)** A
(c) C   **67.** contradiction; $\emptyset$ **69.** conditional; $\{0\}$ **71.** identity;
{all real numbers}   **73.** identity; {all real numbers}

Section 10.3 (pages 808–819)

1. (a) $7x + 8 = 36$ **(b)** $ax + k = tc$ **2. (a)** $7x + 8 - 8 = 36 - 8$
(b) $ax + k - k = tc - k$ **3. (a)** $7x = 28$ **(b)** $ax = tc - k$
4. (a) $x = 4$ **(b)** $x = \dfrac{tc - k}{a}$ **5.** $a \neq 0$; If $a = 0$, the denominator is 0.
6. To solve an equation for a particular variable, such as solving the second
equation for x, go through the same steps as you would in solving for x in
the first equation. Treat all other variables as constants.

7. $W = \dfrac{A}{L}$ **9.** $L = \dfrac{P - 2W}{2}$, or $L = \dfrac{P}{2} - W$ **11. (a)** $W = \dfrac{V}{LH}$
(b) $H = \dfrac{V}{LW}$ **13.** $r = \dfrac{C}{2\pi}$ **15. (a)** $h = \dfrac{2A}{b + B}$ **(b)** $B = \dfrac{2A}{h} - b$, or
$B = \dfrac{2A - bh}{h}$ **17.** $C = \dfrac{5}{9}(F - 32)$ **19.** $y = \dfrac{11 - 4x}{9}$
21. $y = \dfrac{5 + 3x}{2}$ **23.** $y = \dfrac{7 - 6x}{-5}$, or $y = \dfrac{6x - 7}{5}$ **24.** $F = \dfrac{k}{d - D}$
25. $m = \dfrac{Mv}{v - V}$ **26.** $W = \dfrac{A - 2LH}{2H + 2L}$ **27.** 3.275 hr   **29.** 113°F
31. 230 m   **33.** radius: 185 in.; diameter: 370 in.   **35.** 2 in.
37. 75% water, 25% alcohol   **39.** 3%   **41.** $10.51   **43.** $45.66
45. (a) .543   **(b)** .488   **(c)** .444   **(d)** .426   **47.** 52%   **49.** $82,304
51. 17%; yes   **53.** 8%   **55.** 3.8%   **57.** 47.5%

Section 10.4 (pages 820–835)

1. (a) $x + 12$ **(b)** $12 > x$ **3. (a)** $x - 4$ **(b)** $4 < x$ **5.** D
7. $2x + 18$ **9.** $15 - 4x$ **11.** $10(x - 6)$ **13.** $\dfrac{5x}{9}$
15. $x + 6 = -31$; -37 **17.** $x - (-4x) = x + 9$; $\dfrac{9}{4}$
19. $12 - \dfrac{2}{3}x = 10$; 3   **21.** expression   **23.** equation   **25.** expression
27. *Step 1:* We are asked to find the number of patents each university
secured;   *Step 2:* the number of patents Stanford secured;
Step 3: x; $x - 38$;   *Step 4:* 134;   *Step 5:* 134, 96;   *Step 6:* 38;
MIT patents; 96; 230   **29.** width: 165 ft; length: 265 ft
31. 850 mi, 925 mi, 1300 mi   **33.** Eiffel Tower: 984 ft; Leaning Tower:
180 ft   **35.** Yankees: $209.1 million; Tigers: $138.7 million
37. $35.67   **39.** 252,887   **41.** $225   **43.** $4000 at 3%; $8000 at 4%
45. $10,000 at 4.5%; $19,000 at 3%   **47.** $13,500   **49.** 5 L
51. 4 L   **53.** 1 gal   **55.** 150 lb   **57.** We cannot expect the final
mixture to be worth more than either of the ingredients.   **59. (a)** $800 - x$
(b) $800 - y$ **60. (a)** $0.05x$; $0.10(800 - x)$ **(b)** $0.05y$; $0.10(800 - y)$
61. (a) $0.05x + 0.10(800 - x) = 800(0.0875)$
(b) $0.05y + 0.10(800 - y) = 800(0.0875)$ **62. (a)** $200 at 5%;
$600 at 10%   **(b)** 200 L of 5% acid; 600 L of 10% acid   **63.** The
processes are the same. The amounts of money in Problem A correspond
to the amounts of solution in Problem B.

Section 10.5 (pages 836–843)

1. $4.50   **3.** 55 mph   **5.** 17 pennies, 17 dimes, 10 quarters
7. 23 loonies; 14 toonies   **9.** 28 $10 coins, 25 $20 coins
11. 872 adult tickets   **13.** 8.08 m per sec   **15.** 8.40 m per sec
17. $2\frac{1}{2}$ hr   **19.** 7:50 P.M.   **21.** 45 mph   **23.** $\frac{1}{2}$ hr   **25.** 60°, 60°, 60°

27. 40°, 45°, 95° **29.** 40°, 80° **30.** 120° **31.** The sum is equal to the measure of the angle found in Exercise 30. **32.** The sum of the measures of angles 1 and 2 is equal to the measure of angle 3. **33.** Both measure 122°. **35.** 64°, 26° **37.** 24, 25, 26 **39.** 57 yr old

Section 10.6 (pages 844–853)

1. inverse **3.** direct **5.** joint **7.** combined **9.** 36 **11.** 0.625 **13.** $222\frac{2}{9}$ **15.** increases; decreases **17.** If y varies inversely as x, x is in the denominator; however, if y varies directly as x, x is in the numerator. Also, for $k > 0$, with inverse variation, as x increases, y decreases. With direct variation, y increases as x increases. **19.** $\$4.59\frac{9}{10}$ **21.** about 450 cm^3 **23.** 256 ft **25.** $13\frac{1}{3}$ amperes **27.** $21\frac{1}{3}$ foot-candles **29.** \$420 **31.** 448.1 lb **33.** approximately 68,600 calls **35.** 11.8 lb **37.** (0, 0), (1, 4.45) **38.** 4.45 **39.** $y = 4.45x + 0$, or $y = 4.45x$ **40.** $a = 4.45, b = 0$ **41.** It is the price per gallon and the slope of the line. **42.** It can be written in the form $y = kx$ (where $k = a$). The value of a is called the constant of variation.

Chapter 11 Linear Graphing

Taken from *Prealgebra & Introductory Algebra* by Lial, et. al (0321578732)

Section 11.1 (pages 856–870)

1. 2005, 2006, 2007 **3.** 2001: about 165 billion lb; 2007: about 185 billion lb **5.** from 2000 to 2005; about \$0.85 **7.** The price of a gallon of gas was decreasing. **9.** does; do not **11.** y **13.** 6 **15.** yes **17.** yes **19.** no **21.** yes **23.** no **25.** No. For two ordered pairs (x, y) to be equal, the x-values must be equal and the y-values must be equal. Here we have $4 \neq -1$ and $-1 \neq 4$. **27.** 11 **29.** $-\frac{7}{2}$ **31.** -4 **33.** -5 **35.** 4; 6; -6; (0, 4); (6, 0); (-6, 8) **37.** 3; -5; -15; (0, 3); (-5, 0); (-15, -6) **39.** -9; -9; -9 **41.** -6; -6; -6 **43.** 8; 8; 8 **45.** (2, 4); I **47.** (-5, 4); II **49.** (3, 0); no quadrant **51.** negative; negative **53.** positive; negative **55.** If $xy < 0$, then either $x < 0$ and $y > 0$ or $x > 0$ and $y < 0$. If $x < 0$ and $y > 0$, then the point lies in quadrant II. If $x > 0$ and $y < 0$, then the point lies in quadrant IV.

57.–68.

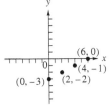

69. -3; 6; -2; 4

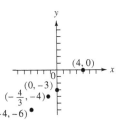

71. -3; 4; -6; $-\frac{4}{3}$

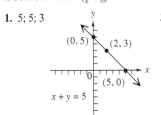

73. -4; -4; -4; -4

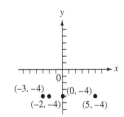

75. The points in each graph appear to lie on a straight line. **77. (a)** (5, 45) **(b)** (6, 50) **79. (a)** (2000, 32.4), (2001, 31.6), (2002, 31.6), (2003, 30.1), (2004, 29.0), (2005, 27.5) **(b)** (2007, 27.1) means that 27.1 percent of 2-year college students in 2007 received a degree within 3 years.

(c) 2-YEAR COLLEGE STUDENTS
COMPLETING A DEGREE
WITHIN 3 YEARS

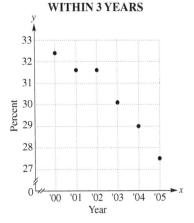

(d) With the exception of the point for 2002, the points lie approximately on a straight line. Rates at which 2-year college students complete a degree within 3 years are generally decreasing. **81. (a)** 157, 141, 125, 109 **(b)** (20, 157), (40, 141), (60, 125), (80, 109)

(c) TARGET HEART RATE ZONE
(Upper Limit)

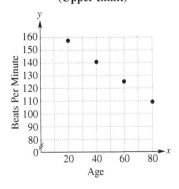

The points lie in a linear pattern.

Section 11.2 (pages 871–884)

1. 5; 5; 3 **3.** 1; 3; -1

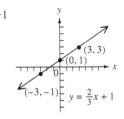

5. $-6; -2; -5$

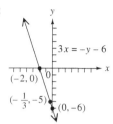

$3x = -y - 6$
$(-2, 0)$
$\left(-\frac{1}{3}, -5\right)$
$(0, -6)$

7. (a) A   **(b)** C   **(c)** D   **(d)** B   **9.** $(12, 0); (0, -8)$ **11.** $(0, 0); (0, 0)$

13.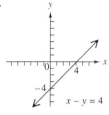

$y = x - 2$

15.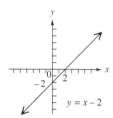

$x - y = 4$

17.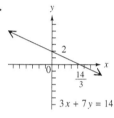

$2x + y = 6$

19.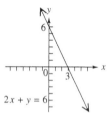

$3x + 7y = 14$
$\frac{14}{3}$

21.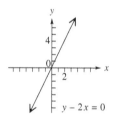

$y - 2x = 0$

23.

$y = -6x$

25.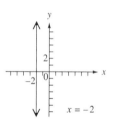

$x = -2$

27.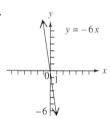

$y - 3 = 0$

29.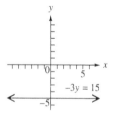

$-3y = 15$

In Exercises 31 and 33, descriptions may vary.
31. The graph is a line with x-intercept $(-3, 0)$ and y-intercept $(0, 9)$.
33. The graph is a horizontal line with y-intercept $(0, -2)$.
35. Choose a value *other than* 0 for either x or y. For example, if $x = -5, y = 4$.
37. (a) 151.5 cm, 159.3 cm, 174.9 cm   **(b)** $(20, 151.5), (22, 159.3), (26, 174.9)$

(c)

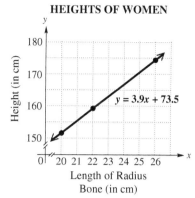

HEIGHTS OF WOMEN

$y = 3.9x + 73.5$

Height (in cm)

Length of Radius Bone (in cm)

(d) 24 cm; 24 cm
39. (a) $62.50; $100   **(b)** 200   **(c)** $(50, 62.50), (100, 100), (200, 175)$
(d)

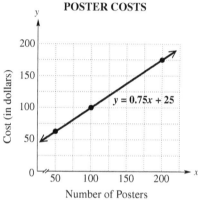

POSTER COSTS

$y = 0.75x + 25$

Cost (in dollars)

Number of Posters

41. (a) $30,000   **(b)** $15,000   **(c)** $5000   **(d)** After 5 yr, the SUV has a value of $5000.   **43. (a)** 1990: 24.1 lb; 2000: 29.5 lb; 2005: 32.2 lb **(b)** 1990: 25 lb; 2000: 30 lb; 2005: 32 lb   **(c)** The values are quite close.

Section 11.3 (pages 885–896)

1. $\frac{3}{2}$ **3.** $-\frac{7}{4}$ **5.** 0   **7.** Rise is the vertical change between two different points on a line. Run is the horizontal change between two different points on a line.

9.–12. Answers will vary.

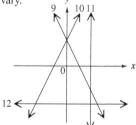

13. (a) falls from left to right   **(b)** horizontal   **(c)** vertical   **(d)** rises from left to right   **15.** Because he found the difference $3 - 5 = -2$ in the numerator, he should have subtracted in the same order in the denominator to get $-1 - 2 = -3$. The correct slope is $\frac{-2}{-3} = \frac{2}{3}$.

17. $\frac{5}{4}$ **19.** $\frac{3}{2}$ **21.** -3 **23.** 0   **25.** undefined   **27.** $-\frac{1}{2}$ **29.** 5

31. $\frac{1}{4}$ **33.** $\frac{3}{2}$ **35.** 0   **37.** undefined   **39.** 1   **41. (a)** negative

(b) 0   **43. (a)** positive   **(b)** negative   **45. (a)** 0   **(b)** negative

47. $\frac{4}{3}; \frac{4}{3}$; parallel   **49.** $\frac{5}{3}; \frac{3}{5}$; neither   **51.** $\frac{3}{5}; -\frac{5}{3}$; perpendicular

53. $\dfrac{8}{27}$ **55.** 232 thousand, or 232,000 **56.** positive; increased
57. 232,000 students **58.** -0.95 **59.** negative; decreased
60. 0.95 student per computer

Section 11.4 (pages 897–910)

1. (a) D **(b)** C **(c)** B **(d)** A   **3.** $y = 3x - 3$

5. $y = -x + 3$ **7.** $y = -\dfrac{1}{2}x + 2$ **9.** $y = 4x - 3$ **11.** $y = 3$

13. (a) C **(b)** B **(c)** A **(d)** D

15. 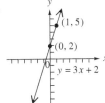   **17.**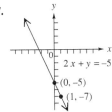

19. 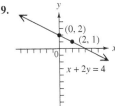   **21.** $y = \dfrac{1}{2}x + 4$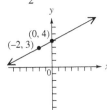

23. $y = -\dfrac{2}{5}x - \dfrac{23}{5}$ 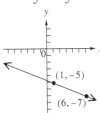   **25.** $y = 2$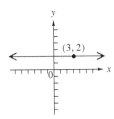

27. $x = 3$ (no slope-intercept form)   **29.** $y = \dfrac{2}{3}x$

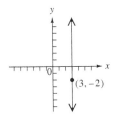   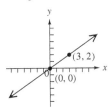

31. $y = 2x - 7$ **33.** $y = -2x - 4$ **35.** $y = \dfrac{2}{3}x + \dfrac{19}{3}$

37. $y = x - 3$ **39.** $y = -\dfrac{5}{7}x - \dfrac{54}{7}$ **41.** $y = -\dfrac{2}{3}x - 2$

43. $x = 3$ (no slope-intercept form)   **45.** $y = \dfrac{1}{3}x + \dfrac{4}{3}$

47. $y = \dfrac{3}{4}x - \dfrac{9}{2}$ **49.** $y = -2x - 3$ **51.** (0, 32); (100, 212)   **52.** $\dfrac{9}{5}$

53. $F - 32 = \dfrac{9}{5}(C - 0)$ **54.** $F = \dfrac{9}{5}C + 32$ **55.** $C = \dfrac{5}{9}(F - 32)$

56. 86°   **57.** 10°   **58.** $-40°$ **59. (a)** \$400 **(b)** \$0.25
(c) $y = 0.25x + 400$ **(d)** \$425 **(e)** 1500   **61. (a)** (1, 1909), (2, 2079),
(3, 2182), (4, 2272), (5, 2361)

(b) yes

**AVERAGE ANNUAL COSTS AT
2-YEAR COLLEGES**

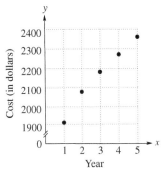

(c) $y = 94x + 1891$ **(d)** \$2455

Chapter 12 Exponents and Polynomials

Taken from *Prealgebra & Introductory Algebra* by Lial, et. al (0321578732)

Section 12.1 (pages 912–920)

1. 7; 5 **3.** 8 **5.** 26 **7.** 1; 6 **9.** 1; 1 **11.** 1; $\dfrac{1}{5}$ **13.** 2; $-19, -1$

15. 3; $1, -8, \dfrac{2}{3}$ **17.** $2m^5$ **19.** $-r^5$ **21.** $\dfrac{2}{3}x^4$ **23.** cannot be simplified;
$0.2m^5 - 0.5m^2$ **25.** $-5x^5$ **27.** $5p^9 + 4p^7$ **29.** $-2y^2$
31. already simplified; 4; binomial **33.** already simplified;
$6m^5 + 5m^4 - 7m^3 - 3m^2$; 5; none of these **35.** $x^4 + \dfrac{1}{3}x^2 - 4$; 4;
trinomial **37.** 7; 0; monomial **39.** $1.5x^2 - 0.5x$; 2; binomial
41. (a) -1 **(b)** 5 **43. (a)** 19 **(b)** -2 **45. (a)** 36 **(b)** -12
47. (a) -124 **(b)** 5 **48.** 5; 175 **49.** 87 ft; (1, 87) **50.** \$16.00
51. \$27 **52.** 2.5; 130 **53.** $5m^2 + 3m$ **55.** $4x^4 - 4x^2$
57. $\dfrac{7}{6}x^2 - \dfrac{2}{15}x + \dfrac{5}{6}$ **59.** $12m^3 - 13m^2 + 6m + 11$
61. $2.9x^3 - 3.5x^2 - 1.5x - 9$ **63.** $8r^2 + 5r - 12$
65. $5m^2 - 14m + 6$ **67.** $4x^3 + 2x^2 + 5x$
69. $-18y^5 + 7y^4 + 5y^3 + 3y^2 + y$ **71.** $-2m^3 + 7m^2 + 8m - 9$
73. $-11x^2 - 3x - 3$ **75.** $2x^2 + 8x$ **77.** $8x^2 + 8x + 6$
79. $8t^2 + 8t + 13$ **81.** $13a^2b - 7a^2 - b$ **83.** $c^4d - 5c^2d^2 + d^2$
85. $12m^3n - 11m^2n^2 - 4mn^2$ **87. (a)** $23y + 5t$ **(b)** 25°, 67°, 88°

Section 12.2 (pages 921–928)

1. 1 **3.** false **5.** false **7.** t^7 **9.** $\left(\dfrac{1}{2}\right)^5$ **11.** $(-8p)^2$ **13.** The
expression $(-3)^4$ means $(-3)(-3)(-3)(-3) = 81$, while -3^4 means
$-(3 \cdot 3 \cdot 3 \cdot 3) = -81$. **15.** base: 3; exponent: 5; 243 **17.** base: -3;
exponent: 5; -243 **19.** base: $-6x$; exponent: 4 **21.** base: x; exponent: 4
23. The product rule does not apply to $5^2 + 5^3$ because it is a *sum*, not
a product. $5^2 + 5^3 = 25 + 125 = 150$ **25.** 5^8 **27.** 4^{12} **29.** $(-7)^9$
31. t^{24} **33.** $-56r^7$ **35.** $42p^{10}$ **37.** The product rule does not apply.
39. The product rule does not apply. **41.** 4^6 **43.** t^{20} **45.** $343r^3$
47. 5^{12} **49.** -8^{15} **51.** $5^5x^5y^5$ **53.** $8q^3r^3$ **55.** $\dfrac{1}{8}$ **57.** $\dfrac{a^3}{b^3}$ **59.** $\dfrac{9^8}{5^8}$
61. $-8x^6y^3$ **63.** $9a^6b^4$ **65.** $\dfrac{5^5}{2^5}$ **67.** $\dfrac{9^5}{8^3}$ **69.** $2^{12}x^{12}$ **71.** -6^5p^5
73. $6^5x^{10}y^{15}$ **75.** x^{21} **77.** $4w^4x^{26}y^7$ **79.** $-r^{18}s^{17}$ **81.** $\dfrac{125a^6b^{15}}{c^{18}}$
83. $25m^6p^{14}q^5$ **85.** $16x^{10}y^{16}z^{10}$ **87.** $30x^7$

Section 12.3 (pages 929–934)

1. $x^2 + 7x + 12$ **3.** $2x^3 + 7x^2 + 7x + 2$ **5.** distributive

7. $-6m^2 - 4m$ **9.** $6p - \dfrac{9}{2}p^2 + 9p^4$ **11.** $6y^5 + 4y^6 + 10y^9$

13. $12x^3 + 26x^2 + 10x + 1$ **15.** $6r^3 + 5r^2 - 12r + 4$

17. $20m^4 - m^3 - 8m^2 - 17m - 15$ **19.** $5x^4 - 13x^3 + 20x^2 + 7x + 5$

21. $m^2 + 12m + 35$ **23.** $n^2 + n - 6$ **25.** $8r^2 - 10r - 3$ **27.** $9x^2 - 4$

29. $9q^2 + 6q + 1$ **31.** $15xy - 40x + 21y - 56$ **33.** $6t^2 + 23st + 20s^2$

35. $-0.3t^2 + 0.22t + 0.24$ **37.** $x^2 - \dfrac{5}{12}x - \dfrac{1}{6}$ **39.** $\dfrac{15}{16} - \dfrac{1}{4}r - 2r^2$

41. $2x^3 + x^2 - 15x$ **43.** $6y^5 - 21y^4 - 45y^3$ **44.** $(30x + 60)$ yd^2

45. $30x + 60 = 600$; $\{18\}$ **46.** **(a)** 10 yd by 60 yd **(b)** 140 yd

47. \$2100 **48.** \$1260 **49.** The answers are $x^2 - 16$, $y^2 - 4$, and
$r^2 - 49$. Each product is the difference of the square of the first term and
the square of the last term of the binomials.

Section 12.4 (pages 935–940)

1. **(a)** $4x^2$ **(b)** $12x$ **(c)** 9 **(d)** $4x^2 + 12x + 9$ **3.** $p^2 + 4p + 4$
5. $z^2 - 10z + 25$ **7.** $16x^2 - 24x + 9$ **9.** $4p^2 + 20pq + 25q^2$
11. $0.64t^2 + 1.12ts + 0.49s^2$ **13.** $25x^2 + 4xy + \dfrac{4}{25}y^2$

15. $9t^3 - 6t^2 + t$ **17.** $-16r^2 + 16r - 4$ **19.** **(a)** $49x^2$ **(b)** 0
(c) $-9y^2$ **(d)** $49x^2 - 9y^2$; Because 0 is the identity element for
addition, it is not necessary to write "$+ 0$." **21.** $q^2 - 4$ **23.** $4w^2 - 25$

25. $100x^2 - 9y^2$ **27.** $4x^4 - 25$ **29.** $49x^2 - \dfrac{9}{49}$ **31.** $9p^3 - 49p$

33. $(a + b)^2$ **34.** a^2 **35.** $2ab$ **36.** b^2 **37.** $a^2 + 2ab + b^2$
38. They both represent the area of the entire large square.
39. 1225 **40.** $30^2 + 2(30)(5) + 5^2$ **41.** 1225 **42.** They are
equal. **43.** $m^3 - 15m^2 + 75m - 125$ **45.** $y^3 + 6y^2 + 12y + 8$
47. $8a^3 + 12a^2 + 6a + 1$
49. $81r^4 - 216r^3t + 216r^2t^2 - 96rt^3 + 16t^4$
51. $3x^5 - 27x^4 + 81x^3 - 81x^2$
53. $-8x^6y - 32x^5y^2 - 48x^4y^3 - 32x^3y^4 - 8x^2y^5$ **55.** 512 cu. units

Section 12.5 (pages 941–952)

1. negative **3.** negative **5.** positive **7.** 0 **9.** 1 **11.** 1 **13.** -1

15. 0 **17.** 0 **19.** 2 **21.** $\dfrac{1}{64}$ **23.** 16 **25.** $\dfrac{49}{36}$ **27.** $\dfrac{1}{81}$ **29.** $\dfrac{8}{15}$

31. $-\dfrac{7}{18}$ **33.** 1 **34.** $\dfrac{5^2}{5^2}$ **35.** $5^{2-2} = 5^0$ **36.** $5^0 = 1$; This supports the

definition of a 0 exponent. **37.** $\dfrac{1}{9}$ **39.** $\dfrac{1}{6^5}$, or $\dfrac{1}{7776}$ **41.** 216 **43.** $2r^4$

45. $\dfrac{25}{64}$ **47.** $\dfrac{p^5}{q^8}$ **49.** r^9 **51.** $\dfrac{x^5}{6}$ **53.** $3y^2$ **55.** x^3 **57.** $\dfrac{yz^2}{4x^3}$

59. $a + b$ **61.** 343 **63.** $\dfrac{1}{x^2}$ **65.** $\dfrac{64x}{9}$ **67.** $\dfrac{x^2z^4}{y^2}$ **69.** $6x$

71. $\dfrac{1}{m^{10}n^5}$ **73.** $\dfrac{5}{16x^5}$ **75.** $\dfrac{36q^2}{m^4p^2}$

Summary Exercises on the Rules for Exponents (pages 951–952)

1. $\dfrac{6^{12}x^{24}}{5^{12}}$ **2.** $\dfrac{r^6s^{12}}{729t^6}$ **3.** $100{,}000x^7y^{14}$ **4.** $-128a^{10}b^{15}c^4$ **5.** $\dfrac{729w^3x^9}{y^{12}}$

6. $\dfrac{x^4y^6}{16}$ **7.** c^{22} **8.** $\dfrac{1}{k^4t^{12}}$ **9.** $\dfrac{11}{30}$ **10.** $y^{12}z^3$ **11.** $\dfrac{x^6}{y^5}$ **12.** 0 **13.** $\dfrac{1}{z^2}$

14. $\dfrac{9}{r^2s^2t^{10}}$ **15.** $\dfrac{300x^3}{y^3}$ **16.** $\dfrac{3}{5x^6}$ **17.** x^8 **18.** $\dfrac{y^{11}}{x^{11}}$ **19.** $\dfrac{a^6}{b^4}$ **20.** $6ab$

21. $\dfrac{61}{900}$ **22.** 1 **23.** $\dfrac{343a^6b^9}{8}$ **24.** 1 **25.** -1 **26.** 0 **27.** $\dfrac{27y^{18}}{4x^8}$

28. $\dfrac{1}{a^8b^{12}c^{16}}$ **29.** $\dfrac{x^{15}}{216z^9}$ **30.** $\dfrac{q}{8p^6r^3}$ **31.** x^6y^6 **32.** 0 **33.** $\dfrac{343}{x^{15}}$

34. $\dfrac{9}{x^6}$ **35.** $5p^{10}q^9$ **36.** $\dfrac{7}{24}$ **37.** $\dfrac{r^{14}t}{2s^2}$ **38.** 1 **39.** $8p^{10}q$ **40.** $\dfrac{1}{mn^3p^3}$

41. -1 **42.** $\dfrac{3}{40}$ **43.** Using the product rule, simplify as follows:
$(10^2)^3 = 10^{2 \cdot 3} = 10^6 = 1{,}000{,}000$. **44.** The negative sign is not part of
the base: $-5^4 = -1(5)^4 = -1 \cdot 625 = -625$.

Section 12.6 (pages 953–956)

1. $6x^2 + 8$; 2; $3x^2 + 4$ **3.** $3x^2 + 4$; 2 (These may be reversed.); $6x^2 + 8$
5. To use the method of this section, the divisor must be just one term.
This is true of the first problem, but not the second. **7.** $30x^3 - 10x + 5$

9. $-4m^3 + 2m^2 - 1$ **11.** $4t^4 - 2t^2 + 2t$ **13.** $a^4 - a + \dfrac{2}{a}$

15. $-2x^3 + \dfrac{2x^2}{3} - x$ **17.** $-9x^2 + 5x + 1$ **19.** $\dfrac{4x^2}{3} + x - \dfrac{2}{3x}$

21. $9r^3 - 12r^2 - 2r + 1 - \dfrac{2}{3r}$ **23.** $-m^2 + 3m - \dfrac{4}{m}$

25. $\dfrac{12}{x} - \dfrac{6}{x^2} + \dfrac{14}{x^3} - \dfrac{10}{x^4}$ **27.** $-4b^2 + 3ab - \dfrac{5}{a}$ **29.** $6x - 2 + \dfrac{1}{x}$

31. $15x^5 - 35x^4 + 35x^3$ **33.** 1423
34. $(1 \times 10^3) + (4 \times 10^2) + (2 \times 10^1) + (3 \times 10^0)$
35. $x^3 + 4x^2 + 2x + 3$ **36.** They are similar in that the coefficients of
the powers of ten are equal to the coefficients of the powers of x. They are
different in that one is a number while the other is a polynomial. They are
equal if $x = 10$.

Section 12.7 (pages 957–962)

1. The divisor is $2x + 5$; the quotient is $2x^3 - 4x^2 + 3x + 2$. **3.** Divide
$12m^2$ by $2m$ to get $6m$. **5.** $x + 2$ **7.** $2y - 5$ **9.** $p - 4 + \dfrac{44}{p + 6}$

11. $r - 5$ **13.** $2a - 14 + \dfrac{74}{2a + 3}$ **15.** $4x^2 - 7x + 3$

17. $3y^2 - 2y + 2$ **19.** $2x^2 - 2x + 3 + \dfrac{-1}{x + 1}$ **21.** $3k - 4 + \dfrac{2}{k^2 - 2}$

23. $x^2 + 1$ **25.** $x^2 + 1$ **27.** $2p^2 - 5p + 4 + \dfrac{6}{3p^2 + 1}$

29. $x^3 + 6x - 7$ **31.** $2x^2 + \dfrac{3}{5}x + \dfrac{1}{5}$ **33.** $(x^2 + x - 3)$ units **35.** 33
36. 33 **37.** They are the same. **38.** The answers should agree.

Section 12.8 (pages 963–968)

1. 6.1309×10^9; 5.8689×10^9 **3.** in scientific notation **5.** not in
scientific notation; 5.6×10^6 **7.** not in scientific notation; 4×10^{-3}
9. not in scientific notation; 8×10^1 **11.** A number is written in
scientific notation if it is the product of a number whose absolute value is
between 1 and 10 (inclusive of 1) and a power of 10. **13.** 5.876×10^9
15. 8.235×10^4 **17.** 7×10^{-6} **19.** -2.03×10^{-3} **21.** 750,000
23. 5,677,000,000,000 **25.** 1,000,000,000,000 **27.** -6.21
29. 0.00078 **31.** 0.000000005134 **33.** 6×10^{11}; 600,000,000,000
35. 1.5×10^7; 15,000,000 **37.** 8×10^{-3}; 0.008 **39.** 2.4×10^2; 240
41. 6.3×10^{-2}; 0.063 **43.** 6.426×10^4; 64,260 **45.** 3×10^{-4};

0.0003   **47.** 4×10^1; 40   **49.** 1.3×10^{-5}; 0.000013   **51.** 5×10^2;
500   **53.** 2.6×10^{-3}; 0.0026   **55.** 7.205×10^{-6}; 0.000007205
57. 1.5×10^{17} mi   **59.** $3554

Chapter 13 Solving Inequalities/Absolute Values/Intro Functions

Taken from, *Intermediate Algebra* (0321574974)

Section 13.1 (pages 970–983)

1. {1, 2, 3, 4, 5}   **3.** {5, 6, 7, 8, . . .}   **5.** {10, 12, 14, 16, . . .}
7. ∅   **9.** {−4, 4}   **11.** {x | x is an even natural number less than
or equal to 8}   **13.** {x | x is a multiple of 4 greater than 0}

15.   **17.**

19. (a) $5, 17, \frac{40}{2}$ (or 20)   **(b)** $0, 5, 17, \frac{40}{2}$ **(c)** $-8, 0, 5, 17, \frac{40}{2}$

(d) $-8, -0.6, 0, \frac{3}{4}, 5, \frac{13}{2}, 17, \frac{40}{2}$ **(e)** $-\sqrt{5}, \sqrt{3}, \pi$ **(f)** All are

real numbers.   **21.** false; Some are integers, but others, like $\frac{3}{4}$,

are not.   **23.** false; No irrational number is an integer.   **25.** true
27. true   **29.** true   **31. (a)** −6   **(b)** 6   **33. (a)** 12   **(b)** 12
35. (a) $-\frac{6}{5}$ **(b)** $\frac{6}{5}$ **37.** 8   **39.** $\frac{3}{2}$ **41.** −5   **43.** −2   **45.** −4.5
47. 5   **49.** 6   **51.** 0   **53. (a)** Louisiana; It decreased 4.1%.
(b) West Virginia; It increased 0.6%.   **55.** Pacific Ocean, Indian
Ocean, Caribbean Sea, South China Sea, Gulf of California
57. true   **59.** true   **61.** false   **63.** true   **65.** true   **67.** $7 > y$
69. $5 \geq 5$ **71.** $3t - 4 \leq 10$ **73.** $5x + 3 \neq 0$ **75.** $-6 < 10$; true
77. $10 \geq 10$; true   **79.** $-3 \geq -3$; true   **81.** $-8 > -6$; false
83. greater than   **85.** California (CA), Florida (FL)   **87.** $x < y$

Section 13.2 (pages 984–1000)

1. D   **3.** B   **5.** F   **7. (a)** $131 \leq s \leq 155$ **(b)** $s > 155$
(c) $9 \leq x \leq 12$ **(d)** $x > 18$ **9.** Reverse the direction of the inequality
symbol only when multiplying or dividing by a *negative* number.
The solution set is $[-16, \infty)$.

11. $(-\infty, 7]$

13. $[5, \infty)$

15. $(-5, \infty)$

17. $(-4, \infty)$

19. $(-\infty, -40]$

21. $(-\infty, 4]$

23. $(7, \infty)$

25. $\left(-\infty, -\frac{15}{2}\right)$

27. $(-\infty, -7)$

29. $\left[\frac{1}{2}, \infty\right)$

31. $(3, \infty)$

33. $(-\infty, 4)$

35. $\left(-\infty, \frac{23}{6}\right]$

37. $\left(-\infty, \frac{76}{11}\right)$

39. {−9}

40. $(-9, \infty)$

41. $(-\infty, -9)$

42. We obtain the set of all real numbers.

43. $(-\infty, -3)$

45. $(1, 11)$

47. $[-14, 10]$

49. $[-5, 6]$

51. $(-6, -4)$

53. $\left[-\frac{1}{3}, \frac{1}{9}\right)$

55. $\left[-\frac{1}{2}, \frac{35}{2}\right]$

57. from about 2:30 P.M. to 6:00 P.M.   **59.** about 84°F–91°F
61. 26 months   **63.** at least 80   **65.** 26 DVDs   **67. (a)** 140 to 184 lb
(b) Answers will vary.   **69.** all numbers between −2 and 2, or (−2, 2)
71. all numbers greater than or equal to 3, or $[3, \infty)$
73. all numbers greater than or equal to −9, or $[-9, \infty)$

Section 13.3 (pages 1001–1012)

1. true   **3.** false; The union is $(-\infty, 6) \cup (6, \infty)$.   **5.** {4}, or D
7. ∅   **9.** {1, 2, 3, 4, 5, 6}, or A   **11.** {1, 3, 5, 6}

13.   **15.**

17.

19. Answers will vary. One example is: The intersection of two streets is
the region common to *both* streets.

21. $(-3, 2)$

23. $(-\infty, 2]$

25. ∅

27. $[5, 9]$

29. $(-\infty, 4]$

31. $(-\infty, 8]$

```
0        8
```

33. $[-2, \infty)$

```
   -2  0
```

35. $(-\infty, \infty)$

```
        0
```

37. $(-\infty, -5) \cup (5, \infty)$

```
   -5   0   5
```

39. $(-\infty, -1] \cup (2, \infty)$

```
   -1 0   2
```

41. $(-\infty, 2) \cup (2, \infty)$

```
     0   2
```

43. $[-4, -1]$ **45.** $[-9, -6]$ **47.** $(-\infty, 3)$ **49.** $[3, 9)$

51. intersection; $(-5, -1)$

```
   -5    -1 0
```

53. union; $(-\infty, 4)$

```
     0        4
```

55. intersection; $[4, 12]$

```
  0 2 4      12
```

57. union; $(-\infty, 0] \cup [2, \infty)$

```
       0   2
```

59. Mario, Joe   **60.** none of them   **61.** none of them   **62.** Luigi, Than   **63.** Mario, Joe   **64.** all of them   **65.** {Tuition and fees}   **67.** {Tuition and fees, Dormitory charges}

Section 13.4 (pages 1013–1026)

1. E; C; D; B; A   **3. (a)** one   **(b)** two   **(c)** none   **5.** $\{-12, 12\}$

7. $\{-5, 5\}$ **9.** $\{-6, 12\}$ **11.** $\{-5, 4\}$ **13.** $\left\{-3, \frac{11}{2}\right\}$

15. $\left\{-\frac{19}{2}, \frac{9}{2}\right\}$ **17.** $\{-10, -2\}$ **19.** $\left\{-8, \frac{32}{3}\right\}$

21. $(-\infty, -3) \cup (3, \infty)$

```
   -3    0    3
```

23. $(-\infty, -4] \cup [4, \infty)$

```
   -4    0    4
```

25. $(-\infty, -10) \cup (6, \infty)$

```
  -10    0 2  6
```

27. $\left(-\infty, -\frac{7}{3}\right] \cup [3, \infty)$

```
   -7/3  0   3
```

29. $(-\infty, -2) \cup (8, \infty)$

```
   -2 0 2     8
```

31. (a)

```
   -5    0    4
```

(b)

```
   -5    0    4
```

33. $[-3, 3]$

```
  -3    0    3
```

35. $(-4, 4)$

```
  -4    0    4
```

37. $[-10, 6]$

```
 -10    0 2   6
```

39. $\left(-\frac{7}{3}, 3\right)$

```
  -7/3 0    3
```

41. $[-2, 8]$

```
  -2 0      8
```

43. $(-\infty, -2) \cup (10, \infty)$

```
  -2 0        10
```

45. $\{-6, -1\}$

```
  -6         -1 0
```

47. $\left[-\frac{10}{3}, 4\right]$

```
 -10/3   0     4
```

49. $\left[-4, -\frac{4}{3}\right]$

```
  -4   -4/3 0
```

51. $\{-5, 5\}$ **53.** $\{-5, -3\}$ **55.** $(-\infty, -3) \cup (2, \infty)$ **57.** $[-10, 0]$

59. $\{-1, 3\}$ **61.** $\left\{-3, \frac{5}{3}\right\}$ **63.** $\left\{-\frac{1}{3}, -\frac{1}{15}\right\}$ **65.** $\left\{-\frac{5}{4}\right\}$

67. $(-\infty, \infty)$ **69.** $\emptyset$ **71.** $\left\{-\frac{1}{4}\right\}$ **73.** $\emptyset$ **75.** $(-\infty, \infty)$

77. $\left\{-\frac{3}{7}\right\}$ **79.** $(-\infty, \infty)$ **81.** $\left(-\infty, -\frac{7}{10}\right) \cup \left(-\frac{7}{10}, \infty\right)$

83. $(-\infty, \infty)$ **85.** $|x - 1000| \le 100; 900 \le x \le 1100$ **87.** 475.6 ft

88. 1201 Walnut, City Hall, Fidelity Bank and Trust Building, Kansas City Power and Light, Hyatt Regency Crown Center   **89.** City Center Square, Commerce Tower, Federal Office Building, 1201 Walnut, City Hall, Fidelity Bank and Trust Building, Kansas City Power and Light, Hyatt Regency Crown Center   **90. (a)** $|x - 475.6| \ge 75$ **(b)** $x \ge 550.6$ or $x \le 400.6$ **(c)** Town Pavilion, One Kansas City Place   **(d)** It makes sense because it includes all buildings *not* listed in the answer to Exercise 89.

Summary Exercises on Solving Linear and Absolute Value Equations and Inequalities (pages 1025–1026)

1. $\{12\}$ **2.** $\{-5, 7\}$ **3.** $\{7\}$ **4.** $\left\{-\frac{2}{5}\right\}$ **5.** $\emptyset$ **6.** $(-\infty, -1]$

7. $\left[-\frac{2}{3}, \infty\right)$ **8.** $\{-1\}$ **9.** $\{-3\}$ **10.** $\left\{1, \frac{11}{3}\right\}$ **11.** $(-\infty, 5]$

12. $(-\infty, \infty)$ **13.** $\{2\}$ **14.** $(-\infty, -8] \cup [8, \infty)$ **15.** $\emptyset$

16. $(-\infty, \infty)$ **17.** $(-5.5, 5.5)$ **18.** $\left\{\frac{13}{3}\right\}$ **19.** $\left\{-\frac{96}{5}\right\}$

20. $(-\infty, 32]$ **21.** $(-\infty, -24)$ **22.** $\left\{\frac{3}{8}\right\}$ **23.** $\left\{\frac{7}{2}\right\}$ **24.** $(-6, 8)$

25. $(-\infty, \infty)$ **26.** $(-\infty, 5)$ **27.** $(-\infty, -4) \cup (7, \infty)$ **28.** $\{24\}$

29. $\left\{-\frac{1}{5}\right\}$ **30.** $\left(-\infty, -\frac{5}{2}\right]$ **31.** $\left[-\frac{1}{3}, 3\right]$ **32.** $[1, 7]$

33. $\left\{-\frac{1}{6}, 2\right\}$ **34.** $\{-3\}$ **35.** $(-\infty, -1] \cup \left[\frac{5}{3}, \infty\right)$ **36.** $\left[\frac{3}{4}, \frac{15}{8}\right]$

37. $\left\{-\frac{5}{2}\right\}$ **38.** $\{60\}$ **39.** $\left[-\frac{9}{2}, \frac{15}{2}\right]$ **40.** $(1, 9)$ **41.** $(-\infty, \infty)$

42. $\left\{\frac{1}{3}, 9\right\}$ **43.** $(-\infty, \infty)$ **44.** $\left\{-\frac{10}{9}\right\}$ **45.** $\{-2\}$ **46.** $\emptyset$

47. $(-\infty, -1) \cup (2, \infty)$ **48.** $[-3, -2]$

Section 13.5 (pages 1027–1034)

1. solid; below   **3.** dashed; above   **5.** The graph of $Ax + By = C$ divides the plane into two regions. In one of these regions, the ordered pairs satisfy $Ax + By < C$; in the other, they satisfy $Ax + By > C$.

7.

9.

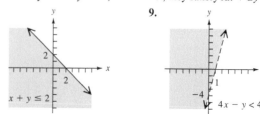

11.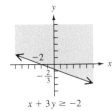

13.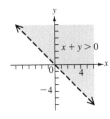

15.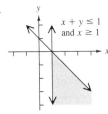

17.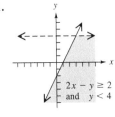

19.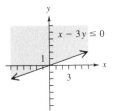

21.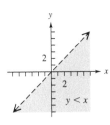

23.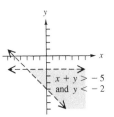

25.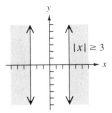

27.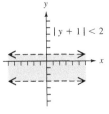

29.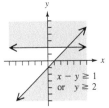

31.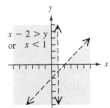

33.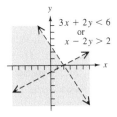

$(-\infty, 0) \cup (0, \infty)$ **35.** function; domain: $\left[-\frac{1}{2}, \infty\right)$ **37.** function; domain: $(-\infty, 9) \cup (9, \infty)$ **39. (a)** $[0, 3000]$ **(b)** 25 hr; 25 hr   **(c)** 2000 gal   **(d)** $g(0) = 0$; The pool is empty at time 0.   **41.** Here is one example. The cost of gasoline; number of gallons purchased; cost; number of gallons   **43.** 4   **45.** -11 **47.** $-3p + 4$ **49.** $3x + 4$ **51.** $-3x - 2$ **53.** $-\frac{p^2}{9} + \frac{4p}{3} + 1$ **55. (a)** 2   **(b)** 3   **57. (a)** 15   **(b)** 10   **59. (a)** 3   **(b)** -3 **61.** line; -2; linear; $-2x + 4$; -2; 3; -2 **63. (a)** $f(x) = -\frac{1}{3}x + 4$ **(b)** 3   **65. (a)** $f(x) = 3 - 2x^2$ **(b)** -15 **67. (a)** $f(x) = \frac{4}{3}x - \frac{8}{3}$ **(b)** $\frac{4}{3}$

69. domain: $(-\infty, \infty)$; range: $(-\infty, \infty)$

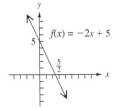

71. domain: $(-\infty, \infty)$; range: $(-\infty, \infty)$

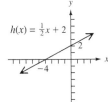

73. domain: $(-\infty, \infty)$; range: $\{-4\}$

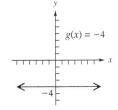

75. (a) $0; $2.50; $5.00; $7.50   **(b)** $2.50x

(c)

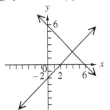

77. 194.53 cm   **79.** 177.41 cm

Chapter 14 Systems of Equations

Taken from *Prealgebra & Introductory Algebra* by Lial, et. al (0321578732) and *Intermediate Algebra* (0321574974)

Section 14.1 (pages 1052–1060)

1. B, because the ordered pair must be in quadrant II.   **3.** There is no way that the sum of two numbers can be both 2 and 4 at the same time.   **5.** no   **7.** yes   **9.** yes   **11.** no
We show the graphs here only for Exercises 13–17.
13. $\{(4, 2)\}$ **15.** $\{(0, 4)\}$

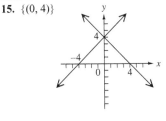

Section 13.6 (pages 1035–1050)

1. independent variable   **3. (a)** A relation is a set of ordered pairs.   **(b)** The domain is the set of all first components (*x*-values).   **(c)** The range is the set of all second components (*y*-values).   **(d)** A function is a relation in which each domain element is paired with one and only one range element.   **5.** function; domain: $\{5, 3, 4, 7\}$; range: $\{1, 2, 9, 3\}$ **7.** not a function; domain: $\{2, 0\}$; range: $\{4, 2, 6\}$ **9.** function; domain: $\{-3, 4, -2\}$; range: $\{1, 7\}$ **11.** not a function; domain: $\{1, 0, 2\}$; range: $\{1, -1, 0, 4, -4\}$ **13.** function; domain: $\{2, 5, 11, 17, 3\}$; range: $\{1, 7, 20\}$ **15.** not a function; domain: $\{1\}$; range: $\{5, 2, -1, -4\}$ **17.** function; domain: $(-\infty, \infty)$; range: $(-\infty, \infty)$ **19.** function; domain: $(-\infty, \infty)$; range: $(-\infty, 4]$ **21.** not a function; domain: $[3, \infty)$; range: $(-\infty, \infty)$ **23.** function; domain: $(-\infty, \infty)$ **25.** not a function; domain: $[0, \infty)$ **27.** function; domain: $(-\infty, \infty)$ **29.** not a function; domain: $(-\infty, \infty)$ **31.** function; domain: $[0, \infty)$ **33.** function; domain:

17. $\{(4, -1)\}$

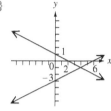

19. $\{(1, 3)\}$ **21.** $\{(0, 2)\}$ **23.** Ø (inconsistent system)
25. $\{(x, y) \mid 2x - y = 4\}$ (dependent equations) **27.** $\{(4, -3)\}$
29. Ø (inconsistent system) **31. (a)** neither **(b)** intersecting lines
(c) one solution **33. (a)** dependent **(b)** one line **(c)** infinite number of
solutions **35. (a)** inconsistent **(b)** parallel lines **(c)** no solution
37. 1980–2000 **39. (a)** 1997–2002 **(b)** 2001 **(c)** 2002 **(d)** (2004, 70)
(The y-value is approximate.) **(e)** During the period 1997–2004, debit card
use went from least popular to most popular of the three methods depicted.

Section 14.2 (pages 1061–1068)

1. The y-value must also be determined. The solution set is $\{(3, 0)\}$.
3. $\{(3, 9)\}$ **5.** $\{(7, 3)\}$ **7.** $\{(-2, 4)\}$ **9.** $\{(-4, 8)\}$ **11.** $\{(3, -2)\}$
13. $\{(x, y) \mid 3x - y = 5\}$ **15.** $\left\{\left(\frac{1}{3}, -\frac{1}{2}\right)\right\}$ **17.** Ø
19. $\{(x, y) \mid 3x - 4y = 2\}$ **21.** $\{(2, -3)\}$ **23.** $\{(10, -12)\}$
25. $\{(-4, 2)\}$ **27.** $\{(7, -3)\}$ **29.** $\{(20, 30)\}$ **30.** To find the total cost,
multiply the number of bicycles (x) by the cost per bicycle (400 dollars) and
add the fixed cost (5000 dollars). Thus, $y_1 = 400x + 5000$ gives this total
cost (in dollars). **31.** $y_2 = 600x$ **32.** $y_1 = 400x + 5000$, $y_2 = 600x$;
solution set: $\{(25, 15{,}000)\}$ **33.** 25; 15,000; 15,000

Section 14.3 (pages 1069–1078)

1. true **3.** true **5.** $\{(-1, 3)\}$ **7.** $\{(-1, -3)\}$ **9.** $\{(-2, 3)\}$
11. $\left\{\left(\frac{1}{2}, 4\right)\right\}$ **13.** $\{(3, -6)\}$ **15.** $\{(7, 4)\}$ **17.** $\{(0, 4)\}$
19. $\{(-4, 0)\}$ **21.** $\{(0, 0)\}$ **23.** Ø **25.** $\{(x, y) \mid x - 3y = -4\}$
27. $\{(2, 9)\}$ **29.** $\{(-6, 5)\}$ **31.** $\left\{\left(-\frac{6}{5}, \frac{4}{5}\right)\right\}$ **33.** $\left\{\left(\frac{1}{8}, -\frac{5}{6}\right)\right\}$
35. $\{(11, 15)\}$ **37.** Ø **39.** $\{(x, y) \mid 2x + y = 0\}$ **41.** $1339 = 1996a + b$
42. $1536 = 2004a + b$ **43.** $1996a + b = 1339$, $2004a + b = 1536$;
solution set: $\{(24.625, -47{,}812.5)\}$ **44.** $y = 24.625x - 47{,}812.5$
45. 1486.8 (million); This is quite a bit less than the actual figure.
46. Since the data do not lie in a perfectly straight line, the quantity
obtained from an equation determined in this way will probably be "off"
a bit. We cannot put too much faith in models such as this one, because
not all sets of data points are linear in nature.

Summary Exercises on Solving Systems of Linear Equations (pages 1077–1078)

1. (a) Use substitution since the second equation is solved for y.
(b) Use elimination since the coefficients of the y-terms are opposites.
(c) Use elimination since the equations are in standard form with no
coefficients of 1 or -1. Solving by substitution would involve fractions.
2. The system on the right is easier to solve by substitution because the
second equation is already solved for y. **3. (a)** $\{(1, 4)\}$ **(b)** $\{(1, 4)\}$
(c) Answers will vary. **4. (a)** $\{(-5, 2)\}$ **(b)** $\{(-5, 2)\}$ **(c)** Answers
will vary. **5.** $\{(2, 6)\}$ **6.** $\{(-3, 2)\}$ **7.** $\left\{\left(\frac{1}{3}, \frac{1}{2}\right)\right\}$ **8.** Ø **9.** $\{(3, 0)\}$

10. $\left\{\left(\frac{3}{2}, -\frac{3}{2}\right)\right\}$ **11.** $\{(x, y) \mid 3x + y = 7\}$ **12.** $\{(9, 4)\}$
13. $\left\{\left(-\frac{5}{7}, -\frac{2}{7}\right)\right\}$ **14.** $\{(4, -5)\}$ **15.** Ø **16.** $\{(-4, 6)\}$
17. $\left\{\left(\frac{19}{3}, -5\right)\right\}$ **18.** $\left\{\left(\frac{22}{13}, -\frac{23}{13}\right)\right\}$ **19.** $\{(-12, -60)\}$
20. $\{(2, -4)\}$ **21.** $\{(18, -12)\}$ **22.** $\{(-2, 1)\}$ **23.** $\left\{\left(13, -\frac{7}{5}\right)\right\}$
24. $\{(10, -9)\}$ **25.** $\{(0.04, 0.9)\}$

Section 14.4 (pages 1079–1088)

1. The statement means that when -1 is substituted for x, 2 is substituted
for y, and 3 is substituted for z in the three equations, the resulting three
statements are true. **3.** $\{(3, 2, 1)\}$ **5.** $\{(1, 4, -3)\}$ **7.** $\{(1, 0, 3)\}$
9. $\left\{\left(1, \frac{3}{10}, \frac{2}{5}\right)\right\}$ **11.** $\{(0, 2, -5)\}$ **13.** $\left\{\left(\frac{20}{59}, -\frac{33}{59}, \frac{35}{59}\right)\right\}$
15. $\{(4, 5, 3)\}$ **17.** $\{(2, 2, 2)\}$ **19.** $\{(-1, 0, 0)\}$ **21.** $\left\{\left(\frac{8}{3}, \frac{2}{3}, 3\right)\right\}$
23. Answers will vary. Some possible answers are **(a)** two perpendicular
walls and the ceiling in a normal room, **(b)** the floors of three
different levels of an office building, and **(c)** three pages of this
book (since they intersect in the spine). **25.** Ø; inconsistent system
27. $\{(x, y, z) \mid x - y + 4z = 8\}$; dependent equations
29. $\{(x, y, z) \mid 2x + y - z = 6\}$; dependent equations **31.** $\{(0, 0, 0)\}$
33. Ø; inconsistent system **35.** $\{(3, 0, 2)\}$ **37.** $128 = a + b + c$
38. $140 = 2.25a + 1.5b + c$ **39.** $80 = 9a + 3b + c$
40. $a + b + c = 128$; $2.25a + 1.5b + c = 140$; $9a + 3b + c = 80$;
$\{(-32, 104, 56)\}$ **41.** $f(x) = -32x^2 + 104x + 56$ **42.** height; time
43. 56 ft **44.** 140.5 ft

Section 14.5 (pages 1089–1102)

1. wins: 96; losses: 66 **3.** length: 78 ft; width: 36 ft **5.** Wal-Mart:
$316 billion; ExxonMobil: $340 billion **7.** $x = 40$ and $y = 50$, so
the angles measure 40° and 50°. **9.** NHL: $247.32; NBA: $267.37
11. Junior Roast Beef: $2.09; Big Montana: $4.39 **13. (a)** 6 oz
(b) 15 oz **(c)** 24 oz **(d)** 30 oz **15.** $1.29x **17.** 6 gal of 25%; 14 gal
of 35% **19.** 6 L of pure acid; 48 L of 10% acid **21.** 14 kg of nuts;
16 kg of cereal **23.** $1000 at 2%; $2000 at 4% **25. (a)** $(10 - x)$ mph
(b) $(10 + x)$ mph **27.** scooter: 25 mph; bicycle: 10 mph **29.** boat:
21 mph; current: 3 mph **31.** $0.75-per-lb candy: 5.22 lb; $1.25-per-lb
candy: 3.78 lb **33.** 76 general admission; 108 with student ID **35.** 8 for
a citron; 5 for a wood apple **37.** $x + y + z = 180$; angle measures: 70°,
30°, 80° **39.** first: 20°; second: 70°; third: 90° **41.** shortest: 12 cm;
middle: 25 cm; longest: 33 cm **43.** Independent: 38; Democrat: 34;
Republican: 28 **45.** $14 tickets: 300; $20 tickets: 225; $50 tickets: 60
47. bookstore A: 140; bookstore B: 280; bookstore C: 380 **49.** wins: 46;
losses: 25; ties: 11

Section 14.6 (pages 1103–1110)

1. (a) $0, 5, -3$ **(b)** $1, -3, 8$ **(c)** yes; The number of rows is the
same as the number of columns (three). **(d)** $\begin{bmatrix} 1 & 4 & 8 \\ 0 & 5 & -3 \\ -2 & 3 & 1 \end{bmatrix}$

(e) $\begin{bmatrix} 1 & -\frac{3}{2} & -\frac{1}{2} \\ 0 & 5 & -3 \\ 1 & 4 & 8 \end{bmatrix}$ **(f)** $\begin{bmatrix} 1 & 15 & 25 \\ 0 & 5 & -3 \\ 1 & 4 & 8 \end{bmatrix}$

3. $\begin{bmatrix} 1 & 2 & | & 11 \\ 2 & -1 & | & -3 \end{bmatrix}$; $\begin{bmatrix} 1 & 2 & | & 11 \\ 0 & -5 & | & -25 \end{bmatrix}$; $\begin{bmatrix} 1 & 2 & | & 11 \\ 0 & 1 & | & 5 \end{bmatrix}$; $x + 2y = 11$;

$y = 5$; $\{(1, 5)\}$ **5.** $\{(4, 1)\}$ **7.** $\{(1, 1)\}$ **9.** $\{(-1, 4)\}$ **11.** $\emptyset$

13. $\{(x, y) \mid 2x + y = 4\}$ **15.** $\{(0, 0)\}$

17. $\begin{bmatrix} 1 & 1 & -1 & | & -3 \\ 0 & -1 & 3 & | & 10 \\ 0 & -6 & 7 & | & 38 \end{bmatrix}$; $\begin{bmatrix} 1 & 1 & -1 & | & -3 \\ 0 & 1 & -3 & | & -10 \\ 0 & -6 & 7 & | & 38 \end{bmatrix}$;

$\begin{bmatrix} 1 & 1 & -1 & | & -3 \\ 0 & 1 & -3 & | & -10 \\ 0 & 0 & -11 & | & -22 \end{bmatrix}$; $\begin{bmatrix} 1 & 1 & -1 & | & -3 \\ 0 & 1 & -3 & | & -10 \\ 0 & 0 & 1 & | & 2 \end{bmatrix}$; $x + y - z = -3$;

$y - 3z = -10$; $z = 2$; $\{(3, -4, 2)\}$ **19.** $\{(4, 0, 1)\}$

21. $\{(-1, 23, 16)\}$ **23.** $\{(3, 2, -4)\}$ **25.** $\emptyset$

27. $\{(x, y, z) \mid x - 2y + z = 4\}$ **29.** $\{(0, 0, 0)\}$

Chapter 15 Factoring

Taken from *Prealgebra & Introductory Algebra* (0321578732)
by Lial, et. al. and *Intermediate Algebra* (0321574974) by Lial, Hornsby
and McGinnis

Section 15.1 (pages 1112–1120)

1. 4   **3.** 4   **5.** 6   **7.** 1   **9.** 8   **11.** $10x^3$ **13.** xy^2 **15.** 6   **17.** $3m^2$

19. $2z^4$ **21.** $2mn^4$ **23.** $y + 2$ **25.** $a - 2$ **27.** $2 + 3xy$

29. $x(x - 4)$ **31.** $3t(2t + 5)$ **33.** $\frac{1}{4}d(d - 3)$ **35.** $-6x^2(2x + 1)$

37. $5y^6(13y^4 + 7)$ **39.** no common factor (except 1)   **41.** $8m^2n^2(n + 3)$

43. $-2x(2x^2 - 5x + 3)$ **45.** $13y^2(y^6 + 2y^2 - 3)$

47. $9qp^3(5q^3p^2 + 4p^3 + 9q)$ **49.** $(x + 2)(c + d)$

51. $(2a + b)(a^2 - b)$ **53.** $(p + 4)(q - 1)$ **55.** $(5 + n)(m + 4)$

57. $(2y - 7)(3x + 4)$ **59.** $(y + 3)(3x + 1)$ **61.** $(z + 2)(7z - a)$

63. $(3r + 2y)(6r - x)$ **65.** $(w + 1)(w^2 + 9)$ **67.** $(a + 2)(3a^2 - 2)$

69. $(4m - p^2)(4m^2 - p)$ **71.** $(y + 3)(y + x)$ **73.** $(z - 2)(2z - 3w)$

75. commutative property   **76.** $2x(y - 4) - 3(y - 4)$

77. No, because it is not a product. It is the difference between
$2x(y - 4)$ and $3(y - 4)$.   **78.** $(2x - 3)(y - 4)$; yes

Section 15.2 (pages 1121–1126)

1. a and b must have different signs.   **3.** A prime polynomial is one that
cannot be factored using only integers in the factors.   **5.** 1 and 12, -1 and
-12, 2 and 6, -2 and -6, 3 and 4, -3 and -4; The pair with a sum of 7 is
3 and 4.   **7.** 1 and -24, -1 and 24, 2 and -12, -2 and 12, 3 and -8, -3
and 8, 4 and -6, -4 and 6; The pair with a sum of -5 is 3 and -8.   **9.** C

11. $x + 11$ **13.** $x - 8$ **15.** $y - 5$ **17.** $x + 11$ **19.** $y - 9$

21. $(y + 8)(y + 1)$ **23.** $(b + 3)(b + 5)$ **25.** $(m + 5)(m - 4)$

27. $(x + 8)(x - 5)$ **29.** $(y - 5)(y - 3)$ **31.** $(z - 8)(z - 7)$

33. $(r - 6)(r + 5)$ **35.** $(a - 12)(a + 4)$ **37.** prime

39. $(r + 2a)(r + a)$ **41.** $(x + y)(x + 3y)$ **43.** $(t + 2z)(t - 3z)$

45. $(v - 5w)(v - 6w)$ **47.** $4(x + 5)(x - 2)$ **49.** $2t(t + 1)(t + 3)$

51. $-2x^4(x - 3)(x + 7)$ **53.** $a^3(a + 4b)(a - b)$

55. $mn(m - 6n)(m - 4n)$ **57.** The factored form $(2x + 4)(x - 3)$
is incorrect because $2x + 4$ has a common factor of 2, which must be
factored out for the trinomial to be *completely* factored.

Section 15.3 (pages 1127–1130)

1. $(m + 6)(m + 2)$ **3.** $(a + 5)(a - 2)$ **5.** $(2t + 1)(5t + 2)$

7. $(3z - 2)(5z - 3)$ **9.** $(2s - t)(4s + 3t)$ **11.** $(3a + 2b)(5a + 4b)$

13. B   **15. (a)** 2; 12; 24; 11   **(b)** 3; 8 (Order is irrelevant.)

(c) $3m$; $8m$ **(d)** $2m^2 + 3m + 8m + 12$ **(e)** $(2m + 3)(m + 4)$

(f) $(2m + 3)(m + 4) = 2m^2 + 11m + 12$ **17.** $(2x + 1)(x + 3)$

19. $(4r - 3)(r + 1)$ **21.** $(4m + 1)(2m - 3)$ **23.** $(3m + 1)(7m + 2)$

25. $(2b + 1)(3b + 2)$ **27.** $(4y - 3)(3y - 1)$ **29.** $3(4x - 1)(2x - 3)$

31. $2m(m - 4)(m + 5)$ **33.** $-4z^3(z - 1)(8z + 3)$

35. $(3p + 4q)(4p - 3q)$ **37.** $(3a - 5b)(2a + b)$ **39.** $(5 - x)(1 - x)$

41. The student stopped too soon. He needs to factor out the common
factor $4x - 1$ to get $(4x - 1)(4x - 5)$ as the correct answer.

Section 15.4 (pages 1131–1136)

1. B   **3.** A   **5.** A   **7.** $2a + 5b$ **9.** $x^2 + 3x - 4$; $x + 4$, $x - 1$, or
$x - 1$, $x + 4$ **11.** $2z^2 - 5z - 3$; $2z + 1$, $z - 3$, or $z - 3$, $2z + 1$

13. The binomial $2x - 6$ cannot be a factor because it has a common
factor of 2, but the polynomial does not.   **15.** $(3a + 7)(a + 1)$

17. $(2y + 3)(y + 2)$ **19.** $(3m - 1)(5m + 2)$ **21.** $(3s - 1)(4s + 5)$

23. $(5m - 4)(2m - 3)$ **25.** $(4w - 1)(2w - 3)$

27. $(4y + 1)(5y - 11)$ **29.** prime   **31.** $2(5x + 3)(2x + 1)$

33. $-q(5m + 2)(8m - 3)$ **35.** $3n^2(5n - 3)(n - 2)$

37. $-y^2(5x - 4)(3x + 1)$ **39.** $(5a + 3b)(a - 2b)$

41. $(4s + 5t)(3s - t)$ **43.** $m^4n(3m + 2n)(2m + n)$

45. $-1(x + 7)(x - 3)$ **47.** $-1(3x + 4)(x - 1)$

49. $-1(a + 2b)(2a + b)$ **51.** $5 \cdot 7$ **52.** $(-5)(-7)$

53. The product of $3x - 4$ and $2x - 1$ is $6x^2 - 11x + 4$.

54. The product of $4 - 3x$ and $1 - 2x$ is $6x^2 - 11x + 4$.

55. The factors in Exercise 53 are the opposites of the factors
in Exercise 54.   **56.** $(3 - 7t)(5 - 2t)$

Section 15.5 (pages 1137–1146)

1. 1; 4; 9; 16; 25; 36; 49; 64; 81; 100; 121; 144; 169; 196; 225; 256;

289; 324; 361; 400   **3.** 2   **5.** $(y + 5)(y - 5)$ **7.** $\left(p + \dfrac{1}{3}\right)\left(p - \dfrac{1}{3}\right)$

9. prime   **11.** $(3r + 2)(3r - 2)$ **13.** $\left(2m + \dfrac{3}{5}\right)\left(2m - \dfrac{3}{5}\right)$

15. $4(3x + 2)(3x - 2)$ **17.** $(14p + 15)(14p - 15)$

19. $(4r + 5a)(4r - 5a)$ **21.** prime   **23.** $(p^2 + 7)(p^2 - 7)$

25. $(x^2 + 1)(x + 1)(x - 1)$ **27.** $(p^2 + 16)(p + 4)(p - 4)$

29. The teacher was justified, because it was not factored *completely*;
$x^2 - 9$ can be factored as $(x + 3)(x - 3)$. The complete factored form
is $(x^2 + 9)(x + 3)(x - 3)$.   **31.** No, it is not a perfect square since the
middle term would have to be $30y$.   **33.** $(w + 1)^2$ **35.** $(x - 4)^2$

37. $\left(t + \dfrac{1}{2}\right)^2$ **39.** $(x - 0.5)^2$ **41.** $2(x + 6)^2$ **43.** $(4x - 5)^2$

45. $(7x - 2y)^2$ **47.** $(8x + 3y)^2$ **49.** $-2h(5h - 2y)^2$

51. $(2x + 3)(5x - 2)$ **52.** $5x - 2$ **53.** Yes. We saw in Exercise 51
that $(2x + 3)(5x - 2)$ is the factored form of $10x^2 + 11x - 6$.

54. The quotient is $x^2 + x + 1$, so $x^3 - 1$ factors as $(x - 1)(x^2 + x + 1)$.

Summary Exercises on Factoring (pages 1143–1146)

1. F   **2.** G   **3.** A   **4.** B   **5.** D   **6.** H   **7.** C   **8.** E   **9.** H   **10.** D

11. $8m^3(4m^6 + 2m^2 + 3)$ **12.** $2(m + 3)(m - 8)$

13. $7k(2k + 5)(k - 2)$ **14.** prime   **15.** $(6z + 1)(z + 5)$

16. $(m + n)(m - 4n)$ **17.** $(7z + 4y)(7z - 4y)$

18. $10nr(10nr + 3r^2 - 5n)$ **19.** $4x(4x + 5)$ **20.** $(4 + m)(5 + 3n)$

21. $(5y - 6z)(2y + z)$ **22.** $(y^2 + 9)(y + 3)(y - 3)$

23. $(m - 3)(m + 5)$ **24.** $(2y + 1)(3y - 4)$ **25.** $8z(4z - 1)(z + 2)$

26. $(p - 1.2)^2$ **27.** $(z - 6)^2$ **28.** $(3m + 8)(3m - 8)$

29. $(y - 6k)(y + 2k)$ **30.** $(4z - 1)^2$ **31.** $6(y - 2)(y + 1)$

32. $\left(x + \dfrac{1}{4}\right)^2$ **33.** $(p - 6)(p - 11)$ **34.** $(a + 8)(a + 9)$ **35.** prime

36. $3(6m - 1)^2$ **37.** $(z + 2a)(z - 5a)$ **38.** $(2a + 1)(a^2 - 7)$

39. $(2k - 3)^2$ **40.** $(a - 7b)(a + 4b)$ **41.** $(4r + 3m)^2$

42. $(3k - 2)(k + 2)$ **43.** prime   **44.** $(a^2 + 25)(a + 5)(a - 5)$

45. $4(2k - 3)^2$ **46.** $(4k + 1)(2k - 3)$ **47.** $6y^4(3y + 4)(2y - 5)$

48. $5z(z - 2)(z - 7)$ **49.** $(8p - 1)(p + 3)$ **50.** $(4k - 3h)(2k + h)$

51. $6(3m + 2z)(3m - 2z)$ **52.** $(2k - 5z)^2$ **53.** $2(3a - 1)(a + 2)$

54. $(3h - 2g)(5h + 7g)$ **55.** $7(2a + 3b)(2a - 3b)$

56. $(5z - 6)(2z + 1)$ **57.** $5m^2(5m - 13n)(5m - 3n)$

58. $(3y - 1)(3y + 5)$ **59.** $(3u + 11v)^2$ **60.** prime

61. $9p^8(3p + 7)(p - 4)$ **62.** $5(2m - 3)(m + 4)$ **63.** $(2 - q)(2 - 3p)$

64. $\left(k + \dfrac{8}{11}\right)\left(k - \dfrac{8}{11}\right)$ **65.** $4(4p + 5m)(4p - 5m)$

66. $(m + 4)(m^2 - 6)$ **67.** $(10a + 9y)(10a - 9y)$

68. $(8a - b)(a + 3b)$ **69.** $(a + 4)^2$ **70.** $(2y + 5)(2y - 5)$ **71.** prime

72. $-3x(x + 2y)(x - 2y)$ **73.** $(5a - 7b)^2$ **74.** $8(t^2 + 1)(t + 1)(t - 1)$

75. $-4(x - 3y)^2$ **76.** $25(2a + b)(2a - b)$ **77.** $-2(x - 9)(x - 4)$

78. $(m + 3)(2m - 5n)$ **79.** $2(2x + 5)(3x - 2)$ **80.** $(y^2 + 5)(y^4 - 3)$

81. $(y + 0.8)(y - 0.8)$ **82.** $6p(2p + 1)(p - 5)$

Section 15.6 (pages 1147–1150)

1. $(10a + 3b)(10a - 3b)$ **3.** $6p^3(3p^2 - 4 + 2p^3)$ **5.** $(x + 7)(x - 5)$

7. prime   **9.** $(6b + 1)(b - 3)$ **11.** $3mn(3m + 2n)(2m - n)$

13. $(2p + 5q)(p + 3q)$ **15.** $(2k + 7r)^2$ **17.** $(m - 2)(n + 5)$

19. $(x + 3)^2(x - 3)$ **21.** prime   **23.** $(3k + 1)(2k - 1)$

25. $(x^2 + 25)(x + 5)(x - 5)$ **27.** $(a + 6)(b + c)$ **29.** $4y(y - 2)$

31. $(7z + 2k)(2z - k)$ **33.** $16(4b + 5c)(4b - 5c)$

35. $8(5z + 4)(25z^2 - 20z + 16)$ **37.** $(5r - s)(2r + 5s)$

39. $8x^2(4 + 2x - 3x^3)$ **41.** $(2x - 5q)(7x + 5q)$ **43.** $(y + 5)(y - 2)$

45. $2a(a^2 + 3a - 2)$ **47.** $(9p - 5r)(2p + 7r)$

49. $(x - 2y + 2)(x - 2y - 2)$ **51.** $(5r + 2s - 3)^2$

53. $(z + 2)(z - 2)(z^2 - 5)$ **55.** $(p + 2)(4 + m)$

57. $2(5p + 9)(5p - 9)$ **59.** $(4a + b)^2$

Section 15.7 (pages 1151–1158)

1. $\{-5, 2\}$ **3.** $\left\{3, \dfrac{7}{2}\right\}$ **5.** $\left\{-\dfrac{5}{6}, 0\right\}$ **7.** $\left\{0, \dfrac{4}{3}\right\}$ **9.** $\left\{-\dfrac{1}{2}, \dfrac{1}{6}\right\}$

11. $\{9\}$ **13.** Set each *variable* factor equal to 0, to get $2x = 0$ or

$3x - 4 = 0$. The solution set is $\left\{0, \dfrac{4}{3}\right\}$.   **15.** $\{-2, -1\}$ **17.** $\{1, 2\}$

19. $\{-8, 3\}$ **21.** $\{-1, 3\}$ **23.** $\{-2, -1\}$ **25.** $\{-4\}$ **27.** $\left\{-2, \dfrac{1}{3}\right\}$

29. $\left\{-\dfrac{4}{3}, \dfrac{1}{2}\right\}$ **31.** $\left\{-\dfrac{2}{3}\right\}$ **33.** $\{-3, 3\}$ **35.** $\left\{-\dfrac{7}{4}, \dfrac{7}{4}\right\}$ **37.** $\{-11, 11\}$

39. $\{0, 7\}$ **41.** $\left\{0, \dfrac{1}{2}\right\}$ **43.** $\{2, 5\}$ **45.** $\left\{-4, \dfrac{1}{2}\right\}$ **47.** $\left\{-12, \dfrac{11}{2}\right\}$

49. $\{-2, 0, 2\}$ **51.** $\left\{-\dfrac{7}{3}, 0, \dfrac{7}{3}\right\}$ **53.** $\left\{-\dfrac{5}{2}, \dfrac{1}{3}, 5\right\}$ **55.** $\left\{-\dfrac{7}{2}, -3, 1\right\}$

57. (a) $64; 144; 4; 6$ **(b)** No time has elapsed, so the object hasn't fallen (been released) yet.

Section 15.8 (pages 1159–1170)

1. Read; variable; equation; Solve; answer; Check; original

3. *Step 3:* $45 = (2x + 1)(x + 1)$; *Step 4:* $x = 4$ or $x = -\dfrac{11}{2}$;

Step 5: base: 9 units; height: 5 units; *Step 6:* $9 \cdot 5 = 45$

5. *Step 3:* $192 = 4x(x + 2)$; *Step 4:* $x = 6$ or $x = -8$; *Step 5:* length: 8 units; width: 6 units; *Step 6:* $8 \cdot 6 \cdot 4 = 192$ **7.** length: 14 cm; width: 12 cm   **9.** length: 15 in.; width: 12 in.   **11.** height: 13 in.; width: 10 in.

13. mirror: 7 ft; painting: 9 ft   **15.** 20, 21   **17.** $-3, -2$ or 4, 5

19. $-3, -1$ or 7, 9   **21.** $-2, 0, 2$ or 6, 8, 10   **23.** 12 cm   **25.** 12 mi

27. 8 ft   **29. (a)** 1 sec   **(b)** $\dfrac{1}{2}$ sec and $1\dfrac{1}{2}$ sec   **(c)** 3 sec

(d) The negative solution, -1, does not make sense since t represents time, which cannot be negative.   **31. (a)** 46 million; The result using the model is a little more than 44 million, the actual number for 1996.

(b) 14   **(c)** 184 million; The result is a little more than 182 million, the actual number for 2004.   **(d)** 318 million   **32.** \$58.6 billion; 16%

33. 2003: \$522.1 billion; 2004: \$610.8 billion; 2005: \$699.5 billion.

34. The answer using the linear equation is close to the actual data for 2004, but not for the other years.   **35.** 2003: \$503.9 billion; 2004: \$601.8 billion; 2005: \$718.2 billion   **36.** The answers in Exercise 35 are fairly close to the actual data. The quadratic equation models the data better.

37. $(1, 365.1), (2, 423.7), (3, 496.9), (4, 612.1), (5, 714.4)$

38.   **U.S. TRADE DEFICIT** (Goods and Services)

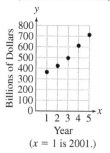

$(x = 1 \text{ is } 2001.)$

39. \$853.1 billion   **40. (a)** The actual deficit is quite a bit less than the estimate.   **(b)** No, data for later years might not follow the same pattern.

Chapter 16   Rational Expressions

Taken from *Prealgebra & Introductory Algebra* (0321578732) by Lial, et. al. and *Intermediate Algebra* (0321574974) by Lial, Hornsby, and McGinnis

Section 16.1 (pages 1172–1180)

1. (a) $3; -5$ **(b)** $q; -1$ **3.** A rational expression is a quotient of polynomials, such as $\dfrac{x + 3}{x^2 - 4}$.   **5.** $y \neq 0$ **7.** $x \neq -6$ **9.** $x \neq \dfrac{5}{3}$

11. $m \neq -3, m \neq 2$ **13.** never undefined   **15.** never undefined

17. (a) 1   **(b)** $\dfrac{17}{12}$ **19. (a)** 0   **(b)** -1 **21. (a)** $\dfrac{9}{5}$ **(b)** undefined

23. (a) $\dfrac{2}{7}$ **(b)** $\dfrac{13}{3}$ **25.** $3r^2$ **27.** $\dfrac{2}{5}$ **29.** $\dfrac{x - 1}{x + 1}$ **31.** $\dfrac{7}{5}$ **33.** $m - n$

35. $\dfrac{3(2m + 1)}{4}$ **37.** $\dfrac{3m}{5}$ **39.** $\dfrac{3r - 2s}{3}$ **41.** $\dfrac{x + 1}{x - 1}$ **43.** $\dfrac{z - 3}{z + 5}$

45. $\dfrac{a + b}{a - b}$ **47.** -1 **49.** $-(m + 1)$ **51.** -1

Answers may vary in Exercises 53–57.

53. $\dfrac{-(x + 4)}{x - 3}, \dfrac{-x - 4}{x - 3}, \dfrac{x + 4}{-(x - 3)}, \dfrac{x + 4}{-x + 3}$

55. $\dfrac{-(2x - 3)}{x + 3}, \dfrac{-2x + 3}{x + 3}, \dfrac{2x - 3}{-(x + 3)}, \dfrac{2x - 3}{-x - 3}$

57. $\dfrac{-(3x - 1)}{5x - 6}, \dfrac{-3x + 1}{5x - 6}, \dfrac{3x - 1}{-(5x - 6)}, \dfrac{3x - 1}{-5x + 6}$ **59.** $x^2 + 3$

Section 16.2 (pages 1181–1186)

1. (a) B **(b)** D **(c)** C **(d)** A **3.** $\dfrac{4m}{3}$ **5.** $\dfrac{40y^2}{3}$ **7.** $\dfrac{2}{c+d}$

9. $\dfrac{16q}{3p^3}$ **11.** $\dfrac{7}{r^2+rp}$ **13.** $\dfrac{z^2-9}{z^2+7z+12}$ **15.** 5 **17.** $-\dfrac{3}{2t^4}$ **19.** $\dfrac{1}{4}$

21. To multiply two rational expressions, multiply the numerators and multiply the denominators. Write the answer in lowest terms.

23. $\dfrac{10}{9}$ **25.** $-\dfrac{3}{4}$ **27.** -1 **29.** $\dfrac{9(m-2)}{-(m+4)}$, or $\dfrac{-9(m-2)}{m+4}$ **31.** $\dfrac{p+4}{p+2}$

33. $\dfrac{(k-1)^2}{(k+1)(2k-1)}$ **35.** $\dfrac{4k-1}{3k-2}$ **37.** $\dfrac{m+4p}{m+p}$ **39.** $\dfrac{10}{x+10}$ **41.** $\dfrac{5xy^2}{4q}$

Section 16.3 (pages 1187–1192)

1. C **3.** C **5.** 30 **7.** x^7 **9.** 72q **11.** $84r^5$ **13.** $2^3 \cdot 3 \cdot 5$

15. The least common denominator is their product. **17.** $28m^2(3m-5)$

19. $30(b-2)$ **21.** $c-d$ or $d-c$ **23.** $k(k+5)(k-2)$

25. $(p+3)(p+5)(p-6)$ **27.** $\dfrac{20}{55}$ **29.** $\dfrac{-45}{9k}$ **31.** $\dfrac{26y^2}{80y^3}$

33. $\dfrac{35t^2r^3}{42r^4}$ **35.** $\dfrac{20}{8(m+3)}$ **37.** $\dfrac{8t}{12-6t}$ **39.** $\dfrac{14(z-2)}{z(z-3)(z-2)}$

41. $\dfrac{2(b-1)(b+2)}{b^3+3b^2+2b}$

Section 16.4 (pages 1193–1202)

1. E **3.** C **5.** B **7.** G **9.** $\dfrac{11}{m}$ **11.** b **13.** $\dfrac{4}{y+4}$ **15.** $\dfrac{m-1}{m+1}$

17. x **19.** $y-6$ **21.** Combine the numerators and keep the same

denominator. For example, $\dfrac{3x+2}{x-6}+\dfrac{-2x-8}{x-6}=\dfrac{x-6}{x-6}$. Then write in

lowest terms: $\dfrac{x-6}{x-6}=1$. **23.** $\dfrac{3z+5}{15}$ **25.** $\dfrac{10-7r}{14}$ **27.** $\dfrac{-3x-2}{4x}$

29. $\dfrac{57}{20x}$ **31.** $\dfrac{x+1}{2}$ **33.** $\dfrac{5x+9}{6x}$ **35.** $\dfrac{3x+3}{x(x+3)}$ **37.** $\dfrac{-k-10}{k(k+5)}$

39. $\dfrac{x+4}{x+2}$ **41.** $\dfrac{x^2+6x-8}{(x-2)(x+2)}$ **43.** $\dfrac{3}{t}$ **45.** $m-2$ or $2-m$

47. $\dfrac{-2}{x-5}$, or $\dfrac{2}{5-x}$ **49.** -4 **51.** $\dfrac{-5}{x-y^2}$, or $\dfrac{5}{y^2-x}$

53. $\dfrac{x+y}{5x-3y}$, or $\dfrac{-x-y}{3y-5x}$ **55.** $\dfrac{-6}{4p-5}$, or $\dfrac{6}{5-4p}$ **57.** $\dfrac{-(m+n)}{2(m-n)}$

59. $\dfrac{-x^2+6x+11}{(x+3)(x-3)(x+1)}$ **61.** $\dfrac{-5q^2-13q+7}{(3q-2)(q+4)(2q-3)}$

63. $\dfrac{9r+2}{r(r+2)(r-1)}$ **65.** $\dfrac{2x^2+6xy+8y^2}{(x+y)(x+y)(x+3y)}$, or $\dfrac{2x^2+6xy+8y^2}{(x+y)^2(x+3y)}$

67. $\dfrac{15r^2+10ry-y^2}{(3r+2y)(6r-y)(6r+y)}$ **69. (a)** $\dfrac{9k^2+6k+26}{5(3k+1)}$ **(b)** $\dfrac{1}{4}$

Section 16.5 (pages 1203–1210)

1. (a) $6;\dfrac{1}{6}$ **(b)** $12;\dfrac{3}{4}$ **(c)** $\dfrac{1}{6}\div\dfrac{3}{4}$ **(d)** $\dfrac{2}{9}$ **3.** -6 **5.** $\dfrac{1}{pq}$ **7.** $\dfrac{1}{xy}$

9. $\dfrac{2a^2b}{3}$ **11.** $\dfrac{m(m+2)}{3(m-4)}$ **13.** $\dfrac{2}{x}$ **15.** $\dfrac{8}{x}$ **17.** $\dfrac{a^2-5}{a^2+1}$ **19.** $\dfrac{3(p+2)}{2(2p+3)}$

21. $\dfrac{40-12p}{85p}$ **23.** $\dfrac{t(t-2)}{4}$ **25.** $\dfrac{-k}{2+k}$ **27.** $\dfrac{2x-7}{3x+1}$

29. $\dfrac{3m(m-3)}{(m-1)(m-8)}$ **31.** $\dfrac{6}{5}$

Section 16.6 (pages 1211–1220)

1. (a) $-1, 2$ **(b)** $\{x\mid x\neq -1, 2\}$ **3. (a)** $-\dfrac{5}{3}, 0, -\dfrac{3}{2}$

(b) $\left\{x\mid x\neq -\dfrac{5}{3}, 0, -\dfrac{3}{2}\right\}$ **5. (a)** 0 **(b)** $\{x\mid x\neq 0\}$ **7. (a)** $4, \dfrac{7}{2}$

(b) $\left\{x\mid x\neq 4, \dfrac{7}{2}\right\}$ **9. (a)** $0, 1, -3, 2$ **(b)** $\{x\mid x\neq 0, 1, -3, 2\}$

11. $\{1\}$ **13.** $\{-6, 4\}$ **15.** $\left\{-\dfrac{7}{12}\right\}$ **17.** $\varnothing$ **19.** $\{-3\}$

21. $\{5\}$ **23.** $\{5\}$ **25.** $\varnothing$ **27.** $\left\{\dfrac{27}{56}\right\}$ **29.** $\varnothing$ **31.** $\{-10\}$

33. $\varnothing$ **35.** $\{0\}$ **37.** $\left\{x\mid x\neq -\dfrac{3}{2}, \dfrac{3}{2}\right\}$

39. $x = 0; y = 0$ **41.** $x = 2; y = 0$

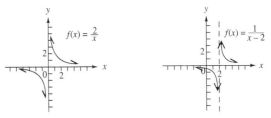

43. (a) 0 **(b)** 1.6 **(c)** 4.1 **(d)** The waiting time also increases.

45. Substituting -1 for x gives a true statement, $\dfrac{4}{3}=\dfrac{4}{3}$.

Substituting -2 for x leads to 0 in the first and third denominators.

46. $C = -4; \{-2\}; -1$ is rejected. **47.** $C = 24; \{-4\}; 3$ is rejected. **48.** Answers will vary.

Summary Exercises on Rational Expressions and Equations (pages 1219–1220)

1. equation; $\{20\}$ **2.** expression; $\dfrac{2(x+5)}{5}$ **3.** expression; $-\dfrac{22}{7x}$

4. expression; $\dfrac{y+x}{y-x}$ **5.** equation; $\left\{\dfrac{1}{2}\right\}$ **6.** equation; $\{7\}$

7. expression; $\dfrac{43}{24x}$ **8.** equation; $\{1\}$ **9.** expression; $\dfrac{5x-1}{-2x+2}$, or

$\dfrac{5x-1}{-2(x-1)}$ **10.** expression; $\dfrac{25}{4(r+2)}$ **11.** expression;

$\dfrac{x^2+xy+2y^2}{(x+y)(x-y)}$ **12.** expression; $\dfrac{24p}{p+2}$ **13.** expression; $-\dfrac{5}{36}$

14. equation; $\{0\}$ **15.** expression; $\dfrac{b+3}{3}$ **16.** expression; $\dfrac{5}{3z}$

17. expression; $\dfrac{2x+10}{x(x-2)(x+2)}$ **18.** equation; $\{2\}$

19. expression; $\dfrac{-x}{3x+5y}$ **20.** equation; $\{-13\}$ **21.** expression;

$\dfrac{3y+2}{y+3}$ **22.** equation; $\left\{\dfrac{5}{4}\right\}$ **23.** equation; $\varnothing$ **24.** expression;

$\dfrac{2z-3}{2z+3}$ **25.** expression; $\dfrac{-1}{x-3}$, or $\dfrac{1}{3-x}$ **26.** expression; $\dfrac{t-2}{8}$

27. equation; $\{-10\}$ **28.** expression; $\dfrac{13x+28}{2x(x+4)(x-4)}$

29. equation; $\varnothing$ **30.** expression; $\dfrac{k(2k^2-2k+5)}{(k-1)(3k^2-2)}$

Section 16.7 (pages 1221–1234)

1. A **3.** D **5.** 65.625 **7.** $\dfrac{25}{4}$ **9.** $G = \dfrac{Fd^2}{Mm}$ **11.** $a = \dfrac{bc}{c+b}$

13. $v = \dfrac{PVt}{pT}$ **15.** $r = \dfrac{nE-IR}{In}$ **17.** $b = \dfrac{2A}{h} - B$, or

$b = \dfrac{2A-Bh}{h}$ **19.** $r = \dfrac{eR}{E-e}$ **21.** Multiply each side by $a-b$.

23. 21 girls, 7 boys   **25.** $\frac{1}{2}$ job per hr   **27.** 5.4 in.   **29.** 7.6 in.

31. 100 games   **33.** 25,000 fish   **35.** 6.6 more gallons   **37.** 2.4 mL

39. $x = \frac{7}{2}$; $AC = 8$; $DF = 12$ **41.** 3 mph   **43.** 1020 mi   **45.** 480 mi

47. 190 mi   **49.** $6\frac{2}{3}$ min   **51.** 30 hr   **53.** 20 hr   **55.** $2\frac{4}{5}$ hr

Chapter 17   Roots and Radicals

Taken from Prealgebra & *Introductory Algebra* (0321578732)

Section 17.1 (pages 1236–1246)

1. true   **3.** false; Zero has only one square root.   **5.** true

7. $-3, 3$ **9.** $-8, 8$ **11.** $-13, 13$ **13.** $-\frac{5}{14}, \frac{5}{14}$ **15.** $-30, 30$

17. 1   **19.** 7   **21.** -16 **23.** $-\frac{12}{11}$ **25.** 0.8   **27.** not a real number

29. not a real number   **31.** 100   **33.** 19   **35.** $\frac{2}{3}$ **37.** $3x^2 + 4$

39. a must be positive.   **41.** a must be negative.   **43.** rational; 5

45. irrational; 5.385   **47.** rational; -8 **49.** irrational; -17.321

51. not a real number   **53.** irrational; 34.641   **55.** C   **57.** $c = 17$

59. $b = 8$ **61.** $c = 11.705$ **63.** 24 cm   **65.** 80 ft   **67.** 195 ft

69. 158.6 ft   **71.** 11.1 ft   **73.** 9.434   **75.** 1   **77.** 5   **79.** -3

81. -6 **83.** 2   **85.** 4   **87.** 6   **89.** not a real number

91. -5 **93.** -4

Section 17.2 (pages 1248–1256)

1. E   **3.** D   **5.** C   **7.** C   **9.** C   **11. (a)** not a real number

(b) negative   **(c)** 0   **13.** -9 **15.** 6   **17.** -4 **19.** -8 **21.** 6

23. -2 **25.** not a real number   **27.** 3   **29.** not a real number

31. $\frac{8}{9}$ **33.** 0.7   **35.** $\frac{4}{3}$ **37.** $-\frac{1}{2}$ **39.** 0.1

41. domain: $[-3, \infty)$; range: $[0, \infty)$ **43.** domain: $[0, \infty)$; range: $[-2, \infty)$

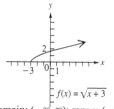

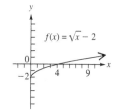

$f(x) = \sqrt{x} - 2$

$f(x) = \sqrt{x + 3}$

45. domain: $(-\infty, \infty)$; range: $(-\infty, \infty)$

$f(x) = \sqrt[3]{x} - 3$

47. 12   **49.** 10   **51.** 2   **53.** -9 **55.** -5 **57.** $|x|$ **59.** $|z|$ **61.** x

63. x^5 **65.** $|x|^5$ (or $|x^5|$)   **67.** 97.381   **69.** 16.863   **71.** -9.055

73. 7.507   **75.** 3.162   **77.** 1.885   **79.** 1,183,000 cycles per sec

81. 10 mi   **83.** 392,000 mi^2 **85.** 1.732 amps

Section 17.3 (pages 1257–1266)

1. C   **3.** A   **5.** H   **7.** B   **9.** D   **11.** 13   **13.** 9   **15.** 2

17. $\frac{8}{9}$ **19.** -3 **21.** not a real number   **23.** 1000   **25.** 27

27. -1024 **29.** 16   **31.** $\frac{1}{8}$ **33.** $\frac{1}{512}$ **35.** $\frac{9}{25}$ **37.** $\sqrt{12}$

39. $\left(\sqrt[4]{8}\right)^3$ **41.** $\left(\sqrt[8]{9q}\right)^5 - \left(\sqrt[3]{2x}\right)^2$ **43.** $\dfrac{1}{\left(\sqrt{2m}\right)^3}$

45. $\left(\sqrt[3]{2y + x}\right)^2$ **47.** $\dfrac{1}{\left(\sqrt[3]{3m^4 + 2k^2}\right)^2}$

49. $\sqrt{a^2 + b^2} = \sqrt{3^2 + 4^2} = 5$; $a + b = 3 + 4 = 7$; $5 \neq 7$

51. 64   **53.** 64   **55.** x^{10} **57.** $\sqrt[6]{x^5}$ **59.** $\sqrt[15]{t^8}$ **61.** 9   **63.** 4

65. y **67.** $x^{5/12}$ **69.** $k^{2/3}$ **71.** $x^3 y^8$ **73.** $\dfrac{1}{x^{10/3}}$ **75.** $\dfrac{1}{m^{1/4} n^{3/4}}$ **77.** p^2

79. $\dfrac{c^{11/3}}{b^{11/4}}$ **81.** $\dfrac{q^{5/3}}{9p^{7/2}}$ **83.** $p + 2p^2$ **85.** $k^{7/4} - k^{3/4}$ **87.** $6 + 18a$

89. $5 + \dfrac{5}{m^3}$ **91.** $y^{3/2}$ **93.** $\dfrac{1}{k^{2/3}}$ **95.** $x^{1/3} z^{5/6}$ **97.** $k^{1/6}$ **99.** $y^{1/30}$

101. $x^{5/27}$ **103.** 72 in.; 6.0 ft   **105.** $-12.3°$; The table gives $-12°$.

Section 17.4 (pages 1267–1280)

1. true; Both are equal to $4\sqrt{3}$ and approximately 6.92820323.

3. true; Both are equal to $6\sqrt{2}$ and approximately 8.485281374.

5. Because there are only two factors of $\sqrt[3]{x}$, $\sqrt[3]{x} \cdot \sqrt[3]{x} = \left(\sqrt[3]{x}\right)^2$, or $\sqrt[3]{x^2}$.

7. D   **9.** $\sqrt{30}$ **11.** $\sqrt{14x}$ **13.** $\sqrt{42pqr}$ **15.** $\sqrt[3]{14xy}$ **17.** $\sqrt[4]{33}$

19. $\sqrt[4]{6xy^2}$ **21.** This product cannot be simplified using the product

rule.   **23.** $\dfrac{8}{11}$ **25.** $\dfrac{\sqrt{3}}{5}$ **27.** $\dfrac{\sqrt{x}}{5}$ **29.** $\dfrac{p^3}{9}$ **31.** $-\dfrac{3}{4}$ **33.** $\dfrac{\sqrt[3]{r^2}}{2}$

35. $-\dfrac{3}{x}$ **37.** $\dfrac{1}{x^3}$ **39.** $2\sqrt{3}$ **41.** $12\sqrt{2}$ **43.** $-4\sqrt{2}$ **45.** $-2\sqrt{7}$

47. cannot be simplified further   **49.** $4\sqrt[3]{2}$ **51.** $-2\sqrt[3]{2}$ **53.** $2\sqrt[3]{5}$

55. $-4\sqrt[4]{2}$ **57.** $2\sqrt[5]{2}$ **59.** His reasoning was incorrect. Here 8 is

a term, not a factor.   **61.** $6k\sqrt{2}$ **63.** $12xy^4\sqrt{xy}$ **65.** $11x^3$

67. $-3t^4$ **69.** $-10m^4z^2$ **71.** $5a^2b^3c^4$ **73.** $\dfrac{1}{2}r^2t^5$ **75.** $5x\sqrt{2x}$

77. $-10r^5\sqrt{5r}$ **79.** $x^3y^4\sqrt{13x}$ **81.** $2z^2w^3$ **83.** $-2zt^2\sqrt[3]{2z^2t}$

85. $3x^3y^4$ **87.** $-3r^3s^2\sqrt[4]{2r^3s^2}$ **89.** $\dfrac{y^5\sqrt{y}}{6}$ **91.** $\dfrac{x^5\sqrt[3]{x}}{3}$

93. $4\sqrt{3}$ **95.** $\sqrt{5}$ **97.** $x^2\sqrt{x}$ **99.** $\sqrt[6]{432}$ **101.** $\sqrt[12]{6912}$

103. $\sqrt[6]{x^5}$ **105.** 5   **107.** $8\sqrt{2}$ **109.** $2\sqrt{14}$ **111.** 13   **113.** $9\sqrt{2}$

115. $\sqrt{17}$ **117.** 5   **119.** $6\sqrt{2}$ **121.** $\sqrt{5y^2 - 2xy + x^2}$

123. 27.0 in.   **125.** 0.003   **127.** 15.3 mi

Section 17.5 (pages 1281–1284)

1. B   **3.** 15; Each radical expression simplifies to a whole number.

5. -4 **7.** $7\sqrt{3}$ **9.** $14\sqrt[3]{2}$ **11.** $5\sqrt[4]{2}$ **13.** $24\sqrt{2}$ **15.** cannot be

simplified further   **17.** $20\sqrt{5}$ **19.** $12\sqrt{2x}$ **21.** $-2m\sqrt{2}$

23. $\sqrt[3]{2}$ **25.** $2\sqrt[3]{x}$ **27.** $-\sqrt[3]{x^2y}$ **29.** $-x\sqrt[3]{xy^2}$ **31.** $19\sqrt[4]{2}$

33. $x\sqrt[4]{xy}$ **35.** $9\sqrt[4]{2a^3}$ **37.** $\dfrac{5\sqrt{5}}{6}$ **39.** $\dfrac{7\sqrt{2}}{6}$ **41.** $\dfrac{5\sqrt{2}}{3}$

43. $5\sqrt{2} + 4$ **45.** $\dfrac{5 - 3x}{x^4}$ **47.** $\dfrac{m\sqrt[3]{m^2}}{2}$ **49.** $\dfrac{3x\sqrt[3]{2} - 4\sqrt[3]{5}}{x^3}$

51. $\left(12\sqrt{5} + 5\sqrt{3}\right)$ in.   **53.** $\left(24\sqrt{2} + 12\sqrt{3}\right)$ in.

Section 17.6 (pages 1285–1294)

1. E   **3.** A   **5.** D   **7.** $6 - 4\sqrt{3}$ **9.** $6 - \sqrt{6}$ **11.** 2   **13.** 9

15. $3\sqrt{2} - 5\sqrt{3} + 2\sqrt{6} - 10$ **17.** $3x - 4$ **19.** $4x - y$

21. $16x + 24\sqrt{x} + 9$ **23.** $81 - \sqrt[3]{4}$ **25.** Because 6 and $4\sqrt{3}$ are not like terms, they cannot be combined. **27.** $\sqrt{7}$ **29.** $5\sqrt{3}$

31. $\dfrac{\sqrt{6}}{2}$ **33.** $\dfrac{9\sqrt{15}}{5}$ **35.** $-\sqrt{2}$ **37.** $\dfrac{-8\sqrt{3k}}{k}$ **39.** $\dfrac{6\sqrt{3}}{y}$

41. To rationalize a cube root, three factors of the quantity under the radical sign are needed. We must multiply by $\sqrt[3]{2^2}$, or $\sqrt[3]{4}$, to rationalize $\sqrt[3]{2}$.

43. $\dfrac{\sqrt{14}}{2}$ **45.** $-\dfrac{\sqrt{14}}{10}$ **47.** $\dfrac{2\sqrt{6x}}{x}$ **49.** $-\dfrac{7r\sqrt{2rs}}{s}$

51. $\dfrac{12x^3\sqrt{2xy}}{y^5}$ **53.** $\dfrac{\sqrt[3]{18}}{3}$ **55.** $\dfrac{\sqrt[3]{12}}{3}$ **57.** $-\dfrac{\sqrt[3]{2pr}}{r}$

59. $\dfrac{2\sqrt[4]{x^3}}{x}$ **61.** $\dfrac{\sqrt[4]{2yz^3}}{z}$ **63.** $\dfrac{2\left(4-\sqrt{3}\right)}{13}$ **65.** $3\left(\sqrt{5}-\sqrt{3}\right)$

67. $\sqrt{3}+\sqrt{7}$ **69.** $\sqrt{7}-\sqrt{6}-\sqrt{14}+2\sqrt{3}$

71. $2\sqrt{3}+\sqrt{10}-3\sqrt{2}-\sqrt{15}$ **73.** $\dfrac{4\left(\sqrt{x}+2\sqrt{y}\right)}{x-4y}$

75. $\dfrac{x\sqrt{2}-\sqrt{3xy}-\sqrt{2xy}+y\sqrt{3}}{2x-3y}$ **77.** $\dfrac{5+2\sqrt{6}}{4}$ **79.** $\dfrac{4+2\sqrt{2}}{3}$

81. $\dfrac{6+2\sqrt{6x}}{3}$ **83.** $\dfrac{319}{6\left(8\sqrt{5}+1\right)}$ **84.** $\dfrac{9a-b}{\left(\sqrt{b}-\sqrt{a}\right)\left(3\sqrt{a}-\sqrt{b}\right)}$

85. $\dfrac{\left(3\sqrt{a}+\sqrt{b}\right)\left(\sqrt{b}+\sqrt{a}\right)}{b-a}$ **86.** In Exercise 84, we multiplied the numerator and denominator by the conjugate of the numerator, while in Exercise 85 we multiplied by the conjugate of the denominator.

Summary Exercises on Operations with Radicals and Rational Exponents (pages 1295–1296)

1. $-6\sqrt{10}$ **2.** $7-\sqrt{14}$ **3.** $2+\sqrt{6}-2\sqrt{3}-3\sqrt{2}$ **4.** $4\sqrt{2}$

5. $73+12\sqrt{35}$ **6.** $\dfrac{-\sqrt{6}}{2}$ **7.** $4\left(\sqrt{7}-\sqrt{5}\right)$ **8.** $3\sqrt[3]{2x^2}$

9. $-3+2\sqrt{2}$ **10.** -2 **11.** -44 **12.** $\dfrac{\sqrt{x}+\sqrt{5}}{x-5}$ **13.** $2abc^3\sqrt[3]{b^2}$

14. $5\sqrt[3]{3}$ **15.** $3\left(\sqrt{5}-2\right)$ **16.** $\dfrac{\sqrt{15x}}{5x}$ **17.** $\dfrac{8}{5}$ **18.** $\dfrac{\sqrt{2}}{8}$

19. $-\sqrt[3]{100}$ **20.** $11+2\sqrt{30}$ **21.** $-3\sqrt{3x}$ **22.** $52-30\sqrt{3}$

23. 1 **24.** $\dfrac{\sqrt[3]{117}}{9}$ **25.** $t^2\sqrt[4]{t}$ **26.** $3\sqrt{2}+\sqrt{15}+\sqrt{42}+\sqrt{35}$

27. $2\sqrt[4]{27}$ **28.** $\dfrac{1+\sqrt[3]{3}+\sqrt[3]{9}}{-2}$ **29.** $\dfrac{x\sqrt[3]{x^2}}{y}$ **30.** $-4\sqrt{3}-3$

31. $xy^{6/5}$ **32.** $x^{10}y$ **33.** $\dfrac{1}{25x^2}$ **34.** $\dfrac{-6y^{1/6}}{x^{1/24}}$ **35.** $7+4\cdot3^{1/2}$, or $7+4\sqrt{3}$ **36.** 1

Section 17.7 (pages 1297–1304)

1. (a) yes **(b)** no **3. (a)** yes **(b)** no **5.** no; There is no solution. The radical expression, which is positive, cannot equal a negative number. **7.** $\{11\}$ **9.** $\left\{\dfrac{1}{3}\right\}$ **11.** $\emptyset$ **13.** $\{5\}$ **15.** $\{18\}$

17. $\{5\}$ **19.** $\{4\}$ **21.** $\{17\}$ **23.** $\{5\}$ **25.** $\emptyset$ **27.** $\{0\}$ **29.** $\{0\}$

31. $\left\{-\dfrac{1}{3}\right\}$ **33.** $\emptyset$ **35.** We cannot just square each term. The right side should be $(8-x)^2=64-16x+x^2$. The correct first step is $3x+4=64-16x+x^2$, and the solution set is $\{4\}$. **37.** $\{1\}$

39. $\{-1\}$ **41.** $\{14\}$ **43.** $\{8\}$ **45.** $\{0\}$ **47.** $\emptyset$ **49.** $\{7\}$ **51.** $\{7\}$

53. $\{4,20\}$ **55.** $\emptyset$ **57.** $\left\{\dfrac{5}{4}\right\}$ **59.** $\{9,17\}$ **61.** $\left\{\dfrac{1}{4},1\right\}$

63. $K=\dfrac{V^2m}{2}$ **65.** $C=\dfrac{L}{Z^2}$ **67.** $L=\dfrac{1}{4\pi^2f^2C}$ **69.** $r=\dfrac{a}{4\pi^2N^2}$

Section 17.8 (pages 1305–1315)

1. i **3.** $-i$ **5.** Any real number a can be written as $a+0i$, a complex number with imaginary part 0. **7.** $13i$ **9.** $-12i$ **11.** $i\sqrt{5}$

13. $4i\sqrt{3}$ **15.** -15 **17.** $-\sqrt{57}$ **19.** -10 **21.** $i\sqrt{33}$

23. $\sqrt{3}$ **25.** $5i$ **27.** $-1+7i$ **29.** 0 **31.** $7+3i$ **33.** -2

35. $1+13i$ **37.** $6+6i$ **39.** $4+2i$ **41.** -81 **43.** -16

45. $-10-30i$ **47.** $10-5i$ **49.** $-9+40i$ **51.** 153

53. (a) $a-bi$ **(b)** $a^2;b^2$ **55.** $1+i$ **57.** $-1+2i$

59. $2+2i$ **61.** $-\dfrac{5}{13}-\dfrac{12}{13}i$ **63. (a)** $4x+1$ **(b)** $4+i$

64. (a) $-2x+3$ **(b)** $-2+3i$ **65. (a)** $3x^2+5x-2$

(b) $5+5i$ **66. (a)** $-\sqrt{3}+\sqrt{6}+1-\sqrt{2}$ **(b)** $\dfrac{1}{5}-\dfrac{7}{5}i$

67. Because $i^2=-1$, two pairs of like terms can be combined in Exercise 65(b). **68.** Because $i^2=-1$, additional terms can be combined in the numerator and denominator. **69.** $\dfrac{5}{41}+\dfrac{4}{41}i$

71. -1 **73.** i **75.** 1 **77.** $-i$ **79.** Since $i^{20}=(i^4)^5=1^5=1$, the student multiplied by 1, which is justified by the identity property for multiplication. **81.** $\dfrac{1}{2}+\dfrac{1}{2}i$ **83.** $(1+5i)^2-2(1+5i)+26$ will simplify to 0 when the operations are applied.

Chapter 18 Quadratics

Taken from *Intermediate Algebra* (0321574974) by Lial Hornsby, and McGinnis and *Prealgebra & Introductory Algebra* (0321578732) by Lial, et. al.

Section 18.1 (pages 1318–1324)

1. true **3.** false; If k is a positive integer that is not a perfect square, then the solutions will be irrational. **5.** false; For values of k that satisfy $0\le k<10$, there are real solutions. **7.** $\{-9,9\}$

9. $\left\{-\sqrt{14},\sqrt{14}\right\}$ **11.** $\left\{-4\sqrt{3},4\sqrt{3}\right\}$ **13.** $\left\{-\dfrac{5}{2},\dfrac{5}{2}\right\}$

15. $\emptyset$ **17.** $\{-1.5,1.5\}$ **19.** $\left\{-\sqrt{3},\sqrt{3}\right\}$ **21.** $\left\{-\dfrac{2\sqrt{7}}{7},\dfrac{2\sqrt{7}}{7}\right\}$

23. $\left\{-3\sqrt{2},3\sqrt{2}\right\}$ **25.** $\left\{-2\sqrt{6},2\sqrt{6}\right\}$ **27.** $\left\{-\dfrac{2\sqrt{5}}{5},\dfrac{2\sqrt{5}}{5}\right\}$

29. $\{-2,8\}$ **31.** $\emptyset$ **33.** $\left\{8+3\sqrt{3},8-3\sqrt{3}\right\}$ **35.** $\left\{-3,\dfrac{5}{3}\right\}$

37. $\left\{0,\dfrac{3}{2}\right\}$ **39.** $\left\{\dfrac{5+\sqrt{30}}{2},\dfrac{5-\sqrt{30}}{2}\right\}$

41. $\left\{\dfrac{-1+3\sqrt{2}}{3},\dfrac{-1-3\sqrt{2}}{3}\right\}$ **43.** $\left\{-10+4\sqrt{3},-10-4\sqrt{3}\right\}$

45. $\left\{\dfrac{1+4\sqrt{3}}{4},\dfrac{1-4\sqrt{3}}{4}\right\}$ **47.** The answers are equivalent. If the answer of either student is multiplied by $\dfrac{-1}{-1}$, it will look like the answer of the other student. **49.** about $\dfrac{1}{2}$ sec **51.** 9 in. **53.** 5% **55.** 2%

Section 18.2 (pages 1323–1332)

1. $25; (x + 5)^2$ **3.** $1; (x + 1)^2$ **5.** $\frac{25}{4}; \left(p - \frac{5}{2}\right)^2$ **7.** D

9. $\{1, 3\}$ **11.** $\{-3, -2\}$ **13.** $\left\{-1 + \sqrt{6}, -1 - \sqrt{6}\right\}$

15. $\left\{4 + 2\sqrt{3}, 4 - 2\sqrt{3}\right\}$ **17.** $\{-3\}$

19. $\left\{\dfrac{-1 + \sqrt{5}}{2}, \dfrac{-1 - \sqrt{5}}{2}\right\}$ **21.** $\left\{-\dfrac{3}{2}, \dfrac{1}{2}\right\}$

23. $\left\{\dfrac{2 + \sqrt{14}}{2}, \dfrac{2 - \sqrt{14}}{2}\right\}$ **25.** $\varnothing$

27. $\left\{\dfrac{-7 + \sqrt{97}}{6}, \dfrac{-7 - \sqrt{97}}{6}\right\}$ **29.** $\{-4, 2\}$

31. $\left\{4 + \sqrt{3}, 4 - \sqrt{3}\right\}$ **33.** $\left\{1 + \sqrt{6}, 1 - \sqrt{6}\right\}$

35. 1 sec and 5 sec   **37.** 3 sec and 5 sec   **39.** 75 ft by 100 ft

Section 18.3 (pages 1333–1340)

1. The fraction bar should extend under the term $-b$.   **3.** $\{3, 5\}$

5. $\left\{\dfrac{-2 + \sqrt{2}}{2}, \dfrac{-2 - \sqrt{2}}{2}\right\}$ **7.** $\left\{\dfrac{1 + \sqrt{3}}{2}, \dfrac{1 - \sqrt{3}}{2}\right\}$

9. $\left\{5 + \sqrt{7}, 5 - \sqrt{7}\right\}$ **11.** $\left\{\dfrac{-1 + \sqrt{2}}{2}, \dfrac{-1 - \sqrt{2}}{2}\right\}$

13. $\left\{\dfrac{-1 + \sqrt{7}}{3}, \dfrac{-1 - \sqrt{7}}{3}\right\}$ **15.** $\left\{1 + \sqrt{5}, 1 - \sqrt{5}\right\}$

17. $\left\{\dfrac{-2 + \sqrt{10}}{2}, \dfrac{-2 - \sqrt{10}}{2}\right\}$ **19.** $\left\{-1 + 3\sqrt{2}, -1 - 3\sqrt{2}\right\}$

21. $\left\{\dfrac{3}{2} + \dfrac{\sqrt{59}}{2}i, \dfrac{3}{2} - \dfrac{\sqrt{59}}{2}i\right\}$ **23.** $\left\{3 + i\sqrt{5}, 3 - i\sqrt{5}\right\}$

25. $\left\{\dfrac{1}{2} + \dfrac{\sqrt{6}}{2}i, \dfrac{1}{2} - \dfrac{\sqrt{6}}{2}i\right\}$ **27.** $\left\{-\dfrac{2}{3} + \dfrac{\sqrt{2}}{3}i, -\dfrac{2}{3} - \dfrac{\sqrt{2}}{3}i\right\}$

29. B   **31.** C   **33.** A   **35.** D   **37.** The equations in Exercises 29, 30, 33, and 34 can be solved by factoring.

Section 18.4 (pages 1341–1354)

1. Multiply by the LCD, x.   **3.** Substitute a variable for $r^2 + r$.
5. The proposed solution -1 does not check. The solution set is $\{4\}$.

7. $\{-4, 7\}$ **9.** $\left\{-\dfrac{2}{3}, 1\right\}$ **11.** $\left\{-\dfrac{14}{17}, 5\right\}$ **13.** $\left\{-\dfrac{11}{7}, 0\right\}$

15. $\left\{\dfrac{-1 + \sqrt{13}}{2}, \dfrac{-1 - \sqrt{13}}{2}\right\}$ **17.** $\left\{\dfrac{2 + \sqrt{22}}{3}, \dfrac{2 - \sqrt{22}}{3}\right\}$

19. (a) $(20 - t)$ mph   **(b)** $(20 + t)$ mph   **21.** 25 mph
23. 80 km per hr   **25.** 3.6 hr   **27.** 9 min   **29.** $\{1, 4\}$

31. $\{3\}$ **33.** $\left\{\dfrac{8}{9}\right\}$ **35.** $\{16\}$ **37.** $\left\{\dfrac{2}{5}\right\}$ **39.** $\{-3, 3\}$

41. $\left\{-\dfrac{3}{2}, -1, 1, \dfrac{3}{2}\right\}$ **43.** $\left\{-2\sqrt{3}, -2, 2, 2\sqrt{3}\right\}$

45. $\left\{\dfrac{\sqrt{9 + \sqrt{65}}}{2}, -\dfrac{\sqrt{9 + \sqrt{65}}}{2}, \dfrac{\sqrt{9 - \sqrt{65}}}{2}, -\dfrac{\sqrt{9 - \sqrt{65}}}{2}\right\}$

47. $\{-6, -5\}$ **49.** $\{-4, 1\}$ **51.** $\left\{-\dfrac{1}{3}, \dfrac{1}{6}\right\}$ **53.** $\{-8, 1\}$

55. $\{-64, 27\}$ **57.** $\{25\}$ **59.** It would cause both denominators to equal 0, and division by 0 is undefined.   **60.** $\dfrac{12}{5}$

61. $\left(\dfrac{x}{x - 3}\right)^2 + 3\left(\dfrac{x}{x - 3}\right) - 4 = 0$ **62.** The numerator can never equal the denominator, since the denominator is 3 less than the numerator.   **63.** $\left\{\dfrac{12}{5}\right\}$; The values for t are -4 and 1. The value 1 is impossible because it leads to a contradiction $\left(\text{since } \dfrac{x}{x - 3} \text{ is never equal to 1}\right)$.   **64.** $\left\{\dfrac{12}{5}\right\}$; The values for s are $\dfrac{1}{x}$ and $\dfrac{-4}{x}$. The value $\dfrac{1}{x}$ is impossible, since $\dfrac{1}{x} \neq \dfrac{1}{x - 3}$ for all x.

Summary Exercises on Solving Quadratic Equations 1353–1354

1. square root property   **2.** factoring   **3.** quadratic formula
4. quadratic formula   **5.** factoring   **6.** square root property

7. $\left\{\sqrt{47}, -\sqrt{47}\right\}$ **8.** $\left\{-\dfrac{3}{2}, \dfrac{5}{3}\right\}$ **9.** $\left\{-4 + \sqrt{10}, -4 - \sqrt{10}\right\}$

10. $\{-3, 11\}$ **11.** $\left\{-\dfrac{1}{2}, 5\right\}$ **12.** $\left\{-3, \dfrac{1}{3}\right\}$

13. $\left\{\dfrac{9 + \sqrt{33}}{6}, \dfrac{9 - \sqrt{33}}{6}\right\}$ **14.** $\left\{2i\sqrt{3}, -2i\sqrt{3}\right\}$ **15.** $\left\{\dfrac{1}{2}, 2\right\}$

16. $\left\{-\dfrac{\sqrt{6}}{3}, -\dfrac{1}{2}, \dfrac{1}{2}, \dfrac{\sqrt{6}}{3}\right\}$ **17.** $\left\{\dfrac{-5 + 2\sqrt{3}}{2}, \dfrac{-5 - 2\sqrt{3}}{2}\right\}$

18. $\left\{\dfrac{4}{5}, 3\right\}$ **19.** $\left\{-\sqrt{7}, -\sqrt{2}, \sqrt{2}, \sqrt{7}\right\}$

20. $\left\{\dfrac{-2 + \sqrt{14}}{2}, \dfrac{-2 - \sqrt{14}}{2}\right\}$ **21.** $\left\{-\dfrac{1}{2} + \dfrac{\sqrt{7}}{2}i, -\dfrac{1}{2} - \dfrac{\sqrt{7}}{2}i\right\}$

22. $\left\{\sqrt{4 + \sqrt{15}}, -\sqrt{4 + \sqrt{15}}, \sqrt{4 - \sqrt{15}}, -\sqrt{4 - \sqrt{15}}\right\}$

23. $\left\{\dfrac{3}{2}\right\}$ **24.** $\left\{\dfrac{2}{3}\right\}$ **25.** $\left\{6\sqrt{2}, -6\sqrt{2}\right\}$ **26.** $\left\{-\dfrac{2}{3}, 2\right\}$

27. $\{-4, 9\}$ **28.** $\{13, -13\}$ **29.** $\left\{1 + \dfrac{\sqrt{3}}{3}i, 1 - \dfrac{\sqrt{3}}{3}i\right\}$

30. $\{3\}$ **31.** $\left\{-\dfrac{1}{3}, \dfrac{1}{6}\right\}$ **32.** $\left\{\dfrac{1}{6} + \dfrac{\sqrt{47}}{6}i, \dfrac{1}{6} - \dfrac{\sqrt{47}}{6}i\right\}$

33. $\{3\}$ **34.** $\left\{-\dfrac{8}{3}, -1\right\}$ **35.** $\left\{-i, i, -\dfrac{1}{2}i, \dfrac{1}{2}i\right\}$ **36.** $\{-2, 7\}$

Section 18.5 (pages 1355–1362)

1. Solve for w^2 by dividing each side by g.   **3.** $m = \sqrt{p^2 - n^2}$

5. $t = \dfrac{\pm\sqrt{dk}}{k}$ **7.** $d = \dfrac{\pm\sqrt{skI}}{I}$ **9.** $v = \dfrac{\pm\sqrt{kAF}}{F}$

11. $r = \dfrac{\pm\sqrt{3\pi Vh}}{\pi h}$ **13.** $t = \dfrac{-B \pm \sqrt{B^2 - 4AC}}{2A}$ **15.** $h = \dfrac{D^2}{k}$

17. $\ell = \dfrac{p^2 g}{k}$ **19.** 2.3, 5.3, 5.8   **21.** eastbound ship: 80 mi; southbound ship: 150 mi   **23.** 1 ft   **25.** 20 in. by 12 in.
27. 2.4 sec and 5.6 sec   **29.** 9.2 sec   **31.** It reaches its *maximum* height at 5 sec because this is the only time it reaches 400 ft.   **33.** $0.80
35. (a) 2750 billion   **(b)** 2750 billion; They are the same.
37. 2001; The graph indicates that vehicle-miles reached 2800 in 2001.
39. 5.5 m per sec   **41.** 5 or 14

Section 18.6 (pages 1363–1374)

1. (a) B **(b)** C **(c)** A **(d)** D   **3.** $(0, 0)$ **5.** $(0, 4)$ **7.** $(1, 0)$
9. $(-3, -4)$ **11.** In Exercise 9, the parabola is shifted 3 units to the left and 4 units down. The parabola in Exercise 10 is shifted 5 units to the right and 8 units down.   **13.** down; wider   **15.** up; narrower
17. (a) I   **(b)** IV   **(c)** II   **(d)** III
19. 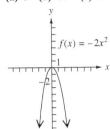 **21.**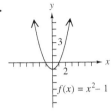

23.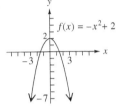

25. vertex: $(4, 0)$; axis: $x = 4$; domain: $(-\infty, \infty)$; range: $[0, \infty)$
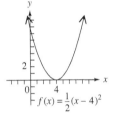

27. vertex: $(-2, -1)$; axis: $x = -2$; domain: $(-\infty, \infty)$; range: $[-1, \infty)$
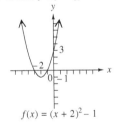

29. vertex: $(-3, 4)$; axis: $x = -3$; domain: $(-\infty, \infty)$; range: $(-\infty, 4]$
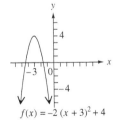

31. vertex: $(-2, 1)$; axis: $x = -2$; domain: $(-\infty, \infty)$; range: $(-\infty, 1]$
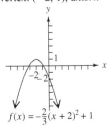

33. It is shifted 6 units up.

34.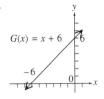

35. It is shifted 6 units up.   **36.** It is shifted 6 units to the right.
37.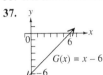

38. It is shifted 6 units to the right.   **39.** quadratic; positive
41. quadratic; negative   **43.** linear; positive
45. (a) **DIGITAL CAMERA SALES IN U.S.**

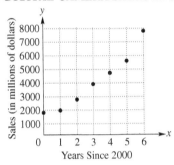

(b) quadratic; positive   **(c)** $f(x) = 99.3x^2 + 400.7x + 1825$
(d) \$9496 million   **(e)** No. The number of digital cameras sold in 2007 is far below the number approximated by the model. Rather than continuing to increase, sales of digital cameras fell in 2007.
47. (a) 2005: 14%; 2007: 2.4%
(b) The approximations using the model are far too low.

Section 18.7 (pages 1375–1386)

1. If x is squared, it has a vertical axis; if y is squared, it has a horizontal axis.   **3.** Use the discriminant of the corresponding quadratic equation. If it is positive, there are two x-intercepts. If it is 0, there is just one x-intercept (the vertex), and if it is negative, there are no x-intercepts.   **5.** $(-1, 3)$; up; narrower; no x-intercepts
7. $\left(\dfrac{5}{2}, \dfrac{37}{4}\right)$; down; same; two x-intercepts
9. $(-3, -9)$; to the right; wider
11. vertex: $(-2, -1)$; axis: $x = -2$; domain: $(-\infty, \infty)$; range: $[-1, \infty)$
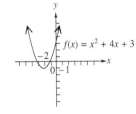

13. vertex: $(1, -3)$; axis: $x = 1$; domain: $(-\infty, \infty)$; range: $(-\infty, -3]$

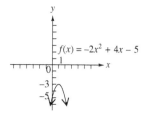

15. vertex: $(1, 5)$; axis: $y = 5$; domain: $(-\infty, 1]$; range: $(-\infty, \infty)$

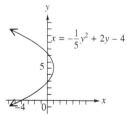

17. vertex: $(-7, -2)$; axis: $y = -2$; domain: $[-7, \infty)$; range: $(-\infty, \infty)$

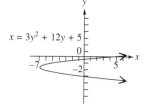

19. F   **21.** C   **23.** D   **25.** 30 and 30   **27.** 160 ft by 320 ft
29. 16 ft; 2 sec   **31. (a)** $R(x) = 20{,}000 + 200x - 4x^2$ **(b)** 25
(c) \$22,500   **33. (a)** maximum   **(b)** 1993; 13.2%
35. (a) The coefficient of x^2 is negative because the parabola opens
down.   **(b)** $(18.45, 3860)$ **(c)** In 2018 Social Security assets will reach
their maximum value of \$3860 billion.

Square

Perimeter: $P = 4s$

Area: $A = s^2$

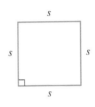

Rectangle

Perimeter: $P = 2L + 2W$

Area: $A = LW$

Triangle

Perimeter: $P = a + b + c$

Area: $A = \dfrac{1}{2}bh$

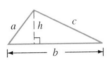

Parallelogram

Perimeter: $P = 2a + 2b$

Area: $A = bh$

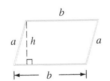

Trapezoid

Perimeter: $P = a + b + c + B$

Area: $A = \dfrac{1}{2}h(b + B)$

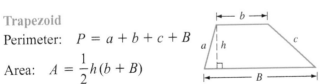

Circle

Diameter: $d = 2r$

Circumference: $C = 2\pi r$

$C = \pi d$

Area: $A = \pi r^2$

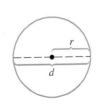

Rectangular Solid

Volume: $V = LWH$

Surface area: $A = 2HW + 2LW + 2LH$

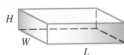

Cube

Volume: $V = e^3$

Surface area: $S = 6e^2$

Right Circular Cylinder

Volume: $V = \pi r^2 h$

Surface area: $S = 2\pi rh + 2\pi r^2$

(Includes both circular bases)

Cone

Volume: $V = \dfrac{1}{3}\pi r^2 h$

Surface area: $S = \pi r \sqrt{r^2 + h^2} + \pi r^2$

(Includes circular base)

Right Pyramid

Volume: $V = \dfrac{1}{3}Bh$

$B = $ area of the base

Sphere

Volume: $V = \dfrac{4}{3}\pi r^3$

Surface area: $S = 4\pi r^2$

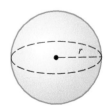

Right Triangle

Triangle has one 90° (right) angle.

Pythagorean Formula (for right triangles)

$a^2 + b^2 = c^2$

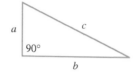

Right Angle

Measure is 90°.

Isosceles Triangle

Two sides are equal.

$AB = BC$

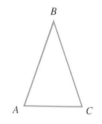

Straight Angle

Measure is 180°.

Equilateral Triangle

All sides are equal.

$AB = BC = CA$

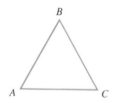

Complementary Angles

The sum of the measures of two complementary angles is 90°.

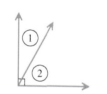

Angles ① and ② are complementary.

Sum of the Angles of Any Triangle

$A + B + C = 180°$

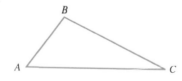

Supplementary Angles

The sum of the measures of two supplementary angles is 180°.

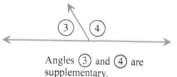

Angles ③ and ④ are supplementary.

Similar Triangles

Corresponding angles are equal; corresponding sides are proportional.

$A = D, B = E, C = F$

$$\frac{AB}{DE} = \frac{AC}{DF} = \frac{BC}{EF}$$

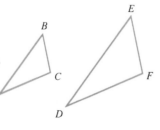

Vertical Angles

Vertical angles have equal measures.

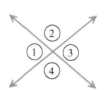

Angle ① = Angle ③

Angle ② = Angle ④